CALCIUM

To help build bones and teeth
To help blood to clot
To help the muscles and nerves
    react normally

CARBOHYDRATE

To su...
To hel...
nut...

HEALTH . . .

WE NEED

CONTAIN IT

VITAMIN A

To help keep the skin and mucous
    membranes healthy and
    resistant to infection
To protect against night blindness

ASCORBIC ACID

To help cement body cells together
    and to strengthen the walls of
    the blood vessels
To help resist infection
To help in healing

VITAMIN D

To help the body absorb calcium
To help build strong bones

The Yearbook of Agriculture 1959

Food

The Yearbook of Agriculture 1959

THE UNITED STATES DEPARTMENT

OF AGRICULTURE, WASHINGTON, D.C.

A 1. 10 : 959

The United States Government Printing Office

100464

Foreword

EZRA TAFT BENSON

Secretary of Agriculture

FOOD IS IMPORTANT in keeping our people and our country strong. The Department of Agriculture is, in a sense, a department of food—food for health and food for fitness. Much of our work has to do with the production, marketing, and use of food.

An abundance of food is one of our blessings. The problems caused by our excessive supplies of a few commodities are quite in contrast to the hunger experienced daily by large numbers of people in many countries of the world. As Secretary of Agriculture I am grateful that we struggle with problems of too much rather than too little.

We are using our supplies not only to meet our own needs but also to assist millions of less fortunate people abroad. We have been generous with our abundance. Our shipments of food are helping the free world meet its challenges by saving some people from starvation, by raising living standards, by building good will, by laying the groundwork for future trade.

To be assured of an abundance of food of good quality, we must increase our knowledge. We are blessed with rich land. We must guard it well, conserving and improving it by means of the most up-to-date knowledge and techniques. We are blessed with intelligent, informed, and industrious farm people who put the results of agricultural research to work in highly effective ways. Research—agricultural research, food research—must go forward. We must learn to produce ever more efficiently, to process and package to meet increasing demands, to market ever more effectively, and to use our abundance ever more wisely.

Much remains to be learned about food in all these aspects. Research on a wide, continuous basis will help give us the more complete knowledge we need to employ our food resources wisely.

v

Accompanying research there must always be more and more education. Facts must be made available widely to get full use. This is the service which this Yearbook of Agriculture can help perform.

This book reports much that is new from the research of scientists in the Department and elsewhere. It tells many things we all need to know about food. It is a very important book. But the full measure of its importance depends on how well and how widely it is read and how well and widely the information it contains is used. I feel sure that it will be a powerful force pointing the way to stronger bodies, stronger homes, and a stronger country.

Preface

ALFRED STEFFERUD

Editor of the Yearbook

EVEN THOUGH women did much of the planning and writing of this Yearbook and women and women-to-be dominated our thinking, it is a book as well for men and men-to-be.

Food is a big part of a man's world, too. He produces, processes, and markets food. He buys, cooks, and eats food. He earns daily bread, worries about his waistline, and sometimes feeds the baby. He is his family's Food Expert.

We hope therefore that men will read this book. Maybe not all of it—to present as many aspects as possible of this complex subject, we prepared some chapters with many groups in mind, among them students, farmers, teachers, administrators, and technicians.

We suggest that men try on for size at least these chapters: *Carbohydrates,* page 88; *Calories and Body Weight,* page 101; *Water,* page 168; *Nutritional Needs After 25,* page 311; *Fish and the Fishing Industry,* page 353; *What Your Food Money Buys,* page 557; *Don't Be Fooled by Fads,* page 660; *Feeding 6,280 Million,* page 671.

We think students—tomorrow's husbands, wives, and parents—will find in these pages grist for themes and thought. If studies, TV, and dates permit no more, we recommend especially for them: *The Story of Nutrition,* page 7; *Adolescents and Young Adults,* page 303; *Youth Learns About Food,* page 647; *Trends in Heights and Weights,* page 181.

They may need to look up some terms in a dictionary, although we did what we could by providing a glossary, which is pretty good reading in itself.

Farmers have been the main readers of the Yearbooks of Agriculture these 111 years. Here they will find information about nutritional values of the products they grow, but not about ways to grow more. To any farmer who may think this book is not "practical" for him, we offer the reminder that keeping his body and mind in prime working order is as important as oiling his tractor and feeding his livestock.

Farmers may like especially: *Quality in Animal Products,* page 327; *Marketing, Quality, and Cost,* page 408; *Freezing Food at Home,* page 461; *Storing Perishable Foods at Home,* page 477; *Conserving Nutritive Values,* page 483; *The Years Ahead,* page 701.

To teachers we recommend especially these chapters: *The Story of Nutrition,* page 7; *Questions and Answers,* page 23; *The Nutriture of People,* page 186; *Recommended Allowances,* page 227; *A Table of Food Values,* page 231; *A Guide to Eating,* page 267; *Planning Meals for the Family,* page 510; *Habits—and More,* page 631.

To parents also those chapters should be helpful.

For the many persons who regard nutrition as more than today's meals, we put food in a national and international framework, as in: *The Development of New Foods,* page 434; *Are We Well Fed?,* page 620; *Feeding 6,280 Million,* page 671; *Sharing Our Bounty,* page 681; *School Lunches,* page 691; *The Years Ahead,* page 701.

Our subject, to repeat, is complex. Our knowledge of it is comparatively new and is developing constantly. Some of it is controversial. We did not expect of the writers, therefore, that they would interpret data in the same way, draw predetermined conclusions, write in some prescribed fashion, or try to reflect the thinking of any particular person or unit in the Department of Agriculture. Scientists cannot work that way.

We have tried to present the facts clearly, but we have not tried to process them into an instant, ready-mix, no-trouble-at-all pap.

Our goal was a solid, authoritative, complete book that will put details of nutrition in proper perspective and counteract some of the nonsense or half-truths about food we read and hear so often.

The members of the 1959 Yearbook Committee are:

Agricultural Research Service: Georgian Adams, T. C. Byerly, Faith Clark, George W. Irving, Jr., Ruth M. Leverton, Hazel K. Stiebeling, *Chairman.*

Agricultural Marketing Service: Martin Garber, Omer W. Herrmann, Frederick V. Waugh.

Federal Extension Service: Frances Scudder.

Office of Information: Alfred Stefferud.

Contents

III. *Food*

HEALTH

IV. *Food*

ALLOWANCES

V. *Food*

OUR NEEDS

VI. *Food*

QUALITY

VII. *Food*

PREPARATION

xii

Food

Food

BACKGROUNDS

Food in Our Lives

HAZEL K. STIEBELING

FOOD contributes to physical, mental, and emotional health. Food nourishes our bodies. When we eat in a favorable setting, we get another kind of well-being: A sense of belonging and other psychological and social values accrue from the pleasures of mealtime and from having our food with friendly companions.

People devote much time and effort and thought to food—to producing the assortments of food that they need and want and to processing, distributing, and serving food in the places, at the times, and in the forms it is wanted.

People always have known they must eat to live—children to grow normally and adults to keep strong. But food can do more than satisfy physiological hunger and carry psychological and social values. Modern science shows that all of us, regardless of purse, can add years to our life and life to our years if we apply knowledge about nutrition to our selection and use of food.

Both the kind and the amount of food are important to those engaged in strenuous physical work—farmers, athletes, lumbermen, miners, to mention only a few.

Indeed, studies made by German physiologists in the 1940's showed that each kind of work activity requires a specific amount of food energy (calories) over and above the amount just to maintain life. For example, the output of miners in the Ruhr district directly paralleled the food energy available for work, which during and immediately after the Second World War was controlled by food rationing.

Management in industry in the United States and other countries became increasingly aware during the war of the value of providing good meals for the workers. Proper food during work hours made for increased efficiency of the labor force.

Brain and nerve are nourished by the same blood stream that builds brawn and bone. Persons of every age and in every occupation require food of kinds and amounts that enable their bodies to maintain the best possible internal environment for all of the cells and tissues.

THE GENERAL ASSOCIATION of diet and health comes from many observations.

Wilbur Olin Atwater, the first director of investigations of nutrition in the United States Department of Agriculture, commented on the contrast between the great beauty of the children and young girls in some parts of the Appalachian highlands and the prematurely aged appearance of the women by the time they reached their midthirties. Dr. Atwater attributed this condition largely to the poor nutritional quality of diets in that area in the 1890's and early 1900's.

Major General Sir Robert McCarrison, a British physician and the director of the nutrition research of the Indian Research Fund Association from 1927 to 1935, was impressed by the great differences in stature and physical well-being of people in different sections of India. He fed laboratory animals rations much like the diets of the different groups. He concluded that diet was a major factor in the differences he observed in the longevity and health of the people.

Lord John Boyd-Orr, a Scottish physician and scientist, studied the nutrition, physique, and health of two African tribes for the British Medical Research Council. He described the superior stature and vigor of members of the tribe that had an abundance of milk and meat. He compared their condition with the lesser stature and vigor of the tribe whose food was primarily cereals and other foods of plant origin.

Margaret A. Ohlson and her research colleagues in the State agricultural experiment stations in Iowa and Michigan reported in 1948 on the dietary practices of 100 Midwest women 30 to 70 years old. The women who were in good general health had borne and reared healthy children and had no history of chronic or debilitating disease. The women in poorer health, although well enough to take part in the day-by-day life of their families, often had too little vitality to do much else. Their medical histories recorded chronic disease processes and many complaints of vague ill health, such as fatigue and irregularities of digestion. The women who were in good health were drinking more milk and eating more eggs, vegetables,

and whole-grain breads and cereals than the less healthy group.

Dietitians, psychologists, and physiologists of the College of Medicine of the State University of Iowa studied the importance of breakfast to men of all ages, college women, and schoolboys. Physical and mental efficiency was sustained better throughout the day when they ate breakfasts that supplied about a quarter of their day's needs for protein and calories than when they omitted the morning meal.

We of the 19th and 20th centuries were not the first ones to link wellbeing with the quality and sufficiency of diets.

Dr. Mary Swartz Rose, researcher, author, and the first professor of nutrition in Columbia University, abstracted Biblical history in these words:

"In an ancient chronicle [Daniel I: 1–15] we may read: 'In the third year of the reign of Jehoiakim, king of Judah [607 B.C.] came Nebuchadnezzar, king of Babylon, unto Jerusalem, and besieged it.' When the city fell into his hands, the king ordered that certain noble youths, 'well-favored and skilful in all wisdom,' be selected for training as courtiers. They were to have a special education and a daily portion of the king's meat, and of the wine which he drank. Living a carefully prescribed life, at the end of three years they would presumably be fit to stand before the great monarch.

"One of these youths 'with knowledge and skill in all learning and wisdom' objected to the dietary part of the program and purposed in his heart that he would not eat the king's meat nor drink his wine; but the prince of the eunuchs, who had him in charge, protested, saying, 'I fear my lord the king.' The young man countered with a reasonable proposal: 'Prove thy servants, I beseech thee, ten days; and let them give us pulse to eat and water to drink. Then let our countenances be looked upon before thee, and the countenance of the youths that eat of the king's meat.'

"This seemed a fair bargain and so

the nutrition experiment was undertaken, with the result that at the end
of the ten days 'their countenances
appeared fairer and fatter in flesh than
all the children which did eat the portion of the king's meat. So the steward
took away their meat and the wine
which they should drink and gave
them pulse [peas or other leguminous
seeds or porridge]'; and when at the
end of their probationary period the
king examined them they passed with
a score ten times better than all the
magicians and enchanters in his
realm."

THE SCIENTIFIC EXPLANATION of why
food makes a difference comes mainly
from well-designed experiments in
nutrition with domestic and laboratory
animals whose metabolic, or life, processes have points in common with or
can be related to those of human
beings. Only in species of relatively
short life can an investigator follow
the influence of diet on growth and on
health throughout the life span and
through successive generations. Only
with lower forms of life can the effects
of different diets be compared while
keeping other environmental conditions rigidly constant.

From long experience with domestic
and laboratory animals, Prof. Elmer
V. McCollum, of the University of
Wisconsin and of The Johns Hopkins
University, has concluded that human
diets could contribute to what he
called the preservation of the characteristics of youth if they were richer
than average in certain components of
food—the nutrients calcium and vitamins A and C. He gave the name
"protective food" to foods rich in these
nutrients. Outstanding for these nutrients are milk, dark-green and deep-
yellow fruit and vegetables, and citrus
and some other fruits and vegetables
that are important for the vitamin C
they contain.

Maintaining certain of the characteristics of youth for a large part of the
life span is important to the individual
and to society. Creative thinking and

outstanding productivity have tended
to occur oftenest in early adulthood,
especially during the thirties.

An interesting report on this subject
by Harvey C. Lehman was published
for the American Philosophical Society in 1953. While recognizing that
some persons succeed in making great
discoveries and original contributions
to science and art in their later years,
Dr. Lehman remarked that such men
had not only good minds but also the
physiological luck that enabled them
to go on through their later years doing
(or completing) notable creative work.

Could it be that good nutrition was
an important part of this physiological
luck? Whether devoted to creative
work or to leadership, the entire span
of adult life will undoubtedly be most
fruitful when undergirded by good
nutrition from conception to the end.

Prof. Henry Clapp Sherman and his
associates in Columbia University
found they were able to accelerate
growth and development in laboratory
animals by feeding a ration richer in
calcium, protein, and vitamin A than
the usual ration that had been adequate enough to produce 88 generations of animals that were considered
normal by all usual standards. The
ration richer in these particular nutrients also prolonged life by about 10
percent and deferred the onset of visible old age in the same animals that
had gained their growth and maturity
relatively early in life. This extra time
in life thus was an extension of the
period of the prime of life.

That fact is important and encouraging. Most of us want to be healthy
during a long prime of life; we do not
prize long life if it means a long period
of immaturity or a long period of
senescence.

Dr. Sherman's work demonstrated
what he called the principle of the nutritional improvability of the norm.
He meant that through better nutrition things can be better than our accepted ideas of what is normal.

The principle has ample support in
agricultural research. Scientists in-

creasingly are able to match nutritional needs in developing rations for animals—the dairy cow, pig, sheep, hen. As a result, they are achieving higher rates of gain in calves, hogs, and broilers and greater production of milk and eggs for each unit of feed.

Agricultural scientists are concerned mostly with improved nutrition as a means of achieving better growth in an animal or better performance during its reproductive life. For the human being, the period of growth and reproduction covers only the first half of the normal life span. We want to know what promise the best possible nutrition at every stage of the life cycle can hold for our entire lives.

The belief that proper nutrition is an important contributor to our health throughout life rests on observations of the comparative well-being of population groups that have subsisted for generations on diets that differ widely in nutritional qualities, on short-term investigations with human subjects to learn the influence of the quantity of various components of food on life processes, and on short- and long-term experiments with animals.

KNOWLEDGE OF NUTRITION has been developed to the point where we know that the human body must get some half-hundred different substances from food. These substances collectively are called nutrients. Each nutrient has specific functions, and each is needed, although in many instances several nutrients must work together closely to perform the assigned services for the body.

Indispensable nutrients include proteins, fats, and carbohydrates—organic substances that can serve as fuel (calories) and suppliers of essential amino and fatty acids; many inorganic or mineral elements, from calcium to zinc; and many chemically unrelated substances known as vitamins.

Nutrients are the building materials for new or repaired tissues and are the substances from which the body daily makes its regulators of digestive and other processes involved in its use of nourishment. Taken together in proper amounts and proportions, nutrients derived from food enable the body to function normally and to achieve orderly changes in composition and structure throughout the life cycle.

Our growing knowledge about nutritional needs and the nutritive characteristics of various foods is helping us to choose diets that can help keep us well and permit our inherited abilities to develop and function fully.

Nurture determines the extent to which we can achieve the upper limits of well-being set by Nature. While no one would want to underestimate the influence of modern medicine, good housing, and other environmental conditions in promoting health, everyone can be sure that food comes first.

Learning the lessons of nutritional science and making the principles a part of our lives is one of the prices Nature demands for health.

Some experiments with animals suggest that specific appetites may develop for indispensable amino acids, minerals, and vitamins when they are short in rations, but human beings cannot depend on any such a mechanism to govern their appetite for food. The food habits of many of us do not insure that we select the variety and amount of foods we need. Most of us need guidance in nutrition.

GUIDANCE in planning diets is given in scientific terms by the Food and Nutrition Board of the National Academy of Sciences-National Research Council. This Board, made up of 24 scientists from universities, research organizations, and industry, interprets scientific opinion on problems of food and nutrition for the Government. A representative of each Government agency concerned with food and nutrition attends the Board meetings. The Board publishes dietary allowances that say how much of each nutrient is recommended for persons differing in age and activity. These scientific goals can be used in planning diets and in evaluating food supplies from the nutritional point of view.

Food guides and weekly market lists, developed by nutritionists of the Department of Agriculture, translate the scientific facts about nutrition into terms of everyday foods. Diet plans of this sort were first issued in 1930, and they are revised from time to time as knowledge of food needs and of nutritive values of food advances. The market lists show how the same nourishment can be supplied by combinations of food that differ widely in cost. Account may also be taken of personal taste and the variations that occur from time to time in market supplies and prices of foods.

These guides and lists put emphasis on the needed amounts of several kinds of foods that some people tend to neglect. They emphasize milk, an excellent source of calcium, riboflavin, and protein, among other nutrients. They emphasize deep-green and dark-yellow fruit and vegetables, foods that are rich in carotenes, which the body can convert into vitamin A. They emphasize the citrus fruits and other fruits and vegetables rich in ascorbic acid.

THE FOOD CONSUMED by some families in the United States still falls somewhat short of scientific goals in one or more nutrients, despite the general availability of present-day knowledge about nutrition. Shortages are seldom severe enough to cause obvious dietary deficiency diseases, however. Rickets, beriberi, simple goiter, pellagra, and scurvy are rarely seen in this country now because most people can afford good diets and have come to understand that proper food can prevent such diseases.

The increase in life expectancy in this country since 1900 has come about largely from a decrease in death rates among children under 5 years and the control of infectious diseases.

The least change has occurred among adults older than 45 years, among whom deaths are more likely to be associated with abnormal developments in the structure and functioning of organs or tissues. This situation is a challenge to nutritional as well as to medical science. There are, for example, many indications that diet is one of the complex set of conditions of modern life that is associated with impairments of the liver, kidney, heart, and blood vessels.

Understanding of these relationships is as yet imperfect. The prevalence of obesity and dental caries as well as early aging or premature physical impairments of many kinds indicate that some nutrition problems still are widespread in this country.

Improvement in many aspects of our diet has occurred since the mid-1930's, however. A third of our families then had diets that were classed as poor. If the same nutritional yardsticks were applied in 1959, only about 10 percent of households would have poor diets.

Improved economic conditions; developments in producing, processing, and marketing foods; and research and education in nutrition have had a large part in this betterment.

Some of the improvement comes from a program initiated in 1941 to enrich white bread and flour with certain minerals and vitamins. We are particularly favored in this country because we have a wide assortment of foods from which to choose our meals, and because our food supplies have been increased far more rapidly than our population. Most of us have much freedom in choosing what shall comprise our daily bread.

A higher proportion of the population is attaining the vigor and physical stature once achieved only by a favored few. With better nutrition, today's children grow sturdier and taller. Young men and women in the United States are about 2 inches taller than the average of 50 years ago. This tendency to grow faster and to become taller adults has been noted also in some other countries.

You may ask whether there is any advantage in having a big body. Certainly there is an advantage in having a healthy body—and what contributes to a healthy body also increases the possibility of attaining the body build permitted by inherited capacity.

That the strongest and ablest minds in science generally go with strong, healthy bodies is a conclusion reached by Dr. Ales Hrdlicka, curator for physical anthropology at the United States National Museum of the Smithsonian Institution for about 40 years. He reported in 1929 on measurements made on 100 (about half) of the members of our National Academy of Sciences. He showed that nearly all of these outstanding representatives of the sciences were superior to the average man in physique, health, and longevity.

Francis Galton of London was similarly impressed during the course of his study into the laws and consequences of hereditary genius. He wrote in 1869:

"I think most of my readers would be surprised at the stature and physical frames of the heroes of history, who fill my pages, if they could be assembled together in a hall. . . . I do not deny that many men of extraordinary mental gifts have had wretched constitutions, but deny them to be . . . the usual accompaniment. . . . A collection of living magnates in various branches of intellectual achievement is always a feast to my eyes; being, as they are, such massive, vigorous, capable-looking animals."

EVERYONE in the United States should be able to have a nutritionally adequate diet. The growing knowledge of nutrition will undergird it, and increased productivity can provide it.

Food in this country costs less in proportion to income than in most parts of the world. Wages for an hour of work in 1959 bought more food, a greater variety of food, and food of higher market quality than ever before. Middle-income groups, both farm and city, spend about one-third of the family budget for food. Low-income city families spend a much larger share and for them the situation is still about as Henry Clapp Sherman once put it:

"Half the struggle of life is a struggle for food in the sense that a majority of the world's people must spend as much of their time or their earnings in providing themselves with food as with all other necessities together."

It takes effort to get our food to us in sufficient quantities and in wholesome form. Agriculture has increased production to meet increased demands for milk, fruit, vegetables, meat, poultry, and eggs. Processing, warehousing, transportation, and marketing industries have done well—but can do better—the task of bringing food to consumers in wholesome condition. Public services help protect the consumer by certifying to wholesomeness of food and freedom from adulteration, establishing standards of identity, requiring truth in labeling, and preventing misleading statements in advertising.

From the planning by the producer to the final eating of the food by the individual, we as a Nation have profited from research and education on food and nutrition.

Shall we in this country and the people around the earth be able to meet the food needs of the future?

The demands of rapidly growing populations will be for more and more of all kinds of food. Demands may also come for change in proportions among the different kinds of foods as nutritional knowledge advances and as standards of living rise.

To meet these demands, we shall need increased knowledge for efficiency in consumption as well as in the production, processing, and marketing of food.

We can and shall meet these challenges.

HAZEL K. STIEBELING, *Director of the Institute of Home Economics, the Agricultural Research Service, has guided the Department's research program in human nutrition and other phases of home economics since 1942. With a doctor's degree in chemistry from Columbia University, she came to the Department of Agriculture in 1930 to undertake research in food economics.*

The Story of Nutrition

ELIZABETH NEIGE TODHUNTER

THIS is the story of man's long search for exact knowledge of the food his body needs.

It is a story of laboratories, experiments, failures, successes, and discoveries. It is even more a story of men and women with curiosity, ideas, persistence, and a driving desire to help people live better.

It is a story of a fight against ignorance and superstitions and the strange ideas people always have had—now, too!—about the things they eat.

It is an old story that could begin with the first man and the little he knew beyond the fact that he liked to eat.

It is, though, primarily a story of accomplishments in this century—indeed, in the last few years; a story so new that it is far from its end.

Although for centuries people tried to solve some of their problems of what to eat and how much and why, they made little progress until chemistry was well developed and we could analyze foods and know what they are made of. We also had to wait until physiology became a science that could provide understanding of the human body and how it functions. We needed as well the contributions of physics, medicine, agriculture, and biology.

Because it is a "new" science, then, let us begin with the man who has been called "the father of American nutrition" and later go back to the men and ideas that preceded him—for nutrition, like every science and almost every other great development, has been built on things that went before.

Wilbur Olin Atwater was born in 1844 in Johnstown, N.Y. He attended the University of Vermont and Wesleyan University in Middletown, Conn. For his thesis for his doctor's degree at Yale University in 1869 he—for the first time in this country—used modern methods to analyze corn fodder.

He went to Europe in 1869 to study agricultural and physiological chemistry at the Universities of Leipzig and Berlin. When the first experiment station in the United States was established at Middletown in 1875, he became its first director. He later became director of the Connecticut Agricultural Experiment Station at Storrs when it was organized in 1887.

His studies on the acquisition of atmospheric nitrogen by plants and on the composition of feeds, begun several years earlier, he continued as part of the work at Storrs during the 14 years he was director. These investigations led to his interest in the composition of man's food.

Dr. Atwater made a series of analyses of fish for the United States Fish Commission and of the flesh of domestic animals for the Smithsonian Institution between 1879 and 1883. He conducted studies of the dietaries of people in Massachusetts and Canada.

Dr. Atwater returned to Europe in 1887. He worked in the laboratory in Munich where Carl Voit was doing outstanding work in studies of respiration—the exchange of gases between the blood and the tissues—and calorimetry, the measurement of heat, the first steps toward quantitative knowledge of nutritional requirements.

Another American student who worked in Dr. Voit's laboratory was Graham Lusk, who brought back with him a small model of a calorimeter Voit had made and later built others at Cornell University Medical College in New York City for studies with dogs and children. We shall come back to Dr. Voit later.

Dr. Atwater also returned to this country inspired to do further calorimetry studies at Wesleyan University. With his coworkers be built a calorimeter for studies on man and designed a bomb calorimeter for measurement of caloric value of foods. He made adjustment for the indigestible fraction in food and the incomplete oxidation of protein in the body and gave the values, widely used ever since, of 4, 9, 4 Calories per gram of carbohydrate, fat, and protein in a mixed diet.

The Congress in 1894 appropriated 10 thousand dollars "to enable the Secretary of Agriculture to investigate and report upon the nutritive value of the various articles and commodities used for human food, with special suggestion of full, wholesome, and edible rations less wasteful and more economical than those in common use."

This work was assigned to the Office of Experiment Stations under Dr. Atwater, who was designated "chief of nutrition investigations."

From that time forward, biochemists, nutritionists, home economists, and investigators in animal and poultry husbandry at agricultural experiment stations throughout the country have steadily and continuously helped build the newer knowledge of nutrition.

Headquarters for the work were established at Middletown, and Dr. Atwater was made chief. He and his colleagues investigated the diets of hundreds of persons of different occupations and compared the results of similar studies in other countries. They made many experiments with men on digestion and carried on special studies of the nutritive value of cereals, meats, vegetables, fruit, and nuts and the effects of cooking and other forms of preparation on nutritive values.

He and his coworkers demonstrated that the amount of heat—energy—a person develops during a given period is the amount that can be derived from the energy liberated in the oxidation of food materials during the period.

Dr. Atwater studied digestibility of food, made numerous dietary studies, and analyzed many foods. He prepared in 1896 the famous Bulletin 28 of the United States Department of Agriculture. It was the first extensive table of food values ever prepared in this country.

Atwater sought to find what was the best and most economical diet for man. At that time only protein and Calories, as supplied by fat and carbohydrate, were considered of importance, and such foods as green, leafy vegetables and fruit were regarded as expensive purchases or luxuries.

A chapter Dr. Atwater wrote for the 1894 Yearbook of Agriculture has meaning for us today. I quote a few sentences from it:

"Materials for the food of man make up the larger part of our agricultural production and the largest item of our export abroad. Our food production is one-sided. It includes a relative excess of the fat of meat, of starch, and of sugar, the substances that serve the body for fuel to yield heat and muscular power, while the nitrogenous substances, those which make blood and muscle, bone and brain, are relatively deficient. . . . What is needed is more nitrogen in the soil for plant food, more nitrogen in plants to make better food for animals and man, and more nitrogen in the food of man. Better culture of the soil and better manuring will bring not only larger crops, but crops richer in nitrogen. . . .

"The power of a man to do work depends upon his nutrition. A well-fed horse can draw a heavy load. With less food he does less work. A well-fed man has strength of muscle and of brain, while a poorly nourished man has not."

He defined food as "that which, when taken into the body, builds up its tissues and keeps them in repair, or which is consumed in the body to yield energy in the form of heat to keep it warm and create strength for its work. . . ."

"The most healthful food is that which is best fitted to the wants of the user. . . .

"The cheapest food is that which furnishes the most nutriment at the least cost.

"The most economical food is that which is both most healthful and cheapest.

"To make the most out of a man, to bring him up to the desirable level of productive capacity, to enable him to live as a man ought to live, he must be well fed.

"One of the ways in which the worst economy is practiced is in the buying of high-priced foods. For this error, prejudice, the palate, and poor cooking are mainly responsible. There is a prevalent but unfounded idea that costly foods, such as the tenderest meats, the finest fish, the highest priced butter, the choicest flour, and the most delicate vegetables possess some peculiar virtue which is lacking in the less expensive materials. . . . The maxim that 'the best is the cheapest' does not apply to food."

LET US GO BACK now for a glimpse at the beliefs and knowledge on which Atwater and other scientists of the 20th century built. Such a quick survey will help us to understand better the growth of the science of nutrition— and the speed with which it has grown.

Back in the days of the Greeks, before the birth of Christ, man's inquiring mind was asking questions about the world in which he lived. The "science" of that day believed that there were four elements—earth, air, fire, and water; four qualities— dry, cold, hot, and wet; and four humors, or liquids, that comprised the body—blood, phlegm, black bile, and yellow bile.

Hippocrates, the father of medicine, taught the value of diet, but he believed in one universal aliment, an idea that prevailed until the early part of the 19th century.

Galen, a Greek physician who settled in Rome in A.D. 164, wrote many books about anatomy, diet, and health. His word was accepted without question through the centuries that saw the decline of Rome, the Dark Ages, and the first light of the Renaissance, until Andreas Vesalius (1514– 1564), a Flemish student of anatomy, overthrew some of Galen's ideas and dared to investigate for himself, rather than follow blindly the master's dicta.

One original thinker in Italy tried to study nutrition. He asked the right questions, but he could not get the answers because he had neither a knowledge of chemistry nor the necessary tools. Santorio Sanctorius (1561– 1636) day after day sat on his big balance and weighed himself and the food he ate, but could not find the answer to the difference in weight after he had eaten. He has truly been called the father of experiments in metabolism, but it was some 300 years later before investigators could explain the nutrition problem he had posed.

In the 17th century, "the Golden Age of Science," the experimental method began to take hold. The British William Harvey revolutionized our concept of the human body by demonstrating that blood circulates from the heart throughout the body. The Dutch Anton van Leeuwenhoek developed the microscope and studied the red cells or corpuscles of the blood stream. At meetings of the Royal Society, which received its charter in 1662, scientists discussed their experiments and the curiosities of nature they had found.

The 18th century brought the rise of modern chemistry. Joseph Black, a professor at Glasgow, discovered the gas that to us is carbon dioxide. Wealthy, eccentric Henry Cavendish discovered hydrogen. Daniel Rutherford, a Scottish physician, discovered nitrogen. Joseph Priestly, the English minister who was happiest when he was in his laboratory, was credited with discovering oxygen.

Antoine Lavoisier of France, outstanding in his ability to interpret and integrate the new discoveries, showed that the life process is one of respiration and that as oxygen was consumed by the body, carbon dioxide was exhaled. He measured those gases and calculated the body's heat production. He realized that the working man expended more calories and therefore needed more food than those who were less active.

Interest in physiology grew. René Réaumur (1683–1757), a French naturalist and physicist, fed various foods to birds and then, after short periods of time, retrieved the food and studied the changes that had taken place during digestion.

Lazzaro Spallanzani (1729–1799) in Italy experimented on himself. He swallowed linen bags containing meat and bread and withdrew them later by strings attached to the bags. From the changes he found in the partly digested food, he realized that some chemical changes were taking place.

A Scottish naval physician, James Lind, conducted a carefully controlled experiment, the first of its kind, and demonstrated how to prevent and cure scurvy, "the scourge of the sea," that killed hundreds of sailors on ships taking long voyages. Dr. Lind in 1747 found that lemon juice could cure or prevent this disease; yet it was more than 50 years later before the British Navy required that lemon juice be provided on all ships. Even then no one seemed to realize the significance of the cure; some 150 years later vitamin C was discovered as the antiscurvy vitamin.

The 19th century was the period of chemical investigation and measurement of respiration and energy use by animals.

Hippocrates had taught that there was one ultimate principle in food, and not till 1834 did this idea change. William Prout, a London physician, published a book, *Chemistry, Meteorology and the Functions of Digestion*, in which he put forward the idea that food contained three staminal principles, which he called saccharine, oily, and albuminous material.

A new era began in 1816 when Francois Magendie, the great French physiologist, discovered that dogs died if given only sugar or oil or butter but would live if given a nitrogen-containing food. Soon Jean Boussingault, a French chemist and experimental farmer, made the first experiment of nitrogen balance with a horse and a cow. Gerrit Jan Mulder, the Dutch physician and chemist, exploring the nitrogen-containing foods, introduced the term "protein" in 1838. He was wrong in what he thought these proteins were, but the name stuck.

The chemistry of the albuminous (protein) substances, as these were first called, began to be understood when some of the "building units" of these complex substances were isolated. The first amino acid, cystine, was discovered in 1810 by the English chemist and physicist William Wollaston when working with kidney stones. He failed to recognize its true chemical nature. The simplest of all the amino acids is glycine. It was first identified by M. H. Braconnot, the French chemist who obtained glycine as a breakdown product from hydrolysis of gelatin.

By the end of the 19th century, 12 of the 22 amino acids now known to be present in proteins of food had been discovered.

The spotlight was on protein. Organic chemistry developed, and Justus von Liebig, the great German chemist, branched out to develop the new agricultural chemistry that was later to lead to biochemistry.

Studies of nitrogen balance were made on dogs and other experimental animals in attempts to determine the amount of protein they needed. Chemists were busy improving methods of food analysis, and the general belief was that through knowledge of chemical composition of foods one would be able to plan an adequate diet.

The French chemist Jean Dumas evolved an accurate method for quantitative measurement of nitrogen. The protein content could be calculated from it. But it was such a long, painstaking process that not many studies could be made. Then the keen mind of Johann Kjeldahl, a Danish chemist, devised a new and relatively easy method of determining nitrogen in organic matter (1883), and the work could push ahead more rapidly. The availability of equipment and suitable chemical methods of analysis have always been an influencing factor in the development of the science of nutrition.

In America, physiology and the study of digestion of food were aided by the work of a backwoods surgeon, William Beaumont. He was on Army duty at Fort Mackinac in Michigan Territory when a gunshot wound of a French Canadian trapper, Alexis St. Martin, gave him an opportunity to show his medical and surgical skill. The trapper's life was saved, but he lived with a hole in his stomach. The hole let Dr. Beaumont have a living organ for the study of digestion. Patiently and accurately, he made his experiments so that the findings presented in his book, *Experiments and Observations on the Gastric Juice and the Physiology of Digestion* (1833), were unsurpassed until the researches of the Russian physiologist, Ivan Petrovich Pavlov.

Dr. Beaumont might have accomplished more, but Alexis did not like being experimented with. He slipped away to Canada and declined to return. Chemistry was not far enough advanced in Beaumont's day to be able to identify what was in the sample of gastric juice that he sent to the leading chemists to analyze. But digestion was clearly recognized now as a chemical process of breaking down food, and men could begin to find out what it involved.

Next came the study of respiration and calorimetry that led to the measurement of man's energy needs—the first steps to quantitative knowledge of nutritional requirements.

Foremost in this work was Carl Voit, who had learned his chemistry from Liebig and later provoked his former teacher by daring to disagree with some of his findings.

Voit, with the help of Max von Pettenkofer, who had been Liebig's assistant, built an apparatus for the study of respiratory exchanges in man and animals. Between 1866 and 1873, these two men published seven long papers on the metabolism of healthy persons during fasting and at work. Dr. Voit showed that, contrary to current belief, nitrogen metabolism is not increased by muscular work.

One of the greatest of all Voit's pupils was Max Rubner, who continued the calorimetry studies begun under his master teacher. He determined caloric values of 4.1, 9.3, and 4.1 per gram of carbohydrate, fat, and protein.

Rubner also established the law of surface area in basal metabolism from his experiments, which showed that heat production of man in the resting state is proportional to the surface area of the body. He showed that the law of conservation of energy—which says that energy must have a source; it cannot come from nothing, nor can it disappear into nothing; it only changes form—holds true for the animal world as for the physical. Rubner also demonstrated that fat and carbohydrate are interchangeable in nutrition on the basis of energy value.

An entirely different concept of food values was introduced some 20 years later.

Elmer V. McCollum in 1918 published a book, *The Newer Knowledge of Nutrition*—a title that was used by many workers from then on to describe the change which had taken place in our understanding of nutrition. In that book, Dr. McCollum also introduced a term that has been widely used ever since—"the protective foods." Milk and the leaves of plants, he wrote, are to be regarded as protective foods and should never be omitted from the diet.

The rapid growth of knowledge of nutrition in the 20th century is also illustrated by the book. The first edition in 1918 had 189 pages. It went through five editions, and the latest in 1939 had 684 pages.

The 20th century opened with the general recognition that protein, fats, and carbohydrates as sources of energy and some inorganic salts were the necessary components of the diet.

This, despite the fact that some two centuries earlier, Dr. Lind had shown that because lemon juice would cure scurvy there must be something else in food. Other investigators some 10 to 20 years earlier also had unusual things happen with diets they were using. Christiaan Eijkman, a Dutch army surgeon, discovered that chickens fed polished rice developed a neuritis, like beriberi, which he could cure or prevent by feeding brown rice. He was the first person to produce a dietary deficiency disease experimentally. In Japan, Baron Kanekiro Takaki had found that he could pre-

vent beriberi, which took the lives of many Japanese sailors, by increasing the amount of meat and fish in their diets.

Nicolai Lunin, a young student in a Russian laboratory, found in 1880 that mice thrived on milk, but they died if they were given a mixture of protein, fat, sugar, and ash of milk. These findings could not be explained and attracted little attention in a world that was making rapid progress in chemistry and bacteriology. The time was coming when the limited viewpoint provided by chemical analysis would be replaced by the new biological method.

VITAMINS now are household words, but the term was coined only in 1912 by a Polish chemist who was working at the Lister Institute in London.

Casimir Funk was trying to isolate some substance from rice polishings that would forestall beriberi. He reasoned that if there was something in food that prevented beriberi, scurvy, and pellagra, this something was vital for life.

His laboratory preparation, which was effective in curing beriberi in birds, was an amine compound, and so he coined the name "vitamine." The name caught on.

Support was given to Dr. Funk's suggestion of the existence of vitamines by the work of Frederick G. Hopkins, biochemist in Cambridge University, England. Dr. Hopkins fed rats an artificial diet prepared from constituents of the same nature as those present in milk. He used a diet of casein, starch, cane sugar, lard, and inorganic salts, each constituent as carefully purified as possible. The rats grew for a short time but then drooped and died. A similar group of rats grew normally when they were given as little as 2 cubic centimeters of milk daily in addition to the artificial diet.

Dr. Hopkins showed that it was not a lack of calories that caused the death of the animals, nor was it lack of palatability of the diet—a reason often given then to explain the failure of growth in animals on special diets. He postulated that there were unsuspected dietetic factors, or accessory food substances, that were essential for health.

Louis Pasteur's brilliant researches of the 1870's helped establish the new science of bacteriology and fixed the germ theory of disease firmly in the minds of scientists.

Cleanliness and sanitation in the handling of food were recognized as essential. But the idea that something not present in food, something lacking, could cause disease was indeed difficult to accept. Men's minds must be ready for the acceptance of new ideas and the findings of research; there was much resistance to the vitamin theory for a decade at least.

Some experiments started at the University of Wisconsin in 1907 were to lead, by halting steps at first, to the actual discovery of the first of the many vitamins with which we are familiar. Rations of the same chemical composition, but each from a different single plant, were fed to cows. The corn-fed animals were sleek, trim, healthy looking after a year. Those receiving the ration from the wheat plant had a rough coat and a gaunt appearance. Those fed the oat plant were midway between. The experiment proved that chemical analysis did not give the complete answer about nutritive values.

Elmer V. McCollum was one of the assistants in those early classic experiments with cows. He was a farm boy from Kansas with a thirst for knowledge and a retentive mind, and he had studied under the great Lafayette Benedict Mendel at Yale University.

Dr. McCollum was given the assignment to try to find what was the cause of the difference in the three rations, which were chemically similar, at least according to the analytical methods then available, although they gave different results.

The young McCollum read and pondered. He came to the conclusion that he must experiment with the simplest of rations prepared from purified foodstuffs if he was to find the cause of the difference. Because a large amount of foodstuff would have to be prepared and it would take a long time for results to show up in cows, he decided he must use some small animal. He chose the rat, and so started what was probably the first rat colony and first extensive series of experiments with these widely used test animals.

By 1913 Dr. McCollum had found an artificial diet of protein, lactose, starch, and inorganic salts, that, with butterfat, gave good growth. If he used the same diet, but replaced the butterfat with olive oil or lard, the rats failed in growth and health. Some essential unknown factor was thus shown to be present in butterfat. It was first called fat-soluble A and, later, vitamin A.

Further study of the purified diets then being used disclosed that the lactose was not "pure"; when it was further purified, the rats developed polyneuritis, or beriberi, which could be cured by feeding a water extract of rice germ. Thus water-soluble B—vitamin B—was discovered.

Similar findings were reported almost at the same time by Thomas Burr Osborne and Dr. Mendel at Yale, and so opened up the era of what Mendel has called "the little things" in nutrition.

Back in 1907, two Norwegian investigators—Axel Holst and Theodor Frölich—wanted to study what was "ship beriberi," which was common among Norwegian seamen. They tried to produce beriberi in guinea pigs. Like the Princes of Serendip, they found something other than what they were seeking. The diet used produced scurvy in the guinea pigs, and thus by lucky chance a suitable test animal was found. They were able to feed different foods and find which ones would cure scurvy. Once vitamins A and B were discovered, it was realized that the "unknown" in fruit and vegetables must be another vitamin, and vitamin C was added to the list.

The change in spelling, with the dropping of the final "e", was made in 1920, because it was realized that these unknown substances were not "amines."

The nutritional deficiency diseases scurvy and beriberi thus were known to be curable by proper food. What about rickets, pellagra, and pernicious anemia—would they, too, respond to a vitamin?

A pooling of knowledge gained from the early writers, clinicians, pathologists, experimental nutritionists, and biochemists soon set the investigations of vitamins in high gear.

More young scientists were being attracted by the new science of nutrition and did their study under great teachers at Yale, The Johns Hopkins University, Columbia, and Wisconsin. These young men and women went forth to the colleges, universities, and experiment stations throughout the country to set up laboratories and to continue the search for new nutrients and the study of how they function.

They encountered difficulties. The rats, guinea pigs, chickens, and dogs with which they worked did not all react in the same way, and soon many letters of the alphabet were used up as designations for what were believed to be new factors.

Vitamin D and vitamin E were identified.

By 1926, what had been called vitamin B was found to be at least two separate factors. One was destroyed by heat and was the antiberiberi factor. Another new substance was stable to heat.

Each new discovery made it possible to prepare more highly purified diets and thus lead to more new discoveries, as other deficiency symptoms showed up in animals and the new curative substances were sought—and found.

A young chemist, Charles G. King, at the University of Pittsburgh, in 1932 prepared pure crystals of vitamin C from lemon juice. It was the first of the vitamins to be isolated in pure form. It was later named ascorbic acid.

Soon others were isolated and identified chemically, their functions and food sources studied, and the amount required daily for maintenance of health and vigor was determined. The old terms of "antiberiberi," "antiscorbutic," and so forth were dropped when it became apparent that the vitamins did much more than just prevent disease. They were essential for health and well-being and functioned as part of many systems of the body.

The latest discovery is vitamin B_{12} (1948). It was found to be a preventive factor for pernicious anemia, which had been described by Dr. Thomas Addison about 100 years before.

The vitamin story has developed mainly since the 1920's. Vitamins held the spotlight, but many advances were being made in our knowledge of proteins, trace elements, and other aspects of nutrition.

ONLY PROTEIN received much attention at the beginning of this century.

Dr. Atwater advocated 125 grams daily for a laboring man. Rubner had declared that a large protein intake was the right of civilized man, a view that was shared by many persons in temperate climates who enjoyed meat, cheese, and eggs. Those who preferred a vegetarian or a more limited diet strongly advocated a much lower intake of protein, and controversy raged in the early decades. Later discoveries showed that the kind of protein was a key factor, but we still hear of the early differences of opinion.

Russell H. Chittenden, first university teacher of physiological chemistry in this country, helped lay the foundations of nutrition science through his own investigations at Yale University and his training of many men. He published in 1904 his revolutionary studies of groups of athletes, soldiers, and professional men who were maintained in nitrogen equilibrium on what corresponded to 44 to 53 grams of protein for a man of average weight.

Slowly they learned that protein was not just protein—there are many different proteins in food. Thomas Burr Osborne, a chemist at Yale, was a leader in these studies. He learned that not all proteins are equally efficient in promoting growth or maintaining nitrogen equilibrium.

Karl Thomas, of Germany, introduced in 1909 the term "biological value" of protein and a formula for determining it. Basically, the biological value of a protein means the percentage of nitrogen retained by the body. Comparisons of many proteins were made in this way by feeding experiments with animals and a few similar studies with human beings.

The biological value of a protein was seen to be related to the composition of amino acids in it. Frederick G. Hopkins at Cambridge University was a pioneer in these studies. He and Sidney Cole in 1901 had discovered a new amino acid, tryptophan. Later, when Dr. Hopkins and his coworkers fed mice a diet with casein as the sole nitrogen-containing constituent, the animals flourished. They died when zein, a protein from corn, replaced casein. If tryptophan was added to the zein, however, the mice lived but did not grow.

Dr. Osborne was joined in 1909 by Dr. Mendel at Yale. They were "the most fertile combination of minds ever directed toward studies of nutrition." They studied almost every phase of nutrition, especially protein and amino acids, and conducted feeding experiments with rats that led to the discovery of vitamins A and B. They measured the biologic value of isolated proteins and showed that amino acids were the limiting factors. In history-making experiments in 1915 they showed that gliadin, a protein in wheat, would maintain life but would not promote growth in rats unless lysine was added and that zein must be supplemented with tryptophan and lysine for life and growth.

At this time proteins were described as being "complete" (they were adequate to maintain life and promote growth) and "incomplete"—that is, they lacked certain amino acids. The concept of quality as well as quantity of protein thus was introduced.

More amino acids were discovered. Nineteen were known then to occur in food proteins. The next step was to find whether they were essential in the diet. Some were hard to get in pure form and in amounts sufficient to feed to test animals.

William C. Rose, one of Dr. Mendel's students, by 1930 at the University of Illinois was able to combine the 19 amino acids as the sole source of protein in diets for rats. The animals failed to grow. Something was still lacking. Because casein or gelatin added to the diet gave good growth, he concluded that some other amino acid, rather than a vitamin or mineral, was the missing factor.

A search for the new amino acid began. It turned out that the new compound was closely tied to another amino acid, isoleucine, and so was difficult to separate and identify, but 4 years of patient work on the problem finally yielded the answer. The new amino acid essential for growth of rats was identified in 1934 and was named "threonine" because of its close relationship to the sugar threose. Continuing his protein researches with mixtures of pure amino acids, Dr. Rose was able by 1938 to prove that nine were essential for normal rate of growth in rats. If arginine was omitted, animals grew at about two-thirds the normal rate—an indication that the organism would synthesize this amino acid but not at a rate that would permit normal growth.

Amino acids could then be grouped as essential and nonessential—needed and unneeded. The next step was to find whether people needed these amino acids. With young men as volunteer subjects, Dr. Rose learned that eight of the amino acids are essential to maintain nitrogen equilibrium.

He then set for himself the task of determining exactly how much of each was required each day. These were the first long-continued series of studies in which human beings were maintained on diets of purified nutrients. Patiently and persistently, the work went forward, until by 1955 Dr. Rose presented data for the recommended daily intake of each of the amino acids essential for people.

Investigators in many laboratories have been at work since 1930 on the protein problem, including the nutritive value of individual proteins and the specific function of individual amino acids.

Protein has been found to be the material for building muscle and body tissue, and to be part of the hemoglobin molecule in red blood cells. Enzymes and hormones have been crystallized and found to be derived from proteins. Enzyme systems contain protein. Antibodies present in the blood stream, an aid in resistance to infection, are protein in nature.

We usually discuss pellagra along with the vitamins. A "pellagra-preventive vitamin" was sought in the early 1920's. The search continued until 1937, when Conrad Elvehjem, of the University of Wisconsin, fed nicotinic acid (which had been on the chemists' shelves for a long time) to dogs with blacktongue, a disease comparable to pellagra in humans. Nicotinic acid cured the blacktongue, and soon was found to be effective in treating human pellagra. Nicotinic acid was added to the list of known vitamins. Its name was changed to niacin to avoid confusion in the mind of the public.

But the story of the fight against pellagra belongs with the proteins. Investigations were carried on by Joseph Goldberger throughout the South, where pellagra was serious from early 1900's till the late 1930's. He found that certain protein-rich foods prevented or cured pellagra. The complexities of this relationship were difficult to unravel and illustrate the interrelationship between nutrients. The answer was found not long ago: The amino acid tryptophan can be converted to niacin. Approximately 60 milligrams of tryptophan are equivalent to 1 milligram of niacin.

Problems of metabolism of protein and its requirement are still being investigated.

Attention also has centered on world problems of nutrition—especially on the nutritional disease, kwashiorkor. The first description of this disease of young children was given in 1933, and attempts to identify the cause have gone on ever since. Kwashiorkor is prevalent in the Tropics and in many poor countries where carbohydrate foods form the bulk of the diet and protein-rich foods are unavailable or too costly. "Protein malnutrition" often is used as the term for kwashiorkor, but present knowledge indicates that they are not synonymous.

Kwashiorkor may be due to a deficiency in the kind and the amount of protein or of many of the other essential nutrients. The advances since 1900 in our knowledge of proteins and amino acids have centered attention on people the world over who do not get enough protein. We also know we need to study the vegetable proteins further.

FATS AND OILS have been foods since ancient times, but not until 1814 did a chemist, Michel Eugene Chevreul of France, discover that fats are made of fatty acid and glycerol. He also named margarine.

A century ago heated arguments went on over whether the animal body could change carbohydrates into fat. Experiment was the only way to find an answer. Fat-free diets were fed to pigs, ducks, and geese. Analysis of the carcasses later disclosed the presence of fat in the body; it could have arisen only from the carbohydrate of the diet.

The use of the calorimeter demonstrated that fats have two and one-fourth times the caloric value of carbohydrate and protein. By the beginning of the 20th century, it was accepted that fats and carbohydrates could be used interchangeably in the diet. It was thought therefore that fats were not essential in the diet. Fats were consumed in large amounts because of their flavor and satiety value, but comparatively little nutritive importance was attached to them, except for their energy value. Then in 1915 came the startling discovery that certain fats, such as butter, were sources of the newly discovered vitamin. Soon other fat-soluble vitamins were discovered.

New interest was aroused in 1929 when scientists observed that rats kept on a fat-free but otherwise adequate diet (with vitamins supplied in other preparations) did not maintain health. The animals lost hair from the body and developed a skin disease and necrosis of the tail. This condition could be prevented by feeding fatty acids that were highly unsaturated in structure. Linoleic acid was identified as the essential fatty acid. Linolenic and arachidonic acids serve the same function. This new knowledge made it possible for researchers to prepare experimental diets, which led to the discovery of more of the vitamins. Once again, interest centered on the vitamins in nutrition.

The high content of fatty substances in the thickened artery walls that is often associated with heart ailments has again aroused interest in the possible relation of dietary fat to those conditions. Much work is being done on fats, the amount and chemical nature of the fats, and the fatty acids that should form part of man's daily diet. Perhaps there is yet to be found a pattern of the kind and amount of fatty acids needed in the diet, as was done for amino acids.

INORGANIC ELEMENTS—or mineral constituents, ash, or inorganic salts, as they have been called—were known a century ago to be essential for plant-life. Farm animals did not thrive if common salt was omitted from their diet.

At the beginning of this century, Henry C. Sherman began studies on calcium, phosphorus, sulfur, and iron in human nutrition, first at Wesleyan University under Dr. Atwater and later at Columbia University. These elements were recognized as essential in the diet, and many experiments were conducted to try to determine just how much of each was needed, exactly how they functioned in the body, and how they were affected by food preparation. Some of these questions are not yet satisfactorily answered.

Doubt existed for a time as to the form of these mineral elements, but belief in the special virtues of organic combinations, especially of phosphorus and iron, gradually gave way to the recognition that inorganic combinations were equally well utilized.

By 1930, as newer techniques and apparatus made it possible for chemists to measure minute amounts of certain inorganic substances, the significance of the trace elements in nutrition was recognized.

Iodine had been identified a century earlier. In the 1920's it was identified as an essential nutrient. The thyroid gland at the base of the neck enlarges when it is deprived of iodine. The condition is known as simple goiter. In the Great Lakes area, where iodine has been leached out of the soil and so is not available in food or drinking water, goiter used to be a common occurrence among children, especially girls.

One of the earliest large-scale controlled human experiments was conducted by David Marine and O. P. Kimball in 1921 with 6 thousand schoolchildren in Akron, Ohio. They showed that children given iodine in drinking water did not develop goiter; a large proportion of those not so treated did develop this condition. A more effective way of providing a readily available and safe supply of iodine for all people was developed later by adding potassium iodide to table salt. Use of this salt has always been on a voluntary basis, but it provides a wise public health measure available to all people.

Investigators in the University of Wisconsin in 1928 found that pure iron salts were ineffective in curing anemia in rats and that small amounts of copper had to be present in the diet before the iron could be utilized.

Manganese, magnesium, and zinc were next added to the list of elements that are needed to maintain growth and health in experimental rats.

Cobalt was found necessary to prevent disease in cattle and sheep (1935). With the discovery of vitamin B_{12} (1948) and the later chemical identification of cobalt as one of its constituents, this element has joined the list of those which are known to be essential for people.

These are the major nutrients that have been identified so far.

The story of nutrition is more than one of discoveries of new compounds needed by the body, however.

The problems of nutrition continue to grow more complex. New discoveries reveal that there is close interrelationship between many of the nutrients. Numerous factors affect the availability of the different nutrients as they exist in food. The biochemical individuality of each person must be kept in focus in providing for man's nutritional needs.

Food nutrients are converted into body structure. For a long time it was thought that the body material, especially the fat deposits, was more or less stable.

How could one tell? It was possible to analyze and know exactly what was taken in by mouth and what was excreted, but what happened inside the body was pretty much unknown.

This was so until the early 1930's brought the discovery of heavy hydrogen and heavy nitrogen by Harold C. Urey, an Indiana boy who became a professor in Columbia University and in 1934 won the Nobel Prize for chemistry.

His discovery was put to work by biochemist Rudolf Schoenheimer, who incorporated heavy hydrogen into fatty acids and fed them to mice. By sacrificing the animals, he could determine where the heavy hydrogen was deposited. He found that the fatty acids of the stored fats are constantly transported to and from organs. They merge indistinguishably with the fat from the diet and are converted into other fatty acids of both longer and shorter chains. Only the essential unsaturated fatty acids did not take up heavy hydrogen—thus further confirming the earlier finding that the unsaturated fatty acids cannot be synthesized in the body but must be supplied in food.

Another series of experiments was made in a similar way. Heavy nitrogen was used as part of the amino acids fed to mice. As with fats, there was a rapid interchange between dietary amino acids and those of the blood and tissues. The amino acid lysine was the only one that did not take up heavy nitrogen from the "labeled" amino acids. Dr. Schoenheimer demonstrated that the body constituents were in a dynamic state. Another new concept of nutrition was introduced.

Radioactive isotopes of other elements—calcium, phosphorus, iron—are now available, valuable tools for following the pathway of nutrients within the body.

DIETARY STUDIES on man have been carried out through the ages, and I mention some examples to show progress by this avenue of study. Most of the nutrition studies have been made on experimental animals. One cannot deliberately deprive man of essential foods, but history and geographical and economic circumstances have provided opportunities for the experimental study of man.

Sanctorius in the 17th century sought an explanation of metabolism as he weighed himself and his food.

The outcome was a book of aphorisms—a happier ending than the one a young physician, William Stark, had in the 18th century. He was a healthy young man of 29, with a desire to find the effect of diet on health. He ate carefully weighed amounts of bread and water, and added various other foods one at a time. He fell ill in a few months and died from what in the light of today's knowledge was probably severe vitamin deficiencies.

James Lind was more fortunate. His classic experiment was the first clinically controlled one and showed that lemon juice cured scurvy.

Toward the end of the 19th century, Max Rubner in Germany, Lyon Playfair in England, and Wilbur O. Atwater in the United States made many studies of diets. They reasoned that groups that were vigorous and healthy surely had adequate diets. By analysis of diets of these groups, they believed they could find what was an adequate intake of calories and protein.

Atwater recommended 3,400 Calories and 125 grams of protein for a man who does moderately active muscular work. He considered fat and carbohydrate to be interchangeable as a source of calories.

The newer knowledge of nutrition was well established by 1926, and adequate human diets could readily be obtained from natural foods.

The inquiring mind of Dr. H. C. Corry Mann, an English physician who was in charge of a boys' home, led him to wonder if he could improve what was considered by all standards of the day to be an adequate diet. One group of his boys remained on the regular diet. Six other groups received, respectively, additions of sugar, butter, margarine, casein, watercress, and milk. All the groups that got the extra items increased more in weight and height at the end of a year than the group on the regular diet. The group that got milk made far greater gains.

Later discoveries of vitamins and further knowledge of nutrients have contributed some of the answers regarding the value of milk as a food. This study again demonstrated the value of the concept introduced early in the century by Dr. McCollum that biological investigation provides information that cannot be obtained by chemical analyses.

Another study was that of Lord John Boyd-Orr and his coworkers in 1931 of the health of two African tribes living in the same area but with different food customs.

Physical and medical examinations, blood analyses, and careful examination of food intakes were made on several thousand tribesmen. The Masai tribe was a pastoral group that lived mainly on milk, meat, and raw blood—a diet relatively high in protein, fat, and calcium. The Akikiyu were agriculturists living on cereals, roots, and fruit—a diet relatively high in carbohydrate and low in calcium. The Akikiyu had a higher incidence of bone deformities, dental caries, anemia, pulmonary conditions, and tropical ulcer. The full-grown Masai males averaged 5 inches taller and 23 pounds heavier and had greater muscular strength than their neighbors.

Once again, the evidence suggests that laboratory findings about nutritive value of foods are borne out by direct studies of human beings.

Further emphasis of the importance of nutrition was given by the studies of Dr. Frederick Tisdall and coworkers in Toronto, who in 1941 found that the physical condition of infants at birth was markedly superior when the mothers had received an adequate diet during pregnancy.

The findings were verified in 1943 by Dr. Harold Stuart and Mrs. Bertha Burke in Boston. They took records of 216 pregnant women whose diets could be classed as good, fair, poor, and very poor. The health of each baby reflected the quality of the mother's diet. Most of the infants born to mothers who had good or excellent diets during pregnancy were in good or excellent physical condition at birth. Infants born to mothers on poor diets were mostly in fair or poor physical condition, stillborn, or prematurely born. The poor diet during pregnancy did not appear to affect the mother's health, but it did affect the health of the infant. The amount of protein in the mother's diet also was correlated with the weight and length of the infant at birth.

SCIENTISTS have wondered for a long time whether nutrition affects the length of a person's life.

Luigi Cornaro, a Venetian of the 16th century, was overindulgent in his youth, but after the age of 40 he kept to a strict dietary regimen. The results were fine for Cornaro; he lived to be 100. In his old age he wrote enthusiastically of the joy of living.

Science demands better evidence than that, however.

It is difficult, if not impossible, to study longevity in relation to diet of man under controlled experimental conditions; no one investigator lives long enough to complete such a study. But if results from experimental rats can be applied to man (and there is evidence that such findings are in many cases applicable), then Henry C. Sherman's experiments at Columbia University have provided an answer.

Beginning in 1920, Dr. Sherman started two series of rats on different diets. Diet A, of dried whole milk and ground whole wheat, was adequate for growth and reproduction. Diet B had a higher proportion of milk powder, and so was better. Succeeding generations from the original animals were maintained on the same two diets. By 1949, the 70th generations were still thriving. This is somewhat like taking two families before the time of Julius Caesar and studying their descendants continuously up to the present time.

Diet A was adequate for growth and reproduction through all the generations of rats. On diet B, the better diet, the animals showed differences which were statistically significant: A more rapid and efficient growth, earlier maturity, longer duration of reproductive life, greater success in rearing of young, and increased length of life.

Other studies by Dr. Sherman showed that the increased vitamin A

and calcium from the added milk powder in diet B definitely contributed to the improved growth and longevity of these animals.

The depression years provided clinical material for the study of nutritional deficiencies in man. They also aroused nationwide concern that our people be adequately fed.

What is an adequate diet is hard to say. Lord Boyd-Orr has defined health as a "state of well-being such that no improvement can be effected by a change in diet." But what kind of a diet will maintain such a state of health?

Hazel K. Stiebeling, now Director of the Institute of Home Economics in the Department of Agriculture, was one of the scientists who considered the problem of the hungry 1930's and set up a working pattern of amounts of nutrients and food required daily for individuals of different ages, sex, and activities. Dr. Stiebeling guided a nationwide study of food consumption of a representative sampling of the population of the United States in the mid-1930's. The diets were evaluated in terms of adequacy as compared with the standard of requirements. The publication, "Are We Well Fed? A Report on the Diet of Families in the United States," aroused widespread concern and led President Franklin D. Roosevelt to call the National Nutrition Conference for Defense in May 1941. At the same time the National Academy of Sciences-National Research Council appointed a Committee on Food and Nutrition to develop a table of "Recommended Daily Allowances for Specific Nutrients."

War problems provided a further stimulus to the study of nutritional needs of all people. Representatives of 44 nations met at Hot Springs, Va., in 1943 to consider ways and means by which each country might increase the food resources and improve the diets of their people. From this conference came the meeting in 1945 in Quebec when the Food and Agriculture Organization of the United Nations was established. It has done much through the years to study malnutrition, determine nutritional needs, and promote food production and improvement of diets of people all over the world.

Enrichment and fortification of food was another milestone in nutrition progress. Enrichment was made possible in the 1940's by the chemists' ability to prepare pure nutrients in inexpensive forms and was made necessary by the findings that the average American diet of that period was inadequate.

I have mentioned the incidence of goiter and its prevention by the addition of small amounts of iodine. Potassium iodide was added to table salt and made available to the public on the grocery-store shelves in 1924 and the benefits of this public health measure have been demonstrated.

Vitamin A has been added to margarine to make it a good source of vitamin A. Such fortification is mandatory in some States, and margarine with 15 thousand International Units of vitamin A per pound is available in most parts of the country.

The Danes first realized the need for adding vitamin A in this way. During the First World War, practically all the butter of Denmark was exported. Subsequently an eye ailment was observed in young children and was recognized as a vitamin A deficiency. As a preventive measure, vitamin A concentrates were added to margarine. Other countries adopted the practice. The Council on Foods and Nutrition of the American Medical Association approved it in 1939, and it has since been advocated by the Food and Nutrition Board.

The discovery of vitamin D as the antirachitic vitamin and the recognition of fish-liver oils as a potent source led to the advice that babies should receive cod-liver oil or some concentrate of vitamin D. Prevention of rickets and development of strong bones in young children depend on an adequate intake of calcium and phosphorus, as well as vitamin D, and therefore forti-

fication of milk with vitamin D was begun in the early 1930's. The Council on Foods and Nutrition of the American Medical Association approved the fortification of milk with 400 International Units of the vitamin per quart.

Considerable evidence had accumulated by 1941 that many American families were consuming diets that were inadequate in thiamine, riboflavin, niacin, and iron. Because we also were concerned with the problems of war in Europe, the National Nutrition Conference for Defense was called in May of that year. The Government was studying proposals to add some vitamins to flour and bread. A Committee on Food and Nutrition (later called the Food and Nutrition Board) had been established in 1940 to provide direction for the national nutrition program. The committee proposed the use of the term "enriched" and set up minimum and maximum limits for the enrichment of bread and flour with thiamine, riboflavin, niacin, and iron. With the support of the millers, enriched flour became available to the public and was used by the Army and Navy. Riboflavin, however, was not available in adequate amounts to use until the end of 1943.

The bread-and-flour-enrichment program has been a controversial one. Some have maintained that the public should be educated to the use of natural foods that would supply all nutrients, but experience of centuries has shown that people are reluctant to change their food habits and that education regarding food choices is a slow process. More than half the States require the enrichment of flour and bread. South Carolina was the first to do so.

Dietary studies give evidence of the nutritional improvement of the food intake of various groups and clinicians have reported declines in nutritional deficiency symptoms. But there have been improvements in family income and family food expenditures since the enrichment program began and these are contributing factors. Nevertheless, all experimental evidence to date shows that nutritional improvement of diets brings improvement in health. Especially is this so when the article of food is a staple.

FROM THE MINDS of men have come the ideas and from the laboratories have come the proof (and sometimes disproof) of the ideas on which our knowledge of nutrition is based. Nutrition laboratories are expensive to maintain.

Therefore the story of progress would not be complete without reference to some of the organizations and agencies that have contributed funds for support of research in nutrition and have provided opportunities to know the work of others through professional meetings and publications.

Our account of how the study of nutrition emerged as a science began with Wilbur O. Atwater and his research in the Office of Experiment Stations. Experiment stations in every State now carry on the search for knowledge. Other divisions of the Department of Agriculture are engaged in a wide variety of basic and applied problems related to nutrition. Chief among them is the Institute of Home Economics, which was established in 1923 as the Bureau of Home Economics.

The United States Public Health Service also has made an outstanding contribution. The story of the fight against pellagra and the use of iodine to prevent endemic goiter have been told. Men of the Public Health Service were in the forefront.

Three professional organizations have among their members many men and women who were the students of Mendel, McCollum, and Sherman and who have carried on research and teaching in all phases of nutrition. These organizations are the American Home Economics Association (1909), the American Dietetic Association (1917), and the American Institute of Nutrition (1933).

The Food and Nutrition Board of the National Academy of Sciences-National Research Council (1940) has guided the application of the science of nutrition through its recommended dietary allowances. The members of the Board also prepare bulletins summarizing and interpreting current research in nutrition.

Nutrition research workers in the laboratory have been greatly aided by grants from the Williams-Waterman Fund (1940). This fund was named for Robert R. Williams, "the father of enrichment," who devoted 26 years to the search for thiamine. Robert E. Waterman was Williams' partner in the last 12 years of his search. Together they found the way to make thiamine so cheaply that it can be used for enriching bread, flour, cornmeal, and rice.

Another important source of financial aid to the research works in nutrition is the Nutrition Foundation (1941). Food manufacturers throughout the country support the foundation, and Dr. Charles G. King, who isolated pure vitamin C in 1932, in 1942 became director of its program of aid for research and dissemination of information about nutrition.

Alone and in teams, in private laboratories and the State experiment stations, and in colleges, universities, clinics, medical schools, and industrial firms, men and women in this and many other countries have sought the answers to the intricate problems of man's health and well-being as influenced by his food. Great progress has been made. Much remains to be learned, however, and that is the challenge we have now.

ELIZABETH NEIGE TODHUNTER *is the Dean of the School of Home Economics, University of Alabama, and a past president, 1957–1958, of the American Dietetic Association. She has done extensive research in nutrition and written widely on the history of nutrition. She is a graduate of the University of New Zealand and of Columbia University, New York.*

Questions and Answers

MOST of the questions that are answered here were asked of home demonstration agents by people all over the United States. They indicate the widespread interest of Americans in nutrition and the kinds of information they want. The questions are barometers, in a sense, and guides that are useful in a number of projects.

Not all the questions fitted into the purpose of this book. Many others are considered at length in the chapters that follow. Some questions from various sources were added to round out this section and reflect more fully the scope of the book—although all the questions and answers together do not form a summary.

How old is man's knowledge of nutrition?
As early as 1900 B.C., Egyptians recognized that diet might be a factor in the development of night blindness and related eye symptoms. For these, raw liver, which we now know is rich in vitamin A, was recommended as a curative procedure.

In 525 B.C., Herodotus recorded that in an examination of Persian and Greek skulls it appeared that the bone structure of the Greeks was considerably stronger, perhaps as related to differences in exposure to sunlight. We now know the importance of vitamin D in bone development and the effectiveness of sunlight in promoting vitamin D activity in the body.

The fascinating sequence of ideas in nutrition investigations has been related by Dr. Elmer V. McCollum, a pioneer investigator himself, in his comprehensive book, *A History of Nutrition* (Houghton Mifflin Company, 1957). Dr. McCollum suggested that Cato the Censor, the grim Roman statesman of the first century B.C., was perhaps the earliest effective teacher of sound dietetics because of his discourse on the value of cabbage, currently recognized as a relatively good source of the essential nutrient, vitamin C, as a restorer and preserver of health in times when dried or cooked cereals, lacking in vitamin C, were subsistence items among the populations.

Biblical references to the effects of certain foods or variations in food supplies, both feast and famine, are numerous. Similar observations through the Middle Ages have been recorded.

Dr. McCollum reviewed reports from throughout the world during the 17th, 18th, and 19th centuries that describe extensive epidemics, which we now recognize included symptoms of nutritional deficiency diseases, such as rickets, scurvy, pellagra, the neurological symptoms of beriberi, night blindness, anemia, and goiter.

23

What's a good way to lose weight?

Here are a few simple rules to follow in choosing low-calorie meals:

Select a varied diet that contains the different kinds of foods important for health—milk, meat (or alternates), fruit and vegetables, and whole-grain or enriched or restored cereals and bread.

Choose the foods with fewer calories in each of these groups. For instance, skim milk and buttermilk provide fewer calories than whole milk.

Prepare and serve foods in ways that do not add calories. Avoid fried foods, rich sauces, gravies, salad dressings, rich desserts, and so forth.

Reduce the amount of food eaten.

Take smaller servings.

Avoid snacking and between-meal eating unless such foods are planned as part of the total allowance of calories.

Take some exercise regularly to increase your expenditure of calories and to keep the body physically fit.

How do I know if I am getting enough calories?

Your weight is a good guide to whether you are getting enough calories. An adult should eat enough to maintain the weight that is desirable for him. Usually your weight at 25 to 30 years of age is considered your desirable weight for the rest of your life. If you weigh more than this amount, you probably are getting too many calories. If your weight is below this standard, you may need more calories. The child and teen-ager, who are still growing, need enough food to permit normal gains in weight.

How many calories are there in a plain gelatin dessert? Why do some doctors recommend it?

One-half cup of ready-to-serve gelatin dessert, eaten plain with no fruit added, furnishes about 80 Calories and about 2 grams of protein.

Doctors may recommend this food because it is easily digested, bland in flavor, and is acceptable to most people. It may be used in calorie-restricted diets as a substitute for desserts of higher calories.

Can vegetable protein be substituted equally for animal protein?

Vegetable proteins generally are of lower quality than animal proteins because they fail to provide the complete assortment of amino acids in the amounts the body needs for tissue building. Certain foods of plant origin—soybeans, nuts, dry beans, and peas—are better than others from plants. It takes only a small amount of protein from animal sources, however, to supplement the protein in vegetable foods. Combinations like cereal and milk, macaroni and cheese, egg and bread, and beans and frankfurters provide better protein than foods of plant origin used alone.

Is bread that is advertised as high-protein bread a good substitute for meat?

No. Many of the breads advertised as "high-protein" bread contain very little more protein than ordinary bread. Four slices of the ordinary white bread contain less than half as much protein as in an average serving of lean meat (2 to 3 ounces cooked). The protein in bread must be combined with some protein from foods of animal origin in order to provide all of the amino acids needed by the body.

What can we eat to give us protein and few calories?

Good sources of protein that are relatively low in fat and thus in calories are skim milk, cottage cheese, eggs, lean meat and fish, chicken, and turkey.

What foods, if any, enhance fertility in women and virility in men?

There is no food that enhances fertility in women and virility in men. Foods contribute nutrients that are important to good health, and the overall state of health may affect fertility and virility.

What is inositol? What is its value?

Inositol is included often among the

vitamins of the B complex. It is required for the growth and proper nutrition of animals, but its role in human nutrition is not yet known.

My child likes candy very much. How much should I give him?

Be sure he is eating all of the foods he needs for growth and health before giving him candy. Then be sure that the candy does not add more calories than he needs.

How does the protein content of peanut butter compare with that of meat?

Four tablespoons of peanut butter supply about the same amount of protein as 2 ounces of lean cooked meat (without bone).

Is fat essential in my diet?

Yes; some fat is necessary for good nutrition. Fat is a concentrated source of calories. Some fats provide vitamins A and D, and some are important as sources of essential fatty acids.

What is lecithin? What is its value in nutrition?

Lecithin occurs in various animal and vegetable tissues. It is chemically related to the fats. Lecithin is added to many foods because it has unusual properties, such as those of retarding oxidation, retaining moisture, and dispersing globules of fat.

What is glutamic acid?

Glutamic acid is one of the simple amino acids. It does not have to be provided as such in our diets because the human body can make it from other amino acids provided by our food.

What is wheat germ?

Wheat germ is the portion of the kernel called the embryo, from which the new plant starts its growth. It is about 2 to 3 percent of the kernel. The germ is a concentrated source of protein, iron, vitamin E, and the B vitamins. Its nutritional contribution to the ordinary diet is limited, however, because of the small amounts generally eaten, alone or combined with other foods.

How much vitamin E is required?

Little is known about the human requirement for this vitamin. Vitamin E is so widely distributed in common foods that there is little likelihood of a dietary deficiency. Wheat germ oil is the richest natural source of vitamin E, but the vitamin is present also in other vegetable and seed oils, green leaves, meat, eggs, and dairy products.

Which foods are especially important for sound teeth in children?

A diet adequate in all nutrients is necessary for the formation and maintenance of good teeth.

What is the value of brewer's yeast?

Brewer's yeast is a concentrated source of high-quality protein and of many of the B vitamins. Because it is also a good source of the minerals iron and phosphorus, it sometimes is prescribed for patients needing dietary supplements.

What is "royal jelly"? Has it any value in nutrition?

"Royal jelly" is a substance from the salivary glands of bees and fed by the worker bees to the queen bee. No important nutrient has been reported to be present in "royal jelly" that cannot be obtained readily from ordinary foods in our regular food supplies. Some food faddists claim that "royal jelly" has special health values for human beings, but there is no scientific basis for such claims.

Is it safe to cook acid foods in aluminum?

Yes. There is no scientific evidence to prove that cooking acid foods in aluminum pans is harmful.

Does beer furnish any nutrients?

Beer furnishes calories and very small amounts of some nutrients. The amounts of minerals and vitamins present are too small to be important in an ordinary diet.

Are carbonated beverages good for children?

The nutritive value of carbonated beverages is mainly in their sugar and calories. Children's diets may be deficient in essential nutrients if carbonated beverages are used in place of nutritionally important foods.

What is the difference in the nutritive values of ice cream and sherbet?

Ice cream is prepared largely from milk products and sweetening agents and contains the nutrients contributed by these foods. Sherbet is made with fruit or fruit juices, sweetening ingredients, and usually small amounts of milk or egg white.

Why are vitamins essential?

Vitamins, although they are required in minute amounts, are essential for growth and reproduction; formation of antibodies; coagulation of the blood; resistance to infection; formation of intercellular substances; and integrity of bones, teeth, skin, blood, and nervous tissue. They also function as coenzymes for innumerable chemical reactions concerned with the metabolism of food, on which the nutrition of the body depends.

Why can't I eat and drink whatever I please and take vitamin and mineral capsules to make sure I get essential nutrients?

A diet chosen by chance is not safe. It may lack protein and energy and other essential nutrients. It may supply too much carbohydrate and not enough of the other essentials. Vitamin and mineral preparations cannot take the place of the food sources of nutrients.

Which is higher in food value—liver from beef, pork, lamb, or calf?

All kinds of liver are excellent sources of good-quality protein, iron, riboflavin, and niacin.

What are the standards for hamburger?

Hamburger is prepared from chopped fresh beef with or without added beef fat. The fat content cannot exceed 30 percent. No other meats and no water may be added.

Are frankfurters already cooked?

Yes. Frankfurters are fully cooked when purchased and are safe to eat without further heating.

Does the thawing juice from frozen meat have any nutritive value?

Yes. It contains small amounts of water-soluble nutrients.

How can we tell a blade roast from chuck roast?

A blade roast comes from the rib end of the chuck. It contains a section of the shoulder blade and portions of rib bones. Another chuck roast is the arm roast, from the lower part of the chuck. It can be distinguished from a blade roast by the cross section of the round shank bone that is present. The arm also contains the ends of several of the ribs.

Is ground meat inspected?

Yes. Ground meat prepared in federally inspected establishments is made from wholesome carcasses. The process of grinding and seasoning the meat is fully supervised for good sanitary practices and use of meat from healthy animals.

Is commercially frozen stuffed turkey safe to use?

Commercially frozen stuffed turkeys are produced under rigid sanitary conditions. The size of the turkeys is limited. Both turkeys and stuffing are kept at low temperatures while they are handled. A mechanically mixed precooked stuffing in controlled amounts is mechanically stuffed into the body cavity and the turkeys are frozen at $-30°$ F. or lower. This quick process under sanitary conditions and under constant laboratory control results in stuffed poultry of extremely low bacterial count. The directions on the packages specify cooking times long enough for the bird and the stuffing to reach a temperature of at least 165°, which is sufficient to destroy any micro-organisms that might be harmful.

Are turkey roasts practical for outdoor cooking?
Small turkeys about 4 pounds in weight ready-to-cook may be cooked outdoors on the grill. They are best cut in quarters to shorten the cooking time. When the coals are glowing, place the turkey parts on the grill, brush with barbecue sauce, and cook until tender, turning often. Larger turkeys, 10 to 12 pounds ready-to-cook, can be barbecued on a revolving spit. Allow about 20 minutes per pound for the larger birds.

Why is it unsafe to stuff poultry and freeze it at home?
Freezing stuffed poultry at home is not recommended because the rapid handling and freezing necessary for a safe product cannot be assured under home conditions. When poultry and stuffing are held at temperatures from 50° to 120° F., micro-organisms associated with food poisoning may multiply and produce toxins. Even a bird taken directly from the refrigerator may reach room temperature while it is being prepared for freezing, and the stuffing is likely to be still warmer. At 0°, the temperature of most home freezers, the freezing process is so slow that portions of the bird and the stuffing may remain in the danger zone too long, especially if the bird is a large one. It is better, therefore, to freeze poultry without stuffing and stuff it just before cooking.

How can you tell good cuts of meat?
Guides to be used in selecting meat include the stamps showing United States Government inspection and grade and the appearance of the cut. The inspection stamp certifies that the meat is from healthy animals, slaughtered under exacting sanitary conditions. The grade stamps are related to quality. The Prime and Choice grades

contain more fat, are usually more tender, and may have a more pronounced flavor than the other grades— Good, Standard, and Commercial. High-quality meat is well marbled (fat intermingled with lean) and fine grained, and has a typical color.

Why is fat in beef sometimes yellow and sometimes white?
The color of beef fat is related to the ration of the animal. Cattle that have a large proportion of grass in their feed store some carotene in their fat; carotene gives a yellow color. Cattle on a ration high in grain have whiter fat with a low content of carotene. Color of fat is no longer used as a basis for Federal grading of carcasses.

What are some cheap meat substitutes?
Common meat alternates include poultry, fish, eggs, dry beans and peas, and cheese. Dry beans and peas are likely to be the cheapest of these foods on the basis of cost per serving. Cheese like the cottage, Swiss, and Cheddar-type may be more economical to buy than many cuts of meat—also poultry and eggs, especially when they are in plentiful supply. Certain fish, depending on the locality and supply, are inexpensive.
The cost of meat varies with the cut, quality, and kind of meat. You may find that some meats are as inexpensive as certain alternates.

What's the difference between a ham and picnic ham?
A ham is the cut from the upper part of the hind leg of a pig or hog. The cut of pork called a picnic or picnic shoulder is the shank end of the shoulder.

What are the signs of spoilage in fresh poultry?
Off-odors and off-flavors are the first indications of spoilage. Sliminess, mold, discoloration, and a putrid odor indicate advanced spoilage.

Does "USDA Inspected and Graded" mean higher quality in poultry?

The ready-to-cook poultry marked "USDA Inspected and Graded" has been graded for quality as well as inspected for wholesomeness. The grade designations are A, B, and C and are based on conformation, fleshing, fat covering, and the extent to which pin feathers have been removed.

What does "USDA Inspected" mean on fresh poultry?

"USDA Inspected" on poultry means that the poultry has been examined for wholesomeness and found fit for food by a trained inspector of the Department of Agriculture.

Should meat be washed before it is cooked?

Meat does not ordinarily need to be washed. Wiping with a damp cloth or scraping with the blunt edge of a knife usually is enough.

Can you oven-roast a beef round?

Roasts from the round of beef vary greatly in tenderness, depending on the age and finish of the animal. The beef round contains considerable amounts of connective tissue and therefore is a less tender cut. Round roasts of beef usually are cooked by moist heat—braised or pot roasted.

When I buy frozen meat and bring it home, it is slightly thawed. Can I refreeze it?

Frozen meat can be safely refrozen if it has not thawed completely. The meat may be less tender and juicy when it is refrozen after having been partially thawed. It will have higher quality if it is kept frozen.

What is the best buy in broilers when buying in quantity for freezing—live or ready-to-cook?

This depends on the price per pound. A live broiler will yield about 70 percent of its purchased weight when it is prepared ready-to-cook excluding neck and giblets. A broiler that weighed 3.5 pounds live will yield about 2.5 pounds ready-to-cook. A live broiler is cheaper when it costs less than two-thirds as much per pound as one ready-to-cook.

Do eggs contain as much iron as meat?

Yes. Equal quantities by weight of eggs and the lean part of meat contribute about the same amount of iron.

Is there any difference in food value between dried and fresh eggs?

There is practically no loss of nutritive value of eggs in the drying process. When reconstituted to the same moisture content as fresh eggs, dried eggs supply the same nutrients in about the same quantities.

Do brown eggs have the highest food value?

No. The color of the shell makes no difference in the nutritive value of an egg. Color of the shell is a characteristic of the breed of poultry.

Why are eggs necessary in the diet?

No single food is essential. The nutrients the body needs are found in many foods. Eggs are a good source of high-quality protein, iron, and vitamin A.

How can I identify a fresh egg in the shell?

The quality of an egg in the shell can be determined by candling. An egg of high quality has only a small airspace and its yolk is well centered. A large proportion of the white is thick.

Grade labeling provides the consumer with a basis for selecting eggs by quality. The letters *U.S.* mean the eggs were officially graded and the letters *AA, A, B,* or *C* designate the quality. *AA* is the highest grade. The date stamped on the carton tells when the eggs were graded. The grade mark is an assurance of the quality specified if the eggs have been kept under good conditions after grading.

How many eggs should we eat per week?

An egg a day, or at least 3 to 4 a week, is a sound recommendation.

Are frozen eggs used like fresh eggs in cooking?

Frozen eggs can be measured after thawing and used as fresh eggs in the following proportions: 3 tablespoons of thawed frozen whole egg equal one whole fresh egg; 2 tablespoons of thawed frozen egg white equal one fresh egg white; 1.3 tablespoons of thawed frozen egg yolk equal one fresh egg yolk. Whole eggs or egg yolks to which salt was added before freezing are best used in scrambled eggs, salad dressing, or main dish. If sweetening was added, use them in cakes, custards, or other sweet food.

What are some ways of cooking and using dried egg?

Dried egg may be used instead of shell eggs in such cooked foods as cakes, cookies, muffins, popovers, long-cooked casseroles, and baked custards.

Two and one-half tablespoons of sifted dried egg plus an equal amount of water take the place of one shell egg. For some recipes, the dried egg is sifted with the dry ingredients. The water needed to replace the water removed from the egg in drying is added to the liquid in the recipe. For other recipes, the dried egg is blended with water first, then used as fresh eggs are used.

What is the difference between eggs of grade AA and grade A eggs?

Before breaking: An egg of grade AA has less airspace than an egg of grade A. The white of a grade AA egg must be clear and firm; that of a grade A egg, clear and reasonably firm. The yolk of a grade AA egg must be well centered, its outline slightly defined, and it must be free from defects. The yolk of a grade A egg may be fairly well centered, its outline fairly defined, and it must be practically free from defects.

After breaking: A grade AA egg covers relatively less area and has more thick white than does a grade A egg. A grade AA egg covers only a small area, has much thick white, and the yolk is round and upstanding. A grade A egg in comparison covers a moderate area, has considerable thick white, a medium amount of thin white, and the yolk is round and upstanding.

How can you tell what size eggs are the best buy?

The size of eggs is based on the total weight of a dozen eggs. The four common sizes of U.S. graded eggs are Extra Large, Large, Medium, and Small. Each of these terms refers to a size that has a specified minimum weight per dozen. The minimum weight for Extra Large eggs is 27 ounces per dozen; for the Large, 24 ounces; for the Medium, 21 ounces; and for the Small, 18 ounces.

For the same weight of eggs of the same grade:

Small eggs are as economical as Large ones when they cost no more than three-fourths as much as the Large ones;

Medium-sized eggs are more economical than Large ones if they cost no more than seven-eighths as much as the Large ones;

Extra Large eggs are cheaper than Large eggs when they cost no more than one-eighth more.

Is lumpy evaporated milk safe to use?

Lumps in evaporated milk are formed by the solids settling during storage. The lumps do not harm the milk. Cans of evaporated milk can be turned or shaken at frequent intervals during storage to prevent lumping.

How much cottage cheese is needed to supply the same amount of calcium as a glass of milk?

Eleven ounces or about one and one-half cups of cottage cheese will supply about the same amount of calcium as an 8-ounce glass of whole milk.

How does low-fat cottage cheese differ in food value from creamed cottage cheese?

Low-fat cottage cheese has very little fat and vitamin A. Creamed cottage cheese usually has about 5 percent fat and therefore furnishes more calories and vitamin A.

How is milk homogenized?

Milk is homogenized by a mechanical process that breaks up the fat into small particles and distributes them throughout the milk. Cream does not form in homogenized milk because the fat particles do not rise to the top of the milk.

Is it possible for a person to drink too much milk?

Yes; if milk is consumed in such large amounts that it crowds out other important foods from the diet.

What is the value of yoghurt?

Yoghurt has the same food value as the milk from which it is made. When made from a partially skimmed milk, which is often the case, yoghurt is lower in fat, vitamin A value, and calories than when it is made from whole milk. Yoghurt is a good source of the other nutrients obtained from milk, however, especially calcium, riboflavin, and protein.

How many vegetables should be included in a dinner menu?

There are no fixed rules for the kinds and amounts of foods to include in each meal. This is a matter of individual preference. A daily food guide, a plan for choosing a nutritionally good diet, suggests at least four servings of vegetables or fruits each day.

Which is cheaper—canned or frozen peas?

The price and yield of canned and frozen peas must be compared to determine which is cheaper. A No. 2 can of peas, for instance, gives about 2 cups; a 10-ounce frozen package, about 1.5 cups. If you consider a half-cup as a serving, the can gives 4 servings; the package, 3. Divide the price of the can and package by the number of servings provided to see whether the frozen or canned peas are the cheaper.

Does white cabbage have a lower food value than red?

Not necessarily. Some varieties of white cabbage have as much vitamin C (the main nutrient) as red cabbage. The amount present depends in part upon the conditions under which the cabbage has been stored and the length of storage period. The method of cooking also affects the final value.

Is there any difference in food value between green and yellow dried peas?

Food values of green and yellow dried peas are very similar.

Is tomato juice a good source of vitamin C?

Yes. One-half cup of tomato juice will supply about one-fourth of the daily allowance of vitamin C recommended by the National Research Council.

How do canned and frozen vegetables compare in value with the fresh products?

Canned and frozen vegetables contain a high proportion of the nutrients originally present when the vegetables are handled and prepared commercially or in the home by modern scientific methods.

Are onion and parsley blood builders?

Foods that are good sources of iron or of high-grade protein improve the quality of the blood. Onions provide little of either of these nutrients. Parsley is a good source of iron, but is not likely to be eaten in a large enough quantity to supply a significant amount of iron.

How do you cook corn outdoors in an open fire?

Select sweet, young corn and strip the husks down to the end of the ear, but do not tear it off. Remove the silk and soak the corn in cold salted water for about 30 minutes. Drain and then brush kernels with butter or margarine and sprinkle with salt and pepper. Pull the husks up around corn again. Wrap each ear of corn in heavy-duty aluminum foil and twist the ends to close tightly. Roast the corn in hot coals after the fire has died down to embers. Turn frequently and roast for about 25 minutes or until done to taste.

What makes potatoes waxy?

Potatoes with a low content of starch and high content of water have a tendency to be waxy when cooked. Potatoes with a high content of starch, on the other hand, are mealy when cooked. New or early-crop potatoes, which are harvested before they are fully mature, are likely to be more waxy than late-crop potatoes.

How do you care for onions after harvest?
Onions are best stored in a basket or crate in a cool, well-ventilated place. To have good keeping quality, onions must be mature and thoroughly dry.

How much loss is there when the liquid in canned vegetables is poured off?
Approximately one-third of the minerals and vitamins present are lost.

How do you keep raw pared potatoes from turning dark?
Pared potatoes often are placed in cold water for short periods to prevent darkening. The water keeps the air with its oxygen from the potato.

Why is it necessary to blanch vegetables before freezing?
Blanching is done by subjecting the vegetables to steam or boiling water, followed by quick cooling in ice water. This process slows or stops the action of enzymes, which otherwise would cause off-flavors, color changes, and toughness in frozen vegetables. Blanching also tends to inactivate enzymes responsible for destruction of vitamins.

Should vegetables be cooked in covered pans to retain vitamins?
Covering the pan helps to retain some of the vitamins by making it possible to cook vegetables in only a little water. The percentage of water-soluble vitamins dissolved in the cooking liquid is less when a small amount of water is used than when a large amount is used.

How can you select potatoes that will not turn dark when cooked?
The tendency to blacken after cooking varies with the variety of potato, season, locality where grown, and differences in chemical composition. You cannot tell from looking at the raw potatoes whether they will darken after cooking. Buy a small quantity to try out before deciding to buy a large amount. Much research has been conducted on the problem of the after-cooking darkening of potatoes, but as yet definite answers are not available.

Does rhubarb have any nutritive value?
Rhubarb furnishes small amounts of several nutrients, including vitamins A and C, and the minerals calcium, phosphorus, and iron. The calcium present, however, may not be available to the body as it may be bound by the oxalic acid that is present in rhubarb.
Rhubarb leaves should never be eaten. Their high content of oxalic acid makes them toxic in some cases.

How do you tell a ripe melon?
Ripeness in most kinds of melons is indicated by the softening of the fruit around the slight depression at the blossom end, which yields to the pressure of the finger. Usually the characteristic odor of the melon becomes stronger and is most perceptible when the full stage of ripeness has been reached. In some kinds of melons, a change of color to a lighter and sometimes a slightly yellowish tinge is an indication of ripeness.

Is there as much food value in canned grapefruit sections as there is in fresh grapefruit?
Grapefruit, like all citrus fruit, is a stable source of vitamin C. Only small losses occur in canning and during the usual storage periods.

Do fresh oranges have values that are lost in frozen, condensed orange juice, crystals, and canned orange juice?
The original content of vitamin C of the fresh juice determines the amount that will be in the canned or frozen product made from it. Canning and freezing methods now in use cause very little loss. Even vitamin C, which usually is destroyed more quickly than other nutrients, is remarkably stable

in these products. The canned juice may lose up to a fifth of its original vitamin C content after long storage at room temperature.

What causes fruit to turn dark when drying?
Discoloration is caused by contact of fruit with oxygen in the air and is speeded up by the enzymes present in the fruit. Darkening can be reduced or prevented in the drying of fruit by using a sulfur dioxide solution to the surface of the fruit or by cooking to destroy the enzyme activity.

Can lemon juice be substituted for ascorbic acid for use on peaches before freezing?
Lemon juice is not so effective as ascorbic acid in preventing darkening in frozen peaches. Also, the large amounts needed to prevent darkening would in some instances make the fruit too sour or mask the natural fruit flavor.

I cooked applesauce in a darkened aluminum kettle and now the kettle is clean and shiny. Will it hurt us to eat the applesauce?
No. The darkening of an aluminum pan when water or low-acid food is boiled in it is due to the formation of grayish-black metallic oxides. These may be from the aluminum pan or from iron salts that are in the water or food. When an acid food is cooked in the darkened aluminum pan, the oxides are dissolved by the acid, and the pan becomes shiny again. The food is not harmed.

How can I get the bottom crust of a pie to brown?
The pastry recipe and the baking temperature are important to the browning of piecrust. Pastry made by a rich formula—one that contains a large proportion of fat—browns more readily than that made by a lean formula. For good browning, the dough must be evenly mixed and the piepan must be dry before the crust is placed in it. An oven temperature of 400° to 450° F. to start baking is recommended primarily to brown the lower crust.

What makes pie dough tough?
Pie dough is tough when too little fat or too much water is used or when the fat is not mixed properly. Overmixing pastry after adding the water also will make it tough.

What causes pastry dough to crumble?
Too little water or too much fat will cause pastry dough to crumble.

Can shrinkage of a baked piecrust be prevented?
Some shrinkage is normal in baked piecrust. Excessive shrinkage may be the result of overhandling or using too much water.

What causes uncooked spots on the bottom crust of a pie?
There are several possible causes: Inadequate blending of fat and flour; insufficient mixing after the addition of the water to moisten the dough evenly—especially if too much water is used; combining warm dough with cold dough. Uncooked spots on a bottom crust may result also from drops of water in the piepan.

What is raw sugar?
Raw sugar is the unrefined residue after the removal of molasses from cane juice. It contains a fairly high proportion of some minerals, but, like refined sugar, is mainly carbohydrate.

How do the following rank in content of vitamin C—orange juice, grapefruit, pineapple juice, cranberries?
Orange juice and grapefruit are among the excellent sources of vitamin C. Pineapple juice has from one-fifth to one-fourth the content of the two citrus items. Cranberries, as they are usually eaten in sauce, contain even less than pineapple juice.

Does jam add nutrients to the diet?
Jam is principally a carbohydrate

food, and it is a concentrated source of calories. It contains small amounts of minerals and vitamins. In the quantities usually eaten, the nutrients contributed are not significant in the diet.

What is the value of molasses?

Molasses is a concentrated sugar food. Its value in the diet is chiefly for its flavor and for the variety it provides. The content of iron and calcium is high, especially in the darker kinds, but because molasses generally is used in small quantities it does not make an important contribution to the ordinary diet.

Can saccharin and Sucaryl be used for jellymaking?

Yes; if recipes designed especially for making jellies without sugar are used. Such recipes have been developed by manufacturers of these sugar substitutes.

Can beet sugar be used for making jams and jellies?

Yes. Beet and cane sugar are identical in chemical composition and can be used with equal success in making jams and jellies.

Is there a difference between cane sugar and beet sugar?

No. Cane sugar and beet sugar have the same chemical composition although they come from different sources. Granulated sugar on the market is practically pure sucrose, whether obtained from the beet or cane.

Does beet sugar cause candy to crystallize?

Beet sugar, like cane sugar, will crystallize under certain conditions. Controlled crystallization is necessary in making candies. In fondant and fudge, the crystals are so small that they cannot be felt in the mouth. Overcooking or beating while hot will make a candy hard or grainy and will destroy its creaminess. Insufficient beating will allow coarse sugar crystals to develop. To help insure smooth candies, do not scrape the saucepan, let the candy cool

undisturbed before beating it, and beat until the entire mixture begins to lose its shiny appearance and the candy holds its shape when dropped from a spoon.

What causes a cake to fall?

A cake is likely to fall if too much sugar or fat or baking powder or liquid is used. Undermixing or insufficient baking, too low an oven temperature, or moving a cake during baking before it has "set" also may cause a cake to fall and be soggy.

How can cake failures be prevented at high altitudes?

Special recipes are required at high altitudes. Usually a decrease in the amount of leavening agent (baking powder or soda) or sugar (or both) and an increase in the amount of liquid are needed. It is sometimes necessary to reduce the shortening when making very rich cakes at high altitudes.

How do you substitute sweet milk and baking powder for soda and sour milk in recipes?

Use the same amount of fresh milk as sour milk called for in the recipe and substitute one teaspoon of baking powder for each one-fourth teaspoon of baking soda.

What causes excessive shrinkage in cake?

This may result from too much liquid or too much fat in the cake recipe or from too much batter in the pan. Or, a cake may shrink if the pan is too heavily greased. Baking in too hot or too cool an oven may result in poor volume in cake.

What causes a cake to have a peaked or cracked top?

A cake batter that is low in shortening or has been overmixed may form a peak while baking. Too little leavening (baking powder or soda) or too much flour may also cause a peaked top. Cracking of the top crust may result from baking the cake in too hot an oven.

477248°—59——4

What causes poor texture in quick breads made with baking powder?

Overmixing is often the cause. A batter, such as a muffin batter, that contains about twice as much flour as liquid should be mixed only enough to moisten the dry ingredients. Too much stirring or beating develops the gluten in the flour, and as a result tunnels are formed. Too high a baking temperature also may cause poor texture in quick breads.

What makes biscuits dry and small in volume?

Biscuits may be dry and have a poor volume because too little liquid or baking powder was used, or they may have been mixed too much or baked at too low a temperature.

Why are muffins sometimes soggy?

Too much liquid or baking at too low an oven temperature will cause muffins to be soggy.

What is the difference between straight dough bread and sponge bread?

In the straight dough method, all the flour and other ingredients of the bread are mixed together in the dough at the beginning. The sponge method requires two steps in mixing. First a sponge is prepared by combining the softened yeast, some sugar, and part of the flour and liquid, and allowing the mixture to ferment until it is full of bubbles. The remaining ingredients then are added to make a dough stiff enough to knead.

What causes loaves of bread to have a flat top and sharp corners?

The dough has been overmixed, or not enough time has been allowed for rising.

When my homemade bread made with yeast lacks volume, how can this be corrected?

If your bread lacks volume, you may have used too little yeast, allowed too little time for rising, or held the dough at too low a temperature. Or you may have added the yeast to liquid that was too hot or let the dough rise at too high a temperature. Under the right conditions, yeast produces carbon dioxide gas, which leavens the bread. Warmth is needed for the process, but too much heat kills the yeast cells. A temperature of about $80°$ F. is best. Overkneading the dough, which may injure the baking quality of the gluten in the flour, is another possible cause of poor volume in bread.

What causes a sour flavor to develop in yeast bread?

A sour flavor will develop in bread if a poor yeast is used, or if the dough has been allowed to rise too long or at too high a temperature. Insufficient baking or baking at too low a temperature also will affect the flavor of yeast bread.

What makes homemade yeast bread coarse textured?

Allowing the loaf to rise too much before baking is the most common cause of coarse texture in bread.

What substances other than the usual food ingredients are permitted in bread? What's their purpose? Are they harmful?

The Federal Standards of Identity under the Federal Food, Drug, and Cosmetic Act permit certain mineral salts to be used in bread as yeast foods and dough conditioners. They are used in commercial baking to give the dough and the finished loaf desirable physical properties. Sodium propionate or calcium propionate are often added as mold inhibitors. Also permitted are certain emulsifying agents which tend to produce a softer crumb. All of these substances are harmless.

Can I substitute 1 cup of butter or margarine for 1 cup of vegetable shortening in recipes for baked goods?

Butter or margarine may be used in place of vegetable shortening in baking, but a slightly larger amount is needed because butter and margarine contain only about 80 percent fat as contrasted with vegetable shortening which is 100 percent fat. One cup of vegetable shortening is equivalent to 1 cup plus 2 tablespoons of butter or margarine.

Does altitude make any difference in the pressure used in pressure cookers for canning foods?

At altitudes high above sea level, it takes more than 10 pounds pressure in a pressure cooker to reach 240° F., the temperature required for processing meats and low-acid vegetables. One additional pound of pressure is needed for each 2,000 feet above sea level. For example, at an altitude of 10,000 feet, you need to use 15 pounds pressure to get a temperature of 240°.

Should I use gelatin to prevent ice crystals from forming when making ice cream?

The purpose of using gelatin and other stabilizers in making ice cream is to prevent the formation of large ice crystals that cause a coarse texture. A stabilizer makes a film around small ice crystals as they form and around the air bubbles incorporated by stirring the mixtures during freezing. This keeps large crystals from forming.

Is chocolate that has turned white spoiled?

No. A whitish appearance in chocolate is due to the cocoa butter that has separated out. At a temperature of about 85° F., the cocoa butter in the chocolate melts and comes to the surface. When the cocoa butter hardens again it turns white. Only the appearance of the chocolate is affected; usually there is no loss of flavor or other quality.

What chemical process takes place when salt is used as a preservative?

Salt draws water from the food by the process of osmosis. A brine is formed that retards or prevents the growth of micro-organisms.

Why is salt used in foods?

Salt has many uses in food preparation. It is a seasoning and brings out flavor of other ingredients. It aids in the coagulation of proteins. Salt lowers the freezing point of water and is added to ice for freezing ice cream and other mixtures. As ice melts, heat is absorbed, and the temperature of the surrounding material is lowered. Salt also raises the boiling point of water solutions. Salt controls the fermentation of yeast to make more desirable baked products. Salt in high concentration is used in preserving foods to retard bacterial action.

Does monosodium glutamate have any food value?

It is used only for flavoring, and the amounts consumed are too small to make any worthwhile contribution to the ordinary diet. It is one of the more concentrated sources of sodium, however, and would not be permitted in diets in which sodium intake must be kept low.

What are some Government publications about food and nutrition?

Single copies of the publications listed below are free from the United States Department of Agriculture, Washington 25, D.C.:

Food for Fitness . . . A Daily Food Guide. Leaflet 424
Nutrition—Up To Date, Up To You. Home and Garden Bulletin Separate No. 1
Eat a Good Breakfast To Start a Good Day. Leaflet 268
Food for the Family With Young Children. Home and Garden Bulletin No. 5
Food for Families With School Children. Home and Garden Bulletin No. 13
Food Guide for Older Folks. Home and Garden Bulletin No. 17
Getting Enough Milk. Home and Garden Bulletin No. 57
Money-Saving Main Dishes. Home and Garden Bulletin No. 43
Turkey on the Table the Year Round. Home and Garden Bulletin No. 45
Cooking With Dried Egg. Home and Garden Bulletin No. 50
Dry Beans, Peas, Lentils . . . Modern Cookery. Leaflet 326

Peanut and Peanut Butter Recipes. Home and Garden Bulletin No. 36
Potatoes in Popular Ways. Home and Garden Bulletin No. 55
Freezing Combination Main Dishes. Home and Garden Bulletin No. 40
Home Freezing of Fruits and Vegetables. Home and Garden Bulletin No. 10
Home Canning of Fruits and Vegetables. Home and Garden Bulletin No. 8
How To Make Jellies, Jams, Preserves at Home. Home and Garden Bulletin No. 56
A Fruit and Vegetable Buying Guide for Consumers. Home and Garden Bulletin No. 21
Poultry Buying Guides for Consumers. Home and Garden Bulletin No. 34
How To Buy Eggs by USDA Grade and Weight Classes. Leaflet 442
U.S. Grades for Beef. Leaflet 310

Publications for sale by the Superintendent of Documents, Government Printing Office, Washington 25, D.C.:

Essentials of an Adequate Diet . . . Facts for Nutrition Programs. U.S. Department of Agriculture Home Economics Research Report No. 3. 15 cents
Foods Your Children Need. Unnumbered. Children's Bureau in cooperation with the Institute of Home Economics. 10 cents
Nutrition and Healthy Growth. Children's Bureau Publication No. 352. 20 cents
The Foods You Eat and Heart Disease. Public Health Service Publication No. 537. 10 cents
Principles of Good Nutrition. Public Health Service Publication 165. Health Information Series 31. 15 cents
Tips on Cooking Fish and Shellfish. Bureau of Commercial Fisheries, Department of the Interior. 10 cents
Basic Fish Cookery. Bureau of Commercial Fisheries, Department of the Interior. Test Kitchen Series No. 2. 25 cents
How To Cook Halibut. Bureau of Commercial Fisheries, Department of the Interior. Test Kitchen Series No. 9. 20 cents

How To Cook Tuna. Bureau of Commercial Fisheries, Department of the Interior. Test Kitchen Series No. 12. 20 cents
How To Cook Crabs. Bureau of Commercial Fisheries, Department of the Interior. Test Kitchen Series No. 10. 20 cents
How To Cook Lobsters. Bureau of Commercial Fisheries, Department of the Interior. Test Kitchen Series No. 11. 20 cents
Shrimp Tips From New Orleans. Bureau of Commercial Fisheries, Department of the Interior. Circular 41. 15 cents
Fresh and Frozen Fish Buying Manual. Bureau of Commercial Fisheries, Department of the Interior. Circular 20. 25 cents

You may request up-to-date lists of publications on foods and nutrition from the United States Department of Agriculture and the Department of Health, Education, and Welfare, and on fish and fish cookery from the Bureau of Commercial Fisheries, Department of the Interior, Washington 25, D.C. Lists of publications that are for sale on various topics are also available without charge from the Superintendent of Documents, Government Printing Office, Washington 25, D.C.

How can I get help on diets and menus for diabetics?

These must be prescribed by the physician who knows the needs and problems of the individual patient.

General information on diabetes can be obtained from the following sources:

Chronic Disease Branch
Division of Special Health Services
Public Health Service
United States Department of Health, Education, and Welfare
Washington 25, D.C.

American Diabetes Association
1 East 45th Street
New York 17, N.Y.

Food

THE NUTRIENTS

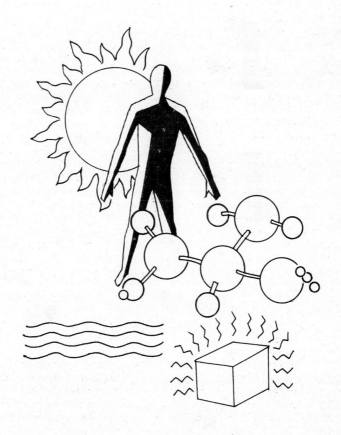

Food Energy

RAYMOND W. SWIFT

OUR need for energy rather than our need for the other nutrients in food undoubtedly is the basis of our instinct and desire to eat. A person could die for lack of a particular food nutrient other than energy with no feeling of hunger.

The energy content of fuels or foods signifies the potential chemical energy which may be released as heat upon combustion and which is measured in heat units—Calories. This measure of the gross energy of foods is the basis of calorimetry.

We use the bomb calorimeter to determine the heat evolved during combustion. It is a steel container in which the food is burned. The container is immersed in a known amount of water. A weighed amount of food is ignited by an electric fuse in the bomb calorimeter, which is filled with oxygen under high pressure. The rise in the temperature of the water (and bomb) upon ignition provides the means of measuring the heat produced.

A calorie (spelled with a small c), a unit measure of heat, is the amount of heat necessary to raise the temperature of 1 gram of water 1 degree centigrade (specifically, from 14.5° to 15.5° C.).

The Calorie (spelled with a capital C) is the amount of heat necessary to raise the temperature of 1 kilogram (1,000 grams) of water 1 degree centigrade. This is the unit commonly used in expressing energy values of foods. A kilogram is equal to 2.2 pounds. A teaspoonful of sugar (4 grams), for example, provides about 16 Calories (16,000 calories).

METABOLISM is a term used to denote the chemical changes constantly taking place in living matter. The oxidation of foodstuffs by the human body provides the energy that serves it in a manner somewhat like that of a fuel in a furnace or machine.

Our bodies may be thought of as machines, which run 24 hours a day throughout life. The machines must continue to run, even when no food is available. Then the energy comes from the oxidation of body tissue. The body itself, particularly its fat, is thus a readily available reserve supply of food and is used continually in metabolism.

But when we think of the body as a machine that gets its fuel in the form of food, we must be aware of some differences. We can make a clear distinction between an engine and its fuel. In the human body, the food is absorbed and becomes a part of the body before it is available for any purpose.

Dr. Henry P. Armsby (1853–1921), a nutrition expert of international renown, has likened the intake, storage, and disposal of food energy to the exchange of water in a millpond:

"The water in the pond may represent the materials of the body itself, while the water running in at the upper end represents the supply of matter and energy in the food, and that going down the flume to the millwheel the metabolism required for the production of physiological work. . . . The water flowing into the pond does not immediately turn the wheel, but becomes part of the pond and loses its identity. Part of it may be drawn into the main current and enter the flume comparatively soon, while another part may remain in the pond for a long time."

Our bodies are not heat engines. A steam engine receives its mechanical power from the heat evolved during the combustion of the fuel. Fuel is burned before any work is done.

Muscular activity is more like the operation of a storage battery. Muscular contraction takes place as a result of a discharge of energy stored in the muscle. The energy is replenished during the recovery period. The net result in a complex series of reactions is the oxidation of lactic acid, a product formed when sugar is metabolized by the muscle. The heat associated with muscular activity is a waste product.

Heat is not a food nutrient. The common statement that the primary purpose of carbohydrates is to furnish calories is not wholly true. A part of the potential energy of ingested carbohydrate may take the form of mechanical energy, or it may be converted into fat and stored. In any event, our bodies do not use heat as their source of energy.

Heat from outside our bodies cannot replace the heat produced by the oxidative reactions in normal metabolism. Heat and mechanical energy are end products of the potential chemical energy of the food nutrients that are oxidized within the body. All forms of energy can be converted into heat. It is convenient to express the energy exchanges of the body processes in terms of heat units—Calories.

Another distinction between the human body and a mechanical engine is that the "human engine" can perform 10 times more work for a time than its current oxygen supply would permit. This process involves an "oxygen debt," which is made up during periods of rest—the recovery periods.

Our bodies differ from mere machines also in that all repairs are made while they operate at full schedule.

The absorption of oxygen does not cause the oxidation of food. There is no lack of oxygen in diabetes, but sugar is not oxidized.

Absorption of oxygen does not cause metabolism, but the amount of the metabolism determines the amount of oxygen to be absorbed. The body heat produced is a manifestation—rather than a cause or regulator—of metabolism.

All organic nutrients can serve the body as sources of energy. Their energy values provide a common basis for expressing nutritive value.

The main sources of energy are the carbohydrates, fats, and proteins. These nutrients, particularly protein, have other unique and specific functions as well, but that does not detract from their usefulness as sources of energy.

The gross energy of food as determined by the bomb calorimeter is not the same as the heat derived from it by the human body: Some of the food may be indigestible and so does not enter the body proper; some of the energy of the food may be represented by the storage of body tissue or by mechanical work; protein is oxidized in the body less fully than in the bomb calorimeter.

The heat-of-combustion values of all fats (and also of carbohydrates and proteins) are not identical. Differences in any one class are not very great, however. The heat-of-combustion value of fat is much higher than that of carbohydrate, because a much larger portion of the carbon and hydrogen in the carbohydrate molecule is already oxidized.

Studies with the bomb calorimeter have given us these averages in Calories per gram: Carbohydrates, 4.1; fats, 9.5; proteins, 5.7.

Carbohydrates—sugars and starches—are about 98 percent digestible and therefore furnish energy equivalent to a little more than 4 Calories per gram (98 percent of 4.1).

Human beings can digest different types of fat more or less equally well. The digestibility is commonly taken as 95 percent. One gram of dietary fat (equivalent to 9.5 Calories) makes available to the body 9 Calories (9.5 Calories×95 percent). Thus a given weight of dietary fat furnishes to the body 2.25 times as much energy as does the same weight of carbohydrate. (The apparent digestibility of the ether extract—"fat"—of certain foodstuffs, such as whole-wheat flour, may be as low as 60 percent).

The end products of carbohydrate and fat when oxidized by the normal healthy person are the same as are obtained from combustion in the bomb calorimeter—carbon dioxide, water, and heat.

The body does not oxidize protein completely but eliminates in the urine a residue of the protein molecule in the form of urea, creatinine, uric acid, and so on. This incomplete oxidation and the 92-percent absorption of the food protein make about 4 Calories available to the body for every gram of protein we eat.

Thus if we know the total carbohydrate, fat, and protein in a food we can estimate the total available Calories contained in it.

For example, 100 grams of ordinary white bread contain an average of 9.1 grams of protein, 53.3 grams of carbohydrate, and 1.6 grams of fat. By using these factors, we find that 100 grams of bread (3.42 ounces) furnish 264 available Calories—$(9.1\times4)+(53.3\times4)+(1.6\times9)$.

This method of evaluating foods is general and does not try to determine any value of the food except its approximate total available energy, which often may be different from the actual energy of a particular sample, as determined by combustion analysis.

THE OXIDATION of carbohydrates is a process in which oxygen unites with carbohydrates to form carbon dioxide, water, and heat.

The relative amounts of each item involved are known precisely. An ounce of carbohydrate oxidized by the body requires 1.19 ounces of oxygen for its combustion. The end products are 1.63 ounces of carbon dioxide, 0.55 ounce of water, and 119 Calories of heat. The volumes (not the weights) of oxygen consumed and of carbon dioxide produced are equal to each other.

The end products, water and carbon dioxide, are of secondary interest as far as nutritive value is concerned. Heat, however, represents the energy available for the maintenance of body temperature. Some of the energy that is represented by this reaction may take the form of muscular activity.

Fats need more oxygen for oxidation than carbohydrates do.

For each liter (approximately 1 quart) of oxygen absorbed in the oxidation of fat, 0.707 liter of carbon dioxide and 4.686 Calories of heat are produced.

The oxidation of proteins also produces carbon dioxide, water, and heat, but (unlike carbohydrates and fats) protein is not completely oxidized to carbon dioxide and water. Proteins contain nitrogen, and the residual nitrogen from the incomplete combustion of protein is eliminated in the urine. Urea is the most important incompletely oxidized fragment of protein oxidation. The chemical analysis of urine to determine its content of nitrogen is the basis for calculating the amount of protein that has been actually used by the body.

One gram of urinary nitrogen signifies that 5.94 liters of oxygen were consumed by protein and that 4.76 liters of carbon dioxide and 26.51 Calories of heat were eliminated. The caloric value of oxygen in the oxidation of protein is: $26.51 \div 5.94 = 4.46$ Calories per liter.

THE RESPIRATORY QUOTIENT (commonly abbreviated R.Q.) is the volume of carbon dioxide produced divided by the volume of oxygen consumed. (The factor for converting grams of oxygen to liters of oxygen—760-millimeter pressure, dry, at 0° C.—is 0.6998. The corresponding factor for carbon dioxide is 0.5094.)

The average value for the heat of combustion of carbohydrates ordinarily accepted is 4.1 Calories per gram, the caloric value of the oxygen absorbed being 5.047 Calories per liter.

If the organism were burning only carbohydrate, the heat production could be computed by determining the liters of oxygen consumed and multiplying by the factor 5.047. Similarly, in the oxidation of fats, the caloric value of oxygen is 4.686 Calories per liter. It is obvious that the "caloric value of oxygen" refers to the amount of heat evolved for each liter of oxygen absorbed. Oxygen is not combustible.

By subtracting the carbon dioxide and oxygen concerned with protein oxidation from the total amounts of each and allowing for the heat produced from protein, we can measure the remaining amounts of carbon dioxide, oxygen, and heat that involve the oxidation of fat and carbohydrate. This procedure is widely used to determine heat production of people.

We have to be on guard to avoid misinterpretation, especially in short experiments, of high respiratory quotients that may result from overventilation of the lungs or deep breathing. This may occur as a result of excitement, exercise, or exposure to cold. Carbon dioxide stored in the body is released. If the period of observation is longer, however, a recovery period

will follow, during which the apparent respiratory quotient will be correspondingly low. Because of this fluctuation in output of carbon dioxide, a measure of oxygen absorption (rather than production of carbon dioxide) is to be preferred.

THE PRODUCTION OF HEAT, the chief end product of food, may be measured by direct or by indirect calorimetry. Our bodies normally are maintained at an essentially constant temperature, 98.6° F. Heat must be supplied continuously to maintain body temperature, and heat must be eliminated to prevent a rise in it.

Before we consider the items that affect heat production and energy requirements, let us examine briefly the techniques of measuring energy metabolism and the basic principles they are based on.

Direct calorimeters are rooms or chambers large enough to accommodate the subject—the person who is being studied—under comfortable conditions.

Most direct calorimeters in use today remove the heat eliminated via radiation and conduction by means of a stream of cold water flowing through copper tubing in the chamber. The part of the heat that is eliminated by the evaporation of water from the skin and lungs must also be determined. The ventilation of the chamber may be of the closed type, into which oxygen is introduced as needed, or an open-circuit type, where outdoor air is continuously introduced into the chamber.

Normally the chamber is equipped with devices that prevent the flow of heat through the walls in either direction. An apparatus so equipped is called adiabatic. Some direct calorimeters, however, are used without such regulation and are calibrated for heat loss by introducing a known amount of heat into the chamber and noting the amount recovered under standard operating temperatures of the chamber and room.

Others employ a compensating principle by means of which the amount of heat required to keep a second chamber in balance with the animal chamber is directly measured in terms of electrical input to the heating elements.

Gradient, or heat-flow, calorimeters also are used. In them the heat passing through the walls is measured electrically.

A large respiration calorimeter designed by Dr. Henry P. Armsby at The Pennsylvania State University is used for determining the 24-hour metabolism of people. It exemplifies the principles and design of an adiabatic respiration calorimeter.

The person is confined in a triple-wall, airtight chamber. An air lock permits us to give him his food and water and remove excretion products without causing changes in the temperature. The walls of the chamber are controlled at the proper temperature to prevent any heat loss through them in either direction.

A carefully measured stream of water is passed through copper tubes in the chamber to remove from him all heat produced by radiation and conduction. The temperature of the water entering and leaving the chamber is recorded at 4-minute intervals. The amount of heat removed in this way is regulated to the amount of heat eliminated by radiation and conduction from the person so that the temperature in the chamber is always constant and in balance with the temperature of the walls.

Air is supplied by means of a constant-speed measuring pump, which draws outdoor air through the calorimeter. Continuous samples are obtained of the air before it enters and after it leaves the chamber. The water content of the samples is determined by passing the air through preweighed, glass-stoppered U-tubes filled with sulfuric acid pumice.

The difference in water content between the ingoing and outcoming air represents the water evaporated by the subject. The heat equivalent of the water evaporated is added to the amount removed by the water flowing through the tubing in the chamber. The carbon dioxide production also is measured ordinarily, although it is not a part of the measurement of direct heat.

The essential data obtained for computing the heat production are the amount of water that has flowed through the heat absorbers, the rise in its temperature, and the amount of water vapor produced by the person.

For example, a person's heat production in a day can be derived from the following data we obtained with a respiration calorimeter:

The volume of water through the absorbers was 2,216 liters.

The average rise in temperature was 0.624° C.

The water vapor produced was 1,016 grams.

The heat of vaporization of water (18° C.) was 0.586 Calories per gram.

The heat by radiation and conduction is 1,383 Calories (2,216×0.624). That, added to the 595 Calories represented by the evaporation of water (1,016×0.586), makes a total heat production of 1,978 Calories.

THE INDIRECT METHODS of determining heat production are essentially chemical methods, in contrast to the purely physical measurements employed in direct calorimetry. An indirect method may be preferable to direct calorimetry, especially in studies in which the period of observation is short.

There are at least four methods of indirect calorimetry. All are based upon heat-of-combustion values, which are determined by the bomb calorimeter, but each method involves somewhat different initial data.

The first method requires a measure of the urinary nitrogen, the carbon dioxide produced, and the oxygen absorbed.

The second involves a record of the change in live weight, the urinary nitrogen, and carbon dioxide.

The carbon-nitrogen-energy balance method, the third, does not require any measure of oxygen absorption.

The fourth involves no measures of urinary nitrogen, oxygen, or carbon dioxide (CO_2).

The first method is the one used oftenest with human subjects. It is based on the quantitative relationships between the amount of the foodstuff burned, the amount of oxygen required for the combustion, and the amounts of CO_2, urinary nitrogen, and heat that are produced.

The two items actually measured are the oxygen consumed and the carbon dioxide produced.

The method requires no information about the diet. It can be adapted to relatively short periods of measurement. It is a very useful method if the air analysis is accurate.

In the process of the oxidation of fat, carbohydrate, or protein, one of the end products is water. This fact is not of primary interest in a study of energy metabolism, but it may be an important consideration in instances when the subject is deprived of water. A given weight of fat, absorbed and oxidized, makes available to the body more water than would the ingestion of the same weight of water itself.

The second method, which involves the determination of urinary nitrogen, change in live weight, and the production of carbon dioxide, often is referred to as the Haldane procedure. It is based on the idea that the live weight of the experimental subject supplied with dry air free of carbon dioxide will be affected only by the absorption of oxygen and the loss of carbon dioxide and water.

The weight of the animal and container is determined at the start and at the end of the experiment. The change in weight of the animal is equivalent to the algebraic sum of the water and carbon dioxide produced and the oxygen absorbed. No food or water may be given to the experimental subject during the actual test. The oxygen absorption is obtained as the sum of the water and carbon dioxide eliminated minus the loss in live weight.

This method is especially adaptable for use with small animals and for studying effects following the ingestion of a test meal. The period of observation may be about 8 hours. The urinary nitrogen is best determined in a separate collection period.

The nitrogen-carbon-energy balance method requires that the subject be maintained on a constant dietary intake. The oxygen consumption is not measured. The nitrogen, carbon, and energy content of the diet and excreta (including the carbon dioxide) are determined. From these data one can figure the heat produced and the daily gain or loss of protein and fat by the body. When ruminants are used as experimental subjects, the carbon and energy of the methane produced are included in the items tabulated.

The body-balance method is the most accurate method of indirect calorimetry. Its use is limited to small animals, which are sacrificed at the end of the test period. It gives a single value for heat production representing a relatively long period of time.

The computation rests on the law of the conservation of energy: The total heat production is equal to the feed energy minus the energy of the excreta and of the body gain.

BASAL METABOLISM is the energy expenditure of the body under specific conditions. It represents the energy needed to maintain body temperature and for all vital processes not under voluntary control, such as the heart beat and respiratory mechanisms.

The person must be in a postabsorptive state (no food during the previous 12–14 hours), free from strong emotions or discomforts, awake, and relaxed, with no muscular movements during the test.

It has been said that basal metabolism is reduced by sleep to the extent of 10 percent or more. A more carefully considered statement would be that the metabolism during sleep is less than the basal metabolic rate by 10 percent or more. Basal metabolism by definition requires that the subject be awake.

A large person naturally has a greater total basal metabolism than a small individual. When results are expressed on a unit surface area basis or on a formula that takes size (weight and height) into account, however, the basal metabolisms of small and large individuals are found to be alike if they are comparable in sex and age.

These two factors have been taken into account in the compilation of tables that serve as standards in judging the basal metabolism of an individual.

Basal metabolism, expressed as the heat production per square meter of body surface, becomes progressively lower from youth to old age. (One square meter is about 1.1 square yards.)

The newborn infant has a low basal metabolism, but the rate increases rapidly within a few weeks. The maximum rate (55 Calories per square meter per hour) is reached at 2 to 4 years. With the possible exception of a rise at the time of adolescence, the rate declines progressively to 32 Calories per square meter per hour at age 90.

The basal metabolic rate of women follows a similar pattern but is about 8 percent lower than for men.

Many thousands of basal metabolism tests have been made of persons of different races and living on various kinds of diets and under quite different climatic conditions.

Some observations have indicated a slightly lower basal metabolism of people in the warmer climates, but the differences are not marked or entirely consistent.

Athletes and laborers with greater development of muscular tissue tend to have a higher basal metabolism than their counterparts living a sedentary life. The basal metabolism in simple obesity definitely falls within the normal range.

As in most other physiological processes, there is a small variation—5 or 10 percent—between comparable normal individuals and, in fact, between measurements taken on the same individual from time to time.

A significant feature of basal metabolism is its uniformity throughout the human race. The average hourly basal rate of normal men between the ages of 20 and 50 years is 40 to 38 Calories per square meter of body surface whether they be tall, short, fat, thin, large, or small. This uniformity makes a measure of the basal metabolism a valuable tool in the diagnosis of certain diseases or of glandular ailments.

The basal metabolism is below normal in cases of obesity that are due to pituitary or hypothalmic disorders, in Addison's disease, in hypothyroidism (myxedema), and lipoid nephrosis and in starvation and undernutrition.

The basal metabolism may be reduced 50 percent in cases of severe and prolonged undernutrition. This reduction represents an adaptation of the body to conserve energy in order to maintain life on a total energy intake far less than would be required for normal basal metabolism alone.

The basal metabolism is higher than normal in hyperthyroidism (exophthalmic or toxic goiter), in leukemia, polycythemia, cardiorenal disease with dyspnea, diabetes insipidus, and fever.

The basal metabolism of a normal healthy person is thus predictable from the knowledge of age, sex, and size (height and weight). This is not true with regard to total energy requirement, which is affected by several additional items.

While the total basal metabolism is proportional to the size (surface area) of the individual, the total daily heat production may or may not be so related. A small furnace may burn more coal (and produce more heat) than a large one. Available food energy may be transformed into heat, work, or body tissue.

A moderate increase in heat produc-

Typical Disposal of Food Energy

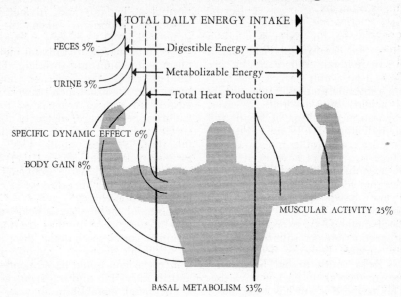

tion occurs as a result of the ingestion of food. This increase in heat production is known as the heat increment or specific dynamic effect of food.

THE DISPOSAL of food energy under ordinary conditions gives us the basis for a proper perspective in studying the various factors affecting energy metabolism.

The accompanying chart depicts the situation prevailing with a normal man 22 years old, weighing 154 pounds, moderately active, and having a daily energy intake of 3,250 Calories. He was gaining weight—fat—at the rate of nearly one-half pound a week.

As shown in the chart, the largest energy expenditure is the basal metabolism. Relatively small amounts are represented by the gain of body tissue, the specific dynamic effect, the urine, and the feces.

It is important in dealing with any aspect of energy metabolism to keep in mind the relative magnitudes of the end products of food energy. The specific dynamic effect (SDE) of food is a rather small item compared to the basal metabolism or to the total energy intake. The relative amounts of energy represented by activity and by body gain on a given intake of energy will vary in a reciprocal manner in accord with the subject's muscular activity.

In the illustration given in the chart, the daily body gain of energy, as fat, is approximately equivalent to the extra energy expended as Calories in sawing wood for 1.5 hours.

An important part of our diet is composed of animal products. It is interesting to note that, compared with feeds for ruminants, the ordinary diets of human beings are highly digestible. The unavailable energy in rations for cattle is in the order of 43 percent, compared to 8 percent in human diets.

Ruminants (cattle, sheep, goats) are able to utilize carbohydrate in the form of coarse fiber. This is accomplished by a "fermentation factory," a term sometimes used to describe the rumen or the first stomach (of four) which receives the food. Bacterial action here breaks down the fiber into digestible fragments. In the process, which involves an overhead expense of utilization, methane, an inert gas, is produced as a waste product in the animal's economy.

Feed energy not used by cattle is represented by the feces, urine, and methane to the extent of about 30, 5, and 8 percent, respectively, of the feed energy.

The food energy represented by the feces and urine of human beings is about 8 percent; 92 percent of the energy intake therefore is available to the body.

MUSCULAR ACTIVITY and environmental temperature are the two most important factors that affect energy requirement and heat production.

Because a person's heat production may vary severalfold, particularly as a result of exercise or the temperature, there must be a corresponding flexibility in the body's ability to eliminate the heat as it is produced. Otherwise, a marked increase in the heat produced would result in an increase in body temperature.

The human body eliminates its heat chiefly by radiation and conduction and by the evaporation of water from the skin and lungs. In the absence of exercise and at a comfortable temperature (72° F.), the percentages are about 70–75 percent (radiation and conduction) and 30–25 percent (evaporation of water).

Strenuous exercise increases the total heat produced and also the percentage that is eliminated by the evaporation of water.

If a person is exposed to an environmental temperature higher than that of the body, as on a hot day, no heat can be eliminated by radiation, and all the heat produced must be eliminated by the evaporation of water.

The efficiency of the human body to do work has been determined many times. A definite and measurable amount of work is a necessary item in such a calculation. Work done may be measured in foot-pounds. If a weight of 132 pounds is raised to a height of 17 feet, the work accomplished is 2,244

foot-pounds (17×132). Work may also be expressed in electrical units or as Calories. One foot-pound is equal to 0.000324 Calorie.

Efficiency may be defined as the ratio of the work done to the energy supply. Efficiencies of 6 to 30 percent have been reported—the differences being due chiefly to the methods of computing the values.

The total metabolism, including the dynamic effect of food, may be considered as a necessary overhead expense and should be included in any calculation of work efficiency.

Efficiency, however, often is computed by dividing the amount of work done (foot-pounds or other work units being expressed as Calories) by the amount of extra heat that was produced in doing the work.

Such computations usually include the recovery period as a part of the extra energy expenditure.

The baseline from which the extra heat is computed is the metabolism of the subject in position (such as sitting on a bicycle ergometer) but doing no work. A man may perform a measured amount of work equivalent to 230 Calories and produce some 850 extra Calories of heat during the process. This represents an efficiency of about 27 percent (230÷850).

If the total work performed in a day is expressed as a percentage of the 24-hour metabolism, however, the efficiency of work performance is about 6 percent. That is a more realistic figure, for it takes into account the unavoidable overhead expense of energy output regardless of whether any measurable work is accomplished.

The speed at which a given amount of work is performed affects the energy required. More energy is required to sprint a given distance than to cover it at a slow walk. Similarly an automobile performs more economically at 35 miles an hour than at high speeds.

Training reduces the amount of energy required in the performance of a given task. A part of the improvement in the performance of athletes brought about by training is due to increased efficiency of the muscles to convert the potential energy of food into mechanical energy.

The position of the body in relation to the task to be performed affects the efficiency with which the work is accomplished. For example, a housewife washing dishes at a sink 9 inches below the proper level will expend more energy than the actual task would otherwise require. No measurable work is done in many activities.

THE EXTRA ENERGY expenditure that accompanies the performance of typical tasks identified by various occupations is of more practical interest than the evaluation of performance on a basis of efficiency.

The total available food energy required per day for a man engaged in strenuous work is much greater than for one of sedentary occupation. Hard work may increase temporarily the heat production to a level of 10 times that of the basal level. That, however, does not mean that the daily food energy intake must be increased to that extent, because such strenuous work is not maintained throughout the 24-hour day.

In computing energy requirements in accord with occupation, one has to consider the time actually spent in following the occupation and the remaining parts of the day, including the time when the person is neither working nor asleep.

We can calculate a person's daily output of energy if, for instance, we find that his basal metabolism is 75 Calories per hour, that during 8 hours of the day while at hard work his heat output averages 275 additional Calories per hour, and that during a period of 8 hours when he is not working or asleep his heat production is 90 Calories per hour above the basal level.

The basal metabolism will involve a daily expenditure of 1,740 Calories (allowing for a 10-percent drop during 8 hours of sleep). The working hours increase this amount by 2,200 Calories. The remaining 8 hours involve an extra expenditure of 720 Calories. The total daily energy expenditure is 4,660 Calories. Assuming an availability of 92 percent, the gross energy of the daily food should be about 5,060 Calories for him to maintain energy equilibrium. This high requirement is brought about by the 8 hours of strenuous work.

A large person expends more extra energy than a small one in performing a given day's activities because a larger mass of body is involved.

Tests with boys, 8 to 11 years of age, washing and wiping dishes, reveals that the increase in energy output is increased above that of the basal metabolism by 52 Calories per hour. The corresponding value obtained with girls was 38 Calories. This difference would seem to justify a boy's claim that his sister can do the job more economically.

The metabolism of boys 7 to 8 years old playing quietly was found to increase 76 Calories per hour during bicycle riding. The increase was 98 Calories for boys 12 to 14 years old.

The activities associated with the performance of common household activities such as preparing food, washing dishes, cleaning, making beds, storing utensils and supplies, laundering, and so on, involve reaching, bending, stooping, and twisting. Some of these characteristic motions have been studied to determine the relative energy expenditure required for their performance. Results are of practical interest in the design of equipment and work areas.

Reaching from the floor to a height of 46, 56, and 72 inches, respectively, at the rate of 44 times a minute requires an extra energy expenditure (over that of standing) of 8, 16, and 32 Calories an hour for the 46-, 56-, and 72-inch reaches, respectively.

Stepping up onto a step 7 inches high at the rate of 50 times per minute increased the heat output by 84 Calories per hour.

Stooping by means of a "deep knee bend" to reach a height of 3 inches above the floor at the rate of 40 times a minute increased the energy expenditure 158 Calories an hour.

Such tests are of short duration and some of them are too strenuous to be performed for an hour continuously. Results are expressed on the extra Calories per hour basis, however, for comparison with corresponding values involving other occupations that are uniform throughout the working day.

Many occupations involve at least a moderate amount of the motions just described. The extra energy expended per hour by a man weighing about 154 pounds is indicated by this list of Calories expended:

Bicycling (century run), 532 Calories; bicycling (moderate speed), 175 Calories; bookbinding, 56 Calories; boxing, 798 Calories; carpentry (heavy), 161 Calories; cello playing, 91 Calories; crocheting, 28 Calories; dancing, foxtrot, 266 Calories; dancing, waltz, 210 Calories; dishwashing, 70 Calories; dressing and undressing, 49 Calories; driving an automobile, 63 Calories; eating, 28 Calories; fencing, 511 Calories; horseback riding (walk), 98 Calories; horseback riding (trot), 301 Calories; ironing (5-pound iron), 70 Calories; knitting a sweater, 49 Calories; laundry, light, 91 Calories; lying still, awake, 7 Calories; organ playing (30 percent to 40 percent of energy is hand work), 105 Calories; painting furniture, 105 Calories; paring potatoes, 42 Calories; playing table tennis, 308 Calories; piano playing (Mendelssohn's songs), 56 Calories; piano playing (Liszt's "Tarantella"), 140 Calories; reading aloud, 28 Calories; rowing in a race, 1,120 Calories; running, 490 Calories; sawing wood, 399 Calories.

Further illustrations are: Sewing, hand, 28 Calories; sewing, foot-driven machine, 42 Calories; sewing, motor-driven machine, 28 Calories; shoe-making, 70 Calories; singing in loud voice, 56 Calories; sitting quietly, 28 Calories; skating, 245 Calories; standing at attention, 42 Calories; standing relaxed, 35 Calories; stone masonry, 329 Calories; sweeping with broom, bare floor, 98 Calories; sweeping with carpet sweeper, 112 Calories; sweeping with vacuum sweeper, 189 Calories; swimming (2 miles per hour), 553 Calories; tailoring, 63 Calories; typewriting rapidly, 70 Calories; violin playing, 42 Calories; walking (3 miles per hour), 140 Calories; walking rapidly (4 miles per hour), 238 Calories; walking at high speed (5.3 miles per hour), 581 Calories; washing floors, 84 Calories; writing, 28 Calories.

Such values are a basis for estimating energy requirements, but one should keep in mind that these values deviate from time to time according to the effort expended—notice the range indicated for a housemaid.

Even though the caloric requirements for given tasks vary with the size of the individual and the speed or activity with which he does the work, the variations tend to equalize when populations are considered.

Caloric requirements generally are based on the needs of the healthy individual who leads an active, useful life of productivity in his occupation. Chronic disease reduces vitality, activity, and appetite. A lack of food energy (undernutrition) also reduces vitality, resistance to disease, basal metabolism, and the initiative to perform mental or physical work. The energy requirement to maintain the status quo under such conditions represents the capacity of the human being to maintain life by physiological adjustment to imposed conditions.

Nutritionists who work with such groups have to recommend caloric allowances greatly above the intake that merely permits life to continue.

Children's energy requirements are relatively greater than those of adults because of their greater muscular activity and because they must manufacture and store body tissue.

A parent knows that the average child may do no "work," but nevertheless is expending much energy in his day's activities.

The daily energy requirement of children 1 to 6 years old may be estimated as 37 to 30 Calories per pound of body weight, respectively.

Boys 13 to 20 years old need 33 to 23 Calories, respectively.

Girls 13 to 20 years old need 27 to 20 Calories.

A very large or a very active child will require more than the average energy allowance to meet his requirement.

The allowance for an undernourished child (or adult) should be based on the estimated weight of the individual in good health.

The energy requirement of older people diminishes progressively with age because of a lesser basal metabolism and, ordinarily, because muscular activity is less. Requirements may be calculated, however, just as satisfactorily as for the young adult.

ENVIRONMENTAL TEMPERATURE is another factor in heat production.

We observe the constriction of the peripheral blood vessels in our hands when we are exposed to cold. This reaction reduces the blood supply to the surface and helps to conserve the heat within our bodies.

Animals conserve heat by curling up to expose a minimum of surface to the surrounding air. Conversely, a warm environment produces dilation of the superficial blood vessels, with an increased supply of blood to the surface.

The loss of heat from the body by evaporation of water from the skin depends not on the amount of sweat produced but on the amount evaporated. Evaporation in humid weather is slow; we are uncomfortable in a hot, humid atmosphere. Actual tests show that men can work with comparative comfort in a hot, dry atmosphere with adequate ventilation at a temperature of 120° F., but the same work can be performed only with considerable discomfort at a temperature of 90° in an atmosphere of high humidity.

There exists a range of environmental temperature in which metabolism of warm-blooded animals is not affected. This range, or zone of thermal neutrality, is not the same for all animals and is influenced by the ingestion of food, the coat of hair, clothing, degree of fatness, and so on.

As the environmental temperature is lowered, a point is reached at which the heat production is increased. This point is called the critical temperature.

Lowering the environmental temperature further brings about a further increase in heat production. At the upper extreme of the zone of thermal neutrality, metabolism is increased again, although a constant body temperature may still prevail.

Critical temperatures, as determined on the quiet, postabsorptive animal, have been found to be: Guinea pig, 90° to 92°; rabbit, 82°; swine, 70°; man (lightly clothed), 59°; rats and mice, 84° to 86°.

The range of thermal neutrality may be quite limited. A fasting rat may have a definite rise in heat production when the environmental temperature reaches 95°, the reliable range for metabolism experimentation being from 86° to 91°, inclusive. In studies of energy metabolism, it is necessary to consider and to control environmental temperature.

The ability to maintain a constant body temperature is not well developed in many species of animals at birth. The point at which an animal takes up a separate existence or the point commonly called birth does not represent the same evolutionary point of development in all animals. It is not surprising, therefore, that the inherited ability to walk, or to fly, or to regulate body temperature should become perfected in different species at different time intervals following birth.

About two-thirds of the body weight is represented by its content of water, the high specific heat of which helps to prevent rapid changes in temperature of the body.

Water also has a high heat of vaporization, which determines its effectiveness in the elimination of heat by vaporization from the skin and lungs. Perspiration may be lost in droplets or by absorption by clothing, but there is no cooling effect unless evaporation takes place from the skin or close to it. The evaporation of 1 kilogram of water signifies the elimination of about 586 Calories.

Man avoids actual exposure to cold by means of clothing and heated houses. But when the body is actually exposed to a lower environmental temperature, it must produce more heat in order to maintain normal body temperature. This increase in heat output takes place without voluntary effort on the part of the person and more than likely without his knowledge.

The "automatic" severalfold increase in heat production that accompanies shivering due to cold is one of the most interesting of the many physiological regulatory mechanisms.

There is also a "chemical regulation" of body temperature, which is associated with the function of the adrenal gland. It is by no means certain, however, that increased secretion of adrenalin (a hormone secreted by the adrenal gland) occurs during the exposure of normal humans to low temperatures, as no increase in blood sugar or heart rate is observed.

The correlation of the mechanisms that govern body temperature seems to be accomplished by means of a nervous "heat center" in the corpus striatum of the brain. The increase in metabolism due to chemical regulation in the absence of increased muscular tension or shivering is very small.

One of the first responses to cold is a constriction of the peripheral blood vessels that reduces the flow of blood to the skin and thus helps to cut heat loss. Next comes the sensation of tightening up—of greater muscular tension before shivering begins. The tension alone, without shivering, may raise the metabolism 36 percent. It is nearly impossible to lie relaxed in a cold place. The onset of shivering is gradual and may begin by slight tremors in various places. Definite and vigorous shivering raises the heat output to four times the basal level.

The fat just under the skin is like a blanket and helps greatly in protecting a person against cold. A fat person may not shiver and may not produce any extra heat when he is exposed to the conditions that produce a marked response in the lean person.

When you wait on a street corner for a bus on a cold winter day and feel chilled to the bone, you can get some small comfort from knowing that Nature has taken over and is dutifully running your body furnace under forced draft in order to maintain body temperature.

ALCOHOL is one of the organic compounds that food energy is derived from. Alcohol yields 7.1 Calories per gram upon oxidation (196 Calories per ounce).

The subject of the metabolism of ethyl alcohol in people and laboratory animals has been investigated from time to time. The purpose of these studies has been to determine whether alcohol may serve the same purposes in the energy economy as does ordinary carbohydrate—to spare protein and to provide the energy for muscular activity, the deposition of fat, and the generation of heat to maintain body temperature.

Investigators seem to have established that in the albino rat alcohol is available for all these physiological purposes to the extent of at least three-fourths that of sucrose.

Similarly, in human metabolism under conditions of moderate intake, most of the potential energy of the ingested alcohol is available for muscular work and for the production of body heat. The partial replacement of carbohydrate or fat in the diet by an amount of alcohol equal in energy content has been shown also to be effective in the synthesis of body tissue.

The body can oxidize alcohol at a limited rate. When absorption exceeds this rate, the unoxidized alcohol in the blood stream makes one drunk. A moderate intake may be considered to be an amount that does not exceed 50 percent of the basal metabolism energy requirement and is taken at less than a specified rate. A quart of wine consumed gradually throughout the day will furnish 650 Calories of available energy. Less alcohol is absorbed if food is eaten at the same time.

It is hard to assess the Calories in the alcoholic beverages Americans drink because some beverages contain sugar and other constituents besides alcohol and because a determination of average consumption is impossible.

Excess consumption of alcohol may result directly and indirectly in malnutrition. Data are needed as to the proportion of total energy intake of individuals that is provided by alcoholic beverages. Such energy intake as a food up to 10 percent of the total intake could be accepted at face value.

THE SPECIFIC DYNAMIC effect of food also affects heat production. The term refers to the increase in metabolism that begins soon after food has been ingested and attains a peak at about the third hour.

Countless studies of it have been made with people and experimental animals. Most of the studies have involved periods of measurement (by indirect calorimetry) lasting a few hours.

Such work, dating from the time of Max Rubner, a German physiologist (1854–1932), indicated that the ingestion of protein produced a greater dynamic effect (increase in heat production) than an amount of fat or carbohydrate that was equal to it in Calories.

He fed food components (protein, carbohydrate, or fat) individually to a subject (animal or man) that had been maintained in a basal or fasting state just before the test. He concluded that protein dominated the dynamic effect of diets.

Some general principles have been established to put in proper perspective the whole question of the dynamic effect of food.

First, the dynamic effect of a complete diet is less than the sum of the dynamic effect of its components, as determined individually.

Second, an individual food component expresses its normal and most characteristic nutritive value (and dynamic effect) only as it is a part of a complete diet.

Extensive studies with albino rats that had diets which contained 10 or 20 percent of protein but which furnished equal amounts of energy disclosed that the diet higher in protein produced greater body gain and less heat.

In referring to the misunderstanding and perplexity of many persons regarding specific dynamic effect of food, Dr. W. W. Hawkins, of the National Research Council of Canada, pointed out that the subject is often presented in such a way that one might ask, "Why do we not waste away because we eat?"

He added: "Practically all our knowledge of specific dynamic action has been derived from studies of animals kept warm in the fasting state, but otherwise under basal conditions. Practically nothing is known about it in human beings under ordinary conditions of activity and everyday living, and under normal food consumption at the usual intervals."

IT SEEMED IMPORTANT therefore to establish the facts as determined by the measured 24-hour metabolism of people maintained on definite amounts of diets of known composition.

Accordingly, in 1957, the Departments of Animal Nutrition and of Foods and Nutrition of The Pennsylvania State University selected four male college students, 21 years old, as subjects for a study of the dynamic effects of two diets that had the same energy content but differed in protein content.

We chose the students on the basis of normal basal metabolism, their uniform weight (about 150 pounds), willingness to accept the diets, and interest in the investigation. They were housed and fed in a cottage used exclusively for the purpose.

The two diets were composed of ordinary food items such as ground beef, eggs, milk, green beans, potatoes, and fruit. The intake of all nutrients, as calculated, exceeded the allowances of the National Academy of Sciences-National Research Council except for the daily intake of protein on the low-protein diet.

One of each of the meals to be used in the experiment was prepared and analyzed for nitrogen and energy before the experiment began. That was necessary to assure that the two diets were equal in Calories and had a definite protein content. Each diet furnished 3,111 Calories daily. The protein supplied by the low-protein diet was 38 grams a day. The high-protein diet furnished 128.6 grams.

The meals were served each day at 7:15 a.m., 12:15 p.m., and 5:30 p.m. The cooked foods were prepared by standardized procedures. All foods were weighed to the nearest gram on a Toledo scale. Each young man was required to eat all the food served him. He used bread to wipe the last traces from the plate. To minimize any possible undesirable psychological responses, the subjects on the low- and high-protein diets were served in separate dining rooms.

Minor modifications in the interior of the Armsby respiration calorimeter were made to adapt the apparatus for use with human beings. A room large enough to contain two cots and chairs and provide limited space for standing and moving about was provided. The usual preliminary tests were made for tightness of the chamber and ventilation lines and for quantitative recovery of known amounts of carbon dioxide.

Before the actual test, the students entered the chamber several times and remained for a few hours to become accustomed to the routine.

They were paired, each pair serving as a unit in the calorimeter. The use of two subjects as a unit provided an appropriate amount of carbon dioxide and undoubtedly helped to keep the boys from getting worried about it.

Two operators were on duty at all times. One of them was always visible to the students. That and the possibility of talking with the operator at any time by means of an intercommunication system prevented any feeling of claustrophobia on their part.

After a preliminary period of 6 hours in the respiration chamber, total metabolism was measured continuously for 24 hours.

The students were free to read or study during this time. Three times a day each was required to take 5 minutes of exercise in the form of knee bends, pushups, and such. The limited exercise reduced boredom and standardized the activity during the 24-hour period, so that we could interpret any differences in total heat production as being due to specific dynamic effect.

The boys got about 7 hours of sleep. They had to retire at a given hour, when all lights were turned off. They were required to arise at a definite hour, when the lights were turned on. The heat generated by the lights was measured as a part of the "blank run," and was subtracted from the direct heat measurement of each experimental period.

The heat production in 24 hours was measured by direct and by indirect calorimetry. The indirect method was the nitrogen-carbon-energy balance method. It involved a 5-day collection period. It (along with the carbon dioxide determined in the calorimeter period) provided the data for computing the daily balance of fat and protein.

The experiment had three objectives:

To compare the 24-hour metabolism of human beings on a high-protein diet with the 24-hour metabolism resulting from a diet of the same energy content but low in protein;

To determine whether high-protein diets affect the manner of heat disposal (Max Rubner reported that a high-protein diet put a load on the sweat glands);

And to determine whether evidence would be found of an adaptation to a given protein intake as concerned the energy metabolism.

The third objective made it seem desirable to conduct the first calorimeter period very soon after the students went on experiment.

THE FIRST MEAL of the low-protein diet preceded the 24-hour metabolism measurement in the respiration calorimeter by 54 hours. Following the first calorimeter period while the boys continued to receive exactly the same diet for a total of 63 days, the 24-hour heat productions were measured at the end of 2, 5, and 7 weeks, respectively. Exactly 1 week after the beginning of the experiment on the low-protein diet, the feeding of the high-protein diet to the second pair of subjects was initiated. Exactly the same sequence was followed.

After this schedule was completed, the assignment of the diets was reversed, and six more calorimeter periods took place, three with each pair of subjects—following the same time schedule as the one I mentioned.

Of a total of 14 calorimeter periods scheduled, 13 took place as planned. We had to omit the sixth period because of a death in the family of one of the students. The dietary intake, however, was maintained constant during this period, even though a calorimeter test could not be made.

While they were in the respiration calorimeter, the students continued to receive three meals a day in accord with the dietary regime under study. Meals were prepared in the calorimeter room and served immediately at the same hours each day.

With one pair of subjects, the 24-hour heat production was 5 percent higher when they were getting the high-protein diet. With the second pair, however, the heat productions on the two diets were identical.

This would seem to permit the conclusion that if any difference exists in the overall energy utilization of equal-calorie diets of widely different protein contents with human beings, such differences must be very small and should bring into proper perspective the distortion that has resulted from the interpretation of very short periods of metabolism measurements. There seems to be little basis for the contention that high-protein diets are "wasteful."

With the low-protein diet, 30.4 percent of the total heat produced was eliminated by the evaporation of water from the skin and lungs. The percentage was 31.8 with the high-protein diet. This tiny difference signifies that there is no reason—on this basis—for avoiding protein foods in hot, humid weather. Environmental temperature and exercise, rather than the composition of the diet, determine the pathways of heat elimination.

As far as adaptation is concerned, the 24-hour heat productions from week to week showed no tendency toward an increase or decrease. The uniformity gives assurance that a given diet is as correctly represented by the heat production measured at the end of a few days as when measured after several weeks.

It is well to keep in mind that it is the amount of food rather than its protein content that determines the magnitude of its dynamic effect. In any event, it is a much smaller item in the energy economy than may be supposed.

After an average meal, the metabolism may be in the order of 22 Calories per hour greater than the basal metabolic rate. That is less than the extra energy expended in standing relaxed. The dynamic effect may ordinarily amount to 5 or 6 percent of the total food energy.

Many scientists have investigated the specific dynamic effect of food in fat people.

Most of the evidence indicates no difference between obese and normal subjects, although some investigators have reported a lesser dynamic effect in the obese.

Even if the average increase of 6 percent in normal people were abolished in obese subjects, it could not account for the tremendous discrepancies between the alleged food intake and weight changes. The total metabolism of normal (and obese) individuals may vary several hundred percentage points in accord with muscular activity, yet the appetite keeps them in energy balance. It is difficult to believe that the appetite can adjust itself easily to such huge changes and fail to respond to a 6-percent demand.

I have cited muscular activity, environmental temperature, and the dynamic effect of food as factors affecting expenditure of energy.

Intense mental effort, on the contrary, involves only a negligible increase in the metabolism. The metabolism of the brain is relatively high and accounts for 8 to 10 percent of the entire basal metabolism, but the extra Calories required for 1 hour of intense mental effort can be met by eating one-half of a salted peanut.

THE INTERRELATIONSHIPS between the three major items affecting energy expenditure—muscular activity, environmental temperature, and specific dynamic effect—have been the subject of investigation since Rubner's time.

The most prevalent understanding is that the specific dynamic effect of food, ordinarily a waste or cost of utilization, may serve a useful purpose when the body is exposed to a low environmental temperature—that it may substitute for some of the extra heat that is produced reflexly because of exposure to cold.

When food and its dynamic effect are not involved, the extra heat needed to maintain body temperature in a cold environment must come from the increased oxidation of body tissue, which may be brought about by voluntary exercise or by reflex action (shivering). The energy expenditure accompanying muscular activity at ordinary environmental temperature is superimposed upon that represented by the dynamic effect of food.

It is apparent from this discussion of food energy intake and outgo that the problem of avoiding simple obesity is as simple as a bank balance—and equally difficult to manage. This aspect of food energy, of great importance from the standpoint of optimum health, is set forth in a later chapter and I give it little more than passing mention here.

Many people without voluntary effort maintain a constant weight for many years. The wide fluctuations in energy requirement that accompany changes in their activity are balanced by corresponding food intakes dictated by appetite.

A slight excess of intake of food energy, if continued for a long time, can be just as effective in producing overweight as any other type of overeating. An excess in intake of only one bottle of soft drink daily or of somewhat less than one-third of an ounce of butter can account for the deposition of more than 7 pounds of fat at the end of a year.

Because that half ounce of butter will provide the extra energy needed to walk a mile and a half, it would seem more feasible in combating overweight to reduce the intake rather than to increase the energy output. In combating simple obesity, it is obvious that one or both must be changed in the appropriate direction.

Most protein and carbohydrate foods contain more water than do foods of high fat content. This increases the energy ratio between them as computed on the fresh basis as eaten. A given weight of butter furnishes about 3.5 times as much energy as does an equal weight of bread.

The notion that a particular food, usually of high carbohydrate content, is especially "deadly" in causing overweight is without foundation. Any dietary fat is more than twice as "deadly" as any carbohydrate.

In any case, there is only one source of body fat—food.

In summarizing the more important aspects of energy metabolism, it is not necessary to refute the law of the conservation of energy. All the energy represented by absorbed nutrients must ultimately appear as heat, body tissue, or work.

From the quantitative standpoint, much more food is required to provide for normal energy metabolism than for all other purposes combined. This is not to imply that the other essential nutrients are less vital to the maintenance of life and good health. In the normal healthy adult of constant weight, at least 90 percent of the food

energy is represented by the heat produced by the oxidation of the food. More than 50 percent of this heat produced is represented by the basal metabolism. Muscular activity accounts for most of the remainder.

Heat is not a food nutrient, and, strictly speaking, we do not "add Calories to a diet." Overweight people find to their consternation that carbohydrates do not indeed merely produce Calories, but, instead, body fat.

RAYMOND W. SWIFT *is head of the Department of Animal Nutrition, The Pennsylvania State University. He is the senior author of textbook, "Energy Metabolism and Nutrition."*

Counting the calories with every meal is common practice for many. In fact, the very word "calories" has come to be part of our everyday vocabulary. But what is the calorie, and why do we associate it with food values and nutritional requirements?

The calorie is a unit measure of heat. The word itself is derived from the Latin "calor," meaning heat. Heat quantity is measured by the change of temperature produced. The calorie, therefore, is the quantity of heat necessary to raise the temperature of 1 gram of water, 1 degree centigrade. The unit quantity of heat varies slightly at different points on the thermometric scale. If the degree interval chosen is from 14.5° to 15.5° C., the value of the unit is almost exactly that of the "mean" calorie, which is 1/100 of the quantity of heat necessary to raise the temperature of 1 gram of water from 0° to 100 ° C.—that is, from the melting point of ice to the boiling point of water.

The calorie, thus defined as the amount of heat required to raise the temperature of 1 gram of water from 14.5° to 15.5° C., is a very small unit, and is referred to as the small calorie (spelled with a small c).

A larger unit, often convenient to use, is the kilogram calorie. This is the Calorie (spelled with a capital C). It represents the amount of heat necessary to raise the temperature of 1 kilogram (2.2 pounds) of

water 1° C. The Calorie, equal to 1,000 small calories, is also called the "large" or "great" calorie. It is the unit generally used in expressing the heat-producing or energy-producing value of food. A teaspoonful of sugar (4 grams), for example, provides about 16 Calories (16,000 calories).

The body requires a source of energy, which is normally supplied by food. In the process, food is fragmented by digestion into simple components, which are absorbed through the intestinal wall and transported to the body tissues. When these food components are oxidized within the tissues, energy is released, to be utilized in maintaining body temperature and muscle tone or to be expended in muscular work and other body activities. If the food intake is more than enough to meet the body's energy needs, there is storage of the excess, chiefly as body fat, and a gain in weight results. If the food intake is insufficient, the body draws on its own reserves, oxidizing them to furnish needed energy, with resultant loss in body weight. Whether we gain, lose, or maintain weight depends on food energy intake in relation to body energy requirements. These requirements, also expressed in terms of Calories, have been studied in metabolic experiments. Several chapters in this book have more to say about these matters and provide further background for understanding why we count the Calories.—GEORGIAN ADAMS.

Proteins

RUTH M. LEVERTON

YOU are looking at a superb package of proteins when you see yourself in a mirror. All that shows—muscles, skin, hair, nails, eyes—are protein tissues. Teeth contain a little protein.

Most of what you do not see is protein, too—blood and lymph, heart and lungs, tendons and ligaments, brain and nerves, and all the rest of you.

Genes, those mysterious controllers of heredity, are a particular kind of protein.

Hormones, the chemical regulators of body processes, and enzymes, the sparkplugs of chemical reactions, also are proteins.

Life requires protein. A Dutch physician turned chemist, Gerrit Jan Mulder, first observed this fact, which we now take for granted. He announced in 1838 his conclusion from many investigations that all living plants and animals contain a certain substance without which life is impossible. He did not know what was in it, but he was sure it was vital. He named it protein, from a Greek word meaning first place.

Scientists since then have discovered that there are hundreds of different kinds of protein—not just the one substance Mulder observed. They also learned that proteins are unique in that they contain the element nitrogen. All our foodstuffs—fats, starches, sugars, and proteins—contain the elements carbon, hydrogen, and oxygen in varying proportions. Because proteins contain them and also nitrogen, they have a special importance and power.

Proteins have to be made by living cells. Proteins do not exist in air, like nitrogen or oxygen. They do not come directly from the sun, like energy.

Most plants make their own protein by combining the nitrogen from nitrogen-containing materials in the soil with carbon dioxide from the air and with water. The energy they need for the process comes from the sun. Legumes, which include beans, peas, and peanuts, can use the nitrogen directly from the air for combining with the other substances to make protein.

Animals and people cannot use such simple raw materials for building the proteins. We must get our proteins from plants and other animals. Once eaten, these proteins are digested into smaller units and rearranged to form the many special and distinct proteins we need.

57

Although we sometimes hear plant proteins referred to as "inferior" to animal proteins, plants are the basic factory of proteins. All proteins come directly or indirectly from plants.

We depend heavily on farm animals to convert plant proteins into animal proteins for us, but most animals, too, must have some animal protein supplied to them. The ruminant animals—cattle, sheep, goats—are an exception, because they can use the simple nitrogen-containing substance in young pasture grasses; the micro-organisms in their paunches can make microbial proteins, which the animal can then digest and use.

NEXT TO WATER, protein is the most plentiful substance in the body. If all the water were squeezed out of you, about half your dry weight would be protein. About a third of the protein is in the muscle. About a fifth is in the bone and cartilage. About a tenth is in the skin. The rest is in the other tissues and body fluids. Bile and urine are the only fluids that do not contain protein.

There are several dozen proteins in the blood alone.

One of the busiest is hemoglobin, which constantly transports oxygen from the lungs to the tissues and brings carbon dioxide back from the tissues to the lungs. Ninety-five percent of the hemoglobin molecule is protein. The other 5 percent is the portion that contains the iron.

Other proteins in the blood are defenders, for they give us the means of developing resistance and sometimes immunity to disease.

Gamma globulin can also form antibodies, substances that can neutralize bacteria and viruses and other micro-organisms. Different antibodies are specific for different diseases.

Once we have had a disease, like measles, and the antibody for measles has been formed, it stays in the blood, and we are not likely to have measles again. A vaccination, such as for poliomyelitis, introduces a tiny amount of the inactive or dead virus into the body to stimulate the blood to form the specific antibody needed for neutralizing the virus that causes poliomyelitis. The presence of an antibody in the blood may give the person immunity to the disease. At least it gives him a head start in fighting the virus, and the disease will be less severe.

Gamma globulin also helps the scavenger cells—phagocytes—engulf disease microbes.

Proteins help in the exchange of nutrients between cells and the intercellular fluids and between tissues and blood and lymph. When one has too little protein, the fluid balance of the body is upset, so that the tissues hold abnormal amounts of liquid and become swollen.

The proteins in the body tissues are not there as fixed, unchanging substances deposited for a lifetime of use. They are in a constant state of exchange. Some molecules or parts of molecules always are breaking down and others are being built as replacements. This exchange is a basic characteristic of living things; in the body it is referred to as the dynamic state of body constituents—the opposite of a static or fixed state. This constant turnover explains why our diet must supply adequate protein daily even when we no longer need it for growth. The turnover of protein is faster within the cells of a tissue (intracellular) than in the substance between the cells (intercellular).

Proteins, like starches, sugars, and fats, can supply energy.

One gram of protein will yield about 4 Calories when it is combined with oxygen in the body. One ounce will give 115 Calories. That is about the same amount as starches and sugars give.

The body puts its need for energy above every other need. It will ignore the special functions of protein if it needs energy and no other source is available. This applies to protein coming into the body in food and to protein being withdrawn from the tissues. Either kind gets whisked through the liver to rid it of its nitrogen and then is oxidized for energy without having a chance to do any of the jobs it is especially designed to do. The protein-sparing action of carbohydrates means that starches and sugars, by supplying energy, conserve protein for its special functions.

WE CANNOT TALK about proteins very long without getting into the subject of the amino acids, the chemical units of which proteins are made. I discuss them in the next chapter, but I must point out here that the kinds and amounts of amino acids in a protein determine its nutritive—or biological—value.

The amino acid composition of animal muscle, milk, and egg is similar, though not identical, to the amino acid composition of human tissues. Because these animal proteins can supply all of the amino acids in about the same proportions in which they are needed by the body, they are rated as having a high nutritive value.

The proteins from fruits, vegetables, grains, and nuts supply important amounts of many amino acids, but they do not supply as good an assortment as animal proteins do. Their nutritive value therefore is lower. The proteins from some of the legumes—especially soybeans and chickpeas—are almost as good as those from animal sources.

To have the nutritive value of the mixture of proteins in our diets rate high requires only that a portion of the protein come from animal sources.

TO STUDY THE NEEDS of people and animals for proteins, scientists commonly study the nitrogen balance.

Nitrogen is easier to measure than protein. The amount of nitrogen, properly determined, is an accurate index of the amount of protein involved. Because the common proteins average 16 percent nitrogen, we can measure the amount of nitrogen in a food, mul-tiply the amount by 6.25, and get our answer in grams of protein.

A nitrogen-balance study is based on the principle that if we know the amount of nitrogen that goes into the body in the food and the amount that leaves the body in the excreta, we can calculate what has been used. The amount that has been used reflects the amount that has been needed.

The body constantly uses materials for maintenance, regardless of the supply. It operates best when the supply of materials from food is generous and regular, but it does not stop functioning immediately when the food fails to supply what is needed. It mobilizes material from its tissues to meet these needs as long as that supply will last.

Suppose that the diet does not furnish enough protein for the body's daily operating and repair needs. The first thing the body does is to draw on some of its own tissue protein to supply this daily wear-and-tear quota. As a result, the operating and repair needs are met, and the normal kind and amount of end products of protein metabolism leave the body.

In a balance study, each person's food intake is weighed. Samples of the food are analyzed for nitrogen. Then the output, the urine and feces, is collected and analyzed. The study lasts a number of days or weeks in order to get a typical picture of the body's metabolism, including its day-to-day variations.

The balance is found by subtracting the output from the intake. When the intake is larger than the output, there is a positive balance, indicating that some nitrogen has been retained in the body.

If the daily intake is 10 grams of nitrogen and output is 9 grams, the balance or retention is 1 gram.

When the intake is smaller than the output, the balance is negative, indicating a loss of nitrogen (and thus protein or protein derivatives) from the body tissues.

If the nitrogen intake is 10 grams and the output is 12 grams, the balance is a minus 2 grams. When the intake and the output are equal, the body is in nitrogen equilibrium.

Nitrogen equilibrium is the usual condition in adults when body proteins are being maintained and replenished as needed and when protein is neither being stored in the tissues nor withdrawn from them.

Positive balance is essential for growth. Only by having a large enough supply to permit storage can the body add to itself.

Negative balance is not a desirable condition. It happens when the food intake supplies too little protein to meet the body's needs.

A positive balance occurs in women during pregnancy, when new tissue is being formed, and during the nursing period, when the mother needs to store nitrogen for the protein of the milk she produces. An adult may be in positive nitrogen balance after any illness or injury that has caused a drain on the protein stores of the body.

Especially during illnesses with continued fever or severe tissue damage, or in the shock of accident, the patient is likely to be in a negative balance. Then, during recovery, protein that has been lost from the tissues is replaced before the person establishes nitrogen equilibrium again.

When an adult is increasing the amount of his muscle tissues—developing larger muscles for strength and endurance—he must be in positive balance to store the protein and other materials from which to make the added muscle. Once this is done, he will return to nitrogen equilibrium.

For children, it is important to supply the amount of protein that will permit the best retention and thus the best growth. Sometimes we refer to this as a level of protein intake above which no improvement in nitrogen retention will occur.

As an example, consider the balance study of a boy 7 years old: Perhaps on a daily intake of 20 grams of protein he just stays in nitrogen equilibrium but retains none for growth. This in-take is too low for him. Then on an intake of 30 grams he stores one-half gram of nitrogen a day; on an intake of 40 grams, he stores 1 gram of nitrogen. If his protein intake is increased to 50 grams but he still retains only 1 gram of nitrogen, no more than he did when he was getting 40 grams of protein, the 40 grams then would be considered just as adequate a supply as the larger amount.

THE PROTEIN REQUIREMENT depends on how fast the body is growing and how large it is: The faster the body is growing, the more protein it needs for building. The larger the mass of living tissue, the more protein it must have for maintenance and repair.

A child grows faster during the first year than at any other time in his life. His second fastest growing period is during adolescence. His total need increases as he gets bigger, because there is more and more tissue to keep supplied and replenished with protein. Protein (or any other material) cannot be used for growth until after the needs for maintenance have been met. When there is not enough protein for both purposes, growth suffers first. The protein need is not increased by exercise or any kind of voluntary muscular activity except when the muscle is growing.

The amounts of protein needed by boys, girls, men, and women of different ages have been established through nitrogen-balance studies. The scientists who make up the Food and Nutrition Board of the National Research Council have evaluated the results obtained by the many investigators who have studied hundreds of normal men, women, and children. On that basis, the Board has set up recommended daily dietary allowances designed for the maintenance of good nutrition of healthy persons in the United States. The Board has done this for all nutrients about which there is enough information.

The recommended amounts of protein include the amount indicated by the nitrogen-balance studies plus an

Protein—Recommended Daily Dietary Allowances (1958)

FOOD AND NUTRITION BOARD—NATIONAL RESEARCH COUNCIL

Person	Age, years	Weight		Height		Protein
		Pounds	Kilograms	Inches	Centimeters	Grams
Men..............	25	154	70	69	175	70
	45	154	70	69	175	70
	65	154	70	69	175	70
Women...........	25	128	58	64	163	58
	45	128	58	64	163	58
	65	128	58	64	163	58
Pregnant (2d half)..+20						
Lactating (28 ounces daily)..+40						
Children...........	1–3	27	12	34	87	40
	4–6	40	18	43	109	50
	7–9	60	27	51	129	60
	10–12	79	36	57	144	70
Boys..............	13–15	108	49	64	163	85
	16–19	139	63	69	175	100
Girls.............	13–15	108	49	63	160	80
	16–19	120	54	64	162	75

amount (usually about 50 percent) to cover individual variations in requirements of normal people and possible differences in the protein quality of foods selected by different people. Adding an amount for a safety factor converts a minimum requirement, as determined under rigid laboratory control, to a recommended allowance suitable for broader application.

The exact amounts of protein recommended by scientists are given in terms of grams. Body weight is given in terms of kilograms. In scientific work, weights are usually expressed in micrograms, milligrams, grams, and kilograms (each one being 1,000 times the one before it) rather than in ounces and pounds and tons. The gram system is used in most countries. An ounce is really too big for measuring most of the nutrients, and using ounces to express the amount of protein needed would be a little like using gallons to express the amount of orange juice to give the baby—the fractions or decimals would be cumbersome. There are 28.4 grams in an ounce, 454.4 grams in a pound, and 2.2 pounds in a kilogram.

The protein requirement often is given as the amount needed for a specified amount of body weight. This is the simplest way to indicate the special needs for both speed of growth and body size. On a body-weight basis, the amount of protein recommended begins with as much as 3.5 grams per kilogram for the young infant (somewhat less if he is breast fed), gradually decreases to 1.5 grams in early childhood, rises again to 2 grams in late childhood and adolescence, and then settles to about 1 gram per kilogram for the average adult.

The total daily protein needs increase steadily from birth to adolescence and then decrease to a maintenance level for adulthood. The recommended allowance climbs from 40 grams of protein for children 1 to 3 years old to 70 grams for children 10 to 12 years old. At those ages, there is no difference in the recommendations made for boys and for girls.

Beginning with the age group from 12 to 15 years old, boys and girls have different patterns of growth and therefore different dietary allowances of protein. Girls mature physically earlier than boys do, and begin their rapid adolescent growth earlier. The recommended allowance therefore is highest for girls 13 to 15 years old (80 grams daily) and drops to 75 grams for girls 16 to 19 years old.

Because boys 13 to 15 years old are bigger than girls of that age, 85 grams of protein daily is the amount recommended for them. Then from 16 to 19 years, when most boys are growing most rapidly, the allowance is increased to 100 grams daily.

The recommended daily protein allowances for adults are 70 grams for the average man who weighs about 154 pounds, and 58 grams for the average woman who weighs 128 pounds. These amounts are equivalent to 1 gram of protein per kilogram of body weight, or 0.46 gram per pound, for both men and women. These figures can be used to calculate the allowances for persons who are larger or smaller than average.

A woman has another period of rapid growth, and thus an increased protein need, when she is an expectant mother. During the second half of pregnancy, when the fetus is growing rapidly, the recommended daily allowance is for an additional 20 grams of protein, which raises her total intake to 78 grams daily. At this time she needs a chance to store protein not only for the growth of the baby but for her own tissues in preparation for milk production. Much of the success in nursing a baby depends on the mother's nutrition before the baby comes.

The mother's total protein allowance when she is nursing her baby is the highest of any time in her life. Forty grams, in addition to her prepregnancy needs, are recommended, so that her total daily recommended intake is now 98 grams. Sometimes it is hard for a mother to realize that she needs more of every kind of nutri-

ent during lactation than she did during pregnancy.

ADULTS CAN BE in nitrogen equilibrium on intakes considerably lower than the recommended allowances.

The body adjusts itself to a low intake by reducing its body stores of the protein in order to cut down the amount it needs for maintenance or overhead. This does not mean that low intakes are advisable. In fact, the reverse is true. Studies of the nutrition of individuals and groups of adults and children show that a generous supply of protein in the diet contributes noticeably to nutritional status and well-being at every age.

All these recommendations for people in the United States assume that some of the protein will come from animal sources. They also assume that the diet will be adequate in calories and other essential nutrients, so that the protein can be used with greatest efficiency and benefit to the body.

SUPPLYING ENOUGH protein is not a major nutritional problem in this country. The average diet is more likely to be adequate, or is more nearly adequate, in protein than in almost any other nutritional essential except calories. There is an average of 97 grams of protein per capita in available household food supplies; two-thirds of this protein is from animal sources. This reflects a high level of economic prosperity as well as certain food preferences.

Despite the high average figures for the amount of protein consumed by the people, certain groups of individuals in some situations have an inadequate supply—for example, during periods of adolescence, pregnancy, and lactation; in reducing diets; when people prefer foods high in starch, sugar, or fat; and among poor people.

Supplies of protein foods are a major problem for many countries—especially the underdeveloped, populous countries. Protein malnutrition in children and adults may result in stunted growth, lack of muscle development, and lowered resistance to disease. It is most prevalent in children 1 to 5 years old. Many children have the protein-deficiency disease, kwashiorkor (quashi-or'-kor). This disease occurs soon after a child is weaned and yet is too young to thrive on the food that the adults have. The adult diet in many countries is far from adequate for normal growth and sometimes is barely sufficient to keep the adult body alive.

Because of its prevalence, high death rate, and its preventable nature, kwashiorkor was of serious concern to health and nutrition workers in many parts of the world in 1959. Progress has been made in learning how to supply the needed protein and in helping families learn about improved feeding and care of children.

In underdeveloped and heavily populated countries, cereal grains have to be the chief item of diet because they are the quickest, easiest, and cheapest food to produce in quantity. The proteins from cereals alone are not of high enough nutritional value for normal growth and efficient maintenance. Although some proteins from animals or certain legumes are essential, enough of them may not always be available.

We have come to realize that perhaps some of the chemical units that make meat, milk, and eggs superior foods for filling the protein needs of people may be supplied by skillfully combining certain foods from plant sources in special proportions. For that, our knowledge of the chemistry and requirements of amino acids is most useful.

RUTH M. LEVERTON *became Associate Director of the Institute of Home Economics in the Agricultural Research Service, Department of Agriculture, in 1958. From 1937 to 1954 she was on the faculty of the University of Nebraska and in the Nebraska Agricultural Experiment Station. During this time she spent a year as Fulbright professor assigned to the Philippines. From 1954 to 1957, she was at Oklahoma State University as assistant director of the agricultural experiment station in charge of home economics research.*

The diet revolution is likely to take two directions "fairly rapidly," predicts Dr. C. G. King, executive director of the Nutrition Foundation. About half of the world's population will increase its food intake, the other half eat less.

In this country, particularly, less consumption in quantity is expected. The constant reminder of health authorities that 25 per cent of the population is overweight, and that obesity is associated with seven of the 10 leading causes of death and crippling diseases, is expected to influence diet habits. The trend toward less physical work as a result of mechanization should also lighten food consumption.

Yet the temptation to overeat will also increase, Dr. King warns, because of relatively high incomes and an abundance of attractive foods.

In fact, the lower income groups could wind up the better fed. In areas where population and economics limit food supplies, research advances, Dr. King predicts, may permit blending of low-cost plant proteins to furnish desired intakes of amino acids. This supplementation of animal protein foods, he says, "will be of critical importance for infants, growing children and mothers."— MALVINA LINDSAY. Washington Post, November 27, 1958.

Amino Acids

RUTH M. LEVERTON

AMINO acids form the alphabet of the proteins. They have the same relation to proteins that letters have to words. At least 22 different letters make up the amino acid alphabet, and combinations of the same or different amino acids make a great variety of proteins.

Not all of the amino acids are present in each protein, but there are many, many more amino acids in a protein than there are letters in any word.

The number of amino acids contained in a single protein can be imagined by comparing the weight of a molecule of an amino acid with the weight of a molecule of protein.

The amino acids range in molecular weight from a low of 89 for glycine to a high of 777 for thyroxine. The wheat protein, gliadin, has a molecular weight of 27,500; zein in corn, 50,000. The molecular weight of hemoglobin in human blood is 63,000. One of the serum globulins in blood may have a molecular weight of more than a million.

The amino acids in a protein determine its chemical characteristics and its nutritive value and how it functions in the metabolism of the body.

All amino acids contain carbon, hydrogen, oxygen, and nitrogen. Three amino acids have sulfur, and two contain iodine.

The chemical structure of each amino acid includes an acid group and an amino group on adjoining carbon atoms.

The acid group looks like this:

$$\underset{HO}{\overset{O}{\diagup}}C-\cdot$$

The amino group looks like this:

$$H-\underset{|}{N}-H.$$

It is attached to the carbon, which in turn is attached to the acid group.

So THE CHEMICAL structure common to all amino acids is this arrangement:

$$\underset{HO}{\overset{O}{\diagup}}C-\underset{\underset{H}{|}}{\overset{\overset{H-N-H}{|}}{C}}-\ ?$$

One amino acid differs from another in the special group that is attached to the same carbon atom as the amino group, where the question mark appears. (Chemists use an *R* to represent this part of the molecule.)

The attachment may be as simple as a lone hydrogen atom to make the amino acid glycine. It may be a certain chain of carbon and hydrogen atoms to make leucine; a chain plus another amino group to make lysine; or a chain that includes an atom of sulfur to make methionine. Adding a more complicated arrangement, such as a ring of carbon and hydrogen atoms, would make phenylalanine; two rings, with some iodine attached, would make thyroxine. Regardless of what is added, however, the characteristic acid and amino groups are common to all amino acids.

A unique feature of the amino acids is that the arrangement of the carbon, hydrogen, oxygen, and nitrogen atoms (and others if they are present) can exist in two patterns.

One pattern is the mirror image of the other, like your left and your right hand. Nature makes only the left-hand pattern, called the L-form of amino acids, and this is the pattern found in all our foods. In general, the body can use only the L-form.

WHEN CHEMISTS make amino acids synthetically in the laboratory, they come out with a mixture of equal parts of the left-hand and the right-hand (D-form) patterns. The body cannot use the right-hand pattern of an amino acid except as a source of carbon and nitrogen, which it may build into the L-form of certain amino acids.

The amino group makes it possible for an amino acid to act like a base (also called alkali), while the acid group makes it possible for it to act like an acid. This dual action is one of the special characteristics of amino acids.

Whether they can act as an acid or a base depends on which is needed at the moment to keep the acid-base balance of the body, especially of the blood, within normal limits. Proteins are often referred to as buffers because of this ability, through their amino acids, to protect the body against sudden or great changes in its acid-base relationships.

It is through their amino and their acid groups that amino acids are joined together to make proteins. The acid group of one molecule of amino acid reacts with the amino group of another just as any acid and alkali react together. A molecule of water is formed and travels off, leaving the nitrogen of one amino acid joined to the carbon of the next amino acid. Such a joining is called a peptide linkage. A protein is a group of amino acids held together by peptide linkages.

Specific enzymes in the gastrointestinal tract attack the peptide linkages when proteins are digested. First, the protein is separated into many clumps of amino acids. And then the clumps are separated further into single amino acids, which are absorbed from the intestine and carried by the blood to the liver.

But the amino acids do not stay single for long. As soon as they leave the liver and are carried by the blood to different tissues, they are reassembled into the special combinations that make the proteins to replace cell material that has worn out, to add to tissue which needs to grow, or to make some enzyme or hormone or other active compound.

It is remarkable how the normal body has unerring accuracy in assembling amino acids into the vital substances needed in every location. If any amino acids are left over, they cannot be stored in the body for use at a later time. They are returned instead to the liver and stripped of their amino groups in a process called deaminization. The nitrogen leaves the body chiefly as urea through the urine, but the carbon, hydrogen, and oxygen fragments that are left can be used to provide energy. If the energy is not needed immediately, the fragments can be converted to fat and stored for use at a later time.

EIGHTEEN DIFFERENT amino acids commonly occur in our food supply.

477248°—59——6

A Peptide Linkage

Many different amino acids can be joined together
by this peptide linkage to form proteins

Some are more important to us than others. The body can manufacture many of them from the materials supplied by the protein and other substances in our food.

There are eight amino acids that the body must have but cannot make from any materials. Our food must supply them completely formed and ready for use. They are valine, lysine, threonine, leucine, isoleucine, tryptophan, phenylalanine, and methionine. They are called the essential or indispensable amino acids because it is essential to have them supplied ready made.

Other amino acids are essential to life and health, too, but if our food does not provide any or enough of them, the body can make them from the raw materials supplied by the food. Therefore they are called nonessential or dispensable amino acids in reference to the fact that it is not essential for the food to furnish them ready made. They are glycine, tyrosine, cystine, cysteine, alanine, serine, glutamic acid, aspartic acid, arginine, histidine, proline, and thyroxine.

The presence in a protein of all of the essential amino acids in significant amounts and in proportions fairly similar to those found in body proteins classifies it as a complete protein— meaning that it could supply com

pletely the needs of the body for these amino acids.

The proportions in which the essential amino acids are required are as important as the amounts. Apparently the body wants these amino acids to be available from food in about the same proportions each time for use in maintenance, repair, and even growth.

Meat, fish, poultry, eggs, milk, cheese, and a few special legumes contain complete proteins.

Gelatin is the only food from an animal source that does not meet the specifications. It contains almost no tryptophan and has very small amounts of threonine, methionine, and isoleucine.

Often the proteins in grains, nuts, fruit, and vegetables are classed as partially complete or incomplete because the proportionate amount of one or more of the essential amino acids is low or because the concentration of all of the amino acids is too low to be helpful in meeting the body's need. Grains, nuts, and legumes are more concentrated sources of amino acids than fruit and vegetables.

Timing, or the distribution of the amino acids among our daily meals, is a factor to consider in meeting our protein needs. In building body proteins, whether for growth or replacement, the body uses all of the essential amino acids plus the nonessential ones.

Knowing that some foods and some combinations of foods used in a meal would not supply enough of all the essential amino acids for building tissue, scientists asked themselves, "Do all the essential amino acids need to be available at the same time, or can the ones that come into the body at one mealtime be held awhile until the others arrive in the next meal or in a meal the next day?"

Dr. Paul Cannon, of the University of Chicago, devised an experiment with rats to help answer the question. He fed them purified amino acids instead of proteins so that he could control more exactly the supply of amino acids.

Instead of giving the rats all the amino acids at each feeding, he divided their ration of acids into two portions. One contained half of the essential amino acids and was fed at the beginning of the day. A few hours later he fed the other portion, which contained the rest of the amino acids. He alternated feeding the two portions, at first spacing the two feedings 8 hours apart and later only 4 hours apart.

The results proved that the animals needed all of the amino acids present at the same time. They could not hold part of the amino acids in their tissues, waiting for the others to come along later. To build the proteins needed for maintenance and growth, all of the essential amino acids had to be on hand at the same time.

Other studies with rats and dogs gave similar results. If even one essential amino acid was absent or was present in too small an amount, the deficiency would limit the utilization of the other amino acids.

Dr. Cannon summarized his findings in this way: "The synthesizing mechanisms operate on an all-or-none principle and are perfectionistic to the extent that if they cannot build a complete protein they will not build it at all."

The same principle holds true for the human body when foods are a source of the amino acids. That was demonstrated in research at the University of Nebraska. Fifteen college girls volunteered to be subjects on a rigidly controlled diet, which supplied the recommended allowances for energy, protein, minerals, and vitamins.

Their breakfasts the first 3 weeks included fruit, bread products (made without milk), butter, jelly, and coffee. All of the animal protein was served at the noon and evening meals, and a part of it was supplied as 1 glass of milk at noon and 2 glasses of milk in the evening.

In the second 3 weeks of the study, the menu was exactly the same, except that a glass of milk was taken from the evening meal and added to the breakfast. Because the daily intake of protein remained constant in amount and quality, the only difference between the two experimental periods was that of timing, or the distribution of amino acids among the meals.

Nitrogen-balance studies showed that the girls made better use of the amino acids from the protein when milk was included in each of the three meals rather than when there was milk at only two meals with none for breakfast.

When incomplete proteins are metabolized, they supply the body with enough of some of the essential amino acids but inadequate amounts of others. The amino acids that are supplied, however, are not used unless the other essential amino acids are present from other food sources. Instead, they are oxidized, and the nitrogen portion is excreted—the amino acids cannot be stored for use at a later time when other acids become available.

The reason that milk was used in the Nebraska study as the protein to shift around was that it is a practical and acceptable form of high-quality protein, which can be included in a breakfast menu without adding an undue amount of food or expense or labor. An egg or a bowl of cereal plus milk or any of the meats could be expected to do the same job.

Minimal requirements for the essential amino acids are determined by nitrogen-balance studies similar to those described for studies of protein needs. Instead of using foods as a source of the amino acids, however, the investigator has to feed the acids as purified chemicals. Only in that way can he single out one amino acid at a time from the others and accurately measure and control the intake. Here, as with the protein studies, nitrogen is the index of the amount of an amino acid involved in the body's metabolism.

If the intake of any one of the essential amino acids is too small to meet the body's need, none of the other essential acids being fed can be used for growth or maintenance of tissue. They will be deaminized, and the nitrogen will be excreted. Also, the body will be in negative nitrogen balance because it has to use some of its own tissue protein as a source of the needed amino acids. The goal in the studies with adults then is to find the amount of each essential amino acid that will maintain the person in nitrogen equilibrium when adequate amounts of the other essential ones are fed also.

We are indebted to college students for serving as subjects for these studies, which are difficult for both the subjects and the investigators. Thirty-two men at the University of Illinois and 60 women at the Universities of Nebraska, California (at Los Angeles), and Wisconsin have given us most of the information now available about the amino acid requirements of adults.

The experimental diet in the studies was no ordinary bill of fare. It could not include any foods that contained protein. Almost every kind of ordinary food therefore was ruled out.

The menu was a variety of purified foods—purified cornstarch, sugar, and fat, plus vitamins and minerals. To this basic diet was added a solution of the amino acids in their chemically pure forms and some extra nitrogen in a simple chemical for the body to use in making the nonessential amino acids.

Comparison of Amino Acid Patterns of Common Foods

	Tryptophan	Lysine	Methionine plus cystine
FAO pattern.....	1	3	3
Milk, cow........	1	5.5	2.4
Milk, human.....	1	4.0	2.5
Buttermilk.......	1	7.7	3.0
Cheese, Cheddar..	1	5.4	2.3
Cheese, cottage...	1	8.0	3.4
Cheese, cream....	1	9.0	3.9
Egg.............	1	3.9	3.3
Beef.............	1	7.5	3.2
Lamb............	1	6.2	2.9
Pork............	1	6.3	2.8
Chicken..........	1	7.2	3.2
Fish.............	1	8.8	4.3
Heart...........	1	6.3	2.6
Kidney..........	1	4.9	2.2
Liver............	1	5.0	2.4
Tongue..........	1	6.9	2.9
Beans, common...	1	8.0	2.2
Chickpeas........	1	8.5	3.4
Cowpeas, dried...	1	6.8	3.0
Lentils..........	1	7.1	1.8
Lima beans......	1	7.1	3.3
Peanuts..........	1	3.2	2.2
Peas, dried.......	1	6.9	2.4
Pigeon peas......	1	13.3	4.7
Soybeans........	1	4.6	2.3
Soybean milk.....	1	5.3	2.5
Coconut.........	1	4.6	4.0
Cottonseed flour..	1	3.6	2.5
Sesame meal.....	1	1.8	3.4
Sunflower meal...	1	2.5	2.6
Barley...........	1	2.7	2.8
Bread (4 percent dry milk solids).	1	2.5	3.8
Buckwheat flour..	1	4.2	2.6
Cornmeal........	1	4.7	5.2
Pearlmillet.......	1	1.5	1.7
Oatmeal.........	1	2.9	2.8
Rice.............	1	3.7	2.9
Rye.............	1	3.6	3.2
Sorghum.........	1	2.4	3.0
Wheat...........	1	2.2	3.0
Flour, white......	1	1.9	2.7
Corn, raw.......	1	5.9	5.8
Cowpeas, raw....	1	6.2	......
Lima beans, raw..	1	4.9	1.7
Peas, raw........	1	5.7	2.3
Spinach.........	1	3.8	2.3
Turnip greens....	1	2.8	2.1
Potatoes.........	1	5.0	2.1
Sweetpotatoes....	1	2.7	2.0
Broccoli.........	1	3.9	......

Calculated from "Amino Acid Content of Foods," by Martha Louise Orr and Bernice Kunerth Watt. Home Economics Research Report No. 4, Agricultural Research Service.

Such a test diet cost about 25 dollars a person a day, but the cost did not keep the amino acids from being mildly distasteful. The diet was terribly monotonous. It was adequate nutritionally, but it was a poor substitute for meat and vegetables, milk, bread, and other foods the students would have liked.

Sometimes the students were on this nitrogen-balance study for as long as 60 days while the intake of one of the amino acids was reduced gradually to find the least amount which would keep them in nitrogen equilibrium.

Now, thanks to the teamwork of the students, research leaders, laboratory workers, and the research organizations that furnished the money for the work, we have a fairly good idea of the amounts of the essential amino acids needed by this representative group of normal adults.

The daily requirements of amino acids for nitrogen equilibrium range from about 0.25 gram of tryptophan to as much as 1 gram of leucine, methionine, and phenylalanine. Intermediate amounts of the others are needed. These amounts actually are very small compared with the amounts we eat in our protein foods every day.

The amino acids phenylalanine and methionine each has a special helper in a related but nonessential amino acid. Tyrosine can help phenylalanine so well that about three-fourths of the phenylalanine requirement can be met by tyrosine.

There are still some functions that only phenylalanine can do—but if there is only a limited supply of phenylalanine, it can be saved for these special functions by supplying plenty of tyrosine.

Cystine is the helper for methionine and is the only other common and plentiful amino acid that contains sulfur. At least three-fourths of the methionine requirement can be met by cystine. Because of this high degree of interchangeability, we are likely to refer to the requirement for total sulfur-containing amino acids, realizing, of course, that at least a small amount of methionine must be present.

THE INFORMATION on requirements and the amino acids in foods gives us a chance to check the food we eat to see how well it meets our needs as we know them now.

Almost any diet that includes a variety of everyday foods supplies generous amounts of all of the essential amino acids and the nonessentials, too.

When foods with proteins of high nutritive value (which means it has a high content of essential amino acids in good proportions) are included in the diet regularly, as they are in this country, a person need not be concerned about the adequacy of the amino acids he gets.

We need to know much more about amino acid requirements, but we have some facts now to reassure us about our own food supply in the United States. We also have information that is most helpful in evaluating the food supplies of other countries and planning ways to supply the nutrients that are in shortest supply.

We need not be concerned about the proportions of different amino acids when the supply of protein is generous and comes from a mixture of ordinary foods. In countries where the protein supply is small and perhaps inadequate, diets are low in calorie value, and the protein chiefly comes from a single food; however, the proportion or ratio of the amino acids may be highly important.

It is possible that an oversupply of one amino acid may reduce the utilization of another amino acid so that a deficiency will occur. Also, an excess of one amino acid may increase the requirement of another acid. The high leucine content of corn, for example, may increase the requirement for isoleucine.

Protein malnutrition in early childhood is one of the most serious deficiency diseases in the world today. Everything possible must be done to find ways to combat and prevent it.

One step has been to translate the figures for requirements of amino acids into a pattern of desirable ratios for the eight essential ones. Such a pattern can be used as both a goal and a measuring stick in developing and supplying food supplements.

The tryptophan requirement has been given the value of 1, and the amounts of the other acids are expressed as multiples of this. The provisional pattern in use by the Food and Agriculture Organization of the United Nations is: Tryptophan, 1; threonine, 2; phenylalanine, 2; lysine, valine, isoleucine, and the sulfur-containing ones, 3; and leucine, 3.4. This means that for efficient use there needs to be twice as much threonine and phenylalanine as tryptophan and three times as much lysine and the others—except leucine, of which there should be 3.4 times.

Usually it is sufficient to consider only tryptophan, lysine, and the sulfur-containing acids (methionine plus cystine). The pattern for them could be written 1:3:3. A study of the ratios in which these amino acids occur in common foods shows that lysine is more plentiful than the sulfur-containing ones.

This pattern can be a guide when selecting foods that in combination will complement each other in providing these essential amino acids.

Consider the pattern for bread, which is tryptophan 1, lysine 2.5, and methionine plus cystine 3.8. The pattern for milk is 1:5.5:2.4. Milk has the lysine to supplement the bread, and the bread has the methionine plus cystine to supplement the milk. One cup of milk and 2 slices of bread therefore have a pattern of 1:4.8:3.

Cornmeal is high in lysine and methionine plus cystine. Peanuts are low in methionine plus cystine. By using 3 parts of cornmeal with 1 part of peanuts, we have a pattern of 1:3.2:3.2.

Supplementation can mean increasing the amount of tryptophan and the other amino acids as well as improving the pattern. Cornmeal is relatively low in tryptophan (0.066 gram in a cupful). White flour is relatively better in tryptophan than it is in lysine. By using equal parts of these, instead of cornmeal alone, we have 58 percent more tryptophan and a better pattern as well. The addition of as little as 10 percent of cottonseed flour to white flour increases the tryptophan 36 percent, the lysine 79 percent, and the methionine plus cystine 33 percent. It also improves the pattern.

Our knowledge of the patterns and the amounts of amino acids in food challenges us to find ways to improve both the quality and quantity of the protein supply wherever the need exists. Sometimes this can be done by careful combinations of foods that are already available in a country. One way is to use a relatively small amount of a protein from an animal source to improve the quality of a protein from a plant source. Animal proteins are not always available, however, and then different plant proteins must be combined in a way to supplement each other. In some instances the main cereal grain can be supplemented with another grain—such as supplementing corn with wheat to improve the amount and proportion of tryptophan. Legumes, too, may be used as supplements. To achieve the goal of a good protein supply for everyone, adjustments may have to be made in some countries in the kinds of crops grown, in the methods of food processing and preparation, and in the food habits of the people.

RUTH M. LEVERTON, *Associate Director of the Institute of Home Economics in the Agricultural Research Service, won the Borden Award for outstanding achievement in fundamental research in 1953 and was corecipient of the award in 1942 for achievement in applied nutrition. She holds a doctor's degree from the University of Chicago.*

The table on the following pages, prepared by Martha Louise Orr, gives the amounts of protein and some amino acids in a number of foods.

Protein and Amino Acid Content of Foods

Food	Measure Weight	Measure Unit	Protein	Tryptophan	Threonine	Isoleucine	Leucine	Lysine	Methionine	Cystine	Total	Phenylalanine	Tyrosine	Valine
			Gm.	Gm.	Gm.	Gm.	Gm.	Gm.	Gm.	Gm.	Gm.	Gm.	Gm.	Gm.
MILK AND MILK PRODUCTS:														
Milk, cow:														
Whole or nonfat, fluid.	244 gm.	1 cup	8.5	0.12	0.39	0.54	0.84	0.66	0.21	0.08	0.29	0.41	0.43	0.59
Nonfat dry, instant.	5 gm.	1 tbsp.	1.8	.03	.08	.11	.17	.14	.04	.02	.06	.09	.09	.12
Buttermilk, cultured.	248 gm.	1 cup	8.7	.09	.41	.54	.86	.72	.20	.08	.28	.46	.34	.65
Milk, goat.	244 gm.	1 cup	8.1	.10	.53	.21	.68	.76	.16	.08	...	.30	...	.34
Milk, human.	244 gm.	1 cup	3.4	.06	.15	.18	.30	.22	.07	.07	.14	.15	.17	.21
Cheese:														
Cheddar.		1 oz	7.1	.10	.26	.48	.69	.52	.18	.04	.22	.38	.34	.51
Cheddar, processed.		1 oz	6.6	.09	.24	.44	.64	.48	.17	.04	.21	.35	.31	.47
Cottage.		1 oz	4.8	.05	.23	.28	.52	.40	.13	.04	.17	.26	.26	.28
Cream.		1 oz	2.6	.02	.12	.15	.26	.20	.06	.02	.08	.16	.12	.15
EGGS:														
Whole, large.	50 gm.	1 egg	6.4	.11	.32	.42	.56	.41	.20	.15	.35	.37	.28	.48
MEAT, POULTRY, AND FISH, RAW:														
Beef, medium fat, without bone.		4 oz	20.6	.24	.91	1.08	1.69	1.80	.51	.26	.77	.85	.70	1.15
Chicken, fryer, flesh only.		4 oz	23.4	.28	.99	1.23	1.69	2.05	.61	.31	.92	.92	.82	1.15
Fish.		4 oz	20.6	.21	.89	1.05	1.56	1.81	.60	.28	.88	.77	.56	1.10
Heart, beef or pork.		4 oz	19.2	.25	.88	.97	1.71	1.57	.46	.19	.65	.87	.71	1.10
Kidney, beef.		4 oz	17.0	.25	.75	.83	1.48	1.23	.35	.21	.56	.80	.63	.99
Lamb, leg, without bone.		4 oz	20.4	.26	.93	1.06	1.58	1.65	.49	.27	.76	.83	.71	1.01
Liver, beef or pork.		4 oz	22.3	.34	1.06	1.17	2.06	1.67	.53	.28	.81	1.13	.84	1.41
Pork, loin, without bone.		4 oz	18.6	.24	.86	.95	1.37	1.53	.46	.22	.68	.73	.66	.97

Sulfur-Containing columns: Methionine, Cystine, Total.

Protein and Amino Acid Content of Foods—Continued

Food	Measure Weight	Unit	Protein	Tryptophan	Threonine	Isoleucine	Leucine	Lysine	Sulfur-Containing Methionine	Cystine	Total	Phenylalanine	Tyrosine	Valine
			Gm.	Gm.	Gm.	Gm.	Gm.	Gm.	Gm.	Gm.	Gm.	Gm.	Gm.	Gm.
MEAT, POULTRY, AND FISH, RAW—Continued														
Sausage:														
Bologna	1 oz	1 slice	4.2	0.04	0.17	0.20	0.30	0.34	0.09	0.05	0.14	0.15	0.14	0.21
Frankfurter	1/10 lb	1	6.4	.05	.26	.31	.46	.52	.14	.08	.22	.23	.21	.32
Pork links	2 oz		6.1	.05	.25	.30	.44	.49	.13	.08	.21	.22	.20	.31
Turkey, flesh only	4 oz		27.2		1.15	1.43	2.08	2.46	.75	.37	1.12	1.09	.80	1.35
Veal, round, boneless	4 oz		22.1	.29	.96	1.17	1.62	1.85	.51	.26	.77	.90	.80	1.14
MATURE LEGUMES AND THEIR PRODUCTS:														
Beans, common	1 oz		6.1	.06	.26	.34	.52	.45	.06	.06	.12	.33	.23	.37
Chickpeas, garbanzo	1 oz		5.9	.05	.21	.34	.44	.41	.08	.08	.16	.29	.20	.29
Cowpeas	1 oz		6.5	.06	.26	.31	.49	.42	.10	.08	.18	.34	.19	.37
Lentils	1 oz		7.1	.06	.25	.37	.50	.43	.05	.06	.11	.31	.19	.39
Lima beans	1 oz		5.9	.06	.28	.34	.49	.39	.09	.09	.18	.35	.15	.37
Peas	1 oz		6.7	.07	.26	.38	.56	.49	.08	.09	.17	.34	.27	.38
Soybeans	1 oz		9.9	.15	.43	.58	.84	.68	.15	.19	.34	.54	.34	.57
Soybean flour, low fat	101 gm	1 cup	45.1	.68	1.95	2.66	3.81	3.12	.66	.88	1.54	2.44	1.57	2.59
Soybean milk	4 oz		3.9	.06	.20	.20	.35	.31	.06	.08	.14	.22	.22	.21
SEEDS, NUTS, AND THEIR PRODUCTS:														
Brazil nuts	1 oz		4.1	.05	.12	.17	.32	.13	.27	.14	.41	.17	.14	.23
Coconut, fresh	1 oz		1.0	.01	.04	.05	.08	.04	.02	.02	.04	.05	.03	.06
Cottonseed flour	1 oz		12.0	.17	.50	.53	.83	.61	.19	.23	.42	.74	.39	.70
Filberts	1 oz		3.6	.06	.12	.24	.27	.12	.04	.05	.09	.15	.12	.26
Peanuts	1 oz		7.6	.10	.23	.36	.53	.31	.08	.13	.21	.44	.31	.43
Peanut butter	16 gm	1 tbsp	4.2	.05	.13	.20	.29	.17	.04	.07	.11	.24	.17	.24
Pecans	1 oz		2.7	.04	.11	.16	.22	.12	.04	.06	.10	.16	.09	.15
Sesame meal	1 oz		9.5	.16	.35	.47	.82	.29	.31	.24	.55	.71	.47	.43
Sunflower meal	1 oz		11.2	.17	.44	.62	.85	.42	.22	.23	.45	.59	.31	.66
GRAINS AND THEIR PRODUCTS:														
Barley	1 oz		3.6	.05	.12	.15	.25	.12	.05	.07	.12	.19	.13	.18

Food	Measure	Weight												Protein, gm.
Bread (4 percent nonfat dry milk, flour basis)	1 slice	½0 lb	.10	.06	.11	.08	.05	.03	.05	.15	.10	.06	.02	1.9
Buckwheat flour, dark	1 cup	98 gm	.59	.24	.43	.42	.22	.20	.67	.67	.43	.45	.16	11.5
Corn and soy grits	1 cup	50 gm	.53	.28	.42	.30	.16	.14	.39	.83	.42	.40	.08	9.0
Corn products:														
Flakes	1 cup	25 gm	.10	.07	.09	.07	.04	.03	.04	.26	.08	.07	.01	2.0
Grits	1 cup	160 gm	.71	.85	.63	.44	.18	.26	.40	1.80	.64	.56	.08	13.9
Meal, whole	1 cup	118 gm	.55	.66	.49	.34	.14	.20	.31	1.41	.50	.43	.07	10.9
Oatmeal	1 cup	80 gm	.68	.42	.61	.42	.25	.17	.42	.85	.59	.38	.15	11.4
Pearlmillet	1 oz		.19		.14	.12	.04	.08	.11	.49	.18	.13	.07	3.2
Rice, white	1 cup	191 gm	1.01	.66	.73	.46	.20	.26	.57	1.25	.68	.57	.16	14.5
Rye flour, light	1 cup	80 gm	.39	.24	.35	.27	.15	.12	.31	.51	.32	.28	.08	7.5
Sorghum, grain	1 oz		.18	.09	.16	.10	.05	.05	.08	.50	.17	.11	.03	3.1
Wheat products:														
Flakes	1 cup	35 gm	.20	.11	.17	.11	.07	.04	.13	.31	.17	.12	.04	3.8
Flour, whole grain	1 cup	120 gm	.74	.60	.79	.59	.35	.24	.44	1.07	.69	.46	.20	16.0
Flour, white	1 cup	110 gm	.50	.39	.63	.38	.23	.15	.26	.89	.53	.33	.14	11.6
Germ	1 cup	68 gm	.93	.60	.62	.47	.20	.27	1.04	1.16	.80	.91	.18	17.1
Macaroni, elbow	1 cup	123 gm	.90	.52	.82	.54	.30	.24	.51	1.04	.79	.61	.18	15.7
Noodles	1 cup	73 gm	.54	.23	.45	.33	.18	.15	.30	.61	.45	.39	.10	9.2
Shredded wheat	1 biscuit	1 oz	.16	.07	.14	.10	.06	.04	.09	.19	.13	.11	.02	2.9
VEGETABLES, RAW:														
Beans, lima	2 oz		.27	.15	.22	.10	.05	.05	.27	.34	.26	.19	.05	4.3
Beans, snap	2 oz		.07	.03	.03	.03	.01	.02	.07	.08	.06	.05	.02	1.4
Cabbage	2 oz		.02	.02	.02	.03	.02	.01	.04	.03	.02	.02	.01	.8
Carrots	2 oz		.03	.01	.02	.03	.02	.01	.03	.04	.03	.02	.01	.7
Collards	2 oz		.11	.09	.07	.06	.03	.03	.11	.12	.07	.06	.03	2.2
Corn, sweet	2 oz		.13	.07	.12	.08	.04	.04	.08	.23	.08	.09	.01	2.1
Cowpeas	2 oz		.29		.30	.30		.07	.35	.37	.26	.20	.06	5.3
Kale	2 oz		.10	.04	.09	.04	.02	.02	.07	.14	.08	.08	.02	2.2
Okra	2 oz		.05	.04	.04	.02	.01	.01	.04	.06	.04	.04	.01	1.0
Peas, green	2 oz		.16	.09	.15	.07	.04	.03	.18	.24	.17	.14	.03	3.1
Potatoes	2 oz		.06	.02	.05	.02	.01	.01	.06	.06	.05	.04	.01	1.1
Spinach	2 oz		.07	.04	.06	.05	.03	.02	.08	.10	.06	.06	.02	1.3
Sweetpotatoes	2 oz		.08	.05	.06	.04	.02	.02	.05	.06	.05	.05	.02	1.0
Turnip greens	2 oz		.08	.06	.08	.06	.03	.03	.07	.12	.06	.07	.03	1.6
MISCELLANEOUS:														
Gelatin	1 tbsp	10 gm	.24	.04	.20	.09	.01	.08	.42	.29	.14	.19	.00	8.6
Yeast:														
Compressed		1 oz	.24	.16	.17	.10	.03	.07	.26	.33	.19	.19	.03	3.0
Brewer's, dried	1 tbsp	8 gm	.22	.15	.15	.11	.04	.07	.26	.26	.19	.19	.06	3.0

Fats and Fatty Acids

CALLIE MAE COONS

FATS often have been prized articles of diet in man's struggle for food. From early times they have denoted prosperity and hospitality, as when the fatted calf was prepared for merrymaking and the widow shared her oil with the prophet.

Scientific and economic concern about dietary fats goes in cycles.

Sometimes the cycle is geared to war and famine, when fats tend to be scarce and are among the first foods to be conserved and rationed. When food surpluses mount, fats float to the top and are among the first to be used extravagantly.

Pioneers in every civilization have been ingenious in ways of conserving and using fats and in bartering them in international trade. Still today many peoples have a low consumption of fats and oils.

Our food technology in the United States has made possible improved supplies of separated fats and oils from meats, grains, cottonseed, soybeans, peanuts, olives, and coconut.

Agricultural research has led to higher acreage yields of the oilseeds and grains and meat animals of high fatness. The flavors of cooked fats have been imparted to many kinds of processed foods, from roasted nuts to main dishes.

Our total and proportional consumption of fats and oils has climbed to an alltime peak, and the kind and amount of fats we eat have come under the scrutiny of economists and scientists.

Fat makes our meals palatable and satisfying. It is the most concentrated dietary source of energy—9 Calories a gram, compared to 4 Calories in carbohydrate and protein. It promotes efficiency in the utilization of protein and carbohydrate. It facilitates the utilization of fat-soluble vitamins.

Some fats and oils are important sources of vitamins A, D, E, and K.

Fats provide various amounts of fatty acids known to be essential in diets and many other fatty acids, which may have nutritional functions that we do not know now.

The amounts of fat, visible and invisible, in food supplies in the United States at retail level have been estimated at 32 percent of the Calories in 1910, 35 percent in 1930, and 40 percent in 1950. They have continued to rise more steeply during the 1950's.

The amounts used in households are much the same—about 30 to 33 percent of the Calories before 1900, 35 to

74

38 in the mid-1930's, and 42 to 44 in the mid-1950's.

Farm families tend to use more fat than city families do, and northern families more than southern families.

As the proportion of Calories from protein has remained about the same—an average of 11 to 12 percent at the household level—the shift to larger proportions of Calories from fat has been at the expense of carbohydrate.

Thus, in the North Central States, farm families in 1955 had 44 to 46 percent of their Calories from fat and about the same proportion from carbohydrate; 40 years earlier, Calories from fat ran 33 to 35 percent and from carbohydrate 53 to 55 percent.

Families with high incomes tend to have even more Calories from fat than from carbohydrate. Low-income groups select more Calories from carbohydrate.

The few reports of individual food intake—the amounts people actually ingest—by adults since 1900 indicate 38 to 42 percent of Calories from fat, 45 to 55 percent from carbohydrates, and 13 to 15 percent from protein. The proportions are about the same for women as for men and for the few groups of elderly people on whom reports were made.

These scattered figures on individual intake do not confirm the time trends noted for household diets and retail food supplies, but they confirm the tendency to a high level of intake of fat in the United States.

Figures from chemically analyzed diets and school lunches support the conclusion that the average diet carries more than 40 percent of its Calories from fat and that diets of some individuals carry 50 percent or more.

The fat may drop to 30 percent or even 20 percent of the Calories in times of war or economic stress.

Often 25 to 30 percent is recommended as desirable for any population at any time. The lowest averages reported from any study in the United States, however, was for two groups of families in the southern mountains just after 1900. Their diets contained, respectively, 26 and 30 percent of the Calories from fat, 8 and 9 percent from protein, and 66 and 61 percent from carbohydrate.

People in densely populated countries are said to subsist on such food patterns, often with even less than 30 percent from fats at any time. People in some countries who have fat intakes that are one-third to one-half that in the United States get less than 20 percent of the dietary fat from all animal sources, as much as 40 percent from cereal grains, and 25 percent from peanuts and other oilseeds.

THE SOURCES of fats consumed in the United States follow changing food patterns. The proportions of Calories from dairy and meat products and from separated fats and oils have increased steadily since 1900.

The average household diet in 1955 had about 25 percent of its fats from dairy products; 24 percent from pork products; 14 percent from beef, veal, and lamb; 13 percent from margarines and shortenings; 6 percent from oils and salad dressings; 6 percent from poultry, fish, and eggs; and 12 percent from baked goods, nuts, fruit, and vegetables.

Of the 25 percent from dairy products, more than half was from milk and cheese; 7 percent was from butter, separated from the other milk nutrients; and the rest was from cream and ice cream.

We should bear in mind that natural unseparated fats are associated with the protein, minerals, and vitamins characteristic of the food, as in milk or pork, and also carry some vitamins, such as A, D, and E, which are useful in the metabolism of fats.

HOW SHALL we choose fats to eat when we have much and many kinds of them in the store and on the table?

Some who want to control weight may be interested in whether the fat is visible (as in butter, shortening, salad oils, and other separated fats or in the visible fat on meat). The fat on meat can be trimmed away, but that means waste. The less readily apparent fats, those mingled, blended, or absorbed into food products, make good eating, but they cannot be trimmed away by the consumer.

Some fats are solid—more or less firm—at room temperature. Others are plastic. Many come naturally as oils. These characteristics are important for baking, deep frying, and making salad dressings.

Almost any fat can be used for any culinary purposes by suitable adaptations in cooking procedures, however. The melting point of a fat can be altered in many ways by the technologist, but consistency does not always denote properties important in diet.

ONE WILL do well to understand the composition and structure of fats and fatty acids in order to know their complicated role in nutrition. The details are technical, however, and some readers may wish to skip this section.

A pure fat is composed of molecules of glycerol (a trihydroxy alcohol, the same as glycerin), to each of which 1, 2, or 3 fatty acids are linked to form monoglycerides, diglycerides, or triglycerides, respectively.

Fatty acids are hydrocarbons consisting of a chain series of carbons, each of which is able to carry 2 hydrogens, but with 3 hydrogens (methyl group) at one end, and an acid (carboxyl) group at the other end, which connects to the glycerol.

Natural fats, as in meats, grains, and nuts, are made up mostly of triglycerides with only trace amounts of the mono- and di- forms and some free fatty acids. Processed fats, such as hydrogenated commercially hardened shortenings, may contain up to 20 percent of monoglycerides and diglycerides.

It makes some difference nutritionally which fatty acid is attached in the middle position on the glycerol molecule and whether an outer position is open or is linked to another substance.

Much variety in fats comes from the kinds of fatty acids linked to the glycerol—whether all three are alike or all are different, whether all are saturated (contain all the hydrogen they can carry) or of various degrees of unsaturation, and whether they are mostly short-chain (under 12 carbons), long-chain (12 to 18 carbons), or extra long-chain (20 carbons or more) fatty acids.

Fatty acids that have 18 carbons in a chain make up about 80 percent and those with 16 carbons comprise about 10 to 15 percent of the fatty acids in average diets.

Short-chain fatty acids occur mostly in milk fat and in coconut oil. Extra long chains occur in fish oils.

Fatty acids that are common in food fats and oils fall into three broad classes according to their degree of saturation.

The fully saturated fatty acids make up about 40 to 45 percent of those in average diets in this country. They are rather stable chemically and account for much of the firmness of fats at room temperatures.

Saturated fatty acids may be of any chain length, from 4 to 18 or more carbons. The most common ones and their chain lengths are: Stearic (18), palmitic (16), myristic (14), and lauric (12).

Beef fat contains 20 percent of stearic acid and lard about 12 percent. Other animal fats run higher. Most animal fats and cottonseed oil contain about 25 to 30 percent of palmitic acid. Palm oil has about 40 percent.

The monounsaturated fatty acids (monoenoic) are those with one reactive unsaturated ("doublebond") linkage, which has 2 hydrogens missing. The best example and the one most abundant in foods is oleic acid containing 18 carbons, which alone furnishes about 40 percent of all the fatty acids in the average diet in this country. It represents 70 to 75 percent of the fatty acids in olive oil and the hydrogenated (commercially hardened) shortenings; 50 percent or more of the fatty acids in lard and peanut oil; and 40 percent in beef, lamb, and poultry fat. Its nutri-

Structure of Mixed Triglyceride—A Monosaturated Fat

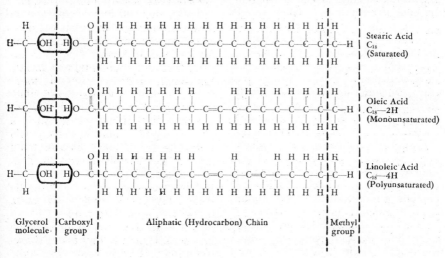

tional role in man has not been fully defined, however.

The polyunsaturated fatty acids, a heterogeneous group, include some essential fatty acids and the extra long-chain fatty acids (20 to 26 carbons) common in fish oils. The degree of unsaturation may involve 2, 3, 4, or more linkages in the chain, with correspondingly 4, 6, 8, or more hydrogens missing. Polyunsaturated fatty acids are sometimes classed as dienoic, trienoic, and tetraenoic, and so on, depending on the number of linkages affected.

The position of unsaturation along the chain is important chemically and nutritionally as well as technologically in processing.

Nutritionally, the position of unsaturation may determine the point of breakup of the chain in metabolism and how well the body can handle the remaining fragments.

The positions of carbons in fatty acids are numbered successively, beginning at the carboxyl (acid) end of the chain, which attaches to the glycerol. The position of linkage carries the number of the lower or first of the 2 carbons that it joins.

Most common monounsaturated fatty acids, including oleic, have the reactive unsaturated linkage in the 9th position—that is, between the 9th and 10th carbons. Linoleic acid, with 2 reactive linkages, has them in the 9th and 12th positions. The descriptive chemical name is 9,12-octadecadienoic. Arachidonic acid, with 4 reactive linkages, has this chemical name: 5,8,11,14-eicosatetraenoic.

The polyunsaturated fatty acids considered essential for nutrition are linoleic, linolenic, and arachidonic.

Because arachidonic acid can be formed from linoleic acid in the body, it is not really a dietary essential. Besides, it constitutes less than 1 percent of animal fats (except in liver and some pig fats, which contain more than 2 percent) and less than 1 percent or none of vegetable fats. Therefore it may be disregarded in choosing dietary fats.

Linolenic acid has a different and perhaps less important nutritional role than linoleic and occurs only in small amounts in food fats. Soybean oil, with 7 percent, is the highest.

Of the three, linoleic becomes the center of dietary importance. It is relatively more abundant in foods than the other two and must come from diet because it cannot be formed by the human body.

Sources of linoleic acid include many grain oils and seed oils, which contain 50 percent or more. Fats from nuts, peanuts, and poultry carry 20 to 30 percent. Outstanding exceptions are fat from walnuts, which has more than 60 percent of linoleic acid, and fat from coconuts, which has about 2 percent.

Fats from such fruits as avocado and olive contain about 10 percent of linoleic acid. Those from leafy vegetables and legumes run higher, 30 percent or more, but the total amount of fat in greens is low.

Doubtless the diet should provide some linoleic acid every day unless the body (as in weight reduction) is mobilizing tissue fat known to contain this fatty acid.

Linoleic acid is necessary for growth and reproduction and helps protect the animal against excessive loss of water and damage from radiation. It is essential for normal skin conditions in babies, who require about 5 percent of the Calories from this source.

When it is fed as 25 percent or more of the fat, linoleic acid lowers blood cholesterol in adults under •certain dietary conditions. It appears to have other metabolic functions that have not yet been defined fully. (Cholesterol is a complex, fatlike material that occurs in all animal tissues, notably nerve tissue, bile, gallstones, egg yolk, liver, spleen, brain tissue.)

Some animal fats and vegetable fats or oils are fairly similar chemically. Both butterfat and coconut oil, for example, contain high proportions of short-chain fatty acids. Beef fat and coconut oil contain less than 2 percent of linoleic, one of the fatty acids that are essential in the diet. Corn oil contains more than 6 times as much linoleic as olive oil, and chicken fat up to 10 times as much as the fat of ruminant animals.

Both animal and vegetable fats contain up to 5 percent of various fatty

substances that are not true fats but may be nutritionally important.

There are processed fats and natural fats and many kinds in each class, so that this distinction is not a good basis for selection by consumers.

Hydrogenation, one type of processing, induces hydrogen to enter points of unsaturation in the fatty acid chains to increase the saturation of the fat and achieve varying degrees of firmness sought for specific uses. It also prevents oxidative rancidity and thus greatly prolongs the storage life of the fat. Only about 15 percent of the dietary fat that reaches the consumer has been exposed to hydrogenation.

When hydrogenation was first used, only a fraction of the fat was exposed to the process and then blended with the untreated oil to a desired consistency.

A later practice is to expose an entire lot in a continuous controlled process, so that more fatty acids are altered but to lesser degrees of saturation. This process tends to cover up most of the essential linoleic acid and convert it to the already abundant oleic acid.

The technologist refers to non-selective hydrogenation, by which saturation of monounsaturated and polyunsaturated fatty acids proceed simultaneously, and to selective hydrogenation, by which polyunsaturated fatty acids are converted largely to monounsaturated before much of either is converted to saturated. Selective hydrogenation thus changes most of the essential linoleic acid to oleic acid, which is already abundant.

By changing the conditions of hydrogenation, the technologist can get various physical and chemical characteristics in the finished product. Many of the characteristics can be obtained also by blending proper assortments of natural fats and oils.

The chemist has not yet found out all that happens to a fat or oil during processing. Biochemists and physiologists cannot yet tell us how the body utilizes some of the products formed during hydrogenation, such as isoacids, transisomers, and conjugated fatty acids.

At least one study has shown these "unnatural" products to be ineffective as essential fatty acids. Another study indicated that conjugated forms favor high blood cholesterol.

Obviously it is not enough to distinguish saturated and unsaturated "fats" for nutrition purposes, because there are varying degrees of saturation in all fats. All oils contain some saturated fatty acids. All solid fats contain some unsaturated fatty acids even though fats that are firm at room temperatures consist mostly of saturated fatty acids.

Fats that are soft or liquid at room temperature may be called unsaturated but may contain different assortments of fatty acids. Olive oil, for example, is liquid because it contains 75 percent or more of oleic acid (one linkage unsaturated); safflower oil contains nearly 75 percent linoleic acid (two linkages unsaturated); linseed oil may contain up to 65 percent of linolenic acid (with three linkages unsaturated).

Iodine value, based on a laboratory test showing uptake of iodine by all unsaturated points in the fatty acid chains, is a gross measure of total unsaturation or potential hydrogen uptake, but it does not indicate the particular fatty acids present.

Iodine value runs below 10 in a near-saturated fat like coconut oil, more than 100 in most vegetable oils, and up to 200 in a highly unsaturated oil, such as linseed oil and some fish oils.

The use of radioactive elements makes it possible to follow fatty acids, cholesterol, and other lipids (fatlike substances) through digestion and absorption to their destinations in the body organism.

In the digestive tract, fat-splitting enzymes in the gastric, pancreatic, and intestinal juices take their turn in separating some of the fatty acids from glycerol. Those in the outer position on the glycerol molecule are split off first. Those in the middle position are split off less rapidly, if at all.

The rate of digestion and absorption depends also on chain length and on the amount and position of the saturated fatty acids, if any, on the glycerol.

The rate depends at first on the degree of emulsification (separation into fine droplets) of the fat, which is none in separated fats or oils and partial in others, as in egg yolk, milk fat, and mayonnaise. Emulsification in the intestinal tract is greatly aided by the bile.

Persons with defective or limited secretions of bile have less efficient digestion of fats than normal persons.

Early experiments showed digestibility by normal young adults to be 90 percent or more for various fats, but we need new studies with fats fed in customary mixed diets and a better understanding of the chemistry of fats and the physiology of absorption and transport.

The various products of fat digestion—some diglycerides and monoglycerides, but mostly free fatty acids and glycerol—are absorbed from the intestine along with lecithin, cholesterol, and other lipids, which also are linked with some fatty acids.

Some fatty acids may be recombined into glycerides, and some positions may be interchanged for others in passing across the intestinal wall into blood and lymph systems. The short-chain fatty acids appear less likely to be reformed and may go more directly through the blood to the liver. They may present more problems in metabolism than the common long-chain ones.

After absorption, about half of the fatty acids in circulation appear linked with cholesterol and phospholipids, the remainder as glycerides or free.

The proportions in such combinations are indicators of normalcy in lipid metabolism and of the effects of various food fats and diets. Values regarded normal in the plasma of persons after fasting overnight are 45 percent of the fatty acids in glycerides, 35 percent in phospholipids (mostly lecithin), and 15 percent in cholesterol. The rest are free or in loose protein combinations.

In plasma of blood and lymph, the products of fat absorption, some of which have been through the liver, are transported to tissues along with other lipids from internal body sources. The lipids travel as parts of complex particles of various sizes called lipoproteins, in "wraps" of protein, which keep the fatty substances miscible with the watery plasma during transport.

The largest of these particles, called chylomicrons, may cause the plasma to appear milky after fat-rich meals. Other particles, graded into successively smaller sizes down to ultramicroscopic, are known as alpha- (the heavier) and beta- (the lighter) lipoproteins, and probably are elaborated in the liver.

The level of beta-lipoproteins is often elevated in abnormal fat metabolism and can be raised experimentally by feeding some fatty acids. Ratios of alpha- to beta-lipoproteins below 0.5 are found in myocardial infarction (coronary artery damage). Ratios around 0.7 or more occur in persons considered well.

Levels of lipoproteins normally are elevated after meals and are cleared out of the plasma in 3 to 6 hours. The various lipids are delivered where they are needed to the skin, brain, and nerve tissues or to fat depots or are oxidized by the tissues to produce energy for heat or activity.

During high lipid levels, the blood tends to clot more easily, regardless of the kind of fat ingested, but clotting also depends on the age of the person, the blood enzyme levels, and other metabolic states.

High lipid levels after meals return to normal more slowly—in 12 hours or longer—in extremely obese persons, in elderly persons with atherosclerosis (a condition accompanied by thickened walls in arteries of the heart), and in persons with high blood lipid levels

from other causes, including liver injury.

The lipid levels return to normal more readily in persons accustomed to physical activity than in persons sedentary or inactive for hours before and after meals. Lipids arising within the body, such as during conversion of excessive nonfat Calories to fat, may augment the burden of disposal.

Sustained elevated plasma lipid levels are considered undesirable. The underlying cause may be that the body has lost some hormone or enzyme capacity to convert, oxidize, or dispose of excesses, or that the circulatory system is being flooded continually with lipids from the foods eaten as well as from internal biosynthesis, but in any case the longtime consequences may be serious.

Fatty acids that are used for muscular energy may be oxidized in any tissue of the body.

The first step in oxidation is breaking off from the fatty acid chain, a two-carbon fragment known as an active acetate. Failure in oxidation may arise from inability to break off the acetates because of the unnatural structure of the fatty acid chain or because of physiologic defects of the body. The failure is due more commonly to lessened ability of the body to proceed with completion of the oxidation of the acetate to carbon dioxide and water as a result of deficiency of some hormone, enzyme, or vitamin.

If the kind of fat being laid down in adult human tissues comes mainly from absorbed fatty acids, it will resemble the fat from the food eaten, especially the long-chain saturated and unsaturated fatty acids.

If the fat is synthesized internally from excess total Calories, such as from sugars and proteins, saturated fatty acids will predominate in the fat deposits, and none will be linoleic, because the body cannot synthesize it. In this respect man metabolizes fat as do pigs, which lay down a firmer, more saturated fat on a corn ration high in carbohydrate, from which fat must be synthesized, than on a peanut-containing ration, from which a preformed oil containing as much as 20–25 percent linoleic acid is absorbed.

Ruminant animals, like cows, absorb short-chain fatty acids, which have been synthesized by micro-organisms in the rumen. Short-chain fatty acids thus predominate in the fat of cow's milk. The shortest is butyric acid, with a chain length of only 4 carbons. More than 30 kinds of fatty acids occur in butterfat.

The fat in human milk contains 2 to 4 times as much linoleic acid as the fat of cow's milk, but we do not know whether this is merely a reflection of diet or is due to liver function or to some special activity of the mammary gland to meet particular needs of the offspring.

Human body fat contains about 11 percent of linoleic acid, according to German analyses made nearly 30 years ago. This figure is only a little higher than the 10 percent estimated content of the average diet in the United States in 1955.

THE IMPORTANCE of blood cholesterol in the metabolism of fat and what regulates its formation and distribution in the body has been an area of intensive research, which so far has given us only partial answers.

Common indicators of abnormal fat metabolism include plasma cholesterol levels, cholesterol-phospholipid ratio in plasma, serum lipoprotein patterns, and the distribution of fatty acids among the lipid fractions—glyceride, cholesterol, and phospholipid—in the blood. Measurement of the plasma cholesterol is the oldest and simplest method of testing, and the results are most easily interpreted.

High cholesterol levels in plasma are among the complications in diabetes in consequence of abnormal metabolism of fats (as well as sugars), although the high levels are somewhat better controlled since insulin began to be used in the 1920's. More than 100 years ago (1847) cholesterol was found

present in atheroma (plaque formations on arterial walls).

Modern analytical methods have shown that the total free and combined cholesterol in atheroma is no higher than the total in normal circulating blood plasma, but that the free cholesterol is about five times as high as that in normal blood. Oleic acid also has been shown to be twice as high in atheroma as in normal plasma.

Many investigators have reached a conclusion that atherosclerosis, with its generalized thickening of the inner arterial wall, might be a consequence of abnormal cholesterol metabolism, whatever the metabolic failure.

This view has been supported also by studies with experimental animals—rabbits, chickens, mice, rats, guinea pigs, dogs, and monkeys—in which elevated blood cholesterol produced by diet, drugs, or other means tended to result eventually in arterial damages resembling in many respects those found in human atherosclerosis. Thus attention has continued to be centered on blood cholesterol.

In the depression of the 1930's, a paucity of atheroma was noted in the poorly nourished bodies on which autopsies were performed. As early as 1904, an increase of 40 percent was observed in diseases of the circulatory apparatus and kidneys and a 15-percent increase in cancer in one generation.

Attention was directed in 1940 to the fact that heart disease was then a worldwide problem. The war period, however, imposed food restrictions on peoples throughout the world and slackened the mortality rates from diabetes and other metabolic disorders as well as from cardiovascular diseases.

The trends reversed after the war to accelerated rates, particularly from coronary damage, and aroused worldwide attention of scientists and clinicians, while cardiovascular diseases rose rapidly to top place as the reported cause of deaths in the United States.

Revived interest in metabolism of cholesterol has continued as research has associated atherosclerosis with high plasma cholesterol and more or less with an estimated high level of fat consumption.

Other observers linked it with a high level of protein from foods of animal origin. The availability of radioactive elements after the war made it possible to use labeled carbon to follow the course and fate of different parts of the cholesterol molecule in metabolism and thus greatly refined the techniques of research.

Cholesterol is a normal and essential constituent of blood, nerve tissue, and other parts of the body of animals. Corresponding substances found in plants are known as plant sterols and include the sitosterols commonly found in vegetable oils. They may be poorly absorbed by people, however. Some may prevent the absorption of some fats. Others elevate blood cholesterol.

Cholesterol is normally synthesized in all cells of the body and especially in the liver from a substance called squalene, which has been formed from acetates (2-carbon fragments). Squalene fed to human beings causes a rise in blood cholesterol in an hour. It reaches a maximum in 7 to 21 hours.

Dietary fat is not essential for the formation of cholesterol, but some fatty acids favor its absorption, and excessive lipids in circulation may favor its formation.

Dietary cholesterol from food, about 0.5 gram daily in the average diet, usually is a minor source compared with the amounts, 2 to 3 grams daily, that the body is capable of forming.

Excessive intakes of cholesterol-rich foods can push the amount up toward 5 grams daily, but that is seldom the case. Moreover, high dietary cholesterol tends to suppress normal body synthesis of cholesterol.

Cholesterol normally transports about 15 percent of the fatty acids of the blood, mostly the unsaturated. It may influence some immunological reactions in protecting the body from certain injurious substances.

Cholesterol is used in the production of steroid or sex hormones. Cholesterol is converted by the liver into bile acids and secreted into the intestines, where part of the cholesterol is reused in the emulsification of fats and absorption of fatty acids. This initiates another metabolic round for the cholesterol, which is shown by isotope measurements to require 2 to 3 days.

Some cholesterol in various forms may be disposed of through the bowel, eventually half or more, and such disposal seems to be favored by diets high in linoleic acid. Failure of conversion to bile acids or of disposal through the bowel may result in backlog accumulations that show up in high blood cholesterol. Within limits, however, the level of plasma cholesterol may be less important to the system than is the kind of fatty acids carried, its relation to the phospholipid level, or to the level of beta-lipoprotein, which also transports cholesterol.

A cholesterol-phospholipid ratio (C/P) of 0.70 to 0.80 is characteristic in persons with normal or low cholesterol. Higher ratios, 0.90 to 1.0 and above, suggest abnormal fat metabolism, whether due to high cholesterol or to low phospholipid in the plasma.

HUMAN PLASMA cholesterol levels differ widely because of many conditions, the most common of which are associated with advancing age.

Other conditions include the kinds and amounts of fat and other constituents in the diet, the planes of regular physical activity, the nature and extent of emotional stress, and periods of menstruation and menopause in women.

In the same individuals over periods of months, the level may fluctuate in a wide range, 15 percent above and below in normal persons and as much as 30 to 40 percent in persons with high cholesterol.

In children, cholesterol levels in the plasma range from 150 to 250 milligrams percent, with erratic trends in adolescence.

In this country, women before menopause have levels of 180 to 200 milligrams percent or even less.

Men under 50 years of age have levels around 200 to 220 milligrams.

After these ages, the average level in men continues to rise gradually. The average level in women rises sharply and exceeds that of men after about 55 years of age, when both are in the range of 240 to 260 or even 300.

A lower average level has been noted in persons older than 65 years, but that may mean persons with low levels are more likely to live beyond that age.

Men with histories of coronary artery damage have been found to have much higher plasma cholesterol levels, especially in ages 25 to 40 years, when the levels were 50 to 100 milligrams above the average for men apparently normal.

Men living in a county home on a limited diet were found to have plasma cholesterol levels markedly below retired men of like ages who lived in their own homes on more liberal, freely chosen diets.

Plasma cholesterol is elevated in diabetes, during periods of gain in weight, low thyroid activity, and other conditions of depressed energy metabolism. It is elevated by several dietary factors, including calories in excess of energy needs, high intakes of fat, particularly certain saturated fatty acids and dietary cholesterol; by high protein intakes, especially of animal proteins and those high in the sulfur-containing amino acids (methionine and cystine and perhaps others); and by choline and rapidly absorbed sugars.

High cholesterol in the plasma is lowered by relatively high intakes of linoleic and perhaps other polyunsaturated fatty acids, by high intakes of nicotinic acid, by dietary starches in place of sugars, and by strict vegetarian-type diets, as well as by stepped-up energy metabolism such as from regular exercise, thyroid hormone, and other agents that stimulate metabolism.

Damage to arterial walls in the presence of high plasma cholesterol has been lessened or averted in experimental animals by higher dietary intakes of magnesium, pyridoxine, and vitamin E. Dietary levels of sodium, potassium, and calcium appear also to be involved.

THE LOW CHOLESTEROL levels characteristic of some nationality groups doubtless reflect a combination of factors—hereditary, hormonal, dietary, occupational, or other environmental factors—although usually a diet low in fat is one factor.

For example, Yemenites are said to have lived apart for some 2,000 years on diets of grain, vegetables, and vegetable oils, with less than 18 percent of the Calories from fat.

Yemenite immigrant men arriving in Israel have been found to have average cholesterol levels of 160 milligrams at ages 55 to 60 years. Those who had lived in Palestine 20 years or more, having diets containing more than 20 percent of the Calories from fat, including some animal fats, averaged 200 milligrams. European Jewish immigrants, who had more liberal diets, averaged more than 240 milligrams percent at similar ages.

The death rates from atherosclerosis in the three groups were reported to be around 5, 35, and 85 per 100,000, respectively.

Similar observations have been made on the cholesterol levels of Japanese living in Japan with less than 15–20 percent of the Calories from fat; those in Hawaii, with about 20 percent; and those in the United States, with more than 30 percent.

Differences in the amount and kind of dietary fat among these groups, however, appear small compared to levels of 40–45 percent in diets in this country and certainly were not the only dietary differences in these situations. The occupations, physical activity, and emotional stresses also were different. For example, laboring Japanese who worked on the plantations had cholesterol levels well below the average for this race in the same location.

Fatty Acids in Some Animal and Plant Products

[Grams per 100 grams of total fatty acids]

Source of fat	Saturated fatty acids			Unsaturated fatty acids		
	Total	Palmitic C 16	Stearic C 18	Oleic C 18–2 H	Linoleic C 18–4 H	Other unsaturated
MILK:						
Buffalo	66	31	15	27	1	6
Cow	59	27	12	35	3	3
Goat	66	29	8	26	5	5
Human	48	23	7	36	8	8
Mare	41	16	3	19	8	32
MEATS:						
Pork:						
Bacon	33	22	10	50	10	7
Fatback	40	27	12	48	6	6
Pork cuts	38	22	14	44	9	9
Pork liver	36	14	19	28	5	31
Rabbit	39	29	4	37	12	11
Ruminant animals:						
Beef	50	29	20	46	2	2
Deer	66	25	35	25	3	6
Goat	61	28	26	35	2	2
Lamb	59	30	26	37	2	2
POULTRY PRODUCTS:						
Egg	34	26	7	47	8	11
Chicken	34	26	7	40	21	5
Duck	27	(20)	(5)	42	24	7
Goose	30	(22)	(6)	57	8	5
Turkey	30	23	6	46	22	4
FISH PRODUCTS:						
Cod-liver oil	15	12	2	26	}	59
Eel	24	18	2	38	}	38
Halibut-liver oil	20	15	2	34	}	47
Herring	20	12	1	20	}	60
Menhaden	25	16	3	16	4	55
Salmon	16	12	2	27	}	55

Tuna	26	19	4		26	48
Whale blubber	27	16	2		37	36
FRUITS, VEGETABLES, NUTS:						
Almond	9	7	2	70	21	
Avocado	22	20	2	50	15	13
Beechnut	9	5	4	57	33	1
Brazil nut	21	14	6	50	28	1
Cashew	18	6	11	73	8	1
Coconut	91	10	2	7	1	1
Filbert (hazelnut)	6	2	2	56	17	21
Hickory nut	8	6	1	72	19	1
Olive	12	9	2	80	7	1
Peanut	23	12	5	46	30	1
Pecan	8	6	1	70	21	1
Pistachio	10	8	2	69	20	1
Walnut, black	6	4	2	37	50	7
Walnut, English	7	5	2	16	65	12
GRAINS, WHOLE:						
Barley	(14)	7	3	26	44	(6)
Corn, white	12	9	1	37	47	4
Millet, foxtail	33	11	15	23	38	6
Oats, rolled	23	13	4	33	43	1
Rice	19	13	2	42	38	1
Sorghum	12	7	5	40	47	
Wheat	16	12	4	28	48	6
SEPARATED FATS AND OILS:						
Butter	59	27	12	35	3	3
Cacao butter	59	24	35	38	2	1
Corn oil	12	8	3	30	55	3
Cottonseed oil	26	23	8	22	51	1
Lard	40	32	(2)	48	11	1
Linseed oil	10	(8)	3	22	18	50
Margarine	27	22	2	60	60	4
Olive oil	12	9	5	80	9	
Palm oil	48	41	6	42	8	2
Peanut oil	19	8	7	50	31	
Shortening, hydrogenated	24	15	4	15	76	1
Safflower oil	8	3	5	40	44	1
Sesame oil	15	9	6	21	55	6
Soybean oil	18	9	5	21	66	1
Sunflower oil	12	6				

A report on one national group continuing in the same environment is of interest in reference to the effect of occupation and physical activity. A study of clinical cases of British men in their sixties revealed that the coronary disease in those in all sedentary occupations combined was twice as frequent as in those who engaged in much activity and was three times as frequent in those sedentary occupations characterized by severe emotional demands—that is, by a combination of emotional stress and limited physical activity.

Thus John Dryden's advice in 1680 echoes almost 300 years later:

"By chase our long-lived fathers earned their
    food;
Toil strung the nerves, and purified the
    blood;
But we, their sons, a pampered race of men,
Are dwindled down to threescore years and
    ten.

"Better to hunt in fields, for health unbought,
Than fee the doctor for a nauseous draught;
The wise, for cure, on exercise depend;
God never made his work, for man to
    mend."

Although elevated blood cholesterol is often associated with atherosclerosis, the nature and extent of the relationship remain to be defined.

Not all persons with atherosclerosis or coronary disease have high blood cholesterol. Conversely, not all persons with high blood cholesterol have cardiovascular disorders. Nevertheless, continuing high blood cholesterol indicates a disturbed metabolism and is undesirable, whatever the factors involved or the likely ultimate consequences.

DIET has held the attention of scientists as well as laymen because it is one of the contributing factors in the formation of cholesterol.

How well do diets in this country measure up to some of the evolving concepts of desirable kinds and quantities of fats in diets?

Average diets reported by households in this country in 1955 were estimated to supply about 44 percent of the Calories from fat.

This fat was calculated to contain on the average about 42 percent saturated fatty acids, mainly stearic and palmitic, 43 percent oleic, and 10 percent linoleic. These estimates of fatty acids were partly substantiated when a composite sample of fats fairly typical of the proportions consumed in 1955 was found by laboratory analysis to contain 40 percent saturated fatty acids, 46 percent oleic acid, and 9 percent linoleic acid.

FAT FROM MILK and dairy products, beef, veal, and lamb in 1955 furnished 56 percent of the saturated fatty acids and only 10 percent of the linoleic, a ratio of almost 6 to 1. Pork, margarine, and shortenings furnished 30 and 32 percent of each, respectively, or about equal shares of saturated and linoleic acids.

Salad oils furnished only 3 percent of the saturated and 28 percent of the linoleic, a ratio of nearly 1 to 10, or more than the reverse of the first group of foods.

The sources of fatty acids varied characteristically with the four regions of the country—Northeast, North Central, West, and South.

The Northeast had the highest proportion of total fat (39 percent) from fats of ruminant animals, and the lowest (28 percent) from pork, margarines, and shortenings.

The South was at the other extreme—lowest (29 percent) in fat from ruminant animals and highest (40 percent) from pork, margarines, and shortenings.

A statistical analysis by the Public Health Service showed regional differences in death rates in 1950 from heart disease, including coronary, with the Northeast highest, 263 deaths per 100,000 and the South lowest, 169.

OTHER DIETARY factors should not be overlooked.

The South had the lowest dietary protein (113 grams) compared with

Percentages of Fat from Different Sources

	U. S.	Northeast	North Central	West	South
	\multicolumn{5}{c}{Household consumption, 1955}				
Milk, dairy....................	25	29	28	25	19
Beef, veal, lamb...............	14	17	16	17	10
Pork, bacon, lard.............	24	17	21	17	35
Margarine, shortening.........	13	11	12	14	14
Oils, salad dressings...........	6	6	5	7	6
Poultry, fish, eggs.............	6	7	6	7	6
Bakery goods, nuts, et cetera....	12	13	12	13	10

the West, where the protein consumption was highest (129 grams), and a death rate of 217. Also, the South had far more Calories from grain products, 1,335, compared with the low of 941 in the Northeast.

The influence of nondietary environmental factors with reference to probable sedentary occupations and emotional stresses of urban life, however, was in the same direction as the dietary factors noted. The Northeast had the highest proportion (79 percent) of its population in towns of 2,500 and over. The South had 49 percent.

Elsewhere are described the shifts in consumption of foods in the United States during the past half century.

Of particular interest is the longtime downward trend in the use of fat (a 30-percent decrease in 50 years) and in the use of grain products, of which we now eat more in the highly processed forms that are lower than natural grains in unsaturated fatty acids, vitamin E, pyridoxine, and other important nutrients.

Also noteworthy is the upward trend in the proportion of dietary fats from meats and milk and the higher intake of animal proteins.

Observations, such as these from several population surveys, present strong challenges to basic research to find out which dietary components are supplementary and which may be antagonistic to normal fat metabolism in the long run and what are the zones of desirable limits for each.

CALLIE MAE COONS *is Director of the Human Nutrition Research Division of the Department of Agriculture. She has engaged in or supervised food and nutrition research in the University of Chicago, the University of Indiana, and Oklahoma State University. Her publications of original research have been in the field of human metabolism. She taught home economics subjects in colleges and universities for some 20 years.*

One of the greatest mysteries of life is the power of growth, that harmonious development of composite organs and tissues from protoplasmic cells, with the ultimate formation of a complex organism with its orderly adjustment of structure and function . . .

Development, growth and vital capacity all depend upon the availability of food in proper amounts and proper qualities.— RUSSELL HENRY CHITTENDEN. Quoted in the Journal of Home Economics, February 1957.

Carbohydrates

A. E. HARPER

FROM carbohydrates we get most of the energy which we need to act and move, perform work, live. Among the carbohydrates are sugars, starches, and celluloses. All green plants form carbohydrates.

Carbohydrates make up about half of the usual American diet and an even greater proportion of the diets of the peoples of most other countries, for the seeds of cereals, high in carbohydrates, form a staple food almost everywhere. They grow almost everywhere. They give the highest yields of energy per unit of land cultivated. They are easy to store and transport. They are inexpensive.

Carbohydrates are important in nutrition for many reasons other than as a source of energy. Some of them make our food sweet. Some of them cling to our teeth and serve as food for bacteria that cause tooth decay. Some determine what types of bacteria will grow in our intestines. The bulk in our food, which helps to prevent constipation, consists mostly of carbohydrates. The body needs carbohydrates in order to use fat efficiently. Some diseases, such as diabetes, develop because the body is unable to use carbohydrates properly.

To understand how carbohydrates perform these functions and how they are used in our bodies, we need to know something about their chemistry. This requires a little discussion of a technical nature, which, if you will bear with me, will help to make some of the more interesting aspects clearer.

The carbohydrates contain carbon, hydrogen, and oxygen.

The hydrogen and oxygen usually occur in the same proportion as in water. When they are burned, water is formed and carbon is left. Early chemists thought therefore that carbohydrates were hydrates of carbon and gave them the name carbohydrate. That turned out to be incorrect, but the name remains.

Some carbohydrates are relatively small molecules. Others, larger and more complex, consist of a few or many of the smaller molecules linked in chains. The chains of the largest molecules may contain more than one thousand units. They may be straight or branched. Some contain only one kind of unit. Some contain several different kinds.

The members of the simplest class, the monosaccharides, have a single unit. Those in the next class are oligosaccharides. They contain only a few units.

These two groups are commonly known as sugars and include such familiar foodstuffs as cane sugar and milk sugar.

Carbohydrates made up of long chains of monosaccharides are known as polysaccharides. Among them are starch, cellulose, plant gums and mucilages, and other structural and storage carbohydrates.

The individual members of each of these classes differ in the types of small units they contain and in the way the units are linked together.

Glucose is the commonest of the monosaccharides. It was named after the Greek word meaning "sweet," long before its chemical structure was determined. It is now known to be a polyhydroxyaldehyde (a long chemical name which I shall explain later) and may be taken as representative of the class of simple carbohydrates.

Glucose contains 6 atoms of carbon, 12 of hydrogen, and 6 of oxygen. The molecular formula is $C_6H_{12}O_6$. It may exist in more than one form, but the structure can be visualized by picturing the 6 carbon atoms as joined in a line.

The carbon atom at one end has attached to it 1 hydrogen atom and 1 oxygen atom to form the aldehyde group.

The carbon at the other end has 2 hydrogens and 1 hydroxyl group. The hydroxyl group, which is present in all alcohols, consists of a hydrogen atom linked to an oxygen and is represented chemically as —OH.

Each of the remaining four carbons of the glucose molecule carries 1 hydrogen and 1 hydroxyl group. Thus we have a polyhydroxyaldehyde. Glucose is called a pentahydroxyaldehyde because it contains 5 hydroxyl groups.

The other simple carbohydrates, or sugars, contain essentially the same groups. They differ in the way the groups occur in relation to each other. Some carbohydrates contain one or more groups that are different from those in glucose.

The properties of the individual monosaccharides depend partly on the positions of the hydroxyl groups within

Open-chain and cyclic structures for glucose.

the molecule and partly on whether the molecule contains groups that differ from those in the glucose structure.

They may differ also in the number of carbon atoms in the chain. Most common monosaccharides — pentoses and hexoses, respectively—contain 5 or 6 carbon atoms.

The more complex carbohydrates, as stated, consist of chains of monosaccharide units. In the formation of each link between units, a hydrogen atom (H) is split away from one unit and a hydroxyl group (OH) from the other, to yield a molecule of water (H_2O).

The properties of the complex carbohydrates depend on the number of units they contain, the types of units of which the chains are composed, and the position of the links that join the individual units together. In the oligo- and polysaccharides, the monosaccharide units are in one of several possible ring forms rather than in the straight chain form described earlier.

MOST OF THE different kinds of carbohydrates are plant products. Plants make them by photosynthesis, a complex chemical process that consists of a series of reactions, at least one of which can occur only with the aid of sunlight and the green plant pigment, chlorophyll.

Energy from sunlight is trapped by the pigment and is used to transfer hydrogen from water to a substance that binds it. The bound hydrogen can then be passed on to other compounds. Carbon dioxide from the air enters the plant and is also combined with substances in the plant tissue, probably without the aid of sunlight. The bound hydrogen is transferred to the substance containing the carbon and oxygen from the carbon dioxide to give a product containing carbon, hydrogen, and oxygen.

Repetition of this series of reactions provides a continuous supply of small building blocks from which the plant can make the most complex carbohydrates and other chemical compounds.

The final result of photosynthesis is that light energy from the sun is converted into chemical energy, largely in the form of carbohydrate.

A large part of this chemical energy is eventually consumed by people and animals when they use plants and plant products as food. As the dry matter of most plants consists of 60 to 90 percent of carbohydrate, man consumes a great deal of the energy trapped by plants directly in this form. A part of it he consumes indirectly, after it has been converted into the flesh of animals.

Although the point has little to do with nutrition, it is interesting that many of the other sources of energy used extensively by man—wood, coal, oil, and peat—also arise directly or indirectly from carbohydrates of plant origin.

ALTHOUGH CARBOHYDRATES, as I said at the outset, function in nutrition primarily as a source of energy, there is no definite nutritional requirement for carbohydrates.

People and animals very likely can survive quite well on diets containing no carbohydrate, because the body can also use fats and proteins directly as sources of energy and because the body can make enough carbohydrate for its special needs from other com-

pounds, such as amino acids, the building blocks of proteins. If the animal body were unable to use carbohydrates as a source of energy, however, the available food materials—and, therefore, the population of the world—would be very limited.

Many different kinds of carbohydrates occur in foods. Not all are of equal importance in nutrition. Their chemical structures determine which of the different carbohydrates can be digested, absorbed, and used by the body and, therefore, their value as foodstuffs. Actually, relatively few of the many carbohydrates that occur in nature are used efficiently by man, but these few make up by far the greatest proportion of the carbohydrates found in most common foods.

Starch, which consists of glucose units, is the only polysaccharide that man can use efficiently. Nutritionally it is far and away the most important carbohydrate.

Cereal grains, our most important source of carbohydrates, are rich in starch. Rice, wheat, sorghum, corn (maize), millet, and rye contain about 70 percent of starch. Potatoes and other tubers and roots are also rich in starch. Beans and the seeds of many other legumes are high in protein, but 40 percent or more of their dry matter is starch.

Only two of the disaccharides (these contain two monosaccharide units) are of much importance nutritionally.

One is sucrose—cane sugar or beet sugar, which is available as a highly refined and relatively pure carbohydrate. It is also one of the carbohydrates in many fruits and vegetables and represents almost one-fourth of the carbohydrates eaten in the United States.

The other important disaccharide is lactose, or milk sugar, which makes up almost 40 percent of the solids in fresh whole milk. It is the only disaccharide synthesized by animals. It is the only carbohydrate of animal origin that is of significance in nutrition. It is made up of one glucose unit and one galactose unit. Galactose is a hexose and differs only slightly in chemical structure from glucose.

Section of starch chain formed through loss of water from glucose molecules. Reversal of this reaction would represent hydrolysis of starch.

The monosaccharides are important in nutrition mainly because they are the units of the more complex carbohydrates. A few of them do occur and are eaten in the free form. Glucose and fructose, a hexose quite closely related structurally to glucose, are in honey and fruits. Fructose derives its name from the Latin word for fruit and sometimes is known as fruit sugar.

The monosaccharides in honey arise largely from the breakdown of sucrose, which contains one glucose and one fructose unit. Fruits, honey, and certain fresh vegetables are the richest sources of the monosaccharides we eat.

Relatively few of the other carbohydrates occur widely enough or are utilized well enough by the body to have much nutritional importance.

The pentoses do not occur to any great extent in the free form and in any event are not well utilized by the body.

The sugar alcohol, mannitol, occurs in a number of fruits and vegetables. Several varieties of trees and shrubs exude it. Some primitive tribes, particularly in Australia, use this so-called manna as a food in time of famine, but as pure mannitol is not well utilized by the body, manna must contain other substances or else be of limited

nutritional value. The manna the Israelites found during their wanderings may have come from the tamarisk tree or from an insect on it.

If the body is to use the complex carbohydrates for energy, they must be split into monosaccharides and then be absorbed. This splitting (or hydrolysis, as the chemists call it), is part of the process of digestion: One molecule of water is added at each of the links in the polysaccharide chain.

A hydrogen atom from water is transferred to one of the units and a hydroxyl group to the other. This reaction, which gives rise to monosaccharides, occurs rapidly under the influence of enzymes in the mouth and in the small intestine.

Enzymes are catalysts produced by living organisms. As catalysts, they increase the rate of a chemical reaction but they themselves are not altered during the reaction. The enzymes, which are biological catalysts, are proteins.

Not all of the carbohydrates in foodstuffs undergo hydrolysis in the digestive tract. There are, for example, no enzymes in the body that will enable it to break down cellulose, the main structural material of plants. In fact, most polysaccharides other than starch are indigestible. They generally are grouped as fiber and pass through the body unchanged. Some raw starches, particularly starch in raw potatoes, occur in granules that are not readily broken down in the digestive tract. They must be finely ground or boiled before they are digested.

Generally, however, only small amounts of these materials are present in our food. The carbohydrates in the diets of most people in civilized areas are about 97 percent digestible.

Even cattle and other ruminants, which use the carbohydrates in the fiber of straw, do not have enzymes of their own that enable them to break these products down. They depend for this on enzymes produced by the bacteria in their special stomach, or rumen. All animals that can thrive on fiber (including insects, such as termites, which live largely on wood) need bacteria to enable them to use cellulose and related carbohydrates as food.

THE DIGESTION of starch begins in the mouth, where salivary amylase, an enzyme, is secreted. Under its influence, the chains of glucose units are split into smaller fragments. Hydrolysis continues in the stomach after the food is swallowed until the stomach contents become too acidic.

The starch fragments and undigested starch and sugars then pass into the small intestine. There the acid is neutralized, more amylase is secreted into the intestine from the pancreas, and the starch is eventually broken down to maltose, a disaccharide that consists of two glucose units.

Maltose (with sucrose and lactose, which pass through to the small intestine unchanged) is then split into its constituent monosaccharides by the action of still other enzymes. The hydrolysis of lactose does not take place so fast as that of the other disaccharides, probably because of its lower solubility.

The monosaccharides—those eaten as such and those arising from the digestive processes—are then absorbed from the intestine and pass into the blood.

Glucose enters the blood directly. Fructose and galactose are thought to be at least partly converted into glucose as they pass through the intestinal wall.

Studies of the rates at which the monosaccharides disappear from the intestine indicate that the most common hexoses (galactose, glucose, and fructose) are absorbed most rapidly. Mannose and pentoses are absorbed more slowly.

Most of our information about the absorption of sugar comes from experiments in which the subjects were given only a simple sugar solution. We need more information about the way other factors affect absorption. Our limited information indicates that both digestion and absorption are influenced by the presence of other substances in the intestine, the nature and the amount of those substances, hormonal factors, and other conditions.

Not all of the monosaccharides that are absorbed are readily utilized by the tissues as a source of energy.

Galactose, for example, is rapidly absorbed, but it accumulates in the blood and tissues when large amounts are eaten, and much of it is excreted in the urine.

Pentoses, too, are poorly utilized. So are the sugar alcohols, with the possible exception of sorbitol, the alcohol arising from glucose.

The different monosaccharides must be converted to glucose before they can be used by the body. Therefore only sugars that can be converted readily to glucose can be used quickly by the body.

WE CAN APPRECIATE better the importance of the conversion of other monosaccharides to glucose when we realize what an important and central role glucose has in body processes. It is the sugar normally found in blood. Because it is highly soluble, is neither acid nor alkaline, and is utilized directly by the tissues, it serves as a fuel that can be easily moved from one part of the body to another. Its energy can be released wherever it is required.

Also, an excess of glucose can be converted by the tissues, particularly in the liver and the muscles, into the polysaccharide glycogen. Glycogen is a branched-chain polysaccharide composed of glucose units. It is similar to starch and is sometimes called animal starch. It (and therefore glucose) is the form in which carbohydrate is stored in the body.

THE LIVER is an important storehouse of glycogen and an important organ in bringing about the conversion of other carbohydrates into glucose. Also, it can synthesize glucose from short-chain organic acids that arise during the oxidation of carbohydrates and amino acids.

Lactic acid, which is formed from carbohydrate breakdown in the muscles during exercise or hard work, enters the blood and is returned to the liver, where it may be converted back to glucose.

When energy is needed urgently in other parts of the body, the liver releases glucose into the blood from its store of glycogen or through synthesis. The blood then carries the glucose to the tissues that need it. It is broken down in the tissues to provide energy. Incomplete breakdown yields organic acids. Complete oxidation yields carbon dioxide and water.

In order for the muscles and various organs to obtain glucose there must be sufficient glucose in the blood. A person's blood sugar is high immediately after he has eaten. As the various tissues and organs take up the extra glucose, the blood sugar falls but is maintained at a constant level. This level (about 80 milligrams per 100 milliliters of blood) is maintained by the flow of glucose to the blood from the liver when the blood sugar level falls. This maintenance of blood sugar level depends on a complex series of reactions involving a number of hormones, which are discussed later.

BECAUSE CARBOHYDRATES are used mainly for energy, we should know something about their energy content.

I mentioned that energy from the sun is required for the synthesis of carbohydrate from carbon dioxide and water. The same amount of energy should then be released if carbohydrates are broken down to carbon dioxide and water.

When we burn carbohydrate in a calorimeter, the heat so released can be used to heat water. We can then measure the change in the temperature of the water. If the volume of water is known, we can calculate the amount of energy released. Values of 3.76 Calories per gram are obtained for glucose and 4.1 Calories per gram for starch by this method. A Calorie is the amount of heat required to raise 1 thousand grams of water 1 degree centigrade.

As most foods contain a large amount of starch, we use a value of 4 Calories per gram of carbohydrate in estimating the energy value of the carbohydrates in ordinary mixed diets. This average value is useful in determining the number of Calories in crude foodstuffs, but it is unsatisfactory for calculating the energy content of the highly refined diets often used in experiments, in which the carbohydrate may be provided as glucose or sucrose rather than as starch.

Because all carbohydrates must be broken down to monosaccharides before they can be absorbed and used by the body, we say sometimes that the fuel value of all the carbohydrates that can be used for energy is probably the same. What we lose sight of, though, is that one molecule of water is formed each time a monosaccharide unit is added to the polysaccharide chain. During hydrolysis in the digestive tract, the water is added back. Therefore, for each gram of a complex carbohydrate eaten, a little more than a gram of monosaccharide is obtained.

Because the gram molecular weight (G.M.W. is the sum of the weights of the atoms in the molecule expressed in grams) of glucose is 180 and the gram molecular weight of the average unit in starch is 162, during the digestion of 162 grams of starch 18 grams of water is added and this results in the formation of 180 grams of glucose in the intestine. The caloric value per unit weight of starch therefore is about 10 percent greater than that of glucose.

THE ENERGY from carbohydrates becomes available to the body when glucose is broken down in the tissues. Complete breakdown involves oxidation and yields carbon dioxide and water. The process is essentially that of burning—but with a difference.

When carbohydrate is burned, all of the energy is converted to heat and is rapidly dissipated. Oxidation in the tissues is slower. It occurs stepwise, with many intermediate reactions. It is like a reversal of photosynthesis in many ways. Hydrogen is removed from many of the breakdown products under the influence of enzymes and is passed to coenzymes, which are complex chemical compounds that act as hydrogen carriers. The hydrogen is passed from the coenzymes and eventually combines with oxygen to form water. Carbon dioxide is split off from the residues in other reactions, and the oxidation is complete.

Small amounts of energy are released during many of these reactions, particularly during the stepwise passage of the hydrogen from the carbohydrates to combine with oxygen to form water. This energy is not dissipated but is used to form a special group of compounds—high-energy phosphates—which are among the most important in the body. When they are broken down, their energy is released in such a way that the tissues can use it for the synthesis of other compounds, to provide heat or to provide the energy for muscular contraction—that is, for work.

Thus light energy trapped by the plant is converted by an intricate series of chemical reactions into kinetic energy—energy used for movement or work—in the animal body.

These oxidative processes, which release energy for our activity, involve many enzymes and coenzymes. A full course in biochemistry would be needed to describe them in detail. Many of the dietary essentials discussed in other chapters are important in them.

The enzymes, for example, must be synthesized from amino acids, the units of which the proteins in our diet are composed. The coenzymes contain vitamins and often minerals that also are essential nutrients. A lack of any one of them can depress or inhibit important steps in the body's utilization of carbohydrate.

ALTHOUGH THE MAIN FUNCTION of these processes is considered to be the provision of energy for bodily activity, they are important in other ways, too.

Many small molecules, such as organic acids, are formed during the series of oxidative reactions. They represent intermediate stages during the breakdown of the carbohydrates to water and carbon dioxide. They also represent intermediate stages in the synthesis of certain larger molecules.

Fat can be made from carbohydrate in the animal body. An example: The carcass of a pig that is kept for a few months on a diet that contains very little fat but a great deal of carbohydrate will contain far more fat than it consumed.

The carcass fat is built up by condensation of several molecules of acetic acid, a small, two-carbon acid that is the acid of vinegar. It is an intermediate in the oxidation of carbohydrate and occurs in the body bound to a coenzyme, of which pantothenic acid, a vitamin, is a part.

The ability of the animal body to produce fat from carbohydrates makes it possible for us to consume a part of the plant carbohydrates in the form of animal fats. This process also makes it possible for us to store efficiently part of the energy we get from carbohydrates. Fats have a heat content of about 9 Calories per gram, compared to 4 for carbohydrates. Thus less space is needed to store a given amount of energy as fat than as carbohydrate.

The knowledge that carbohydrates can be converted to fat in the body has given rise to the saying that if you want to reduce you should eat less of the carbohydrates. This is misleading. If we want to reduce we must eat fewer Calories—that is, we must eat less food.

It is important that we eat sufficient proteins because the amino acids of proteins are dietary essentials. We cannot get along without them. Also, because some of the fatty acids of fats are dietary essentials, we cannot cut all fats out of our diet. Nevertheless it is surprising how little fat and protein are needed to supply the essential fatty acids and amino acids.

Therefore if we want to reduce there is no reason for cutting down only on our intake of carbohydrates. It is much better to eat a balanced diet and to eat less of it. If one component of our diets is to be restricted more than another, it would be much more effective to restrict our intake of fats, which provide many more Calories per pound than do the carbohydrates.

Besides acetic acid, other organic acids containing 3, 4, 5, or 6 carbon atoms are intermediates in the breakdown of carbohydrates. At least three of them can be converted directly into amino acids, the building blocks of proteins, if nitrogen is available from ammonium salts, urea, or other amino acids. This process occurs in the tissues of man and animals that have only one stomach, but is much more important to animals that have more than one stomach.

The paunch, or rumen, of cattle, sheep, and goats contains untold numbers of bacteria, which carry out this process efficiently. These microorganisms can synthesize many more amino acids than the animal body can. If they have a source of nitrogen, therefore, much of the carbohydrate from plants (even carbohydrates such as cellulose, which have no nutritive value for man) can be converted by the micro-organisms in the rumen into the building blocks of the proteins and the fat of beef and mutton.

THE CONVERSION of other monosaccharides into glucose I mentioned as a step in the utilization of the various carbohydrates as a source of energy.

These reactions are reversible—that is, other monosaccharides can be formed from glucose. These interconversions are important because some biologically important compounds in the body contain carbohydrate units other than glucose.

Among the carbohydrates involved are two pentoses, ribose and deoxy-ribose; galactose; sugar acids, such as glucuronic acid; and sugar amines, which arise from glucose and galactose. Thus a single dietary carbohydrate may be converted into others that serve as building blocks for such compounds as some of the complex lipids, which contain galactose; for nucleic acids, which contain pentoses; and for some of the structural elements in cartilage, which contain certain sugar acids and sugar amines.

Another important function of carbohydrate and of the series of reactions by which carbohydrate is oxidized in the body is to facilitate the oxidation of fat.

It is often said that fat is burned in a flame of carbohydrate: If not enough carbohydrate is available, it is difficult for the body to oxidize fat completely to carbon dioxide and water. The reason is that one of the organic acids formed during carbohydrate oxidation is required for the complete oxidation of fat. The incomplete products of fat oxidation are the short-chain, usually four-carbon, organic acids (known as ketone bodies). An accumulation of them can cause the blood and the urine to become acidic. These acids are excreted as salts, so their excretion may lead to severe losses of sodium. This in turn reduces the ability of the blood to carry carbon dioxide and in severe cases may result in coma.

This occurs sometimes in diabetic individuals, whose tissues cannot oxidize carbohydrate. It also occurs during starvation (when the body must use its stored fat for energy) and when diets very high in fat are eaten. The administration of insulin (a hormone from the pancreas that is needed for the utilization of carbohydrates) with carbohydrate to diabetic persons, and carbohydrate alone to starving ones, restores the ability of their body cells to oxidize fat completely.

This is also one of the reasons why it is unwise to try to lose weight by going without food for several days. The body's store of carbohydrate is quickly used up, and then large amounts of body fat must be used for energy. Without some carbohydrate, the fat may not be completely oxidized, and ill effects may result.

CARBOHYDRATES also exert a protein-sparing effect—that is, they reduce the wastage of body or dietary protein that occurs in certain conditions.

For example, the bodies of starving persons and those who restrict their Calories must oxidize amino acids from protein along with fat in order to obtain energy. The result is a loss of amino acids. If carbohydrates are supplied, the body oxidizes them for energy in preference to protein, and thus the amino acids of the protein are spared for other purposes. This sparing effect on protein is primarily an effect of Calories. Calories supplied as fat can also spare protein. We have some evidence, however, that carbohydrates exert a sparing effect on the protein, besides that of supplying Calories, and therefore are more effective than fat in this role.

Several hormones are important in the body's utilization of carbohydrates. Insulin, a hormone from the pancreas, facilitates the entry of glucose into tissue cells. A lack of insulin causes a rise in the amount of sugar in the blood.

When carbohydrates are eaten, insulin stimulates the formation of glycogen from the absorbed sugar, either by directly stimulating absorption by the cells or by stimulating certain enzymes. Extra sugar is thereby removed from the blood.

The pancreas also secretes another hormone, glucagon, which has just the opposite effect. Injections of glucagon cause a rise in the amount of sugar in the blood. Its effect is of short duration, and we do not know how significant it is in the overall utilization of carbohydrate.

The adrenal gland also produces hormones that affect the utilization of carbohydrates. One is adrenalin, or epinephrine, which arises from the adrenal medulla, the central part of the gland. It is released during anger or fear. It stimulates the breakdown of glycogen in the liver, and the glucose released raises the level of sugar in the blood. This serves as a source of extra energy, and enables the body to respond more effectively to emotions and crises.

Other hormones are produced by the adrenal cortex, the outer part of the gland. These are known as adrenal cortical hormones. The one with the greatest effect on the utilization of carbohydrates is hydrocortisone. The adrenal cortical hormones are thought to counteract in some way the action of insulin, because an animal from which the adrenal cortex has been removed becomes extremely sensitive to injections of insulin. Injections of hydrocortisone stimulate the liver to form glucose from amino acids and result in the accumulation of glycogen in the liver.

A hormone from the anterior pituitary gland also exerts some control over the utilization of carbohydrate. The rise in blood sugar that follows removal of the pancreas is alleviated by removal of the pituitary gland as well. Prolonged injections of pituitary extracts can cause the development of diabetes.

SEVERAL CONDITIONS prevent the body from making proper use of carbohydrates. The commonest is diabetes.

Certain carbohydrates cannot be utilized in some rarer hereditary conditions. One of these, known as glycogen-storage disease, is a condition in which abnormal amounts of glycogen accumulate in the liver. Another is congenital galactosemia, in which the lactose of milk cannot be utilized.

Diabetes has been known for centuries. Hippocrates (460?–?377 B.C.) described the sweet urine of diabetic patients. Excretion of sugar in the urine is characteristic of the disease. The amount of sugar in the blood rises. Organic acids appear in the blood and urine. Loss of weight is pronounced. In severe cases of diabetes, cataracts develop and, if the disease is untreated, death ensues. These symptoms are primarily a result of the body's inability to use glucose.

Diabetes is caused mainly by the failure of the pancreas to secrete enough insulin. Some forms of the disease are caused by imbalances of other hormones. Administration of insulin promptly relieves the signs of diabetes and permits normal utilization of carbohydrate when the disease is caused only by the loss of function of the cells of the pancreas that produce this hormone.

The condition known as glycogen-storage disease is rare. Some cases are so severe that infants suffering from it survive only a short time. Other cases may be mild and merely limit the activity of the individual a little. It results from a lack in the liver of an enzyme, glucose-6-phosphatase, which is required for the removal of phosphate from a glucose phosphate. Glucose phosphates are intermediates in the formation of glucose from glycogen. Unless the phosphate is split off, the glucose cannot pass into the blood and become available as a source of energy in other parts of the body.

Congenital galactosemia, or galactose diabetes, is a disorder in man in which the ability to utilize galactose is low. Infants having this defect show it only after they have been given milk for a few days. The galactose level of the blood rises, the liver becomes enlarged, and jaundice occurs. These infants develop cataracts and mental deficiency and may die if they continue to receive only milk.

The disorder results from the lack of (or lowered activity of) an enzyme necessary for the conversion of galactose to glucose. Infants suffering from this disorder recover quickly if they are given a diet that contains no galactose or lactose.

Some toxic effects have been observed in animals eating large amounts of lactose, galactose, and xylose. The quantities that produce these effects are beyond what a person would normally consume, but because the effects can be produced in animals, they deserve consideration.

Rats fed a diet containing 70 percent of lactose develop cataracts (the lens of the eye becomes opaque). Galactose and xylose, fed as a large percentage of the diet, also cause cataracts. Galactose and xylose are absorbed but are not readily utilized by the tissues and accumulate in them when they are fed in large quantities. These sugars apparently interfere in some way with the normal utilization of glucose.

BESIDES PROVIDING ENERGY, carbohydrates affect food consumption indirectly through their flavors and through their influence on the amount of water drawn into the stomach.

The sweetness of sugar makes many foods more palatable. We use the sugars of fruits in jams and jellies to make bread and toast taste better.

We add sugar to many sour foods, such as fruit juices that contain a lot of acid, to sweeten them.

We may prefer the foods that are sweetened by their own sugars—for example, young peas and corn and other vegetables, compared to older, riper ones that contain little sugar. This sweetening power may not be of any direct nutritional importance, but it can be a valuable aid in getting young children and people on diets to eat the foods that are best for them.

It can, of course, be a disadvantage, too, in tempting them to eat too much of certain sweet foods that they would be better off without.

Sugars are not all equally sweet. Table sugar, or sucrose, is a standard with which the others can be compared. If we set the sweetness of sucrose at 100, glucose would be given a value of about 75. Fructose is sweeter than sucrose, and has been rated at 110 to 175 by individual tasters. The value of galactose may probably lie somewhere between 35 and 70. Lactose is 15 to 30.

Food passes from the mouth to the stomach. The stomach supplies enzymes for the digestion of protein and is a temporary storage organ in which food is diluted. It also influences the amount of food that is eaten.

Carbohydrate molecules, as I said, vary greatly in size. Carbohydrates also vary in solubility. They therefore vary greatly, too, in the osmotic pressure they exert.

Osmotic pressure can be defined loosely as the water-attracting power of concentrated solutions—for example, when red blood cells are put into water, it is the osmotic pressure of the solution inside the cells that causes water to pass into the cells until they swell sufficiently to burst. When a large amount of glucose or sucrose is eaten, the osmotic pressure of the solution in the stomach is high, and water passes from the tissues to dilute the stomach contents. This can cause distention of the stomach and lessen the desire to eat.

If an animal is fed a diet that contains an inadequate amount of some essential component, such as protein, the drop in the consumption of food—because of the presence of a large amount of a carbohydrate of low molecular weight in the stomach—may be enough to lower the rate of growth.

The substitution of starch for sucrose in the diet stimulates food consumption and growth, apparently because starch exerts less osmotic pressure and therefore causes less water to be drawn into the stomach. Such an effect may account for the observation of many mothers that the appetite of a child who has eaten a relatively small amount of candy just before a meal seems to be reduced out of all proportion to the amount eaten.

These observations appear worthy of consideration in planning the diets of infants and of rapidly growing children. They may also be important in the feeding of patients whose stomachs have been removed. The loss of this organ of dilution may lead to unde-sirable osmotic effects in the intestine when one eats a large amount of a sugar of low molecular weight.

CARBOHYDRATES FUNCTION as energy sources for us and also for the bacteria that inhabit the mouth and the intestinal tract. It is because of this that they influence the development of dental caries—tooth decay—and the condition of the intestinal tract.

Many nutritional and hereditary factors influence the development of dental caries. One should not place too much emphasis on any one of them. Carbohydrates are certainly one of the important nutritional factors. Bacteria, probably through their production of acid and enzymes, cause dental caries. They, like other forms of life, require a readily available supply of energy. The carbohydrates used most extensively by man, sucrose and starch, are also readily used by micro-organisms responsible for dental caries. Diets that are low in carbohydrate and high in fat and protein cause fewer dental caries than those that are high in carbohydrate.

The physical characteristics of the carbohydrates determine to a great extent their influence on dental caries. Carbohydrates that are sticky and those that are finely ground adhere to the teeth and promote the growth of bacteria more than do coarser, cruder preparations.

Less tooth decay develops if the sugars are eaten with meals than if they are eaten between meals. Carbohydrates in solution are less damaging than those in solid form.

Little tooth decay develops in experimental animals that drink only milk, even though more than one-third of the solids of milk is carbohydrate. This is partly because milk sugar is not readily broken down in the mouth and partly because of the flushing action of the dilute solution, which leaves little food for the bacteria.

It is clear, therefore, that carbohydrates must remain in the mouth and must be available to bacteria to cause dental caries. The longer they remain, the greater will be the bacterial growth.

It is impractical to recommend diets low in carbohydrate for the control of dental caries. Nevertheless, attention to the form in which carbohydrate is eaten can aid in the control of caries. Less refined carbohydrates, little carbohydrate between meals, and rinsing the carbohydrate from the mouth can help to deprive the bacteria that cause decay of the nutriment they require.

TWO ROLES of carbohydrates in the intestine also should be considered.

One is their effect on the intestinal flora—the bacteria and other micro-organisms that grow in the intestinal tract.

The other is their role in providing fiber or bulk.

Both are important in maintaining the intestine in a healthy condition.

Carbohydrates serve as a source of energy for the bacteria that grow in the intestines, just as they do for those in the mouth. The type of dietary carbohydrate influences greatly the nature of the intestinal flora.

Highly soluble carbohydrates, such as sucrose and glucose, are absorbed quickly from the intestine, leaving primarily protein and fat, which favor the growth of micro-organisms that can use these substances efficiently.

Carbohydrates that are less soluble and less rapidly digested, such as lactose and starch, remain in the intestine longer and favor the growth of other bacteria that can use carbohydrates more readily.

Lactose, the sugar of milk, is relatively insoluble and slowly digested. It is not rapidly removed from the intestine and is used most efficiently by certain types of bacteria that produce organic acids. The acids help check the growth of some of the less desirable bacteria. They also increase the solubility, and therefore the absorption, of calcium.

Lactose is tolerated well by the infant who receives most of its carbohydrate in this form from milk. It seems to be tolerated better in animals fed a diet that is high in fat. Its slow rate of absorption can cause diarrhea in adults who take in large amounts of it. That may be due to its osmotic pressure, which causes water to be drawn into the intestine. Lactose in limited amounts helps keep the intestine in a healthy condition and prevent constipation.

Carbohydrates that are not absorbed quickly from the intestine also stimulate the growth of micro-organisms that synthesize many vitamins of the B complex. Most of our information about them comes from experiments with animals. The first observations were of a phenomenon, refection.

The term was used to describe a condition observed when rats were fed a large amount of raw-potato starch in a diet that contained no obvious source of B vitamins (water-soluble vitamins). For a time they failed to grow. Then, if they were kept on the diet longer, they began to grow quite well, apparently because the bacteria in their intestines were synthesizing the needed vitamins.

In later studies, the water-soluble vitamin requirements of animals fed on diets containing starch, lactose, and certain other carbohydrates that disappear slowly from the intestine were found to be lower than those of animals fed a diet containing a highly soluble carbohydrate. Apparently vitamins synthesized by the intestinal bacteria were absorbed and used by the animal.

The sugar alcohol, sorbitol, has been found to stimulate the production of B vitamins by micro-organisms in the intestinal tract.

Further evidence that intestinal micro-organisms are important suppliers of B vitamins was obtained from experiments in which deficiencies of the vitamins biotin and folic acid, which are required in minute amounts, could be produced only if the intestinal micro-organisms were inhibited by a sulfa drug. The deficiencies could be produced faster if the carbohydrate was highly soluble.

In a few studies involving people, a complex carbohydrate in the diet has been found to increase the amounts of some of the B vitamins available to the body. People eating a diet that contained a complex carbohydrate were found to excrete more of certain of the B vitamins than they consumed. These observations and others suggest that certain carbohydrates—through their influence on the intestinal flora—can be highly important in preventing the development of vitamin deficiencies in people and animals.

Carbohydrates in the intestine also help maintain normal peristaltic action—rhythmic contraction—which is favored by the presence of a certain amount of bulk in the diet. Bulk consists largely of cellulose and a number of other polysaccharides and related substances, such as agar-agar, pentosans, and pectins, which are not digested by the enzymes of the body. They accumulate in the intestine and expand it. Since they absorb water (some of them much more than others) they contribute appreciably to the bulk of the feces and help to prevent constipation.

A. E. HARPER *is associate professor of biochemistry in the University of Wisconsin. He has degrees from the University of Alberta and the University of Wisconsin. He has held teaching positions in those institutions and for a year was research fellow at Cambridge University, England. Dr. Harper is the author of a number of scientific publications dealing mainly with the nutritional significance of carbohydrate, protein, and fat.*

The Associated Press reported from Tokyo on Oct. 21, 1958: Bumper rice crops mean malnutrition. That is a paradox Japan is trying to overcome.

A welfare ministry survey shows that one of four persons in Japan was suffering in 1957 from such nutritional diseases as beriberi, anemia, and dropsy.

It warned that more and more people are reversing a postwar trend and returning to rice as their main source of food at the expense of valuable proteins, fats, vitamins and minerals.

Japan has enjoyed bumper rice crops for four years. This year the second highest harvest in history is expected.

School girls of 10 grew more than an inch taller and one pound heavier than their sisters of the same age group before the war.

Dieticians and health officials credited the occupation-introduced dietary reforms—plus the postwar rice shortages.

But the welfare ministry said since 1956 cases of vitamin B₁ deficiency have increased.

It found 25.9 out of every 100 persons suffering from malnutrition last year. This was 3.3 persons more than in 1956. The rate of physical growth, both in rural and urban areas, has leveled off. The highest rate of growth was in 1955.

Rural children—who consume more rice—were found to be a quarter of an inch to three-quarters of an inch shorter than city children.

—From The Evening Star, Washington, D.C. Reprinted by permission.

Calories and Body Weight

KATHERINE H. FISHER AND RAYMOND W. SWIFT

PEOPLE need a continual supply of food to supply energy for good health and well-being. The energy of food, in the form of stored chemical energy, is released as heat when the food is oxidized by the body. How much food a person needs depends on his activity and the weight he should maintain.

National and international groups of specialists in nutrition have suggested energy needs for people of all ages. The recommended energy allowances of the Food and Nutrition Board of the National Academy of Sciences-National Research Council (NRC) are the standards used in the planning of food supplies and in the evaluation of diets of Americans. The Committee on Calorie Requirement of the Food and Agriculture Organization of the United Nations (FAO) has prepared recommendations for use elsewhere.

In both systems of caloric assessment, the suggested energy values do not represent actual requirements but rather caloric levels that take into account the variations that occur within a population group.

The addition of carbohydrate to a diet provides a source of energy that the body may later oxidize to produce

heat (Calories), or it may be stored as fat, or its energy may be represented by muscular exercise.

The recommended energy allowances for normal, healthy Americans have been grouped into two general categories: The Calorie allowances for adults and the Calorie allowances for children and adolescents.

The allowances for adults were patterned after the needs of a man who weighs 154 pounds and is 69 inches tall and a woman who weighs 128 pounds and is 64 inches tall, who are 25 years old, live in a temperate climate, and are fairly active physically. Adjustments for age and pregnancy and lactation were made so as to include adults who differ from such a "reference" man and woman.

The Calorie allowances suggested for children and adolescents were based mostly on standard patterns of growth rates early in life.

Although the recommended allowances are to be used solely as a guide in assessment of Calories, the values suggested for children and adolescents are less applicable to individuals than are those proposed for adults. The reasons therefor stem from the differences in physical activity, appetite, and size and composition of the body among children of all ages.

CALORIE ALLOWANCES for adults have been proposed by the NRC in terms of levels at ages 25, 45, and 65 years.

During early adulthood, when physical performance may be high, daily intakes of 3,200 and 2,300 Calories have been proposed for the 25-year-old man and woman, respectively.

As adults approach middle age and physical activity lessens, 3,000 and 2,200 Calories each day, respectively, have been suggested as enough to meet the energy demands of most 45-year-old men and women.

A further reduction in caloric intake has been recommended at age 65 in order to account for still lower physical expenditures and for the gradually decreasing basal metabolism. (Basal metabolism is the energy expenditure of the body during physical, digestive, and emotional rest.)

The daily Calorie values suggested for older people are 2,550 Calories for men and 1,800 Calories for women.

Extra Calories are needed to compensate for the increased energy demands of women during pregnancy and lactation. Because the energy costs and the reduced activity in the early stages of pregnancy balance one another, the addition of 300 Calories each day has been recommended only for the second half of the reproduction period.

The extra needs for Calories during lactation, however, are greater and more constant. It has been suggested that a daily supplement of 1,000 Calories should more than satisfy the energy needed for the average rate of human milk production (about 29 ounces a day). Nevertheless, about 130 Calories of food energy should be allotted for each 3.5 ounces of milk produced.

Size, activity, and rate of growth are the standards used in assessing the caloric needs of infants 12 months old or less. Based on body weight, a recommendation of about 55 Calories per pound (age 2 to 6 months) and about 45 Calories per pound (age 7 through 12 months) has been made to meet the energy demands during this period of fast growth. No recommendation was made for the first month of life, when many babies are breast fed.

The same caloric value has been recommended for both boys and girls in the preschool and early school years. The 1- to 3-year-old child has a daily need of about 1,300 Calories, and 1,700 Calories should provide enough energy for the 4- to 6-year-old boy or girl. For boys and girls 7 to 9 years old, 2,100 Calories are recommended; for those 10 to 12 years old, 2,500 Calories.

The adolescent years, 13 through 19, have an additional need for all nutrients, including food for energy. Because the curves of maximum growth are different for boys and girls at this period, separate energy values have been proposed.

The adolescent girl has her greatest daily energy need between the ages of 13 and 15 years—2,600 Calories. In the postadolescent period (16 through 19 years), 2,400 Calories are recommended.

The period of greatest energy need of adolescent boys occurs during the years 16 through 19. A daily intake of 3,600 Calories is recommended for them. Before this period of maximum energy intake, 3,100 Calories a day (age 13 to 15) are suggested.

The number of Calories should be adjusted when the conditions of environmental temperature, size of body, or activity differ from the factors used in determining the standard energy allowances of adult men and women.

The average temperature within the continental United States corresponds rather closely to 68° F. (20° C.) used in the standard energy allowances. Although metabolism is affected by environmental temperature, most people avoid actual exposure to excessive heat or cold by means of clothing and control of indoor temperatures.

Desirable Weights for Height

| Height in inches | Weight in pounds | |
	Men	Women
58.............	....	112±11
60.............	125±13	116±12
62.............	130±13	121±12
64.............	135±14	128±13
66.............	142±14	135±14
68.............	150±15	142±14
70.............	158±16	150±15
72.............	167±17	158±16
74.............	178±18	....

Calorie Allowances for Individuals of Various Body Weights

[At mean environmental temperature of 68° F. and assuming moderate physical activity]

MEN

| Desirable weight Pounds | Calorie allowances | | |
	25 years	45 years	65 years
110..........	2,500	2,350	1,950
121..........	2,700	2,550	2,150
132..........	2,850	2,700	2,250
143..........	3,000	2,800	2,350
154..........	3,200	3,000	2,550
165..........	3,400	3,200	2,700
176..........	3,550	3,350	2,800
187..........	3,700	3,500	2,900

WOMEN

88............	1,750	1,650	1,400
99............	1,900	1,800	1,500
110..........	2,050	1,950	1,600
121..........	2,200	2,050	1,750
128..........	2,300	2,200	1,800
132..........	2,350	2,200	1,850
143..........	2,500	2,350	2,000
154..........	2,600	2,450	2,050
165..........	2,750	2,600	2,150

When a person's body size differs from the values stated for the "reference" man and woman (154 pounds and 128 pounds, respectively), an adjustment in the energy intake must be made.

The first step in calculating the approximate Calorie need of an individual is to determine his desirable weight for his height (table 1, above).

For example, the desirable weight of a man 5 feet 6 inches tall (66 inches) is 142±14 pounds. This means that the desirable weight may be from 128 to 156 pounds.

The second step in calculating the approximate Calorie need of an individual is a consideration of age for this desirable weight (table 2). For example, a 43-year-old woman, weighing 110 pounds, needs about 1,950 Calories a day.

The one factor that may cause considerable variation in the actual energy requirement of adults, children, and adolescents is the amount of physical activity they perform. An adjustment must be made when a person's degree of physical performance differs from the rate of activity described in the standard energy allowance.

In the normal person who maintains a desirable and constant body weight, the fluctuation in the rate of activity is accompanied by a corresponding fluctuation in his voluntary intake of food.

No simple formula has been devised to adjust for these variations in need for energy. It is suggested that for heavy work the addition of 25 percent of the standard allowance of energy should be sufficient to meet the demands for the extra activity. For example, a 45-year-old farmer who does heavy work would need about 3,000 Calories (the standard allowance) plus 750 Calories (25 percent of 3,000 Calories), or 3,750 Calories.

Persons who work in a sedentary occupation or lead a sedentary life should reduce their standard energy allowance in order to balance the lesser expenditures for a lower physical activity.

Because these adjustments for differences in size and activity must be made on an individual basis, it is best to consult the family physician or a nutritionist (available in departments of public health) in the determination of one's best energy intake.

IDEALLY, you should maintain at each stage of life the body weight that is desirable for you. It has been suggested that one's desirable weight at age 25 should be maintained throughout life. We estimate, however, that one out of every five adults in the United States is overweight.

Underweight is apparently less prevalent among adult Americans. These marked deviations among our citizens are of major concern to medical and nutritional specialists.

Desirable body weights for individuals of the same age, sex, and height may vary considerably from the weight values given in height-weight tables. These weight standards, which are commonly used in the United States to predict ideal weight, represent average values of thousands of measurements but do not consider individual variations of body size or composition.

Standard values therefore should not be used as exact values but rather as a guide for predicting desirable weight. For example, the standard weight value for two men (A and B) may be stated to be 150 pounds, but actually A weighs 140 pounds and B weighs 160 pounds. According to the standard weight value, A would be 10 pounds underweight and B would be 10 pounds overweight, but the actual weight of A and of B may be desirable for his own build (table 1).

The control of body weight is based on the law of the conservation of energy: Energy can neither be created nor destroyed, but it can be changed from one form to another. Body tissue therefore is neither lost nor gained when the intake of food energy equals the actual body need for energy. If, however, the intake exceeds the body's need for energy, the extra energy intake may be stored as fat in the tissues. But when the caloric intake is below the body's energy requirement, the body has to use fats stored in the tissues for fuel.

Control of weight has been compared to a bank balance. If more money is deposited in the bank than is needed for expenditures, money accumulates. Deficits occur when more money is spent than deposited.

Changes in body weight from day to day should not be interpreted at face value, for there may be a gain in weight due to retention of water even when the body is losing fat. Weights obtained at the same time of day at weekly intervals constitute a more reliable measure of the extent and direction of actual change in the body weight.

The terms commonly used to describe a deviation from the desirable weight are overweight, obesity, and underweight.

Overweight means an excess of 10 to 20 percent in body weight.

When the excess weight represents more than 20 percent of the desirable weight, we refer to the condition as obesity.

If the actual weight of an individual is 20 percent or more below the desirable weight, the person may be considered to be underweight.

Overweight occurs when a person day after day takes in more energy than his body needs.

The pounds of excess body weight he accumulates are related directly to the amount of extra food he eats. For example, you may gain 11 pounds of body fat in a year if you drink only one bottle of soft drink (which contains about 105 Calories) each day beyond the energy your body needs.

All age groups—not only adults—have overweight persons.

Dr. Ercel S. Eppright, at Iowa State College, studied about 1,200 Iowa schoolchildren. Almost 11 percent of the boys and 17 percent of the girls were very heavy or obese.

Among 325 college freshmen examined at the Cooper Union for the Advancement of Science and Art, Dr. Charlotte M. Young, of Cornell University, found that about 23 percent of the men and almost 36 percent of the women were overweight.

Overweight and obesity are symptoms of overeating.

Dr. Jean Mayer, of the Harvard School of Public Health, suggested that the primary causes of obesity may be classified as genetic, traumatic, and environmental.

In the first one, the cause of overeating is related to the influence of heredity.

The traumatic factor relates the cause to an injury to some part of the body's metabolic processes.

The third factor relates the cause of overeating to environmental conditions—that is, the influences of the availability of food.

It is hard to classify the cause of overeating that results from emotional disturbances into one of these three general primary causes. Since this cause may be due to any one of the three factors, it could be included in any category. Some productive studies of the primary causes of overweight and obesity have been made, but more research is needed before we can establish fully the definite causes and different types of obesity.

The place of genetic factors in the causes of obesity has been observed in studies with animals.

Yellow obesity, a condition that may occur in litters of mice, has been directly related to heredity. The affected animals have a yellow coat of hair and are obese as compared with their littermates, who are normal in size and have nonyellow hair. The dominant gene that causes the disorder carries both the characteristic for yellow hair and the characteristic for obesity.

The results from these studies with animals cannot be translated directly to man, but there is less tendency now to disregard heredity completely as a factor tending toward a greater food intake than is required for good health.

Obesities caused by a traumatic factor have been observed in mice by Dr. Jean Mayer and his coworkers at Harvard University. The thin littermates of genetically obese mice were subjected to two types of lesions, which interfered with the normal metabolic processes of the animals.

In one study, obesity was produced by injections of a chemical substance (LD$_{50}$—lethal dose required to kill 50 percent of animals—of goldthioglucose).

In another study, a lesion to the interbrain (the hypothalamus) led to obesity. The goldthioglucose-obese animals, which showed normal patterns of physical activity, ate 50 to 75 percent more food than normal. The hypothalamic-obese animals showed a lower amount of physical activity, although their intake of food was 50 to 100 percent above normal.

Again, these observations cannot be translated directly to man in order to explain types or causes of human obesity, but the data are significant in that they show that obesity can be induced in the animal organism when some phase of the metabolic processes is interfered with.

Overeating caused by environmental factors is apparently the commonest cause of overweight and obesity. The more important environmental factors that may be responsible for overeating are availability of food, nature of the diet, and too little physical activity.

A relationship seems to exist between the incidence of overweight and obesity and the availability of food within a population group. In India, where the food supply is short, for example, overweight and obesity are not a problem as they are in the United States. Advances in the processing, marketing, and storage of food have increased the availability of more kinds of food to our people. We must consider also the ability of most families to purchase enough food or more food than they actually need.

The nature of the diet as a contributing cause of overweight and obesity may have been overrated in the past, but it is still a factor that we cannot disregard. Poor food habits and attitudes about food undoubtedly are responsible for many instances of overeating. The intake of large quantities of high-energy foods—for example, sweets, with no regard to other dietary essentials—will lead to overweight.

The place of food in our social life is another factor. The custom of serving food at parties and giving gifts of food often invites overeating.

A main environmental factor that gives rise to overweight and obesity is the lack of enough physical activity to balance the food intake. The average rates of physical activity are less than they were 50 years ago. Few occupations today require heavy work because of the development of laborsaving machines and devices. Working hours are shorter. More people are in occupations that we can consider sedentary. Time and distance and maybe laziness mean that few of us now walk to work and school. More leisure time and more dollars to spend for food tend to create an imbalance between intake and outgo of energy.

Psychological or emotional disturbances sometimes are a direct cause of obesity. In this type of obesity, the value of food and the obese condition acquire exaggerated values for the person, who may use eating as a substitute for love and security or his obesity as a kind of security.

The most obvious effect of overweight and obesity is the accumulation of surplus body fat. That in itself presents both economic and esthetic problems to man. The extra pounds add a great physical burden to the body's work—25 pounds of excess weight is like a 25-pound bag of flour tied to the back of a person and carried during all his activities.

The onset of certain human degenerative diseases has been attributed to obesity, although in studies Ancel Keys made of men in Minnesota it was reported, "There is no tendency for coronary disease to single out overweight men." (*Weight Changes and Health of Men*, Iowa State College Press, 1955.) Other studies also have indicated that overweight is not related to coronary heart disease.

Statistics from life-insurance companies, however, have indicated that the overweight policyholders are predisposed to diabetes, cirrhosis of the liver, appendicitis, chronic nephritis, cerebral hemorrhage, gallbladder disease, and heart disease.

Excess weight throws out of balance the body's entire system of energy exchanges. For that reason alone it is a hazard.

THE ONLY KNOWN CURE for overweight or obesity is to eat food that furnishes less energy than one needs for body maintenance. Then body fat will be oxidized as a supplemental contribution to the total energy requirement.

A successful reducing program, however, is not a simple matter. At least five factors must be considered if one is to lose weight successfully.

First, one should consult a medical doctor to determine whether or not weight reduction is desirable from a health standpoint.

Second, one must want to lose weight.

Third, the amount of weight to be lost and the rate of loss should be decided upon and approved by a medical doctor or a nutritionist.

Fourth, the diet used for weight reduction should be nutritionally adequate in protein, minerals, and vitamins as well as low in Calories.

Fifth, after weight is reduced, the new weight should be maintained by controlling the intake of Calories and having enough physical activity regularly.

No person should begin a reducing diet without first consulting a medical doctor to be certain that the physiological stresses encountered in losing weight will not injure the health. The doctor also can do much to encourage and manage his patient's campaign to gain better health.

How to convince overweight or obese people that they should lose weight often is a job in itself.

Dr. Young learned that grouping overweight people into three general types has been helpful.

The first type of patient, who has no apparent emotional problems, usually overeats because he does not understand the relationship between caloric intake and caloric need. Giving him the information he needs about food and nutrition may be enough to make him want to lose weight.

A second type includes people who have minor emotional problems. They may or may not want to lose weight. They need to learn ways to relieve their anxieties before instruction about nutrition can be effective.

Patients who have deep emotional problems are included in the third group. Psychiatric help may be necessary before attempts at motivation can even begin. Some medical and nutritional specialists believe, however, that in this type of patient overeating itself is a better adjustment to life than are other manifestations of their emotional disturbances.

THE SURPLUS POUNDS will determine how much will have to be lost. This is an individual matter, and the family physician will be helpful in determining the goal.

The weekly rate of loss will depend on the caloric limitations of the diet. Some authorities recommend that nobody should lose more than 2 pounds in a week.

Since it takes a deficit of 3,500 Calories to lose 1 pound of body fat, a daily reduction of 500 Calories in the actual energy intake will result in the loss of 1 pound of body weight each week—500 (Calories) times 7 (days) equals 3,500 Calories. Because it is easy to overestimate the caloric need and underestimate the caloric intake, the actual loss of body weight may vary from this calculation.

"The merry-go-round of reducing diets" describes the many plans for weight reduction that have been published in recent years. They have been both sound and unsound in respect to nutritional content. The structure of many has been satisfactory nutritionally, but many persons have found some of them unsatisfactory for reducing because of the excessive hunger or fatigue experienced while subsisting on them or because of the unfamiliar foods they call for.

The best diet for reducing weight is one that has been scientifically planned and then tested to prove its effectiveness.

A low-energy diet was developed at Michigan State University and tested there and at Cornell University. It is adequate in all dietary essentials except energy, is high in protein (90 grams) and moderate in fat (90 grams), and contains enough carbohydrate to supply 1,500 Calories each day. Actually, more than one-half of the energy in the diet comes from fat, which tends to reduce the feeling of hunger. After 16 weeks on this diet, 7 of the subjects at Michigan State University lost 19 to 37 pounds. At Cornell, where the diet was fed at the 1,400-Calorie level and contained only 80 grams of fat, 10 subjects lost between 9 and 23.5 pounds each in 8 to 9 weeks. Weight was lost without flabbiness of tissue or looseness of skin and without a feeling of hunger between meals.

Here is an example of a day's menu from a weight-reduction diet that provides almost 1,500 Calories, with about 40 percent coming from fat, 35 percent from carbohydrate, and 25 percent from protein:

Breakfast consists of one-half cup of orange juice; 1 cooked egg; 1 slice of bread; 1 teaspoon of butter; and 1 cup of skim milk.

The noon meal includes a 4-ounce broiled beef pattie; two-thirds cup of green beans, with 1 teaspoon of butter; 1 medium apple; and 1 cup of skim milk.

Dinner includes a 4-ounce serving of broiled halibut; two-thirds cup of cooked carrots, with 1 teaspoon of butter; one-half slice of bread, with 1 teaspoon of butter; 2 medium peach halves, with 2 tablespoons of sirup; and 1 cup of skim milk.

Coffee and tea may be used in this diet, but alcoholic and sweetened beverages are avoided because they contribute Calories to the food intake.

Other meats, fruit, and vegetables may be substituted in this pattern to give variety and to fit individual food likes and dislikes.

A 4-ounce serving of any lean meat, fish, or poultry can be used in this diet plan, but the fatty kinds should be avoided. Cheese may replace part of the meat. A medium slice or a 1-inch cube of cheese or 2 tablespoons of cottage cheese constitute a 1-ounce serving.

In this diet, the fruit juice at breakfast contributes about 50 Calories. The fruit at lunch and dinner contains approximately 100 Calories.

Other portions of commonly eaten fruits that supply about 100 Calories are: Apricots (canned, 4 medium halves plus 2 tablespoons sirup); banana (1 medium); cantaloup (1 melon); grapefruit (one-half); grapes (1 cup); grape juice (one-half cup); orange (1 large); peach (raw, 2 medium); pear (raw, 1 medium); raspberries (1 cup); and fresh strawberries (2 cups).

Vegetables differ in their caloric values. In the diet we gave, the portion of green beans served at lunch supplies fewer than 25 Calories. The carrots served at dinner contribute 25 to 50 Calories.

Other vegetables that supply fewer than 25 Calories per two-thirds cup are asparagus, cabbage, cauliflower, celery, cucumber, endive, escarole, kale, lettuce, mustard greens, parsley, pepper, radishes, sauerkraut, spinach, summer squash, and tomatoes.

A two-thirds cup of beets, broccoli, brussels sprouts, or rutabaga supplies between 25 and 50 Calories. That amount of corn, green peas, onions, lima beans, parsnips, sweetpotatoes, white potatoes, or winter squash contains more than 50 Calories.

One should avoid certain foods in any weight-reduction program— candy, jelly, jams, and other sweets; rich desserts (cake, pie, ice cream, and pudding); salad dressings (mayonnaise and french dressing); nuts; and rich gravies and dessert sauces.

We suggest several points you can use for judging the acceptability of a reducing diet.

First, the energy content of the diet must be below the caloric need, otherwise you will not lose weight. You must take care, however, that your intake of nutrients other than energy remains adequate. A 1,200- to 1,600-Calorie diet, with slower loss of weight, therefore will be a better diet than a 1,000-Calorie diet, which very likely lacks one or more food essentials.

Beware of the reducing plan that advocates eating all the Calories you want—such a program simply does not make sense.

Second, the plan of the diet should include familiar foods that you can easily get. Because weight reduction may be a long-range project, a dietary plan that specifies seasonal or costly food items may not be feasible.

Third, the diet should be composed of a variety of foods, which with some additions can serve as the dietary pattern after weight loss has been achieved. Some reducing diets highlight the intake of one particular food at each meal—for example, cereal, or eggs, or fruit. Such a diet soon becomes monotonous and cannot be used for long periods.

Fourth, the diet should contain a mixture of foods that satisfy you in order to check and train the appetite.

Dr. Margaret A. Ohlson and her coworkers at Michigan State University said:

"The most frequent patient reaction to the classical reduction diets providing a gram or less of protein per kilogram weight, almost no fat, and 1,000 to 1,200 Calories is that such mixtures result in an almost constant desire for food." (*Control Through Nutritionally Adequate Diets;* M. A. Ohlson, W. D. Brewer, D. Kereluk, A. Wagoner, and D. C. Cederquist; Iowa State College Press, 1955.)

A sound reducing diet therefore will contain enough fat to curb the appetite even though equal portions of either carbohydrate or protein contain less than one-half as many Calories.

Fifth, the diet should provide for three meals a day. Some people try to diet by skipping meals—particularly breakfast. We now know from research studies that a person's efficiency is reduced in the late morning hours when breakfast is omitted.

Sixth, tablets or pills that depress the appetite should be followed in a reducing program only under the prescription and continuous supervision of a medical doctor.

AFTER WEIGHT has been reduced to the right point, the next step is to maintain it at a constant level. This can be managed only by a controlled intake of Calories and enough physical activity. That may require supplemental exercise.

A person's best energy intake for the maintenance of desirable body weight after weight reduction can be estimated in the following way. Extra portions of food should be gradually added to the low-calorie diet used for weight loss until little or no fluctuation occurs in the body weight in a week's time. If weight gain should occur, however, it is suggested that the extra food portions be reduced until the weight is stabilized.

Exercise must be considered in the maintenance of body weight even though it cannot take the place of diet in weight control.

It is unrealistic to suggest that a man who is 10 pounds overweight can lose weight by exercise alone, because it would take work equal to about 35,000 Calories to remove this excess tissue. For example, if 1 hour of heavy work required 200 extra Calories of energy, it would take this man, working 8 hours a day, almost 22 days to use up the 10 pounds of body fat. On the other hand, it would have been possible for him to have prevented the accumulation of 10 pounds of weight by a small amount of exercise each day. For example, 30 minutes of heavy work each day will correspond to about 10 pounds a year.

UNDERWEIGHT occurs in an individual as a result of a food energy intake that is below the actual body need for energy. For example, an energy deficit of as few as 100 Calories each day, which is the amount of energy contained in about 1.5 slices of white bread or 2 pats of butter, will account for the loss of about 10 pounds of body fat in a year.

A survey of 223 farm, nonfarm, and village families in Groton Township, N.Y., revealed that 17 percent of the group examined (837 individuals) were underweight. Underweight was most prevalent among adults 20 to 39 years old.

A study of 39 families of miners in West Virginia disclosed that more of the men and children among them were underweight than overweight, even though more than one-half of the women were overweight and about one-fourth of them were underweight.

A survey of about 2,600 individuals from diverse population groups in the Northeastern States indicated that approximately one-fifth of them were underweight by 10 percent or more.

The problem of underweight has not received the same attention as has the problem of overweight, but underweight should be regarded as one of our nutritional problems.

Underweight sometimes is the result of certain diseases or glandular disturbances, but in healthy persons it is apparently caused by poor food and living habits.

Some persons who are underweight just do not eat enough food to meet the energy demands of the body. Others skip meals because they do not take the time to eat properly. Still others have not learned to use foods that contribute nutrients necessary for general good health.

Too little rest, the inability to relax, and tensions of modern living are factors that may give rise to poor food habits.

The underweight person may be

more susceptible to infection or to digestive disturbances, may lack ambition or the ability to concentrate, or may tire more easily than a person of desirable weight.

Underweight may be overcome by the intake of more food than is necessary for the body's energy expenditures. In such a case, the excess energy will be stored in the form of body tissue.

Although the prescription to eat more food than is actually needed may seem an easy thing to do, the management of a weight-gaining program may be just as difficult as one for weight reduction.

At least four factors must be considered for a successful program of weight gain.

An underweight person should undergo a complete examination by a medical doctor in order to discover any physical defects that may contribute to suboptimal body weight. The family physician may act as the principal figure in the encouragement and management of his patient's weight gain.

A person may have to correct his food and living habits before he can gain weight.

A nutritionally adequate diet with extra food energy must be eaten.

After the proper weight has been reached, the new body weight should be maintained at a constant level.

An underweight person may need to establish new eating and living habits before he can gain weight. For example, the person who does not drink milk because he prefers coffee will need to learn to use milk in addition to his coffee because of its excellent nutritional contribution. The person who skips breakfast because he is too tired to eat so early in the morning will need to acquire more rest at night in order to feel like eating this important meal.

The diet used for gaining weight must contain energy in excess of the body's need; extra amounts of protein, minerals, and vitamins may also be required. Since a pound of body fat represents 3,500 stored Calories, a daily 500-Calorie intake above the actual energy need of a person will result in the gain of 1 pound of body fat each week.

It is easy to say that extra energy can be obtained by eating concentrated food sources of carbohydrates and fats—rich desserts and butter. Actually, however, such a directive may only lead to a feeling of extreme fullness, and an inadequate food intake may still prevail.

The most desirable weight-gaining diet is one that advocates three adequate meals each day plus snacks between meals.

The following example is a day's menu for a weight-gaining diet that provides about 3,500 Calories.

Breakfast comprises 1 cup of orange juice, 1 cooked egg, 2 slices of cooked bacon, 2 slices of bread with 2 teaspoons of butter and 1 tablespoon of jam, and 1 cup of whole milk. A banana in midmorning adds extra Calories.

Lunch consists of a 4-ounce broiled beef pattie; a medium-size baked potato, with 1 teaspoon of butter; one-half cup of green beans, with 1 teaspoon of butter; 1 slice of bread, with 1 teaspoon of butter and 1 tablespoon of jam; 2 medium peach halves, with 2 tablespoons of sirup; and 1 cup of whole milk. A one-half cup of ice cream is suggested for the afternoon snack.

Dinner consists of a 4-ounce ham steak; 1 small candied sweetpotato; one-half cup of cooked carrots, with 1 teaspoon of butter; 1 slice of bread, with 1 teaspoon of butter and 1 tablespoon of jam; 1 cup of vanilla pudding; and 1 cup of whole milk. A bedtime snack of 1 cup of whole milk and 2 graham crackers will add more energy.

Coffee or tea and other meat, fruit, vegetables, and miscellaneous foods may be substituted in the weight-gaining diet to give variety to the food intake and to coincide with the person's food likes.

After the desirable weight gain has been achieved, the new weight should be maintained at a constant level. The formula for this procedure is just the reverse of that prescribed in a weight-reduction program. Here, some of the extra food portions, such as the in-between-meal snacks, should be eliminated gradually until little or no fluctuation of body weight occurs within a week. Extra food portions should be added back to the diet if and when weight loss does occur.

KATHERINE H. FISHER *is associate professor, Department of Foods and Nutrition, The Pennsylvania State University, and coauthor of a textbook, "Principles of Nutrition."*

RAYMOND W. SWIFT *is head, Department of Animal Nutrition, The Pennsylvania State University.*

100-CALORIE PORTIONS OF SOME COMMONLY USED FOODS

Cereals and Breads	
biscuit or plain muffin	3/4 medium
bread, white, enriched	1 1/2 slices
corn flakes	1 cup
crackers, saltines	6 crackers
oatmeal, cooked	2/3 cup
rice, white, cooked	1/2 cup
roll, plain	5/6 medium
wheat, puffed	2 1/3 cups
Dairy Products	
butter	1 tbsp.
buttermilk	1 1/6 cups
cheese, Cheddar	7/8 oz.
cheese, cottage	3 2/3 oz.
cream, heavy	2 tbsp.
ice cream, plain	1/3 cup
milk, whole	4 4/5 oz.
milk, nonfat solids	3 1/2 tbsp.
Vegetables	
beans, lima, canned	2/3 cup
beans, soup, green, canned	2 2/3 cups
broccoli, cooked	2 1/4 cups
cabbage, shredded, raw	4 1/6 cups
carrots, raw	4 3/4 medium
cauliflower, cooked	3 1/3 cups
celery, diced, raw	5 1/2 cups
corn, canned	3/4 cup
lettuce	1 1/2 lb. head
onion, cooked	1 1/4
peas, green, canned	2/3 cup
pepper, green, raw	5 7/8 medium
potato, white, baked	1 medium
potato, white, mashed	2/3 cup
sweetpotato, baked	1/2 medium
spinach, cooked	2 1/6 cups
tomatoes, canned	2 1/6 cups
Fats and Oils	
french dressing	1 2/3 tbsp.
mayonnaise	1 tbsp.
salad oil	4/5 tbsp.
Fruit	
apple, raw	1 1/3 medium
apricot, canned	1/2 cup
banana	1 1/8 medium
grapefruit juice, canned	1 1/10 cups
orange juice, fresh	9/10 cup
peaches or pears, canned	3/5 cup
pineapple, canned, crushed	1/2 cup
strawberries, raw	1 5/6 cups
Meat, Fish, Poultry, and Nuts	
bacon, cooked	2 slices
beef, cooked	1 oz.
chicken, breast, cooked	3 4/5 oz.
egg, whole	1 1/4
frankfurter	4/5
haddock, cooked	2/3 fillet
ham, cooked	9/10 oz.
liver, beef, cooked	1 3/4 oz.
luncheon meat	1 1/5 oz.
peanut butter	1 1/10 tbsp.
pork, cooked	1 1/10 oz.
tuna fish, canned	1 4/5 oz.
Sugars and Sweets	
carbonated beverages	8 oz.
candy bar, chocolate	2/3 oz.
cake, plain, iced	5/8 medium
cookies, plain	9/10 medium
jellies	2 tbsp.
pie, apple	1/21 medium
sirup, corn	1 3/4 tbsp.
sugar, white	6 1/4 tbsp.

Calcium and Phosphorus

MILICENT L. HATHAWAY AND RUTH M. LEVERTON

CALCIUM, the most abundant mineral in the body, comprises 1.5 to 2.0 percent of the weight of an adult's body. It usually is associated with phosphorus, which is 0.8 to 1.1 percent of the body weight. A person who weighs 154 pounds would have 2.3 to 3.1 pounds of calcium and 1.2 to 1.7 pounds of phosphorus in his body.

About 99 percent of the calcium and 80 to 90 percent of the phosphorus are in the bones and the teeth. The rest is in the soft tissues and body fluids and is highly important to their normal functioning.

Calcium is essential for the clotting of blood, the action of certain enzymes, and the control of the passage of fluids through the cell walls. The right proportion of calcium in the blood is responsible for the alternate contraction and relaxation of the heart muscle.

The irritability of the nerves is increased when the amount of calcium in the blood is below normal.

Calcium in a complex combination with phosphorus gives rigidity and hardness to the bones and teeth.

Phosphorus is an essential part of every living cell. It takes part in the chemical reactions with proteins, fats, and carbohydrates to give the body energy and vital materials for growth and repair. It helps the blood neutralize acid and alkali.

Both calcium and phosphorus are essential for the work of the muscles and for the normal response of nerves to stimulation.

The human embryo at 12 weeks contains about 0.2 gram of calcium and 0.1 gram of phosphorus. (There are 28.4 grams in an ounce.) The values are 5.5 and 3.4 grams, respectively, for these two minerals by the 28th week, and 11 and 7 grams by the 34th week. The most rapid increase in the calcium and phosphorus content of the unborn child occurs from the 34th week to the 40th week.

One-half of the total calcium and more than one-third of the total phosphorus in the baby's body at birth are deposited during the last 6 weeks. The baby's body contains about 23 grams of calcium and 13 grams of phosphorus at birth.

The calcium content of the body increases faster in relation to size during the first year of life than at any other time. About 60 grams of calcium are added. A child is depositing only about 20 grams a year when

112

he is 4 or 5 years old and weighs about 40 pounds. He may be depositing as much as 90 grams a year when he is 13 to 14 years old and weighs 110 pounds. He will deposit more if he weighs more.

All these gains in calcium content depend on an adequate supply of calcium in the diet and the ability of the body to use it for normal growth.

The percentage as well as the total amount of calcium and phosphorus increases during growth. The infant's body is about 0.8 percent calcium and the adult's is about twice as much—1.5 to 2 percent. The phosphorus content of the body increases from 0.4 percent at birth to 0.8 to 1.1 percent in adulthood.

Bone is composed of tiny, complex crystals of calcium and phosphorus, which are set in honeycomb fashion around a framework of softer protein material, called the organic matrix.

The crystals contain about twice as much calcium as phosphorus. They also contain oxygen and small amounts of hydrogen and other minerals.

The honeycomb structure gives strength and an enormous surface area to a small amount of bone material— as much as 3,100 square yards to 1 ounce. Connecting canals containing blood and lymph vessels, nerves, and bone marrow pass throughout the matrix and bone crystals. Intercellular fluid surrounds the crystals and keeps them supplied with the materials for repair.

Crystals of the same kind are deposited to make the enamel and dentin of the teeth. The crystals are larger, however, than those in bone. That may be the reason why enamel and dentin are harder than bone.

Phosphorus and calcium are of equal importance in the bones. Phosphorus is involved in ossification or calcification just as much as calcium. When bone is formed, phosphorus is deposited with the calcium. When the bone loses calcium (by decalcification), it also loses phosphorus. They are closely associated in blood and foods.

Phosphorus is included, therefore, even though it is not named each time that calcium is mentioned.

The major change during growth is in the size and the compactness of the bone material. The shape of the bones in a young child is much the same as it will be when he is an adult. The bones in an infant are like firm cartilage and have a low content of calcium and phosphorus. They become firmer as these minerals are deposited in and around the cartilage. This process of bone building is called ossification or calcification. The bones and teeth are said to ossify or to calcify.

Certain bones in the wrist and ankle and the permanent teeth do not begin to calcify until after birth. Groups of specialized cells that are present at birth have the ability to deposit calcium and phosphorus around them and thus become bones and teeth. They are called ossification centers and tooth buds.

Eight small bones in the wrist are mere ossification centers at birth. Two of them usually are calcified in the 1st year, one in the 3d year, two in the 5th year, one each in the 6th and 8th years, and the last one in the 12th year. The exact time of ossification varies among children. Girls often are a little ahead of boys in this process.

The tooth buds of the first teeth begin to form in the human embryo at about 4 to 6 weeks and begin to calcify at about 20 weeks. The upper and lower first molars of the permanent teeth begin to calcify very soon after birth. Others begin at 3 months to 3 years. The wisdom teeth may not begin to calcify until sometime between the 8th and 10th year.

Bones and teeth calcify more slowly in children who have diets deficient in calcium and phosphorus and other essential nutrients. Severe deficiencies can cause permanent stunting of size or malformations of bones and teeth.

Changes occur on both the inside and outside of a bone as it grows larger. New bone is deposited around the outside of the shaft of a long bone. Bone on the inside of the shaft is absorbed at the same time and used elsewhere. Thus the cavity that contains the bone marrow is widened. Bone is added also to the outside of each end of the shaft and then taken from the outside of the area just beneath it.

Adding material to the outside of bone and subtracting it from the inside gives the skeleton size and strength without unnecessary weight. If bones grew only by adding material to the outside and none were subtracted from the inside, the skeleton would weigh so much that the muscles could not move it around.

The intricate process of bone building requires many nutrients besides calcium and phosphorus. Vitamin D is essential for absorption from the intestinal tract and the orderly deposition of the bone material. Protein is needed for the framework and for part of every cell and circulating fluid. Vitamin A aids in the deposition of the minerals. Vitamin C is required for the cementing material between the cells and the firmness of the walls of the blood vessels.

Bones can accumulate a reserve supply of calcium and phosphorus at any age if the diet provides enough for the growth and repair and some is left over for storage.

When the intake is generous, the minerals are stored inside the ends of the bones in long, needlelike crystals, called trabeculae. This reserve can be used in times of stress to meet the body's increased calcium needs if the food does not supply enough.

When there is no reserve to use, the calcium has to be taken from the bone structure itself—usually first from the spine and pelvic bones. The dentin and enamel of the teeth do not give up their calcium when the body must provide what the diet lacks.

If the calcium that is withdrawn in times of increased need is not replaced, the bone becomes deficient in calcium and subnormal in composition. From 10 to 40 percent of the normal amount of calcium may be withdrawn from

mature bone before the deficiency will show on an X-ray film. Height may be reduced as much as 2 inches because of fractures of the vertebrae, which are caused by pressure and result in rounding of the back. Such fractures may occur with relatively minor jolts or twists of the body and may not be recognized at the time they happen.

Bones with a low content of calcium are weaker and break more easily than bones well stocked with calcium. Breaks in older persons often are related directly to the thinness and brittleness of the bones and are difficult to treat. The bones may be too weak to hold pins or other means of internal repair, and healing may be slow because of the low activity of bone-forming cells.

The calcium and phosphorus and other minerals in our food are dissolved as the food is digested. Then they are absorbed from the gastrointestinal tract into the blood stream. The blood carries them to the different parts of the body where they are used for growth and upkeep.

Calcium as it is present in food dissolves best in an acid solution. It begins to dissolve in the gastric juice of the stomach. The calcium is absorbed when the contents of the stomach move into the small intestine. Farther along in the intestine, the contents change from an acid to alkaline reaction, which does not favor the absorption of calcium.

Usually 10 to 50 percent of the calcium eaten is not absorbed but is excreted in the feces. A small portion of the excreted calcium comes from the intestinal fluids.

The calcium that is absorbed travels in the blood to places where it is needed, particularly the bones. If any of the absorbed calcium is not needed, it is excreted by the kidneys into the urine. Normal functioning of the kidneys is essential for the normal metabolism of calcium and other minerals.

Vitamin D is essential for the absorption of calcium from the gastrointestinal tract. Vitamin D does not occur naturally in many foods. Egg yolk, butter, fortified margarine, and certain fish oils are the chief sources. To a few foods, notably milk and cereals, some vitamin D is added.

A special substance, cholesterol, is present in the skin and is changed to vitamin D by the ultraviolet rays of the sun. We cannot be sure that enough of the rays reach the skin and produce vitamin D in all seasons of the year and in all parts of the country to insure normal growth. Most infants and young children therefore are given daily a concentrated source of vitamin D, such as cod-liver oil or some other fish oil. Adults normally do not need more vitamin D than they customarily get from food and exposure of the skin to the effective rays of sunshine.

Adults who stay out of the sun entirely or wear clothing that covers all of the body except the face probably do not get enough vitamin D naturally and therefore need to have some added to their diet.

Too much vitamin D can be dangerous. It overloads the blood and tissues with calcium. Infants who are given several times the amount of vitamin D that they actually need may suffer gastrointestinal upsets and retarded growth. This condition is called hypercalcemia—meaning too much calcium in the blood. It can be cured, if it is recognized soon enough, by omitting the vitamin D from the diet.

A hormone secreted by the parathyroid glands has an important part in the body's use of calcium and an indirect part in the use of phosphorus. There are two of these tiny glands on each side of the neck near or in the thyroid gland.

The parathyroid hormone keeps the amount of calcium in the blood at a normal level of about 10 milligrams per 100 milliliters of blood serum. (Serum is the watery part of the blood that separates from a clot.)

Any wide deviation from this amount is dangerous to health and life. The hormone can shift calcium and phosphorus from the bone into the blood. If the blood levels are too high, it can increase the excretion of these minerals by the kidneys. If anything reduces the secretion of the parathyroid hormone, the calcium in the blood drops quickly, the phosphorus rises, and severe muscular twitchings result.

The amount of calcium absorbed into the body is affected by the body's need for it, the amount supplied by the diet, the kind of food that supplies it, and the speed with which the food passes through the gastrointestinal tract.

The body will absorb more calcium when it is needed for growth and for storage during pregnancy and lactation or after periods of loss than it will when such needs do not exist.

The body is likely to absorb a larger proportion of calcium from a low intake than from a generous intake. The body tries in this way to make full use of a small supply, especially when its needs are great. In terms of total amount, however, more calcium is absorbed from a generous intake than from a low one.

Lactose, the form of sugar present in milk, is especially good in promoting the absorption of calcium. Certain proteins and amino acids also are effective. Perhaps the combination of these is responsible for the excellent absorption of calcium from milk.

The absorption of calcium from vegetables is somewhat lower. The high content of fiber, especially in the coarse, leafy, green vegetables, makes them move through the intestine rapidly, and the amount of calcium absorbed is reduced.

Spinach, beet greens, chard, and rhubarb contain a chemical, oxalic acid, which combines with the calcium to make calcium oxalate. Because it is insoluble in the intestinal fluids, the calcium cannot be absorbed but is excreted in the feces.

The outer husks of cereal seeds, such as wheat, contain phytic acid, a substance that combines with phosphorus to form phytates. The phytates can interfere with the absorption of calcium, especially in a child when a high intake of phytic acid is accompanied by an inadequate supply of calcium and vitamin D. Phytates are not likely to hinder the absorption of calcium in the diets commonly used in the United States.

Laxatives also are likely to lower the absorption of calcium.

The requirements for calcium have been determined by balance studies, in much the same way as the requirements for protein were learned. Studies with children have determined the amount of calcium that will result in the maximum storage for growth. Studies with adults have determined the amount needed for repair and maintenance of the mature body.

The allowances of calcium recommended by the Food and Nutrition Board of the National Academy of Sciences-National Research Council in 1958 are 0.8 gram daily for adults, 1.5 grams during the second half of pregnancy, and 2 grams when a mother is nursing her baby.

Daily allowances for children are 1 gram of calcium for all children 1 to 9 years old and 1.2 grams for children 10 to 12 years old. Boys 13 to 19 years old need 1.4 grams. Girls 13 to 19 years old need 1.3 grams daily.

How to supply these amounts in the day-to-day selection of food is told in chapters devoted to the nutrition of persons in different age groups.

Adults should have the same amount of phosphorus as they have of calcium. Children should have about one and one-half times as much phosphorus as calcium.

The needs of normal persons for phosphorus are supplied by the same foods that supply their needs for calcium and protein.

Diets that provide enough protein and calcium very likely furnish enough phosphorus as well.

The calcium content of different foods is shown in the table that begins on page 243.

Milk is the best source. It is almost impossible to supply the amounts of calcium that are recommended unless milk in some form is used daily and cheese and other milk-containing products are eaten frequently.

Sometimes a pure chemical form of calcium is prescribed when for some reason enough milk is not available or cannot be used. Calcium in this form is available to the body, but it cannot supply the many other essential nutrients that are present in the foods that supply calcium.

The body benefits in many ways from having a good reserve of calcium and accompanying minerals and a generous daily supply of calcium from food to maintain that reserve.

The difference between a minimum and a generous intake of calcium can be measured in terms of the body's nutritional status. A body well-nourished with calcium and other nutrients can be expected to have good bone growth and development, a well-functioning nervous system, a high level of vigor and positive health at every age, and a longer period of the prime of life.

In many countries, especially in the Orient, little milk is available, and calcium must come from other sources. Infants are breast fed as long as possible to give them the benefit of the calcium and other nutrients in mother's milk. The bones of small fish and other animals that are eaten are good sources of calcium. Some of the bone minerals are dissolved and made available when bony meats are cooked in water with a little acid, such as vinegar. Grains and vegetables are eaten in large amounts, and the small amount of calcium present in them becomes relatively important. The drinking water in some areas contains a little calcium. Tortillas supply sizable amounts of calcium when they are made with corn that is soaked in lime before it is ground. The people who chew the betel nut mixed with lime get some calcium this way.

These and other sources of calcium seldom add up to even a minimum supply. Deficiency of calcium and stunted growth are among the serious nutritional problems in many countries. Abnormal bone conditions occur when there are disturbances in the body's supply or use of nutrients.

Osteomalacia, often referred to as adult rickets, is caused chiefly by a deficiency of vitamin D and calcium. Because not enough calcium is available for the upkeep of the bones, they gradually weaken. This condition is particularly prevalent among the women in the Orient and other parts of the world who have diets extremely low in calcium, get little sunshine, and yet need more calcium and vitamin D because of frequent pregnancies. It is less prevalent among the peasant women who wear less clothing and work outdoors, even if their calcium intakes are low.

Osteoporosis is a condition in which the formation of bone does not proceed normally because of dietary deficiency or some disorder in metabolism. The organic matrix of the bone may be abnormal, too. The bone actually becomes porous and thin because calcium is being taken from it and is not being replaced. The chief cause probably is an inadequate supply of protein, minerals, and vitamins over a period of years. Poor use of nutrients by the body and an imbalance of hormones also may be causes. Some women have osteoporosis after the menopause, but it is more likely to occur in older people. Extreme inactivity may be a contributing cause.

Another disturbance in calcium metabolism is the milk-alkali syndrome, or group of symptoms. There is excess calcium in the blood, calcium is deposited in the soft tissues, and the kidneys may not function properly. Vomiting, gastrointestinal bleeding, and high blood pressure also may be present. This disturbance occurs chiefly in persons with ulcers who for many years have used an almost exclusively milk diet with large amounts of antacids to neutralize the excess acid of the gastric juice. Recovery depends on changing the diet under medical supervision to rid the body of the excess calcium. No cases have been known to develop on a diet of milk without the antacids.

CALCIUM appears to have an added function in the atomic age. It may reduce the amount of radioactive strontium 90 that may be deposited in the body.

Strontium 90 is a product of atomic explosions and may become a health problem. Its radioactivity is slow to disappear, and its accumulation in the body could be dangerous. Strontium 90 is absorbed into the body from the food and then deposited and retained in the bones. High concentrations of it can cause bone cancers and possibly leukemia, the blood cancer that begins in the bone marrow.

Major atomic explosions (described as megaton size) send the strontium 90 into the upper atmosphere and scatter it widely. When it returns to earth, it is deposited rather thinly on the soil and plant foliage over large areas.

The smaller atomic explosions (described as of kiloton size) do not send the strontium 90 up so far, and it is deposited more thickly on the soil and plants near the site of the explosion.

Strontium 90 was first detected in animal bones, dairy products, and soil in 1953. It now occurs in all human beings regardless of their age or where they live.

Amounts found to date in human beings are small compared with what is thought to be the permissible limit for them—100 micromicrocuries per gram of calcium. A curie is the unit used to measure radioactivity, and a micromicrocurie is one millionth of one millionth of a curie. The amount of radioactivity from strontium 90 in a food or in a tissue or bone usually is expressed on the basis of its calcium content. Plants take up this radioactive strontium along with their necessary calcium. Animals eat the plants, and human beings eat both plants and animal products such as milk, meat, and eggs. The relation of the amount of strontium 90 to the amount of calcium is referred to as the strontium-to-calcium ratio.

Plants show little discrimination between their absorption of calcium and their absorption of strontium 90. The strontium-to-calcium ratio is reduced markedly as these two minerals pass from the fodder to the cow's body and then to the milk she secretes. The ratio in meat is about one-fourth of that in fodder, and in milk the ratio is only about one-tenth of that in the fodder. Because of these differences in the strontium-to-calcium ratios among common foods, milk supplies calcium that is less contaminated with strontium than are other foods.

In the United States, 70 to 75 percent of the calcium in our diet comes from milk and other dairy products, 15 to 20 percent from plant foods, about 5 percent from meat and eggs, and some from water and the compounds containing calcium that are used in commercial food processing.

The strontium-to-calcium ratio that is found in human and animal tissues is related directly to the amounts in the diet. Not all of the strontium and calcium that is present in the food is absorbed into the body, however.

The average diet in the United States in 1957 supplied about 6.5 to 8 micromicrocuries of strontium 90 for each gram of calcium it supplied. Only part of this amount reached the tissues from the gastrointestinal tract. Fortunately the body absorbs strontium 90 less readily than it absorbs calcium, and it excretes the strontium more readily than it does the calcium.

Data available from skeletons of North American children in 1957 and 1958 show that up to 1 year of age there were between 0.46 and 1.84 micromicrocuries of strontium 90 per gram of calcium. Skeletons of children from 1 to 4 years of age contained between 1.23 and 1.53 micromicrocuries per gram of calcium. Above that age, the strontium-to-calcium ratio gradually decreased to adult values. The worldwide average for human adult skeletons in 1957 and 1958 was 0.19 micromicrocurie of strontium 90 per gram of calcium. The average of human skeletons of all ages was 0.52 micromicrocurie per gram of calcium.

Animals in one experiment were fed diets high in calcium, and they deposited less radioactive strontium than those that had diets low in calcium. Rats fed 2 percent of calcium in their ration for 38 days and then given small amounts of radioactive strontium for 7 days retained only about one-fourth as much of the strontium as rats that had rations with 0.5 percent calcium. The same kind of results was obtained with cows.

If people react in the same way, it will be important to have high intakes and body reserves of calcium as built-in protection against radioactivity.

MILICENT L. HATHAWAY *came to the Department of Agriculture in 1946 as nutrition specialist in the Human Nutrition Research Division, Agricultural Research Service. She taught in the University of Illinois and Cornell University. Her primary research has been in studies of the needs of children and adults for minerals and vitamins. She was recipient in 1947 of the Borden Award of the American Home Economics Association for outstanding research in applied nutrition. She has a doctor's degree in biochemistry from the University of Chicago.*

RUTH M. LEVERTON, *Associate Director of the Institute of Home Economics, has studied the metabolism and requirements of calcium and phosphorus of women from 16 to 70 years of age. Her studies in the Philippines showed that the bones of the small fish dilis which are eaten with the fish were an excellent source of calcium and phosphorus.*

It is the alert, the well-educated, the economically favored housewife, who responds promptly to new and attractive food products and to information about foods and feeding. It is the less well-informed, the isolated and remote family which learns slowest and avails itself least of technological advances. The benefits start largely in nonmarginal homes, thence filter down through the strata of society and often fail to reach areas at the lower levels.—R. R. WILLIAMS.

Sodium, Potassium, and Magnesium

RUTH M. LEVERTON

SODIUM, potassium, and magnesium are essential in nutrition. They are among the most plentiful minerals in the body. Calcium and phosphorus are present in the largest amounts, and then come potassium, sulfur, sodium, chlorine, and magnesium in descending order of amounts.

A person who weighs 154 pounds has about 9 ounces of potassium, 4 ounces of sodium, and 1.3 ounces of magnesium in his body.

Sodium and potassium are similar in chemical properties but different in their location within the body. Sodium is chiefly in the fluids that circulate outside the cells, and only a small amount of it is inside the cells. Potassium is mostly inside the cells, and a much smaller amount is in the body fluids.

The interrelation between amounts of these minerals in their different locations permits substances to pass back and forth between the cells and the surrounding fluids. This process of exchange is called osmosis.

Sodium and potassium are vital in keeping a normal balance of water between the cells and the fluids. A decline in the sodium content of the fluids results in a transfer of water from the fluids into the cells. An increase in sodium causes a transfer of water from the cells into the fluids.

Sodium and potassium are essential for nerves to respond to stimulation, for the nerve impulses to travel to the muscles, and for the muscles to contract. All types of muscles, including the heart muscle, are influenced by sodium and potassium.

Sodium and potassium also work with proteins, phosphates, and carbonates to keep a proper balance between the amount of acid and alkali in the blood.

We do not have enough information to establish the exact requirements for these minerals. Dietary deficiencies are uncommon, however. Deficiencies are more likely to result from unusual losses from the body.

The body normally conserves its supply of sodium and potassium when the intake is low by reducing the amount that it excretes in the urine. Excessive sweating can cause a major loss of sodium from the body. Such a loss can be replaced easily by increasing the intake of common table salt—sodium chloride.

Severe diarrhea and vomiting reduce the amount of sodium in the body and upset seriously the relationship between the sodium and potassium in the fluids and the cells. A solution of sodium chloride sometimes has to be given intravenously to correct this imbalance.

The body usually can take care of great variations in the amount of sodium taken in because it excretes promptly what it does not need. This may not be true in some types of heart disease and poor functioning of the kidneys.

The intake of sodium for persons in the United States has been estimated to be 3 to 7 grams per person per day. Salt is the main source of sodium in a person's diet, and taste and habit determine the amount of salt he eats.

Sodium is one of the nutrients that we can eat in too large amounts. An oversupply comes from the excess salt we add to our food rather than from the sodium that is present in our foods as they are grown or produced.

Sodium is present in most of our foods and in some of the materials we use in preparing and processing food. Ordinary table salt is 43 percent sodium and our most concentrated source. A large proportion of our daily intake of sodium comes from the salt we add to our food when we prepare and eat it. Baking soda is about 30 percent sodium. Ordinary baking powders contain about 10 percent.

Foods from animal sources, including meat, fish, poultry, milk, and cheese, contain more sodium than do foods from plant sources. Seafoods are higher in sodium than fish from fresh water.

Most fresh and frozen vegetables contain only small amounts of sodium, unless salt is added when they are prepared for eating. Beets, carrots, celery, chard, kale, beet and dandelion greens, and spinach are exceptions; they contain several times more sodium than other vegetables.

Canned vegetables contain more sodium than fresh or frozen ones because of the salt added during the process of canning.

All fresh, canned, and frozen fruits are low in sodium.

Breakfast cereals are low in sodium if none has been added to the grain during processing. The same is true of rice, macaroni, and spaghetti. The label usually gives this information.

Yeast breads that contain salt and other baked goods that contain salt and baking powder or soda have relatively large amounts of sodium.

Butter and margarine have a high content of sodium unless they are made without salt. The label gives this information. Shortenings and salad oils do not have salt added.

Coffee and tea contain very little sodium unless they are made with water that has a great deal of sodium.

The water supplies in some areas contain appreciable amounts of sodium. Some of the ion-exchange systems for softening water add sodium to it.

Foods contain the most sodium when salt has been added to them directly or by brining or pickling or by curing. A raw potato, for example, contains about 0.001 gram of sodium, but the same weight of potato chips may have as much as 0.340 gram of sodium. Cured ham has about 20 times more sodium than fresh pork.

Large intakes of sodium may aggravate a tendency toward high blood pressure. A moderate rather than a high intake of sodium therefore is one of the many measures advocated to prevent the development of high blood pressure. This means intakes at the lower end of the range of 3 to 7 grams of sodium a day, which is our estimated intake.

One can have a moderate intake of sodium if he does not add extra salt to foods after they are prepared and if he eats salted, pickled, and cured foods sparingly.

A person's intake of sodium can be limited to 1.5 to 2.5 grams daily if no salt is added at any time in preparing the food, and if no salted, pickled, and cured foods are used.

The daily intake of sodium sometimes is restricted to 1 gram or less as part of the treatment of diseases accompanied by high blood pressure or edema, which is the swelling of the tissues caused by retention of water. This can be done only under medical supervision.

Expert care must go into planning diets that are restricted severely in sodium, or they will be inadequate in other essential nutrients, especially high-quality protein and vitamins of the B complex.

ORDINARY DIETS of persons in the United States supply 1.4 to 6.5 grams of potassium per person per day.

The intake of potassium is related to the calorie value of the diet because this mineral is so widely distributed among different kinds of foods. We have no evidence that the healthy person needs to limit or otherwise control his intake of potassium.

MAGNESIUM is closely related to both calcium and phosphorus in its location and its functions in the body. About 70 percent of the magnesium in the body is in the bones. The rest is in the soft tissues and blood. Muscle tissue contains more magnesium than calcium. Blood contains more calcium than magnesium.

Magnesium acts as starter or catalyzer for some of the chemical reactions within the body. It also becomes a part of some of the complex molecules that are formed as the body uses food for growth and for maintenance and repair. It plays an important role as a coenzyme in the building of protein. There is some relation between magnesium and the hormone cortisone as they affect the amount of phosphate in the blood.

Animals on a diet that is deficient in magnesium become extremely nervous and give an exaggerated response to even small noises or disturbances. Such unnatural sensitiveness disappears when they are given enough magnesium. In extreme deficiencies, the blood vessels expand, the heart beats faster, and damage in the midbrain causes such irritability that the animals die in convulsions.

A deficiency of magnesium in human nutrition is not common, but it may occur more frequently than it is diagnosed. It disturbs the calcification of bone. An excess of magnesium causes a deposition of calcium in the soft tissues.

An adult requires about 0.3 gram of magnesium a day. A child needs more magnesium in proportion to his size than an adult does, but we do not know the exact amounts. One estimate is that he requires about 0.006 gram of magnesium daily for each pound of body weight. A child who weighs 40 pounds thus would need 0.24 gram daily.

Magnesium is present in foods from both animal and plant sources—meats, milk, cereals, vegetables, and fruit. They vary greatly in the amount of magnesium they contain. Nuts, legumes, and cereal grains have more magnesium than other foods. Fresh fruits contain less than other foods.

A diet that is adequate in other essential nutrients, especially protein of high quality, is likely to supply enough magnesium.

Scientists know that there is much more to be learned about the actions and purposes of magnesium in the normal functioning of the body. For example, evidence is growing that magnesium may play an important part in the body's use of fats. But we do not have the facts to prove this and other suspected relationships. Research will provide the facts in time, however, and we then can apply them to improve our diet and health.

RUTH M. LEVERTON *is Associate Director of the Institute of Home Economics in the Agricultural Research Service.*

The Trace Elements

KENNETH J. MONTY AND WILLIAM D. McELROY

ALL living things contain a variety of minerals. Some occur in such small amounts that early chemical analyses could barely detect them. They therefore became known as the trace minerals, metals, or elements.

For only a few of them have nutritional requirements or biological functions been demonstrated. It is likely that many of the others occur in living things only by accident, having been acquired in the food or water, or absorbed through the skin, or even inhaled.

At the present stage of our biological knowledge, however, we cannot ignore the possibility that some of the trace elements we now think of as nonessential do have as yet unrecognized functions in the body's processes.

People found out about the need for trace elements when they saw that some deficiency diseases in livestock, and sometimes in human beings, could be treated by large doses of a specific mineral.

An example is iodine, which was used in a somewhat hit-or-miss way to treat goiter as long ago as 1820. A study of the distribution of iodine in soils and water later led to the belief that goiter often is a nutritional disease, especially in places where the natural supply of iodine is low. Scientists in 1895 proved that iodine is a normal component of the thyroid gland and is depleted in cases of endemic goiter. Today we recognize iodine as a component of the hormones produced by the thyroid gland.

Another example is cobalt. Investigators in 1935 discovered that this element prevented certain wasting diseases of sheep and cattle in localities in Australia and New Zealand. Subsequent studies demonstrated that a deficiency of cobalt was responsible for similar diseases in Florida, parts of England and Scotland, and Kenya. As with iodine, the function of cobalt remained obscure for some time after the need for it in animal nutrition was recognized.

Scientists in later years have brought about artificial deficiencies in animals in order to study further their requirements of trace elements. They carefully purify or combine various diets that omit the trace element they are studying in order to see whether it is essential for health. Feeding such unbalanced diets to small laboratory animals demonstrated the essentiality of copper, manganese, and zinc in animal nutrition.

We now know that trace elements required for the growth of animals include copper, iodine, iron, magnesium, manganese, and zinc. Cobalt is essential for the growth of ruminants.

Selenium can prevent certain degenerative conditions of the liver in animals and birds.

Also important to animals are molybdenum and fluorine. Molybdenum is a component of certain enzymes, but a deficiency of molybdenum usually does not depress growth.

One exception has been noted. Researchers at the Missouri Agricultural Experiment Station demonstrated that molybdenum is necessary for micro-organisms of the rumen of sheep to carry out their function of degrading cellulose to a form in which the sheep can utilize it. Molybdenum also may be required for best growth of chicks.

Fluorine has never been reported to influence the growth of animals, but it is beneficial in the diet because it helps prevent dental caries. In a sense, it may be considered as essential to the formation of perfect teeth.

ONE OF THE GREAT PROBLEMS today is to set standards for fixing the need for trace elements or any constituent of diet.

The old attitude was that a constituent is essential if slow growth or none or death results from failure to include it in the diet. It has been apparent for some years that that definition is not good enough.

An example is vitamin E. Too little of it leads to sterility in many mammals but often has no effect upon other physiological processes, such as growth. Yet vitamin E is essential.

Other examples lead us to question whether we can take inadequacy of growth as a sole criterion of essentiality. Deficiencies of fluorine and molybdenum are not necessarily incompatible with the continuation of life or the maintenance of normal growth, although both have beneficial biological functions.

It seems wise, then, to introduce into nutrition the concept of functional nutrients. A diet must supply a proper balance of essential nutrients and functional nutrients to insure overall physiological perfection.

THE ESTABLISHMENT of minimal dietary requirements for the trace elements is a difficult problem, for many factors may affect their absorption and utilization. Besides the effects trace elements may have on each other is the fact that other nutrients may modify the degree of absorption, utilization, and excretion of the trace elements, usually by entering into chemical complexes (chelates) with the trace elements and thereby modifying their solubility properties.

We must consider also the degree of physical activity and various other minor physiological stress conditions. Scientists therefore have been unable to assign exact requirements, even to small laboratory animals. Because human beings consume large amounts of food, it is technically difficult and expensive to prepare suitable test and experimental diets.

Human requirements for trace elements have been estimated from studies of normal intake and excretion. The recommended daily requirements we list here probably greatly exceed the minimum daily requirements, but they certainly are adequate to supply the body's needs under normal circumstances.

Data from several sources indicate the following daily allowances:

Copper, 2 milligrams;

Iodine, 0.1 to 0.2 milligram;

Iron, 1 milligram per kilogram of body weight for infants and children (up to about 9 years), 10–12 milligrams for adults, 15–20 milligrams for pregnant women;

Manganese, 0.3 milligram per kilogram of body weight;

Zinc, 0.3 milligram per kilogram of body weight.

(A kilogram is approximately 2.2 pounds. There are approximately 30,-

000 milligrams in an ounce. Thus an 11-pound—5 kilograms—baby requires about 1.5 ten-thousandths of an ounce—5 milligrams—of iron a day.)

If molybdenum is in fact essential for humans, its daily requirement is considerably less than 0.3 milligram per kilogram of body weight.

The optimum level of fluorine for drinking water is 0.0001–0.00015 percent.

Cobalt apparently is required only as part of vitamin B_{12}.

No information is available as to a possible requirement for selenium in human beings.

TRACE ELEMENTS carry out a variety of functions in a variety of ways in the animal body. Several are parts of complex molecules that are indispensable to body processes.

Cobalt, for example, is a component of vitamin B_{12}, the extrinsic factor in pernicious anemia. As far as we know, cobalt is indispensable to the activity of vitamin B_{12}, which functions in the production of hemoglobin, in the phase of intermediary metabolism known as one-carbon transfer (the transfer of methyl groups) and in the preparation of amino acids for assembly into protein chains.

Iodine, like cobalt, seems to have its sole function as part of a complex organic molecule. Iodine is an essential part of the thyroid hormone, and as such is of great importance in regulating the rates at which many body functions are carried out.

A third trace element may fall into this category of function. Evidence has been obtained at the National Institutes of Health that the active form of selenium in the animal body is an organic molecule that has not been identified. This molecule may function in oxidative reactions in metabolism.

SOME TRACE ELEMENTS carry out their specific duties as parts of protein molecules.

For example, the transport of oxygen in the blood stream of most animals is the function of a group of metal-containing proteins.

The iron-containing protein, hemoglobin, is the chief respiratory protein in mammals and many other animals. Different iron-containing proteins, the erythrocruorins, perform this function in some invertebrates. Oxygen transport is assigned to copper-containing proteins (hemocyanins) in many of the common shellfish (crabs, lobsters, and snails) and in squids and octopuses.

In all of these respiratory pigments, the metal is attached quite rigidly to the protein molecule, often through some subsidiary organic molecule (called a prosthetic group). Thus the iron in hemoglobin is attached primarily to a porphyrin molecule, which in turn is attached to the protein, globin.

The iron-containing respiratory pigments are red or brown. Those containing copper are blue. Myoglobin, an iron protein similar in many ways to hemoglobin, serves as a storage site for oxygen in muscle tissue. Related oxygen-storage proteins occur in many animals. Oxygen is carried as a complex with the metal in all of the respiratory proteins.

ENZYMES, a group of proteins that direct and hasten—catalyze—chemical reactions in living things, sometimes contain trace elements as integral parts of their structures.

Iron is involved in many such proteins that catalyze a variety of oxidative reactions. As with hemoglobin, the iron is attached to the protein through a porphyrin molecule.

Among the iron-containing enzymes are catalase, which decomposes hydrogen peroxide; the peroxidases, which catalyze the oxidation by hydrogen peroxide of a variety of molecules; and the cytochrome enzymes, which are essential to the trapping of energy during the oxidation of carbohydrate and fat by oxygen.

Molybdenum is a part of at least two animal enzymes, xanthine oxidase and aldehyde oxidase. How it is attached to the protein is not fully understood.

Another example of the inclusion of a trace element in a protein molecule is chlorophyll, the green pigment in plants. Magnesium is attached to the protein of chlorophyll through a porphyrin molecule similar to those involved in many of the iron-containing proteins.

THE OTHER FUNCTIONS of trace elements involve less rigid associations between the element and an enzyme. In these cases, we refer to the trace element as a cofactor for the enzyme. Most enzyme requirements for metals are in this group. One should not think that because the trace element is less firmly attached to the enzyme it is any less important to the function of the enzyme. Manganese, for example, apparently fulfills its many functions in the animal body by this type of loose connection with enzymes.

Among the enzymes that depend on trace elements for their activity, one group absolutely requires a specific metal. The enzymes we have discussed, in which the trace element is a fixed part of the molecule, usually are made inactive by any attempt to substitute a different metal group in place of the one that occurs naturally. Many enzymes that depend on less rigid affiliations with trace elements also require an exact cofactor.

By contrast, a number of enzymes (all of the type that displays the relatively loose affiliations with metals) accept one of two or more metals as a cofactor. Manganese and magnesium appear to be interchangeable as cofactors for several enzymes. In certain instances, metals like aluminum and chromium, which are not recognized to be essential to animals, will serve nearly as well. Even in these instances, the enzyme usually displays an order of preference for the various acceptable metals, as reflected in the relative catalytic ability of the enzyme when in combination with the metals.

To understand why many enzymes depend on metals for their activity, it is necessary to have some insight into the mechanism whereby enzymes accelerate chemical reactions.

Most chemical reactions depend on the chance collision of the two reacting molecules. Not every such collision is effective, for it is important that the reacting sites of the two molecules concerned be appropriately arranged. Only a very small percentage of such collisions is effective in permitting the reaction to occur.

One of the ways that the enzymes increase the rates of chemical reactions is by holding the two reacting molecules in this proper space relationship, thus insuring that nearly every collision will result in a reaction. The enzymes can be visualized as presenting organized surfaces that attract and hold the reacting molecules in the spatial arrangement necessary for reaction.

Three of the trace metals are important to enzymes whose entire action seems to be explainable as the orientation of molecules.

The function of zinc appears to be to hold the molecules diphosphopyridine nucleotide and triphosphopyridine nucleotide (derivatives of the vitamin niacin) in proper orientation for reactions involving the transfer of hydrogen atoms and electrons between these nucleotides and a number of other organic molecules. The zinc is thought to be attached to the surface of the enzyme, and the nucleotide attached in turn to the zinc. The metal in this case may be envisioned as important in properly modifying the surface of the enzyme. Zinc also functions in at least two other types of enzymes, carboxypeptidase and carbonic anhydrase, both of which catalyze reactions involving water.

Magnesium and manganese are cofactors for a large number of the enzymes. Magnesium is required by many of the enzymes that catalyze the transfer of phosphate groups. It is therefore of great importance to the glycolytic pathways in metabolism, for here the transfer of the phosphate groups is the primary means for gleaning utilizable energy from the chemical reactions involved.

Manganese is essential to many reactions that involve the removal of carboxyl groups and is therefore the primary metal for the enzymes of the citric acid cycle, the central scheme of metabolism wherein most of the final oxidation to carbon dioxide occurs.

Many of the enzymes in these two groups will accept either magnesium or manganese, and sometimes other metals, as activators.

SOMETIMES ENZYMES may capitalize on inherent properties of metals in an amazingly efficient way. As an example, very small amounts of iron in solution will hasten the reaction of the oxygen of the air with other components of the solution.

Today we recognize that such phenomena involve a series of events—the oxidation of the iron by oxygen, a rapid reaction, followed by the oxidation of the second molecule by the oxidized iron.

The two reactions often proceed many hundreds of times faster than the single direct reaction that would be necessary in the absence of iron. Since the amount of iron present is not altered by the reaction, it has acted as a catalyst in hastening the oxidation.

The ease with which iron and copper may be oxidized and reduced is utilized by many enzymes. The incorporation of the metal into the enzyme molecule usually results in the magnification of this inherent property for catalyzing oxidative reactions, again increasing the rate of reaction many hundredfold.

The enzyme molecule further places restrictions upon what molecules shall find access to the catalytic power of the metal. Whereas the free metal would catalyze oxidations in a hit-or-miss fashion, the metallo-enzyme usually is a highly specific catalyst, commonly speeding up only a single reaction.

The enzymes that use metals for the catalysis of oxidative and reductive reactions generally have the metal built into their structure.

WE HAVE MENTIONED some of the iron-containing enzymes—catalase, peroxidase, and the enzymes of the cytochrome system. The last are worth some additional comments.

The most important oxidative reactions in biology do not involve the direct reaction of oxygen with carbohydrates, fats, or amino acids. Instead, a complicated sequence of reactions provides the same result—the complete oxidation to carbon dioxide and water. The series of reactions has evolved to release the energy of these oxidations in small, utilizable bursts.

Oxidation usually proceeds through the stepwise transfer of hydrogen atoms from the metabolite to either diphospho- or triphosphopyridine nucleotide. These are then oxidized by a group of enzymes known as cytochrome c reductases. In this reaction, the cytochrome c reductase becomes reduced. It is in turn oxidized by cytochrome c, which is oxidized by cytochrome oxidase. Finally cytochrome oxidase reacts with oxygen, and the cycle begins again. The overall result is that two hydrogens have been removed from a simple molecule and combined with oxygen to form water.

By performing this oxidation in the stepwise fashion, much of the energy available is successfully trapped for use in other chemical reactions. This is the central energy-producing system in animals, as in most forms of life. The enzymes cytochrome c and cytochrome oxidase contain iron, and are examples of the way in which enzymes capitalize on the natural properties of iron.

The details of the functions of copper in human beings are obscure, although in other forms of life copper often is involved in enzymes that catalyze the direct reaction between oxygen and organic molecules. It is probably concerned with the oxidation of an amino acid, tyrosine, and of vitamin C.

The formation of melanin, the pigment of skin, depends on copper. Copper also is involved in many aspects of iron metabolism in animals and plants.

The function of molybdenum seems to be in the catalysis of oxidative and reductive reactions.

Dr. Alvin Nason and his coworkers in the McCollum-Pratt Institute of The Johns Hopkins University showed that it is oxidized and reduced during reactions catalyzed by the enzyme nitrate reductase, a molybdenum-containing enzyme found in molds, certain other micro-organisms, and plants.

Molybdenum is a component of the animal enzymes xanthine oxidase and aldehyde oxidase, both of which catalyze oxidative reactions, but the functioning of molybdenum in a fashion comparable to that in nitrate reductase has never been demonstrated experimentally.

Selenium also can catalyze oxidative reactions. Its biological function is unknown, but selenium may be part of an enzyme that catalyzes oxidative reactions.

NOT ALL NUTRITIONAL requirements for trace elements are explainable in terms of functions within the animal body.

Within the alimentary canal (stomachs and intestines) of higher animals reside a host of bacteria that depend on the diet of the animal for the satisfaction of their nutritional requirements and in turn perform certain tasks for the animal. Thus, ruminants are able to obtain nutritive value from the cellulose of plants only because bacteria within the rumen, the first of the four stomachs of these animals, break down the cellulose into smaller molecules utilizable by the animal. To perform this degradation of cellulose, the bacteria require molybdenum, which must be supplied in the feed.

Similarly, ruminants sometimes do not get enough cobalt. This element is required by the rumen bacteria for the production of vitamin B_{12}, to satisfy both their own requirements for this vitamin and those of the animal as well.

It is likely that many more functions will be recognized for trace elements in the bacteria of the alimentary canal.

As IS TRUE of many of the essential nutrients, including the vitamins, the major minerals, and even water, excessive intake of the trace elements may lead to detrimental effects upon the body.

Toxicities of trace elements among livestock have created problems in many localities. Notable among them are molybdenum and selenium. Naturally occurring toxicities due to copper and fluorine were reported.

The toxic effects of most of the other trace elements have been observed only with laboratory animals.

Well-documented toxicities of trace elements have been described only rarely among human beings, other than those that result from occupational hazards (like lead poisoning from paint) or inadequate disposal of industrial wastes. We shall reconsider this aspect shortly.

The toxicities have served to point out some interesting facts concerning interrelationships between the trace elements.

Excessive intake of molybdenum may create problems in the utilization of copper by animals. Many of the symptoms of a copper deficiency appear, even though the level of copper in the diet is seemingly adequate. A possible explanation of this effect of molybdenum on copper metabolism has appeared with the observation in our laboratory that molybdenum toxicity in the rat leads to a depression of the enzyme sulfide oxidase, normally responsible for the detoxification of hydrogen sulfide. Should this compound accumulate in even very small amounts in the body, it would cause the precipitation of copper sulfide, an extremely insoluble material. In this fashion the copper of the body would be rendered unavailable for fulfilling its normal tasks.

Experiments have been undertaken to obtain a more careful evaluation of this explanation of the copper-molybdenum interrelationship.

Dr. Robert Van Reen, at the McCollum-Pratt Institute, demonstrated that an excessive intake of zinc also may lead to an impairment of the function of copper in experimental animals. We do not know whether any relationship exists between the effects of zinc and of molybdenum on copper.

Studies in a number of laboratories have indicated that in pigs and rats copper is essential to many aspects of iron utilization, including its absorption from the alimentary canal and its incorporation into hemoglobin and such iron-containing enzymes as cytochrome oxidase and catalase. The normal functioning of iron depends entirely on an adequate intake and utilization of copper.

THE SOIL is the ultimate source of trace elements.

Plants reflect the soil condition with respect to most trace elements, up to the point that the conditions become incompatible with life, because plants also have nutritional requirements and are subject to toxicities.

The animals we raise for food are largely herbivorous and convert into meat the plant tissues that to man are indigestible and unpalatable. The meat animals, to the extent that they exist on the plants grown nearby, are in turn subject to the condition of the soil with respect to trace elements. Naturally occurring deficiencies and toxicities are commonest among these animals.

Meat-eating animals are less likely to show abnormalities with respect to trace elements, simply because their food source either has corrected the problems presented by the soil or has not survived to serve as a food source.

Animals and people that eat a mixed diet of plant and animal foods seldom encounter deficiencies of trace elements, and toxicities usually result from the drinking water rather than the food. Man has the advantage that his food usually comes to him from a large area. Local soil problems therefore are less important to him.

The only deficiencies of trace elements that have been clearly shown for man involve fluorine, iodine, and iron.

The first is relatively common, but apparently it affects only the resistance of the teeth to dental caries and is not a serious hazard to general health. The local supplementation of drinking water is the main device for correcting this situation.

A deficiency of iodine may lead to endemic goiter and related conditions in local areas in many parts of the United States. This deficiency is easily circumvented by the use of such nutritional aids as iodized table salt.

A deficiency of iron has been cited as the commonest of all deficiency diseases in man, but most of these anemias are due to factors other than dietary inadequacy—as, for example, chronic loss of blood due to such pathological conditions as infections or malignant conditions involving the stomach, intestines, or urogenital system. Infants, however, not uncommonly display symptoms of iron deficiency.

Girls and women require more iron than do males, largely because of three important losses of iron to which males are not subject—menstruation, gestation, and lactation. Administration of iron during late pregnancy and lactation safeguards against the anemias of pregnancy and deficiencies in the infant. It has been estimated that up to 40 percent of all pregnant women would benefit from such therapy.

OUR DISCUSSION has pointed up the fact that our knowledge concerning trace elements in human nutrition is small. We know considerably more about the nutritional problems of the animals that we raise for food.

The motivating force in such investigations in the past has been the correction of the agricultural problems and economic losses, reflecting the human trait of placing a concern for one's pocketbook above one's health.

The emphasis in research has begun to shift. The function of trace elements in the action of enzymes has become one of the central problems in biochemistry today, and the nutritional research with respect to the trace elements now is motivated more by the desire to understand these constituents of living things than by economic necessity.

We cannot foresee what practical applications will be made of this more fundamental research. It is important to remember that life is a delicate balance of a seemingly infinite number of competing chemical and physio-logical processes. The trace elements are obviously of great importance to these processes and to that balance.

Health, we are beginning to realize, is more than the absence of disease. It is, rather, the ideal in which the perfect balance of the processes of life is achieved. The study of trace elements and their functions is therefore the study of health.

KENNETH J. MONTY *is assistant professor, Department of Biology, The Johns Hopkins University and the McCollum-Pratt Institute.*

WILLIAM D. MCELROY *is chairman, Department of Biology, The Johns Hopkins University, and director of the McCollum-Pratt Institute, a unit of the university.*

The types of food most generally required to improve people's diets and health are in many cases those produced by methods of farming best calculated to maintain the productivity of the soil and to increase and make more stable the returns to agricultural producers. In short, better nutrition means better farming.—From the Official Summary of the United Nations Conference on Food and Agriculture, held at Hot Springs, Va., 1943.

It is hypocritical to lament the wide extent of malnutrition while quantities of food are not reaching consumers, or while producers are being required to restrict output. It is equally hypocritical, and indeed irresponsible, to urge farmers to produce more if the food already at hand cannot be sold at reasonable prices.—From the Report of the First Session of the Conference on Food and Agriculture, Quebec, 1945.

Vitamins A, D, E, K

ERNESTINE B. McCOLLUM AND ELMER V. McCOLLUM

ANALYSTS a half century ago used chemical methods to estimate the proteins, fats, carbohydrates, mineral elements, and water in foods. They separated the substances in relatively pure form from such natural foods as milk, meat, and cereal grains. They fed mixtures of the purified nutrients to animals, which soon sickened and died. It became plain to the scientists that proteins, fats, carbohydrates, minerals, and water are not the only essential constituents of foods.

Animals grew well and remained healthy when small amounts of water-soluble material from yeast or wheat germ—the embryo or heart of the wheat—were added to the purified diets and when the right fat was included. All fats have essentially equal caloric value, but experiments on rats showed that some fats are superior to others for growth and the maintenance of health. Studies such as these led to the discovery of the vitamins.

We classify vitamins on the basis of their solubility. Vitamin C (ascorbic acid) and the vitamins of the B complex are water soluble. Vitamins A, D, E, and K in their natural forms are soluble in fats and such fat solvents as ether and chloroform. We call them the fat-soluble vitamins.

Elmer V. McCollum and Marguerite Davis, then of the University of Wisconsin, discovered in 1912 that the provision of something in butterfat or egg yolk fat made the difference between moderate success in the nutrition of young rats on certain diets and prompt nutritive failure. This something was vitamin A.

Some months later Thomas Burr Osborne and Lafayette Benedict Mendel, in investigations at Yale University, corroborated and extended Dr. McCollum's observations on the effects of a deficiency of vitamin A.

They described the condition as a "type of nutritive deficiency exemplified in the form of an infectious eye disease prevalent in animals inappropriately fed." They said it was alleviated speedily by adding butterfat to the diet.

They discovered first that young animals deprived of vitamin A fail to gain weight, an effect caused by a deficiency of any of the known essential nutrients.

An eye disease, xerophthalmia or dry eye, is a specific result of too little vitamin A, however. It occurs in human beings and in experimental animals. It was observed in infants in Japan in 1904 and among children in Denmark in 1917. It was attributed in both countries to scarcity of food fats.

A DEFICIENCY of vitamin A injures the epithelial tissues throughout the body. These cells form the outer layer of the skin and the mucous membranes that line the mouth and the digestive, respiratory, and genitourinary tracts. The secretory glands, such as the tear glands and digestive glands, are composed of specialized epithelial cells. Epithelial cells dry and flatten and slough off when vitamin A is lacking. The cells, instead of being soft and moist, become hard and dry like the scales of dry skin.

The mucous membranes are barriers against many kinds of bacterial invasion. Impairment of their structure and function when vitamin A is deficient lowers resistance to respiratory and other infections. Severe infections of the eyes, genitourinary tract, and mouth may occur.

This deficiency also is said to be the cause of much blindness among the populations of the Orient.

Vitamin A is necessary for vision. The retina of the eye contains a pigment, visual purple, which is composed of vitamin A and protein.

Visual purple is converted first to visual yellow and then to visual white when the eye is exposed to light. Vitamin A is lost in this conversion. Visual purple is regenerated if a fresh supply of the vitamin is available. Without this regeneration, vision in subdued light is impaired following exposure to bright light—a condition known as night blindness.

Night blindness has a long medical history, in which it is associated with diet. It was common in Newfoundland among fishermen who worked in open boats in bright sunshine and exposed their eyes to the glare on the water. There was an old belief that if a man could not see at night, his vision would be restored by the next night if he ate the liver of a codfish or a sea gull.

Vitamin A profoundly influences the development of the teeth. When the tooth buds buried in the child's jaw are ready for the formation of enamel, certain epithelial cells from what later become gum tissue fold inward and form a cap over the part of the tooth that is to be enameled. These then become specialized as to function. Each cell forms a minute, six-sided prism of enamel substance. The prisms finally reach a length equal to the thickness of the enamel on the erupted tooth. The many enamel prisms are laid together so perfectly as to make a dense, thick, smooth enamel.

If the child gets too little vitamin A when his teeth are developing, the enamel-forming cells become abnormal and lose their effectiveness in forming enamel prisms. Some prisms in the finished enamel may be missing, and pits are formed. Such pits may later harbor food deposits, which may ferment and form acids that etch the enamel and lead to decay.

Vitamin A occurs only in foods of animal origin.

It is not found in any plant. All yellow and green plants, however, contain yellow pigments that can be converted by chemical cleavage into fragments, one of which is vitamin A.

The commonest of these pigments is carotene, so called because it was first prepared from carrots. There are three carotenes. One of them can be converted into two molecules, and the others into one molecule of vitamin A.

The yellow pigment of corn, cryptoxanthine, also can be converted into vitamin A in the body.

The conversion of carotene into vitamin A is thought to take place in the intestinal mucosa.

Because carotene can be converted into vitamin A, it is often called provitamin A.

Experiments generally have shown that carotene is utilized less efficiently than vitamin A. Individuals differ in their ability to convert it into the vitamin.

An example is the difference in the yellowness of milks of a Jersey cow, a Holstein cow, a ewe, a goat, and a sow that graze on the same green grass. The milk of the Jersey is yellower than that of the Holstein. The milks of the other three species are nearly white.

The yellow color of milk and cream is due to carotene. Vitamin A is almost colorless. Animals with great ability to convert carotene to the vitamin produce white or slightly yellow milk. Those that are not so efficient put more carotene and less vitamin A into their milk.

The total vitamin A value of milk, cream, butter, and eggs is the sum of the vitamin A and the carotene present, but one cannot estimate the vitamin A value of such foods on the basis of their color alone.

The biologic activities of vitamin A and carotene are expressed in I.U. (International Units) or U.S.P. units (United States Pharmacopoeia). These units have the same value, and the terms are used interchangeably. They are defined in terms of standardized, pure, crystalline vitamin A or beta-carotene. Three-tenths of a gamma of crystalline vitamin A or six-tenths of a gamma of pure beta-carotene is equal to one unit. A unit is very small. There are 1 million gamma in a gram and about 30 grams in an ounce. An ounce of the pure, crystalline vitamin equals 30 million units. This is enough to meet the needs of one person for almost 30 years!

We estimate that two-thirds of the vitamin A activity in the average American diet comes from carotene and related compounds. One-third is provided by the vitamin itself present in foods of animal origin.

Not all of the carotene present in the food eaten is converted into vitamin A. Some passes through the digestive tract and is excreted as such. Some

circulates in the blood, and some is changed in the intestine or liver.

The amount of ingested carotene that is converted into vitamin A varies with different foods and with methods used in preparing them. Other substances present in foods or served with them may also affect the body's ability to take up carotene from the intestinal tract and convert it into vitamin A.

Feeding experiments on human beings indicated that cooked carrots put through some blender (Waring Blender, Osterizer, or similar device) were more than twice as good a source of carotene as cooked carrots that were sliced or mashed. When cooked spinach was compared with carrots prepared in the two ways described, it was found to be equal in carotene value to the blended carrots.

Other dietary factors also influence the requirement for vitamin A. Vitamin E protects carotene and vitamin A against oxidative destruction within and outside the body. The livers of animals deprived of vitamin E are depleted rapidly of vitamin A. The store of vitamin A in the liver can increase when vitamin E is provided again.

Mineral oil reduces the absorption of carotene and vitamin A. It is undesirable to combine mineral oil with the food. Anybody who uses it should take it on rising or long enough after a meal to prevent interference with the utilization of the fat-soluble vitamins.

The National Academy of Sciences-National Research Council has recommended a daily intake of 5 thousand I.U. of vitamin A. This allowance is approximately twice that required to meet the minimum needs of the average healthy adult on a good diet. It assumes that two-thirds of the total vitamin A is provided by carotene present in the yellow and green, leafy vegetables and yellow fruits, like kale, spinach, collard greens, mustard greens, carrots, pumpkin, yellow sweetpotatoes, apricots, yellow peaches, and cantaloup. Foods from animal sources, like whole milk, butter, eggs, liver, kidney, and some fish, contain the vitamin itself.

Vitamin A accumulates in the liver. A well-nourished individual is likely to have a sufficient store to last for months even if his food is completely devoid of the vitamin and carotene.

Overdosing with vitamin A may cause serious injury to health. Self-administration of highly potent concentrates is likely to result in hypervitaminosis A, a serious condition from which recovery is slow. It has been observed in children who were given excessive intakes of 75 thousand units or more daily for some time.

The recommended allowance for vitamin A can be met by including yellow and green, leafy vegetables, such as collards, turnip greens, kale, carrots, squash, and sweetpotatoes in the diet every day. Yellow peaches, apricots, cantaloups, and papayas are also good sources. Liver of all animals is an excellent source. A 2-ounce serving of cooked beef liver provides more than 30 thousand I.U. of the vitamin.

Other good sources are whole milk, butter, cheese made from whole milk or cream, margarine enriched with vitamin A, eggs, and kidney.

Carotene and vitamin A are insoluble in water. Thus there is no loss by extraction during cooking. Exposure to air or oxygen, especially in the presence of heat, however, causes destruction of vitamin A and carotene. Air drying of such foods as eggs and vegetables results in significant loss of vitamin A value. Vacuum drying prevents such loss.

THE CAUSE of rickets was unknown until 1919, when scientists produced it in young rats and dogs by feeding them experimental diets. Thus they made it possible to study the cause of the disease. If the diet contained cod-liver oil, the bones of the animals remained normal. The same diet, but with the cod-liver oil replaced by various vegetable fats or oils or by body fats of animals, produced rickets. Twenty per-

cent of butterfat, which is rich in vitamin A and contains small amounts of the antiricketic vitamin, had some preventive effect.

Scientists discovered in 1922 that the vitamin A in cod-liver oil could be destroyed by oxidation without loss of its antiricketic properties. Then it was apparent that cod-liver oil contains a second fat-soluble vitamin. It was named vitamin D.

Determining the existence of vitamin D and how it functions was complicated by the need to understand its relationship with calcium and phosphorus. That came through clinical experience with rickets and research on experimental animals.

Before it was produced in laboratory animals, rickets was assumed to be due to faulty environment and poor hygiene, especially lack of sunshine and exercise. It is a disease of the bones and occurs mostly in infants, children, and young adults. It results in deformities of varying degrees of severity. It occurs almost entirely in the temperate regions. It is rare in the far north and the Tropics.

A few physicians noted that severe rickets occurred in children in deep valleys in the Swiss Alps. Children who lived up in the nearby mountains escaped the disease. The doctors rightly surmised that the mountain sunshine had a beneficial effect. The valley children were predisposed to rickets because the mountains shut out sunshine from the valleys.

Ricketic children in Europe were successfully treated during the First World War by exposing them to the rays of ultraviolet lamps.

American scientists learned that experimental rickets in young rats could be prevented by exposure to summer sunlight. Furthermore, if the diet that produced severe rickets was exposed for a short time to ultraviolet light, it not only prevented the development of the disease in rats but it would promptly cure those that were ricketic.

Further experiments proved that the remarkable action of light was due to the transformation of a substance called sterol into a form of vitamin D. Before irradiation, the sterol was not protective against rickets.

Sterols are organic compounds widely distributed in animal and plant tissues. They are white, crystalline substances that have physical properties like those of candles. Antiricketic activity can be induced by irradiation or other means in at least 11 different sterols.

Human skin and the skins of all animals contain a sterol called cholesterol. It is transformed into vitamin D_3 when it is exposed to ultraviolet light. Sunlight in the Tropics and subtropics is rich in ultraviolet rays. There is less of these rays in sunlight at higher latitudes. Ultraviolet rays are more abundant in mountain sunlight than at sea level in temperate regions.

Clouds, fog, and dust in the atmosphere absorb ultraviolet rays. Sunlight in cities accordingly is inferior to sunlight in open country. Because window glass absorbs ultraviolet rays, the light that has passed through ordinary glass has practically no antiricketic activity.

People in northern latitudes wear heavy clothing during the colder months and shield the skin against such sunlight as is available. This custom and the dearth of ultraviolet rays in city sunlight and in cloudy weather make it imperative that children in temperate regions be given some source of vitamin D.

The vitamin D produced by irradiation of a sterol (ergosterol) from yeast is called calciferol, or vitamin D_2. It is dissolved in oil and sold commercially as viosterol. It efficiently protects infants, rats, pigs, calves, and other mammals, but even large doses of this form of the vitamin have little protective action in preventing the development of rickets in birds. Vitamin D_3, which is present in cod-liver oil and other fish-liver oils, is effective in the prevention and cure of rickets in both mammals and birds.

Vitamin D promotes the absorption of calcium from the digestive tract and lessens the amount in the feces.

Urinary excretion of phosphorus is also less in children and animals when vitamin D is included in the diet.

The absorption of phosphorus depends partly on the absorption of calcium. Any factor that exerts a favorable or an unfavorable effect on the utilization of one affects the other likewise. Thus, by improving the absorption of calcium and phosphorus and by aiding in the maintenance of the normal blood levels of these two essential bone builders, vitamin D makes both available in a concentration that is suitable for the formation and growth of bones.

The levels of blood calcium and phosphorus fall in children deprived of the vitamin. Amounts necessary for the formation of strong and rigid bones are not available. An excess of preosseous tissue accumulates, which fails to calcify normally. The joints enlarge, and bowed legs, knock-knees, beaded ribs, and skull deformities may result. Such changes are characteristic of rickets.

Rickets also causes the ribs to soften and the muscles of the body to lose tone and become weak and flabby. That interferes with breathing, produces unventilated areas in the lungs, and predisposes to respiratory diseases.

The teeth, like the bones, normally contain large amounts of calcium and phosphorus. The enamel and the dentin are composed almost entirely of the two elements. Teeth may not develop normally if the calcium and phosphate of the blood are too low in concentration while the teeth are forming. The teeth of ricketic animals and children have thin, poorly calcified enamel, with pits and fissures. Such teeth are especially prone to decay.

Conditions that predispose to the development of rickets in children may result in adults in osteomalacia, in which changes occur in the shafts of bones and bone structure softens. It has been observed in Asian countries, especially in women who have borne children and nursed them over extended periods. It occurred in Germany in the First World War, when food supplies were low.

Very few foods contain significant amounts of the vitamin D. We have no way of measuring the amount of vitamin D formed in the body by the action of ultraviolet light. It varies with climate, season, and mode of life.

The requirement for vitamin D for infants has been intensively studied. Pediatricians recommend 300 to 400 units of vitamin D daily for a full-term baby that is bottle fed. The same is recommended for the full-term baby that is breast fed, even though the mother's milk may provide some vitamin D.

Because prematurity precludes the storage of calcium and phosphorus that normally occurs during the last months of pregnancy, the premature babies should be given twice as much (800 units a day) during the period of most rapid growth and thereafter the same amount as full-term infants.

For children between infancy and adolescence, 300 to 400 units a day are recommended, plus a pint and a half of milk to assure desirable retention of calcium and phosphorus.

Adolescents should receive 400 units of vitamin D a day.

Vigorous adults who lead normal lives and have opportunity for exercise and exposure to sunlight probably require no extra source of the vitamin. However, for nightworkers and others whose mode of life precludes exposure to sunlight and for the elderly and infirm whose lives are spent indoors, a daily supplement of 400 units of vitamin D is wise practice.

Because of the increased need for calcium and phosphorus during pregnancy and lactation and because vitamin D promotes their retention and utilization, a daily supplement of 400 units is recommended for pregnant and lactating women.

The recommendations of the National Research Council for vitamin D are as we indicated. They make no specific recommendation for adults.

For infants, children, adolescents, pregnant women (last 3 months), and nursing mothers, the Council recommends 400 units a day.

Salt-water fish generally contain large amounts of vitamin D. Herring, mackerel, and canned salmon and sardines are good sources. Vitamin D is present in the body oil as well as in the fat of the liver. Egg yolk and liver (beef, chicken, hog) contain the vitamin. The amount present depends largely on the amount in the feed.

Cow's milk generally is not a good source of vitamin D. Increasing the vitamin content of milk by feeding large amounts to the cow, adding a vitamin concentrate to the milk, or irradiating milk with an ultraviolet lamp is a common practice. Such enrichment insures a content of 400 units per quart of milk.

Most evaporated milk and much of the dried whole milk contain enough vitamin D to give 400 units per quart after reconstitution with the recommended amount of water. Milk contains calcium and phosphorus in amounts and ratios conducive to their absorption, retention, and utilization. The addition of vitamin D to milk further promotes this relationship.

Cod-liver oil, percomorph oil, and halibut-liver oil provide vitamin A as well as vitamin D. Because percomorph oil is a much richer source of both vitamins than cod-liver oil, it is administered in drops rather than by the teaspoonful. Irradiated ergosterol dissolved in oil is standardized as to its D content and sold as viosterol. This, too, is a concentrated preparation and is given in drops. It should be remembered, too, that viosterol is pure vitamin D in an oil. It contains no vitamin A as do the fish-liver oils and preparations made from them.

Too much vitamin D can be harmful. Toxic effects result in children on 40 thousand or more units a day and in adults on 100 thousand or more units a day. Overdosing with concentrates of the vitamin results in loss of appetite, vomiting, diarrhea, and drowsiness. Blood calcium and phosphorus rise to abnormal levels, and calcification of the walls of the blood vessels, heart, and various soft tissues may occur. Death may follow.

Hypervitaminosis D has been produced in infants by mistakes in dosage and in adults treated for arthritis with excessive amounts.

A NEW CONCEPT in nutritional research arose in 1922, when investigators observed that nutrition failed in unborn rats when a certain experimental diet was fed. This failure was prevented by the provision of an unknown substance present in various natural foods. It could not be identified with any known nutrient. It was called vitamin E.

Lettuce and wheat germ were found to be rich sources of vitamin E. It was shown to be fat soluble and to have the properties of an alcohol. To characterize the vitamin as a factor essential for reproduction, the word "tocopherol" was coined from a combination of the Greek words "tokos" (childbirth), "phero" (I bring), and the suffix "ol," indicating it has the properties of an alcohol.

Alpha, beta, gamma, and delta tocopherols have been isolated from natural sources. All have physiologic activity. Alpha tocopherol is the most potent and is referred to as vitamin E. Its chemical composition is known, and the pure vitamin is now made commercially.

Sterility, premature delivery, fetal death before or at term, and failure of the mother to deliver her young had been described previously in nutrition studies on animals fed experimental diets. But the effects produced by diets deficient in vitamin E differed from all of these.

The early stages of reproduction in the female rat are normal in the absence of the vitamin. The ovulation cycle is normal. The eggs can be fertilized. The fertilized ova develop in the uterus without attaching themselves to the uterine wall until the sixth day after fertilization. On that day the ova begin to implant and placentae are formed, through which the fetuses secure nutrients from the mother's blood.

The rat's normal gestation period is 21 or 22 days. A deficiency of vitamin E interferes with placental function and the development of the young at about the eighth day of pregnancy. If it is administered as late as the fifth day after mating, the young may develop without mishap and be normally born. Otherwise the fetuses die and undergo dissolution. The mother loses weight day by day until she returns to her normal weight before pregnancy. In the absence of the vitamin, repeated pregnancies may succeed each other and always end in failure. Administration of the vitamin will again permit successful pregnancy and the birth of normal young.

A male rat that gets a ration deficient in vitamin E becomes sterile in 75 to 100 days. His sperm-forming structures are injured. At first nonmotile sperms are formed. They tend to be liberated in clumps and cannot fertilize the ova. Once such damage occurs, it is not possible to restore fertility in the male, even though large doses of the vitamin are given.

The view was once held that the function of vitamin E was limited to the reproduction mechanism. This concept is too narrow. Young rats born of mothers kept on diets containing only enough of the vitamin to last through one gestation period developed paralysis when they were about 21 days old. This could be prevented by giving small doses of vitamin E to rats before they were 15 days old.

Rats born of mothers fed adequate amounts of vitamin E grow at the normal rate and appear to remain healthy when placed at weaning on an E-deficient diet. After 3 to 4 months, when the body reserves of the vitamin have been exhausted, growth slackens, and weight remains the same or declines. The animals become paralyzed and drag their hindquarters. Administration of vitamin E arrests but does not cure this affliction.

In guinea pigs, rabbits, sheep, goats, hamsters, and calves, severe degeneration of skeletal muscles develops on rations devoid of vitamin E. Reproductive failure such as that described in rats on E-deficient diets does not occur. Cattle deprived of vitamin E may die from a heart ailment.

Hens fed rations deficient in vitamin E produce eggs of low hatchability. The mortality rate among the chicks hatched from such eggs is high. Young chicks reared on E-deficient diets may develop brain injury and exudative diathesis, which is characterized by an accumulation of fluid in the tissues.

The red blood corpuscles of adult rats on rations low in vitamin E are abnormally susceptible to destruction by an oxidizing agent like hydrogen peroxide. The blood of newborn young of such females shows the same abnormality. The administration of small amounts of alpha tocopherol protects the corpuscles against such damage.

In similar manner, alpha tocopherol protects the blood of newborn, full-term infants from the hemolytic (blood-destroying) action of hydrogen peroxide. Feeding the vitamin to a newborn infant results in a marked decrease in susceptibility to the blood-destroying action of this chemical.

Vitamin E is an antioxidant—that is, it unites with oxygen both within and outside the body. Oxidation makes fats rancid and destroys vitamin A.

Tocopherols are the main antioxidants present in natural fats and serve to prevent the development of rancidity. By accepting oxygen and combining with it, the tocopherols prevent the oxidation of adjacent compounds. This property is probably responsible for the protection of the red blood cells in the presence of hydrogen peroxide as well as the protection of vitamin A and carotene in food and in the body. For, as we mentioned earlier in connection with vitamin A, the stores of vitamin A are depleted in the livers of

animals deficient in vitamin E and are increased when vitamin E is provided.

Vitamin E deficiency has not been identified in people.

Except for the protection afforded red blood cells in the presence of a blood-destroying agent like hydrogen peroxide, no specific role for the vitamin has been observed in human nutrition. Hence requirements have not been determined and there is no recommended allowance.

The symptoms of vitamin E deficiency in experimental animals, especially the death of young in the uterus and muscular dystrophy, have led to the clinical use of vitamin E in spontaneous abortion, multiple sclerosis, various muscular and neuromuscular disorders, and cardiovascular diseases. None of these conditions treated with the vitamin has been shown so far to be due to its deficiency or to be definitely benefited by vitamin E therapy.

Vitamin E is widely distributed in both plant and animal tissues. Green leaves and the oil found in the germs of cereal seeds, especially wheat germ oil, are excellent sources of the tocopherols. So, too, are corn oil and cottonseed oil. Considerable tocopherol is present in milk, butter, eggs, and liver.

Because vitamin E is insoluble in water, there is no loss by extraction in cooking. Exposure to oxygen and development of rancidity result in the destruction of the tocopherols.

People whose diet includes fruit, vegetables, milk, whole-grain cereals, meat, and eggs every day are not apt to have deficiencies of vitamin E.

THE DISCOVERY of vitamin K followed the observation that certain experimental diets produced fatal hemorrhages in chicks. The symptoms looked like those of scurvy, but they did not respond to the administration of lemon juice, a rich source of the antiscorbutic vitamin. Feeding alfalfa or other green leaves to the sick birds brought dramatic relief from the symptoms.

It was found that the blood of chicks on diets deficient in this newly discovered nutrient took longer to clot than that of normal birds.

A number of investigators set about trying to isolate and identify the substance capable of influencing the properties of the blood as seen in this deficiency disease.

Of the many green leaves studied, those of the alfalfa plant proved to be exceptionally rich in the new factor. A Danish investigator, Carl Peter Henrik Dam, isolated a fat-soluble substance from dried alfalfa leaves. Because it corrected the clotting or coagulating time of the blood, he called it the Koagulations-Vitamin. This was shortened to vitamin K for convenience.

Vitamin K is essential for normal function of the liver and for the formation of prothrombin by the liver. Prothrombin is a normal constituent of blood. It is one of the several components that react together to form the blood clot. When vitamin K is deficient, the prothrombin content of the blood falls and clotting time is prolonged. The capillaries must also become fragile, since extensive hemorrhage accompanies the reduction of prothrombin.

The administration of the vitamin causes a prompt response of the body with the formation of prothrombin, and the blood returns to its normal composition and physical properties.

Fibrin is one of the chief constituents of a blood clot. Prothrombin is required for its formation.

A deficiency of vitamin K can be produced in chickens and in various animals by the use of special diets. It has been described in individuals with bizarre eating habits.

Human babies and the young of sheep, goats, and guinea pigs are born with no reserves of vitamin K. We attribute this to the fact that at birth the intestinal tract is sterile. Some microorganisms usually present in the human intestinal tract make vitamin K, which can then be used by the host. This source of the vitamin is not available in the newborn.

The newborn infant lacks an intestinal source of vitamin K—hence the presence of low prothrombin levels of the blood and susceptibility to hemorrhagic disease shortly after birth. It is routine in many hospitals to administer vitamin K to the mother just before delivery or to the newborn infant.

Although it is clear that human beings must have vitamin K, no requirements have been established and no allowances have been set up.

It is probable that the normal, healthy person derives much of his vitamin K from synthesis by intestinal flora. The only times when the human intestinal tract does not produce enough for human needs appear to be immediately after birth (before the intestinal flora is established) and possibly during or following prolonged treatment with sulfa drugs or antibiotics.

A deficiency of vitamin K usually is secondary to some other defect. In disturbances of the intestinal tract, such as chronic diarrhea or colitis, obstruction, or sprue, absorption of the vitamin may be impaired and a deficiency may result.

Bile salts are essential for the absorption of vitamin K. Bile salts are lacking in persons with obstructive jaundice, and low prothrombin level of the blood and delayed clotting time occur. Before the discovery of vitamin K and its availability in pure form, such patients were bad surgical risks. The death rate in these cases has been greatly reduced in recent years by the use of the vitamin and bile salts.

In addition to that available through bacterial synthesis in the intestine, vitamin K is so widely distributed in a variety of foods that there is no likelihood of a deficiency. The green, leafy vegetables, tomatoes, cauliflower, egg yolk, soybean oil, and liver of all kinds are good sources. Since it is insoluble in water, there is no loss in ordinary cooking procedures.

Ernestine B. McCollum *and* Elmer V. McCollum *are assistant professor and emeritus professor of biochemistry in the School of Hygiene and Public Health, The Johns Hopkins University, Baltimore.*

Vitamins of the B Complex

GRACE A. GOLDSMITH

AN investigation of beriberi in the late 19th century started the chain of events that led to the discovery of vitamins. Beriberi had long been a common and a serious disease in parts of the world where polished rice was the staple food.

Christiaan Eijkman, a Dutch surgeon, was carrying out studies on fowls in a military hospital in Java in the 1890's. To save money, he fed them scraps—mostly polished rice—from the patients' meals. The fowls unexpectedly developed a bad nerve ailment, which resulted in paralysis.

Somewhat later the director of the hospital withheld permission to use the scraps, and Dr. Eijkman had to buy natural or undermilled rice for the chickens he used in his experiments. The ailing birds improved after they began eating the natural rice.

Dr. Eijkman then began a series of experiments that led to the first clear concept of disease due to nutritional deficiency. He fed polished white rice to pigeons, chickens, and ducks. They developed the paralysis he had observed previously, and they recovered when he fed them natural rice. Birds fed whole rice remained well.

He noted that the disease that resulted from a polished rice diet in birds resembled beriberi in man.

He believed that rice contained too much starch, which poisoned nerve cells, and that the outer layers, removed from the grain in milling, were an antidote. His report was published in Dutch, and some time elapsed before it was known generally.

G. Grijns, another Dutch physician, interpreted Dr. Eijkman's findings in a different way. He concluded in 1901 that beriberi in birds or man was due to a deficiency or absence of an essential nutrient from the diet.

From then on, chemists in many countries tried to concentrate the substance in rice that prevented beriberi in order to obtain it in pure form. Among them was Casimir Funk, of the Lister Institute, London, who coined the term "vitamine" and applied it to the antiberiberi substance.

B. C. P. Jansen and W. P. Donath in Holland in 1926 isolated the antiberiberi vitamin, and in the 1930's

Robert R. Williams and his associates determined its structure and synthesized it.

Thus men discovered the cause and cure of beriberi, which nevertheless remains a serious disease today in countries in which overpolished and overmilled rice is a staple in the diet.

During the first stages of separating and identifying vitamins, the designation "water-soluble B" was given by Dr. Elmer V. McCollum and Marguerite Davis to the concentrates that cured beriberi. Vitamin B at that time was thought to be a single substance. Later research showed that it consists of a number of substances that differ widely in chemical structure but have much the same natural distribution in foods.

Of the 11 substances in the vitamin B complex that now are available in pure form, five are components of one or more coenzymes—thiamine, riboflavin, niacin, pyridoxine, and pantothenic acid. Coenzymes are catalysts that have important and often related functions in the biochemical processes by means of which nutrients are used for energy and for building up or maintaining the cells and tissues of the body.

Two of the B vitamins, folic acid and vitamin B_{12}, have antianemic properties and presumably exert their function in a similar way—that is, as coenzymes.

These seven vitamins are essential in human nutrition and must be included in the daily diet.

Of the other four members of the B complex, choline is important in human nutrition but is probably not an essential dietary constituent because the body can form it from other compounds.

Very likely biotin is required by man, but it is furnished by bacterial synthesis in the intestinal tract as well as by food.

Inositol and p-aminobenzoic acid, other members of the B complex, have not been shown to be essential in human nutrition.

A LACK OF VITAMINS of the B complex is one of the forms of malnutrition that often occur throughout the world. Because of the similar distribution of the B vitamins in foods, a deficiency of several factors is observed oftener than a deficiency of a single substance. The interrelationship of many of these vitamins in life processes means that signs of deficiency often are similar when the diet lacks any one of several factors.

Many physiologic and pathologic stresses influence the need for the B vitamins. Larger amounts are needed during growth and in pregnancy and lactation than in maintenance of health in adult life. The requirement may be increased by diseases that elevate metabolism and by conditions associated with poor absorption, improper utilization, or increased excretion. Administration of antibiotics may lead to vitamin deficiency in some circumstances; in others, antibiotics spare vitamin requirements.

THIAMINE, or vitamin B_1, also known as the antineuritic or antiberiberi vitamin, is a water-soluble compound. It is readily broken down by heat in neutral or alkaline solutions. Its solubility and the ease with which it is destroyed are important, because overcooking food and discarding the water in which the food is cooked may cause large amounts of the vitamin to be lost.

Thiamine is present in many natural foods but is abundant in few. Lean pork is one of the best sources. Dry beans and peas, certain of the organ meats, and some nuts furnish sizable amounts. Whole wheat and enriched cereals and bread are dependable sources. They can contribute valuable amounts to the diet. The small amounts provided by other foods, such as milk, eggs, other meat, fruit, and vegetables, add up and represent a worthwhile contribution to the diet.

The thiamine requirement is related to caloric intake. The minimum need is approximately 0.20 to 0.23 milligram per 1,000 Calories. This requirement is based on experiments in which thiamine in the diet is restricted, on studies of diets of population groups, and on estimates of the amounts excreted in the urine of people having known intakes of thiamine.

The requirement of infants in relation to Calories appears to be comparable to that of the adult. Human milk supplies an average of 0.21 milligram per 1, 000 Calories. We have evidence that the ratio of carbohydrate to fat in the diet influences the requirement.

The recommended dietary allowance for thiamine is 0.5 milligram per 1,000 Calories. When an adult's diet furnishes fewer than 2,000 Calories a day, the thiamine allowance should not be less than 1 milligram daily. This allowance provides a large factor of safety above the minimum need and seems desirable because requirements vary among individuals and because stores of thiamine in the body are not large and may be exhausted readily in diseases associated with an increase in metabolism.

Bacteria in the intestines may synthesize some thiamine, but the amount available to the human body to supplement the dietary supply seems to be small.

Thiamine is absorbed readily from the intestinal tract. It is excreted in the urine in amounts that reflect the amount taken in and the amounts stored in tissues. Measurement of the urinary excretion of thiamine after giving a small dose of thiamine is useful in determining whether body stores are adequate or deficient.

Thiamine functions in the body as a coenzyme, which is called cocarboxylase. It acts as a catalyst in one of the chemical reactions by which glucose (sugar) is broken down in the tissues to supply energy. These reactions proceed stepwise, and cocarboxylase acts at an intermediate stage when a substance known as pyruvic acid has been formed.

In thiamine deficiency, pyruvic acid accumulates in the blood and tissues and there is a change in the ratio of this acid to lactic acid. These metabolic changes are magnified by administration of glucose and by exercise and form the basis of a diagnostic test for thiamine deficiency. The concentration of glucose, lactic acid, and pyruvic acid in blood is determined after the administration of glucose and a standard amount of exercise. Results are expressed as a "carbohydrate index," which increases in thiamine deficiency.

Thiamine deficiency has been produced experimentally in people. Effects of a moderate shortage of thiamine include fatigability; apathy; loss of appetite; nausea; such psychic and personality disturbances as moodiness, irritability, and depression; a sensation of numbness in the legs; and abnormalities of the electrocardiogram.

Advanced deficiency of thiamine, or beriberi, is characterized by peripheral neuritis, heart disease, and edema. Peripheral neuritis is a disease of the nerves of the extremities; usually both legs are affected and sometimes the arms as well. The symptoms include loss of sensation, muscle weakness, and paralysis.

A deficiency of thiamine can also cause damage to the brain, which may be manifested by confusion, delirium, and paralysis of the muscles that move the eyeballs. This condition is called Wernicke's syndrome.

RIBOFLAVIN, formerly known as vitamin B_2 or G, is a water-soluble, yellow pigment. It is widely distributed in foods of plant and animal origin. It is stable to heat, especially in acid solutions, but it is destroyed on exposure to light.

Among the best sources of riboflavin are milk and variety meats, like liver, heart, and kidney. Other lean meat, cheese, eggs, and many of the leafy, green vegetables also furnish valuable amounts. Whole-grain and enriched cereals and bread, in the amounts in which they are eaten in this country, contribute important amounts of riboflavin to the diet.

Pasteurizing and drying milk do not lower its riboflavin content very much, but exposure to sunlight destroys large amounts of the vitamin.

The minimal daily requirement of riboflavin is about 0.6 to 0.7 milligram for adults and 0.4 to 0.5 milligram for infants. Considerable evidence indicates that an intake of 1.1 to 1.6 milligrams daily will provide adequate body stores.

The need for riboflavin does not seem to be related to caloric consumption but may be related to body weight. Both riboflavin and protein requirements are increased by similar conditions, such as growth, pregnancy, and lactation. Riboflavin allowances accordingly are computed from the protein allowances; a factor of 0.025 is used. Recommendations for men and women are 1.8 and 1.5 milligrams daily, respectively.

The recommended intake during the second half of pregnancy is 2 milligrams. During lactation it is 2.5 milligrams. The allowance for infants is 0.5 to 0.8 milligram daily.

Chemical research on riboflavin started in 1879, but its function and importance in nutrition were not understood fully until the 1930's. Otto Warburg and W. Christian of Germany in 1932 studied a yellow enzyme in yeast and were able to split it into a protein and a pigment (flavin).

Later research disclosed riboflavin to be an essential human nutrient, which is combined with protein in the body to form a number of important enzymes. These flavoproteins function in the respiration of tissue and act closely with enzymes containing niacin, another B vitamin. Some flavoproteins are known as oxidases since they catalyze the oxidation of various chemical substances.

The functional association of riboflavin and niacin-containing enzymes helps to explain the similarity of certain findings in deficiency of these two vitamins.

Deficiency of either may result in soreness and redness of the tongue and lips, atrophy of papillae on the surface of the tongue, and cracks at the angles of the mouth. In riboflavin deficiency, dermatitis of the greasy type often involves the scrotum and may affect the face and ears. Another finding is injection of the blood vessels of the eye and growth of the vessels into the cornea, which normally does not contain these vessels.

In animals, too little riboflavin during pregnancy may result in abnormalities in the embryo or in abortion. We do not know whether any congenital defects in man may be due to an inadequate supply of riboflavin in the mother.

Chemical tests are available for estimating the adequacy of riboflavin nutrition. The amount excreted in the urine can be measured and tends to reflect dietary supply and body stores. One feature of riboflavin metabolism can markedly influence the test, however. Riboflavin is excreted when protein of the body is being broken down; it is retained when protein is being accumulated. Thus, in acute starvation, uncontrolled diabetes mellitus, and other conditions associated with negative nitrogen balance, excretion in the urine does not reflect body stores.

The concentration of riboflavin in red blood cells is under investigation as a measure of adequacy of riboflavin intake. This test may prove useful in determining nutritional status.

NIACIN, the pellagra-preventing vitamin, was discovered after long search.

Its elusiveness may be explained partly by a recent finding that one of the amino acids, tryptophan, is a precursor of niacin.

Pellagra was known to be associated with a poor, monotonous diet high in corn, since the disease was first described in the 18th century by Gaspar Casal in Spain and Francesco Frapoli in Italy. Theories regarding the cause of pellagra were many. For years, the disease was believed to be due to a toxic or infectious substance in spoiled corn. Early in the present century, Casimir Funk suggested that pellagra was due to vitamin deficiency. Investigators in Egypt held that the disease was related to lack of an essential amino acid, probably tryptophan. The investigations of Joseph Goldberger, beginning about 1914, demonstrated that pellagra is due to a nutritional deficiency.

Conrad Elvehjem and his associates at the University of Wisconsin in 1937 discovered that niacin (nicotinic acid) cured blacktongue in dogs, a condition previously recognized as similar to pellagra in human beings. Shortly thereafter niacin was shown to be effective in the prevention and treatment of pellagra.

The whole story was not yet complete, however. Diets in parts of the world in which pellagra was rare contained less niacin than did diets in areas in which pellagra was common. Furthermore, some foods such as milk are low in niacin but they effectively prevent pellagra. These discrepancies were cleared up after the discovery by Willard Krehl and his associates in the University of Wisconsin in 1945 that either tryptophan or niacin could counteract a retarded growth in rats produced by diets high in corn. Tryptophan has been shown since then to be a precursor of niacin in many animal species, and the steps by which this amino acid is converted to niacin have been determined.

We found that administration of tryptophan to people was followed by an increased urinary excretion of niacin derivatives and that tryptophan was effective in the treatment of pellagra. Similar findings were reported by other investigators. The efficacy of tryptophan as a precursor of niacin was studied in our laboratory in the Tulane University School of Medicine and by Max K. Horwitt and his associates. Approximately 60 milligrams of dietary tryptophan furnish 1 milligram of niacin, although there is wide variation in this conversion ratio among individuals.

Most foods that are high in animal protein are also high in tryptophan. Gelatin is an exception; it has almost no tryptophan. Lean meat and poultry are good sources of both tryptophan and niacin.

Among plant sources, peanuts are outstanding in niacin and are also among the best sources of tryptophan. Other plants that are good sources of both nutrients include beans, peas, other legumes, most nuts, and several whole-grain or enriched cereal products. Corn and rice are low in tryptophan. Oatmeal is low in niacin.

The requirement of niacin can be determined only in terms of both niacin and tryptophan intake. Our studies and those of Dr. Horwitt indicate that the minimum amount of niacin that will prevent pellagra in adults is about 9 milligrams daily. This includes the niacin formed from tryptophan, if we assume that 60 milligrams of tryptophan are equivalent to 1 milligram of niacin. The term "niacin equivalent" is useful for expressing this total potential niacin value of the diet.

Calculation of the niacin equivalent of the diets used by Dr. Goldberger, which resulted in pellagra, gives a figure of 12 milligrams. These diets were higher in Calories than those used by me and by Dr. Horwitt, and the niacin requirement appears to be related to caloric intake and to body weight.

Dr. Horwitt suggested a minimum need of 4.4 milligrams of niacin equivalent for each 1,000 Calories furnished by the diet.

We found the minimum requirement in relation to body weight to be slightly more than 0.10 milligram of niacin per kilogram when the diet furnished 200 milligrams of tryptophan.

Dr. Emmett Holt's studies and the calculation of the niacin equivalent received by breast-fed infants suggest that the requirement of infants is about 5 milligrams daily, if the conversion of tryptophan to niacin is comparable to that in adults.

Recommended dietary allowances

for niacin expressed as niacin equivalents are 17 to 21 milligrams for adults and 6 to 7 milligrams for infants. These amounts are 50 percent higher than the minimum need, calculated on the basis of caloric intake or body weight, whichever is the greater amount. The many uncertainties make this large factor of safety seem desirable.

Niacin functions in the body as a component of two coenzymes, diphosphopyridine nucleotide (DPN) and triphosphopyridine nucleotide (TPN), in tissue respiration and glycolysis (the process by which sugar is broken down to produce energy). Niacinamide was found to be part of these coenzymes before its nutritional importance was discovered. They work in close association with enzymes that contain riboflavin.

Niacin deficiency is characterized by dermatitis, particularly of areas of skin which are exposed to light or injury; inflammation of mucous membranes, including the entire gastrointestinal tract, which results in a red, swollen, sore tongue and mouth, diarrhea, and rectal irritation; and psychic changes, such as irritability, anxiety, depression, and (in advanced pellagra) delirium, hallucinations, confusion, disorientation, and stupor.

In severe deficiency, hydrochloric acid may be absent from the gastric juice. The excretion of niacin metabolites in the urine falls to low levels. An excretion of less than 2 milligrams in 24 hours is typical of pellagra.

A deficiency of riboflavin often accompanies a deficiency of niacin. Thiamine deficiency may also be present at times.

VITAMIN B₆ consists of a group of three closely related substances, pyridoxine, pyridoxal, and pyridoxamine. They are widely distributed in foods and are present in both free and bound form.

The best sources of vitamin B₆ are muscle meats, liver, vegetables, and whole-grain cereals. The bran from the cereal grains has especially large amounts. Few foods can be classed as poor sources of this vitamin.

The exact requirement of vitamin B₆ has not been determined. Probably 1 to 2 milligrams daily should be enough for an adult, an amount readily provided by the average diet in the United States.

The need of infants can be supplied by milk, which contains 100 micrograms per liter.

In animals, vitamin B₆ requirement is increased by methionine (an amino acid), protein, and sucrose (cane sugar) and apparently is reduced by choline, essential fatty acids, biotin, and pantothenic acid. In the rat, vitamin B₆ is synthesized by intestinal organisms, and some of this seems to be available for metabolic needs. We do not know whether these findings apply to people.

Vitamin B₆ occurs in tissues predominantly as the phosphates of pyridoxal or pyridoxamine.

Pyridoxal phosphate functions as a coenzyme in a number of chemical reactions involving amino acids. This explains the increased need of the vitamin when diets are high in protein.

Enzymes containing vitamin B₆ are important in many reactions that provide material for the citric acid cycle, a metabolic pathway that furnishes energy for the body.

Vitamin B₆ has a role in the conversion of tryptophan to niacin derivatives. This function forms the basis of a test for deficiency of vitamin B₆. When a large amount of tryptophan is administered to deficient animals or man, xanthurenic acid is excreted in the urine in abnormal quantities. Vitamin B₆ may also function in the metabolism of essential fatty acids.

A deficiency of vitamin B₆ due solely to dietary inadequacy has not been observed in adults.

Deficiency has been reported in infants who received a liquid milk formula in which much of the vitamin B₆ was destroyed unknowingly in processing. The infants developed irritability, muscular twitchings, and convulsive seizures. If vitamin B_6 is not supplied in adequate amounts, infants cease gaining weight and may develop anemia.

Experimental deficiency in adults has been produced by the administration of a pyridoxine antagonist, desoxypyridoxine. Symptoms included irritability, depression, and sleepiness. Other findings were a seborrheic (greasy) type of dermatitis, skin lesions that resembled pellagra, soreness of the tongue and lips, conjunctivitis, and peripheral neuritis. These abnormalities resemble those seen in deficiency of riboflavin, niacin, and thiamine and attest the close metabolic relationship of these vitamins of the B complex.

Vitamin B_6 metabolism may be altered during pregnancy, and the requirement may be increased. Pregnant women excrete abnormally large amounts of xanthurenic acid after the administration of tryptophan. There is also an abnormal response to administration of alanine, an amino acid. Blood urea nitrogen remains high for more than 12 hours. Similar findings have been observed in animals deficient in vitamin B_6.

Pyridoxine has been shown to prevent or alleviate the peripheral neuritis that may develop when isoniazid, an antituberculosis medication, is administered.

PANTOTHENIC ACID is needed by man and many species of animals.

It is widely distributed in foods. Liver and eggs, particularly good sources, contain 100–200 micrograms per gram. Broccoli, cauliflower, lean beef, skim milk, white potatoes and sweet potatoes, tomatoes, and molasses are quite high in pantothenic acid.

The human requirement is unknown but is probably not above 5 milligrams daily.

Pantothenic acid has a vital role in metabolic processes as it is a constituent of coenzyme A. This coenzyme is required for acetylation, one of the essential chemical reactions of the body. An important compound, active acetate, is actually the acetylated coenzyme that reacts in numerous ways.

Coenzyme A occupies a central position in metabolism. It functions in the formation and breakdown of fatty acids and in the entry of fat and carbohydrate into the citric acid cycle, a series of chemical reactions that provide energy for the organism. Coenzyme A functions in the synthesis of the porphyrin part of the hemoglobin molecule and in the formation of sterols (such as cholesterol) and steroid hormones (formed by the adrenal and sex glands).

The symptoms of a deficiency of pantothenic acid in animals are more diverse than are observed for most other vitamins, perhaps because of the fundamental importance of coenzyme A in metabolism and the many reactions in which it participates.

A deficiency disease due to lack of pantothenic acid has not been observed in man. Diets may never be sufficiently low in this vitamin to produce deficiency.

William Bean and his associates at the State University of Iowa attempted to induce deficiency by administering a pantothenic acid antagonist, omega-methyl-pantothenic acid, to volunteer subjects who were receiving a diet devoid of pantothenic acid.

(A vitamin antagonist is a substance so similar in structure to the vitamin that the body accepts it in place of the vitamin, but the antagonist is unable to perform the functions of the true vitamin.)

Numerous physical and biochemical disturbances resulted. The subjects became quarrelsome, sullen, and petulant. Some of them developed pains and disturbances of sensation in the arms and legs. Others noted loss of appetite, indigestion, and nausea. Fainting attacks were common. The pulse tended to be unduly rapid. There seemed to be an increase in susceptibility to infection. Laboratory tests showed many abnormal findings related to the numerous functions of pantothenic acid in the chemical reactions of the body.

A deficiency of pantothenic acid may be responsible for the "burning foot syndrome," which is encountered in places where other B complex deficiencies are common. This condition has been reported to respond to doses of pantothenic acid.

Other studies indicate that pantothenic acid may influence the reaction of human subjects to stress.

THE FOLIC ACID group of vitamins are essential for many animal species. They are necessary for the formation of blood cells in man.

Members of this group include folacin (or pteroylglutamic acid), pteroyltriglutamic acid, pteroylheptaglutamic acid, and folinic acid or citrovorum factor, a derivative of folic acid that occurs in natural materials in both free and combined form.

Information is meager concerning the amounts of folacin and folinic acid compounds in foods and their biological availability. Enzymes that can break down conjugated pteroylglutamates (combined forms of folic acid) to folacin occur in many animal tissues. In several natural products, these enzymes or conjugases are accompanied by an inhibitor. This inhibitor appears to influence the availability of the combined forms of folacin to human subjects. These findings illustrate the difficulties involved in estimating the folacin that is available from foods and in determining the human need for it.

The best sources include liver, dry beans, lentils, cowpeas, asparagus, broccoli, spinach, and collards. Other good sources include kidney, peanuts, filberts, walnuts, immature or young lima beans, cabbage, sweet corn, chard, turnip greens, lettuce, beet greens, and whole-wheat products.

Intestinal bacteria synthesize folacin. This source may be important in man, because experimental deficiency has not been induced by diets low in folacin. The dietary requirement of folacin is not known, but available evidence suggests that approximately 0.1 to 0.2 milligram daily may suffice.

Much has been learned about the function of folacin and its derivatives, although their exact metabolic role has not been delineated. It seems likely that a derivative of folinic acid is the functioning form of the vitamin and that this derivative combines with a protein and functions as a coenzyme. Folacin participates in the formation by the body of complex chemical compounds known as purines and pyrimidines that are utilized in the building up of nucleoproteins— that is, proteins that are found in the nucleus of every cell.

The essentiality of folacin for hematopoiesis (the manufacture of blood cells) in man presumably resides in its function in the formation of purines and pyrimidines.

Folic acid stimulates the formation of blood cells in certain anemias, which are characterized by oversized red cells and the accumulation in the bone marrow of immature red blood cells, called megaloblasts. The bone marrow is the organ that manufactures blood cells. It cannot complete the process in the absence of folic acid. Vitamin B_{12} also is needed for the formation of blood cells and is effective in the treatment of many anemias.

The exact biochemical interrelationships of these two vitamins in metabolism have not been clarified. Vitamin B_{12}, like folacin, seems necessary for the formation of nucleoproteins.

Two human anemias appear to be due primarily to folacin deficiency— macrocytic anemia of pregnancy and megaloblastic anemia of infancy. These anemias occasionally respond to treatment with vitamin B_{12}.

Sprue and nutritional macrocytic anemia often improve when either folacin or vitamin B_{12} is administered. Sprue is a disease in which absorption of food from the intestinal tract is seriously impaired, and the stools contain large amounts of fat. Folacin may improve absorption in this condition.

In pernicious anemia, treatment with folacin may bring the blood status to normal, but relapse occurs. Damage to the spinal cord and peripheral nerves, which is a common finding in pernicious anemia, is neither prevented nor alleviated.

The mechanism by which deficiency of folacin develops is not clear. The deficiency may be of dietary origin in some instances but not in others. Defective absorption may explain deficiency at times.

Macrocytic anemia of pregnancy may be related to an increased folacin requirement that is not met by the diet. Folacin has a role in the reproductive process in animals.

The syndrome of folacin deficiency in man is exemplified best by the symptoms that develop when large amounts of a folic acid antagonist such as aminopterin are administered. Manifestations include glossitis (a sore, red, smooth tongue), diarrhea, gastrointestinal lesions, and anemia. Similar findings occur in sprue and nutritional macrocytic anemia; they often revert to normal with folacin therapy.

Folacin is functionally related to ascorbic acid. Megaloblastic anemia of infancy occurs in infants receiving diets deficient in ascorbic acid. It can be prevented by ascorbic acid but responds to treatment only with folacin or folinic acid.

Folacin is related to the metabolism of the amino acid tyrosine, and so is ascorbic acid. An abnormal excretion of tyrosine metabolites in the urine occurs in infants who lack ascorbic acid. Administration of ascorbic acid or large doses of folacin relieve the abnormality.

VITAMIN B_{12}, like many other members of the B complex, is not a single substance but consists of several closely related compounds with similar activity. The term "cobalamin" is applied to this group of substances because they contain cobalt. Vitamin B_{12} is cyanocobalamin, named for the cyanide ion in the molecule. Other compounds are hydroxycobalamin and nitritocobalamin.

The search for vitamin B_{12}, which is the antipernicious anemia factor of liver, forms an interesting chapter in medical investigation. Pernicious anemia was an incurable disease until 1926, when George R. Minot and William P. Murphy, of Boston, showed that feeding whole liver was effective therapy. William Castle and his associates at Harvard demonstrated that mixtures of beef muscle and normal gastric juice would also induce remission in pernicious anemia. Beef muscle alone and beef muscle and the gastric juice of a patient with pernicious anemia were ineffectual.

Castle postulated that a substance in gastric juice (intrinsic factor) combined with a substance in food (extrinsic factor) to form the antipernicious anemia factor of liver. Intrinsic factor was absent from the gastric juice of patients who had pernicious anemia.

As each new B vitamin was discovered, it was tested for antipernicious anemia activity. Folic acid at first was thought to be the active principle of liver, as it caused improvement in the blood picture in pernicious anemia.

Later study indicated that folic acid would not maintain normal blood status and failed to influence the neurologic changes that occur in this disease. A serious handicap in the search for the antipernicious anemia factor was the need to test all materials in human subjects who had pernicious anemia in relapse. No animal developed a comparable disease.

Mary Shorb, of the University of Maryland, in 1947 found that liver extract contained a growth factor that was required by a micro-organism, *Lactobacillus lactis* Dorner. Using this microbiological assay, Edward L. Rickes and his associates, at Rahway, N.J., isolated B_{12} in 1948.

Lester Smith, in England, at about the same time isolated the vitamin by procedures designed to obtain in pure form the red pigment that gave color to active preparations of liver.

Vitamin B_{12} was shown to be effective in the treatment of pernicious anemia by Randolph West, of Columbia University, and others.

Subsequently it was discovered that vitamin B_{12} is not only the antipernicious anemia factor of liver but also the extrinsic factor of food.

Intrinsic factor of gastric juice appears to be necessary for the absorption of vitamin B_{12}, but the mechanism of action has not been determined.

Intrinsic factor may have other functions as well. We have found that intrinsic factor will increase the binding of vitamin B_{12} by proteins in tissues and in human serum.

Vitamin B_{12} is found in animal protein foods. The best sources are liver and kidney. Other sources are muscle meats, milk, cheese, fish, and eggs. As far as we know, fruit and vegetables do not furnish any vitamin B_{12}.

The dietary requirement for the vitamin is unknown. A normal diet is estimated to contain 8 to 15 micrograms. The daily administration by injection of 1 microgram will induce remission in pernicious anemia. The normal adult presumably needs to absorb an amount no larger than this.

The biological availability of vitamin B_{12} in the diet has not been determined.

Much remains to be learned about the specific functions of vitamin B_{12} in bodily processes. It appears to be involved in the synthesis of nucleoproteins through participation in the metabolism of purines and pyrimidines. The close relationship to folic acid in stimulating blood regeneration has been discussed. The specific role of this vitamin in the metabolism of nerve tissue has not been determined.

Vitamin B_{12} is essential for the growth of animals. It may have a growth-promoting effect in man in certain conditions of diet and nutrition.

Pernicious anemia is the most important human disease that is due to too little vitamin B_{12}. The deficiency is not due to dietary inadequacy but to failure of absorption of the vitamin from the intestinal tract in the absence of intrinsic factor from the gastric juice.

Pernicious anemia is characterized by degenerative lesions in the spinal cord and peripheral nerves as well as by macrocytic (large cell) anemia.

The concentration of vitamin B_{12} in blood is extremely low. Failure of absorption of vitamin B_{12} can be demonstrated by administration of Co^{60} vitamin B_{12}—that is, vitamin B_{12} containing radioactive cobalt. If intrinsic factor is given with Co^{60} vitamin B_{12}, absorption is increased to normal.

Macrocytic anemia that follows surgical removal of the stomach is due to failure of absorption of vitamin B_{12}, as in pernicious anemia. Sprue may be associated with a deficiency of vitamin B_{12}, as are some other syndromes due to intestinal malabsorption. In these situations, there is failure of absorption of vitamin B_{12}, even when intrinsic factor is administered with the vitamin.

A deficiency of vitamin B_{12} due to dietary inadequacy is rare. Only two cases of severe macrocytic anemia on this basis have been reported. A small percentage of persons who subsist for years on a strict vegetarian diet, however, have been found to develop other signs of vitamin B_{12} deficiency. Soreness of the mouth and tongue, numbness and tingling of the hands, pains in the back, and (in one instance) combined degeneration of the spinal cord have been observed. Levels of vitamin B_{12} in the blood are lower than normal in vegetarians.

CHOLINE is not a vitamin in the strict sense. It is classified usually as a member of the vitamin B complex. It is an essential nutrient in that methyl groups (part of the choline molecule) must be included in the diet. The amino acid methionine (in protein) and betaine are other dietary sources of methyl groups. It seems likely that choline and methionine are not completely interchangeable as sources of methyl in all species.

A dietary requirement for choline cannot be given, since the compound can be manufactured in the body and the need for choline depends also on other sources of methyl groups. The average diet contains 250 to 600 milligrams of choline.

Foods that supply large amounts of choline are liver, kidney, brain, muscle meats, nuts, beans, peas, and skim milk. Moderate amounts exist in cereals and a number of vegetables.

Choline functions in the body as a source of labile methyl groups and in the formation of phospholipids, a class of fatty substances found in all body tissues. The most important phospholipids are lecithin, cephalin, and sphingomyelin. These compounds are found especially in nerve tissue. Lecithin and cephalin are present in egg yolks. Choline is a component of the compound acetylcholine, which functions in the transmission of nerve impulses across neuromuscular junctions.

Labile methyl groups are used in the synthesis of creatine, N^1-methylnicotinamide (an excretion product of niacin) and probably other vital substances, such as epinephrine, the hormone of the adrenal medulla. Methyl groups have a lipotropic function— that is, they prevent the accumulation of fat in the liver.

Choline deficiency leads to many abnormal findings in various animal species, among them hemorrhagic lesions in the kidney.

Incomplete evidence suggests that choline may have an influence on fatty infiltration of the liver in man. Choline, methionine, vitamin B_{12}, and folic acid are interrelated in the prevention of fatty livers in animals under certain dietary conditions.

BIOTIN is needed in animal nutrition and presumably is essential for man. It is present in many foods and is synthesized by the intestinal bacteria. The urinary excretion of biotin in humans at times is greater than the intake.

Liver, milk, meat, nuts, egg yolk, most vegetables, and a number of fruits (bananas, grapefruit, tomatoes, watermelon, and strawberries) contain significant amounts of biotin.

It seems unlikely that a dietary deficiency of biotin occurs in human beings. The requirement has not been determined.

Biotin seems to be an essential component of a coenzyme in carbon dioxide fixation, an important reaction in intermediary metabolism. Considerable data suggest that one manifestation of this role of biotin is a requirement for purine synthesis. Biotin is the anti-egg-white injury factor. Raw egg white contains the protein, avidin, which combines with biotin to prevent its absorption.

Virgil Sydenstricker and associates at the University of Georgia produced experimental deficiency of biotin in people by feeding large amounts of raw egg white. Manifestations included a dry, scaly dermatitis and changes in the color of the skin. Nervous symptoms, tongue lesions, and abnormalities in the electrocardiogram were noted—findings similar to those produced by deficiency of other vitamins of the B complex.

GRACE A. GOLDSMITH, M.D., *is professor of medicine in the Tulane University School of Medicine, New Orleans. She also is consultant physician, Charity Hospital of Louisiana, New Orleans; chairman, Food and Nutrition Board, National Academy of Sciences-National Research Council; and member of the Council on Foods and Nutrition of the American Medical Association.*

If all that we know about nutrition were applied to modern society, the result would be an enormous improvement in public health, at least equal to that which resulted when the germ theory of infectious disease was made the basis of public health and medical work.—FRANK G. BOUDREAU, M.D.

We know that a lot of people who are regarded as poor prospects for jobs need food. They are set down in personnel records as lazy and dumb. What is really wrong with them is that they are hungry.—PAUL V. McNUTT.

Vitamin C

MARY L. DODDS

THE conquest of scurvy is a landmark in the dramatic story of nutrition. Scurvy once was common during famines and wars and among sailors who ate little except bread and salt meat on long voyages.

Scurvy brings debility, skin degeneration, spongy gums, hemorrhages in body tissues, and sometimes death.

People recognized the symptoms readily enough and concluded that scurvy and diet were related somehow. Naval physicians conducted thorough investigations of causes and the remedies. They learned that eating fresh fruit, especially citrus fruits, and some vegetables can prevent scurvy. The British Navy in 1795 ordered all its ships to carry supplies of lemons or limes.

It took a long time to establish that the effective substance is vitamin C. The way it performs its work is still mysterious.

Charles G. King, then at the University of Pittsburgh and later director of the Nutrition Foundation, and a graduate student, William Waugh, isolated vitamin C from lemons in 1932.

They identified it as the antiscorbutic—scurvy preventing—vitamin.

Hungarian scientists had isolated it 4 years earlier, but they did not recognize it as the scurvy-preventing vitamin, because its striking chemical properties were of greater interest to them.

The vitamin was officially named "ascorbic acid" to indicate its antiscorbutic function.

Its chemical activity may account for its mystifying qualities. It reacts readily under so many circumstances that one is tempted to connect its chemical versatility with its antiscorbutic function—although several compounds have the same chemical properties but little or no antiscorbutic potency.

Its chemical structure is quite simple. Its behavior as a chemical is well known. Relatively satisfactory methods have been developed for determining it. Scientists have analyzed endless biological materials to see if it exists in them.

Vitamin C occurs in animals and vegetables extensively but haphazardly. Fresh raw fruit and vegetables contain it, yet few animals need it. People, monkeys, and guinea pigs get it from sources outside their bodies. Other species make their own.

Some vitamins exist in several forms, but vitamin C occurs naturally in only one. It exists in two states of oxidation.

Closely related forms have been synthesized but are not known to occur in nature. A few of them have slight antiscorbutic activity. Other vitamins, especially those of the B family, carry on their biological duties in combination with partners and become coenzymes, but whether vitamin C does so has not been proved.

People, monkeys, and guinea pigs show similar signs of physical deterioration when they are deprived of it.

Recovery follows the same pattern when vitamin C is given them. The evidences of its function may be observed, but the manner in which it functions remained a secret in 1959.

Vitamin C is the same chemical compound whether it is isolated from foods or is synthesized and sold as pills or capsules.

It is known as L-ascorbic acid in the reduced form and as L-dehydroascorbic acid in the oxidized form.

Chemical pictures or formulas of these two forms can be found in any standard textbook on physiology, such as *Practical Physiological Chemistry*, by Philip B. Hawk, Bernard L. Oser, and William H. Summerson.

The chemical makeup is related to the hexose sugars. These sugars have a backbone of six carbon atoms firmly joined to each other rather like vertebras. On the side these carbons are joined to oxygen and hydrogen. Vitamin C has this form, too, but between the second and third carbons there is a double bond, which means chemically that this backbone is not so firm as that of the hexose sugars. These two carbons in vitamin C are free to make changes.

The hydrogen atoms at this point are especially at liberty to wander off, and they have a high preference for any oxygen that may be about. It is when these two hydrogens have left that the vitamin becomes known as L-dehydroascorbic acid. This feature makes it an extremely changeable chemical in solution, and the ability to drop off the two hydrogens is one of its outstanding features.

Outside the body, in solution, this compelling chemical action takes place easily—the characteristic that is the basis of a number of the analytical methods in use for ascorbic acid.

This chemical activity of vitamin C suggests possible ways in which it may enter into the chemical activities in the living organism.

Glucose, an important hexose sugar in metabolism, is a more stable chemical than vitamin C, although in some ways it resembles it in structure. Glucose is easily stored in the body, and it divides into successively smaller molecules that provide energy during breakdown by well-established routes.

In human beings, ascorbic acid—chemically fragile though it may be—sidesteps vigorous activity, and any excess not needed for its specific function is eliminated in the urine without being changed.

SCURVY now is uncommon in the United States. Nearly all of us get some vitamin C in our food. Infants on formula feeding who get no supplementary vitamin C will develop scurvy. Old people, especially those who live alone on restricted food intakes because they are poor, cannot go to a food market, or are indifferent, may show scorbutic signs. Some diets in institutions are low in fresh fruit and vegetables, and inmates who spend many years in them may show symptoms of scurvy.

Symptoms differ in infants and adults because of the added stress put on the organism by growth.

The normal newborn infant has stores of ascorbic acid adequate to prevent development of scurvy for about 5 months. The breast-fed baby normally gets enough for protection until he begins to eat a variety of foods. Deficiency is rare in children more than 15 months old. Infantile scurvy will develop in 3 months or more after breast feeding is stopped if no antiscorbutic is given either as a food or a supplement.

The most marked symptoms are found in growing bones. Bones may form improperly because the intercellular cementing substance or supporting tissue is missing and mineralization is faulty. Even though the minerals are available, they are disarranged and cannot form normal bones.

Areas at the ends of the bone shafts are especially affected. The soft tissue about the joints swells and is tender. The difficulty tends to be more severe in the legs than in the arms. Walking and sitting become painful, and the child lies on his back to avoid the pain involved in moving his legs.

The front ends of the ribs are sore. Breathing may be difficult. The ribs may be beaded. The child cries when handled or even approached, because he expects pain. If there are teeth, the gums may bleed. Changes in the soft tissues are less common in infants than in adults.

The staff of Vanderbilt University Medical School Hospital worked with deficiency diseases and their diagnoses for many years.

Dr. Calvin Woodruff of that staff reviewed a 28-year record (1926–1954) of 103 cases of infantile scurvy treated there. In an article in the Journal of the American Medical Association for June 2, 1956, he reported that in all cases scurvy resulted because of long periods of feeding when there was no ascorbic acid or negligible amounts of it in the diet. The disease was reversed in 3 to 4 days when even small amounts of ascorbic acid were supplied as foods or in capsules.

His record showed that infantile scurvy is not frequent—but it also showed that there should be no scurvy at all, because it is so easy to supply the vitamin C a baby needs.

The soft tissues of adults who have scurvy are the site of the most evident signs of the deficiency. The cementing material is missing, and the cells literally seem to fall apart. The gums become sore, swollen, spongy, bleed readily, and are easily infected. In extreme cases, the teeth may loosen. This condition is known as gingivitis. The skin is thickened and scaled in spots. Small hemorrhages due to weakness of blood vessels form at the hair follicles; they appear where there is pressure, even as slight a pressure as the binding of clothes. These signs appear first on the legs and thighs. Large discolored patches form as blood leakages continue. A feeling of general weakness and a complaint of breathlessness are common. Anemia may occur because of loss of blood as the capillaries break. Resistance to infection is reduced. Wounds do not heal. Old wounds break open.

As with infants, the healing process is dramatically rapid once a supply of vitamin C is given.

Signs of scurvy now seen are less drastic.

Borderline cases are hard to diagnose by any of the classical symptoms, because weariness may result for many reasons, gums may be infected even when intakes of vitamin C are high, and anemias may have many causes. Unless there is other proof, we can rely on no single symptom to indicate a deficiency of vitamin C.

The amount of ascorbic acid suggested for a person is based on a great deal of research. Vitamins perform their work in unbelievably small amounts. The measures used for them have a strange sound as compared to usual commercial units such as ounces, pounds, and quarts. It may help in appreciating the powerful activity of vitamins to compare the units used in their measurement with the more ordinary units.

A sweetpotato furnishes about 35 milligrams of ascorbic acid for every 100 grams eaten. That means there are 35 parts of ascorbic acid for every million parts of sweetpotato. A sweetpotato of modest size weighs about 200 grams, or a little less than one-half pound.

One hundred milligrams of ascorbic

acid eaten each day is a generous supply. For a person weighing 132 pounds,
this will be about 1 part of the vitamin
to 10 million parts of the body. The
content of vitamin C in the blood is
considered good if there is 1 part in a
million (1.0 milligram per 100 milliliters). One hundred milliliters is close
to one-tenth of a quart.

The authorities who have interpreted
research and set the goals for the
amounts of vitamin C intake by people
have had different objectives—requirement and recommendation.

The requirement is estimated to be
the intake that is adequate to prevent
scurvy.

The recommendation is set to provide certain benefits, over and above
the prevention of scurvy, such as avert-
ing gum disorders and favoring resistance to infections.

The recommendation is more than
twice the requirement. We in the
United States use the recommendation
as an accepted measure, but there is
need to understand the requirement or
low level.

Recommended daily allowances for
maintenance of good nutrition in
healthy persons are based on age and
known increases in the body cellular
activity, such as rapid growth during
adolescence and added needs in pregnancy and lactation. Size and sex also
may be factors, as the adult man may
need a little more than a woman.

Recommendations given in "Recommended Dietary Allowances" (revised
in 1958), publication 589 of the National Academy of Sciences-National
Research Council, are:
For infants, 30 milligrams a day;
for children from 1 to 9 years, start
at 35 and increase to 60 milligrams;
for males 10 to 20 years old, increase
gradually from 75 to 100 milligrams;
for fully grown men, 75 milligrams;
for the adolescent girl 10 to 20 years
old, the increase is from 75 to 80 milligrams;
for fully grown women, 70 milligrams.
In the second half of pregnancy, 100
milligrams are recommended, and in
lactation, 150 milligrams.

Thus a vitamin C tablet, labeled
"100 milligrams," contains more of
the vitamin than is needed in most
states of normal health.

We have evidence that as little as 10
to 20 milligrams daily will prevent
frank scurvy. That is the basis of the
requirement of 30 milligrams for the
adult, as set by British and Canadian
authorities.

The difference between the requirement and the recommendation seems
to be large. There are indications that
the difference provides benefits that
are wise to accept but hard to measure.

THE ACTUAL REQUIREMENT of people
is of perpetual interest. Scurvy is rare,
but it would be useful to have a
measure for physical or biochemical
stages on intakes intermediate between
too little and abundant. Such a
measure would help us distinguish
adequate nutrition from crucial states
that exist before physical symptoms of
deficiency appear.

An informative technique relates
vitamin C levels in some of the blood
fractions, such as plasma, serum,
whole blood, or white cell-platelets
(which are parts of the blood that can
be separated to work with), to sustained known intakes of the vitamin.
Experience justifies assigning significance to the ascorbic acid content of
these fractions. Plasma, serum, and
blood level are conceded to reflect
dietary supply. The content of the
white cell-platelets indicates body
stores.

Data from experiments relate intake
with one or more of these blood measurements.

A famous experiment was reported
by John H. Crandon, Charles C. Lund,
and David B. Dill in 1940 in the New
England Journal of Medicine. Dr.
Crandon kept to a diet that was adequate in all nutrients except vitamin
C until scurvy developed.

His plasma level of ascorbic acid

reached zero in 41 days. The whole blood level of the vitamin reached zero in 124 days. Wound healing took place normally at 4 months, but on the 134th day (10 days after ascorbic acid had disappeared from all the blood components) skin thickening and scaliness appeared on the thighs and buttocks. Small skin hemorrhages showed on the 161st day, and wounds then would not heal.

Dr. Michel Pijoan, in 1941–1942, served as the director of nutrition in the United States Indian Service and observed American Indians who had low intakes of ascorbic acid but no scurvy. He believed that the ability to maintain a fixed level of vitamin C in the plasma—no matter how small— prevents scurvy. To verify his theory, he maintained himself for 20 months on daily average intakes of 16 milligrams of vitamin C. His plasma levels during that time were 0.0 to 0.2 milligram per 100 milliliters, but his white cell-platelet value was constant at 26 milligrams per 100 grams. At the end of 20 months, wound healing was judged to be normal.

Research workers at Cornell University—Betty F. Steele, Rachel L. Liner, Zaida H. Pierce, and Harold H. Williams—reported in 1955 in the Journal of Nutrition that at a lower level of intake (10 milligrams or less) the ascorbic acid content of white cell-platelets went down 40 to 80 percent for 13 subjects in 40 days.

Gradual increases of vitamin C intake by increments of 10 milligrams up to 40 milligrams resulted in slightly increasing concentrations, but the final ascorbic acid content of the white cell-platelets was not equal to the pre-experimental level for any subject, nor was any as high as that which Dr. Pijoan maintained on an intake of 16 milligrams of vitamin C.

The serum levels of the people under survey at Cornell increased only slightly, and at 40 milligrams were close to 0.2 to 0.3 milligram per 100 milliliters.

These records suggest that scurvy develops after long deprivation of as-

corbic acid and that low levels of intake, if regular, will protect for even longer periods.

In our own experience, women who were maintained on 35 milligrams a day had slowly decreasing plasma levels of the vitamin. Increasing the intake to about 60 milligrams a day resulted in increasing levels for most of the 42 women. Dr. Florence L. MacLeod and I reported this finding in Science in 1947.

We learned that a daily intake of 35 milligrams would not maintain indefinitely a positive balance of the ascorbic acid in their plasma—thus the adequacy of the requirement of only 30 milligrams daily may depend on the length of time the diet is so restricted.

We got additional evidence in favor of intakes approaching the recommendation level for young men in our laboratories. On controlled intakes of 75 milligrams a day, the men maintained plasma levels of approximately 0.5 milligram per 100 milliliters for 7 weeks and had a small and constant excretion of about 5 milligrams of ascorbic acid a day.

Work with both men and women at similar levels of intake has indicated that sex may be a factor in the blood levels maintained. In our experience, women maintained on 75 milligrams of vitamin C a day for as long as the men had (in contrast to them) plasma levels of 0.8 to 0.9 milligram per 100 milliliters, with daily excretions of about 12 milligrams.

We cannot attribute this variation solely to differences in the volume of blood. Total volumes of blood in men are about 7.5 percent higher than in women, but plasma volumes are more nearly equal, because men have higher hemoglobin values than women do. The distribution of ascorbic acid among the blood parts, in plasma or serum, red cells, and white cell-platelets, may have some bearing on the observations of sex differences in plasma levels on the same intake.

This is a guide to the relationship

of vitamin C intake to blood levels; one should remember that these are averages and are more useful in the evaluation of groups than individuals, unless a consecutive series of blood values is available for the individual:

On a daily intake of 10 milligrams, plasma levels remain below 0.1 milligram per 100 milliliters; on 23 milligrams, below 0.2 milligram per 100 milliliters. Plasma levels between 0.2 and 0.6 milligram per 100 milliliters may be expected at intakes of 25 to 70 milligrams. Above 70 milligrams, plasma values vary between 0.6 and 1.0 milligram per 100 milliliters. At 100 to 1,000 milligrams, levels remain very close to 1.4 to 1.5 milligrams per 100 milliliters.

The value of ascorbic in white cell-platelets does not increase above 30 milligrams per 100 grams but may drop on intakes of 10 to 23 milligrams daily to 2 to 12 milligrams per 100 grams. A value below 2 milligrams per 100 grams is indicative of inadequate intakes of vitamin C.

Low levels of vitamin C in plasma, 0.2 milligram per 100 milliliters or less (which are accompanied by white cell-platelet levels of 12 to 20 milligrams per 100 grams), show a need for increasing the intake of vitamin C. This combination of measures may serve to define the prescorbutic state without the usual clinical symptoms.

Otto A. Bessey and Oliver H. Lowry at one time worked together to adapt chemical methods for the analysis of nutrients in very small samples of blood. They developed many useful measurements on a micro scale. Their method for determining total ascorbic acid in 0.01 milliliter of blood is accepted generally. Most data that have appeared after 1945 present blood levels as total ascorbic acid values by this micro method. Earlier investigators reported the content as reduced ascorbic acid. The trends of both measures are similar, and the existence of the two types of data does not change our general understanding of the vitamin and its behavior.

The fact that the total ascorbic acid values of blood levels tend to be higher than the reduced values has led to the speculation that blood contains dehydroascorbic acid.

We have concluded a study in our laboratories on the utilization by young men of dehydroascorbic as compared with that of ascorbic acid. We find that either form of the vitamin results in similar levels of reduced blood levels of ascorbic acid. We also find higher values on both forms of intake for the measure of total ascorbic acid, but we are not convinced that the difference is dehydroascorbic acid present in the blood. It seems improbable that with a mechanism so potent in converting ingested dehydroascorbic acid to the reduced form that small amounts will remain unchanged in the blood stream.

AN ANTIOXIDANT will keep food, such as peaches and apples, from darkening during processing. Vitamin C is a good one. When lemon juice is used for this purpose, it is the vitamin C in it that does the work.

The use of D-arabo ascorbic acid sometimes is proposed as an antioxidant for foods. The question then arises as to what effect the practice will have on accepted measures.

Two investigations were made in 1957–1958 to answer this question. One was at the pharmaceutical company of Hoffmann-La Roche, and one was in our laboratory at The Pennsylvania State University. Both showed that the behavior of this close relative is similar to that of ascorbic acid itself and that it is impossible to tell them apart in the blood plasma. Since this synthesized form of ascorbic acid is only slightly antiscorbutic, widespread use of it by the food industry will seriously limit the usefulness of our current measures of the antiscorbutic vitamin in work on human nutrition.

A GREAT IMPETUS was given to the study of human nutrition by the Research and Marketing Act of 1946, which made regional investigations possible.

Large segments of the population were sampled for food habits, nutritive intake, blood measurements, and clinical observations. The general uniformity of methods across the country gives highly informative results, although all tests were not carried out on all population samples. The least extensive work and the least exact information obtained was for men and women in the prime of life, but they also were represented in the investigations.

When nutritive intakes were measured and calculated and compared with recommendations of the National Research Council, sizable parts of the population repeatedly were found to be low in vitamin C intake, although average intakes as a rule exceeded the recommendation.

Blood serum or plasma levels of vitamin C averaged high. Few individuals fell below the critical level of 0.2 milligram per 100 milliliters. The critical level most often used in reporting, however, was 0.4 milligram per 100 milliliters.

FEW CLINICAL SYMPTOMS of a deficiency of vitamin C, except sore and tender gums, were reported. They were found in higher proportions in populations in New Mexico, Colorado, and Maine, where fewer foods rich in vitamin C are eaten. The chief sources there of dietary vitamin C come from foods not high in ascorbic acid, like potatoes in Maine or foods eaten in limited amounts, like chili peppers in New Mexico.

We are not sure how best to evaluate these reports of gum difficulty, or gingivitis, because often the people who were studied had blood levels not associated with scurvy. The gum disorders may be an indication in some persons of an ascorbic acid intake that is below the highest recommended amount.

Dr. Norman Jolliffe, director of the Bureau of Nutrition of the City of New York, in a report in 1958 on the nutritional status of schoolchildren in Cuba, cited an occurrence of 22.5 percent gingivitis in the public schools. He did not attribute it to a lack of vitamin C because such confirmatory signs as skin scaling or hardening were absent.

His opinion was that soreness and bleeding of gums cannot be used as a key sign of a deficiency of vitamin C unless it is accompanied by confirmatory signs. Because only 1 percent of the Cuban children had blood serum levels under 0.3 milligram per 100 milliliters of blood, he ascribed the incidence of gingivitis to other causes.

The observation of gingivitis as a possible deficiency symptom related to a low intake of vitamin C is reported frequently. A number of subjects in any survey will be in brackets that are below the average for any standard for the group. Are they the ones who show gum disorders?

The man in whom Drs. Crandon, Lund, and Dill caused experimental scurvy did not have gingivitis even after a long period without ascorbic acid. Individuals differ, and it may be that certain persons among those in population surveys have gums that are the vulnerable tissue.

A convincing piece of evidence for implicating gum disorders as an early sign of inadequate intakes of vitamin C was reported by Emma D. Kyhos, Edgar S. Gordon, Marian S. Kimble, and Elmer L. Sevringhaus in the Journal of Nutrition in 1944.

They investigated minimum ascorbic acid needs of adults and described the oral and gum disease prevalent in a prison in Wisconsin. The prisoners got no fresh fruit and very few fresh vegetables. Twenty of the 71 men had zero levels of ascorbic acid in the plasma. Nearly 80 percent had levels under 0.2 milligram per 100 milliliters. When a 25-milligram ascorbic acid supplement was given, only a slight improvement in gum disease and no real increase in plasma values occurred. A supplementation of 50 milligrams did not improve the gums, but 75 to 100 milligrams induced healing of the gums. Under those circumstances, a mild scurvy must have existed, its chief symptom being gingivitis.

A group of investigators in the West conducted a survey of a representative group of 577 older men and women. Agnes F. Morgan, Helen L. Gillam, and Romona I. Williams wrote a report on the studies in 1955.

The needs of this group for vitamin C seemed no different from those of any adult group. One observation was that women maintained higher ascorbic acid serum levels on lower intakes than men. The scientists speculated on whether advancing years and the accompanying body changes, such as the production of hormones, were factors.

Many data on ascorbic acid in the diet and vitamin C levels in the blood are available in the reports of the regional studies conducted under the Research and Marketing Act of 1946. They are presented as averages for a number of age and sex groups in different regions.

When the averages are grouped by sex in the age ranges of 4 to 12 years, 13 to 20 years, and more than 20 years, and regression lines—the relationships found by statistical methods—are calculated from the intakes and blood levels, evidence appears of a sex difference in the use made of vitamin C.

For the youngest group, there is little difference in either intake or serum ascorbic acid between the boys and girls. Above 13 years, the males have higher vitamin C intake, yet their serum ascorbic acid levels are below those of the females.

The intake averages for groups of all ages are all high, 70 to 88 milligrams, and in a narrow range. These data, which cover hundreds of cases, point to a significant difference according to sex in the utilization of ascorbic acid beginning at adolescence.

THE SYNTHESIS of vitamin C by plants and animals that provide their own supply has been traced to definite starting materials, the hexose sugars, which I mentioned earlier as having a six-carbon backbone and oxygen and hydrogen neighbors on the side. The structural likeness of ascorbic acid and these sugars and the synthesis of ascorbic acid in the laboratory from them made this family of compounds a natural set of starting materials to investigate in biosynthesis.

We have evidence that a number of the naturally occurring D-hexoses serve as precursors in plants. Rats can convert D-glucose to L-ascorbic acid. These sugars are subject to metabolic arrangements and give rise to a variety of compounds. The pathway by which the change, D-hexose sugar to L-ascorbic acid, takes place is not clearly defined, but a number of inbetween compounds are a part of the process, as they, too, give rise to L-ascorbic acid when they are fed to experimental plants and rats.

The L-hexose sugars, which more closely resemble L-ascorbic acid than D-hexoses, do not seem to act as precursors.

A major change involved in the synthesis must depend on twisting the molecules of the starting material end for end in such a way that their configuration is changed from the dextro- to the levorotatory form—that is, the ability to rotate a beam of polarized light changes during the transformation. This is a remarkable alteration, and the credit for bringing it about is given to an enzyme that only people, monkeys, and guinea pigs must lack.

THE INTERPLAY OF NUTRIENTS is the basis of metabolic activity.

The fact that the omission of vitamin C from an otherwise adequate diet will finally result in physical disaster to a complex organism demonstrates the close relationship it must bear to other nutrients as they function in the body.

A relationship calls for at least two participants. Vitamin C has failed so far to show an association that fully accounts for its functioning. Logical clues have been followed, but findings have suggested only minor participation by the vitamin.

The concentration of ascorbic acid is greatest in tissues of high metabolic activity; and, in a given tissue, the younger the animal the higher the content.

Notable concentrations are found in human beings in the adrenal, brain, pancreas, thymus, spleen, kidney, and liver. These organs therefore often have been chosen to investigate possible functions of the vitamin.

The adrenal, an exceedingly active gland, is involved in the production and activity of hormones. It is enlarged and there are pathological changes when vitamin C is deficient.

Injection of ACTH (adrenocorticotrophic hormone) causes the concentration of ascorbic acid in the adrenal gland to fall temporarily. An injection of cortisone causes a decrease in its size. These changes generally take place in experimental animals regardless of intake of ascorbic acid.

In spite of many investigations with experimental animals, the relationship of vitamin C to the adrenal gland is not clear. The evidence that men and women may have very similar amounts of ascorbic acid in their food, but different concentrations in the blood, suggests that ascorbic acid and the sex hormones may depend on each other in some way.

Phenylalanine and tyrosine, two amino acids, do not follow the usual routes of metabolism in premature infants. Providing vitamin C restores the normal process. This was demonstrated also in guinea pigs that were deficient in vitamin C. Perhaps, therefore, vitamin C has a role in protein metabolism. Proteins are made up of amino acids, and any unusual action of an amino acid is a point of interest.

Other compounds that are reducing agents but have no antiscorbutic activity can bring about this change. Harold H. Williams and his coworkers at Cornell University investigated this relationship in adult human beings. They maintained 10 persons on 7 milligrams of vitamin C daily and fed 2.5 times as much tyrosine as the usual diet supplies.

They found no indication of abnormal behavior in the body of this amino acid nor any changes in the ascorbic acid levels in the blood fractions that were not expected of these low intakes. So, in adult humans, the oxidation of tyrosine does not seem to be a major function of vitamin C, or at least not a measurable one. Scientists will continue to seek an interrelationship between protein and vitamin C, since they have this clue.

Anemia has been associated with a lack of vitamin C. The dietary abuse that results in a lack of vitamin C is likely to produce other deficiencies. An anemia can be expected when loss of blood by persistent small hemorrhages occurs, and both iron and vitamin C therapy will be beneficial.

Some researchers have tried in vain to establish that anemia is a result of low intakes of ascorbic acid. They have been unable to prevent anemia by giving vitamin C alone. Other data, however, indicate a direct relationship between low intakes of vitamin C and low hemoglobin levels, a measure of one kind of anemia.

Maybe we can reconcile the conflicting views on anemias by evidence that there is a relationship between folacin, one of the B family of vitamins, and ascorbic acid. Folacin is transformed in the body to a related substance, citrovorum factor. Vitamin C stimulates this change. The citrovorum factor is active in the human in the treatment of megaloblastic anemia. This may be an effect rather than the unique antiscorbutic function of vitamin C.

THE CONNECTION between vitamin C and infection probably is the reason that nutritionists in this country recommend higher intakes. A deficiency of vitamin C carries with it liability to infections.

In infectious ailments, like pulmonary tuberculosis, the vitamin C status is lowered, and tissue concentrations in infected animals are lower than normal—indications of increased usage or conspicuous loss.

THE SPECULATION is that the production of antibodies—disease-fighting mechanisms—is impaired if vitamin C is lacking and that there is failure of the formative cells to produce new body tissue. A suggestion has been made that activity of white blood cells can be stimulated by ascorbic acid. The white blood cells are able to destroy harmful materials as disease organisms.

Proof is needed, but the theory that the formation of new cells, as antibodies, and the replacement of impaired body tissue depend on the presence of vitamin C is a reasonable one. The failure of wounds to heal in scorbutic persons indicates a need for new building material. The higher concentration of vitamin C in young tissue than in old and the high concentration in actively multiplying cells and tissue indicate that vitamin C must be present where tissue is formed or regenerated.

Protein precursors—builders—must be present if new tissue is to be formed, and we again are searching for a protein interrelationship. How much vitamin C must be available to retain immunity to (or aid in recovery from) infection is not clear. Is it assured by an amount in excess of antiscorbutic requirements? Or will access by cells to a small supply circulating in the blood fill even emergency needs?

It is not strange that possible interrelationships of vitamin C are suggested rather than proved. Many of the metabolic activities demonstrated are oxidations and reductions, and ascorbic acid exhibits a great willingness to enter into such systems. The search goes on for the mechanisms involved in its specific function, the formation of intracellular cementing substances for both soft and bony tissues, which make possible an orderly but infinitively diverse and patterned alinement of the cells.

BECAUSE PEOPLE must depend on outside supplies of vitamin C, we should know which foods furnish it. Thousands of analyses on all manner of foods have given us a great deal of information about which ones supply it and how much they contain.

Three types of foods that contribute vitamin C generously are citrus fruits, tomatoes, and members of the cabbage family. This has been repeated so often that other fruits and vegetables, also useful sources, are overlooked. It is difficult to choose food that during the course of a day's eating will not furnish at least 25 milligrams—unless, of course, a person persists in a strange or finicky diet.

Vitamin C occurs haphazardly in plant tissues. The concentration in some is high. It is low in others. The vitamin content during the growth cycle may vary from high to low or low to high. Growing conditions are vital in the synthesis of ascorbic acid by plants. Conditions that favor a high content in bush and tree crops are not always the same that favor it in root crops.

Light accelerates its synthesis. A cloudy, rainy season will cause a crop to have less ascorbic acid than the same species grown on the same spot in a season with long hours of sunshine. Fruit on the outside of a tree will have more vitamin C than fruit shaded among the branches.

Beyond the growing stage—after harvest—crops vary in their ability to conserve the vitamin. Green beans may lose much of it within hours. Potatoes show gradual losses in several months.

Size may be a factor. A small head of cabbage usually has higher concentration than a larger head grown on the same plot, but the concentration in sweetpotatoes is independent of size.

Processing—freezing and frozen storage, canning, final cooking, and holding—causes changes, too. Research has given us valid generalizations for conserving the vitamin during many types of processing, but they do not insure equal protection for all products.

In certain vegetables, such as squash, cucumbers, and cabbage, the ascorbic acid exists along with an enzyme, ascorbic acid oxidase, or ascorbase. When the tissue of these vegetables is mutilated by crushing or cutting and is exposed to the air, the chief function of this enzyme appears to be that of changing the ascorbic acid to dehydroascorbic acid. Other enzymes in a wide variety of foods cause the same change in more indirect ways.

A point of interest and wonder is that ascorbase has copper as a part of its structure. This enzyme carries the oxidation of the vitamin only to the formation of dehydroascorbic acid, which is antiscorbutic. A trace of copper ion, in solution with the vitamin, catalyzes an oxidation to fragments beyond the dehydroascorbic acid stage and destroys the antiscorbutic power. This destruction is modified in food extracts but it is the reason for making sure that no metallic copper is exposed in equipment used for processing and cooking food.

THE AIM in providing ourselves with the necessary vitamin C is to promote and protect a continuing biological function. When we harvest, process, cook, and eat plant products, the physiological function in the plant is destroyed, and vitamin C in it is no longer protected. Thus, although we deal with the same chemical—the vitamin—we do so under different circumstances, and find that the vitamin behaves in different ways.

The animal organism tends to protect vitamin C. It even discards the excess without destroying much of it. Yet vitamin C, more than any other known vitamin, tends to be destroyed when we prepare foods that contain it. It is unstable. It is soluble in water and leaches out of the food. It reacts eagerly with oxygen when exposed to the air. Its destruction speeds up as temperature increases. The enzymes

that accompany it in a product can start its destruction. Exposure to light hastens its loss.

These quirks of behavior determine a number of precautions that are routine in food processing and preparation, such as storing foods at low temperatures and in the dark, using as little water in cooking as will result in a good product, avoiding lengthy cooking, and putting vegetables in boiling water to destroy enzymes—which is the reason for blanching vegetables in preparation for freezing. We get more of the vitamin C in some fruit and vegetables when we eat them raw.

Citrus fruit or juice for breakfast insures getting the greater part of the vitamin C we need.

Chances are fair that other fruit and vegetables eaten throughout the day will make up the recommended quantity, because other classes of foods provide some vitamin C.

Foods having medium to good levels of vitamin C are potatoes and sweetpotatoes. The green and yellow vegetables make continuous if modest additions of the vitamin.

In a rural, low-income, mountain area in the Southeastern States, 28 percent of the available vitamin C in the food supplies of a group of people came from potatoes and sweetpotatoes. Green and yellow vegetables contributed another 26 percent. Only 17 percent came from citrus fruit and tomatoes. On an average, the total food supplied the recommended amount. Thus an adequate intake does not need to depend on a few types of food.

Some seasonal and local and regional foods are good sources of ascorbic acid. Among them are berries, melons, chili peppers, guavas, pineapple, peppers, broccoli, asparagus, turnip tops and other greens, spinach, chard, and kale.

Not only are oranges, grapefruit, lemons, limes, and tangerines especially endowed with vitamin C—they protect it. In the raw state, they have firm skins. Even when juiced, they retain ascorbic acid tenaciously. The processed products, canned, frozen, and pasteurized, keep approximately 90 percent of their original content. This happy combination of factors has made citrus fruit synonymous with vitamin C to many persons.

THE CHEMICAL METHODS in common use for getting quantitative information on ascorbic acid are not totally satisfactory. Certain types of interference are annoying. The very chemical activity of the vitamin creates problems in analytical procedures. Speed is one of them; changes can be slowed, but are not easily stopped at a known point. Because variability is the essence of biological material, variations due to analytical procedure must be separated from variations in the material.

Recognition of these factors raises doubt as to absolute values of ascorbic acid. But the worth of the great wealth of relative information that has accumulated is unaltered. Besides, the points of agreement far outweigh the uncertainties.

Average values of vitamin C available to populations, as shown by the Survey on Food Consumption and Dietary Levels for Households in the United States, prepared by the Department of Agriculture in 1955, are assuring. Our Nation produces a varied and adequate supply of foods containing the vitamin.

The losses of ascorbic acid during harvesting, trimming, storage, processing, and serving food must be kept in mind in estimating how well needs are met.

Vicissitudes of preparation, unequal distribution, individual likes and dislikes, and lack of knowledge are factors that underlie repeated observations that segments of our population have intakes that fall below the recommended allowances.

The right foods must be chosen. Once chosen, they must be eaten. Once eaten, the problem of utilization of ascorbic acid again arises. The researcher still would like to know how this vitamin accomplishes its amazing effects in the organisms of the species that require it.

MARY L. DODDS *is professor of foods and nutrition in the College of Home Economics, The Pennsylvania State University, and is in charge of research in the department of foods and nutrition. Previously she was a research fellow at Mellon Institute and the University of Pittsburgh and research nutritionist at the University of Tennessee. She has a doctor's degree from the University of Pittsburgh.*

We need less emphasis on the mere measurement of status at a given moment, or age level, and more emphasis on the doing of the organism—more emphasis on what the child is becoming as well as on the "how" and the "why" of the "becoming." The more one considers the striking differences between children, together with the equally striking tendency of each to follow consistently his own pattern of progress, the more one realizes the need for following every child long enough to evaluate the significance for him of his particular characteristics and of the pattern by which he grows.—A. H. WASHBURN. Quoted in the Journal of Home Economics, February 1957.

Unidentified Substances

GEORGE M. BRIGGS

SOME day—and the day may not be far off—a white-coated scientist is going to look up from his data books or his laboratory bench and tell himself, with no more excitement than his scientist's caution allows, "This is it!"

It will be a new vitamin or a new growth factor that he and perhaps many other laboratory workers have tried for a long time to find or identify exactly.

This new vitamin, or a food factor, will be a link between the first findings in nutrition years ago and today's research. It will push farther back the frontiers of man's knowledge. It will benefit people or animals or both. It will be as exciting as the solution of a mystery story and perhaps as outstanding as Dr. Jonas Salk's discovery of vaccine for poliomyelitis.

It may rank alongside the discovery of vitamins A, C, and D and the B-complex vitamins, which were complete mysteries before 1920 and minor mysteries between 1930 and 1955, when their chemical structures were discovered.

For there are still discoveries to be made of unidentified substances in foods.

Natural foods, such as milk, meat, eggs, vegetables, and cereals, contain at least several important nutrients and substances whose identity we still do not know. We call them unidentified factors. The list of them has been dwindling steadily as our knowledge has grown, but the ones remaining in 1959 seem to be important in nutrition.

How do we know that unidentified factors exist?

To find out, we start with a purified diet that contains all known nutrients in ample amounts in the form of a mixture of pure proteins, carbohydrates, vitamins, minerals, and fat. We feed it to an experimental animal and keep a record of the results. If we can get better results—such as improved growth or reproduction—by adding any natural food to this diet, we can be fairly certain that an unidentified factor is present in the natural food. White rats, mice, guinea pigs, chicks, and other small animals are the favorite "tool" for this work.

The next job is to identify the factor. That is not easy. We make concentrates—or extracts—of the factor from the natural food by chemical fractionation. We test the concentrates by adding them to the original purified diet and feeding the diet to the test animal. Thus we can follow the activity through repeated tests to the final isolation of the pure substance and to its identification. This is more difficult than it sounds and may take many months or years. There are many pitfalls and blind alleys, which can slow down the work considerably.

Often it is possible to find a 1- or 2-day test for the unknown factor if we use certain fast-growing microorganisms as the test "animals." That hastens the process. Most of the B vitamins were discovered in this way—by using bacteria.

THE DISCOVERY of vitamin B_{12} in 1948 is an example of how unidentified factors become known and identified.

A number of supposedly different unidentified factors were being studied in different laboratories before 1948. Many of these turned out to be vitamin B_{12}. As far back as 1926, Dr. George Richards Minot and Dr. William Parry Murphy, of Harvard and Boston, discovered that pernicious anemia, an incurable disease in man until then, could be treated by feeding large amounts of liver. Concentrates of the antipernicious anemia factor, as it was called, became available in the form of injectable liver extracts in a few years—but attempts to identify the active factor were unsuccessful.

Two groups of workers at the Agricultural Research Center at Beltsville, Md., had been working with unidentified factors for animals since the 1930's. Their investigations were along two different lines.

A number of investigators in the Poultry Division—Drs. Theodore C. Byerly, H. W. Titus, H. R. Bird, A. C. Groschke, N. R. Ellis, J. C. Hammond, M. Rubin, and others—studied an "animal protein factor." They learned that it occurred in protein concentrates from such sources as fishmeal and meat scraps and helped growth and reproduction of poultry. They discovered by a fortunate observation in 1946 that ordinary cow manure is an excellent source of a

similar unidentified growth factor for chicks. It became known as the cow manure factor. Long and tedious attempts to purify and identify the substance were unsuccessful, but the scientists were able to prove that the factor is synthesized by micro-organisms in the rumen.

C. A. Cary, A. M. Hartman, and their coworkers in the former Bureau of Dairy Industry of the Department of Agriculture were working at the same time on what was thought to be another unidentified factor in milk. It was necessary for the growth and reproduction of laboratory rats. This factor was different from all vitamins and minerals known at that time (1943 to 1947). They called it factor X. Many time-consuming studies were made to identify the factor, but it proved to be elusive and difficult to purify. These scientists found that antipernicious anemia factor concentrates were good sources of factor X, a finding that later proved to be useful to others (even though they believed at the time that the two factors were not identical).

In another laboratory, Lois M. Zucker and T. F. Zucker of Columbia University, a husband-and-wife team, were studying growth effects obtained by adding casein (the protein of milk), liver, or fish solubles to purified diets for rats. They obtained concentrates of an unidentified factor, which they named "zoopherin."

Other workers with rats and chicks in various laboratories, including the University of Wisconsin, Cornell University, and Lederle Laboratories, confirmed these findings and were actively attempting to identify the animal protein factor, as it was most commonly called in 1946 to 1948. All found the animal tests expensive and difficult.

Still another line of attack was being made to isolate this unidentified factor. Mary Shorb, a bacteriologist, working first at Beltsville in the former Bureau of Dairy Industry and later at the University of Maryland, discovered in 1947 that a certain bacterium, *Lactobacillus lactis* (Dorner), would not grow unless concentrates of the antipernicious anemia factor for humans were added to their food. She called this unknown substance the LLD factor, from the initials of the name of the bacterium.

Following this discovery, Dr. Shorb and I, at the University of Maryland Poultry Department, attempted to purify the LLD factor further. We had little success, but we were able to improve the assay enough so that it could be used by ourselves and others in short-time routine tests to identify the compound.

Using the Maryland test with bacteria, research workers in the Merck & Co. laboratories in Rahway, N. J., isolated a deep-red, crystalline compound from liver and other sources in 1948. Like others, the Merck laboratory had spent thousands of dollars and many years in attempts to find the antipernicious anemia factor. The goal was reached by the use of the 2-day bacterial test, which was better than testing each new batch on hospital patients suffering from pernicious anemia. The new compound was named vitamin B_{12}.

Thus a scientific mystery of long standing was solved in 1948, and many loose ends were brought together. After the discovery of vitamin B_{12}, scientists proved that it was not only the LLD factor but also the antipernicious anemia factor for humans, factor X, the animal protein factor, the cow manure factor, and zoopherin for chickens, pigs, and rats!

A discovery of this type leads to a large amount of experimental work and results in many benefits to mankind. It has had much practical use in animal feeding and in human nutrition and medicine. Workers in laboratories all over the world have written more than 1,500 scientific publications on vitamin B_{12} since 1948.

Another example of a recently discovered nutrient is selenium, a trace mineral. It was an unsuspected part of an unidentified factor until 1957, when scientists discovered that compounds containing selenium had important nutritional properties in feed given rats, pigs, chickens, turkeys, and mice.

The recognition of selenium as a trace element in nutrition goes back to 1951 to the work of K. Schwarz and his co-workers at the National Institutes of Health in Bethesda, Md. They discovered that some foods, such as milk, brewer's yeast, meat, and certain cereals (corn, soybeans, and wheat) contain an unidentified substance, which they called factor 3. It prevented liver damage and death in rats fed special diets low in vitamin E and low in cystine, an amino acid.

After 6 years of intensive study and purification, Dr. Schwarz and his group in 1957 discovered that highly purified concentrates of factor 3 contained selenium. Certain crystalline salts of selenium fed in small amounts (0.1 part per million or less) prevented liver damage in rats. This amount is far less than the amounts necessary to produce the well-known toxic effect of selenium in feeds.

Several groups of workers discovered soon thereafter that selenium-containing compounds are also exceedingly active in preventing exudative diathesis in chicks (a condition characterized by fluid under the skin), liver damage in pigs, and heart and kidney damage in mice.

Vitamin E had to be absent from the diet before the selenium compounds were effective in all animals. Vitamin E prevented the conditions, but it was only about one five-hundredth as active as the selenium compounds. Not all the functions of vitamin E could be replaced by the selenium compounds, however.

An active search began in 1957 to find the most active selenium-containing compounds in foods and to find out why selenium-containing compounds are necessary under these conditions. As is typical of such studies, complete answers will not be found until after years of devoted work on thousands of animals and much expense.

NOBODY CAN SAY how many nutritional factors remain unknown or how soon they will be discovered.

I list some of the substances that seem to be necessary for animals and that were not identified in 1958. We have little information about their importance in human nutrition.

STREPOGENIN is the name given to a growth factor for certain bacteria by Dr. D. W. Woolley, of the Rockefeller Institute for Medical Research in New York, in the 1940's. It is present in many natural foods and is associated closely with proteins. Highly purified diets or synthetic media must be used in studies of it.

Certain peptides—compounds containing several amino acids—are known to have strepogenin activity in bacteria. Thousands of man-hours have been spent to identify the substance, but after 15 years of work the final answer has not been found. Its discovery must await the development of new techniques in protein and amino acid chemistry.

Studies with chicks in our laboratories at the National Institutes of Health and in other laboratories have indicated that this unidentified factor may be important for animal growth.

PROTEIN SOURCES, such as egg yolk, liver meal, dried whey, peanut meal, and fishmeal, have been reported to contain an unidentified vitamin (or possibly more than one) for the growth and reproduction of chickens and turkeys and for the growth of swine.

Drs. Henry Menge, Robert J. Lillie, and Charles A. Denton, of the Agricultural Research Service, have conducted extensive studies at Beltsville on this factor. Much work has been done at many State agricultural experiment stations and commercial laboratories.

In order to get growth responses with these materials, levels of as high as 5 to 12 percent of the material must be used in the diet. This would indicate that the protein portion of the crude materials might be responsible for the growth effect. The growth responses cannot be duplicated with pure proteins or with amino acids, however.

Little progress had been made up to 1959 in the identification of the factor (or factors), which at various times has been termed the egg yolk factor, liver factor, whey factor, and fish factor. Much has been written about it. It promises to be important in animal nutrition and possibly for people.

THE GRASS JUICE FACTOR, or the forage juice factor, was reported in 1938 to be necessary for guinea pigs. With the discovery of several other B vitamins in 1938 to 1948, the grass juice factor was almost forgotten. Now there is renewed interest in it. In studies in our laboratory and elsewhere, evidence has been found of this growth-promoting factor in grass, alfalfa, and possibly other green forage and pasture crops. It may also be present in plant seeds, such as corn, soybean meal, and wheat.

One might suspect that the factor would be important to grass-consuming animals, like sheep and cattle. It is not safe to make too many predictions about unidentified factors, however. The unexpected is more usual than the expected.

The grass juice factor is a good example of how long studies on unidentified factors often take. It takes particularly devoted scientists to stick to a problem, for example, that goes on for more than 20 years without a final answer.

UNIDENTIFIED TRACE MINERALS, with nutritional activity for poultry, swine, and ruminants, exist, according to scientists' reports in 1957 and 1958.

A number of trace elements are known to have important functions in plants or in lower forms of life, but their importance to animal nutrition has never been proved. Among them are such minerals as nickel, aluminum, boron, silicon, and vanadium. These elements could not be considered as essential trace elements for animals in 1959, but no one can predict what will be found in future years.

Experiments with trace minerals are just as difficult to perform as studies with vitamins. It is extremely difficult to remove the very last amount of a mineral from purified diets so that their role in animal nutrition can be studied. Often a study becomes completely worthless if as little as one part in a million of a mineral remains in a test diet.

Promising new techniques are being developed, however, for studies on unidentified minerals. Scientists in some laboratories use animals that are the offspring of several generations of animals fed special diets. This is done in order to remove all traces of the mineral from the animal. In other laboratories, compounds are fed that are unique in being able to tie up the last remaining traces of an element within the animal.

In still other studies, animals are given special feeds produced on soils absolutely devoid of certain trace minerals. The curiosity of a nutritionist is unlimited, and he will go to any extremes possible to discover new facts.

THE UNIDENTIFIED ANTITOXIC factors found in natural foods counteract the effects of toxic agents in animal nutrition.

Factors in meat and liver, for example, are known to prevent the toxic effect of large doses of the thyroid hormone and cortisone. Unidentified factors in meat overcome the toxicity of the drug thiouracil.

The study of antitoxic factors is but one pathway that may lead to the discovery of a new vitamin or growth factor. It is possible that a small amount of an antitoxic factor may be necessary by animals even in the absence of the toxic factor. The importance of these factors in animal or human nutrition was not known in 1959.

Growth factors in microbial products (such as brewer's yeast, distiller's solubles, bacterial and mold cultures, and fermentation residues) continue to receive attention by men who study nutrition of animals. Such products appear to contain unidentified factors for bacteria as well as for animals. It is possible that short-time tests for these factors can be developed with bacteria to replace the much longer animal tests.

No predictions can be made at this stage of research as to the actual importance of the factors in animal and human nutrition. However, even now crude sources of these factors are being used with apparent benefit in commercial poultry and swine rations: It is possible to make good use of unidentified factors in nutrition even before they are identified.

BACTERIA, protozoa, insects, and other lower forms of life are known to require unidentified factors besides those I mentioned previously.

Such compounds, when they are identified, are known as growth factors, rather than vitamins, because, by definition, a compound must be shown to have a beneficial physiological function by one or more of the higher animals—vertebrates—before it can be called a vitamin. Furthermore, by definition, the compound must be an organic substance in natural foods but not a fat, carbohydrate, or amino acid.

Unidentified growth factors for lower forms of life include one or more substances in bacterial cultures for *Lactobacillus casei;* a growth factor in liver for *Lactobacillus leichmannii;* a corn-leaf factor for the European corn borer larva; and an unknown substance in spleen for *Escherichia coli.*

Many others have been reported. We do not yet know the importance of these growth factors in the nutrition of higher animals, including people. The answer can only be obtained by further study.

On the one hand, many of our present B vitamins were discovered to be needed by bacteria (folic acid, vitamin B_{12}, and biotin, for example) before we knew they were needed by animals.

On the other hand, many important growth factors for lower forms of life have no known role in vertebrate nutrition. These should not be considered as vitamins. Among them are the purines and pyrimidines, the bifidus factor, para-aminobenzoic acid, melvalonic acid, inositol, lipoic acid (thioctic acid), various sterols (including cholesterol), nucleosides, orotic acid, asparagine, carnitine, shikimic acid, and others.

GROWTH promotants are compounds that stimulate the growth of animals by indirect ways, usually by some type of action in the intestinal tract. Some may improve absorption or stimulate the synthesis of nutrients in the intestine. Some may prevent subclinical diseases—diseases that are present but do not severely affect an animal.

Such growth-promoting compounds as the antibiotics, surface-acting agents (such as ordinary detergents), organic arsenicals, several sulfa drugs, various drugs used for the prevention of coccidiosis, and other drugs act in this manner. These substances, not present in most natural foods, should not be confused with vitamins, which the body cells need for normal metabolism.

Some of the unidentified factors reported to be necessary for animals undoubtedly will fall into the class of growth promotants rather than vitamins when they eventually are isolated.

It is highly possible, for instance, that the so-called vitamin B_{13}, found in fermentation products and distiller's solubles, is really a growth promotant. The only way one can be sure is to characterize chemically the growth-stimulating compound and study it in animals in the laboratory.

A vitamin B_{14} and vitamin B_{15} have been mentioned since 1948, but their real importance to animal or human nutrition is not known, and the terms should be dropped until such information is available.

Known nutrients have been inadvertently rediscovered many times, because of inadequate levels of minerals or vitamins in experimental diets or because of nutritional imbalances. Because of the complexities of experimental work in this field, one should regard unconfirmed announcements of new unidentified factors with caution.

Nutritional knowledge has improved so much since 1930 that today animals are being reared on synthetic diets of known composition composed of highly purified ingredients—sugar, fat, proteins, vitamins, and minerals—with no natural foods at all. In fact, white rats and chickens have been carried through several generations on such diets.

These are convincing demonstrations that the most essential vitamins for these animals have been discovered, except perhaps the substances present in protein. Similar statements cannot be made for the guinea pig, the turkey, or the pig.

Studies with synthetic diets in human nutrition over long periods are especially incomplete.

Because we know that unidentified factors do exist in foods of plant and animal origin, it obviously is wisest to eat a wide variety of foods from the many excellent food groups—milk and milk products, meats, eggs and poultry, fish, cereals and grain products, vegetables, and citrus and other fruits. One who does this routinely does not need to eat vitamin pills or the so-called health foods (like wheat germ, molasses, yoghurt) to supply known nutrients and the unidentified factors that may be necessary for optimal health except on the advice of a physician or except by personal preference.

When scientists develop further information on the present unidentified factors in food, people will benefit.

GEORGE M. BRIGGS *has been doing research in nutrition, particularly on vitamin B complex and unidentified factors, since 1940. He took an active role in early studies on folic acid and vitamins B_{10}, B_{11}, and B_{12}. In 1958 he became Executive Secretary of the Biochemistry Training Committee, Division of General Medical Sciences, National Institutes of Health, Department of Health, Education, and Welfare, Bethesda, Md.*

Water

OLAF MICKELSEN

NEXT to oxygen, water is the most important factor for survival of man and animals. A person can do without food for 5 weeks or more, but without water he can survive for only a few days.

The exact length of time a person can go without water depends on his rate of water loss. An individual who walks in the desert in the heat of the day may lose water so fast that he dies of dehydration in less than 24 hours. Under more normal circumstances an individual can exist without water for a longer period.

I have read about the case of an 8-year-old girl in Wales, who allegedly was able to grow even though she ate and drank nothing. The publicity given her case in the late 1800's prompted a London physician, who was vacationing in the area, to question its validity. As a result, the parents let the child be observed by nurses, who stood watch around the clock. The girl asked for nothing during the observation period, and no attempt was made to give her anything. On the eighth day, showing signs of extreme dehydration, she died.

The longer an individual goes without water, the greater the number and severity of symptoms he shows.

Weakness, lassitude, thirst, and dryness of the mouth are the first signs of dehydration. Loss of weight and mental confusion set in later. The individual becomes uncooperative and sullen. The cheeks become pale, and the lips are dry and bluish. The skin loses its elasticity. The eyeballs have a sunken appearance. The volume of urine decreases, and its specific gravity rises. At the end, the respiration ceases, even though the pulse and general circulation may be well maintained. The volume of blood is maintained at the expense of the water within the body cells. The central nervous system undergoes the same dehydration as the cells in the remainder of the body and is the first area to show functional changes.

If the dehydration occurs in a very warm place, the person may develop heat cramps, heat exhaustion, or heat stroke before the preceding cycle has run its course.

For heat cramps and heat exhaustion, rest and the administration of salt and water, or water alone, often will restore the patients to normal. Heatstroke requires medical attention, since the patient may die if proper measures are not taken promptly.

About 55 to 65 percent, by weight, of a person's body is water. The exact percentage is related to the amount of fat in the body—the more fat, the less water. A 170-pound man with an average amount of body fat contains about 110 pounds of water.

During a football or basketball game, a player may lose as much as 15 pounds—most of it water. This water loss must be replenished within a short time, since a normal person can temporarily lose only 5 to 10 percent of his body weight as water before symptoms of dehydration set in.

Our bodies lose water in various ways. The kidneys are the primary way. Some people routinely have small urine volumes. Others have fairly large volumes. The volume reflects the individual's drinking habits and may be altered by changing the volume of fluid he drinks. The volume of urine is reduced when the water lost by other routes is increased unless the intake is increased proportionately.

When the intake of water (both as such and as other fluids) ceases, the urine volume decreases, but there is a lower limit of approximately one-third quart below which the volume in an adult cannot be reduced. As long as metabolic activity continues, even at a very much reduced rate, nitrogenous waste products are formed and require a certain volume of water for their elimination.

Our bodies also lose water through the air we expire. Ordinarily an adult may lose a third of a quart of water a day in this way. Talking and exercise are two obvious activities that increase the loss of water from the respiratory tract.

High altitude is another factor that increases the loss of water in the expired air. The lower concentration of oxygen in the air at elevations above 8,000 feet produces a compensatory increase in both the rate and depth of breathing. Furthermore, the absolute amount of moisture in the air at high altitudes is low. Since the expired air is practically saturated with moisture, the amount of water removed from the respiratory passages at high altitudes is greater.

An appreciation of such factors may have helped Sir Edmund Hillary in his conquest of Mount Everest. The records of the earlier Swiss expedition that was unsuccessful in its attempt to scale the peak indicated that each climber consumed less than a pint of water a day for the last 3 days of the climb. The marked water deficit resulting therefrom may have contributed to the extreme fatigue and listlessness of the Swiss climbers during the final stage of the expedition. The British took special precautions to carry extra fuel to melt enough snow and ice to insure each man a daily intake of 5 to 7 pints of water in addition to the water in his food. The British attributed the success of their expedition partly to the increased intake of water.

We lose water through our skin by two different mechanisms.

By one of them, we lose the so-called insensible perspiration, which amounts to about a pint a day. The water that collects on a glass surface when we hold the palm of a hand against it is insensible perspiration. The insensible perspiration usually is not detectable, because each area of the skin gives off such a small amount that it evaporates immediately. The cooling produced by the evaporation of the insensible perspiration and the water in our expired air is an important means of maintaining constant body temperature when we are relatively inactive. The heat so lost is related to the amount of energy expended in the absence of visible sweating; it is about one-fourth the caloric expenditure under basal conditions.

Sweating is the other means whereby our bodies lose heat. When our rate of work becomes so great and when the external conditions become so uncomfortable that our bodies begin accumulating heat, we begin to sweat. (We talk about sweat even though some prefer to believe that "horses sweat, men perspire, and women glow.")

Sweat, unlike insensible perspiration, contains sodium chloride, urea, and tiny amounts of calcium, potassium, and some water-soluble vitamins.

The sodium chloride has received a great deal of attention. Many persons believe that extra salt must be consumed during warm weather or when their work exposes them to hot temperatures (blast-furnace workers, cooks, and bakers, for example). They believe extra salt is necessary to replace that lost in the sweat. Actually, an ordinary American diet provides a salt intake of about 10 grams a day, which is enough to permit an adult to withstand even the most vigorous sweating as long as his water intake is maintained.

The water lost in sweat should be replaced as soon as possible to forestall fatigue, which is one of the earliest symptoms shown by individuals who are short of water. To maintain your work efficiency during hot weather, you must consume water throughout the period of exposure to heat.

The evaporation of sweat is an important means of maintaining body temperature in hot climates. The evaporation of 1 quart of sweat dissipates 580 Calories of heat. This amount of energy expended in an hour would represent very heavy work.

Only the sweat that evaporates is effective in cooling the body. As the evaporation of sweat is markedly lower on hot, humid days, we feel more uncomfortable on those days than when the air is dry.

At the beginning of the Second World War, scientists in the Laboratory of Physiological Hygiene in the University of Minnesota were engaged in a study of the factors that influence the ability of soldiers to work in hot, desertlike conditions. Some of the men who were exposed to the high temperatures refused to drink water during the day except with their meals. They explained their situation by saying that one should never drink large amounts of water on an empty stomach. A num-

ber of them persisted in their refusal to drink in spite of all arguments. They were the men who suffered from heat cramps. The soldiers who drank enough water while they were working tolerated sweat losses of a quart an hour.

Tolerance to hot weather is developed over a period of 3 days or more. Adjustments are made during that time in the circulatory system, which permit a larger proportion of the blood to flow through the skin and so increase the rate of body cooling. Changes also occur in the volume and composition of the sweat. As acclimatization to hot weather develops, the concentration of salt in the sweat is reduced, with a consequent conservation of the body's supply of salt. The individual's thirst response improves to the extent that he is likelier to maintain his water intake throughout the period of exposure to heat.

Ideally, the body's water content should be maintained throughout the period of exposure to heat, especially if hard physical work is done at the same time. Even one who is acclimated to hot weather, however, is not likely to achieve ideal water balance. The well-acclimated individual may replenish only two-thirds of his water loss during periods of heavy sweating. The remainder of the deficit is made up at mealtimes or during rest periods.

Under ordinary circumstances, about 100 milliliters of water (about one-half cup) are lost by way of the gastrointestinal tract—in the feces and saliva. The amount so lost is only a small fraction of the total volume that is secreted into and is absorbed from the tract. It has been estimated that 8 quarts of water are secreted into the gastrointestinal tract daily. About 99 percent of it is reabsorbed.

Diarrhea may increase the water loss by this route to such an extent that severe dehydration develops. If the diarrhea persists for some time, especially in infants, the dehydration may become so acute that medical measures are required for the replacement of the lost fluids. When vomiting accompanies diarrhea, it is often necessary to replace the lost minerals as well as the water.

The mechanism that regulates the concentration of body water is unknown. It is a very precise regulation, for the concentration of body water does not change despite the large volumes consumed by each person—200 to 400 quarts a year for an adult, exclusive of the water in his food, which contributes an equal amount.

VARIOUS theories have been proposed to explain the regulating mechanism.

More than a century ago, Claude Bernard, the renowned French physiologist, concluded that the stomach has an important role in regulating body water. He operated on horses and dogs so that the water they drank did not reach their stomachs but was shunted to the outside of the body through a tube. The thirst of these animals could not be satisfied. When the water was permitted to enter their stomachs, however, their continual drinking ceased.

Other investigators have suggested that the mouth and the throat are involved in the regulation of water intake, because thirst is associated with a dry feeling therein. It was suggested that thirst results from a deficiency in the secretion of saliva; some scientists thought the dry feeling resulting therefrom was the primary motivation to drink.

The hypothalamus, an area of the brain located near the pituitary—the so-called master or regulatory endocrine gland—also may regulate water intake. Destruction of small regions in the hypothalamus of rats causes complete loss of thirst. The rats drink no water, and they die unless they are given water by stomach tube. There appears to be another center in the same region of the brain. When it is stimulated, the animals drink large amounts of water in a short time.

These two regions probably regulate the intake of water in somewhat the same way as the appetite centers, also in the hypothalamus, govern appetite. When one of them is destroyed, the animal develops a voracious appetite and becomes obese. When the other center is destroyed, the animal loses its appetite and dies of starvation. It would appear that these two centers operate as a thermostat does in maintaining constant room temperature.

When the body requires food, one center in the hypothalamus is stimulated to initiate reactions which we associate with hunger. When we have eaten enough to supply our caloric requirements, the other center sends out signals which tell us to stop eating. (The latter signals are frequently not heeded; when that happens routinely, we become obese.) This interpretation was advanced by Dr. Norman Jolliffe (*Reduce and Stay Reduced*, Simon & Schuster, New York, 1952), who suggested the name "appestat" for these centers in the hypothalamus.

A number of hormones are involved in the regulation of water metabolism.

One of them is vasopressin, which is produced by the posterior pituitary. A deficiency of it produces diabetes insipidus, a condition characterized by great thirst and large amounts of urine. Treatment with vasopressin reduces the urine volume to normal.

Another group of hormones, produced by the adrenal cortex, influence water in the body through their action on sodium and potassium metabolism. The interrelationship of water and salt metabolism is so close that a change in the amount of sodium in the body is practically always accompanied by a corresponding change in the amount of water.

Some of the female sex hormones may be responsible for the slight increase in weight that many women experience each month just before menstruation starts. Thyroglobulin also regulates water metabolism but to only a minor extent, as evidenced by the fact that persons with a hypofunctioning thyroid have an increased amount of water in the skin and the tissue just under the skin.

IT IS WELL to remember that it is more important to have an adequate intake of water than it is to have enough calories.

Except when a deficit of body water develops, thirst is the best guide to the amount of water a person needs. There is relatively little danger in an increased water intake, except if it persists and is associated with an insatiable thirst—symptoms that suggest diabetes insipidus and should be considered by a physician.

Aside from an edematous (swelling) condition, which occurs only in pathological states, the intake of water beyond the body's needs is excreted in the urine. From this standpoint, the regulation of body water content is more precise than the factors regulating caloric intake; caloric intake in excess of needs is stored as adipose tissue.

WATER FOR DRINKING should be free of unpleasant odors and flavors in order to make sure that the individual will ingest enough to meet his requirements. During periods of severe water shortage, many people refuse to drink water that they consider unpleasant, even though it is perfectly safe.

What does all this mean to you?

If you are in a place where drinkable water is scarce, you should take all possible measures to reduce your water loss.

If you have to work and walk under conditions of extreme heat, do it at night or in the early morning; whenever possible, keep in the shade.

Work at a rate that does not cause the body to become overheated and cause loss of water through the sweat. Should you have to do hard work when the air is hot, spray your body and clothes with any nonpotable water at hand.

Protect the potable water from evaporation and use all possible means for collecting what rainwater there may be.

Where there is a plentiful supply of drinking water, hard physical work is facilitated and fatigue prevented by consuming enough water to replenish what is lost in the sweat. Under conditions of very high temperatures, the water intake may have to be as much as a quart an hour. Thirst governs the actual amount to drink.

OLAF MICKELSEN is Chief, Laboratory of Nutrition and Endocrinology, National Institute of Arthritis and Metabolic Diseases, National Institutes of Health, Department of Health, Education, and Welfare, Bethesda, Md.

Food

HEALTH

Statistics of Health

JAMES M. HUNDLEY

BIRTHS, deaths, disease rates, longevity, and other aspects of health that can be expressed statistically are used almost universally to assess and follow the status of people's health.

Statistics are simply barren figures, however, and we have to relate or compare them to something else before they have life and meaning. Since no one knows what level of health may be attainable ultimately, vital statistics are most useful in showing trends, detecting changes or problems, and comparing conditions of health. They help us determine what has been accomplished and what remains to be done.

Among the most important vital statistics are those that pertain to the growth of population. The population of the United States was estimated at about 75 million in 1900. It was 130 million in 1940, 150 million in 1950, and 177 million on June 14, 1959. If current trends continue, the population will exceed 220 million in 1970.

This remarkable rate of the growth reflects first of all the numbers of births and deaths. Immigration accounted for considerably less than 10 percent of the increase in recent years.

The birth rate was less than 20 per 1 thousand in the 1930's. It was at a fairly steady level of about 25 during the 1950's. That was not much above the level in 1925; about 1 million more children are now born every year, but that is an increase in number, due to the larger total population, and not in the rate itself. It is interesting to note that the estimated birth rate in 1910 was about 30.

Meanwhile the death rate has dropped spectacularly. Except during 1918, when influenza was pandemic, the rate has trended downward, from 17.2 in 1900 to 9.4 in 1956.

Even more striking is the decline in infant mortality (under 1 year of age), which was 162.4 per 1 thousand live births in 1900 and less than 30 in 1955.

Since the birth rate was about 25 in 1959 and the mortality rate about 10, the net population gain was about 15 (per 1 thousand population), a rate of increase of 1.5 percent a year. That is lower than the rates in some of the other countries in the Americas, where increases of 3 percent a year are recorded, but higher than in most of Europe and higher even than in some major Asian countries, such as India.

Some of the reasons for the major

drop in the death rate are evident in comparing the 10 leading causes of death in 1900 and the mortality in later years from those diseases. The figures are given in an accompanying table. The spectacular decline in disease of infectious origin is the main point to note.

These striking decreases in mortality are reflected in figures of life expectancy. The average life expectancy was about 47 years in 1900. It was 69.3 years in 1957. In a little more than a decade, 5 years have been added to man's expected span.

These gains in health have been shared by most of the economically well-developed countries. In many countries, however, malnutrition and disease continue to exact heavy tolls. Average life expectancies are 35 to 45 years in many of them.

Other types of statistics also have some relationship to nutrition—the incidence of premature babies and maternal mortality, for example. At this point, however, it is pertinent to ask what these statistics mean in terms of nutrition.

Data like those I have given often are used to estimate the probable nutrition situation of a population. In countries where malnutrition is widespread, there is no doubt that nutrition is a major factor in most of the usual vital statistics, but it must be remembered that these statistics are influenced by many factors other than nutrition.

Endemic and epidemic diseases, sanitation, the adequacy of medical care, and the public health facilities exercise major influences. The better medical care that can be given mother and infant in a modern hospital, for instance, unquestionably has been a leading factor in reducing the infant mortality rates in the United States, where 94 percent of all deliveries occur in hospitals.

Deaths among boys and girls 1 to 4 years old in many ways are better indicators of nutritional status than infant mortality is. It is the period

Leading Causes of Death in 1900 and Deaths from Those Causes in 1955

[Total Population—Rates per 100,000]

	1900	1955[1]
Influenza and pneumonia..	203.4	27.1
Tuberculosis..............	201.9	9.1
Diarrhea and enteritis.....	133.2	4.7
Diseases of the heart (excluding coronary artery disease)...............	132.1	108.8
Infectious diseases (typhoid, smallpox, measles, scarlet fever, whooping cough)..	115.9	.4
Congenital malformation and diseases of early infancy...................	91.8	39.0
Nephritis................	89.0	9.6
Cerebral hemorrhage and softening...............	71.5	106.0
Cancer..................	63.0	146.0
Bronchitis...............	45.7	1.7

[1] A few of the figures for 1955 may not be strictly comparable to 1900 data because of a change in the classification of diseases and change in reporting systems.

when infants change from breast, formula, or other special feeding to the food available to other members of the family. Protein malnutrition then takes a toll in many countries.

That mortality among children 1 to 4 years old is largely preventable is shown by the spectacular decreases in this country. Mortality rates between 1 and 4 were 19.8 per 1 thousand in 1900. The rate in 1955 was 1.1—almost a twentyfold decrease. Mortality in this age group continues high in many countries with major nutrition problems—for example, Mexico, 27.8; Brazil, 16.2; and Egypt, 49.7 (1947 data).

Even in this group, however, many factors besides nutrition influence mortality. The same must be said of tuberculosis mortality, where nutrition is an important factor. Total deaths from tuberculosis in this country exceeded 80 thousand in 1930 and were less than 20 thousand in 1954. The decline has been especially sharp since about 1945—probably due mainly to better therapy.

This decline in tuberculosis mortality has occurred despite the fact that total new cases reported annually have declined only a little since 1930. The illness now tends to be shorter in duration and less severe.

Other types of statistics, such as rates of occurrence of specific nutritional disease, would be more specific indicators of nutritional change. Such diseases are not reportable, as are many of the infectious diseases. Only death rates are available, and they have declined to the point where they have little meaning as indicators of changes in nutrition.

Deaths reported from various nutritional diseases are listed in the second table. The main points to note are the decline in deaths from pellagra and rickets and the low incidence of all types of nutritional deaths in 1956.

The decline in pellagra is even more striking because in 1928 more than 7 thousand deaths were reported from this nutritional disease. Niacin, the pellagra-preventing vitamin, was discovered in 1938 and its addition to bread became widespread about 1941. It is not safe to assume, though, that these were the main causes of the virtual disappearance of pellagra. Foods that could prevent and cure it were known long before the vitamin was discovered. Besides, as I noted, pellagra had been disappearing at a fairly steady pace over three decades or more. It is more likely that continued improvement in general diet was the main factor.

Some statistics are at hand on endemic goiter, which occurs in some regions of the United States because of a lack of iodine. In parts of Michigan before the introduction of iodized salt, the incidence of endemic goiter in schoolchildren was 38.6 percent. In 1928, after people started using iodized salt, the incidence was 9 percent. It was 1.4 percent in 1952. Similar data are available for sections of Ohio.

The data I have reviewed indicate a good nutritional situation today. They support much other evidence that indicates that the average levels of nutrition have improved considerably in the past several decades.

On the other hand, this type of information does not permit measurement of just how great this improvement has been, nor can it be said with certainty just how much improved nutrition has contributed to the spectacular decline of certain diseases and to improved health and longevity generally. The nutritionist can say with certainty, however, that average levels of nutrition must be good and probably have been improving in recent years. Such spectacular gains in health would otherwise have been impossible.

THREE FACTS must be kept in mind.

First, while health has been improving, no one knows what levels of health may ultimately be reached, or how close we are to reaching them.

Second, pressing problems must be met if further gains are to be made. Growing evidence suggests that diet and nutrition may be involved in some of them.

Third, we know that average diets have improved from the standpoint of supporting good growth and preventing deficiency diseases. But we do not know yet how to change diets to promote the best health—partly, because we do not yet know all of the dietary measures that might improve health further.

Health is much more than just the absence of disease. Good health also implies physical and intellectual vigor, vitality, and freedom from emotional, functional, and minor but incapacitating illnesses.

Therefore it is pertinent to look somewhat more deeply at vital statistics to see what they tell about problems ahead.

It is important to realize that most of the gains in longevity have come about through prevention of mortality at young ages. Great progress has been

Total Deaths Reported in the United States from Several Nutritional Causes

	1956	1949	1945	1940	1935
Beriberi............................	25	47	46	63	7
Pellagra...........................	70	321	914	2, 123	3, 543
Scurvy.............................	7	22	18	26	30
Active rickets.....................	6	65	93	161	261
Other avitaminoses [1]..............	......	......	108	104	......
Malnutrition: general or multiple deficiencies [1]..................	588	799	......	......	......

[1] Changes in the system of reporting deaths have altered the reporting of nutritional diseases from time to time.

Relative Life Expectancy of White Males and Females in the United States (in Years)

	1900			1956		
Year of life	Males	Females	Difference	Males	Females	Difference
1............	48. 2	51. 1	2. 9	67. 2	73. 7	6. 5
50...........	20. 8	21. 9	1. 1	23. 1	27. 7	4. 6
70...........	9. 0	9. 6	. 6	10. 3	12. 2	1. 9

Leading Causes of Death in 1956; Total Population—White Males and Females

[Rates per 100,000]

	Total	White	
		Males	Females
Heart diseases.......................................	360. 5	443. 0	296. 7
Cancers...	147. 9	162. 5	140. 7
Vascular lesions of the central nervous system.......	106. 3	102. 3	107. 0
Accidents...	56. 7	76. 9	33. 5
Certain diseases of early infancy....................	38. 6	40. 1	27. 1
Influenza and pneumonia.............................	28. 2	29. 5	21. 9
General arteriosclerosis.............................	19. 1	19. 6	20. 4
Diabetes..	15. 7	12. 8	18. 6
Congenital malformations............................	12. 6	13. 7	11. 3
Cirrhosis of liver...................................	10. 7	14. 7	7. 4

made in this sector. Relatively little has been gained in older age groups. These facts are brought out in the third table.

The infectious diseases that used to take such a heavy toll in infants and young children have been conquered so completely that (except for accidents) cancer—mainly leukemia—is now the leading cause of death among children 5 to 14 years old.

It is significant also that women are living longer than men and are continuing to gain in this respect at all ages. The reasons therefor are not entirely clear. Under age 50, mortality rates for men and women in the United States are among the lowest in the world. During the age periods after 50, mortality in American females is near the average of other similar countries. Mortality in males in the United States after age 50 is among the highest in the world, however.

ANOTHER consequence of declining mortality and increasing longevity is that older people are becoming a steadily larger part of our population. In 1955, 28.7 percent of our total population were 45 years or older. Of these, 8.5 percent were 65 years or older. Only 16 percent of the people in 1900 were over 45 years; of these, only 3.4 percent were 65 or older.

Population forecasts indicate that the "over 65" group will enlarge somewhat further in the years to come. The special dietary problems of aging people therefore will become more and more important. Likewise it will be more and more important that these groups are nourished as well as possible so that they can maintain vigor, interest, and self-sufficiency.

Those who survive to older ages are more and more susceptible to the so-called chronic diseases, which are the main cripplers and killers in this period. The leading causes of death in 1956, as shown in the fourth table, bring this out.

These 10 leading causes of death accounted for about 85 percent of all deaths. It is of interest to compare the fourth table with the first table, which lists the leading causes of death in 1900. The emergence of the chronic degenerative diseases is clear.

We can understand why so much attention has been given to atherosclerosis, since it is at the root of most of the heart disease (largely coronary artery disease) and the vascular lesions of the central nervous system. It is also involved in diabetes.

Little progress has been made thus far in the prevention of atherosclerosis, although a number of quite promising leads are being explored. Current research suggests that diet and nutrition may be important in prevention.

Some progress has been achieved against some diseases in the chronic disease group. Cardiovascular syphilis has been nearly wiped out. It once constituted nearly 25 percent of all cases of heart disease. Now it is well under 1 percent. Rheumatic heart disease—once the most common type of heart disease—is now waning. Whether nutritional improvement had something to do with this is interesting speculation, but we have no proof. Subacute bacterial endocarditis—once almost universally fatal—now can be cured in 75 to 80 percent of cases. Surgical advances have done much to relieve chronic disability in valvular heart disease, chronic constrictive pericarditis, and congenital heart disease. Hypertensive heart disease can now be treated better through drugs, surgery, and diet.

Important advances against certain chronic diseases have been made in other fields, such as cancer, diabetes, and arthritis. As attested by current mortality figures, however, there is still a long way to go.

Nutrition can claim little of the credit for these advances. On the other hand, it may have a key role in preventing or treating many of the still largely unsolved major chronic diseases—atherosclerosis, diabetes, and perhaps even arthritis.

It is important to know not only what kills older people but also what diseases or ailments cause disability and nonfatal illness. Here the situation is somewhat different from the leading causes of death.

In the 45 to 64 age group, the common cold, bronchitis, accidents, influenza, arthritis and rheumatism, digestive disturbances, sore throat, diseases of the heart, diarrhea and enteritis, headache, neuritis and neuralgia, hypertension and arteriosclerosis, and genital and breast disturbances in females are, in that order, the most frequent complaints.

In those 65 or over, the list is much the same, except that diseases of the heart, hypertension, and arteriosclerosis are more frequent disabilities, and cerebral "strokes" also come into the picture.

The possibility of further reducing mortality and illness in younger persons must not be overlooked. In children under 5, the leading causes of death are immaturity, postnatal asphyxia, birth injury, pneumonia, congenital malformations, accidents, heart disease, other diseases of early infancy, digestive disease, and hemolytic disease of the newborn. The leading causes of disability are various infectious diseases. The facts suggest that there is still an appreciable amount of mortality that can be prevented in young children.

VITAL statistics for the United States depict a rapidly growing, vigorous people whose nutrition is among the best in the world. They tell a story of dramatic, sustained improvements in health and the virtual eradication of recognizable, preventable, nutritional deficiency diseases.

On the other hand, as old problems have been conquered, others have risen in their place. The increasingly large older segment of the population and the chronic diseases that kill or disable so often, are the challenge for the decades ahead.

From the standpoint of nutrition, the challenge is no longer how to prevent the diseases that are due to a lack of vitamins or to some other deficiency. The problem is to maintain the nutritional advantages we now have and at the same time to find the role of diet in the chronic diseases and build better health through feeding for positive health and vigor through a long life.

Much has been accomplished, but there is no reason for complacency. Many new problems in nutrition and health remain to be explored and solved.

JAMES M. HUNDLEY, M.D., *is a medical director in the United States Public Health Service, Department of Health, Education, and Welfare. He joined the Public Health Service in 1940 and since 1943 has been engaged in nutrition research, mainly at the National Institutes of Health in Bethesda, Md. In 1953 he became head of the Laboratory of Biochemistry and Nutrition of the National Institutes of Health. At present he is developing programs to study the interrelations of nutrition and disease for the National Heart Institute and the National Institute for Arthritis and Metabolic Diseases.*

We are handicapped in several ways in our attempt to interpret research results. First, much attention in the past and present has been centered on the so-called normal person, and too often "normal" has been used to indicate yesterday's or today's average which may or may not be normal. Second, observations on so-called "normal persons" have been made with no attempt to relate these observations to food intake and/or food utilization. Third, observations have been of short duration in relation to the entire life span of man. We have records of food intakes for one day, or one week, or one month out of "three score and ten years." Or, we observe calcium balance for one week, hemoglobin values at yearly intervals, or single observations at five- or ten-year intervals. And finally many of the data have been obtained "piecemeal." One laboratory will center its interest on nitrogen utilization, another on calories, and a third on one or more of the minerals. Charles G. King has reminded us there is growing evidence that we must increasingly regard nutrients in terms of the total organism and the interplay or balance of all of the nutrients in the preservation of health on a life span basis.— DENA CEDERQUIST, in Journal of Home Economics, February 1957.

Trends in Heights and Weights

MILICENT L. HATHAWAY

CHILDREN and adults in the United States are taller than children and adults of similar ages were some years ago.

Among the reasons therefor are improved economic conditions, better diets, and advances in medical care and health services.

The figures that show how our population has changed and how individuals differ in size from their parents and grandparents reveal interesting progress, of which many of us may not be aware.

The population of the United States before 1800 consisted of 89 percent English and Scottish, 8 percent German and Dutch, 2 percent Irish, and 1 percent from other countries.

The immigrants in 1800–1900 came mostly from Germany, Ireland, and Poland. Most of the immigrants between 1900 and 1920 were from Canada, Mexico, and countries of southern Europe. The later immigrants were shorter than the earlier ones, who had come from northwestern Europe, and many of them settled in the Eastern States.

Immigration has been restricted since 1920, and the chief change in our population has been the migration of people from east to west.

The earliest data for heights and weights of large groups of the population are from Army measurements. More than 500 thousand Civil War soldiers were measured in 1863–1864. They were largely from "old" American families—at least two generations in the United States—and averaged 67.7 inches in height.

Another early record is that for United States Senators of 1866, who averaged 69.5 inches without shoes. The report pointed out that they were not typical, however: "They exceed (in height) the average of mankind in all parts of the world as well as the average of our own country."

The average height of more than 1 million United States soldiers in 1917–1918 was 67.5 inches. This low overall average probably was due to the larger number of "new" Americans—immigrants or first-generation Americans. The shortest men came from the New England and Middle Atlantic States,

Weights of Men and Women

Height (inches)	Weights of men			Weights of women		
	Low	Median	High	Low	Median	High
	Pounds	Pounds	Pounds	Pounds	Pounds	Pounds
60...........	....	....	....	100	109	118
61...........	....	....	....	104	112	121
62...........	....	....	....	107	115	125
63	(118)	(129)	(141)	110	118	128
64...........	(122)	(133)	(145)	113	122	132
65...........	126	137	149	116	125	135
66...........	130	142	155	120	129	139
67...........	134	147	161	123	132	142
68...........	139	151	166	126	136	146
69...........	143	155	170	130	140	151
70...........	147	159	174	133	144	156
71...........	150	163	178	(137)	(148)	(161)
72...........	154	167	183	(141)	(152)	(166)
73...........	158	171	188	....	....	....
74...........	162	175	192	....	....	....
75...........	165	178	195	....	....	....

Weights were based on those of college men 25 to 29 years old and college women 20 to 24 years old. Measurements were made without shoes and other clothing. The range from "low" to "high" at a given height included the middle 50 percent of the cases. Half the weights were below the median and half above. Body build will determine where, within the ranges given, normal weight should be. Weight at any age probably should not exceed these values by more than 5 pounds for the shorter adults and 10 pounds for the taller ones.

Weights of Men

Dates	Age in years	Height in inches			
		65	68	70	73
		Weight in pounds			
1885–1900 ..	25–29	142	154	163	171
	35–39	148	162	172	191
	40–49	152	166	177	197
1955.......	25–29	156	161	167	172
	35–39	152	166	172	186
	40–49	151	168	170	181

Weights of Women

Dates	Age in years	Height in inches			
		60	63	65	68
		Weight in pounds			
1885–1908 ..	25–29	122	132	140	152
	35–39	129	140	148	159
	40–49	136	146	155	166
1955.......	25–29	116	124	133	146
	35–39	132	133	140	149
	40–49	135	142	151	154

where many of the newest immigrants had settled. Average heights of the men in those States were 66.4 to 67.3 inches.

Men from the mountain sections of North Carolina averaged 68.7 inches and from the Ozark region, 68.6 inches. Nearly all of them were from "old" American families, and were about an inch taller than the "old" Americans of 50 years before.

About 100 thousand Army recruits in 1943 had an average height of 68.1 inches; 85 thousand recruits in 1946 averaged 68.4 inches. Smaller special groups of men in the Armed Forces measured in 1946–1953 averaged 68.4 to 70.2 inches.

Over the years, then, average heights have increased gradually.

The Association of Life Insurance Medical Directors and the Actuarial

Society of America in 1912 compiled data from previous records of heights and weights of civilians who had been accepted for life insurance. Most of them lived in cities in the Eastern States and Canada: 216,583 men in 1885–1900 and 221,819 women in 1885–1908. Measurements were in ordinary indoor clothing with shoes. (On the basis of illustrations of shoe styles in 1900, an allowance of 1 inch for men's heels and 2 inches for women's heels has been made to make possible comparisons with heights of other groups measured without shoes.)

A study of heights and weights was made in 1955 by the Department of Agriculture as part of a survey of eating habits in the United States. Data were reported for 6,340 men and 6,680 women in 6 thousand households representative of all households in the United States.

The men 30 to 35 years old in the life-insurance study published in 1912 had the highest average height of any age group, 67.6 inches. The men 25 to 29 years old in the 1955 Department of Agriculture study had the highest average height, 69.6 inches.

Men in 1955 thus averaged at least 2 inches taller than men 55 to 70 years ago. They attained that average at least 5 years earlier. The average heights in 1955 were similar to those of the "very tall" Senators of 1866.

The two studies also provide information on the percentage of tall men. Fewer than 4 percent of any age group were as tall as 6 feet in 1885–1900. Twenty percent of the 20–29-year-old men were at least 6 feet in 1955, and 3 percent were at least 6 feet 3 inches tall.

Women, too, averaged about 2 inches taller in 1955 than 50 years earlier. Women 20 to 29 years old averaged 62.4 inches in 1900–1908 and 64.3 inches in 1955. Only 4 percent of the 20–29-year-old women in 1900–1908 could be considered tall, 67 inches and over, but 18 percent of this age group in 1955 were that tall.

Older men measured in 1885–1900 were heavier when compared with younger men of corresponding height than those in the 1955 sample. In 1885–1900, for example, the average weight of men 45–49 years old was at least 20 pounds more than that of 25–29-year-old men of corresponding height.

Differences with age among men 68, 70, and 73 inches tall were minor in 1955; the older men weighed, respectively, only 7, 3, and 9 pounds more than those 20 years younger.

The 1955 weights of the taller men (70 and 73 inches) were less at 40–49 years than those for men of the same height in 1885–1900.

Women of comparable ages weighed less for their height in 1955 than in 1885–1908, but the increase in weight was slightly more from the younger to the older age groups among women studied in 1955 than among those measured in 1885–1908. For example, the 25–29-year-old women at all heights weighed 6 to 8 pounds less in 1955 than the corresponding group in 1885–1908. The 45–49-year-old women in 1955, however, were about 18 pounds heavier than those 25–29 years old, whereas the difference in 1885–1908 between the age groups was only about 14 pounds.

Men succeed better than women in keeping their earlier weight. Women were 4 to 8 pounds lighter at 25 to 30 years in 1955 than in 1900, but they gained weight faster in their later years than men did.

Another way to measure changes in size is to study the changes in selected population groups, such as freshmen in colleges. Freshmen in two men's colleges were about 3 inches taller in 1957 than freshmen 75 years before.

The percentage of first-year college men who were 6 feet and over has increased from less than 5 percent in the 1880's to about 30 percent since 1955. Average weights have increased about 20 pounds—from 136 to 157 pounds—slightly more than would be expected for the extra 3 inches in stature.

*Average
Heights
of Girls
Measured
Yearly*

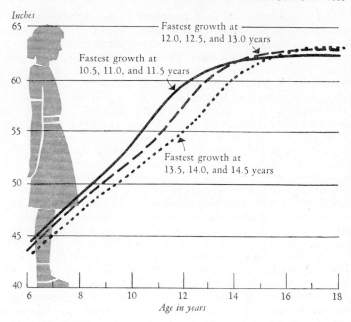

*Average
Heights
of Boys
Measured
Yearly*

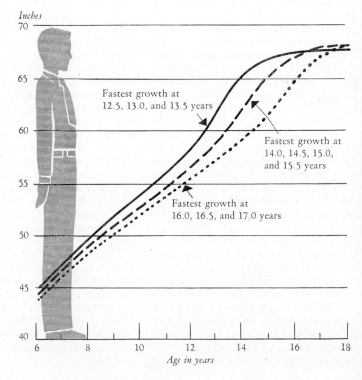

Sixty years of consecutive records in two women's colleges show increases in the average heights of freshmen of about 2 inches—from 63.4 to 65.3 inches. Changes in average weights—from 120 pounds to 127 pounds—are much less than those of men.

The 1912 life-insurance tables, which are still in use, are based on the heights and weights of insured men and women of more than 50 years ago as dressed at that time. Adults usually are advised to try to maintain in later years the weight recommended for their height at age 25 to 29 years rather than to gain the amounts shown in the tables.

THE DEPARTMENT of Agriculture has developed a table of desirable weights for height from data on 25- to 29-year-old men and 20- to 24-year-old women from 100 colleges and universities of the United States in 1948–50. (Data used in preparing the table were made available through the Research Committee of the American College Health Association.)

The data represent nude weight-for-height values for the largest segment of the adult population for which recent data are available. Evidence from the 1955 study by the Department of Agriculture shows that persons with education beyond high school generally maintain a more desirable weight for height than those with less education.

Yearly measurements were made in 1922–1934 of a group of 707 boys and 745 girls throughout their 12 years in the public schools in the Boston area.

The boys and girls who were larger at 6 years grew faster and stopped growing sooner than those who were smaller at 6 years. The fast-growing children generally were heavier at all ages than those who grew more slowly.

Girls 10 to 12 years old usually are taller than boys of that age. When boys are 13 to 15 years old, they catch up with the girls in height and continue to grow at least until they are 18 to 19 years old. Girls usually grow only slightly after they are 13 to 15 years old.

Fat boys and girls tend to mature unusually fast. Only 3 of 100 overweight children studied in Birmingham, England, in 1955 had evidence of endocrine imbalance. When the weight of the others was reduced by diet, their rate of growth in height also slowed down.

The tendency to obesity in a few children may therefore be constitutional and associated with early maturity and early tallness. Growth stops earlier in these early maturing children, and the result is a relative shortness of stature and continued heaviness as an adult.

The most satisfactory method of judging a child's normalcy is to follow his own growth record over the years. He should gain both in height and weight at a fairly regular rate until about a year before he shows signs of pubescence. Then he will have a more rapid spurt of growth, and soon thereafter will reach his maximum height. A boy's gain in weight may continue for several years after he has attained his full height, but a girl shows little change in weight between her 15th and 20th year.

An individual's ultimate size depends on several factors. First is his heredity. The genes a child is born with determine his potential height. He may fall short of his potentialities, but he cannot exceed them. His rate of development is related genetically to his sex and skeletal development, but such factors in his environment as illness, malnutrition, or emotional stress may alter the rate.

MILICENT L. HATHAWAY *joined the Department of Agriculture in 1946 as nutrition specialist in the Human Nutrition Research Division, Agricultural Research Service. She published a research report in 1957 on heights and weights of children and youth in the United States, a compilation and analysis of published and unpublished data. A companion bulletin on heights and weights of adults was prepared in 1959.*

The Nutriture of People

AGNES FAY MORGAN AND LURA M. ODLAND

GOOD, solid information about the actual nourishment of a sizable part of a population—not merely the amounts and kinds of food one person or a family eats—is of value to many.

Those who produce, process, and distribute food need data on the effects of diet on the health of people and the effects of their health and well-being, or lack of it, on their use of food.

Nutritionists and biochemists use the information to estimate recommended dietary allowances and the kinds and amounts of food that provide the necessary nutrients. Along with studies of animals and more laboratory observations of human beings, they also need large-scale investigations of groups of people in order to assess factors of individual variation, environment, habits, geography, origin, and knowledge of the importance of food.

Medical and dental doctors know how vital it is to penetrate the twilight zone between good and poor nutrition—the zone which lies between robust health and deficiency diseases like scurvy and rickets and in which may lie tooth decay and anemia. The observation of one or some persons may help them penetrate that zone, but a

wider knowledge, such as that which comes from extensive surveys, is needed.

Homemakers would like to have some baseline for measuring what they have accomplished and where changes or improvements may benefit themselves and their families.

Government and military authorities get from surveys a better insight into social and economic trends and the comparative vigor and stamina of men who enter the armed services from the various sections of the country.

We have also an interest in the nutrition of people in other countries. A basic association—which we all will do well to know more about—exists between the health of a people and the development of a favorable economic, social, and political climate among them. Vast numbers of people still live amid severe stresses, one of which is malnutrition.

Guiding principles for studies on the nutrition of population groups were outlined in 1939 in a publication of the Health Organization of the League of Nations by Dr. E. J. Bigwood. At that time it was recognized that much basic information was needed to define more clearly the relationships between dietary, clinical, and physiological observations in large-scale investigations of nutrition.

The National Academy of Sciences-National Research Council, through its Committee on the Diagnosis and Pathology of Nutritional Deficiencies, published in 1943 the first comprehensive summary of dietary surveys and nutritional appraisals that had been reported for population groups.

It summarized the available information on nutritional status on a uniform, authoritative, and comparable basis.

The information on the intake of nutrients of persons of all ages in many localities was compared with the recommendations. Many of the diets provided less than half of the recommended dietary allowances for several essential nutrients, but most of the diets provided more than 50 percent of the recommended levels.

Reliable data based on studies of blood serum were available in 1943 for only hemoglobin, protein, and ascorbic acid. All studies in this and other countries indicated a notably high prevalence of anemia, especially among children and pregnant women of the low-income groups. This was thought to indicate an inadequacy of iron in diets. Levels of vitamin C in the blood serum were low in a large proportion of the groups, especially among schoolchildren in all parts of the United States.

Together, the dietary, chemical, and physical-examination surveys in many regions showed that there were few indications of severe, acute deficiencies, but accumulated evidence pointed toward many mild or moderate states of deficiency.

The Council reported in 1943: "All evidence is in agreement that deficiency states are common among the population of the United States. Most of them are not the severe acute type. Rather they are less intense in degree and very much slower in their course. Predominately the deficiency states here are mild, moderate, or severe chronic forms. Because of their slow, gradual development, their presence is commonly unsuspected. In frequency and severity they increase with age and with lowered economic level. As yet optimum nutrition throughout the Nation has not been achieved; on the contrary, deficiency states are present on a large scale."

There has been further development of basic information since 1943 on which to base recommended dietary allowances for healthy people in the United States. Tables of food composition, which indicate the kinds and amounts of nutrients in food, have been expanded. Methods have been developed for determining the levels of essential nutrients in tiny amounts of blood, which can be taken easily from large numbers of people. There has been increased recognition of physical signs and symptoms that may be associated with low intakes of one or several nutrients.

A number of agencies have undertaken joint fieldwork and appraisals of the findings of surveys. Some of the surveys were organized by private research foundations. Others have been made by the Interdepartmental Committee on Nutrition for National Defense, representing nine departments of the United States Government that are concerned with health, agriculture, and defense; the State agricultural experiment stations individually and in regional cooperative efforts; medical and public health units, brought together under the Food and Agriculture Organization of the United Nations; and State and city departments of public health.

The procedures for determining nutritional status have been fairly well agreed upon, but the interpretation of the results is still somewhat variable. Statistical calculations usually must be used because of the bewildering variability of the observations. For that reason also the size of the sample must be large. The interpretation of even the most elaborate examination of the individual is beset by uncertainties, but group examinations may yield clearcut results.

Nutritional status—that is, the degree of well-being of a population as it is affected by food intake—usually is appraised through coordinated studies of health statistics, particularly those on morbidity and mortality, the growth rates of children, birth rates, infant death rates, principal causes of death, and life expectancy;

data on food consumption—that is, amounts of food that are available and that disappear and are presumably consumed;

detailed dietary records and histories;

clinical examinations, with special attention to changes in the skin, eyes, mouth, tongue, gums, muscles, blood pressure, and pulse rate;

biochemical tests of blood for various constituents associated with nourishment and tests of samples of urine, with or without preliminary administration of certain nutrients.

The population studied may include everyone in a city, county, State, or country, or it may be persons of a given age, sex, or physiological condition. The status of an individual can be assessed only by repeated and detailed clinical examinations, biochemical tests, and dietary records.

We divide this presentation into three main parts: Studies made by research workers in colleges, agricultural experiment stations, and independent organizations in the United States and other countries; reports of the cooperative studies on relationships of health, well-being, diet, and environment in the four regions of the United States, conducted by workers in agricultural experiment stations; and the findings of special studies and surveys.

MOST OF THE STUDIES of population groups until 1946 were concerned primarily with the relationships between the kinds and amounts of foods eaten and the general physical condition.

The composition of the blood may reflect nutriture, but taking samples of blood of large numbers of persons was not feasible before 1946 because of the amounts of sample necessary, the inconvenience to the person, and the time required for processing and analyzing the samples.

Microchemical methods of analyzing blood were developed by 1945 by O. A. Bessey, O. H. Lowry, and their associates in the Public Health Research Institute of the City of New York for eight of the dietary essentials or their important tissue derivatives.

The few drops of blood that were required could be obtained easily by puncturing the fingertip. The small—"micro-"—samples could be analyzed efficiently and quickly. These analyses were particularly easy to use in nutritional studies of large groups.

The first extensive studies to use the microchemical methods of blood analysis were carried out in eight high schools in New York State during the fall of 1946. The New York State Joint Legislative Committee on Nutrition requested the survey in order to get data on the nutritional status of schoolchildren. The survey also gave research workers a chance to test the new microchemical methods.

Blood samples were collected from about 1,200 children, 11 to 19 years old, in schools of differing social and economic circumstances.

There seemed to be a fairly even distribution of vitamin A levels in blood serum. On that basis, the intakes of vitamin A were considered satisfactory for nearly all of the children. Serum carotene values, which indicate recent intake of green and yellow vegetables, varied somewhat more than serum vitamin A levels and revealed that some of the children in all the schools were not receiving recommended amounts of green and yellow vegetables.

Among 50 percent of the students in seven schools, low amounts of ascorbic acid (vitamin C) also indicated that fresh fruit and vegetables were not being eaten in recommended amounts.

The amounts of riboflavin in the blood samples varied, but no outstanding differences were found that could be taken to reflect high or low economic levels among the students.

Boys between 12 and 19 years old showed progressive increases in hemoglobin. The hemoglobin among girls remained practically the same as during childhood, although variations in hemoglobin were more pronounced among the girls. The amount of hemoglobin was related to the iron concentration of the serum and suggested the presence of an iron deficiency among girls that had low values of hemoglobin. Only a few boys and girls had hemoglobin values that could be classified as poor, but a significant percentage in most of the schools was classified as only fair.

The level of alkaline phosphatase, an enzyme in the blood, may be an indicator of the growth and development of bones. Characteristic changes in phosphatase levels corresponding to age changes in skeletal development were observed, but no schools had more than a few phosphatase values that could be considered abnormal.

The outstanding conclusions were that there appeared to be no marked differences among the students in the eight schools with the exception that in one school, selected as representative of a reasonably high economic level, the nutritional status appeared to be superior to that of the other schools. The most evident inadequacies in the diet in all the schools were fruit and vegetables, as indicated by the low blood values of carotene and ascorbic acid.

The results indicated generally that it was feasible and practical to use the microchemical methods as one yardstick for estimating the nutritional status of a group. It also gave us a basis for estimating the level of nutriture in children according to the levels of certain blood components.

One study of nutrient intakes of children was outstanding. Successive records were obtained for 30 boys and 34 girls in 1946–1957 at the Child Research Council and the University of Colorado School of Medicine in Denver. It was one of the few studies of the intake of food and nutrients by the same individuals throughout more than a small part of the life cycle.

The reports by Virginia A. Beal, of the Child Research Council and the University of Colorado, for children from infancy to 5 years indicate that the average levels of intake of nutrients may be relatively high through the first years of life.

Most of the children were eating the kinds and amounts of foods that provided the recommended amounts of nutrients. Considerable individual variations were related to individual patterns in the food the children chose.

Each child, notably when 1 to 4 years old, had periods in which likings for certain foods changed greatly. The intake levels for various nutrients, except iron and calcium, were high. Children between 2 and 5 years had little iron. The intakes of calcium, related to the consumption of milk, varied the most.

MUCH OF the research on the nutritional status of younger children has been conducted at institutions. Comparable studies of children of these ages, made in their own homes, were conducted in the regional experiment station studies, and we describe them in a later section.

In studies of child-care agencies in Michigan, Icie G. Macy and her coworkers stressed the point that many children who enter institutions may be poorly nourished or malnourished.

Special efforts therefore should be made to provide an environment suitable for nutritional conditioning and, in many instances, reconditioning.

Many children who have had low levels of food intake over a period of years may need larger amounts of nutrients than are generally considered necessary for maintaining good health.

The studies in Michigan indicated short-term reconditioning effects of a health camp conducted for underprivileged children who might benefit physically and mentally from attendance. Of the 96 children, 6 to 15 years old, who participated in the study, most showed evidence of poor nutritional status as judged by physical and biochemical examinations when they entered the camp. After 6 weeks at camp—6 weeks of good food and good environment—the children improved greatly in nutrient levels of the blood and in physical condition.

About one-fourth of them, when they entered the camp, had the blood serum levels of vitamin C that we generally associate with deficiency states. One-third of the others had levels that were at the threshold of a deficiency. During the 6 weeks, the average vitamin C serum levels doubled for boys and girls; only 3 percent of the children were considered to be at the borderline.

Most of the children had one or more symptoms in skin, eye, or mouth that we associate with low nutrient intakes. How well these symptoms cleared up at the end of the time in camp was not reported, but significant gains in weight by almost all of the children were a sign of improved condition.

The study demonstrated that the children had poor diets before they went to camp and that most of them responded quickly to the improved diet and the better care.

The researchers in Michigan also studied 390 children, 2 to 18 years old, who were referred to them by several institutions and agencies. Many differences were observed in blood levels of ascorbic acid: 11 to 35 percent of the children had blood levels that indicated they were getting too little vitamin C. The serum vitamin C in all the children was consistently related to dietary intake of vitamin C.

Among the children in two of the institutions, the serum values in the fall were consistently higher than in spring—the children were getting more vitamin C foods in summer and au-

tumn. The blood serum values of carotene and vitamin A also differed markedly among children from the different agencies—suggesting differences in dietary patterns—but the differences, by agency, in vitamin C and vitamin A were not closely related, even though the seasonal trends were similar.

EXTENSIVE STUDIES of children in institutions tell us that their nutritional status can be improved considerably through expert guidance in planning daily menus. Food budgets of institutions usually are limited, but judicious buying, preparing, and serving, designed for the maximum conservation of nutrients, help to give children the food they need.

Lydia J. Roberts and her coworkers in the University of Chicago have given us the results of efforts to provide a liberally adequate diet to children in a boarding school. They determined the nutrient intakes and measured gains in weight and height and blood and urine levels of nutrients and their products in 152 children 2 to 14 (most of them 6 to 10) years old before and after their diets were improved.

The diet at the beginning of the study was considered to be about the average diet in children's institutions, which contained some of all the essential nutrients but usually not in the full amounts usually recommended.

The nutrient intakes of 25 of the children, who were representative of the whole group, were determined for foods as prepared for consumption. The children in each age group at the beginning of the study were consuming amounts of nutrients considerably below recommended levels and considerably below the intakes reported for children of similar ages in other studies. Exceptions were iron and vitamin A, which were generally adequate for the children in the school.

Supplements of milk and other dairy products, eggs, whole-grain cereals, and pineapple juice were added to the diet in amounts sufficient to raise the nutritional quality of the diet to recommended levels. The children liked the supplemented diet and soon improved in growth.

The percentage of children whose weights were below the average for their height went down. A definite shift of the group toward a more favorable weight-height status was apparent.

Increases in blood levels of vitamin C were noted, but not enough to bring the levels up to those reported in other studies. The vitamin C in the noncitrus fruit juice in the supplemental foods was not enough to raise serum levels higher. The amount of thiamine in their blood increased markedly. The status of thiamine and riboflavin improved, as indicated by levels of those nutrients in the urine. As with blood levels of nutrients, some indication of nutrient utilization and metabolism can be had by studying the amount of certain nutrients or their byproducts excreted.

The levels of vitamin A in the blood indicated that the children were getting enough vitamin A and its precursors in both the original and supplemented diets.

The findings from physical examinations, tests in the chemical laboratory, and studies of the diets themselves indicated the weak points of the institutional diet, the food supplements that would improve the diet, and the benefits the children attained in nutritional status after their meals had been improved.

THE DEPARTMENT of Health of Pennsylvania has sponsored a number of studies of the effects of nutrition on health.

A report in 1955 on the nutritional status of 2,536 young people 12 to 20 years old indicated that the diets of the girls were much less satisfactory than those of the boys in providing recommended amounts of nutrients. The diets of the youngest and the oldest of the girls among them rated higher than the diets of the girls 13 to 15 years old.

The 12-year-olds among them apparently were retaining some previously established good food habits, but the 13- to 15-year-old girls had the poorest nutrient intake levels of any group. Some improvement was noted among those who were 16 to 20 years old.

The percentage of boys whose meals contained recommended amounts of nutrients was higher generally than the percentage of girls. Among the boys, as among the girls, however, those 13 to 15 years old were least likely to have diets containing adequate amounts of nutrients: Differences in their nutrient intakes were related to their eating habits. The boys had much more milk, meat, and eggs.

Both boys and girls had low intakes of fruit and vegetables, especially citrus fruit and yellow and leafy, green vegetables.

About 85 percent of the boys and girls in all age groups got recommended amounts of vitamin A. About 50 percent of all boys and girls of all ages were consuming recommended amounts of other nutrients except vitamin C.

Studies of the 2,536 students in the Pennsylvania study and more than 5,400 children whose diets were investigated by workers in agricultural experiment stations indicated that boys and girls 13 to 15 years old were least likely to be getting the recommended kinds and amounts of foods. That age, therefore, seems to be the one to which we should pay better attention.

We do not have enough comparable data to say whether over the years there has been a lowering of the age range in which drastic changes take place in the food habits of girls. That, though, is very likely.

It would seem also that with succeeding generations there is an increasing awareness of detrimental changes in the food habits of adolescent girls. This may or may not be a reflection of an increasingly critical situation.

Studies of numbers of persons as

individuals—not as members of a group—through all stages of their life cycle could help us answer this question, but such studies would be difficult and costly.

On the other hand, the levels of nutrient intakes of women of child-bearing age seem to have improved over the past 50 years. It is likely that better economic conditions, which have made possible wider choices of food, rather than better food habits as such, are the reason.

In the study in Pennsylvania, and even more in studies conducted by the experiment stations in the West, among children of practically the same generation, fewer of the 16- to 17-year-old girls met or exceeded the recommended allowances for nutrients than did girls less than 13 years old. Usually fewer than half as many girls over 16 as under 13 years had diets that provided the recommended levels of some nutrients.

The study in Pennsylvania included determination of blood, blood serum, or urinary levels of hemoglobin, alkaline phosphatase, and certain nutrients or their byproducts.

Of particular interest were the results of the hemoglobin studies. About two-thirds of the boys and one-third of the girls had hemoglobin levels considered good. None had extremely low hemoglobin levels.

Hemoglobin levels of the 13- to 15-year-old girls in Pennsylvania were notably lower than those of girls in older or younger age groups. That group also had the smallest number of girls who got recommended levels of iron. Hemoglobin levels were lower among the Pennsylvania girls and boys than among adolescent children in the western and northeastern sections of the United States and in the New York school system.

Low serum levels of vitamin A were reported for about one-fourth of the children in Pennsylvania. The ones who were getting high levels of vitamin A tended to rank better in certain conditions of eyes and skin.

Low excretion levels of thiamine, riboflavin, and niacin byproducts were generally observed among students with low intakes of those nutrients. All the students ranked lower in the clinical and laboratory observations and tests than in their conformity to diet recommendations.

Only 7 girls and 12 boys of these 2,536 students had perfect teeth.

RECORDS of dietary intakes of college students in several parts of the country indicate some continuation of the dietary patterns that have been noted among children 13 to 15 years old.

Some general improvement in intakes among the college women seems apparent, although low amounts of several nutrients, particularly iron, calcium, and ascorbic acid, are reported frequently.

As in the younger, adolescent-age groups, nutrient intakes of the college-age men were generally higher in relation to recommended amounts than were the intakes of college women. Low intakes of ascorbic acid, calcium, and calories were reported often among college men. Most of these studies were not confirmed by biochemical or physical examination data, however.

MANY STUDIES indicate that many families do not have diets considered best for the maintenance of good health and physical well-being.

Most of the surveys indicate that (except among families whose incomes are very low) the nutritional quality of food supplies of families may be associated more closely with food habits and patterns of food purchases than with other social and economic factors, such as size and type of family and income.

In a survey of 146 urban families in Michigan in 1953, for example, the amounts of nutrients available to them tended to increase as food expenditures went up, but the patterns of food purchases were such that some of the families whose average meal cost was in the highest range failed to meet recommended allowances. Other families, whose meal costs were in the lowest range, had food purchases that supplied 100 percent or more of the recommendations for calories and eight nutrients.

Many studies have indicated that the levels of nutrient intake of various members of a family may be quite different from those estimated for the family as a whole.

Levels of nutrient intake of the younger boys and girls usually reflect the levels as calculated from family food records, although the individual food habits of the younger children may vary greatly.

In Maryland, for example, about 60 to 80 percent of the 6- to 12-year-old children whose diets were studied had diets of about the same level of adequacy as their families' diets. Most of the remaining children had poorer diets than the family as a whole, except in calcium, which they got from milk.

Records of 223 families in a rural township in New York in 1948–1949 were evaluated for nutrient content by researchers in Cornell University. Generally, only 10 to 15 percent of the families were consuming less than the recommended amounts for each nutrient, except calcium. About half of the families had intakes of calcium below recommended amounts.

Individual records of 805 males and females 1 year to more than 70 years old indicated that boys and girls under 10 years had the best food records. The adolescent girls and the women of childbearing age fared worst.

The caloric intakes of adolescent girls and young women most frequently were low. That was reflected partly in relatively low intakes of many nutrients, particularly calcium and iron. Low intakes of calcium and protein were apparent among males.

In another study of 27 families, in each of which were two adults at least 50 years old, in Washington State, food habits were considered to be more important than the level of income in the selection of the weekly menus that supplied recommended allowances of nutrients.

The average nutrient intakes were generally high as to recommended allowances for 14 of the 27 families, but their levels were low for one or more nutrients—most frequently ascorbic acid, calcium, and riboflavin.

ALTHOUGH MORE Americans over 60 own their own homes than do younger people, institutions for older persons also are increasing more rapidly than for any other age group.

Institutional food service generally is planned to provide approximately the amounts of nutrients recommended for the largest group in the institution. Several studies between 1948 and 1956 of older groups in institutions have indicated, however, that the daily meals, as served, may provide recommended amounts of nutrients, but the actual nutrient intake levels of the older individuals often are below the recommended amounts.

This situation is not unlike comparisons of intake levels of families as a whole and of the individual members of families. Among the groups in large institutions, however, there is less consideration of individual food habits and food preferences in planning menus than there would be for family groups.

Studies by the California, Florida, and Rhode Island Agricultural Experiment Stations between 1950 and 1956 indicated that the nutrient intake levels of older age groups in institutions generally are substantially lower than the nutrient intake levels of older persons in individual homes. Most of the residents in public institutions consumed considerably less than recommended amounts of all nutrients.

Standard portions of foods served in one institution for older people provided recommended amounts or more of all nutrients. The low nutrient intake for the individual members of the group was related directly to the amount of various foods each of them ate.

When their intakes of iron and of protein were adequate, some relationship was evident between the intake of iron and protein and the hemoglobin. When intakes of iron and protein are generally high, hemoglobin levels may be rather consistent—an indication that hemoglobin beyond certain intake levels does not generally increase with higher intakes.

In most of the surveys among older people, dietary intakes of ascorbic acid were related to blood levels of ascorbic acid, a nutrient that generally is readily absorbed and is not stored to an appreciable extent in the body.

INCREASING NUMBERS of homemakers in the United States have some employment outside the home. Concern has been expressed as to the possible effect of such employment of wives and mothers on food habits of families and the nutritional value of diets.

Studies by researchers in the Mississippi Agricultural Experiment Station have indicated some significant differences in food purchase patterns among 100 gainfully employed rural homemakers and 100 homemakers who did not have outside employment.

The working wives used somewhat more ready-prepared foods, such as luncheon meat, ice cream, bakery products, and ready-prepared soups. The food budget tended therefore to be higher. The full-time homemakers served more home-produced foods, particularly fruit, vegetables, eggs, poultry, and beef. The similarities in the kinds and amounts of food used by the two groups were more striking than were the differences, however, and the calculated nutrient levels of the diets for the two groups of families were similar.

It may be that the shift from home-produced food to more purchased food is slow, partly because the food habits tend to change gradually. Then, too, wives often are seasonal or part-time wage earners, who shift between full-time homemaking and outside employment, and also all families are exposed to the same markets and food advertising.

SEVERAL STUDIES of the nutritional status of pregnant women and its influence on the unborn child have indicated that good nutrition before and during pregnancy gives benefits to both the mother and the infant.

J. H. Ebbs, F. F. Tisdall, and W. A. Scott, Canadian scientists, were among the first to report on relationships between the nutritional level of the mother's diet, the course of the pregnancy, and the infant's condition.

Among 400 Canadian women from the low-income group, the women whose diets were considered to be relatively good—either because of their customary choices of foods or because of the supplementary foods of high nutritive values—appeared to have better health and fewer complications of pregnancy than did women who customarily had poor diets.

The well-fed group had healthier babies and appeared better able to nurse them.

Because it was known that many pregnant women in low-income groups had poor diets, studies were undertaken in the 1940's among several thousand pregnant women in England and Wales to test the effectiveness of supplements of yeast or certain vitamins and minerals. Such an improvement in the diet appeared to reduce the complications of pregnancy and the number of premature births.

A study at the Philadelphia Lying-In Hospital of 1,500 pregnant women was designed to determine whether supplements of protein and vitamins would provide measurable benefits to the health of the mothers and their babies.

The records of food consumption of the women indicated that the general dietary level of most of them was good. After instruction was given them in prenatal clinics, the overall quality of the diets presumably improved. The supplements given them included a protein concentrate or one multiple vitamin capsule or both. The diet records had indicated no differences in the eating habits between the women who did not receive the supplements and those who did. The women who received the supplements tended to have fewer complications during pregnancy and fewer premature births.

The effect of the supplements was of slight, if any, benefit to the infants, who were examined at birth, 1 month, and 1 year. Only 3 percent of all the infants were rated as poor at birth. Two-thirds of them were rated as good or excellent. The researchers believed that few of the Philadelphia mothers whom they studied had diets poor enough to affect very much the development of the infants.

IN A STUDY of 79 pregnant women, Anne W. Wertz and her associates in the Massachusetts Agricultural Experiment Station linked complications of pregnancy in part with low nutrient intakes, although the weights and lengths of infants did not appear to be greatly affected by the adequacy of the mother's diet.

The study was a part of the cooperative regional studies of nutritional status undertaken by the State agricultural experiment stations.

One-fourth to one-third of the 79 women studied had serum levels of carotene, vitamin A, and ascorbic acid below the normal range. Urinary excretions of the B vitamins, thiamine, and riboflavin were related to the amounts of them in the diet. Ten to 20 percent of the women excreted thiamine in amounts that indicated that their intakes were inadequate; this finding was borne out by the diet records. None of the women appeared to be taking inadequate amounts of riboflavin. About three-fourths of them took vitamin and mineral supplements.

THE CORD blood was found to have double the ascorbic acid of the mother's blood, but less vitamin A and carotene than the mother's blood.

The inadequacies in the diets were chiefly in calcium; 63 percent were getting less than two-thirds the recommended amount. Forty percent were lacking in riboflavin and iron, and 30 percent in protein, thiamine, and ascorbic acid.

The women whose diets met at least two-thirds of the recommended allowances had only one-third as many complications of pregnancy as did those whose diets fell below the recommended amounts to this degree in at least one nutrient.

The investigators in Massachusetts indicated (as did those in Pennsylvania) that perhaps the nutrient content of the mother's diets, even those considered least adequate, were not so low as to influence the condition of the infant.

EARLY REPORTS of the nutritional status of pregnant women by Bertha S. Burke and H. C. Stuart, of Harvard University, showed positive relationships between the excellence of the diet and the well-being of the mother as well as the size of the infant and the condition of his bones and teeth.

In their study, 32 percent of the 216 subjects were consuming diets with less than two-thirds of the recommended protein allowances. A definite relationship was established between the mothers' protein intakes and the pediatric rating of the infants.

In studies of 2,129 pregnant women by scientists in the Vanderbilt University School of Medicine, nutrition did not seem to be directly related to the development of commonly encountered obstetric and fetal abnormalities. These women might have been above the nutritional level at which such diseases may occur. The general nutriture of about three-fourths of the women seemed to be satisfactory, as indicated by dietary intake records, serum levels of certain nutrients, and physical evidences of health.

Among the pregnant women whose

intakes of ascorbic acid were considered consistently high, blood levels of ascorbic acid were also in the upper ranges. During lactation, however, blood levels of vitamin C were much lower, despite consistently high intakes of the vitamin. The incidence of gum disorders was associated only partly with the level of vitamin C.

No cases of clinically recognizable deficiency diseases occurred among these women, but some physical signs associated with poor nutrition were observed. Obesity, edema (swelling), and lesions of skin, eyes, and mouth were more pronounced among the older women and among those who had had several children.

Studies by the Research Laboratory of the Children's Fund of Michigan in 1947–1950 provided information on the influence of pregnancy on the needs and uses of nutrients.

Definite patterns in the metabolism of nutrients during pregnancy were indicated through studies of the levels of certain blood components throughout the course of pregnancy. The investigations in Michigan also included basic observation on nutritional relationships between the mother, the developing fetus, and the infant, as indicated by dietary, chemical, and physical findings.

The 1,064 pregnant women studied were patients of physicians associated with a public prenatal clinic for low-income or indigent people, a private prenatal clinic for patients with moderate means, and a group of private patients who were characterized as middle class and wealthy.

Records of their food intake during pregnancy were evaluated in terms of the number of servings from certain food groups considered necessary if the diets were to contain recommended amounts of nutrients. Poor dietary habits existed oftener among the poorer women.

About 40 percent of the women from the public and private clinics and 9 percent of the private patients had low dietary ratings—that is, the diets prob-ably contained less than 60 percent of the recommended amounts of nutrients. These low intakes might be inadequate for many women under the nutritional stress of pregnancy.

The diets appeared to be low in fruit and vegetables, including leafy, green, and yellow vegetables, and citrus fruit. Many diets, especially of the women in the low-income and indigent public clinics, were also low in protein foods.

Data about 427 women, who had no health complications throughout the childbearing period and who were delivered of healthy, full-term infants, were considered as representative of the average pattern and normal variations that might occur during and following pregnancy. Dietary ratings for them were quite similar to average ratings for all women.

Biochemical and dietary findings were related for ascorbic acid. High dietary intakes of foods rich in vitamin C were associated with high-serum levels of this nutrient for the women during pregnancy and for the newborn infants. Hemoglobin levels were generally somewhat lower for the women in the low-income or indigent group whose dietary intake records were classified oftenest as low.

Low blood serum vitamin A and carotene were observed oftenest among women from the indigent group rather than from those in the other groups. Evaluations of dietary intake corroborated the serum findings.

Levels of vitamin A and carotene in the blood serum samples from infants generally were significantly less than those from the mothers; premature infants appeared particularly to be less well fortified with vitamin A.

Clinical and biochemical findings and assessments of dietary intake agreed in indicating that lower income and inferior dietary intake were reflected in low concentrations of some constituents of blood.

SUCCESSIVE SURVEYS of a group over a period of years may be used to estimate trends in health and well-being and the effectiveness of efforts to improve nutrition.

Various studies in Newfoundland before 1944 indicated that nutritional deficiency diseases were prevalent among the inhabitants living in poor economic conditions on this relatively isolated island.

The high incidence of deficiency diseases was attributed to their widespread use of refined white flour, the preference for salt fish and salt meats, and shortage of green vegetables and milk.

The government of Newfoundland in 1944 invited a group of Canadian, British, and American physicians to conduct a survey to provide an evaluation of the nutritional status of the population and a baseline from which the effectiveness of corrective nutritional measures could be judged.

Physical examinations of 868 men, women, and children from various parts of Newfoundland indicated a high prevalence of clinical signs associated with chronic deficiencies of vitamin A, riboflavin, and ascorbic acid. Low levels of these nutrients were found in the blood and urine samples. Some signs suggestive of chronic, mild deficiencies of niacin and thiamine were also encountered. The total food supply of Newfoundland was providing less than a third of the recommended amounts of vitamin A and ascorbic acid, less than half of the calcium and riboflavin, and less than two-thirds of the thiamine. The investigators concluded that the state of health in Newfoundland was unsatisfactory.

Efforts to improve nutrition in Newfoundland were undertaken by the government and other agencies. These included a program for public education in nutrition, the distribution in the schools of hot milk and cod-liver oil, the fortification of margarine with vitamin A, and the enrichment of white flour with thiamine, riboflavin, niacin, iron, and calcium in the form of edible bonemeal.

An improvement in economic conditions in Newfoundland also influenced favorably the food supplies and diet.

A resurvey was conducted in 1948 in the hope of evaluating the effect on health of the measures undertaken after the survey in 1944. The same number of persons was examined, including 227 individuals who participated in the 1944 survey.

The prevalence of symptoms related to deficiencies of vitamin A, thiamine, riboflavin, and niacin was strikingly diminished, although there was no improvement in the occurrence of other signs related to deficiency of vitamin C.

The increasingly favorable economic conditions led to increased imports of all kinds of food, but food production on the island seemed to have declined. It was not possible to estimate whether there had been a substantial increase in the consumption of milk, meat, fruit, and vegetables, because an undeterminable proportion of the civilian food supplies had been consumed by military forces on the island and a large amount of food had gone into stocks and stores. Nevertheless, the improvement in clinical observations associated with vitamin A, thiamine, riboflavin, and niacin could be attributed in part to the fortification of margarine, an increased use of processed milk, and the enrichment of flour.

Of particular interest were the successive observations of pregnant women in 1944 and 1948. As reported in other studies, pregnancy in women consuming diets low in nutrients may lead to an increased severity in the symptoms associated with nutritional deficiency. The pregnant women in 1944 had more obvious deficiencies than nonpregnant women when the dietary intakes of certain nutrients were low. Also, as in other studies, there was generally more striking evidence of malnutrition in women who had been pregnant oftener.

There were declines of 15 percent or more in 1948 in symptoms associated with deficiencies of vitamin A, thiamine, riboflavin, and niacin. Women who had had recent or frequent pregnancies showed the greatest benefits from the measures undertaken to improve nutritional conditions. The main exception was of the severe symptoms related to a deficiency of vitamin C, but (as with the population as a whole) serum levels and intake had remained fairly constant during the 4 years between the surveys. Orange juice supplied to pregnant women added only an average of 1.1 milligrams of ascorbic acid a day of a total recommended level of 100 milligrams a day. Again in the 1948 surveys, as with the total population, increases in blood or urine levels of vitamin A, thiamine, riboflavin, and niacin substantiated and undoubtedly confirmed the improved findings of the physical examinations.

Stillbirth rates and infant mortality were reduced between 1944 and 1948 as nutriture of the mothers improved.

Following the resurvey, the nutrition education program directed toward increased consumption of milk, vegetables, and fruit has been expanded throughout Newfoundland.

Distribution of cod-liver oil and concentrated orange juice for infants and pregnant women, the fortification of margarine, and the enrichment of flour have been continued.

WE GIVE another example of a planned change in staple foods for nutritional benefit. Surveys in Bataan, in the Philippine Islands, disclosed that polished rice contributed 83 percent of the Calories in the diets of 559 families. Protein foods, mainly fish, and vegetables each contributed about 8 percent of the Calories. Sweets provided the rest.

Chemical analyses of the blood and urine and physical examinations of 200 persons also indicated the prevalence of multiple dietary deficiencies. These most pronounced among the pregnant and lactating women were lack of thiamine, vitamin C, protein,

and hemoglobin. Beriberi, a multiple nerve-degeneration syndrome frequently associated with deficiencies of thiamine in the diet, was widely prevalent and caused many deaths.

One major recommendation to improve the nutritional status of the group was the provision of rice enriched with thiamine, niacin, and iron to increase the dietary intake of them to about the recommended levels.

A nutritional resurvey was undertaken 2 years after a rice-enrichment program was started. Of the 200 persons studied, 128 had participated in the original survey.

The resurvey indicated that nutrient intakes were more satisfactory, although the dietary, chemical, and clinical studies indicated that calcium and riboflavin intake levels were still very low.

Symptoms of beriberi had practically disappeared. More favorable levels of thiamine and hemoglobin were noted in chemical analyses of the blood. Improvements in the health of the people could be related to the program of rice enrichment.

STUDIES by scientists of the Food and Agriculture Organization, the World Health Organization, the United Nations Children's Fund (UNICEF), and the Interdepartmental Committee on Nutrition for National Defense have contributed to our knowledge of many aspects of physical health and well-being of people in developing countries where economic, educational, and public-health improvements frequently are basic to the achievement of better nutrition.

Under the auspices of the United Nations, all phases of development have been considered, together with recommendations for raising nutritional conditions. Populations that are under heavy economic and environmental stress often lack good food. Frequently there is a heavy deficit of calories, and with it the possibility of considerable reductions in the intakes of all nutrients.

A major nutritional problem in

the developing countries is kwashi-orkor, which occurs oftenest in young children and is attended by arrested growth, arrested bone development, and finally severe general malnutrition. The condition has been associated primarily with very small amounts of protein in the diet and other dietary deficiencies and nutrient imbalances.

Several United Nations committees are concerned also with an apparent increase in beriberi among isolated populations for whom rice is a staple. The increased incidence of beriberi is due partly to the introduction of small rice mills, which remove the vitamin-containing outer layers of the rice grain. No compensating measures have been taken voluntarily to remedy this or to provide other dietary sources of the important vitamins thus discarded.

A lack of natural food sources of vitamin A appears to be a main factor in a nutritional deficiency disease that is characterized by severe eye lesions and has been cited as a contributory cause of death among children in several countries. The eye symptoms may be alleviated by supplying doses of vitamin A, but improvement in the levels of nutrient intake through changes in compatible dietary habits is most to be desired.

Anemia has been cited as an important cause of maternal mortality in some countries. It has been estimated that in one country 40 percent of the maternal mortality is related to severe anemia. Many factors may be involved, but malnutrition undoubtedly is largely to blame.

Under the auspices of the Interdepartmental Committee, nutrition surveys have been made at the formal requests from the Governments of Korea, Iran, Pakistan, Turkey, the Philippines, Libya, Spain, and other countries as part of a program for technical, military, and economic development.

In the United States surveys have been developed under the auspices of the Interdepartmental Committee on Nutrition for National Defense, which was established in 1954 by the De-partments of Defense, State, Agriculture, and Health, Education, and Welfare, and the International Co-operation Administration. The Committee was later expanded to include the Atomic Energy Commission.

Its primary function is to coordinate nutrition programs of the United States agencies working in foreign countries and to serve as a center for information about nutrition.

The Committee reviews nutrition projects being conducted in special areas and coordinates and participates in field studies.

As a part of the nutrition surveys in each country, a statistical sample of about 2 thousand individuals are given detailed physical examinations. Blood and urine samples are also obtained for chemical analysis for about 500 of them. In addition, 3 thousand to 5 thousand individuals in each country are given a less extensive examination in which signs indicative of nutritional deficiency are recorded.

Average daily food intakes are determined primarily by food inventories and surveys of food preparation techniques. Food samples are collected for chemical analysis for nutrient content because standard reference tables on the nutrient content for certain staple foods are not available.

The nutritional status of the population groups studied has been reasonably good in general, although the surveys indicated the improvements that could be made in each country. Improvement in riboflavin intakes and, in some areas, vitamin A and C were most frequently suggested. As generally noted in most surveys, however, physical signs possibly related to low nutrient intakes were seldom specific for only one nutrient. The incidence of borderline nutritional deficiency symptoms varied greatly between countries and between areas within each country.

Relationships among chemical measurements of the blood and urine and the occurrence of clinical signs of malnutrition were observed. When blood serum levels of vitamin C were low, for example, there were more gum disorders; when riboflavin levels of the urine were low, there was increased prevalence of changes of the skin at the corners of the mouth.

Among the population groups studied, low blood serum levels of various nutrients were observed in large numbers of people. In particular, low blood serum vitamin C was reported in 17 to 72 percent of the persons examined in four countries; low blood serum vitamin A, in 17 to 24 percent in two countries; low hemoglobin, in 25 percent of the subjects in one country; and low blood serum protein, in 29 to 53 percent in two countries.

Following these extensive surveys, recommendations for dietary improvement were formulated in each country with particular regard to the food resources and the customs and habits of the people within the area.

Recommendations often have included the eventual goal of developing facilities for processing, preserving, and storing food, because nutritional needs often can be met by using existing resources better.

A resurvey was conducted in Korea in 1956, 3 years after a survey had indicated possible areas of deficiencies and ways to improve the nutritional status. That the recommendations were feasible and practical was indicated by striking decreases in the percentages of people who showed signs of possible nutritional deficiencies.

In the 3 years, the percentage of underweight persons dropped from 43 to 16; mouth lesions decreased from 45 to 28; and gum disorders declined from 46 to 0. Favorable changes were reported also for the levels of certain blood constituents.

Studies such as these are providing means for the improvement of the nutritional status of populations of developing countries. They also provide information on the basic development and use of criteria for measuring nutritional status.

THE FIRST of a number of regional cooperative studies of nutritional status by State agricultural experiment stations began in 1936, when a group of home economics investigators in several north-central experiment stations inaugurated a study of the nutritional status of college women. The study continued 10 years. Thereafter new and broader projects were undertaken in the north-central and other regions by the State experiment stations.

The original group published 24 reports of their findings: Ten dealt with nutrient intakes and balances of calcium, phosphorus, and nitrogen. Seven dealt with the blood studies, especially hemoglobin, red cells, and other phases of hematology. Five had to do with basal metabolism. Two gave anthropometric measurements.

More than 1,100 basal metabolism determinations of 576 women 17 to 24 years old in Iowa, Kansas, Minnesota, Ohio, and Oklahoma revealed that the basal energy-producing rates of the girls in Kansas and Oklahoma were significantly lower than those of the girls in the three States farther north.

Nearly 1 thousand freshman women were measured as to height, weight, chest breadth and depth, arm and leg girth, and grip strength. Of them, 437 were "old Americans"—that is, their ancestry on both sides had been American for at least three generations. These women excelled in both height and weight all women previously measured in the respective States. Measurements of 209 of them were taken for 4 successive years and showed a consistent annual increase in height.

On the basis of the metabolic balance studies, values for daily intakes of calcium, phosphorus, and protein necessary for equilibrium for women 17 to 24 years old were suggested. These were 1 gram of calcium, 1 gram of phosphorus, and 56 grams of protein. With a diet adequate in the other nutrients, 7 milligrams of iron were found to be sufficient for balance.

The outstanding faults found with the typical self-selected diets of these young women were scarcity of citrus fruit, tomatoes, other green and yellow vegetables and fruit, and milk. Whole-grain cereal products were low or lacking in these diets. The bread-and-cereal-enrichment program of the past decade very likely has overcome somewhat the deficiencies presented by refined grain products.

NEW IMPETUS was given to regional cooperative researches on nutritional status under the Research and Marketing Act of 1946. Funds were provided for the agricultural experiment stations to use in projects in which two or more stations work together toward the solution of a problem.

One of the first such endeavors was on the subject of the nutritional status and dietary needs of selected population groups. All four regions eventually proposed researches in this field.

The reports dealing with the findings by these teams have been appearing since 1947 in bulletins, scientific journals, and extension leaflets. The reports contain a vast amount of data on the nutritional status of men, women, and children in city and rural communities, of varying incomes, occupations, and customs, and in at least 38 of the States.

Since the methods of collecting and evaluating data were fairly uniform in all regions, the results are as nearly suitable for mass comparison and interpretation as such studies can be.

The maps of the United States on the next page indicate the regions and the age and sex of most of the subjects studied.

A total of 4,394 children under 13 years of age were studied in New York, Maine, West Virginia, Iowa, Kansas, Ohio, Louisiana, Virginia, and Utah.

Adolescents, aged 13 to 20 years were examined in Maine, New York, Rhode Island, West Virginia, Iowa, Illinois, Arizona, Colorado, Idaho, Montana, New Mexico, Oregon,

Utah, and Washington, to the number of 4,141.

Adult men and women studied in California, Colorado, New Jersey, Massachusetts, Virginia, Illinois, Iowa, Michigan, Minnesota, Nebraska, Texas and South Dakota numbered 4,210.

Not all the examinations and calculations usually included in studies of nutritional status were recorded for every one of these persons, but dietary intakes, blood composition, and physical examination usually were included. Those three criteria were used in the States in the Northeast, the South, and the West, but in the North Central States (at least in the case of the older women subjects) only dietary intakes have been reported in full.

Both blood composition and dietary findings have been reported for the schoolchildren in Iowa, Kansas, and Ohio. Heights, weights, and other physical measurements were reported for the children in Virginia and Louisiana and for most of the adolescents in the West.

The study of schoolchildren in Iowa was unusually complete but did not include listings of such physical signs as changes in skin, eyes, and mouth, which sometimes are thought to be associated with nutritional deficiencies.

The findings of this group of studies we summarize under six headings:

The amounts of foods consumed by the families and persons of various ages and both sexes in pounds in a week;

the mean daily intake of nine nutrients of these persons, compared with the recommended allowances of these nutrients;

the percentage of each age and sex group who had less than two-thirds the recommended allowance of each of the nutrients;

the blood composition of these subjects, correlated with nutrient intakes;

the heights and weights and channel of development as well as body build of the children and the degree of underweight and overweight of the adults;

and the incidence of superficial signs

Cooperative Research on Nutritional Status

CHILDREN UNDER 13 YEARS OF AGE
4,394 were studied in New York, Maine, West Virginia, Iowa, Kansas, Ohio, Louisiana, Virginia and Utah.

ADOLESCENTS, AGED 13 TO 20 YEARS
4,141 were examined in Maine, New York, Rhode Island, West Virginia, Iowa, Arizona, Colorado, Idaho, Montana, New Mexico, Oregon, Utah and Washington.

ADULT MEN AND WOMEN
4,210 were studied in California, Colorado, New Jersey, Massachusetts, Illinois, Iowa, Michigan, Minnesota, Nebraska, South Dakota and Texas.

Special Studies

INDUSTRIAL WORKERS
in New Jersey

PAPAGO INDIANS
in Arizona

SPANISH AMERICANS
in New Mexico

PREGNANT WOMEN
in Massachusetts

Not all the examinations and calculations usually included under nutritional status studies were recorded for every one of these subjects but usually dietary intakes, blood composition and physical examination were included.

of possible nutritional significance in skin, eyes, mouth, and muscles and their correlation with nutrient intakes and blood composition.

Amounts of the food consumed were not recorded in all of the surveys. Values for seven foods were recorded in the Northeast. A full study of household food consumption was made in the South under the early Food Consumption Cooperative Research, which preceded the nutritional status project.

A somewhat similar but more restricted study was carried out in Kansas and Ohio of 446 families and 1,355 of their children.

We can compare all these records

with the studies of food consumption scientists in the Department of Agriculture made in 1955 of 6 thousand city and rural families in the four sections of the country. The methods used in obtaining the household data were different from those used in the cooperative dietary studies of individuals. The household consumption studies included all waste and no individual intake records. A comparison of the estimated nutrient or food intakes per person per day or per week obtained in these different ways therefore is of considerable interest.

The average food consumption of 750 low-income Negro and white fam-

ilies in the South was much less than that of the families in Kansas and Ohio. The southern families had only 70 percent as much meat and milk and 40 percent as much fruit and vegetables, but 132 percent as much cereal foods as the families in Kansas and Ohio.

The amounts eaten by the children in the latter groups were not similar to their own household surveys or the large north-central study of the Department of Agriculture in 1955 and could not be predicted from those two investigations.

The families in Kansas and Ohio used less meat and more milk, cereal foods, and fruit and vegetables than the regional survey showed. Their children, however, ate only 56 percent as much meat, 60 percent as much fruit and vegetables, 109 percent as much milk, and about 80 percent as much bread and cereal foods as were reported by their families.

The average nutrient intakes of the children in Kansas and Ohio were lower in every instance than those of their families. The percentage of children having less than two-thirds the allowances recommended in 1953 was far larger in every instance than that of the corresponding families.

Thirty to 40 percent of the children (but only 3 to 4 percent of the families) had less than two-thirds the recommended amount of ascorbic acid; 16 to 33 percent of the children (but only 7 and 9 percent of the families) were similarly low in calcium; 13 to 26 percent of the children (but only 4 percent of the families) were low in vitamin A. Similar but less striking discrepancies were disclosed in the other nutrients.

One-fifth to one-third of the low-income southern families, especially the Negro families, had less than two-thirds the recommended amounts of calcium, vitamin A, riboflavin, and ascorbic acid. (The recommended allowances available in 1953 were revised in 1958, but general comparisons are still valid.)

Consumption of six food groups was reported in a study of some 1,700 boys and girls 9 to 11 years old in public schools in Iowa, Kansas, and Ohio. Some of them were the same children included in the family survey in Kansas and Ohio. The children in Ohio ate larger amounts of nearly all the foods reported—notably fruit and vegetables.

Large groups of adolescents in three Northeastern and three Western States had rather similar intakes of food. The western boys and girls drank more milk and ate more meat and other protein foods (except those in Idaho), more cereal foods, fewer potatoes, and more fruit and vegetables than the northeastern group.

Another comparison of adolescents in Iowa, four Northeastern States, and three Western States also indicated rather similar consumption. The Iowa and northeastern boys and girls usually ate more meat but less milk than the western group. The Iowans ate more fruit and vegetables than any of the others. The westerners were next. The northeasterners ate slightly less than the westerners, who, however, ate more bread and cereal than any of the others.

We can compare the food consumption of the older women in the north-central region with that of a group of California women. That of middle-aged men in New Jersey can be compared with a group of older men in California.

The California women ate more meat, more milk, and more sweets and desserts, but less fruit and vegetables, particularly potatoes, and less cereal products and fats than the north-central women.

The New Jersey men were compared only as to consumption of milk, potatoes, and cereal with the older California men. They ate more of each of these foods.

The amount of fat in the diets was recorded in only a few studies—those of the north-central older women, the Iowa children 6 to 18 years old, the

Virginia children 8 to 11 years old, and all the western subjects.

The north-central women and children ate consistently larger amounts of fat (41 to 44 percent of total calories) than did the western children and adults (36.5 percent of total calories) and the Virginia children (37.5 percent of total calories).

These differences are significant and interesting in view of the suspicion in medical circles that dietary fat may contribute to production of arteriosclerotic disease.

The significance of records of food consumption illustrated by the national study of the Department of Agriculture in 1955 and by the studies of family food consumption in the South, Kansas, and Ohio lies in the fact that they establish the amounts of foods available to the population and the cost of the foods and predict the probable market for the farmer's products. They indicate only approximately the nutriture of the population, because, as we previously indicated, they provide no figures of actual food consumption of individuals.

The amounts and kinds of nutrients eaten—that is, the chemical constituents of food of known importance in nutrition—determine nutriture.

There are over 30 indispensable items in nutrition. They include water, 11 or more mineral elements, 12 vitamins, and 8 amino acids. Calories are yielded by all the organic food constituents, chiefly protein, fat, and carbohydrates.

Natural foods contain varied assortments of these nutrients, some in more economical and physiologically efficient proportions than others. Because the composition of foods is roughly constant, we can estimate fairly precisely the nutrient contributions of natural foods and compare the contributions with the normal daily needs of children and adults.

The mean daily intake of nutrients was determined by standardized methods. The individual record of food eaten by a participating subject in these surveys is called a dietary. Much effort was expended by the cooperating stations, especially in the Northeast, in an attempt to insure accuracy and uniformity in such records.

Some of the questions raised have to do with the number of days to be recorded; the choice of recall or of written record; choice of days of the week; measures of quantity (for example, the size of servings of food); accuracy and speed in calculation of nutrients in foods; the number of subjects required for a given degree of confidence in the methods; the effects of season, ethnic origin, and cultural traits; and the economic level of the persons studied.

At regional and interregional meetings of the investigators, agreements were reached on many of these questions. Every effort was expended thereafter to obtain uniform records. The chance for error in such dietary studies is large. The surprising similarity of the mean nutrient intakes by thousands of subjects in all parts of the country, of both sexes and practically all ages, argues for the validity of these records in terms of groups, but probably not of individuals.

The recommended daily allowances have been set up by a committee of the National Academy of Sciences-National Research Council for 10 essential nutrients. Much of the appraisal of dietary records has been directed at them. Besides Calories and protein, the 10 nutrients include 6 vitamins and 2 mineral elements, calcium and iron. One of the vitamins, vitamin D, is not usually appraised in dietary studies because of uncertainties as to actual requirements and because of the role of sunlight in meeting any need for it. Besides, vitamin D is usually present in diets only when it is added, as in milk, or as a supplement. It was not taken into account in the cooperative studies.

Assessed in all these dietaries were the amounts of vitamin A (or its vegetable provitamin carotene); vitamin C (more properly designated ascorbic acid); and three (of the seven or more) B vitamins—thiamine (vitamin B_1), riboflavin (vitamin B_2), and niacin.

Several other vitamins—vitamin B_6, pantothenic acid, vitamin E, and vitamin B_{12}—probably are just as essential to good nutrition as the six chosen for evaluation, but their presence was not determined, chiefly because reliable values for them were not available and because recommended or even minimum daily requirements for them in human nutrition were not established in 1958.

Analyses of calcium and iron in food have long been available, and so-called daily requirements have been set up. A good deal of doubt has arisen in recent years, however, as to the validity of these requirements. Apparently the intestine exerts an automatic control on the absorption and excretion of these elements, so that balances may be established on widely varying levels of intake. This is particularly evident with calcium, the requirements for which have been set up chiefly on the evidence of balance experiments. Such experiments are affected so much by the previous accustomed levels of intake as to make interpretation difficult.

Protein needs have been assessed and reassessed during the past century with numerous and puzzling results. It has been generally accepted in recent years that the physiological need is for certain amino acids designated as essential, which are conveyed in the food in varying proportions in the different naturally occurring proteins. The amount of protein needed in the diet depends partly on the amino acid makeup of that protein. A reasonable assumption, however, can be made as to the origin and therefore as to the value of the proteins in the prevailing American diet, and a generous allowance has been suggested as likely to provide all the needed amino acids.

The question of total requirement of calories is another thorny one, since physical activity affects it acutely

and individuals vary greatly in their amounts of activity.

The basal metabolism—that is, the lowest possible production of calories necessary for life—varies with age, sex, body size and composition, external temperature, and such physiological and pathological conditions as pregnancy, fever, and thyroid derangements.

It is possible nevertheless to estimate the basal calorie output of normal persons from standards based on age, sex, and body size. More calories demanded by the estimated amount of physical exercise may be added to this to provide a total calorie requirement, or allowance. It is obvious that such a calorie allowance is subject to great variation, and criticism of diets on the basis of inadequacy or excess of calories must be advanced cautiously.

The mean regional intakes by age groups of the nine nutrients—calories, protein, calcium, iron, vitamin A, thiamine, riboflavin, niacin, and ascorbic acid—were calculated from the 7-day, 3-day, or 1-day diet records of more than 3 thousand children 4 to 12 years old in all four regions, more than 2,400 boys and girls 13 to 20 years old in three regions, and more than 3 thousand adult men and women 20 to 95 years old in all four regions.

The groups that conducted the studies employed statistical methods to evaluate these means, but in the presentation we give here only the arithmetic means were used. We present the significant differences that were found but without the statistical verbiage.

THE CALORIES consumed by boys up to 14 years of age were approximately the same as the recommended amounts but after that were consistently (although slightly) lower.

The girls at all ages had about 200 calories less than the recommendations.

Both men and women more than 20 years old consumed 100 to 400 fewer calories than the recommended

Average Daily Intake of Calories

Boys and Girls 4 to 20 Years Old

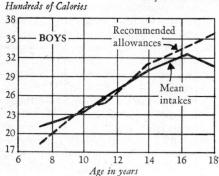

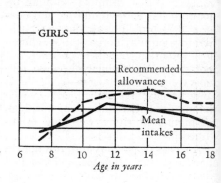

Average Daily Intake of Calories

Men and Women 20 to More Than 80 Years Old

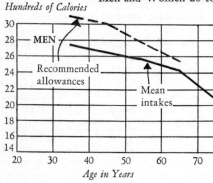

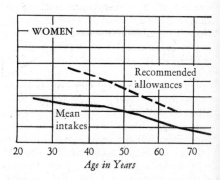

amounts. The gap was less at the older than the younger ages.

If we accept the reasonable completeness of these records, it appears that (although basal metabolism may not have changed) the muscular activity of the population, both young and old, may have been reduced enough in recent years to make the current calorie recommendations excessive.

The protein eaten by the boys and men at all ages averaged 15 to 20 grams a day more than the recommended amounts. The gap closed somewhat in the group over 70 years of age.

The girls up to 12 years old likewise

had high protein intakes, but after that age their intake fell off to 6 to 10 grams below the recommended amount.

From age 20 to 55, the women also had high intakes of protein, but after 55 the amount taken dropped to as low as 50 grams a day. Adolescent girls and elderly women obviously take less protein than the rest of the population, but it is difficult to judge whether this represents a physiological hazard. It is possible that the recommended allowances are higher than necessary.

The calcium intakes showed conditions somewhat similar to those of intake of protein. Boys and men at all ages exceeded the recommended

Average Daily Intake of Protein
Boys and Girls 4 to 20 Years Old

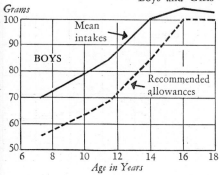
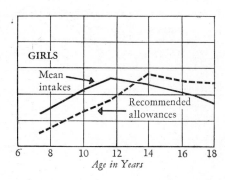

Average Daily Intake of Protein
Men and Women 20 to More Than 80 Years Old

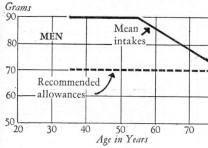
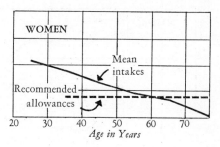

amounts, but girls and women had a wide gap in intake, nearly 0.2 gram below the recommended amount, except at age 20–29 years. This latter figure, however, was supplied by only one small group of women industrial workers in Virginia.

No obvious disadvantage seems to have resulted to these girls and women from the low intake of calcium. Indeed, some doubt as to the validity of the rather high recommended allowance of calcium has been expressed. The amount recommended was chosen chiefly on the basis of studies of calcium balance, which apparently are influenced greatly by the preceding habitual level of calcium intake. Good adjustments to quite low intakes have been seen.

The intakes of iron also followed the pattern shown by protein and calcium. The boys and men had average intakes well above the recommended amounts at all ages. The girls and women at all ages after 12 years had less than the recommended amount, except for the three decades between 30 and 60 years of age. Much the same criticism raised with reference to the calcium allowances may be applied to the iron allowance. The allowance for women has been kept to 12 milligrams, while that for men was reduced in 1958 to 10 milligrams. The argument is that women require

Average Daily Intake of Calcium
Boys and Girls 4 to 20 Years Old

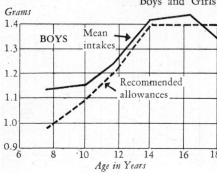
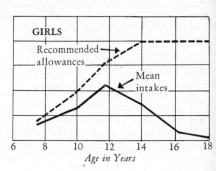

Average Daily Intake of Calcium
Men and Women 20 to More Than 80 Years Old

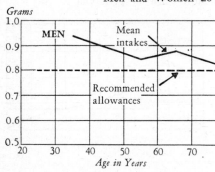
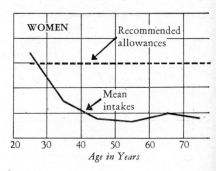

Average Daily Intake of Iron
Boys and Girls 4 to 20 Years Old

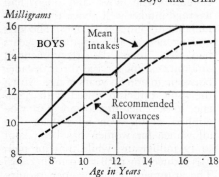
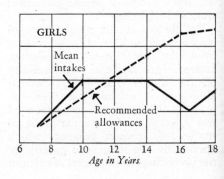

more iron for blood regeneration because of possible losses due to menstruation and reproduction. But again no stigmata of iron deficiency have been recorded for these girls and women with supposedly low intakes of iron.

Vitamin A was consumed at all ages by both the males and females in all four regions in ample amounts—well above the recommended levels of 3 thousand to 5 thousand International Units. Since vitamin A is fat soluble and cumulative, it seems unlikely that many members of these populations would manifest any deficiency.

Thiamine intakes by the boys up to age 14 and the girls to age 10 met the recommended criteria, but the males after age 14 ate consistently less— about 0.1 milligram daily—than the recommended amount. The females from age 10 to 45 had likewise about 0.1 milligram too little. After 45 years, however, the average intake was about the recommended amount. These deficits correlate fairly well with the lower intakes of calories we noted previously, and the thiamine need is proportional to calorie intake.

Riboflavin was obtained by boys and men on the average in amounts well over the recommended allowance at all ages, but the girls after age 14 had increasingly low intakes. The exception again was seen in the records of the 20- to 29-year-old group of women in Virginia.

Niacin was present in adequate amounts in nearly all diets. New amounts of total niacin equivalents have been suggested in the recommended allowances of 1958. Since tryptophan, one of the amino acids of the proteins, can be transformed in the body into niacin, in the average ratio of 60 to 1, the tryptophan value of the diet must be considered in assessing the niacin equivalents present. Males and females had adequate intakes at all ages, except the girls at 16 to 20 years, whose intakes were slightly low. The high content of protein of the diets contributed to this,

although niacin as such was present in generous amounts.

The intake of ascorbic acid of the boys and girls up to 12 years was excellent, but after that in both sexes the intakes were 5 to 15 grams lower than the recommended allowances. The women maintained nearly adequate intakes from age 20 on, and the men had large excesses. The values for the older men were largely obtained from the California group, which had notably high intakes of the vitamin-rich fruit and vegetables compared with men in other regions.

It is interesting to speculate on this recurring pattern of the decrease of intake of nutrients by girls after age 12 and the continuing rise in intake by the boys.

The growth of girls, which we mention in a later section, follows a curve different from that of the boys. A rapid acceleration occurs just before puberty at 10 to 12 years of age and is followed by an equally rapid deceleration. Growth continues but at a sharply decreasing rate.

The spurt of growth of the boys occurs at about age 14 and continues at only a slightly lowered tempo to maturity at about age 20.

The intake of all nutrients follows these lines. Nevertheless we have some indication that the choice of foods made by the teen-age girls may be disadvantageous.

The percentage of subjects who ate less than two-thirds the recommended amounts of the nutrients was determined in nearly all the studies.

These comparisons were generally with the 1953 list of allowances.

Children under 13 years of age in six States showed smaller percentages of subjects with less than two-thirds the recommended amounts of nutrients than persons in any other age group. There were more in this low category in West Virginia and Virginia than in the other four States. The children in New York had many with low intakes of iron and niacin, however. Except for ascorbic acid, only four nutrients were reported lacking in this degree in more than 10 percent of the children's dietaries. These were calcium in Iowa and West Virginia, iron and niacin in New York, and vitamin A in Virginia. Vitamin A values in the West Virginia dietaries were not reported. Ascorbic acid (vitamin C) intakes in less than two-thirds the recommended amount occurred in all States to the extent of 17 to 41 percent, except in Iowa, 12 percent.

Among the schoolchildren, 9 to 11 years old, in Kansas, there were more who ate less than two-thirds the recommended amounts of nearly all the nutrients than among the similar children in Iowa and Ohio. The largest percentages of low intakes were in ascorbic acid, calcium, and vitamin A. These records accord with the relatively low blood values of the Kansas children, which we discuss later.

The adolescent boys and girls in six Western and two Northeastern States had most deficits in ascorbic acid and calcium. The word "deficit" we use here for convenience only—intakes less than two-thirds the recommended allowances for any of the nutrients may be far from deficient because of the generous margin of safety provided in these allowances.

Most of the low intakes were among the Spanish-American children in New Mexico and the adolescents in Colorado. Forty to 60 percent of both groups had low intakes of ascorbic acid and calcium, and only slightly smaller numbers had low amounts of thiamine, riboflavin, niacin, and vitamin A.

The girls in all States had still larger proportions with deficits in calcium, iron, vitamin A, ascorbic acid, thiamine, and riboflavin.

Even in protein, 30 to 40 percent of the Spanish-American girls and girls in Colorado had less than two-thirds the recommended amount.

The adolescents in Maine and New York had fewer deficits than the westerners, except in calcium and vitamin A, and, in the case of the boys, protein. The same picture was seen among the Iowa adolescents— more low intakes among the girls than the boys and more in the older than the younger age group.

College students 16 to 20 years old in three States had the same distribution of low intakes as the adolescents, mostly in calcium and ascorbic acid.

The adult women in the six North Central States showed large numbers with low intakes in the older age groups. The greatest percentage of such low intakes occurred in calcium, vitamin A, ascorbic acid, and riboflavin. The California and Colorado women more than 50 years old had similar but less marked deficits. The younger women, 20 to 50 years old, in Virginia had few such cases, except in ascorbic acid and vitamin A. The similar-aged group of men in New Jersey also had fewer members with these low intakes of nutrients except ascorbic acid and calcium.

Smaller groups of California and Colorado men over 50 years had more members with limited intakes. Nearly 40 percent of Colorado men were low in ascorbic acid and calcium; 30 to 35 percent were low in vitamin A. The California men had fewer low intakes—about 20 percent in ascorbic acid, 15 percent in vitamin A, and fewer than 10 percent in the other nutrients.

The composition of blood of these subjects correlated with the nutrient intakes in many instances.

SINCE IT HAS BEEN established that the composition of the blood reflects the state of nutriture in regard to several nutrients at least, blood sampling and analysis have become routine procedure in nutritional status studies. In most of the cooperative researches, strictly comparable procedures were used, so that the results might be fairly comparable within as well as between regions.

An elaborate effort was made in the

northeastern region to secure similarity of techniques, including the preparation and distribution of a referee blood sample by the West Virginia station. The six participating States analyzed this sample by microchemical methods for hemoglobin, ascorbic acid, vitamin A, and carotene.

The variations in determinations of these four substances within an experiment station were small compared with variation from station to station. Apparently the station-to-station differences were about the same as the day-to-day fluctuations in blood levels of ascorbic acid and carotene in an individual subject. It can therefore probably be assumed that the blood analyses made by these six experiment stations are comparable.

Almost similar, if not identical, methods were used in the other regions. The Iowa, Kansas, and Ohio groups standardized their slightly different methods for determination of hemoglobin by calibrating all instruments against the oxygen-capacity method of Van Slyke. They used the same methods for serum ascorbic acid, vitamin A, and carotene as the northeastern group.

The western experiment stations in some cases used larger blood samples from a vein, but the actual laboratory methods were essentially the same as were used in the other regions. Finger blood was used in the studies in Virginia and Louisiana of 8- to 11-year-old children and the same microchemical methods that were adopted in the other regions.

The hemoglobin of children under 13 years was determined in New York, Iowa, Virginia, Louisiana, Kansas, Ohio, and Utah. The hemoglobin levels of the boys and girls in all groups were much alike at about 13 grams percent of whole blood.

The children in rural schools in Iowa usually had about 1 gram percent less hemoglobin than those in the city schools. Children in New York and Utah were alike at 13 percent hemoglobin; children 9 to 11 years

old in Iowa and Ohio were alike at 13 percent; the children in Kansas had only 11 percent. The white and Negro children in towns of Virginia and Louisiana also had 13 percent, but the rural children in Virginia had 11 percent.

Adolescents in three Northeastern States showed the expected rapid increase in hemoglobin of the boys to 14 or 15 percent, with little change in the girls, who remained at 13 percent. This was shown also in the studies in Iowa and New York and in the extensive sampling in the West.

Men and women in the West, Virginia, and New Jersey maintained fairly steady hemoglobin concentrations of 13 to 14 and 14 to 15 percent.

Correlations were found in the Northeast, California, Montana, New Mexico, Virginia, and Louisiana between the protein and iron of the food and the level of hemoglobin in the blood of the subjects. The positive correlation with both protein and iron was significant in some and in others with one but not with the other. Apparently when the intakes were generous the relationship was not so easy to demonstrate as when borderline amounts of the nutrients were taken.

Altitude affected the hemoglobin. The western subjects generally had higher hemoglobin levels than those in the other regions. This is due undoubtedly to the higher altitudes at which many of the subjects lived. The groups in Colorado, Montana, Utah, New Mexico, and a part of Oregon lived at altitudes of 4 thousand to 10 thousand feet. Raised hemoglobin levels are characteristic of all acclimated people living at these altitudes.

The serum ascorbic acid of children under 13 in Iowa, New York, and Utah showed a steep decline from 5 years to adolescence. The 9- to 11-year-old children in Kansas had blood values of ascorbic acid significantly lower than children in Iowa and Ohio. The white and Negro children in rural Virginia, 8 to 11 years old, had levels

Hemoglobin and Ascorbic Acid Levels of Blood

Children and Adults in Eight Western States

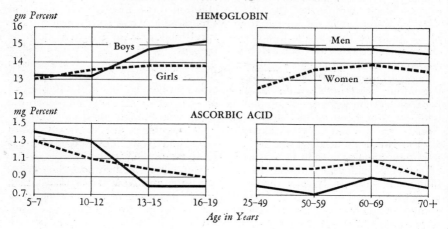

of serum ascorbic acid about half those of the children in towns in Virginia and Louisiana.

Adolescents in the Northeast showed a clear difference in the blood ascorbic acid of the sexes. The girls in all cases maintained the higher levels. The western group showed the same difference, but that was not so in Iowa and New York.

The women in the West, 50 years of age and older, had consistently higher ascorbic acid blood values than the men. In nearly all these studies, a positive correlation of a high order of significance was found between the amount of ascorbic acid in the diet and the level in the blood. Most of the blood levels were judged adequate or good, but the rural children in Virginia; the children, 9 to 11 years old, in Kansas; and many of the adolescent boys in the Northeast had borderline values.

Blood vitamin A and carotene frequently were determined. Carotene is the provitamin A in foods of vegetable origin. It is transformed in the body into vitamin A and must be so transformed to function physiologically. The efficiency of transformation is variable. Serum carotene reflects the recent intake of carotene

from green and yellow vegetables and fruit, but does not necessarily indicate the status of vitamin A.

Serum vitamin A indicates the level of circulating vitamin A and is therefore related to the vitamin A status of the body. Since both carotene and vitamin A occur in foods and are estimated together as International Units of vitamin A, correlation of the dietary intake with serum vitamin A and carotene may be unsatisfactory. Carotene in the food usually correlates well with carotene levels in the blood but total food vitamin A or food vitamin A of animal origin may or may not be correlated with serum vitamin A. It is obvious, therefore, that the significant blood constituent is vitamin A, not carotene.

The children and adolescents in New York had levels of serum carotene that decreased irregularly from the youngest age groups to maturity. The levels of serum vitamin A rose from 5 to 8 years of age, then decreased steadily to average age 18. The lowest level, about 36 micrograms percent, generally is considered adequate for good nutrition. Serum carotene followed almost the identical pattern in the western studies, descending from about 180 micrograms percent at 5 to

Vitamin A and Carotene Levels of Blood
Children and Adults in Eight Western States

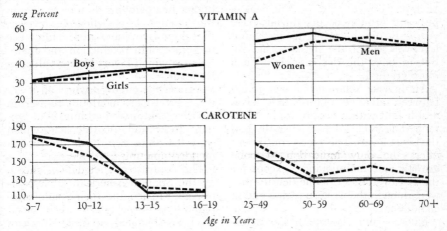

Age in Years

7 years to 110 micrograms percent at 16 to 19 years. The blood vitamin A of the western subjects varied from 30 to 40 micrograms percent in the same age range, but without the peak at 8 years of the children in New York.

The children in Kansas generally had higher serum vitamin A but lower levels of carotene than the children in Iowa and Ohio examined by the same techniques. This shows the possible divergence of these two blood constituents due to variation of the current from previous diet habits.

The 8- to 11-year-old children in Virginia and Louisiana had satisfactory levels of both vitamin A and carotene. The white children in urban Virginia and the children in Louisiana had higher levels than the white and the younger Negro rural children. Adolescents in Maine, Rhode Island, and West Virginia had similar blood values, vitamin A, 30 to 40 micrograms percent, and carotene, under 100 micrograms percent, except for the 16- to 20-year-old group. The girls had higher levels of carotene than the boys.

The older men and women in the West showed higher blood levels of vitamin A than any of the younger groups, usually more than 50 micro-

grams percent for vitamin A and more than 130 micrograms percent for carotene. This may be due to the cumulative nature of high intakes of A.

Positive correlations between blood carotene levels and the vitamin A and carotene of the diets were established for the women in Virginia; the adolescents in Montana, New Mexico, and Washington; and for the older men and women in California.

No significant correlations were found in the northeastern studies, but in this region no separation of dietary vitamin A and carotene was attempted. The studies of preadolescent children in Louisiana and Virginia also revealed significant correlations between food vitamin A and carotene in the blood.

Serum alkaline phosphatase is an enzyme that may indicate the extent and normality of growth or change of bone. High values occur during rapid growth. Low values occur in scurvy, hypothyroidism, and in weight loss. High values also may indicate the presence of rickets or other bone disorders.

Only the experiment stations in New York, Maine, Iowa, Utah, Montana, and Idaho included this among the blood analyses. The same pattern of occurrence was seen in children of the Northeast, Iowa, and the West. A sharp rise occurred in girls at age 10 to 12 and in boys at 13 to 15. The peak of pubertal growth occurs during these years. Rapid lowering to the adult level was seen in the girls after age 12, but in boys the decrease was much more gradual.

An inverse relationship was found between alkaline phosphatase levels and height within sex groups in Montana. The taller subjects generally had the lower levels. This blood constituent offers the only indication of bone growth and maintenance, except for the X-ray studies of bone density that were done in the western region and in Tennessee.

Blood serum cholesterol was determined routinely only by the western stations. The females at all ages had higher serum levels than the males, except for the small group of adults, 20 men and 21 women 25 to 49 years of age, in the study in Utah. The value for adolescents was established fairly clearly at 167 milligrams percent for the girls and 156 milligrams percent for the boys at age 14, and 171 and 162 milligrams percent at age 18. The older women maintained a high value, 260 to 272, during the fifth and sixth decades, with a slow decline thereafter. The men showed a steady decline from 265 at 55 years to 232 at age 70. These studies were among the first to establish the difference in levels of serum cholesterol between males and females.

The subjects in California had a positive correlation between the cholesterol level and dietary fat and cholesterol. Much importance had been attached in recent years to the maintenance of low levels of cholesterol, particularly in men, in the hope of decreasing the danger of arteriosclerotic heart damage. Several special studies on this problem were carried out by the cooperating stations, chiefly with older women as subjects in the northeast, north-central, and western regions.

The blood studies confirmed the dietary records. The higher intakes of protein and iron of the boys and men at all ages were accompanied by higher hemoglobins than were seen in the females. It is believed, however, that there is an inherent sex difference in hemoglobin production and maintenance which favors higher values in the male.

Among the children who had lower mean levels of hemoglobin and serum ascorbic acid more had intakes of protein, iron, and ascorbic acid which were less than two-thirds the recommended amounts.

The contrast of diet deficits shown by the Spanish-American adolescents of New Mexico and their Anglo companions is borne out by their blood level ascorbic acid: Spanish-American boys and girls, 0.7 and 0.8, Anglo 0.8 and 0.9; carotene, Spanish-American 108, Anglo 122; vitamin A, Spanish-American 29, Anglo 32; hemoglobin, Spanish-American boys and girls, 14.1 and 13.5, Anglo 15.2 and 13.8.

THE GROWTH OF CHILDREN and the weights of adults were noted.

Systematic measurements of 1,200 children were part of the program to determine their nutritional status in Iowa. Heights and weights were recorded in Kansas, Ohio, New Mexico, Montana, Arizona, Idaho, Washington, Virginia, and Louisiana. Deviation from standard weight for height, age, and sex was also reported in the Northeast. The standards usually used were taken from the Baldwin and Wood tables, which were compiled in 1923 from measurements of some 129 thousand children of school age in 12 schools in the northeastern and north-central regions.

Another set of standards for both growth and development is the Wetzel grid, a chart published in 1941 for measuring the progress of individual children. The relationship of weight to height determines the physique channel, or build, of the child. It is further adjusted to age to indicate the channel of development, or auxodrome, in which the child is placed. This may be good, doubtful, or poor by comparison with the records of 7 thousand normal children previously studied. Thus a child might have height and weight indicating obese, stocky, medium, thin, or very thin build, and poor, doubtful, or good development for age.

The distribution of body builds among Iowa children indicated what was generally found to be the case—that is, more girls than boys were obese or stocky and fewer were medium or thin at all ages, but the obesity of the girls and the thinness of the boys increased with age. Sixty-five to 75 percent of both boys and girls of ages 6 to 19 years had both good—that is, medium—physiques and a good growth.

The Wetzel grid comparison was applied also to the Iowa, Kansas, and Ohio schoolchildren 9 to 11 years old. More girls in all three States were of obese or stocky build than the standard called for, and more boys were thin or very thin. The Ohio girls had a larger percentage of stocky, thin, and very thin members than did those in Iowa and Kansas and consequently only about 40 percent in the medium class.

Adolescents 14 to 16 years old were classified as to body build in New Mexico, Washington, and Idaho. As usual, the percentage of obese and stocky girls was greater than that of the boys, with more boys in the thin or very thin grouping. The Spanish-American boys in New Mexico had many more thin and very thin members than any of the other groups, but the girls had much the same body builds as the other western girls, except that very few were obese.

Figures as to underweight and overweight for height in the groups of children under 13 years of age in Utah, New York, Virginia, Louisiana, Ohio, Kansas, and Iowa agreed fairly well with each other when compared with the Baldwin and Wood standards. There was somewhat more underweight in Utah and the South and more overweight in New York. There

was more overweight among New York adolescent boys and girls also, as well as West Virginia boys and Rhode Island girls. Oddly enough, West Virginia girls showed disproportionately more underweight than any of the other groups.

The western adolescents manifested fair balances of underweight and overweight, except the Spanish-Americans in New Mexico, of whom 40 to 50 percent of both sexes were 10 percent or more underweight. The Anglo New Mexico and Colorado boys also had nearly this amount of underweight. Twenty-five percent of all the girls, except those in New Mexico, were 10 percent or more overweight for height. The same was true of 10 to 20 percent of the boys.

The average weights and heights of most of the western adolescents were compared. The Papago Indian children studied in Arizona and the Spanish-Americans in New Mexico were 4 to 5 inches shorter and the boys were 15 to 20 pounds lighter than the children of like age and sex in Iowa, Montana, Idaho, and Washington, who were much alike. The Papago Indian girls, however, were heavier than any of the others.

THE AMOUNT OF UNDERWEIGHT and overweight among adults was expressed as more than 10 percent underweight, 10 percent or less above or below normal, 10 to 20 percent overweight, and more than 20 percent overweight. The groups of women in South Dakota, Illinois, Iowa, and Michigan had excessive proportions of overweight; usually 25 to 30 percent were more than 20 percent overweight and were classified as obese.

Among the women in Minnesota, California, and Colorado fewer were overweight and more were underweight. These latter groups on the average were older than the other north-central women. The same comparison holds for the older California and Colorado men, as compared with the New Jersey men.

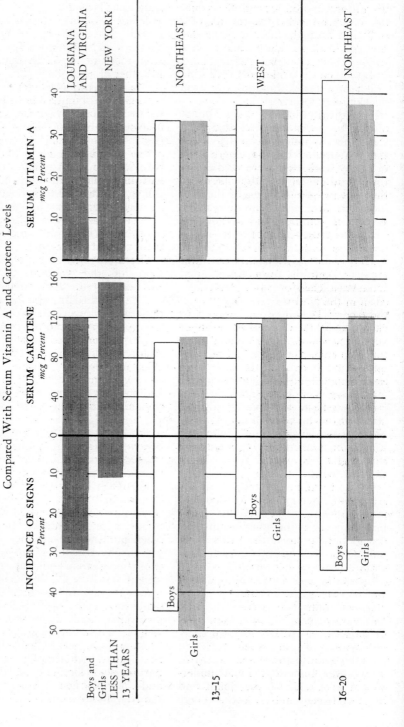

Incidence of Eye and Skin Changes Sometimes Associated With Vitamin A and Riboflavin Deficiencies

Compared With Serum Vitamin A and Carotene Levels

It is clear that among adults over-weight, not underweight, is the problem. Adolescent girls likewise tend to develop overweight more than do the boys, although there were some exceptions—the West Virginia girls 13 to 20 years old and the Maine girls 16 to 20, for example.

THE INCIDENCE of superficial signs of possible nutritional significance in skin, eyes, mouth, and muscle and their correlation with nutrient intakes and blood composition were noted in subjects in the northeastern, southern, and western regions.

An attempt was made to standardize these examinations, or at least to minimize differences in judgment of the examining physicians. The same examiners were used in two or more States in some instances, particularly in the West. Colored photographs were taken in the Northeast for comparison and record. This study was initiated at the Vermont Agricultural Experiment Station. Seven physicians and one dentist rated color slides of selected physical signs supposed to be associated with vitamin deficiencies. Significant differences arose among the ratings of the examiners. Color slides were also used by the Arizona and Washington experiment stations in their study of adolescent children and in conjunction with observations with the slit lamp and biomicroscope.

So much doubt as to their significance has been expressed by those who have studied the reports of these physical signs that the findings must be reported only in a general way. The occurrence of most of these signs—for example, roughening and drying of the skin, swelling and reddening of gums, and reddening and thickening of the mucous membranes covering the eyeball and eyelids—may be caused by a multiplicity of conditions, some of nutritional origin, some not.

Nevertheless, the incidence of any of these conditions in any population may be considered a useful pointer to possible dietary faults. Interpretation in the individual case is by no means so likely to be reliable.

A comparison of the incidence of these signs among the southern and northeastern children under 13 years of age showed that in nearly all cases the Virginia and Louisiana children had much more incidence of skin, mouth, and eye signs than the northeastern children, except for reddening and soreness of lips and gums among the West Virginia children.

The adolescents in the West had about the same percentage of abnormalities of skin, but less of the eyes, mouth, and tongue than the adolescents in the Northeast.

The older people in California and Colorado had more incidence of changes in skin, mouth, tongue, and eyes (conjunctival tissues) than the young adults of West Virginia and the middle-aged men in New Jersey.

An attempt was made to bring together these reports of clinical signs and to compare them with the known facts about the diets and blood composition of the same subjects.

The eye and skin lesions often are said to be due to deficiencies in vitamin A or riboflavin, or both, and the mouth and gum changes to deficiencies in ascorbic acid or riboflavin or both. The total incidence among children and adolescents of the eye and skin signs was compared with the serum vitamin A and carotene levels of these persons. The Louisiana and Virginia children had a high incidence—nearly 30 percent—of these signs. The New York children had a low incidence, 10 percent. But both the serum vitamin A and carotene levels of the New York children were significantly greater than those of the southern children.

The adolescents 13 to 15 years old in the Northeastern States showed a high incidence, nearly 50 percent, of these lesions. The western group had much less, about 20 percent. The blood of the westerners was slightly richer in both vitamin A and carotene. The northeast group 16 to 20 years old were intermediate in both incidence of signs and

Incidence of Changes in Mouth, Gums, and Tongue
Sometimes Associated With Ascorbic Acid Deficiency
Compared With Serum Ascorbic Acid Levels

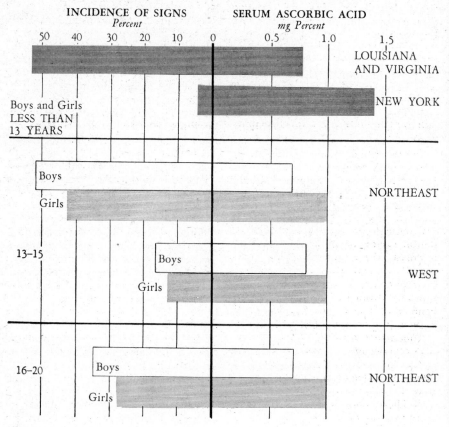

blood carotene, but not blood vitamin A. Riboflavin blood values were not available for this comparison.

A similar comparison of the incidence of mouth signs, chiefly cheilosis, gingivitis, and tongue changes, with the levels of ascorbic acid in the blood serum indicated that high incidence of signs in the southern children was accompanied by low serum ascorbic acid levels; with low incidence and high serum ascorbic acid in the New York children. The same inverse relationship was shown by the northeastern and western adolescents.

Nothing significant came from the

study of mean intakes of vitamin A, riboflavin, and ascorbic acid, or from a study of the percentage of subjects who had less than two-thirds the recommended allowances of these three vitamins compared with the incidence of these physical signs. With apparently adequate intakes, incidence of signs may be high or low.

It seems that blood will tell when dietary records will not—or else the current diets of these subjects were not representative of their accustomed and longtime food habits.

SOME SPECIAL STUDIES were carried

on under these cooperative nutritional status projects.

DENTAL DECAY, the most prevalent disease in the United States, affects more than 95 percent of the population. It has been estimated that the incidence of dental caries in this country is progressing six times faster than the needed number of dentists can be trained.

A significant conclusion was drawn from a 1952 survey by the National Academy of Sciences-National Research Council of the published information available from more than 2 thousand studies on the prevalence of tooth decay and factors that may influence the development of dental caries: Both heredity and environment profoundly affect dental caries.

Many surveys among primitive people indicate extremely low rates of dental caries, even though some differences exist among the groups surveyed. As civilization develops in primitive areas or as the people migrate toward the more civilized centers of living, tooth decay rates appear to increase considerably.

Concurrent with the change in rates of dental decay are substantial changes in the kinds of foods consumed, and often the nutrient content of the diet may be adversely affected. Particularly, there is usually an increase in the consumption of highly processed cereals and refined sugar. In human beings, however, the relationship between dietary sugar and other refined foods in the diet and susceptibility to tooth decay never has been clearly established.

In a review of many reports on food supplies and dental conditions in Norway, Great Britain, and other European countries during the Second World War, Dr. Guttorm Toverud, of the Norwegian State Dental Schools, stated that decreased caries rates were observed generally and that the magnitude of the decline seemed to be correlated chiefly with the restriction in sugar and sugar products. The sugar supply was less than half the prewar level, and there was little candy.

In Norway, for example, where the surveys have been most extensive, between 5 thousand and 6 thousand 7- to 13-year-old children were examined periodically between 1940 and 1953. Several hundred 3- to 6-year-old children also were examined yearly.

The average number of decayed, missing, and filled teeth per child showed a definite drop in 1942 and 1943. The rates of decrease in tooth decay were generally greater for the younger children. For example, decreases of about 75 percent were reported for 3-year-olds between 1939 and 1947. Among older children, reductions were 27 to 64 percent.

There was more variation in the rate of reduction according to the area in which the older children were living. The differences between the youngest and the oldest groups in changes in dental decay rates suggested that the teeth of the younger children reacted more readily to changes in nutritional or environmental condition than did those of the older children.

The rates of tooth decay increased substantially after the war years, but they had not reached the high prewar levels by 1953.

Dr. Toverud suggested that the drastic decrease in consumption of sugar and sugar products might be considered as the main cause of the reduction in tooth decay during the war years and that the postwar increase in tooth decay rates in Norway may be related chiefly to the gradual change to prewar food habits.

The total food restriction was severe in Finland. The reduction in sugar consumption was greatest and so was the reduction in tooth decay rates.

Reduction in tooth decay and changes in food habits, particularly in regard to sugar consumption, have also been reported for Great Britain, Switzerland, Hungary, the Netherlands, Belgium, France, Germany, Italy, and (to a lesser extent) the United States.

Increases during the war years in dietary intakes of calcium and vitamins A and D in Great Britain by mothers and infants, perhaps even more than reduced sugar and sweet intakes, may be related to decreases in dental caries.

Studies of United States repatriated prisoners of war who had existed on drastically reduced food intakes over extended periods indicated that dental caries did not increase with striking reductions in total food and nutrient intakes.

Of the many factors that may affect the development of dental caries, the influence of the amount of fluoride in water supplies has seemed to be outstanding. Many water supplies naturally carry fluorides, but many others do not. Population groups residing in those areas with minute amounts of fluorides in the water supplies generally have significantly lower dental decay rates than those groups residing in areas where fluorides are not present in water supplies. Fluoridation programs have been started in more than 1,500 communities in the United States to counteract the advancement of dental caries.

One of the most carefully controlled studies on the influence of adding minute amounts of fluorine to water supplies upon the rate of dental decay of children has been conducted by the New York State Department of Health. Two cities, Kingston and Newburgh, were selected as the areas for investigation. The cities were quite similar in population and environmental characteristics, including the fact that neither had naturally occurring fluorides in the water supply. Very small amounts of fluorides were added to the water supply in 1945 in Newburgh—only one part of fluorides in every million parts of water.

An extensive study of the number of decayed, missing, and filled teeth among 1,800 children of the two cities—789 children in Newburgh and 1,016 in Kingston—during a 10-year period indicated that the Newburgh children of the age group 6–9 years, who had had the benefits of fluoridated water all of their lives, had 57 percent less dental caries experience than did children of a similar age in Kingston. Newburgh children in the 13–14-, and 16-year age groups who had only 10 years of exposure to fluorides in water showed 48 percent and 41 percent less caries experience, respectively. Thus it appeared that even in the older children there was a significant protective effect of fluorides on the teeth that had erupted before the fluoridation program was started.

The inverse relationship between fluorides in the water supply and the rate of dental caries also has been noted in other countries. Sixteen other countries have begun similar programs. Results of surveys in all nations using fluoridated water supplies show remarkable uniformity.

The occurrence of tooth decay in children has often been thought to be connected in some way with nutritional faults. No general agreement on a specific relationship between caries and diet, however, has so far been demonstrated. Workers at five of the western agricultural experiment stations concentrated on the dental health of children in their studies of nutritional status.

The Oregon Agricultural Experiment Station in particular made a detailed and well-planned attack on this problem, in which Idaho, Montana, Utah, and Washington joined. More than 2 thousand boys and girls, 14 to 16 years old, were the subjects. The rate of occurrence of caries among them was found to be excessively high.

Climatic influence on this occurrence was found only in Oregon and to a lesser degree in Washington. Altitude and sunshine were beneficial. Humidity and precipitation were harmful. But when all the areas were considered together, the climate factor appeared negligible. Dietary differences were also ruled out.

Fluoride in the water supply again was found to be the outstanding protective factor. Thus, when the water contained 0.5 part per million (p.p.m.) of fluoride, dental decay was reduced 37 percent; with 1.0 p.p.m., it was reduced 55 percent; and with 1.5 p.p.m., it was reduced 45 percent. In this area 1 p.p.m. of fluoride in the water had the optimum beneficial effect on the teeth.

The hardness of fluoride-free water also bore a favorable relationship to dental caries. The presence in hard water of some trace element, not fluorine, and not its hardness itself, may be the favorable factor.

The girls had more missing, decayed, or filled teeth than the boys. The difference in eruptive age of teeth did not wholly account for this. In the fluoride-free areas 99 percent of the children, and 91 percent in the fluoride regions had present or past caries experience. Ninety-four and 79 percent of these children needed dental care.

The pilot study of children in three schools in Iowa, Kansas, and Ohio included examination of the teeth and gums. Of 219 Iowa children, 92 percent had open cavities and 10 percent had diseased gums. Of 190 Kansas children, 85 percent had cavities and 5 percent had diseased gums. Of 53 Ohio children, only 3 had no carious teeth. It was concluded that dental caries was the chief physical defect in these children.

THE GROWTH, development, and maintenance of the skeletal system has been assessed primarily through gross observations of bone outlines on X-ray films, with special reference to the appearances and formation of ossification centers.

Many valuable data have been contributed by studies of large numbers of persons who were photographed at different ages and under varying environmental and dietary conditions and of whom some were examined during later growth.

Individuals vary tremendously in the rate of bone growth and development. Even in one individual there is some variation in the rate of the growth and development of the different bones. The rate of skeletal development appears to be influenced by many cumulative factors.

Nutrition is recognized as a primary factor in abnormal skeletal formation in cases of gross malnutrition, such as rickets and scurvy, but objective means of measuring subclinical effects of chronic or acute low intakes of nutrients on skeletal development are still in the process of development.

Reports on a new technique for measuring bone density in human beings quantitatively were published by investigators in Pennsylvania about 1949.

This method involves essentially the use of a calibrated ivory or metal wedge placed on the film at the time of exposure, so that comparative measurements of the density of the film image of a given section of bone and of the calibrated wedge may be then obtained from the exposed film. Bone density in this sense may be defined as the weight of the ivory or metal in grams, which in a similar shape absorbs the same amount of X-radiation as the bone, divided by the volume of the bone in cubic centimeters.

This technique was used in nutritional status surveys in several of the State agricultural experiment stations. It was hoped that the data obtained might provide basic information on "normal" values for bone density for groups of various ages and an indication of the value of bone density measurements in the evaluation of nutritional status of population groups.

For about 2 thousand persons 5 to 95 years of age in the western region, trends in density values of heel and finger bones were associated with age and sex groups. Increases in bone density were observed during the developmental years of childhood and adolescence. Some decreases occurred among older age groups, particularly older women.

In most of the studies to date, no relationship has been readily apparent between measurements of bone density and nutrient intake as calculated from food records obtained at the time X-ray photographs were taken. Bone density may indicate cumulative nutritional status, however, whereas nutrient intake data calculated from short-term dietary records are designed to estimate current dietary trends of the group under study.

It was reported in the western regional studies that the customary dietary patterns of a group of Papago Indian adolescent girls might be associated with consistently low intakes. Comparatively low bone density values were observed among them.

Similar observations of low values of bone density associated with dietary inadequacies have been reported for Quechua Indian boys, 7 to 20 years old, in the north-central Peruvian Sierras. Low values of bone density observed particularly among older boys were associated with long-term inadequate nutrient intakes and also with retarded growth and maturation.

Fluoride content of the water supplies was not found to be related to bone density, even though in the same communities it influenced favorably the caries among the children.

Young women about 21 years of age were studied in Tennessee. Their calcium intakes and outputs were measured and the density of the heel bones was determined before and after supplements of calcium and vitamin were given for 3 months. No effect on bone density could be seen. It was concluded that bone density, as thus measured, is probably influenced by lifetime dietary habits, particularly as to calcium, but is not readily changed by even drastic changes in intake.

In all reports on bone density, it has been recognized that many factors may influence skeletal growth and development. Future population and carefully controlled long-term laboratory studies may define more clearly

Alkaline Phosphatase Concentration in Blood

Children in New York, Iowa, and the West

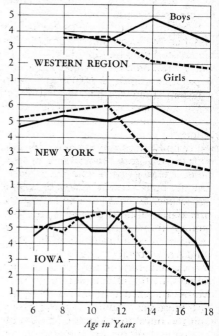

Nitrophenol Units

the relationship between bone density and nutrient intake, physiological development, heredity, and environment.

SOME TYPE OF FOOD service is available to most of the public school children in this country.

Studies of the influence of the availability of school lunches on the nutrition and health of the pupils have been conducted primarily among groups of children in fairly good physical condition.

One typical study among 100 children 6 to 12 years old in Maryland indicated that only mild, if any, physical signs possibly suggestive of malnutrition were seen. Chemical analyses of the blood indicated that hemoglobin values did not appear to be influenced by participation in the school lunch program. Blood levels of vitamin C (associated with intakes of citrus and other fruit and vegetables) and carotene (associated with intakes of green and yellow vegetables and fruit), however, were higher for pupils who had school lunches.

Extensive studies of the physiological response of children and adults to different breakfasts conducted at the State University of Iowa have indicated that a basic breakfast providing approximately one-fourth of the total daily calories and protein may best maintain physical and mental efficiency.

Breakfast habits of some children and of many teen-agers and adults are poor. Among the teen-agers, frequently considerably less than half of the students studied had adequate breakfasts—that is, breakfasts that contained one-fifth to one-third of the recommended allowances of the day's intake of nutrients.

A special study of the breakfasts and school lunches of teen-age children in Maine revealed that the girls' breakfasts were very low in iron and niacin and the boys' in vitamin C. Less than 15 percent of the daily allowance of vitamin C was included in more than 40 percent of these breakfasts.

The lunches eaten by a group of 450 junior high school students in Bangor were examined. The hot school lunch that was served some of them contained less than one-third the daily recommended allowance of calories, iron, niacin, and vitamin C. The box lunches or store lunches eaten by some of the children were much less adequate. The lunches eaten at home were no better, because they usually were inadequate in vitamin A and in the other nutrients listed.

Revision of the school lunch followed this study.

Similar studies were made in New York and Rhode Island, and indicated inadequacy of breakfasts. Fifty percent or more of the children received less than one-fourth of their daily calories and protein at breakfast. Between-meal snacks contributed little in New York and Maine, but were important in the diets of the children in Rhode Island.

The Iowa, Kansas, and Ohio agricultural experiment stations cooperated in the extensive study of school-children we previously mentioned. An effort to discover what measurable effect a hot lunch at school might have led to comparison of the blood composition of children who ate the school lunch and those who brought their own or ate at home or elsewhere.

No significant differences were found. Perhaps the school lunches on the whole did not supplement the home diets.

On the other hand, the Papago Indian children in Arizona showed measurable differences due to the kind of school lunch they ate. The children who attended a private school at which a small and inadequate lunch was served had lower blood vitamin A and ascorbic acid than the children who received a good lunch at a public school. The former group also showed more signs of vitamin A and ascorbic acid deficiencies. The girls who received the limited lunch had poorer bone calcification than those receiving the good lunch.

This is almost the first positive demonstration of the value of a good school lunch, perhaps because the children involved were receiving a really low basic diet.

The adequacy and acceptability of the food served in a rural school in Iowa were criticized in an early study. Recommendations were made for standardizing the quality and size of servings. The amount of plate waste was found to be a fair indicator of acceptance of foods. The acceptance of milk was high; the acceptance of vegetables and salads was low. Further studies of plate waste in a public school lunchroom in Ohio showed that about 14 percent of all vegetables were returned and 10 percent of meat, fish, and poultry dishes, as well as about 9 percent of fruits and desserts.

Another study in Iowa on the breakfast habits of nearly 1,200 children 6 to 19 years old likewise indicated that as a rule foods of cereal origin only were used. Too little fruit, milk, eggs, and meat were included. One-half to two-thirds of all breakfasts were classed as poor. The older girls made the poorest choices of all, but the boys' breakfasts also were of poor quality. Snacks eaten by the children, particularly the girls, were largely of carbohydrates and were low in nutrients. It was noted that when the breakfast meal was inadequate, the total food for the day was likely to be inadequate.

AGNES FAY MORGAN, *professor emerita and former chairman of the Department of Nutrition and Home Economics in the University of California, is the recipient of many outstanding awards and honors, including the Garvan Medal in chemistry and the Borden Award in human nutrition. Dr. Morgan's contributions to knowledge of mechanisms of vitamins, particularly in relation to hormone activity, effect of heat on the biological value of proteins, nutritional status of older age groups, and vitamin analysis of processed foods are recognized as unique and significant contributions to studies of human nutrition.*

LURA M. ODLAND *is a member of the State Experiment Stations Division of the Department of Agriculture. Formerly she was associate professor in Montana State College and nutritionist for the Committee on Food Composition of the National Academy of Sciences-National Research Council. Dr. Odland has published national and international reports of research findings on food composition and the conservation of nutrients in foods, vitamin metabolism, and nutritional status of younger age groups.*

Food

ALLOWANCES

Recommended Allowances

RUTH M. LEVERTON

NUTRITION is a science of the quantity, as well as the nature, of the substances we need from food for good health. Supplying some of any essential nutrient does not insure good nutrition: The body must have a large enough supply of each nutrient to meet all of its needs all of the time. A reserve supply in the body for use during emergencies is most desirable also.

Good judgment must go into interpreting the results of investigations into the quantitative requirements for a nutrient and the application of results to develop dietary standards or guides.

The Food and Nutrition Board of the National Academy of Sciences-National Research Council is the scientific group in the United States that is assembled to interpret the results of research and to set up dietary standards. It has been mentioned in several preceding chapters in connection with the amounts of Calories and nutrients that are recommended for healthy persons.

The Food and Nutrition Board was established by the National Academy of Sciences-National Research Council in 1940 to advise the Government on matters of food and nutrition. The Academy had been set up by a congressional charter in 1863 to advise the Government on subjects of scientific importance.

Members of the Board are appointed from among the leaders in the sciences related to food and nutrition on the basis of their experience and judgment.

One of the first responsibilities of the Board was to develop a dietary guide for the United States—a guide that would state the amounts of Calories and certain nutrients needed to keep the population of the country well nourished and that would be of help in planning adequate diets for healthy individuals and population groups. It would be a basis of comparison in checking the nutritive value of the food consumption of individuals and of groups. It would provide goals toward which to work when planning the country's food supplies.

Members of the Board first studied all of the research reports that threw light on the requirements for Calories and nutrients. Then they set tentative amounts for Calories and the nutrients for which a guide was needed. They could do this, of course, only when the necessary scientific information about requirements was available.

A set of figures was formulated after much study and weighing of evidence

227

Recommended Daily Dietary

FOOD AND NUTRITION BOARD, NATIONAL ACADEMY
Designed for the Maintenance of Good Nutrition
[Allowances are intended for persons

	Age	Weight	Height	Calories	Pro-tein	Cal-cium
	Years	*Pounds*	*Inches*		*Gm.*	*Gm.*
Men........	25	154	69	3, 200	70	0. 8
	45	154	69	3, 000	70	. 8
	65	154	69	2, 550	70	. 8
Women......	25	128	64	2, 300	58	. 8
	45	128	64	2, 200	58	. 8
	65	128	64	1, 800	58	. 8
Pregnant (second half)				+300	+20	1. 5
Lactating (28 ounces daily)				+1, 000	+40	2. 0
Infants (age in	2–6	13	24	lb.×54. 5	(1)	. 6
months).	7–12	20	28	lb.×45. 4	(1)	. 8
Children.....	1–3	27	34	1, 300	40	1. 0
	4–6	40	43	1, 700	50	1. 0
	7–9	60	51	2, 100	60	1. 0
	10–12	79	57	2, 500	70	1. 2
Boys........	13–15	108	64	3, 100	85	1. 4
	16–19	139	69	3, 600	100	1. 4
Girls........	13–15	108	63	2, 600	80	1. 3
	16–19	120	64	2, 400	75	1. 3

[1] *Allowances are not given for protein during infancy, but intakes of 1.5 grams of*

and after several changes in the tentative amounts first suggested. It was called recommended allowances to indicate that the amounts were not minimal requirements and were not hard-and-fast rules that never would be changed. The recommended allowances represented as fully as possible the consensus of scientific judgment of desirable nutritional goals for individuals of different ages and conditions.

The first recommended allowances were announced in May 1941. They included Calories and nine nutrients.

These allowances were slightly revised in 1945, 1948, 1953, and 1958 to keep them up to date with the most recent research findings.

Allowances, Revised 1958

OF SCIENCES-NATIONAL RESEARCH COUNCIL
of Healthy Persons in the United States
normally active in a temperate climate]

Iron	Vitamin A	Thia-mine	Ribo-flavin	Niacin	Ascorbic acid	Vitamin D
Mg.	I.U.	Mg.	Mg.	Mg.	Mg.	I.U.
10	5,000	1.6	1.8	21	75	....
10	5,000	1.5	1.8	20	75	....
10	5,000	1.3	1.8	18	75	....
12	5,000	1.2	1.5	17	70	....
12	5,000	1.1	1.5	17	70	....
12	5,000	1.0	1.5	17	70	....
15	6,000	1.3	2.0	+3	100	400
15	8,000	1.7	2.5	+2	150	400
5	1,500	.4	.5	6	30	400
7	1,500	.5	.8	7	30	400
7	2,000	.7	1.0	8	35	400
8	2,500	.9	1.3	11	50	400
10	3,500	1.1	1.5	14	60	400
12	4,500	1.3	1.8	17	75	400
15	5,000	1.6	2.1	21	90	400
15	5,000	1.8	2.5	25	100	400
15	5,000	1.3	2.0	17	80	400
15	5,000	1.2	1.9	16	80	400

protein for each pound of body weight are ample for healthy infants.

The amounts of Calories and the nine nutrients that are recommended are believed to be wholly adequate to maintain good nutrition in healthy persons in the United States. The allowances are higher than the least amounts required for health. They are intended to cover the needs of most of the persons who have the highest requirements.

The allowances thus provide a margin of safety, more accurately called a margin of sufficiency, above the minimum requirements for protein, minerals, and vitamins but not for Calories. The size of this margin above average requirements varies for different nutrients. It depends on the ability of the body to store a nutrient, the range in the requirement among individuals, and the possibility of dangers from an excess.

The amounts suggested do not cover the additional requirements associated with disease or needed for recovery from malnutrition.

The allowances for Calories and the nutrients are the amounts that are to be consumed, not the amounts present in food at some stage before it is eaten. They do not cover losses in the nutritive content of food during storage, cooking, and serving. They do take account, however, of incomplete availability from food or incomplete absorption from the intestinal tract of certain nutrients, such as iron and carotene.

The table of recommended dietary allowances gives the age and the height and weight of average persons in each age and sex group. The adults are thought of as the "reference man and woman." Their heights and weights are used in discussing or calculating average values for adults.

The calorie allowances must be adjusted for persons who differ in size, age, or physical activity from the reference man and woman and the children described in the table. Many adults are less active than the moderately active reference man and woman and need fewer Calories. Some adults and children are larger or smaller than the average size, and adjustments need to be made for such differences.

The recommended allowances are not referred to as optimal—the best possible—amounts. We know they are much better and safer than minimal amounts. We have to wait for results of further research, however, to know whether larger amounts will bring additional benefits in health.

Diets that supply less than the recommended allowances may not always mean nutritional deficiencies. People differ greatly in their requirements and in their ability to adjust to intakes of the different nutrients which are less than desirable. The allowances are set high enough to care for those having needs higher than average.

The recommended allowances for the United States are higher than dietary guides used in Canada and Great Britain.

The Canadian standard is the smallest amount of each nutrient and Calories that will prevent a deficiency, or the amount below which health cannot be assumed.

The British standard aims to maintain good nutrition in the average person. The standard of the United States, in contrast, is intended to cover the needs of substantially all healthy persons and to provide a margin of safety as well.

The Food and Nutrition Board in its publication (No. 589) on dietary allowances commented on 20 nutrients that are recognized as essential but for which amounts are not specified. These include carbohydrate and fat; water; the minerals sodium, potassium, phosphorus, magnesium, copper, iodine, cobalt, zinc, manganese, and molybdenum; and the vitamins folacin, B_6, B_{12}, pantothenic acid, biotin, E, and K.

Quantitative allowances have not been recommended for these nutrients partly because requirements for some of them are not known and partly because deficiencies are not likely to occur. A mixed diet of ordinary foods that supplies all the recommended amounts of the nine nutrients for which allowances have been set can supply enough of the other nutrients. Foods supply many essential nutrients in addition to the ones for which there are recommended allowances.

The wide use and acceptance of the allowances have been a result of the thorough, careful, and democratic method by which they were developed.

The recommended dietary allowances plus tables showing the amounts of Calories and nutrients found in foods are the tools for planning food supplies and consumption for a healthy individual, family, and Nation.

RUTH M. LEVERTON *is Associate Director of the Institute of Home Economics.*

A Table of Food Values

BERNICE KUNERTH WATT, ANNABEL L. MERRILL, AND
MARTHA LOUISE ORR

THE table we present here provides typical values for the nutrients in foods that are of particular importance in evaluating diets and planning meals.

The nutrients listed are protein, fat, carbohydrate, two minerals (calcium and iron), and five vitamins (vitamin A, thiamine, riboflavin, niacin, and ascorbic acid). Percentages of water in food and also the Calories, which denote the amount of fuel or food energy released to the body by the oxidation of protein, fat, and carbohydrates, are shown.

The table is based on analytical data in scientific and technical journals published all over the world and on all other data available to us from published and unpublished sources.

Future tables of food composition for general use will include additional nutrients and many new kinds and forms of foods.

The growing volume of laboratory findings already has made it possible in the case of one nutrient, protein, to publish separate values for 18 of the component amino acids. Data on specific components of fat and carbohydrate are becoming available.

All the substances we need for good nutrition are in the plants and animals of the world around us. We use leaves, stems, berries, seeds, roots, and tubers of plants; the muscle, liver, blood, and other parts of animals; and many forms of the life of the sea.

Differences in kind and amount of main nutrients are apparent in many foods. Milk, for example, is outstanding for its calcium but has little iron. Meat provides excellent protein but has only negligible amounts of calcium. Oranges are superior sources of ascorbic acid (vitamin C) but have almost no protein.

Similarities in nutrient content exist among many foods. Meat, fish, and poultry, for example, are excellent sources of protein. If to these we add such good sources as eggs, milk, dry beans and peas, and nuts, we have what we call the protein group.

Green and yellow vegetables are good sources of carotenes, precursors of vitamin A. Vitamin A value is a term that may refer to vitamin A itself or to one of the carotenes, which the body can convert to vitamin A.

Citrus fruits, tomatoes, fresh strawberries, and cabbage are among the

231

many foods valuable for their content of ascorbic acid—a vitamin that often is referred to as vitamin C.

Whole-grain cereals, those with added vitamins and minerals, and those restored to the level of whole grains provide sizable amounts of iron, thiamine, riboflavin, and niacin.

These are only a few examples of natural groupings of foods on the basis of similarity of nutrient composition. Such groupings lend themselves to a great variety of uses in appraisals and calculations of diets.

Variations in amount of nutrients also occur in different samples of the same kind of food. The protein content of one sample of wheat may be nearly double that of another. The fat content of milk depends upon many factors, including the breed of the animal. The content of carotene, or vitamin A value, of carrots extends over a wide range.

In the preparation of our table of composition of food, we make such differentiations as seem indicated in order to get representative values.

We subdivide some groups of food according to characteristics that we know are associated with nutrients— as variety, degree of maturity, storage conditions, the way a food is prepared for market, and the kind and degree of processing.

We must take into account the distinguishing characteristics of each food when we set out to derive average or representative nutritive values. Two familiar foods, oranges and potatoes, illustrate the complexity of obtaining values suitable for various purposes.

Oranges are particularly important for their content of vitamin C, but single oranges may show great variation. From the hundreds of analyses of the vitamin C in orange juice, we have learned that 100 grams (a scant half cup) of the juice may have less than 20 to more than 80 milligrams of vitamin C.

The variety of the orange accounts for much of the difference. Navel oranges from California have an aver-age of about 60 milligrams in 100 grams of juice. California Valencias and Florida-grown early and midsea-son varieties (Hamlin, Parson Brown, and Pineapple) average 51 milligrams. Florida late-season Valencias average 37 milligrams of vitamin C.

The vitamin C in orange juice varies also with the time the oranges are picked. It is higher early in the harvesting season than toward the end of the season. We used data on the quantities picked at different times throughout the harvest period to derive an average value of vitamin C for each variety of orange. Then, so as to get the average value for a year on a national basis, we studied data for individual varieties. We took into account the relative proportion of each variety in the total production of oranges shipped for the fresh-fruit market. This year-round, countrywide value for fresh oranges is 50 milligrams of vitamin C per 100 grams of juice. (There are nearly 250 grams in a cupful of juice.)

The average amount of vitamin C in orange juice from the important commercial varieties varies throughout the year. Values are high in November–February, when a cupful of juice provides about 132 milligrams of vitamin C. They are low in August–September, when the average drops to about 110 milligrams. During the other 6 months, the juice has an intermediate value of about 119 milligrams per cupful. The average values on an annual basis for juice from all the important commercial varieties is 124 milligrams per cup.

Frozen orange juice concentrate is prepared mainly from Florida oranges. The average content of ascorbic acid of juice of the commercially important varieties from Florida, including the Temple oranges, is about 45 milligrams per 100 grams of juice—112 milligrams per cupful.

The loss of ascorbic acid during processing is negligible; the value for frozen reconstituted juice is the same as for Florida fresh juice. The value of the reconstituted frozen juice is a little lower than the national, year-round value for fresh orange juice because California-grown oranges comprise a large proportion of the total shipped for use as fresh oranges but only a small proportion of the total oranges used for the frozen concentrate.

Grapefruit, unlike oranges, shows little varietal difference in amount of ascorbic acid but does have a similar seasonal trend of decreasing content as the harvest season progresses. The average values of the four types on the market—white seeded, white seedless, pink seedless, and pink seeded—fall within the range of 36 to 39 milligrams per 100 grams of pulp or juice.

The Florida-grown grapefruit, which makes up the greater share of the total market supply, has the highest content of ascorbic acid in the fall when the harvesting season begins and the lowest content in the late spring at the end of the season.

The high values of September and October average about 42 milligrams per 100 grams for white-fleshed varieties and 44 to 47 milligrams for pink-fleshed grapefruit. The lowest values in May average 33 to 35 milligrams for all varieties.

California and Arizona grapefruit show a similar trend, starting with a value of about 44 milligrams in September and dropping to 36 milligrams in August.

We must keep a different set of characteristics in mind when we derive average values of potatoes.

Potatoes furnish several nutrients. One is ascorbic acid, which may vary widely. Some potatoes have more than 50 milligrams per 100 grams of potato; others, less than 5 milligrams.

Length of the storage period has an important influence on the content of ascorbic acid. Maturity and variety also affect nutritive value.

The highest content of ascorbic acid is in immature potatoes, which sometimes are grabbled for home use before the crop is ready to dig. Their ascorbic acid value averages about 35 milli-

grams per 100 grams. Since few, if any, of these young potatoes get into commercial channels, however, data for these are not included in our average values for potatoes.

"New" potatoes—that is, potatoes recently dug and not stored—are on the market nearly all year. Some plantings are primarily for the production of new potatoes. Usually they are dug before they are fully mature, and do not keep well. Other plantings are for harvest when the crop is mature. Some of these are sold as new potatoes, and the others are put in storage.

The average content of vitamin C for the different varieties of major commercial importance is in the range of 19 to 33 milligrams per 100 grams.

A good general figure for all new potatoes on the regular market is 26 milligrams per 100 grams.

Most of the potatoes sold in winter and spring have been taken out of storage. The vitamin C in stored tubers drops progressively from December to the end of July. About one-fourth of the ascorbic acid is lost by the end of the first month; about one-half after 3 months; and two-thirds after 6 months. Any on hand after 9 months of storage have lost three-fourths or more.

The ascorbic acid value of the total market supply for January, February, March, and April (weighted by the proportion of new and stored potatoes) is 13 to 14 milligrams per 100 grams of potato. The value rises to 18 milligrams in May with the increased volume of new potatoes and goes on up to 25 milligrams in summer and fall. It drops back to about 18 milligrams in December.

The average year-round value for ascorbic acid in potatoes of commerce, taking into account variety and storage, is 20 milligrams per 100 grams.

The derivation of representative composition values brings to light many interesting similarities and differences among foods in the various food groups.

Like members of a family, foods in

a group have some features that are similar and some that are individualistic. We note some of these features in the major groups of foods.

MILK as produced by the cow has a lower percentage of water than many succulent fruits and vegetables.

The average composition of milk is about 87 percent water, 3.5 percent protein, 4 percent fat, 5 percent carbohydrate, and a little less than 1 percent ash (minerals). These milk solids are an outstanding source of calcium and a good source of riboflavin, high-quality protein, vitamin A, thiamine, vitamin B_{12}, and other dietary essentials.

A cream line forms in milk upon standing as fat particles rise to the top. Commercial separation of the cream from the milk is done so effectively that less than 0.1 percent of fat is left in the skim milk.

Homogenized milk, which forms a major portion of the whole milk on the market, has no cream line. The fat globules are broken up by a mechanical process into such tiny particles that they no longer rise to the top. The nutrients are uniformly distributed in homogenized milk, as they are in evaporated milk.

Cans of evaporated milk (including sweetened condensed milk) should be turned every few weeks during storage because the solids tend to settle.

Skim milk, fluid and powdered, has become increasingly important in the family grocery orders. Since nearly all the fat is removed from skim milk, its energy value is reduced greatly. A glass of skim milk has only half the calories of a glass of whole milk.

Removal of the cream removes the fat-soluble nutrients carried in the cream—vitamins A, D, E, and K—the most important of which is vitamin A. A pint of whole milk provides nearly a sixth of the entire daily allowance of vitamin A for an adult, but a pint of nonfat milk has only a negligible amount. The water-soluble nutrients, the minerals, the B vitamins, and the

protein originally present in the whole milk remain in the nonfat portion.

Milk is the basic ingredient of many manufactured dairy products. Their nutrient content depends on whether the starting point was whole milk or one of the fractions (cream or skim milk) separated from it and whether there is any further separation of milk solids. A decrease or increase in nutrients may result from addition of other ingredients.

Buttermilk originally was the fluid portion left after separation of the butterfat. It had nearly all the solids (other than the fat) that were in the cream. Most of the fluid buttermilk on the market now is made directly from skim milk; a culture is used to develop the desired flavor and consistency. Cultured buttermilk has somewhat more lactic acid but otherwise has practically the same composition as the skim milk from which it is made.

Special therapeutic properties are sometimes attributed to buttermilk and other fermented milks, as kumiss, kefir, and yoghurt. The protein precipitate in them is in the form of a fine curd, which may permit them to be digested more quickly than plain milk.

The amounts of the main nutrients in the milk used in making the fermented products are not greatly changed. The same nutritive values may be applied. Yoghurt, for example, can be made many ways—from skim milk, whole milk, evaporated milk, or from mixtures of these. The nutrient content of the milk ingredients used applies to the prepared yoghurt.

CHEESES offer great variety in flavor and texture. All consist of a curd, which essentially is a precipitate of high-quality protein. The watery portion that remains after the curd separates is the whey. The composition—hence, the nutritive value—of the cheese depends chiefly on the kind of milk used and on the conditions under which the curd is precipitated and separated.

The curd carries most of the protein and much of the calcium and riboflavin. The solids carried off by the whey consist mostly of the milk sugar (lactose), some of the protein, and a fairly large portion of riboflavin and the other B vitamins that were present in the milk originally.

Disproportionate losses of valuable nutrients in the whey make it impossible to work out satisfactory nutritional equivalents between milk and cheese except in terms of calcium or some other single nutrient. The amounts of milk and cheese that would be equivalent in terms of any one nutrient would not necessarily be equivalent on the basis of other nutrients.

Cottage cheese is a soft, uncured cheese prepared from a high-moisture curd that is not allowed to ripen. It is usually prepared from skim milk. The conditions of forming the curd are such that it has a smaller portion of the calcium from the milk than most kinds of cheese. Plain cottage cheese has normally less than 0.5 percent of fat.

Creamed cottage cheese is more popular than the plain type because of the extra flavor from the cream. Creamed cottage cheese is required by law to have at least 4 percent fat, but even this is low in comparison with other types of cheese. Terms such as large- or small-curd, farmer style, pot or cup cheese, Dutch cheese, and smearcase sometimes are used locally to identify the texture of cottage cheese.

Cheeses made from cream or whole milk have a much higher content of fat and vitamin A in proportion to their protein content than the cheeses made from part whole milk or from skim milk. In the manufacture of most cheeses, the curd is subjected to a ripening process. This ripening is aided by micro-organisms, which contribute to the increased content of certain B vitamins, a phenomenon that has been noted in some cheeses.

Federal definitions and standards of identity have been issued for some 60 forms of natural cheese, processed cheese, cheese food, or cheese spread. The proportions of fat and solids in the finished product often are specified.

The nutrient composition of processed cheese is about the same as that of the cheese or mixture of cheeses from which it is made. Processed cheese is prepared by grinding the cheese fine and heating and mixing it with an emulsifying agent into a homogeneous, plastic mass.

Process cheese food differs from processed cheese in that it contains in addition one or more of certain dairy products, such as whey, skim milk, milk, or cream.

EGGS are Nature's unique source of nourishment for the developing chick. They are dependable sources of many nutrients also needed by man.

The protein content of eggs is relatively constant, but the hen's ration has an important influence on the vitamin content. In deriving our average values, we gave major consideration to analyses made on eggs from hens receiving usual commercial rations.

The nutrients are unevenly distributed within the egg. Egg yolk, a little more than one-third of the edible part, contains the fat, vitamin A, thiamine, and nearly all of the calcium, phosphorus, and iron in the egg and considerable protein and riboflavin. Egg white is much higher than egg yolk in water content. The white contains protein and riboflavin—not so much as an equal weight of egg yolk, but (because there is nearly twice as much white as yolk) more than half the total protein and riboflavin in an egg are in the white.

MEAT of all kinds is a valuable source of many nutrients, particularly of good-quality protein, iron, and various B vitamins. These nutrients are mainly in the lean portions. The fat surrounding a cut of meat and extending inward that can be readily removed is known as the separable fat. The remainder of the muscle is known as the separable lean and may or may not be marbled.

Lean meat is marbled when it has small streaks or veins of fat. Marbling and the total fat increase as animals are finished to meet the standards for higher market grades.

Round of beef is one of the leanest cuts in the carcass. The separable lean in round of the lower market grades seldom has a content of fat (that is, of chemically determined fat) of less than 2 percent. It probably is 4 to 5 percent in round of the Choice grade.

Rib and loin cuts usually have more marbling, and their lean has a higher fat content than the corresponding rounds.

Cuts from beef loin, including porterhouse, T-bone, and club steaks, average 8 to 10 percent of chemical fat in the separable lean of the most important grade. The content may average 12 to 15 percent in the Prime grade.

Water, protein, and ash (minerals) are present in beef in an almost constant proportion, in which water makes up about 77 percent of the total of these three constituents, protein 22 percent, and ash 1 percent. In the fat cuts, and in any cuts of fat animals, the amount of lean is reduced because in effect it is diluted by fat, but the relationship of water to protein to ash is practically the same.

Pork may have a chemical fat content of 4 to 10 percent in the separable lean of a lean cut, like ham, and 6 to 18 percent of chemical fat in a fat cut, like the loin. These ranges apply to meat from hogs of the 200-pound class—the presently preferred weight class. Heavier and fatter hogs probably would yield lean meat with a higher chemical content of fat.

Lamb and veal have been used in much smaller amounts than beef and pork; nutritionists have studied them much less. Veal is the meat from the young bovine animal that has subsisted largely on milk.

A few differences in their nutrient composition are notable. Veal has more lean and less fat than most beef, lamb, and pork. The lean of veal and lamb seems to carry a little more niacin than beef or pork. Pork runs higher in thiamine than other meats.

Liver, unlike muscle meat, is an ex-cellent source of vitamin C and vitamin A. Since liver is so small a proportion of the edible carcass, however, it is not available in quantities large enough to be an important item of the national food supply.

Cooked meat, as customarily served, includes the lean and varying amounts of adhering fat. Some of us, like Jack Sprat, trim off the fatty tissue and eat only the lean. Others enjoy a part or all of the fat that may be present.

The separable fat portion of cooked meat varies considerably in composition and thus in Calories. It has a small percentage of protein and a somewhat larger percentage of water. It may vary in chemically determined fat from 60 to 80 percent. Values we use as representative for the composition of trimmable fat from cooked beef are 6 percent protein, 15 percent water, and 78 percent chemical fat. Fat of this composition would provide 730 Calories per 100 grams, or about 200 Calories per ounce.

The lean portion of cooked meat has less water than before cooking. Well-done meat is drier than had the cooking been stopped at the rare or medium-done stage. The protein and other nutrients remaining become more concentrated as meat shrinks.

An extremely lean roast of beef, for example, having a composition before cooking of 21 percent protein, 3 percent fat, and 75 percent water, after cooking to medium doneness, would be expected to have about 29 percent protein, 5 percent fat, and 65 percent water. Such lean meat has about 170 Calories per 100 grams, or 48 Calories per ounce of cooked meat.

Meat with some marbling—hence of higher fat content—is more representative of cuts generally available. The fat in the separable lean portion of cooked beef is seldom less than 6 percent and may exceed 20 percent.

Average figures for the separable lean of medium-done beef are 9 percent fat, 30 percent protein, and 60 percent water. Cooked beef of this composition would supply 205 Calories per 100 grams, or 58 Calories to the ounce.

POULTRY, FISH, AND WILD GAME are included in the meat group because of their high-quality protein and similarity in other nutritive values.

Chickens of the broiler-fryer class comprise the largest proportion of the chicken production. They have less fat, and therefore are lower in caloric value, than most meats. Most of the fat occurs in deposits in the abdominal cavity or in and under the skin.

Older birds, roasters and stewers, are higher in fat content; the total edible portion, including skin and giblets, approaches the level of fat in other meats.

The light meat has a lower content of fat than the dark; it is also lower in iron, thiamine, and riboflavin but higher in niacin than dark meat.

Turkeys are generally marketed at a more mature stage than chickens and therefore have a higher content of fat. Younger and smaller turkeys, which are becoming more and more popular, are lower in fat than the older, heavier ones. The mineral and vitamin content in turkey meat is similar to that of chicken meat.

Ducks and geese are higher in fat than chickens and turkeys, but there is a tendency to market them younger than formerly. As with other kinds of poultry, the younger birds are lower in fat content than older ones.

Fish, both the fresh- and salt-water kinds, and shellfish available on American markets are high in protein. Their fat content varies widely, depending on the species and the time of year of the catch. Compared with meats, however, fish and shellfish are low in fat. Even the fattest types of fish rarely average more than 10 percent fat. Many kinds average less than 1 percent. The skin of fish is higher in fat than the flesh. The addition of fats and oils in cooking and canning increases the fat level somewhat.

Shellfish that are eaten whole, such as oysters and clams, are extremely high in iron. Oysters are an unusually rich source of copper. Like other flesh foods, fish are a poor source of calcium, but some that are canned with the bones in, such as salmon and sardines, are excellent sources of calcium. The bones are soft and edible.

The vitamin content of fish may be considered in general as similar to beef. Some kinds contain appreciable amounts of vitamin A in the flesh.

FRUIT AND VEGETABLES at harvest are relatively high in water content. Many of the more succulent ones (tomato, celery, lettuce) contain more water than orange juice and milk. Sweetpotatoes and fresh lima beans have lower moisture than most other foods in this group, but even they are about two-thirds water. Peas and potatoes are about three-fourths water—thus having about the same amount of solid matter as lean meat.

Water, minerals, or the other constituents may change as the product matures. The solids in peas, as an example, may increase from about 19 percent in peas picked at an early stage to about 24 percent at the more mature stage and 35 percent in peas well past their prime.

Fruit and vegetables supply little protein in relation to their weight and only a trace of fat. Garden peas and fresh lima beans are exceptions. They have about 6 to 8 percent of protein.

The fat content of nearly all foods in this group is less than 1 percent. Avocados are unusual. Their fat content varies from less than 5 to more than 20 percent, depending on such factors as variety and time of harvest.

The carbohydrate content of our common fruit and vegetables ranges from less than 3 percent in lettuce to around 23 percent in bananas and lima beans. Calories are closely related to carbohydrate in fruit and vegetables, because most of them have little protein or fat. Classification on the basis of carbohydrate content, as 3, 6, 9, or 12 percent, sometimes is used for dietary purposes.

The carbohydrate in fruit and vegetables consists mainly of sugars and starches. The body uses both forms readily. Fiber and other forms of carbohydrate, which are not well utilized, also are present. Classifications of fruit and vegetables by carbohydrate content is based on the amount remaining after the fiber is deducted.

Many fruits and vegetables have fewer calories than equal weights of other foods. In the early days of nutrition studies, foods were often viewed with an eye to economy as sources of food energy and protein. Fruit and vegetables, except a few of the cheaper staples, like potatoes, were considered luxuries. Foods in this group were recognized as good sources of mineral matter but did not come to the fore until the discovery of vitamins and of man's dependence on this food group for several of the important ones, particularly A and C.

Dark-green leaves are rich in both vitamin A and vitamin C. Depth of color is a fair index of carotene and hence of vitamin A in the green leaves and other green vegetables. Kale, spinach, turnip greens, and broccoli leaves have many times more vitamin A value than lettuce, cabbage, or snap beans. Leaf lettuce has more than the varieties that have pale-green heads.

Sweetpotatoes of the deep-yellow, soft-fleshed varieties, which are the predominant type on the market, have an exceptionally high value of vitamin A. One root of average size (6 ounces) of the commercially important varieties supplies more than 12 thousand International Units of vitamin A, more than twice the amount recommended for the daily needs of the body. Some of the newer varieties that may in time become commercially important have even higher values. The vitamin A value of sweetpotatoes of most varieties increases during the curing period and in the interval of storage before reaching retail channels.

Sweetpotatoes also are a good source of ascorbic acid, particularly when they are eaten soon after they are cured—an average-sized root then contains 30 to 40 milligrams. The content is in the range of 20 to 25 milligrams after several months of storage.

The Jersey-type sweetpotato, characterized by its firm flesh after cooking, has a higher initial content of ascorbic acid than the popular soft-fleshed variety, Porto Rico, which is grown extensively in the South. The average value for a 6-ounce root of the Jersey type is 41 milligrams of ascorbic acid and of the Porto Rico, 32 milligrams. The content is the same for both—about 24 milligrams in a 6-ounce root—after 3 months of storage.

Soft-fleshed, orange-colored sweetpotatoes are called yams in some sections. This is a misnomer. The two belong to completely different classifications. The botanical name for sweetpotato is *Ipomoea batatas*. The true yam belongs to the genus *Dioscorea*.

Carrots are a rich source of carotene. The amount increases as the carrot matures. As with other yellow-pigmented foods, the depth of the color is an indication of the amount of carotene present.

Carrots on the market range in size from small, immature, pencillike carrots weighing 50 grams (about 2 ounces) or less to mature roots that weigh as much as 150 to 175 grams (5 to 6 ounces). The large ones usually have a much deeper color, and their vitamin A value is several times higher than that of the small, young carrots. Values for carrots of marketable size range from 4 thousand to 20 thousand or more International Units per 100 grams (about 3.5 ounces) of carrots. The value increases progressively as the carrot grows in size and matures.

Vitamin C, which we associate with citrus fruits and tomatoes, occurs also in many other fruits and vegetables—cauliflower, cantaloup, strawberries, cabbage, brussels sprouts, sweetpotatoes, peppers, white potatoes, and turnips, to mention a few.

Apples may be a moderately good source of ascorbic acid or furnish only a little, depending on whether it is a summer apple or a fall or winter apple, whether it is eaten soon after harvest or several months later, and whether it is unpared or pared.

A large summer apple, weighing about one-half pound, furnishes about 22 milligrams of vitamin C if eaten whole and 14 milligrams if it is pared. A fall or winter apple of the same size soon after harvest has 14 to 15 milligrams but only 5 to 7 milligrams if it is pared. The values drop by as much as half after long storage.

Seeds, pods, and some of the dark-green leaves are fairly good sources of thiamine. Lima beans and peas, corn, dandelion greens, and young cowpeas in the pod or shelled out have more thiamine than most other vegetables.

Turnip greens, kale, and collards are among the rich sources of riboflavin.

The dark-green, leafy vegetables are notable sources of iron and calcium. The minerals are not uniformly distributed in different parts of the plant. Calcium in the outside green leaves of head lettuce is three to five times higher than in the inner leaves. Outer leaves of cabbage also have more calcium than inner leaves.

Some greens, including beet greens, chard, spinach, and New Zealand spinach, contain calcium. They also contain oxalic acid, which may combine with the calcium and make it unavailable to the body. The oxalic acid may remove calcium from some other food during digestion. When one eats these foods, he should be sure his diet has ample calcium from other foods.

Some foods in this large group are important. We would not want to be without them even though their nutrient content is low. Celery, cucumbers, beets, pears, and onions are examples. These have only small amounts of nutrients; raw, cooked, or pickled, however, they add flavor, texture, and color to meals.

Mature dry legumes include navy, pinto, lima, soya, and all other beans, all dry peas, and different kinds of peanuts. They and the many kinds of tree nuts, like walnuts, hickory nuts, pecans, and others, have a low moisture content and are concentrated sources of many nutrients. These seeds are our richest common sources of protein among foods of plant origin. All are moderately good to rich sources of thiamine.

Cowpeas, an important legume, sometimes called black-eyed peas, crowder peas, and southern peas, are used at various stages—snap green pod, immature shelled bean, and mature dried beans. The protein, thiamine, and phosphorus in them at any of these stages is related to the content of solids. All increase as the cowpeas develop. An extensive study in several Southern States showed the significance of locality on the protein, starch, sugars, thiamine, and riboflavin in dried cowpeas. Their mineral content was influenced more by location than by fertilizer treatments. The content of protein and thiamine varies greatly with variety.

The place where lima beans are grown is reflected in their amount of ascorbic acid and thiamine and riboflavin. These nutrients, calculated on the dry basis, dropped markedly with increasing maturity.

Agronomists in New Mexico demonstrated that location influences significantly the protein, thiamine, riboflavin, and niacin in several varieties of common beans.

Peanuts are extraordinarily good sources of niacin. Their thin, reddish-brown skin is rich in thiamine. The skin is a small fraction of the total weight of the kernel and skin, but the thiamine content of Spanish peanuts with the skins on is more than 15 percent higher than that of the peanuts without skins.

The fat content of peanuts and various tree nuts (except coconut, chestnuts, and a few others) averages about 50 percent or more. The fat includes large amounts of linoleic acid, an unsaturated fatty acid.

Mature legumes and nuts have little

sodium. Soybeans and their products, particularly soybean curd and milk, are relatively good sources of calcium. Legumes and nuts are useful in various special diets and add variety to usual diets that have no specific restrictions.

CEREALS are major foods the world over. Wheat, corn, rice, and oats and their products are the leaders in the United States.

These grains share many nutritional characteristics. They are concentrated food; their moisture contents are of the order of 5 to 15 percent.

They vary somewhat in protein contents—wheats, 9 to 14 percent; oatmeal, about 14 percent; cornmeals, about 9 percent; and rice, about 7 percent.

All are high in carbohydrate. The endosperm (the inner part of the kernel), which makes up the major part of the grain, is largely starch. The outside layers of the kernel are hard and fibrous. Minerals and vitamins are present in higher concentrations in the germ and outer layers of the kernel than in the starchy endosperm. The small amount of fat that the cereal grains contain is concentrated in the germ.

Whole-wheat flour, known also as graham flour, is milled from cleaned wheat kernels. It includes the germ and outer layers and thus retains all the nutritive value of the whole grain. It represents 100 percent extraction. White flour, milled to exclude the germ and most or all of the outer layers, consists mainly of the inner portion of the kernel. Straight-grade and patent flours represent about 72 and 63 percent extractions of the kernel, respectively.

No material toxic to man is present in the grain or added in the milling of grains. White flours, which are made from the endosperm, simply lack the amounts of those nutrients present in the excluded parts.

White flour has a higher proportion of starch and a higher caloric value than an equal weight of whole-wheat flour from the same wheat supply. The greater digestibility of the starch in comparison with the other forms of carbohydrate present in the wheat kernel is the basis for the higher caloric value.

Federal standards have been established for enrichment of white flour whereby the vitamins thiamine, riboflavin, and niacin and iron, are added within specified limits. Provision is made for optional addition of two other nutrients, calcium and vitamin D. Enriched white flour has about 7 times as much thiamine, nearly 6 times as much riboflavin, and about 4 times as much niacin and iron as patent or plain white flour.

The milling procedures for corn and rice differ technically from wheat milling, but the general effect on changes in nutrients is the same.

Oatmeal does not represent the whole oat kernel, but it contains the germ. Nutritionally it is classed with the whole-grain cereals.

The popular demand for refined wheat, corn, and rice products has led nutritionists to encourage the use of enriched cereal products. Federal standards of enrichment have been established for several cereal items besides flour. These include white bread and rolls, cornmeal and corn grits, farina, macaroni and noodle products, and rice.

Parboiled and converted rice are refined products of considerably higher nutritive value than plain white rice. To prepare them, whole brown rice in the husk is steeped in hot water, steamed, dried, and milled. Thiamine and other water-soluble nutrients originally concentrated in the outer layers and germ diffuse into the kernel. When the husk and outside layers are removed in milling, a large portion of the nutrients ordinarily removed are retained by the kernel.

Wildrice (*Zizania aquatica*), also called Indian rice, is an entirely different plant from the ordinary rice (*Oryza sativa*). The seeds are narrow and long—two to three times longer than ordinary rice kernels—and of a dark-brown or purple color.

Wildrice, an annual grass, grows partly submerged along the margins of lakes. It was once an important food of Indian tribes, especially those of the Great Lakes and upper Mississippi Valley regions. The Indians harvest it from their canoes, knocking the ripe grains into the canoes.

The difficulties of cultivation and harvest limit the amount of wildrice available. It is expensive, and usually it is served on special occasions and with wild game or fowl.

Good growing conditions in 1958 in Minnesota, Wisconsin, and Canada meant the production of about 1.5 million pounds; about 275 thousand pounds were harvested in 1957.

The nutritive value of wildrice is about the same as that of other wholegrain cereals.

Cereal products in many ready-to-eat and to-be-cooked forms we have come to associate so closely with the morning meal that we commonly call them breakfast foods. Often they are made of mixtures of several grain products, which have been refined and processed.

The boxes of some breakfast cereals have statements on their labels that they contain added nutrients and that a given amount of the product supplies certain proportions of each nutrient. Such cereals are called "restored," since the added nutrients make partial restoration of losses in milling the whole grains. The term is a loose one, as the selection of nutrients for addition and the levels in the final product are determined entirely by the manufacturer.

PARTLY PREPARED cereal products and mixes are popular. Self-rising flour for making quick breads, long a staple in the South, has the leavening already mixed in. Prepared pancake mixes, cake, cookie, and roll mixes, pastry sticks, and a great number of ready-to-bake products are available.

How do the mixes on the market

compare in nutritive value with products made from ingredients mixed at home?

If all the ingredients used in the preparation of the mixes and the homemade products were the same in kind and in proportion, there would be no difference in nutrient content. For example, if the flour were enriched in both instances, we would expect the flour to contribute the same nutritive value. Information on enrichment should be stated on the package.

It is hard to make precise comparisons between prepared and homemade products, however. Recipes for homemade cakes often call for more eggs or fat; they therefore yield richer cakes than the mixes do.

When butter or margarine is specified, the vitamin A value of the cake will be much higher than when other fats that have no vitamin A value are used.

The homemaker herself must decide between the richer homemade cake with its larger amounts of nutrients and higher caloric value and the cake made from the more convenient mix.

THE FATS AND OILS group includes fats separated from milk and from meat; oils extracted from vegetables, fruit, nuts, and grain; and some foods, largely fat, like butter, margarine, and salad dressings. Bacon and salt pork sometimes are included.

The fats and oils may be classified as animal or vegetable, according to their source. Usually we refer to those that are liquid at room temperature as oils and those that are semisolid or solid as fats. Liquid forms may be converted to solid forms by the process of hydrogenation.

The foods in this group, being predominately fat, provide chiefly energy. Some contain small amounts of minerals. The fat-soluble vitamins, particularly vitamin E and vitamin A, are present in some. Other constituents are fatty acids, including those considered to be essential. Cholesterol occurs only in foods of animal origin.

477248°—59——17

Information on the composition of fats and oils helps in planning variously restricted diets.

Butter and margarine supply the same amount of food energy—3,300 Calories per pound or 100 Calories per tablespoon. Both may be excellent sources of vitamin A.

Butter varies in its vitamin A according to the season. Summer butter, produced when cows have an abundance of green feed, is much richer in vitamin A than winter butter. A nationwide study of vitamin A value of butter produced in this country showed an average of 15 thousand International Units of vitamin A per pound for the year as a whole.

Fats and oils used in the manufacture of margarine have no appreciable vitamin A value, but manufacturers have been fortifying their products. In 1941, under the Federal Food, Drug, and Cosmetic Act, the amount of vitamin A required in margarine in order to print on the label the words "vitamin A added" or "with added vitamin A" was specified as 9 thousand International Units per pound. The regulations were amended in 1952 to require 15 thousand International Units per pound. Nearly all margarine now marketed is so fortified.

SALAD DRESSINGS are important in the fats and oils group for the flavor and variety they provide. The wide range of commercial dressings now available makes it possible to choose according to individual preferences or requirements.

Vegetable oil is the basic ingredient of most salad dressings. Minimum amounts of vegetable oils required to meet Federal specifications for three widely used salad dressings are: Mayonnaise, 65 percent by weight; french dressing, 35 percent; salad dressing, 30 percent. The oil content of many commercial dressings is somewhat higher than the minimum requirement—mayonnaise, 75 to 80 percent, and french and salad dressings, 35 to 40 percent. Nutrients other than fat vary with the ingredients used in the dressings.

Energy values of french and salad dressings average about 50 to 60 Calories per tablespoon and of mayonnaise, about 100 Calories per tablespoon.

Special low-calorie dressings, which may furnish as few as 10 Calories per tablespoon, usually are made with sweeteners other than sugar and with fruit or vegetable juice as a base. Fruit or vegetable juice may be used in place of part or all of the oil ordinarily used.

BERNICE KUNERTH WATT *is a member of the Household Economics Research Branch, Agricultural Research Service. She has responsibility for compiling and evaluating findings of worldwide research on the nutritive value of foods and for the preparation of tables of food composition. Dr. Watt is a graduate of Iowa State College. She received her doctorate from Columbia University. Before coming to Washington, D.C., in 1941, she was a member of the faculty and research staff of Kansas State College in Manhattan.*

ANNABEL L. MERRILL *has been engaged principally in the preparation of food composition tables since joining the staff of the Household Economics Research Branch in 1941. She assisted in the preparation of a number of publications, and coauthored the technical bulletin, "Energy Value of Foods—Basis and Derivation." Miss Merrill is a graduate of Cornell University with degrees in foods and nutrition. She came into Federal Service with a background of experience in college teaching.*

MARTHA LOUISE ORR, *a nutrition analyst, has been with the Household Economics Research Branch since 1947. A native of Michigan, she received degrees in chemistry and bacteriology at the University of Michigan. She has had varied experience in biochemistry in the research laboratories of the College of Physicians and Surgeons, Columbia University, and the American Cyanamid Company before entering Federal Service in 1943. Her principal field is the study of amino acids and vitamins. She is the coauthor of the report, "Amino Acid Content of Foods."*

Explanation of the Table

The values shown in the table that follows are in terms of common units of measure, as one cup, one ounce, or a piece of specified size. The quantities of foods thus shown can be converted readily to particular serving portions. The one-cup amount, for example, can be reduced or multiplied in estimating servings of various sizes.

The cup measure used refers to the standard 8-ounce measuring cup of 8 fluid ounces or one-half liquid pint. The ounce shown is by weight, that is, one-sixteenth of a pound avoirdupois, unless the fluid ounce is indicated.

Most of the foods listed in the table are in ready-to-serve form, but a few items frequently used as ingredients in prepared dishes have been included.

Values for many of the food mixtures have been calculated from typical recipes. The cooked vegetables have no added fat.

A column showing water content is in the table, as the percentage of moisture is frequently useful in identifying and comparing food items.

Parts of some foods, as seeds, skins, bone, are either inedible or may be eaten but usually are discarded. The nutrient values in the table apply to the parts customarily eaten. Values for potato, for example, apply to potato without the skin. If the skin also is eaten, the amounts of some nutrients will be a little larger than shown in the table.

Nutrients in Common Foods in Terms of Household Measures

Item number	Food	Water (Per cent)	Food energy (Calories)	Protein (Grams)	Fat (Grams)	Total carbohydrate (Grams)	Calcium (Milligrams)	Iron (Milligrams)	Vitamin A value (International Units)	Thiamine (Milligrams)	Riboflavin (Milligrams)	Niacin (Milligrams)	Ascorbic acid (Milligrams)
	MILK AND MILK PRODUCTS												
	Milk; 1 cup:												
1	Fluid, whole	87	165	9	10	12	285	0.1	390	0.08	0.42	0.2	2
2	Fluid, nonfat (skim)	90	90	9	Trace	13	298	.1	10	.10	.44	.2	2
3	Buttermilk, cultured (from skim milk)	90	90	9	Trace	13	298	.1	10	.10	.44	.2	2
4	Evaporated (undiluted)	74	345	18	20	24	635	.3	820	.10	.84	.2	3
5	Condensed, sweetened (undiluted)	26	985	25	25	170	829	.3	1,020	.24	1.21	.5	3
6	Dry, whole	2	515	27	28	39	968	.5	1,160	.30	1.60	.5	6
7	Dry, nonfat	3	290	29	1	42	1,040	.5	20	.28	1.44	.7	6
8	Half and half (milk and cream)	80	330	8	29	11	259	.1	1,190	.07	.39	.1	2
	Cream; 1 tablespoon:												
9	Light, table or coffee	72	30	Trace	3	1	15	Trace	120	Trace	.02	Trace	Trace
10	Heavy or whipping	59	50	Trace	5	Trace	12	Trace	220	Trace	.02	Trace	Trace
	Milk beverages; 1 cup:												
11	Cocoa (all milk)	79	235	9	11	26	286	.9	390	.09	.45	.4	2
12	Chocolate flavored drink	83	190	8	6	27	270	.4	210	.09	.41	.2	3
13	Malted milk	78	280	12	12	32	364	.8	680	.18	.56	.....	3
14	Yoghurt (from partially skimmed milk); 1 cup	89	120	8	4	13	295	.1	170	.09	.43	.2	2
	Cheese; 1 ounce:												
15	Cheddar, or American	36	115	7	9	1	221	.3	380	.01	.15	Trace	0
16	Cheddar, processed	39	105	7	9	Trace	214	.2	350	Trace	.12	Trace	0
17	Cheese foods, Cheddar	43	95	6	7	2	163	.2	300	.01	.17	Trace	0
	Cottage:												
18	From skim milk	79	25	5	Trace	1	26	.1	Trace	.01	.08	Trace	0
19	Creamed	78	30	4	1	1	25	.1	50	.01	.08	Trace	0
20	Cream cheese	51	105	2	11	1	18	.1	440	Trace	.07	Trace	0
21	Roquefort, or blue	40	105	6	9	Trace	122	.2	350	.01	.17	.1	0
22	Swiss	39	105	7	8	1	271	.3	320	.01	.06	Trace	0
	Desserts (largely milk):												
23	Cornstarch pudding, plain; 1 cup	76	275	9	10	39	290	.1	390	.07	.40	.1	2
24	Custard, baked; 1 cup, 8 fluid ounces	77	285	13	14	28	278	1.0	870	.10	.47	.2	1

No.	Food											
	Ice cream, plain, factory packed:											
25	1 slice or individual brick, ¼ quart.	62	165	3	10	17	100	.1	420	.03	.15	.1	1
26	1 container, 3½ fluid ounces	62	130	2	8	13	76	.1	320	.03	.12	.1	1
27	1 container, 8 fluid ounces	62	295	6	18	29	175	.1	740	.06	.27	.1	1
28	Ice milk; 1 cup, 8 fluid ounces	67	285	9	10	42	292	.2	420	.09	.41	.2	2
	EGGS											
	Egg, raw, large:											
29	1 whole	74	80	6	6	Trace	27	1.1	590	.05	.15	Trace	0
30	1 white	88	15	4	Trace	Trace	3	Trace	0	Trace	.09	Trace	0
31	1 yolk	51	60	3	5	Trace	24	.9	580	.04	.07	Trace	0
	Egg, cooked; 1 large:											
32	Boiled	74	80	6	6	Trace	27	1.1	590	.05	.14	Trace	0
33	Scrambled (with milk and fat)	72	110	7	8	1	51	1.1	690	.05	.18	.1	0
	MEAT, POULTRY, FISH, SHELLFISH											
34	Bacon, broiled or fried, medium done; 2 slices	13	95	4	9	Trace	4	.5	0	.08	.05	.8	0
	Beef, cooked, without bone: Braised, simmered, or pot-roasted; 3-ounce portion:											
35	Entire portion, lean and fat	43	340	20	28	0	9	2.6	50	.04	.15	3.1	0
36	Lean only, approx. 2 ounces	62	115	18	4	0	8	2.2	Trace	.03	.13	2.7	0
	Hamburger patties, made with—											
37	Regular ground beef; 3-ounce patty	54	245	21	17	0	9	2.7	30	.07	.02	4.6	0
38	Lean ground round; 3-ounce patty	60	185	23	10	0	10	3.0	20	.08	.20	5.1	0
	Roast; 3-ounce slice from— Cut having relatively large amount of fat:											
39	Entire portion, lean and fat	35	420	15	39	0	7	2.0	80	.04	.12	2.8	0
40	Lean only, approx. 1.6 ounces	57	110	13	6	0	6	1.7	Trace	.03	.10	2.4	0
	Cut having relatively small amount of fat:											
41	Entire portion, lean and fat	52	255	22	18	0	9	2.8	30	.06	.16	3.9	0
42	Lean only, approx. 2.3 ounces	63	115	19	4	0	8	2.4	Trace	.05	.14	3.4	0

Nutrients in Common Foods in Terms of Household Measures—Continued

Item number	Food	Water	Food energy	Protein	Fat	Total carbohydrate	Calcium	Iron	Vitamin A value	Thiamine	Riboflavin	Niacin	Ascorbic acid
		Percent	Calories	Grams	Grams	Grams	Milligrams	Milligrams	International Units	Milligrams	Milligrams	Milligrams	Milligrams
	MEAT, POULTRY, FISH, SHELLFISH—Con.												
	Beef, cooked, without bone—Con.												
	Steak, broiled; 3-ounce portion:												
43	Entire portion, lean and fat...	39	375	19	32	0	9	2.6	60	0.06	0.16	4.0	0
44	Lean only, approx. 1.8 ounces..	59	105	17	4	0	7	2.0	Trace	.05	.13	3.3	0
	Beef, canned:												
45	Corned; 3 ounces.........	59	180	22	10	0	17	3.7	20	.01	.20	2.9	0
46	Corned beef hash; 3 ounces......	70	120	12	5	6	22	1.1	10	.02	.11	2.4	0
47	Beef, dried; 2 ounces.......	48	115	19	4	0	11	2.9	......	.04	.18	2.2	0
48	Beef and vegetable stew; 1 cup........	79	250	13	19	17	31	2.6	2,520	.12	.15	3.4	15
	Chicken, without bone:												
49	Broiled; 3 ounces........	71	115	20	3	0	8	1.4	80	.06	.15	10.5	0
50	Canned; 3 ounces.........	62	170	25	7	0	12	1.5	160	.03	.14	5.4	0
	Chile con carne, canned:												
51	Without beans; 1 cup.........	67	510	26	38	15	97	3.6	380	.05	.31	5.6	......
52	Heart, beef, trimmed of fat, braised; 3 ounces.......	61	160	26	5	1	14	5.9	30	.23	1.05	6.8	3
	Lamb, cooked:												
	Chops; 1 thick chop, with bone, 4.8 ounces:												
53	Lean and fat, approx. 3.6 ounces.	44	450	24	39	0	10	2.9	......	.13	.24	5.4	0
54	Lean only, 2.4 ounces.......	62	130	19	5	0	8	2.3	......	.10	.19	4.2	0
	Roast, without bone:												
	Leg; 3-ounce slice:												
55	Entire slice, lean and fat...	51	265	20	20	0	9	2.6	......	.12	.22	4.5	0
56	Lean only, approx. 2.3 ounces.......	62	120	19	5	0	9	2.4	......	.11	.20	4.1	0
	Shoulder; 3-ounce portion, without bone:												
57	Entire portion, lean and fat..	48	300	18	25	0	9	2.3	......	.11	.19	4.0	0
58	Lean only, approx. 2.2 ounces.......	61	125	16	6	0	7	2.1	......	.09	.17	3.5	0

No.	Food												
59	Liver, beef, fried; 2 ounces	57	120	13	4	6	5	4.4	30,330	.15	2.25	8.4	18
60	Pork, cured, cooked: Ham, smoked; 3-ounce portion, without bone	39	340	20	28	Trace	9	2.5	0	.46	.18	3.5	0
	Luncheon meat:												
61	Boiled ham; 2 ounces	48	170	13	13	0	5	1.5	0	.57	.15	2.9	0
62	Canned, spiced; 2 ounces	55	165	8	14	1	5	1.2	0	.18	.12	1.6	0
	Pork, fresh, cooked: Chops; 1 chop, with bone, 3.5 ounces:												
63	Lean and fat, approx. 2.4 ounces	39	295	15	25	0	7	2.1	.....	.60	.17	3.6	0
64	Lean only, approx. 1.6 ounces	53	120	14	7	0	6	1.8	.....	.51	.15	3.1	0
	Roast; 3-ounce slice, without bone:												
65	Entire slice, lean and fat	43	340	19	29	0	9	2.5	.....	.71	.21	4.3	0
66	Lean only, approx. 2.2 ounces	55	160	19	9	0	8	2.4	.....	.68	.20	4.1	0
	Simmered; 3-ounce portion, without bone:												
67	Entire portion, lean and fat	42	355	19	30	0	9	2.4	.....	.43	.20	3.9	0
68	Lean only, approx. 2 ounces	60	120	16	5	0	7	2.0	.....	.37	.17	3.3	0
	Sausage:												
69	Bologna; 8 slices (4.1 by 0.1 inches each), 8 ounces	56	690	27	62	2	16	4.1	.....	.36	.49	6.0	0
70	Frankfurter; 1 cooked; 1.8 ounces	58	155	6	14	1	3	.8	.....	.08	.10	1.3	0
71	Pork, bulk, canned; 4 ounces	55	340	18	29	0	10	2.6	.....	.23	.27	3.4	0
72	Tongue, beef, boiled or simmered; 3 ounces	61	205	18	14	Trace	7	2.5	.....	.04	.26	3.1	0
73	Veal, cutlet, broiled; 3-ounce portion, without bone	60	185	23	9	0	9	2.7	.....	.06	.21	4.6	0
	Fish and shellfish:												
74	Bluefish, baked or broiled; 3 ounces	68	135	22	4	0	25	.6	40	.09	.08	1.6	0
	Clams:												
75	Raw, meat only; 3 ounces	80	70	11	1	3	82	6.0	90	.08	.15	1.4	0
76	Canned, solids and liquid; 3 ounces	87	45	7	1	2	74	5.4	70	.04	.08	.9	0
77	Crabmeat, canned or cooked; 3 ounces	77	90	14	2	1	38	.8	.....	.04	.05	2.1	0
78	Fishsticks, breaded, cooked, frozen; 10 sticks (3.8 by 1.0 by 0.5 inches each), 8 ounces	66	400	38	20	15	25	.9	.....	.09	.16	3.6	0
79	Haddock, fried; 3 ounces	67	135	16	5	6	15	.5	50	.03	.08	2.2	0

Nutrients in Common Foods in Terms of Household Measures—Continued

Item number	Food	Water (Percent)	Food energy (Calories)	Protein (Grams)	Fat (Grams)	Total carbohydrate (Grams)	Calcium (Milligrams)	Iron (Milligrams)	Vitamin A value (International Units)	Thiamine (Milligrams)	Riboflavin (Milligrams)	Niacin (Milligrams)	Ascorbic acid (Milligrams)
	MEAT, POULTRY, FISH, SHELLFISH—Con.												
	Fish and shellfish—Continued												
	Mackerel:												
80	Broiled; 3 ounces..........	62	200	19	13	0	5	1.0	40	0.13	0.23	6.5	0
81	Canned, solids and liquid; 3 ounces.........	66	155	16	9	0	157	1.8	370	.05	.18	4.9	0
82	Ocean perch, fried (dipped in egg and bread crumbs); 3 ounces....	59	195	16	11	6	14	1.3	50	.09	.10	1.7	0
83	Oysters, raw, meat only; 1 cup (13–19 medium-size oysters, selects)....	85	160	20	4	8	226	13.2	740	.30	.39	6.6	0
84	Oyster stew; 1 cup (6–8 oysters)....	84	200	11	12	11	269	3.3	640	.12	.40	1.7	0
85	Salmon, canned (pink); 3 ounces.....	70	120	17	5	0	159	.7	60	.03	.16	6.8	0
86	Sardines, canned in oil, drained solids; 3 ounces..........	57	180	22	9	1	367	2.5	190	.02	.18	4.6	0
87	Shad, baked; 3 ounces............	64	170	20	10	0	20	.5	20	.11	.22	7.3	...
88	Shrimp, canned, meat only; 3 ounces...........	66	110	23	1	.....	98	2.6	50	.01	.03	1.9	0
89	Swordfish; 3 ounces..........	65	150	24	5	0	23	1.1	1,750	.03	.04	9.3	0
90	Tuna, canned in oil, drained solids; 3 ounces............	60	170	25	7	0	7	1.2	70	.04	.10	10.9	0
	MATURE BEANS AND PEAS; NUTS												
91	Almonds, shelled; 1 cup............	5	850	26	77	28	332	6.7	0	.34	1.31	5.0	Trace
	Beans, dry seed:												
	Common varieties, as Great Northern, navy, and others, canned; 1 cup:												
92	Red.............	76	230	15	1	42	74	4.6	0	.13	.13	1.5	Trace
	White, with tomato or molasses:												
93	With pork........	69	330	16	7	54	172	4.4	140	.13	.10	1.3	5
94	Without pork........	69	315	16	1	60	183	5.2	140	.13	.10	1.3	5

95	Lima, cooked; 1 cup	64	260	16	1	48	56	5.6	Trace	.26	.12	1.3	Trace
96	Brazil nuts, broken pieces; 1 cup	5	905	20	92	15	260	4.8	Trace	1.21	.46	1.9	.....
97	Cashew nuts, roasted; 1 cup	5	770	25	65	35	51	5.1	.....	.49	.....	.....	.....
	Coconut; 1 cup:												
98	Fresh, shredded	50	330	3	31	13	15	1.7	0	.06	.03	.5	4
99	Dried, shredded (sweetened)	3	345	2	24	33	13	1.6	0	.04	.02	.4	0
100	Cowpeas or black-eyed peas, dry, cooked; 1 cup	80	190	13	1	34	42	3.2	20	.41	.11	1.1	Trace
101	Peanuts, roasted, shelled; 1 cup	2	840	39	71	28	104	3.2	0	.47	.19	24.6	0
102	Peanut butter; 1 tablespoon	2	90	4	8	3	12	.4	0	.02	.02	2.8	0
103	Peas, split, dry, cooked; 1 cup	70	290	20	1	52	28	4.2	120	.36	.22	2.2	Trace
104	Pecans, halves; 1 cup	3	740	10	77	16	79	2.6	140	.93	.14	1.0	2
	Walnuts, shelled; 1 cup:												
105	Black or native, chopped	3	790	26	75	19	Trace	7.6	380	.28	.14	.9	.....
106	English or Persian, halves	4	650	15	64	16	99	3.1	30	.33	.13	.9	3
	VEGETABLES												
	Asparagus:												
107	Cooked; 1 cup	92	35	4	Trace	6	33	1.8	1,820	.23	.30	2.1	40
	Canned; 6 medium-size spears:												
108	Green	92	20	2	Trace	3	18	1.8	770	.06	.08	.9	17
109	Bleached	92	20	2	Trace	4	15	1.0	70	.05	.07	.8	17
	Beans:												
110	Lima, immature, cooked; 1 cup	75	150	8	1	29	46	2.7	460	.22	.14	1.8	24
	Snap, green:												
	Cooked; 1 cup:												
111	In small amount of water, short time	92	25	2	Trace	6	45	.9	830	.09	.12	.6	18
112	In large amount of water, long time	92	25	2	Trace	6	45	.9	830	.06	.11	.5	12
	Canned:												
113	Solids and liquid; 1 cup	94	45	2	Trace	10	65	3.3	990	.08	.10	.7	9
114	Strained or chopped; 1 ounce	93	5	Trace	Trace	1	10	.3	120	.01	.02	.1	11
115	Beets, cooked, diced; 1 cup	88	70	2	Trace	16	35	1.2	30	.03	.07	.5	11
116	Broccoli, cooked, flower stalks; 1 cup	90	45	5	Trace	8	195	2.0	5,100	.10	.22	1.2	111
117	Brussels sprouts, cooked; 1 cup	85	60	6	1	12	44	1.7	520	.05	.16	.6	61
	Cabbage; 1 cup:												
118	Raw, finely shredded	92	25	1	Trace	5	46	.5	80	.06	.05	.3	50
119	Raw, coleslaw	84	100	2	7	9	47	.5	80	.06	.05	.3	50

Nutrients in Common Foods in Terms of Household Measures—Continued

Item number	Food	Water	Food energy	Protein	Fat	Total carbohydrate	Calcium	Iron	Vitamin A value	Thiamine	Riboflavin	Niacin	Ascorbic acid
		Percent	Calories	Grams	Grams	Grams	Milligrams	Milligrams	International Units	Milligrams	Milligrams	Milligrams	Milligrams
	VEGETABLES—Con.												
	Cabbage; 1 cup—Con.												
	Cooked:												
120	In small amount of water, short time	92	40	2	Trace	9	78	0.8	150	0.08	0.08	0.5	53
121	In large amount of water, long time	92	40	2	Trace	9	78	.8	150	.05	.05	.3	32
	Cabbage, celery or Chinese; 1 cup:												
122	Raw, leaves and stem (1-inch pieces)	95	15	1	Trace	2	43	.9	260	.03	.04	.4	31
123	Cooked	95	25	2	1	5	82	1.7	490	.04	.06	.6	42
	Carrots:												
124	Raw; 1 carrot (5½ by 1 inch) or 25 thin strips	88	20	1	Trace	5	20	.4	6,000	.03	.03	.3	3
125	Raw, grated; 1 cup	88	45	1	Trace	10	43	.9	13,200	.06	.06	.7	7
126	Cooked, diced; 1 cup	92	45	1	1	9	38	.9	18,130	.07	.07	.7	6
127	Canned, strained or chopped; 1 ounce	92	5	Trace	0	2	7	.2	3,400	.01	.01	.1	1
128	Cauliflower, cooked, flower buds; 1 cup	92	30	3	Trace	6	26	1.3	110	.07	.10	.6	34
	Celery, raw:												
129	Large stalk, 8 inches long	94	5	1	Trace	1	20	.2	0	.02	.02	.2	3
130	Diced; 1 cup	94	20	1	Trace	4	50	.5	0	.05	.04	.4	7
131	Collards, cooked; 1 cup	87	75	7	1	14	473	3.0	14,500	.15	.46	3.2	84
	Corn, sweet:												
132	Cooked; 1 ear 5 inches long	76	65	2	1	16	4	.5	1,300	.09	.08	1.1	6
133	Canned, solids and liquid; 1 cup	80	170	5	1	41	10	1.3	1,520	.07	.13	2.4	14
134	Cowpeas, immature seeds, cooked; 1 cup	75	150	11	1	25	59	4.0	620	.46	.13	1.3	32
135	Cucumbers, raw, pared; 6 slices (⅛-inch thick, center section)	96	5	Trace	Trace	1	4	.2	0	.02	.02	.1	4
136	Dandelion greens, cooked; 1 cup	86	80	5	1	16	337	5.6	27,310	.23	.22	1.3	29
137	Endive, curly (including escarole); 2 ounces	93	10	1	Trace	2	45	1.0	1,700	.04	.07	.2	6
138	Kale, cooked; 1 cup	87	45	4	1	8	248	2.4	9,220	.08	.25	1.9	56

#	Food												
	Lettuce, headed, raw:												
139	2 large or 4 small leaves	95	5	1	Trace	1	11	.2	270	.02	.04	.1	4
140	1 compact head (4¾-inch diameter)	95	70	5	1	13	100	2.3	2,470	.20	.38	.9	35
141	Mushrooms, canned, solids and liquid; 1 cup	93	30	3	Trace	9	17	2.0	0	.04	.60	4.8	……
142	Mustard greens, cooked; 1 cup	92	30	3	Trace	6	308	4.1	10,050	.08	.25	1.0	63
143	Okra, cooked; 8 pods (3 inches long, ⅝-inch diameter)	90	30	2	Trace	6	70	.6	630	.05	.05	.7	17
	Onions:												
	Mature:												
144	Raw; 1 onion (2½-inch diameter)	88	50	2	Trace	11	35	.6	60	.04	.04	.2	10
145	Cooked; 1 cup	90	80	2	Trace	18	67	1.0	110	.04	.06	.4	13
146	Young green; 6 small, without tops	88	25	Trace	Trace	5	68	.4	30	.02	.02	.1	12
147	Parsley, raw; 1 tablespoon chopped	84	1	Trace	Trace	Trace	7	.2	290	Trace	.01	.3	7
148	Parsnips, cooked; 1 cup	84	95	2	1	22	88	1.1	0	.09	.16	.3	19
	Peas, green; 1 cup:												
149	Cooked	82	110	8	1	19	35	3.0	1,150	.40	.22	3.7	24
150	Canned, solids and liquid	82	170	8	1	32	62	4.5	1,350	.28	.15	2.6	21
151	Canned, strained; 1 ounce	86	10	1	Trace	2	5	.3	160	.03	.02	.3	2
	Peppers, sweet:												
152	Green, raw; 1 medium	93	15	1	Trace	3	6	.4	260	.05	.05	.3	79
153	Red, raw; 1 medium	91	20	1	Trace	4	8	.4	2,670	.05	.05	.3	122
154	Pimientos, canned; 1 medium	92	10	Trace	Trace	2	3	.6	870	.01	.02	.1	36
155	Peppers, hot, red, without seeds, dried, ground (chili powder); 1 tablespoon	13	50	2	1	9	20	1.2	11,520	.03	.20	1.6	2
	Potatoes:												
	Baked or boiled; 1 medium, 2½-inch diameter (weight raw, about 5 ounces):												
156	Baked in jacket	75	90	3	Trace	21	9	.7	Trace	.10	.04	1.7	20
157	Boiled; peeled before boiling	80	90	3	Trace	21	9	.7	Trace	.11	.04	1.4	20
158	Chips; 10 medium (2-inch diameter)	3	110	1	7	10	6	.4	Trace	.04	.02	.6	2
	French fried:												
159	Frozen, ready to be heated for serving; 10 pieces (2 by ½ by ½ inch)	64	95	2	4	15	4	.8	Trace	.08	.01	1.2	10
160	Ready-to-eat, deep fat for entire process; 10 pieces (2 by ½ by ½ inch)	45	155	2	7	20	9	.7	Trace	.06	.04	1.8	8

¹ Vitamin A based on yellow corn; white corn contains only a trace.

Nutrients in Common Foods in Terms of Household Measures—Continued

Item number	Food	Water	Food energy	Protein	Fat	Total carbohydrate	Calcium	Iron	Vitamin A value	Thiamine	Riboflavin	Niacin	Ascorbic acid
		Percent	Calories	Grams	Grams	Grams	Milligrams	Milligrams	International Units	Milligrams	Milligrams	Milligrams	Milligrams
	VEGETABLES—Con.												
	Potatoes—Con.												
	Mashed; 1 cup:												
161	Milk added	80	145	4	1	30	47	1.0	50	0.17	0.11	0.2	17
162	Milk and butter added	76	230	4	12	28	45	1.0	470	.16	.10	1.6	16
163	Pumpkin, canned; 1 cup	90	75	2	1	18	46	1.6	7,750	.04	.14	1.2	....
164	Radishes, raw; 4 small	94	10	Trace	Trace	2	15	.4	10	.01	.01	.1	10
165	Sauerkraut, canned, drained solids; 1 cup	91	30	2	Trace	7	54	.8	60	.05	.10	.2	24
	Spinach:												
166	Cooked; 1 cup	91	45	6	1	6	223	3.6	21,200	.14	.36	1.1	54
167	Canned, creamed, strained; 1 ounce	90	10	1	Trace	2	19	.3	750	.01	.03	.1	1
	Squash:												
	Cooked, 1 cup:												
168	Summer, diced	95	35	1	Trace	8	32	.8	550	.08	.15	1.3	23
169	Winter, baked, mashed	86	95	4	1	23	49	1.6	12,690	.10	.31	1.2	14
170	Canned, strained or chopped; 1 ounce	92	10	Trace	Trace	2	7	.1	510	.01	.01	.1	1
	Sweetpotatoes:												
	Baked or boiled; 1 medium, 5 by 2 inches (weight raw, about 6 ounces):												
171	Baked in jacket	64	155	2	1	36	44	1.0	[2] 8,970	.10	.07	.7	24
172	Boiled in jacket	71	170	2	1	39	47	1.0	[2] 11,610	.13	.09	.9	25
173	Candied; 1 small, 3½ by 2 inches	60	295	2	6	60	65	1.6	[2] 11,030	.10	.08	.8	17
174	Canned, vacuum or solid pack; 1 cup	72	235	4	Trace	54	54	1.7	17,110	.12	.09	1.1	30
	Tomatoes:												
175	Raw; 1 medium (2 by 2½ inches), about ⅓ pound	94	30	2	Trace	6	16	.9	1,640	.08	.06	.8	35
176	Canned or cooked; 1 cup	94	45	2	Trace	9	27	1.5	2,540	.14	.08	1.7	40
177	Tomato juice, canned; 1 cup	94	50	2	Trace	10	17	1.0	2,540	.12	.07	1.8	38
178	Tomato catsup; 1 tablespoon	70	15	Trace	Trace	4	2	.1	320	.02	.01	.4	2

FRUITS

No.	Food												
179	Turnips, cooked, diced; 1 cup	92	40	1	Trace	9	62	.8	Trace	.06	.09	.6	28
180	Turnip greens, cooked; 1 cup	90	45	4	1	8	376	3.5	15,370	.09	.59	1.0	87
181	Apples, raw; 1 medium (2½ inch diameter), about ⅓ pound	85	70	Trace	Trace	18	8	.4	50	.04	.02	.1	3
182	Apple betty; 1 cup	64	350	4	8	69	41	1.4	270	.13	.10	.9	Trace
183	Apple juice, fresh or canned; 1 cup	86	125	Trace	0	34	15	1.2	90	.05	.07	Trace	2
	Apple sauce, canned:												
184	Sweetened; 1 cup	80	185	Trace	Trace	50	10	1.0	80	.05	.03	.1	3
185	Unsweetened; 1 cup	88	100	Trace	Trace	26	10	1.0	70	.05	.02	.1	3
186	Apricots, raw; 3 apricots (about ¼ pound)	85	55	1	Trace	14	18	.5	2,890	.03	.04	.7	10
	Apricots, canned:												
187	Heavy sirup pack, halves and sirup; 1 cup	78	200	1	Trace	54	34	1.0	4,070	.05	.07	1.1	10
188	Water pack, halves and liquid; 1 cup	90	80	1	Trace	21	27	.7	3,320	.04	.05	.9	8
	Apricots, dried:												
189	Uncooked; 1 cup (40 halves, small)	25	390	8	1	100	100	8.2	16,390	.02	.24	4.9	19
190	Cooked unsweetened, fruit and liquid; 1 cup	76	240	5	1	62	63	5.1	10,130	.01	.13	2.8	8
191	Apricots and applesauce, canned, strained or chopped; 1 ounce	80	20	Trace	Trace	5	3	.2	440	.01	.01	.1	Trace
192	Apricot nectar; 1 cup	85	135	1	Trace	36	22	.5	2,380	.02	.02	.5	7
	Avocados, raw, California varieties (mainly Fuerte):												
193	1 cup (½-inch cubes)	74	260	3	26	9	15	.9	430	.16	.30	2.4	21
194	½ of a 10-ounce avocado (3½ by 3¼ inches)	74	185	2	18	6	11	.6	310	.12	.21	1.7	15
	Avocados, raw, Florida varieties:												
195	1 cup (½ inch cubes)	78	195	2	17	13	15	.9	430	.16	.30	2.4	21
196	½ of a 13-ounce avocado (4 by 3 inches)	78	160	2	14	11	12	.7	350	.13	.24	2.0	17
197	Bananas, raw; 1 medium (6 by 1½ inches), about ⅓ pound	76	85	1	Trace	23	10	.7	170	.05	.06	.7	10
198	Blackberries, raw; 1 cup	85	80	2	1	18	46	1.3	280	.05	.06	.5	30
199	Blueberries, raw; 1 cup	83	85	1	1	21	22	1.1	400	.04	.03	.4	23

² Average vitamin A value for important commercial varieties. Varieties with pale flesh contain very small amounts while those with deep orange-colored flesh have much higher contents than the value shown in the table.

Nutrients in Common Foods in Terms of Household Measures—Continued

Item number	Food	Water	Food energy	Protein	Fat	Total carbohydrate	Calcium	Iron	Vitamin A value	Thiamine	Riboflavin	Niacin	Ascorbic acid
		Percent	Calories	Grams	Grams	Grams	Milligrams	Milligrams	International Units	Milligrams	Milligrams	Milligrams	Milligrams
	FRUITS—Con.												
200	Cantaloups, raw; ½ melon (5-inch diameter)	94	40	1	Trace	9	33	0.8	3 6,590	0.09	0.07	1.0	63
201	Cherries, sour, sweet, and hybrid, raw; 1 cup	83	65	1	1	15	19	.4	650	.05	.06	.4	9
	Cherries, canned:												
202	Red sour, pitted; 1 cup	87	120	2	1	30	28	.8	1,840	.07	.04	.4	14
203	Cranberry juice cocktail, canned; 1 cup	85	135	Trace	Trace	36	10	.5	20	.02	.02	.1	5
204	Cranberry sauce, sweetened; 1 cup	48	550	Trace	1	142	22	.8	80	.06	.06	.3	5
205	Dates, "fresh" and dried, pitted and cut; 1 cup	20	505	4	1	134	103	5.3	170	.16	.17	3.9	0
	Figs:												
206	Raw; 3 small (1½-inch diameter), about ¼ pound	78	90	2	Trace	22	62	.7	90	.06	.06	.6	2
207	Dried; 1 large (2 by 1 inch)	23	60	1	Trace	15	43	.3	20	.02	.02	.2	0
208	Fruit cocktail, canned in heavy sirup, solids and liquid; 1 cup	81	175	1	Trace	47	23	1.0	360	.04	.03	1.1	5
	Grapefruit:												
	Raw; ½ medium (4¼-inch diameter, No. 64's):												
209	White	89	50	1	Trace	14	21	.5	10	.05	.02	.2	50
210	Pink or red	89	55	1	Trace	14	21	.5	590	.05	.02	.2	48
211	Raw, sections, white; 1 cup	89	75	1	Trace	20	31	.8	20	.07	.03	.3	72
	Canned:												
212	Sirup pack, solids and liquid; 1 cup	81	165	1	Trace	44	32	.7	20	.07	.04	.5	75
213	Water pack, solids and liquid; 1 cup	91	70	1	Trace	18	31	.7	20	.07	.04	.5	72
	Grapefruit juice:												
214	Raw; 1 cup	90	85	1	Trace	23	22	.5	4 20	.09	.04	.4	92
	Canned:												
215	Unsweetened; 1 cup	89	95	1	Trace	24	20	1.0	20	.07	.04	.4	84
216	Sweetened; 1 cup	86	120	1	Trace	32	20	1.0	20	.07	.04	.4	78

217	Frozen concentrate, unsweetened: Undiluted; 1 can (6 fluid ounces)	62	280	4	1	72	70	.8	60	.29	.12	1.4	286
218	Diluted, ready-to-serve; 1 cup	89	95	1	Trace	24	25	.2	20	.10	.04	.5	96
219	Frozen concentrate, sweetened: Undiluted; 1 can (6 fluid ounces)	57	320	3	1	85	59	.6	50	.24	.11	1.2	245
220	Diluted, ready-to-serve; 1 cup	88	105	1	Trace	28	20	.2	20	.08	.03	.4	82
221	Dehydrated: Crystals; 1 can (net weight 4 ounces)	1	400	5	1	103	99	1.1	90	.41	.18	2.0	399
222	With water added, ready-to-serve; 1 cup	90	90	1	Trace	24	22	.2	20	.10	.05	.5	92
	Grapes, raw; 1 cup:												
223	American type (slip skin)	82	70	1	Trace	16	13	.4	100	.05	.03	.3	4
224	European type (adherent skin)	81	100	1	Trace	26	18	.6	150	.08	.04	.4	7
225	Grape juice, bottled; 1 cup	82	165	1	1	42	25	.8	......	.11	.06	.7	Trace
	Lemon juice:												
226	Raw; 1 cup	91	60	1	Trace	20	27	.5	Trace	.08	.03	.3	129
227	Canned; 1 cup	91	60	1	Trace	20	27	.5	Trace	.07	.03	.3	102
228	Lemonade concentrate, frozen, sweetened: Undiluted; 1 can (6 fluid ounces)	48	305	1	Trace	113	9	.4	Trace	.05	.06	.7	67
229	Diluted, ready-to-serve; 1 cup	88	75	Trace	Trace	28	2	.1	Trace	.01	.01	.2	17
	Lime juice:												
230	Raw; 1 cup	90	65	1	Trace	22	22	1.5	Trace	.03	.04	.4	80
231	Canned; 1 cup	90	65	1	Trace	22	22	1.5	Trace	.02	.04	.4	52
232	Limeade concentrate, frozen, sweetened: Undiluted; 1 can (6 fluid ounces)	50	295	Trace	Trace	109	11	.7	Trace	.01	.02	.2	262
233	Diluted, ready-to-serve; 1 cup	90	75	Trace	Trace	27	2	.2	Trace	Trace	.01	.1	6
	Oranges, raw; 1 large orange (3-inch diameter):												
234	Navel	86	70	2	Trace	17	48	.3	270	.11	.03	.4	83
235	Other varieties	86	70	1	Trace	18	63	.3	290	.12	.03	.4	66
	Orange juice: Raw; 1 cup:												
236	California (Valencias)	88	105	2	Trace	26	37	.5	500	.20	.05	.6	126
	Florida varieties:												
237	Early and midseason	90	90	1	Trace	23	25	.5	490	.20	.05	.6	127
238	Late season (Valencias)	88	105	1	Trace	26	25	.5	500	.20	.05	.6	92
239	Canned, unsweetened; 1 cup	87	110	2	Trace	28	25	1.0	500	.17	.05	.6	100

[3] Vitamin A based on deeply colored varieties.

[4] Vitamin A value for juice from white grapefruit. The vitamin A value per cup of juice from pink or red grapefruit is 1,080 I.U.

Nutrients in Common Foods in Terms of Household Measures—Continued

Item number	Food	Water	Food energy	Protein	Fat	Total carbohydrate	Calcium	Iron	Vitamin A value	Thiamine	Riboflavin	Niacin	Ascorbic acid
		Percent	Calories	Grams	Grams	Grams	Milligrams	Milligrams	International Units	Milligrams	Milligrams	Milligrams	Milligrams
	FRUITS—Con.												
	Orange juice—Con.												
	Frozen concentrate:												
240	Undiluted; 1 can (6 fl. ounces)	58	305	5	Trace	80	69	0.8	1,490	0.63	0.10	2.4	332
241	Diluted, ready-to-serve; 1 cup	88	105	2	Trace	27	22	.2	500	.21	.03	.8	112
	Dehydrated:												
242	Crystals; 1 can (net weight 4 ounces)	1	395	6	2	100	95	1.9	1,900	.76	.19	2.5	406
243	With water added, ready-to-serve; 1 cup	88	105	1	Trace	27	25	.5	500	.20	.05	.6	108
	Orange and grapefruit juice, frozen concentrate:												
244	Undiluted; 1 can (6 fluid ounces)	59	300	4	1	78	61	.8	790	.47	.06	2.3	301
245	Diluted, ready-to-serve; 1 cup	88	100	1	Trace	26	20	.2	270	.16	.02	.8	102
	Peaches:												
	Raw:												
246	1 medium (2½ by 2-inch diameter), about ¼ pound	89	35	1	Trace	10	9	.5	[5] 1,320	.02	.05	1.0	7
247	1 cup, sliced	89	65	1	Trace	16	15	.8	[5] 2,230	.03	.08	1.6	12
	Canned (yellow-fleshed) solids and liquid:												
248	Heavy-sirup pack; 1 cup	80	185	1	Trace	49	13	.8	1,000	.02	.06	1.3	8
249	Water pack; 1 cup	92	65	1	Trace	17	15	.7	1,100	.02	.07	1.4	9
250	Strained; 1 ounce	82	20	Trace	Trace	5	2	.2	150	Trace	.01	.2	Trace
	Dried:												
251	Uncooked; 1 cup	25	420	5	1	109	80	9.6	6,330	.02	.32	8.4	32
252	Cooked, unsweetened; 1 cup (10–12 halves and 6 tablespoons liquid)	77	220	3	1	58	43	5.1	3,350	.01	.16	4.1	6
	Frozen:												
253	1 12-ounce carton	79	265	1	Trace	69	20	1.4	1,770	.04	.10	1.8	[6] 99
254	1 16-ounce can	79	355	2	Trace	92	27	1.8	2,360	.05	.14	2.4	[6] 132
255	Peach nectar, canned; 1 cup	87	115	Trace	Trace	31	10	.5	1,070	.02	.05	1.0	1

No.	Food												
	Pears:												
256	Raw; 1 pear (3- by 2½-inch diameter)	83	100	1	1	25	13	.5	30	.04	.07	.2	7
	Canned, solids and liquid:												
257	Heavy-sirup pack; 1 cup	81	175	1	Trace	47	18	1.3	10	.02	.05	.4	3
258	Strained; 1 ounce	84	15	Trace	Trace	4	3	.1	Trace	Trace	.01	.1	Trace
259	Pear nectar, canned; 1 cup	86	125	1	Trace	33	8	.2	10	.01	.05	Trace	1
	Pineapple:												
260	Raw, diced; 1 cup	85	75	1	Trace	19	22	.4	180	.12	.04	.3	33
	Canned:												
	Sirup pack, solids and liquid:												
261	Crushed; 1 cup	78	205	1	Trace	55	75	1.6	210	.20	.04	.4	23
262	Sliced; 2 small or 1 large slice and 2 tablespoons juice	78	95	Trace	Trace	26	35	.7	100	.09	.02	.2	11
263	Pineapple juice, canned; 1 cup	86	120	1	Trace	32	37	1.2	200	.13	.04	.4	22
	Plums:												
264	Raw; 1 plum (2-inch diameter), about 2 ounces	86	30	Trace	Trace	7	10	.3	200	.04	.02	.3	3
	Canned (Italian prunes):												
265	Sirup pack, solids and liquid; 1 cup	79	185	1	Trace	50	20	2.7	560	.07	.06	.9	3
	Prunes, dried:												
266	Uncooked; 4 medium prunes	24	70	1	Trace	19	14	1.0	430	.02	.05	.5	1
267	Cooked, unsweetened; 1 cup (17–18 prunes and ⅜ cup liquid)	65	295	3	1	78	57	4.3	1,780	.08	.18	1.7	3
268	Canned, strained; 1 ounce	73	25	Trace	Trace	7	8	.4	170	.01	.01	.2	1
269	Prune juice, canned; 1 cup	80	170	1	Trace	45	36	10.6	......	.01	.03	1.1	4
270	Raisins, dried; 1 cup	18	460	4	Trace	124	99	6.2	30	.13	.12	.7	2
	Raspberries, red:												
271	Raw; 1 cup	84	70	1	Trace	17	49	1.1	160	.03	.08	.4	29
272	Frozen; 10-ounce carton	74	280	2	1	70	79	1.7	220	.03	.12	.5	45
273	Rhubarb, cooked, sugar added; 1 cup	63	385	1	Trace	98	112	1.1	70	.02	......	.2	17
	Strawberries:												
274	Raw; 1 cup	90	55	1	1	12	42	1.2	90	.04	.10	.4	89
275	Frozen; 10-ounce carton	72	300	2	1	75	62	1.7	120	.05	.14	.5	116
276	Frozen; 16-ounce can	72	485	3	2	121	100	2.7	190	.08	.23	.8	186
277	Tangerines; 1 medium (2½-inch diameter), about ¼ pound	87	40	1	Trace	10	34	.3	360	.05	.01	.1	26

[5] Vitamin A value of yellow-fleshed varieties; the value is negligible in white-fleshed varieties.

[6] Content of frozen peaches with added ascorbic acid; when not added ascorbic acid, the content is 14 milligrams per 12-ounce carton and 18 milligrams per 16-ounce can.

Nutrients in Common Foods in Terms of Household Measures—Continued

Item number	Food	Water	Food energy	Protein	Fat	Total carbohydrate	Calcium	Iron	Vitamin A value	Thiamine	Riboflavin	Niacin	Ascorbic acid
		Percent	Calories	Grams	Grams	Grams	Milligrams	Milligrams	International Units	Milligrams	Milligrams	Milligrams	Milligrams
	FRUITS—Con.												
	Tangerine juice:												
278	Canned; 1 cup............	89	100	1	Trace	25	45	0.5	1,050	0.14	0.04	0.3	56
	Frozen concentrate:												
279	Undiluted; 6-fluid-ounce can..	58	315	4	1	80	130	1.5	3,070	.43	.12	.9	202
280	Diluted, ready-to-serve; 1 cup.	88	105	1	Trace	27	45	.5	1,020	.14	.04	.3	67
281	Watermelon; 1 wedge (4 by 8 inches), about 2 pounds (weighed with rind)..	92	120	2	1	29	30	.9	2,530	.20	.22	.7	26
	GRAIN PRODUCTS												
282	Biscuits, baking powder, enriched flour; 1 biscuit (2½-inch diameter)........	27	130	3	4	20	83	.7	0	.09	.08	.7	0
283	Bran flakes (40 percent bran) with added thiamine; 1 ounce........	4	85	3	1	22	17	1.1	0	.13	.07	2.5	0
	Breads:												
	Cracked wheat:												
284	1 pound (20 slices).........	35	1,190	39	10	236	399	5.0	Trace	.53	.42	5.8	Trace
285	1 slice (½ inch thick)......	35	60	2	1	12	20	.3	Trace	.03	.02	.3	Trace
	French or vienna:												
286	Enriched; 1 pound.........	31	1,315	41	14	251	195	10.0	Trace	1.26	.98	11.3	Trace
287	Unenriched; 1 pound......	31	1,315	41	14	251	195	3.2	Trace	.39	.39	3.6	Trace
	Italian:												
288	Enriched; 1 pound........	32	1,250	41	4	256	77	10.0	0	1.31	.93	11.7	0
289	Unenriched; 1 pound......	32	1,250	41	4	256	77	3.2	0	.39	.27	3.6	0
	Raisin:												
290	1 pound (20 slices)........	35	1,190	30	13	243	322	5.9	Trace	.24	.42	3.0	Trace
291	1 slice (½ inch thick)......	35	60	2	1	12	16	.3	Trace	.01	.02	.2	Trace
	Rye:												
	American (light):												
292	1 pound (20 slices)........	36	1,100	41	5	236	340	7.3	0	.81	.33	6.4	0
293	1 slice (½ inch thick)......	36	55	2	Trace	12	17	.4	0	.04	.02	.3	0
	Pumpernickel:												
294	1 pound............	34	1,115	41	5	241	381	10.9	0	1.05	.63	5.4	0

White:[7]
Enriched, made with—

	1-2 percent nonfat dry milk:											
295	1 pound (20 slices)...........	36	1,225	39	15	229	318	10.9	Trace	1.13	.77	10.4	Trace
296	1 slice (½ inch thick).......	36	60	2	1	12	16	.6	Trace	.06	.04	.5	Trace
	3-4 percent nonfat dry milk:											
297	1 pound (20 slices)...........	36	1,225	39	15	229	381	11.3	Trace	1.13	.95	10.8	Trace
298	1 slice (½ inch thick).......	36	60	2	1	12	19	.6	Trace	.06	.05	.6	Trace
	5-6 percent nonfat dry milk:											
299	1 pound (20 slices)...........	35	1,245	41	17	228	435	11.3	Trace	1.22	.91	11.0	Trace
300	1 slice (½ inch thick).......	35	65	2	1	12	22	.6	Trace	.06	.05	.6	Trace

Unenriched, made with—

	1-2 percent nonfat dry milk:											
301	1 pound (20 slices)...........	36	1,225	39	15	229	318	3.2	Trace	.40	.36	5.6	Trace
302	1 slice (½ inch thick).......	36	60	2	1	12	16	.2	Trace	.02	.02	.3	Trace
	3-4 percent nonfat dry milk:											
303	1 pound (20 slices)...........	36	1,225	39	15	229	381	3.2	Trace	.31	.39	5.0	Trace
304	1 slice (½ inch thick).......	36	60	2	1	12	19	.2	Trace	.02	.02	.3	Trace
	5-6 percent nonfat dry milk:											
305	1 pound (20 slices)...........	35	1,245	41	17	228	435	3.2	Trace	.32	.59	4.1	Trace
306	1 slice (½ inch thick).......	35	65	2	1	12	22	.2	Trace	.02	.03	.2	Trace

Whole wheat, graham, or entire wheat:

307	1 pound (20 slices)...........	36	1,105	48	14	216	449	10.4	Trace	1.17	1.03	12.9	Trace
308	1 slice (½ inch thick).......	36	55	2	1	11	23	.5	Trace	.06	.05	.7	Trace

Cakes:

309	Angelfood; 2-inch sector (1/12 of cake, 8-inch diameter).......	32	110	3	Trace	23	2	.1	0	Trace	.05	.1	0
	Butter cakes:											
	Plain cake and cupcakes without icing:											
310	1 square (3 by 2 by 1½ inches).......	27	180	4	5	31	85	.2	[8]70	.02	.05	.2	0
311	1 cupcake (2¾-inch diameter).......	27	130	3	3	23	62	.2	[8]50	.01	.03	.1	0
	Plain cake with icing:											
312	2-inch sector of iced layer cake (1/16 of cake, 10-inch diameter).......	25	320	5	6	62	117	.4	[8]90	.02	.07	.2	0

[7] When the amount of nonfat dry milk in commercial bread is unknown, use bread with 3-4 percent nonfat dry milk.

[8] If the fat used in the recipe were butter or fortified margarine, the vitamin A value for plain cake would be 200 I.U. per large square, item 310; 150 I.U. per cupcake, item 311; 280 I.U. per 2-inch sector, iced, item 312; for rich cake, iced, item 313; for fruit cake 120 I.U. per piece (2 by 2 by ½ inches), item 314.

Nutrients in Common Foods in Terms of Household Measures—Continued

Item number	Food	Water	Food energy	Protein	Fat	Total carbohydrate	Calcium	Iron	Vitamin A value	Thiamine	Riboflavin	Niacin	Ascorbic acid
		Percent	Calories	Grams	Grams	Grams	Milligrams	Milligrams	International Units	Milligrams	Milligrams	Milligrams	Milligrams
	GRAIN PRODUCTS—Con.												
	Cakes—Con.												
	Butter cakes—Con.												
	Rich cake:												
313	2-inch sector of layer cake, iced (1/16 of cake, 10-inch diameter)	21	490	6	19	76	114	0.6	[8] 220	0.03	0.10	0.2	0
314	Fruit cake, dark; 1 piece (2 by 2 by ½ inches)	23	105	2	4	17	29	.8	[8] 50	.04	.04	.3	0
315	Gingerbread; 1 piece (2 by 2 by 2 inches)	30	180	2	7	28	63	1.4	50	.02	.05	.6	0
316	Sponge; 2-inch sector (1/12 of cake, 8-inch diameter)	32	115	3	2	22	11	.6	210	.02	.06	.1	0
317	Cookies, plain and assorted; 1 cookie (3-inch diameter)	5	110	2	3	19	6	.2	0	.01	.01	.1	0
318	Cornbread or muffins made with enriched, degermed cornmeal; 1 muffin (2¾-inch diameter)	49	105	3	2	18	67	.9	[9] 60	.08	.11	.6	0
319	Corn, puffed, presweetened, added thiamine, riboflavin, niacin, and iron; 1 ounce	3	110	1	Trace	26	3	.5	....	.12	.05	.5	0
320	Corn and soy shreds, added thiamine and niacin; 1 ounce	4	100	5	Trace	21	24	1.2	....	.19	.04	.6	0
321	Corn cereal mixture (mainly degermed cornmeal) puffed, added thiamine, niacin, and iron; 1 ounce	3	115	2	1	23	6	1.2	....	.15	.04	.6	0
	Cornflakes:												
322	With added thiamine, niacin, and iron; 1 ounce	4	110	2	Trace	24	3	.5	0	.12	.03	.6	0
323	Presweetened, added thiamine, niacin, and iron; 1 ounce	4	110	1	Trace	26	1	.5	0	.12	.01	.6	0
	Corn grits, degermed, cooked:												
324	Enriched; 1 cup	87	120	3	Trace	27	2	.7	[10] 100	.11	.08	1.0	0

No.	Food												
325	Unenriched; 1 cup	87	120[9]	3	Trace	27	2	.2	[10] 100	.04	.01	.4	0
	Crackers:												
326	Graham; 4 small or 2 medium	6	55	1	1	10	3	.3	0	.04	.02	.2	0
327	Saltines; 2 crackers (2-inch square)	5	35	1	1	6	2	.1	0	Trace	Trace	.1	0
	Soda, plain:												
328	2 crackers (2½-inch square)	6	45	1	1	8	2	.1	0	.01	.01	.1	0
329	10 oyster crackers or 1 tablespoon cracker meal	6	45	1	1	7	2	.1	0	.01	Trace	.1	0
330	Doughnuts, cake type; 1 doughnut	19	135	2	7	17	23	.4	40	.05	.04	.4	0
331	Farina, enriched to minimum levels for required nutrients and for the optional nutrient, calcium; cooked; 1 cup	89	105	3	Trace	22	31	.8	0	.11	.07	1.0	0
	Macaroni, cooked; 1 cup:												
	Enriched:												
332	Cooked 8–10 minutes (undergoes additional cooking as ingredient of a food mixture)	64	190	6	1	39	14	1.4	0	.23	.14	1.9	0
333	Cooked until tender	72	155	5	1	32	11	1.3	0	.19	.11	1.5	0
	Unenriched:												
334	Cooked 8–10 minutes (undergoes additional cooking as ingredient of a food mixture)	64	190	6	1	39	14	.6	0	.02	.02	.5	0
335	Cooked until tender	72	155	5	1	32	11	.6	0	.02	.02	.4	0
336	Macaroni and cheese, baked (enriched macaroni used); 1 cup	58	475	18	25	44	394	2.0	970	.22	.46	1.9	Trace
337	Muffins, made with enriched white flour; 1 muffin (2¾-inch diameter)	37	135	4	4	20	99	.8	50	.09	.10	.7	0
	Noodles (egg noodles), cooked:												
338	Enriched; 1 cup	70	200	7	2	37	16	1.4	60	.23	.14	1.8	0
339	Unenriched; 1 cup	70	200	7	2	37	16	1.0	60	.04	.03	.7	0
340	Oat cereal (mixture, mainly oat flour), ready-to-eat, added B vitamins and minerals; 1 ounce	3	115	4	2	21	45	1.2	0	.22	.04	.5	0
341	Oatmeal or rolled oats, regular or quick cooking; cooked; 1 cup	85	150	5	3	26	21	1.7	0	.22	.05	.4	0

[9] Based on recipe using white cornmeal; if yellow cornmeal is used vitamin A value is 120 I.U.

[10] Vitamin A based on yellow corn grits; white corn grits contain only a trace.

Nutrients in Common Foods in Terms of Household Measures—Continued

Item number	Food	Water	Food energy	Protein	Fat	Total carbohydrate	Calcium	Iron	Vitamin A value	Thiamine	Riboflavin	Niacin	Ascorbic acid
		Percent	Calories	Grams	Grams	Grams	Milligrams	Milligrams	International Units	Milligrams	Milligrams	Milligrams	Milligrams
	GRAIN PRODUCTS—Con.												
	Pancakes, baked; 1 cake (4-inch diameter):												
342	Wheat (home recipe)	55	60	2	2	7	43	0.2	50	0.02	0.03	0.1	Trace
343	Buckwheat (with buckwheat pancake mix)	62	45	2	2	6	67	.3	30	.04	.04	.2	Trace
	Pies; 4-inch sector (⅐ of 9-inch diameter pie):												
344	Apple	48	330	3	13	53	9	.5	220	.04	.02	.3	1
345	Cherry	46	340	3	13	55	14	.5	520	.04	.02	.3	2
346	Custard	58	265	7	11	34	162	1.6	290	.07	.21	.4	0
347	Lemon meringue	47	300	4	12	45	24	.6	210	.04	.10	.2	1
348	Mince	43	340	3	9	62	22	3.0	10	.09	.05	.5	1
349	Pumpkin	59	265	5	12	34	70	1.0	2,480	.04	.15	.4	0
350	Pretzels; 5 small sticks	58	20	Trace	Trace	4	1	1.0	0	Trace	Trace	Trace	0
	Rice, cooked; 1 cup:												
351	Converted	72	205	4	Trace	45	14	.5	0	.10	.02	1.9	0
352	White	71	200	4	Trace	44	13	.5	0	.02	.01	.7	0
353	Rice, puffed, added thiamine, niacin, and iron; 1 ounce	5	110	2	Trace	25	4	.5	0	.12	.01	1.5	0
354	Rice flakes, added thiamine and niacin; 1 ounce	5	110	2	Trace	25	8	.6	0	.10	.01	1.6	0
	Rolls:												
	Plain, pan (16 ounces per dozen); 1 roll:												
355	Enriched	31	115	3	2	20	28	.7	Trace	.11	.07	.8	Trace
356	Unenriched	31	115	3	2	20	28	.3	Trace	.02	.03	.3	Trace
357	Hard, round (22 ounces per dozen); 1 roll	25	160	5	2	31	24	.4	Trace	.03	.05	.4	Trace
358	Sweet, pan (18 ounces per dozen); 1 roll	31	135	4	4	21	37	.3	30	.03	.06	.4	0
	Spaghetti, cooked until tender:												
359	Enriched; 1 cup	72	155	5	1	32	11	1.3	0	.19	.11	1.5	0

No.													
360	Unenriched; 1 cup	72	155	5	1	32	11	.6	0	.02	.02	.4	0
	Waffles, baked, with enriched flour:												
361	1 waffle (4½ by 5½ by ½ inches)	40	215	7	8	28	144	1.4	270	.14	.20	1.0	0
	Wheat, puffed:												
362	Added thiamine, niacin, and iron; 1 ounce	4	100	4	Trace	22	8	1.2	0	.16	.06	2.2	0
363	Presweetened, added thiamine and niacin; 1 ounce	3	105	1	Trace	26	4	.5	0	.12	.01	1.4	0
364	Wheat, rolled, cooked; 1 cup	80	175	5	1	40	19	1.7	0	.17	.06	2.1	0
365	Wheat, shredded, plain (long, round, or bite-size); 1 ounce	6	100	3	1	23	13	1.0	0	.06	.03	1.3	0
366	Wheat and malted barley cereal, added thiamine, niacin, and iron; 1 ounce	3	105	3	Trace	24	13	1.0	0	.13	.05	1.5	0
367	Wheat flakes, added thiamine, niacin, and iron; 1 ounce	4	100	3	Trace	23	13	1.2	0	.16	.05	1.8	0
	Wheat flours:												
368	Whole wheat; 1 cup, stirred	12	400	16	2	85	49	4.0	0	.66	.14	5.2	0
	All purpose or family flour:												
369	Enriched; 1 cup, sifted	12	400	12	1	84	18	[11]3.2	0	[11].48	[11].29	[11]3.8	0
370	Unenriched; 1 cup, sifted	12	400	12	1	84	18	.9	0	.07	.05	1.0	0
371	Wheat germ; 1 cup, stirred	11	245	17	7	34	57	5.5	0	1.39	.54	3.1	0
	FATS, OILS, RELATED PRODUCTS												
372	Butter; 1 tablespoon	16	100	Trace	11	Trace	3	0	[12]460	0	0	......	0
	Fats, cooking:												
	Vegetable fats:												
373	1 cup	0	1,770	0	200	0	0	0	0	0	0	0	0
374	1 tablespoon	0	110	0	12	0	0	0	0	0	0	0	0
	Lard:												
375	1 cup	0	1,985	0	220	0	0	0	0	0	0	0	0
376	1 tablespoon	0	125	0	14	0	0	0	0	0	0	......	0
377	Margarine; 1 tablespoon	16	100	Trace	11	Trace	3	0	[13]460	0	0	......	0
378	Oils, salad or cooking; 1 tablespoon	0	125	0	14	0	0	0	0	0	0	0	0

[11] Iron, thiamine, riboflavin, and niacin are based on the minimal level of enrichment specified in the standards of identity promulgated under the Federal Food, Drug, and Cosmetic Act.

[12] Year-round average.

[13] Based on the average vitamin A content of fortified margarine. Federal specifications for fortified margarine require a minimum of 15,000 I.U. of vitamin A per pound.

Nutrients in Common Foods in Terms of Household Measures—Continued

Item number	Food	Water (Percent)	Food energy (Calories)	Protein (Grams)	Fat (Grams)	Total carbohydrate (Grams)	Calcium (Milligrams)	Iron (Milligrams)	Vitamin A value (International Units)	Thiamine (Milligrams)	Riboflavin (Milligrams)	Niacin (Milligrams)	Ascorbic acid (Milligrams)
	FATS, OILS, RELATED PRODUCTS—Continued												
	Salad dressings; 1 tablespoon:												
379	Blue cheese	28	90	1	10	1	11	Trace	30	Trace	0.02	Trace	Trace
380	Commercial, plain (mayonnaise type)	48	60	Trace	6	2	2	Trace	30	Trace	Trace	Trace	0
381	French	42	60	Trace	6	2	3	.1	0	0	0	0	0
382	Mayonnaise	14	110	Trace	12	Trace	2	.1	40	Trace	Trace	Trace	0
383	Thousand Island	38	75	Trace	8	1	2	.1	60	Trace	Trace	Trace	2
	SUGARS, SWEETS												
	Candy; 1 ounce:												
384	Caramels	7	120	1	3	22	36	.7	50	.01	.04	Trace	Trace
385	Chocolate, sweetened, milk	1	145	2	9	16	61	.3	40	.03	.11	.2	0
386	Fudge, plain	5	115	Trace	3	23	14	.1	60	Trace	.02	Trace	Trace
387	Hard	1	110	0	0	28	0	0	0	0	0	0	0
388	Marshmallow	15	90	1	0	23	0	0	0	0	0	0	0
389	Chocolate sirup; 1 tablespoon	39	40	Trace	Trace	11	3	.3	.....	.....	.....	.....	.....
390	Honey, strained or extracted; 1 tablespoon	20	60	Trace	0	17	1	.2	0	Trace	.01	Trace	1
391	Jams, marmalades, preserves; 1 tablespoon	28	55	Trace	Trace	14	2	.1	Trace	Trace	Trace	Trace	1
392	Jellies; 1 tablespoon	34	50	0	0	13	2	.1	Trace	Trace	Trace	Trace	1
	Molasses, cane; 1 tablespoon:												
393	Light	24	50	.....	.....	13	33	.9	.....	.01	.01	Trace	.....
394	Blackstrap	24	45	.....	.....	11	116	2.3	.....	.02	.04	.3	.....
395	Sirup, table blends; 1 tablespoon	25	55	0	0	15	9	.8	0	0	Trace	Trace	0
	Sugar; 1 tablespoon:												
396	Granulated, cane or beet	Trace	50	0	0	12	[14]10	.....	0	0	0	0	0
397	Brown	3	50	0	0	13	.....	.4	0	0	0	0	0

MISCELLANEOUS

398	Beverages, carbonated, kola type; 1 cup	88	105	....	Trace	28	....	....	....	....	....	....	0
399	Bouillon cubes; 1 cube	5	2	Trace	Trace	0	0	....	....	....	....	....	0
400	Chili sauce (mainly tomatoes); 1 tablespoon	69	15	Trace	Trace	4	2	.1	320	.02	.01	.4	2
401	Chocolate, unsweetened; 1 ounce	2	145	2	15	8	28	1.2	20	.01	.06	.3	0
402	Gelatin dessert, plain, ready-to-serve; 1 cup	83	155	4	0	36	0	0	0	0	0	0	0
	Olives, pickled; "Extra large" size, 12 olives or "Jumbo" size, 7 olives:												
403	Green	78	65	1	7	1	48	.9	170	Trace	Trace	Trace	....
404	Ripe	76	85	1	9	2	45	.9	40	Trace	Trace	Trace	....
	Pickles, cucumber:												
405	Dill; 1 large (4 inches long, 1¾-inch diameter)	93	15	1	Trace	3	34	1.6	420	Trace	.09	Trace	8
406	Sweet; 1 pickle (2¾ inches long, ¾-inch diameter)	70	20	Trace	Trace	5	3	.3	20	0	Trace	Trace	1
407	Sherbet, factory packed; 1 cup (8-fluid-ounce container)	68	235	3	3	58	96	.1	0	.03	.15	.1	0
	Soups, ready-to-serve; 1 cup:												
408	Bean	82	190	8	5	30	95	2.8	....	.10	.10	.8	....
409	Beef	92	100	6	4	11	15	.5	....	....	....	.6	0
410	Bouillon, broth, and consomme	95	10	2	....	0	2	1.0	0	0	0	1.0	0
411	Chicken	94	75	4	2	10	20	.5	....	....	....	....	....
412	Clam chowder	91	85	5	2	12	36	3.6	....	....	....	1.5	....
413	Cream soup (asparagus, celery, or mushroom)	85	200	7	12	18	217	.5	200	.05	.20	.5	0
414	Noodle, rice, or barley	90	115	6	4	13	82	.2	30	.02	.05	.2	0
415	Tomato	91	90	2	2	18	24	1.0	1,230	.02	.05	1.0	10
416	Vegetable	92	80	4	2	14	32	.8	....	.05	.08	.8	8
417	Vinegar; 1 tablespoon	....	2	0	....	1	1	.1	....	....	....	....	....
418	White sauce, medium; 1 cup	73	430	10	33	23	305	.3	1,350	.07	.42	.3	1

[14] Calcium value is based on dark brown sugar; value would be lower for light brown sugar.

A Daily Food Guide
FOR FITNESS

MEAT GROUP

2 or more servings

Beef, veal, pork, lamb,
poultry, fish, eggs

As alternates

dry beans, dry peas, nuts

MILK GROUP

Some milk for everyone

Children............ 3 to 4 cups
Teen-agers......... 4 or more cups
Adults............. 2 or more cups

**VEGETABLE AND
FRUIT GROUP**

4 or more servings

Include

A citrus fruit or other fruit or vegetable important for vitamin C
A dark-green or deep-yellow vegetable for vitamin A—at least every
other day
Other vegetables and fruits, including
potatoes

**BREAD AND
CEREAL GROUP**

4 or more servings

Whole grain, enriched, or restored

plus

Other foods as needed to complete
meals and to provide additional food
energy and other food values

The Basic Seven Food Groups

LEAFY, GREEN, AND
YELLOW VEGETABLES

MILK, CHEESE,
ICE CREAM

CITRUS FRUIT,
TOMATOES,
RAW CABBAGE

MEAT, POULTRY,
FISH, EGGS,
DRIED PEAS, BEANS

POTATOES AND
OTHER VEGETABLES
AND FRUITS

BREAD, FLOUR,
CEREALS
whole-grain, enriched,
or restored

BUTTER AND
FORTIFIED MARGARINE

A Guide to Eating

ESTHER F. PHIPARD AND LOUISE PAGE

TODAY'S markets are overflowing with an abundance of foods. With so much to choose from, how can we be sure that the kinds of foods we select will give a good diet?

The daily food guide is an answer. It points out the main kinds of foods to include in our meals each day. The pattern of choices suggested are based on what we know about people's needs for vitamins, minerals, protein, and other nutrients.

In the guide, foods valuable for proteins and key minerals, vitamins, and other essentials are grouped into four main classes according to their major contributions of nutrients. Then the number of servings that it will take to add up to a good diet is listed.

There is ample choice within groups to allow for varied meals from day to day. Choices within groups allow us to select favorite foods, foods within the family budget, and those in season.

The foods grouped together furnish about the same nutrients, but they vary in the amounts they provide in a serving. They are enough alike that we can make different selections from a group with the assurance that our choices will contribute their share of nutrients toward a good diet.

MILK, cheese, and ice cream make up a group. Milk is outstanding for calcium. Unless some milk is used each day, it is difficult to get the amount of calcium recommended for all.

Milk is also a valuable provider of high-quality protein, riboflavin, and other vitamins and minerals. Whole milk and some fortified milk also offer vitamin A. Much of the homogenized milk and practically all evaporated carry vitamin D.

Suggested amounts of milk for a day are 3 to 4 cups for children, 4 or more cups for teen-agers, and 2 or more cups for adults.

Many forms of milk are available, and any of them can count toward the daily quota. These include whole fluid milk, concentrated milk, evaporated milk, buttermilk, skim milk, and whole or nonfat dry milk. Cheese and ice cream may be used as alternates for milk because they contribute the same nutrients as milk, though in different proportions.

When cheese and ice cream replace milk, enough of them should be eaten to provide the amounts of calcium we would have had from the milk. Here are common portions of a few familiar cheeses and of ice cream with their

267

milk equivalent in calcium: One-inch cube of Cheddar-type cheese equals two-thirds cup of milk; one-half cup of cottage cheese equals one-third cup milk; 2 tablespoons of cream cheese equal 1 tablespoon of milk, and one-half cup of ice cream equals one-fourth cup of milk.

MEAT AND ALTERNATES are another main group. Meat, fish, poultry, and eggs are excellent sources of high-quality protein. They also furnish good amounts of iron, thiamine, riboflavin, and niacin, but some are better providers than others.

Liver is outstanding among meats because of the generous amounts of many vitamins and minerals it contains. Other variety meats, as heart and kidney, also are rich in a number of nutrients. Pork, too, deserves special mention since it is high in thiamine.

Beef, veal, lamb, pork, variety meats, poultry, eggs, fish, and shellfish are examples of possible choices from the meat group. Alternates include lentils, peanuts, and peanut butter in addition to dry beans, dry peas, and nuts.

Suggested amounts for a day from this group of foods are two or more servings of meat, poultry, fish, or eggs, with dry beans, dry peas, and nuts used occasionally as alternates.

Amounts of these foods to count as a serving are 2 to 3 ounces of lean cooked meat, poultry, or fish (this amount is without bone, fat, or gristle); 2 eggs, 1 cup of cooked dry beans, dry peas, or lentils; 4 tablespoons peanut butter.

If less than these quantities of a food is eaten, it counts as only a part of a serving. An egg, for instance, would be one-half serving, and we would need an additional one and one-half servings to make up the two servings recommended as a minimum for a day from the meat group.

VEGETABLES AND FRUIT, a third group, furnish a substantial share of the vitamin A value and nearly all the vitamin C (ascorbic acid) available to us from food.

Four or more daily servings of vegetables and fruit are recommended in the guide. A serving each day of a citrus fruit or other fruit or vegetable important for vitamin C and a serving at least every other day of a dark-green or deep-yellow vegetable for vitamin A are included in this number.

Color, in this instance, is a general guide to food value. The deeper the yellow, as in carrots and winter squash compared with corn, or the darker the green, as in kale or spinach compared with green snap beans, the better the food is for vitamin A. Consequently, we stress the dark-green and deep-yellow vegetables and a few fruits in the guide for this nutrient. These include apricots, broccoli, cantaloup, carrots, chard, collards, cress, kale, mango, persimmon, pumpkin, spinach, sweetpotatoes, turnip greens and other dark-green leaves, and winter squash.

Many dark-green vegetables also are important for calcium, riboflavin, vitamin C, and iron.

Oranges and grapefruit and their juices—fresh, frozen, or canned—are outstanding for vitamin C. Other good sources are broccoli, cantaloup, guava, mango, papaya, peppers, and fresh strawberries.

Some vegetables and fruit, though containing less vitamin C in a common serving than the items just listed, do provide worthwhile amounts. We can have two servings of these foods during a day, if we want, instead of a single serving of the better sources we mentioned. The vegetables include asparagus tips, brussels sprouts, raw cabbage, collards, garden cress, kale, kohlrabi, mustard greens, potatoes and sweetpotatoes cooked in the jacket, spinach, tomatoes and juice, and turnip greens. The fruits include honeydew melon, tangerines and juice, and watermelon.

One-half cup of vegetable or fruit, or a portion as ordinarily served, such as one medium apple, banana, orange, or potato, or half a medium grapefruit, or cantaloup, can count as a serving.

BREAD AND CEREALS are a fourth group. These foods, especially the whole-grain, enriched, and restored kinds, are valued for protein, iron, several of the B vitamins, and food energy (calories).

The four servings suggested from this group may consist of three slices of bread and a serving of cereal. One ounce of ready-to-eat cereal, one-half to three-fourths cup of cooked cereal, including cornmeal, grits, macaroni, noodles, rice, and spaghetti, are amounts to count as a serving. If no cereals are eaten, we may use two slices of bread instead, making a total of five slices for the day. It takes about two slices of bread to give the same food value as we would get from a serving of many cereals.

Any of these, if whole grain, enriched, or restored, can count toward the suggested four daily servings: Bread, cooked cereals, ready-to-eat cereals, cornmeal, crackers, flour, grits, macaroni, noodles, rice, rolled oats, spaghetti, quick breads, and other baked goods. If in doubt as to enrichment, do not count them toward the daily quota.

We probably will use more than the smallest number of servings suggested from the four groups during a day. Moreover, some familiar foods not included in the groups are by custom a part of meals. Butter, margarine, or salad dressing, for example, or sugar, jams, jellies, sirups or other sweets may be added to foods.

The daily guide, then, really provides a framework for the meals of a day rather than a complete diet. But with our choices coming first from the four groups, the nutritional quality of the diet is safeguarded. We can add other foods to this foundation as desired, or as our weight dictates.

FOODS FROM THE GUIDE easily fit into our three-meals-a-day way of eating. Taking the milk group first: Enough milk is suggested for children to have some at each meal and for adults at two meals. Milk can be served as a beverage, used in cooking, or poured over cereals or fruit. Part of the milk can be consumed in the form of cheese or ice cream.

Our usual meal pattern calls for a meat or alternate in the noon and evening meals. We ofttimes have eggs, with or without a breakfast meat, in the morning, as well. This more than takes care of the minimum servings.

A typical breakfast generally includes a fruit or juice. This meal is a good time to make sure of our daily serving of citrus fruit or other source of vitamin C. The additional three or more servings of fruit and vegetables suggested can be divided between the other two meals.

A serving of bread or cereal easily fits into each meal. Cereals include items such as macaroni, spaghetti, noodles, and rice when they are enriched. Brown rice, a whole-grain product, also counts. Some meals might contain both a breadstuff and cereal.

With the foundation servings taken care of, we can make other selections to complete meals and to round out the nutrients provided by our well-chosen first choices.

Foods from each group can be part of every meal, but it is not necessary if we have the suggested servings sometime during the day. It is wise, however, to have in each meal some food, such as milk, cheese, fish, eggs, or legumes, that furnishes protein.

THE FOOD GUIDE IS SO DESIGNED that we can adapt it to individual needs. With so many choices possible from each food group, for instance, we can plan meals that include well-liked foods and meals that fit the budget.

The number of servings indicated from each food group is for the young and old alike, except for the very young child who receives special food.

As a general rule, young children need less of all foods than adults, except milk. This means smaller rather than fewer servings, however. One-fourth cup of vegetables and fruits, for instance, may be more suitable for them than the one-half cup serving suggested for these foods. But the four daily portions are important for young children, not only for a good diet today but to help establish good eating habits that will remain with them.

Another difference in food for the young and old may be in the way it is prepared. However, the same kinds of foods are basic to a good diet for all ages.

Weight watchers can use the pattern of choices suggested by the daily guide in planning low-calorie meals, since they need the same kinds of foods for health as everyone else.

To cut down on calories and fat, fluid and dry skim milk and buttermilk can be used in place of whole milk. Cheese made from skim milk, as cottage cheese without added cream, can be used instead of whole milk cheese. Fat can be trimmed from meat before eating. Meat can be broiled or roasted rather than fried. Vegetables served plain without cream sauces or seasoned with only a small amount of table or other fat, if any, and fruit without added sugar or cream give fewer calories.

Pies, cakes, and other rich desserts can add many calories to the diet. Jam, jellies, sugar, and other sweets used frequently or in generous amounts also mean extra calories.

THERE IS NO SINGLE WAY we must eat for health. Many different combinations of foods can give us the essentials we need for an adequate diet. This means that with a variety of ways to group foods there are many possibilities for food guides.

One of the earliest food guides, developed in 1921, classed foods into five groups according to their food value and use in meals. The groups are vegetables and fruit; meat, milk, and other foods depended on for complete or efficient protein; cereals; sugar and sugary foods; and fats and fat foods.

At the time this early food plan was developed, scientists did not know so much about food values and vitamins and minerals as they do today. The need for energy, or calories, provided the basis for suggesting the amounts of different foods to have daily. Vegetables and fruit, for example, were supposed to furnish about 20 percent of the calories; cereal foods, 25 percent; meat, eggs, milk, and similar foods, 25 percent; sweets, 10 percent; and fats and fat foods, 20 percent.

There are many other food guides or plans, some with as few as 2 or 3 groups and others with 11 to 13 groups.

One, which has been familiar for many years, is the basic seven. Some of the same groups of foods are found in it and the daily food guide.

Foods listed in the basic seven include the leafy, green and yellow vegetables, one or more servings; citrus fruit, tomatoes, raw cabbage, one or more servings; potatoes and other vegetables and fruit, two or more servings; milk, cheese, ice cream, three to four cups of milk for children, and two or more cups for adults; meat, poultry, fish, eggs, dried peas, beans, one or two servings; bread, flour, cereals—whole grain, enriched, or restored—every day; butter and fortified margarine, some daily.

Both the basic seven and the newer daily food guide can be helpful when we select foods at a cafeteria counter and when a housewife checks the kinds of foods she has been including in her meals.

Both guides emphasize foods that have a special importance for us.

ESTHER F. PHIPARD *is Chief of the Diet Appraisal Branch, Household Economics Research Division, Agricultural Research Service. Since coming to the Department of Agriculture, she has been engaged in studies of family food consumption and dietary adequacy and in the interpretation of these data.*

LOUISE PAGE *is a nutrition analyst in the Household Economics Research Division of the Agricultural Research Service. She came to the Department of Agriculture with a background of experience as a dietitian and as a member of a research team in nutrition.*

Food

OUR NEEDS

Food for Expectant and Nursing Mothers

ICIE G. MACY AND HARRIET J. KELLY

THERE is some truth in the saying that the expectant and nursing mother must eat for two, because the processes of reproduction involve growth and adaptation of the mother and her child and usually some degree of nutritional reconditioning of both of them.

During pregnancy and lactation—as during growth and recovery from injury or disease or malnutrition—the body's daily requirements of many food substances are increased, and they have to be added to the usual needs, which are based on varying conditions of activity, environment, and the nutritive plane she previously maintained.

Because the maintenance of a healthy chemical body structure depends on the presence in the food of many nutrients, the diets of expectant and nursing mothers must take into account the kinds and amounts of protein and the deficiencies or excesses of calories, minerals, and vitamins.

Thus the maternal and fetal needs may be fulfilled and their bodies fortified with reserves to withstand the hazards during gestation, labor, puerperium, lactation, and early infancy.

Nutritional needs differ for different people.

A diet that meets the needs at one time may be insufficient under different physiologic conditions. One may retain large amounts of varied nutrients if the body is undergoing growth, pregnancy, or lactation or if it is underfed or undernourished, so that it requires nutritive conditioning or repletion. If the body has matured and is nourished satisfactorily, however, the amounts stored will be much less and in different proportions.

Lately we have been paying more and more attention to the perinatal concept of tying together the care of the mother and baby. The perinatal period includes the time before conception, all of pregnancy, labor, and the period immediately after birth.

A close relationship exists between the nutritional status of the expectant mother at the time of conception and the outcome of pregnancy, lactation, and the survival and health of the baby. Diets containing enough essential nutriments to satisfy the changing maternal needs therefore contribute to improved maternal health, reduced trauma and loss of maternal tissues during and after birth, greater nutritional stability of the infant, less chance of premature birth, and less illness of mother and child.

Experiences in prenatal clinics in this and other countries indicate that many women do not receive enough of the essential nutrients to satisfy their usual body needs; meet the augmented needs of reproduction; acquire enhanced reserves essential to meet sudden and unexpected periods of physiologic and pathologic stress that arise from ineffective fulfillment of biologic demands; and meet new needs of growth and development of the fetus and placenta. The placenta is the organ on the wall of the uterus to which the embryo is attached by means of the umbilical cord and through which it receives its nourishment. At term the placenta is the afterbirth.

Data from many studies confirm the effect of an adequate diet on the outcome of pregnancy when it is adopted early in the reproductive cycle. Furthermore, research demonstrates that women who conceive when their bodies are in an undernourished or malnourished state may not seek medical guidance until after the first 3 months. By then the biologic pattern of maternal growth and the development of the placenta and the organ and tissue structure of the fetus are established, and metabolic adaptations and stress abound and may leave a detrimental imprint on the lives and health of both mother and child.

The establishment of pregnancy and lactation depends initially in large measure on hormonal stimulation, but the nutritional status of the mother's body determines the success and efficiency with which her physiologic, metabolic, and functional needs are met. Nutrients, hormones, and enzymes are interrelated in metabolism, growth, and development.

Pregnancy introduces complex problems because the fetal organism is living in physiologic and metabolic union with the mother's body and depends on her for the performance of its digestive, excretory, and functional processes.

The mother also needs more food to secrete milk. Breast milk, a unique food, meets the requirements of the infant's delicate digestive system. Thus the adequacy of the mother's diet determines her ability to supply enough predigested nutrients to the fetus through the placental blood supply and to produce breast milk of adequate quantity and concentration to meet the infant's physiologic requirements.

Nutritional status involves the metabolic and physiologic condition of the individual who consumes the food. For instance, the full-term newborn infant who is nutritionally 9 months old at birth also has a characteristic biologic age with physiologic, functional, and nutritive requirements that determine its food response and resultant nutritional state.

PREGNANCY has three morphologic phases.

The first, the preimplantation period, extends approximately 2 weeks after conception.

Next is the interval of about 2 to 8 weeks, during which major construction of organs and tissue takes place. It is the biologic time and stage in the growth and development of the fetal organism when its nervous and excretory systems and sensory organs are most susceptible to untoward environmental conditions and when the possibility of abortion is greatest.

The third phase, from 8 weeks to term, is the period of most rapid fetal growth and development and most intensive maternal physiologic growth, nutritional reconditioning, and preparation of reserves for meeting the extra demands of approaching labor, puerperium, and milk production.

Each phase of pregnancy exerts its own characteristic physiologic, functional, and nutritive demands as a result of the many functional and regulatory mechanisms that are initiated by the products of conception.

Each phase of the life cycle has its own nutritive requirements and its own physiologic disturbances and diseases.

The endometrium, the membrane lining the uterus, is prepared for the ovum during the preconceptional periods and early pregnancy.

The implantation of the fertilized ovum, however, brings into play many new hormonal changes. They result in an unbalanced physiologic state, with which are associated disturbances of the gastrointestinal system, such as depressed appetite, reduced food consumption and utilization, nausea, and possibly loss of weight.

Metabolic changes as the result of conception may be observed in the level or distribution of blood components; the level or distribution of urinary components; the retention or loss of nutrients; and the composition and developmental changes of the fetus, the placenta, and the adnexa (other fluids and structures associated with maintenance of the fetus).

THE PRIMARY function of the placenta is to store and transport nourishment from mother to embryo and provide a mechanism for returning the end products of the embryo's metabolism to the mother's blood stream. It is a storehouse for the building and maintenance materials from which the fetus, in a highly selective way, may draw its nutrients for growth and development.

Indeed, the complex mechanism for the nutrition of the human embryo, from the time that the fertilized ovum is embedded in the uterus to maturation and birth, must function through the specialized placental structure.

Normally the chemical composition of the placenta during gestation varies to suit the demands made on it by the growing fetus. The fat and carbohydrate contents, for example, are reduced in the last quarter of pregnancy; the vitamin content of the placenta may increase during the pregnancy and change near its end.

The fetal part of the placenta at term has developed to the extent that it forms the major part of the organ.

We have indications that all the morphologic and metabolic changes that occur in the human body during a person's lifetime take place in the placenta during the short span of gestation.

Changes occur in the thyroid and pituitary glands and in the distribution of the ovarian and placental hormones during gestation.

Gonadotropins, progesterone, and estrogens are hormones primarily concerned with reproductive processes and are particularly important in regulating the internal nutritional environment of cells and modifying their behavior.

Gonadotropins have a dominant role up to about the fourth month of pregnancy in embryonic tissue differentiation (organogenesis) and in fetal growth and associated nutritive and protective structural systems. Biological tests for pregnancy depend on the presence of gonadotropin in the urine.

Progesterone, derived from the corpus luteum, placenta, and adrenal cortex, stimulates changes in secretions, which prepare and maintain the endometrium of the uterus for the implantation of the fertilized ovum and for nourishing the fetus.

Estrogen and progesterone stimulate growth and functional changes in the breasts.

The use of hormone treatment in the stabilization of pregnancy and in the suppression of the flow of milk at the outset of mammary function is common medical practice.

THE COMPOSITION of the human fetus and of breast milk has a significant bearing on metabolism during the reproductive cycle and growth of the infant.

Nitrogen, calcium, magnesium, sodium, potassium, chlorine, and phos-

Maternal and Fetal Storage of Nitrogen and Calcium

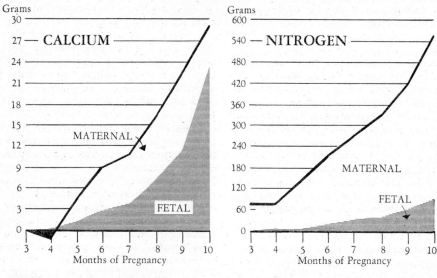

phorus are present in the fetus. During the first 3 months, when fetal tissue is undergoing differentiation and the organism is small, the nutritive requirements are similarly small, yet each essential nutrient or the substance from which it is formed are critically important and must be present in adequate amounts and proportions to permit maximum formation of tissues and organs without blemishes.

The last 3 months is the period of greatest embryologic accumulation of nutrients. The fetus grows most then.

Studies of metabolic balance are of great value in increasing our knowledge of the nutritional status of women. They include analyses of food eaten over a given period of time and analyses of urine and feces. The difference between the food eaten and that excreted is presumed to represent in large measure the amounts of nutriments assimilated by the mother for increases in blood volume, enlargement of the uterus, development of the mammary glands and placenta, formation of amniotic fluid, and the nutritive needs of the embryo.

This method does not tell us which of the retained nutrients are utilized by the mother, the fetus, or the placenta and does not reveal their distribution to target organs in the two organisms. It helps us get a rough approximation, however, by calculating progressive fetal needs from chemical composition of fetal specimens obtained at autopsy. The maternal body generally deposits a large excess of nutrients over and beyond that needed for the fetus and placenta.

Figure 1 illustrates the large amount of maternal calcium and nitrogen stored in excess of fetal and placental needs. The maternal "rest material" is much greater for nitrogen, because it universally participates as protein in all protoplasmic activities. Thus it is needed in the construction, maintenance, and repletion of muscular, neural, and glandular tissues, in the organic matrix portion of the bone of the maternal-fetal unit, and in the reserves requisite to parturition and lactation.

The embryo has laid down on the average approximately 0.9 to 55.9 grams of nitrogen by the fourth to tenth lunar month, respectively. By term, approximately 17 grams of nitrogen have been used in development of the placenta and 1 gram in the amniotic fluid.

The amount of nitrogen utilized by the hypertrophied mammary glands has been estimated to be about 17 grams, and the uterus at term contains nearly 39 grams of nitrogen. It seems that the period of gestation in healthy women is one of appreciable maternal gain over and beyond the measurable requirement of the fetal tissues.

The surplus 200 to 370 grams of nitrogen accumulated during gestation serve as a maternal reserve to take care of the losses encountered during labor and parturition and also to prepare the maternal body for meeting the physiologic needs of lactation.

During parturition there is loss of nitrogen in excess of the food intake. The extent of the deficit depends on the maternal nutritional state, on the type and duration of labor, and on the amount of physiologic bleeding and postpartum hemorrhage. Loss of blood may be as much as 300 to 500 milliliters or more.

The extent of the nutritive reserve may be the determining factor in a woman's ability to convalesce rapidly from the experiences of labor, delivery, and puerperium, especially if she is still growing or is undernourished.

The average daily nitrogen balances during the first 4 weeks after delivery may amount to approximately -3.12, -0.78, $+1.75$, and $+4.33$ grams. The initial loss of nitrogen may be due partly to the involution of the uterus and regression of other maternal tissues.

When new physiologic functions are initiated, the organs of the body involved take on increased activity, which is proportional to the importance and duration of the duty they have to perform. The kidneys, liver, uterus, thyroid, adrenals, and pituitary glands develop enlarged functional activities commensurate with the stage and demands of gestation. They, too, regress after the release of the fetus and thus contribute to the dissipation of nitrogen.

CALCIUM largely is involved in the construction and maintenance of the bones and teeth. It also is important in the blood-clotting mechanism and other essential metabolic and homeostatic functions. The hormonal influences of early gestation may affect metabolism of calcium.

Calcium metabolic balances show that the maternal organism may lose on the average 0.11 and 0.31 gram of calcium daily at the 3d and 4th lunar months, respectively, and accrue 4.22, 8.68, 10.61, 15.84, 22.40, and 29.26 grams of calcium from the 5th to the 10th lunar month, respectively.

The calcium content of the fetus over the same period shows accretion to be about 0.20, 1.3, 3.1, 5.4, 8.5, 13.1, and 22.7 grams of calcium. The total amount of calcium used in the placenta and amniotic fluid is approximately 0.5 gram.

Wide variations exist among individuals under similar circumstances and suggest that nutritive state, physiologic constitution, and previous levels of dietary intake are important and should be considered in relation to dietary requirements for pregnancy.

Mineral disturbances in expectant and nursing mothers require careful dietary practice.

THE FETUS has access only to those nutrients passed to it through the blood circulation of the mother. Only a fraction of the mother's food intake will be distributed to the fetal and maternal bodies.

The maternal organism converts the foodstuff into small units and synthesizes or mobilizes materials that may be essential or conducive to an optimal environment for the embryo.

To a considerable degree, therefore, the nutrition of the fetus is the function of the mother's food. The fetus takes priority over the mother with regard to certain nutrients, but the maternal protective mechanisms spare the fetus from harmful excesses of some nutrients.

Nutritional and hormonal factors influence different steps in metabolism directly or indirectly through the production of enzymes and the interaction of individual vitamins, amino acids, and minerals.

The growth hormone produced during pregnancy increases nitrogen metabolism in the tissues in the form of protein and is an essential part of the growth process. It aids nitrogen conservation when dietary protein and carbohydrates are in short supply.

Maternal basal metabolic rate is influenced by increased thyroid function. After the fourth month of gestation, the increase amounts to 0.13 percent more in excess of that conditioned by the gross increase of maternal body weight as influenced by fetal growth and development. In general, the plasma volume also increases during gestation— approximately 25 percent at term over the nonpregnant amount.

MATERNAL GAIN in weight is only a general indication of the nourishment of the expectant mother and is not a direct measure of storage of tissue-building constituents, because it does not indicate composition of that gain.

Gain in weight, however, is one of the important clinical guides in relation to previous weight, to weight loss or gain in the first and second trimester, to the total gain during pregnancy, and to gain or loss subsequent to delivery.

The well-fed and healthy expectant mother usually gains 16 to 24 pounds and is more apt to pass through the reproduction period in better health and with fewer complications.

Excessive gain or loss in weight indicates the susceptibility of the mother to disease and also increases the health hazards to the infant during the neonatal period and the first year of life.

In studies of women during childbearing and complications that arise,

the late Dr. William J. Dieckmann of the Chicago Lying-In Hospital observed a close relationship between the rate of gain in different phases of pregnancy and the outcome.

His observations were extended by Dr. Winslow T. Tompkins of Philadelphia in his Nutrition Clinic. He found that a normal gain during the first 3 months lessens the hazard of toxemia. If the increase is restricted too severely during this period, the probability of premature labor seriously increases. The possibility of premature labor is greatly reduced, therefore, by an acceptable rate of gain during the first 6 months.

Dr. Tompkins said: "If maximum protection is to be obtained for each individual patient, every effort must be made to establish an adequate nutrient intake for her needs, both qualitatively and quantitatively as early in pregnancy as possible and maintained at this crucial level throughout the duration of the individual gestation concerned. Any deviation of even previously considered minimal degrees, particularly in the patient of lower nutritional adequacy, markedly increases her probability of either premature labor or preeclampsia."

When intakes of minerals and vitamins are low and mineral metabolism is defective during pregnancy, the result is a predisposition to defection in bones and teeth in the intrauterine organism.

In some cases the associated nutritional disturbances in the mother may be one of the causative factors in vomiting, eclampsia, osteomalacia, dental caries, tetany, and premature labor.

A strain on the function of hematogenesis—blood building—is shown by mild secondary anemia, which is common and in some instances becomes severe. The blood requirements of the fetus, the increased maternal blood volume, the blood loss during parturition, and other factors in this anemia contribute to the metabolic overload.

Newborn infants from mothers with hypochromic anemia may show a normal blood picture but develop anemia during the first year of life. Unless the supply of iron in the mother's body is adequate, the fetus of an iron-deficient mother does not accumulate enough of this essential blood component to carry it through infancy.

Factors of health and environment that arrest or distort the development of the embryo before birth or shortly thereafter have important implications. The prenatal phase of development is one of great vulnerability.

Today's most challenging and perplexing problems in public health are concerned with the causes of human reproductive waste; of prematurity and perinatal mortality; of full-term but underdeveloped live infants; of premature onset of labor, eclampsia, and spontaneous abortion; and exact methods for detection of oxygen lack to the fetus and the effect on the fetus of maternal nutrition and of various drugs and biological agents.

LACTATION increases maternal dietary requirements for milk production. The augmented needs greatly exceed those of pregnancy. These two phases of the reproductive cycle, however, are intimately interrelated.

The enlarged storage of nitrogen, calcium, and other nutrients toward the end of gestation should be regarded as having a dual role in preparation for lactation in addition to finishing of the fetus.

Amounts of milk taken daily by healthy breast-fed infants range from 300 to 500 milliliters at the end of the 1st week of age, 400 to 550 milliliters in the 2d week, 430 to 720 milliliters in the 3d week, 500 to 800 milliliters in the 4th week, 600 to 1,030 milliliters from the 5th to the 13th week, and 720 to 1,150 milliliters from the 4th to the 6th month. The mother may lose 1.0 to 1.5 grams of nitrogen and 0.25 to 0.50 gram of calcium daily through breast milk.

We lack precise information about the food eaten by nursing mothers who successfully feed their babies and at the same time preserve their own body tissues and maintain good health.

Milk of the healthy, well-fed mother is generally acknowledged to possess nutritive qualities that provide advantages for her infant, but many of the factors responsible for its superior value have not been fully defined.

Significant losses of calcium during intensive milk flow, despite an apparently adequate diet, point to the need of further knowledge of the various processes involved in lactation.

The increase in protein, energy, minerals, and vitamins in lactation depends on the initial dietary intake and activity. Colostrum, the first milk secreted, has a higher concentration of most nutrients, and for this and other reasons offers special advantages to the newborn.

Knowledge of the composition of milks used in infant feeding is needed by workers in nutrition, obstetrics, pediatrics, and public health.

Two comprehensive tables of composition of human colostrum and human milk have been published. One, "The Composition of Milks, A Compilation of the Comparative Composition and Properties of Human, Cow, and Goat Milk, Colostrum, and Transitional Milk," by the Food and Nutrition Board of the National Academy of Sciences-National Research Council, was published as Bulletin No. 254 in 1953. The other, "Human Milk, Wartime Studies of Certain Vitamins and Other Constituents," by the Medical Research Council, London, was published as Special Report Series No. 269.

The initial tentative Recommended Daily Dietary Allowances of the Food and Nutrition Board of the National Research Council were published in 1943 and revised several times. The values for pregnancy and lactation were based primarily on chemical analyses of human fetuses and placentas of different ages, food consumption records of expectant and nursing mothers, and maternal metabolic data. Because of lack of knowledge

Recommended Daily Dietary Allowances of Young Infants, Women, and Expectant and Nursing Mothers[1]

Age	Weight	Height	Calories	Protein	Calcium	Iron	Vitamin A	Thiam.	Ribo.	Niacin eq.	Asc. acid	Vitamin D
	kg. (lb.)	cm. (in.)		gm.	gm.	mg.	I.U.	mg.	mg.	mg.	mg.	I.U.
Infants:												
2 to 6 months	6 (13)	60 (24)	kg.×120	(2)	0.6	5	1,500	0.4	0.5	6	30	400
7 to 12 months	9 (20)	70 (28)	kg.×100	4	.8	7	1,500	.5	.8	7	30	400
Women:												
25 years	58 (128)	163 (64)	2,300	58	.8	12	5,000	1.2	1.5	17	70	......
45 years	58 (128)	163 (64)	2,200	58	.8	12	5,000	1.1	1.5	17	70	......
65 years	58 (128)	163 (64)	1,800	58	.8	12	5,000	1.0	1.5	17	70	......
Pregnant (second half)	......	......	+300	+20	1.5	15	6,000	1.3	2.0	+3	100	400
Lactating (850 ml. daily)	......	......	+1,000	+40	2.0	15	8,000	1.7	2.5	+2	150	400

[1] National Research Council Recommended Daily Dietary Allowances, Revised 1958.

[2] See page 287.

and of the limitation inherent in the allowances, the Board urged those using them to bear in mind the general principle followed—that the quantitative levels are sufficiently liberal to be "suitable for maintenance of good nutritional status."

The recommendations represent levels of nutrient intakes that are considered normally desirable goals or objectives: "They are not called requirements because they are not intended to represent merely literal (minimal) requirements of average individuals, but levels enough higher to cover substantially the individual variations in the requirements of normal people."

Thus the recommended amounts are generally higher than average requirements but generally lower than the amounts used to meet the needs created by pathologic states or to compensate for an earlier depletion.

Because of the great complexity of the physiologic mechanisms involved in early gestation and a lack of knowledge of the processes that prevent an evaluation of food needs during the first half, daily dietary allowances are recommended for the second half only and for lactation. Both are based on specific increases above the initial dietary intake to cover the greater needs in late pregnancy, when fetal and maternal needs are maximal, and the needs of lactation plus an additional amount to provide for an estimated daily secretion of 850 milliliters of breast milk of average composition.

The recommendations recognize many limiting factors: The pregnant individual becomes less active as she nears term, whereas the nursing mother is not only more active than usual with the new baby but has increased needs for milk production. Both the composition and volume of breast milk may vary from day to day and as the stages of lactation develop. Individuals vary in their nutritive backgrounds.

The required daily calories may be adjusted by allowing an increase of 300

Food Pattern for	NORMAL DIET *plus*			
	Milk	Citrus fruit or tomato	Lean Meat, Fish, Poultry, Eggs, Beans, or Cheese	Leafy, Green Vegetable
PREGNANCY	1 PINT	1 SERVING	1 SERVING	
LACTATION	1 QUART	2 SERVINGS	1 SERVING	1 SERVING

Calories for late pregnancy and 1,000 Calories for lactation above the initial dietary intake.

Proteins, the essential components of living protoplasm and integral participants in vital physiologic processes, are preeminently important to life. The expectant mother should receive an extra daily allowance of 20 grams of protein and 1.5 grams of calcium. The nursing mother should have 40 grams more of protein and 2 grams of calcium.

Vitamin C is vital in metabolism, growth, and repair of tissues. It has high priority in the daily allowances—100 milligrams for pregnancy and 150 milligrams for lactation, in comparison with 70 milligrams before childbearing.

Other known nutrients are needed in larger amounts for the reproductive cycle.

A variety of foods selected in proper amounts from the basic food groups will satisfy the appetite, meet nutritive needs, and reduce unusual cravings.

The basic groups will furnish the protein, calories, minerals, and vitamins for health and enjoyment of eating. They include meat, fish, and poultry; whole grain and enriched flour products; leafy, green vegetables; yellow vegetables; citrus and other fruits; dairy products; and oils and fats.

A quart of milk a day or its equivalent in such calcium-rich foods as cheese is a safeguard for the bones and teeth of the expectant and nursing mother. Skim milk also possesses a rich supply of calcium and other nutrients.

Newborn babies vary in their nutritive needs. The baby is influenced by heredity. Even before birth it is affected by the mother's state of health and nutrition for 9 months. Full-term infants may vary in nutritional endowment, in degree of maturity, and in body size, physique, and composition.

The first few days of life therefore are crucial.

Breast milk, if there is enough of it and if it is produced by a healthy woman who has a satisfactory diet, contains adequate amounts of food elements best adapted to the delicate and physiologically unstable infant for good nutrition in the early days and weeks of life.

Breast milk is safe and has definite therapeutic and preventive values that are extremely important in the early weeks in life. It forms soft, easily digestible curds in the infant's digestive tract and represents a nutritive mixture that is used as a basis for the preparation of formulas. Human milk and cow's milk vary in physical characteristics and chemical composition.

Although feeding infants with other foods than mother's milk usually is based on a standard level of only pro-

Contribution of One Quart of Milk to Daily Food Needs During Lactation

Based on Recommended
Dietary Allowances of the
National Research Council.

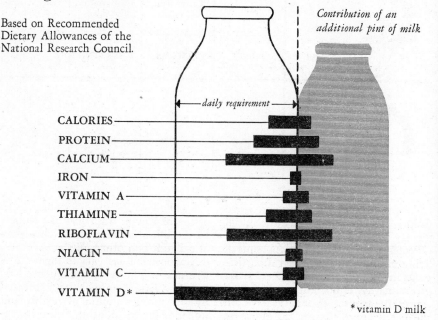

*Contribution of an
additional pint of milk*

daily requirement

CALORIES
PROTEIN
CALCIUM
IRON
VITAMIN A
THIAMINE
RIBOFLAVIN
NIACIN
VITAMIN C
VITAMIN D*

*vitamin D milk

tein and calories, wide differences remain in the amounts and proportions of many other essential nutrients.

In adapting the recommended allowances for young infants, the Food and Nutrition Board recognizes the judgment of some investigators and practitioners who strive to develop children up to and beyond a theoretical "normal" weight for height and age.

Infants given cow's milk retain larger amounts of nitrogen and calcium than those receiving similar amounts of human milk. Some investigators conclude from these observations and gains in weight that the breast-fed infant may not receive enough food and that cow's milk may have certain advantages.

The 1953 and 1958 dietary standards of the young infant are raised to a questionable degree, according to some investigators. It is safe to assume that the healthy nursing mother can provide the best food for her infant up

to 3 and 6 months of age if the quantity is sufficient and her diet has been adequate.

Breast milk is the time-proved physiological food for the small, physiologically unstable human infant. It best satisfies the nutritive requirements of the delicate metabolic mechanisms, as they ebb and flow and support and sustain growth and development.

The size or gain in weight of the child does not give specific information on the chemical composition of its body or on its nutritive stability and health thereafter.

ICIE G. MACY *is a member of the Division of Human Development staff in the Merrill-Palmer School in Detroit. She formerly was director of the Research Laboratory, Children's Fund of Michigan.*

HARRIET J. KELLY *is a biostatistician in the Division of Human Development, Merrill-Palmer School in Detroit. Formerly she was statistician in the Research Laboratory, Children's Fund of Michigan.*

Infants and Toddlers

GENEVIEVE STEARNS

THE newborn infant differs from the adult as greatly in his inner makeup as in his outer dimensions. At birth he not only is small; his body proportions are different. His head is relatively large. His arms and legs are short and at first are almost useless. His body contains more water, and a much greater proportion of its water is outside the cells. Only one-fourth of his total weight consists of muscle, instead of nearly half of it, as in the adult. His skeleton, like the adult's, is about one-fifth of his body weight, but there the resemblance ends, for the newborn baby's skeleton has much more cartilage or gristle and is more than half water.

Only the central sections of the long bones are mineralized in the newborn. As an X-ray film shows only the mineralized portions, a film of a young baby's skeleton looks like a collection of separate bones. All these bones must be mineralized, and the baby has to increase his protein content, on a per pound basis, at least to half again its birth proportion.

Each organ grows at its own rate—growing is a much more complicated process than just getting bigger.

The full-term newborn baby has the ability to digest and absorb proteins, simple carbohydrates, and a moderate amount of fats.

Ordinarily he does not manage starches well, although infants who are given feedings thickened with starch for therapeutic reasons will begin to make amylase (a starch-digesting enzyme) in response to the stimulus.

His kidneys are functioning and can carry off wastes, although he needs more water, relative to his size, than the adult does to manage this excretion. His food needs to be simple and liquid. He can suckle, as can all young mammals, but is not ready to chew or swallow solid or semisolid foods. His alimentary canal can excrete unused food and gastrointestinal juices, after much of their water content has been absorbed.

His nervous system is not entirely complete and functioning. His eyes do not focus. His senses of taste and smell are not acute.

The blood of a newborn infant has a larger number of red cells and a larger amount of hemoglobin, the iron-containing red coloring of the cells, than at any other time in life. Before birth, the baby got his oxygen supply from his mother's blood and he returned the waste carbon dioxide to it. When he breathes air, with its far higher amount of oxygen, he does not need so much hemoglobin, and his body starts almost immediately to break down the excess. The iron in hemoglobin is saved and stored for future use, for his mother's milk contains very little iron.

The baby born at term of a well-nourished mother is usually in excellent nutrition at birth, sturdy, vigorous, and contented. The baby whose mother was in poor nutritional condition during her pregnancy is more apt to be born prematurely and require special care for survival. Even though born at term, he often is smaller, less vigorous, more apt to suckle poorly, and fretful.

An infant who has been born after fewer than 270 days in the womb or who weighs less than 5.5 pounds is considered premature. If the difference in time is small, such a baby can often catch up with the full-term infant. Often the premature infant is in a poor nutritional state. The greater the degree of prematurity, the more difficult are the problems just of keeping the baby alive and growing.

THE BABY BORN 2 months prematurely is a fragile and an unfinished product, weighing only about half as much as the full-term newborn. His body has much more water and much less protein and mineral per pound of body weight than the full-term baby. He has little fat and looks like a wizened ancient. His bones are so poorly calcified that the skull bones can be pressed inward easily. During the birth process, this molding of the skull permits increased pressure on the brain; hemorrhage with brain damage therefore is commoner among the prematurely born than among full-term infants.

Because the development of his nervous system is incomplete, the control of such vital functions as breathing, suckling, coughing, and heart rate are defective. Temperature regulation is poor because of his relatively large surface area and the incomplete development of the sweat glands.

His digestive ability and kidney function are more nearly effective, but much more water must be provided for each unit weight of feeding to enable him to excrete all his wastes. The nutrients which he should have received constantly from his mother's blood in a form that was ready for immediate use by his tissues must now be ingested at intervals, digested, and absorbed. Yet this tiny unfinished product, prematurely thrust into the world, is expected to grow more rapidly than he ever will again.

The causes of prematurity are many, but recent studies have shown that the incidence and degree of prematurity increase as the mother's nutrition worsens.

The death rate of prematurely born infants that were studied by scientists in Iowa was highest among those whose mothers had the poorest diets. The poorly fed young mothers were apt to deliver their first or second infants prematurely. Older mothers, whose food habits were considered fair to good but who had given birth to a series of infants in rapid succession, often could not carry their later infants to term. Their nutritional stores had become exhausted by multiple pregnancies. Such women need an excellent diet at all times.

The child needs to be well nourished during his 9 months of intrauterine life. It is possible, even probable, that he will not be so unless special precautions are taken to improve the mother's nutrition. Nutritional deficiences of mothers in much of the United States are due more to social factors, such as lack of education and resourcefulness, than to economic factors.

If every mother- and father-to-be realized how much safer the baby is from birth injury and how much easier he is to care for throughout infancy if he is kept well-nourished before birth, every precaution to provide sufficient nutriment for the mother and the baby would be taken.

Human milk of good quality and sufficient quantity is the normal food of the full-term infant. He is more likely to thrive smoothly on human milk than any other food. Maintenance of the mother in good nutrition is essential both for the production of a healthy baby and for the establishment of a good flow of milk of good quality.

The standard by which the rate of growth and development of any baby is measured is the average rate of growth and physical development of infants who are born at term of well-nourished mothers and who receive ample breast milk and, in addition, moderate amounts of vitamin D and vitamin C. Normal infants so fed grow well and usually remain healthy and sturdy. A formula-fed baby whose growth and development are significantly slower than those of the standard breast-fed babies is not thriving nutritionally.

Human milk fed directly from the breast of a healthy mother is always fresh and free from disease-producing organisms.

Because mother's milk customarily is not measured in amount or analyzed for quality, we tend to assume both factors are adequate. When the mother is poorly nourished, however, the amount of milk she secretes is small, and duration of lactation is short. Even under those conditions, if the amount of milk secreted permits some growth, the baby may fare better when breast fed if no other safe, properly prepared milk is available. His nutrition, however, is at his mother's expense; the ability to produce milk solely from her own body constituents is limited. If the mother is severely undernourished, her baby will not thrive if breast fed only.

Other factors than malnutrition or starvation also affect a mother's ability to produce enough milk of good quality to nourish her infant adequately. Most mothers in good health, however, if they have the support of their husbands and doctors, can produce enough milk for the needs of their babies.

During the first few days after the baby's birth, the milk secreted by the mother is quite different from that secreted later. This early milk is called colostrum; milk secreted later is called mature milk.

Colostrum is a thin fluid and contains more protein and salts and less sugar and fat than does later milk. The amount of colostrum is small, 1 to 2 ounces in the 24 hours. About the third to fourth day, the milk comes in, and the mother's breasts enlarge and become tender. By the end of 2 weeks, or soon thereafter, the change from colostrum to mature milk is complete.

The baby should get increasing amounts of milk daily and by 6 weeks to 2 months should be getting at least 2.5 ounces per pound to thrive.

Even though the baby can be breast fed only for a month or so, it is well worth while to nurse him. Colostrum and its gradual change to mature milk tide him over the difficult period of adjustment to the changed conditions of independent life. Nursing the baby through 6 months or more is still better. Continuation of nursing past 9 months is unusual in this country. Many physicians consider it unnecessary for the baby's health. Lactation beyond 9 months can be associated with a heavy loss of nutrients from the mother's body. Such length of lactation may be more harmful to the mother than helpful to the infant.

The young breast-fed infant should be given vitamin D in the amount of 300 to 400 I.U. (International Units) daily shortly after birth. It is customary in this country also to give the baby an added source of vitamin C beginning soon after birth, although if the mother has a good intake of vitamin C, her baby will have enough.

Often preparations containing vitamins A, C, and D are prescribed for infants. Additional vitamin A is not needed by the breast-fed infant whose mother is well fed. In countries in which vitamin A deficiency is common, its addition would be wise. The practice of giving orange juice or other natural sources of vitamin C accustoms the baby to the bottle and nipple and to a different flavor at an early date. In case of emergency weaning, the baby accustomed to a nipple is not so disturbed over the process. The baby who is accustomed to two different flavors is not apt to be so reluctant in accepting new foods as the baby who has been given only milk.

Other supplementary foods for the breast-fed infant I discuss later.

HUMAN MILK AND COW'S MILK differ in many respects.

Human milk, though far and away the best first food for the healthy fullterm baby, nevertheless is a food that provides little if any excess of any nutrient. It is a most successful food for the full-term infant when it is adequate in quantity. It is a safe food, for it goes directly from mother to baby without storage or contamination.

The composition of the milk varies widely from woman to woman and from cow to cow. Average cow's milk contains more than twice the protein and about half the milk sugar of average human milk. Each milk has about 20 Calories to the ounce (70 per 100 milliliters). Cow's milk also has a greater proportion of its protein as casein, the protein of the curd. Raw cow's milk therefore produces large, tough curds; human milk produces fine, soft curds. Boiling cow's milk changes the character of the curd to a fine, soft curd resembling that of human milk, except that it is present in greater quantity. Half the protein of human milk (but less than one-fifth of cow's milk protein) is in the whey, which is the watery substance of milk after the curd is removed.

The fat content of the two milks is about the same, but the fatty acid content differs somewhat. Both fats can be digested by a healthy baby. A sick baby may have difficulty with the fat of cow's milk and do better if half the fat is removed (by using equal parts of whole and skim milk).

Average cow's milk contains nearly four times as much calcium and six times as much phosphorus as human milk; these form the chief components of bone mineral. Both human milk and cow's milk are short of iron and vitamin D. The minerals of cow's milk are poorly used unless vitamin D is given.

The vitamin content of both milks varies with the food given the producer. Cows are specially fed for milk production; mothers too often are not. Species differences also occur in vitamin content of the two milks. Human milk has more of vitamins A and E, niacin, and vitamin C than cow's milk. Cow's milk has much more riboflavin and more of some other of the B group vitamins.

Because the vitamin C of cow's milk disappears quickly with pasteurization and standing, for infant feeding it is considered as having none. Neither human milk nor cow's milk has enough iron or vitamin D for the baby. Because some loss of vitamins of the B group occurs with heating and storage, the excess of some of these vitamins in cow's milk is not great when fed; under some conditions all of them may be lost.

The thiamine content of both milks as fed appears to be marginal.

The vitamin content of human milk will vary according to the mother's diet. She should be careful therefore to have an adequate intake of fruit, vegetables, whole-grain cereals, and other foods that contain these vitamins.

Cow's milk can be bought as raw, pasteurized, evaporated, sweetened condensed, dried whole, and skim (nonfat) milk. All forms have been used in infant feeding.

Fresh milk should be boiled or sterilized for infant feeding.

As sweetened condensed milk is nearly half sugar, the milk content is low and the baby grows poorly. It is rarely if ever used now for infant feeding, although it was popular 50 years ago.

Dried whole milk must be packaged so that air is excluded, or the fat becomes rancid. Packaging in tins makes dried whole milk far more expensive than the dried nonfat milks which can be sold in cheaper packaging. Nonfat dry milk often is used for special purposes, such as a supplement to other milks and foods.

Evaporated milk is usually the cheapest form of whole milk. All evaporated milks have vitamin D added in the proportion of 400 units to the reconstituted quart, giving automatic protection to the baby against rickets. Fluid milk also may be homogenized and fortified with vitamin D. In this country, all vitamin D milk contains 400 units to the quart.

An important difference between cow's milk formulas and human milk lies in the fact that, while the milk of a healthy mother is always fresh and free from bacteria, any artificial formula must be heat treated to destroy harmful organisms.

Raw milk should never be given an infant. Even pasteurization cannot be depended on to make milk absolutely safe for young infants. Boiling the formula sterilizes it and produces little change in any of its nutrients except that some of the vitamin C is destroyed. Preparations for sale as complete formulas have been sterilized at high temperatures because of the storage necessary. Bottles and nipples should be well scrubbed with soap and water and boiled after using.

The NUTRITIONAL requirements of full-term infants are high because growth in infancy is rapid. A full-term baby will need 45–55 Calories per pound (100–120 per kilogram), whereas an active adult uses only about 20–30 Calories per pound. The food must be given in a liquid or semiliquid form. The water requirement of the baby is high, and must be planned for, as the baby cannot go and get a drink when thirsty. His need for protein, minerals, vitamins must be met.

Calories are important. The baby must ingest food of sufficient energy value to supply body heat and the energy necessary for the heart, lungs, muscles, and digestive organs to perform their activities. The amount of energy needed for the fasting body is called the basal caloric requirement. To this must be added allowances for growth, for activity, and for loss of undigested food.

The calorie requirement the first 2 weeks after birth is relatively low—about 45 to 50 per pound. By 3 to 4 weeks, the baby is really hungry and may take 55–60 Calories per pound or even more if he is large and active. After 6 months the rate of growth slows somewhat; the baby takes more total food, but his intake per pound decreases slowly until at a year it averages again about 50 Calories per pound.

The baby's water content is much higher than an adult's. He breathes faster and loses much water from the lungs, especially if kept in an overwarm, poorly humidified environment. He also needs more water for excretion of wastes than the adult. All in all, the baby should get at least 2.5 ounces of water per pound of body weight. Most of it will be in his milk feedings.

After the first few months, the infant is taught to accept food with a variety of flavors and textures. These supplementary foods are used also to provide nutrients not in ample amount in the formula or breast feeding.

The breast-fed baby will get most of his nutritional requirements if he gets 2.5 ounces or more of human milk of good quality per pound of baby. The protein requirement of the breast-fed baby is lower than that of the artificially fed infant. The amino acid makeup of human milk protein suits the needs of the human infant, and no destruction occurs as a result of heating or storage. To get the proper mixture of amino acids for the baby from any other milk necessitates a more liberal allowance. Allowance must be made also for loss through heat and storage of the milk and for a somewhat greater loss through the stool.

Although the exact requirement for protein from cow's milk is not known, it seems wiser to provide a generous amount. Even the young baby, the premature, and the severely undernourished infant can digest and utilize protein very well.

It is the general custom of many pediatricians to allow 1.5 to 2 grams of protein per pound (3 to 4 grams per kilogram). Premature infants thrive best on 2 to 2.5 grams per pound. One ounce of cow's milk provides about 1 gram of protein.

The rest of the calories the baby needs will be provided by fat and carbohydrate. Babies thrive on widely differing proportions of these two sources.

A small amount of essential fatty acids (linolenic, linoleic, or arachidonic acid), which occur in both milks, is necessary. The young baby usually has considerable storage of these essential fatty acids, for at least short-term feeding of low-fat milks seems to cause no ill effects or slow the rate of growth. A baby can burn fat completely—that is, oxidize it to carbon dioxide and water. Very young, premature, and feeble infants absorb fat poorly; therefore they should derive a greater part of their energy requirement from carbohydrate.

For most babies, milk containing not more than 3.5 to 4 percent of fat causes no difficulty. Both human milk and cow's milk, containing about 3.5 percent of fat, provide about half their total calories as fat. Jersey and Guernsey milk have a higher content of fat and should be partly skimmed for infant feeding. Premature, small, or sick babies may be given half-skim milk, made from equal parts of whole and skim milk, with added carbohydrate to bring up its energy content.

Certain vegetable oils have a higher proportion of essential fatty acids than do milk fats. Some proprietary foods for premature and immature infants have part or all of the milk fat replaced by vegetable oils.

The carbohydrate of milk is in the form of lactose, or sugar of milk. Average cow's milk contains 4.8 per-

cent of lactose; human milk, 7 percent. The higher content of lactose in human milk brings up its total Calories to equal those of cow's milk. As cow's milk is usually somewhat diluted before being fed to young infants, it is customary to add some carbohydrate to the infant's formula. Some, but not all, infants thrive on boiled cow's milk without dilution.

Many types of carbohydrate can be used in infant feeding. Dextrose needs no digestion, as it is the sugar already present in blood. It is absorbed rapidly. If the blood level gets too high, some of it may be lost in the urine. Lactose, maltose (from grain), or sucrose (cane or beet sugar) can be used. Lactose and maltose are expensive; sucrose accustoms the baby to a sweet feeding.

When starch is hydrolyzed, either by the enzymes of malt diastase or by acid, it breaks down by stages; those soluble in water and somewhat less complex than starch are known as dextrins. Dextrins hydrolyze to maltose and ultimately to dextrose. The solution containing a mixture of dextrins, maltose, and dextrose may be concentrated to a sirup or dried. Usually the products of acid hydrolysis of starch are sold as sirups, commonly called corn sirup. The hydrolysis products after enzyme digestion of starch ordinarily are sold in dry powdered form as dextrin-maltose mixtures for infant feeding.

Cane sugar in concentrations of more than 8 percent and dextrose of more than 6 percent of the feeding draw water from the tissues into the gastrointestinal tract and cause some diarrhea and dehydration.

When enough cow's milk is fed to allow 1.5 to 2 grams of protein per pound (1.5 to 2 ounces of milk per pound), the baby will receive sufficient minerals, except iron and possibly copper, and enough of all vitamins, except C and D.

Vitamin C is required in the amount of 30 milligrams daily for young infants and 50 milligrams for older infants. Premature infants need 30 to 50 milligrams of vitamin C daily. The breast-fed infant whose mother receives 100 milligrams of vitamin C daily usually will thrive without added vitamin C; however, it is customary to give the baby about 30 milligrams daily to make certain.

Orange or tomato juice diluted with warm water is fed from a bottle with a nipple. Orange juice contains 15 milligrams of vitamin C to the ounce; tomato juice, 5 milligrams per ounce. Pot liquor, the concentrated liquid in the pot in which greens are cooked, is cheap and a good source of vitamin C. All fat should be removed before feeding the liquor to the baby. Acerola juice is used in Puerto Rico and is an excellent source of vitamin C. A sirup made from rose hips is used in some countries. Potatoes are a major source of the vitamin in northern Europe. Crystalline ascorbic acid is inexpensive and readily available in the United States for infants who are allergic to natural forms.

All babies should be given 300 to 400 units of vitamin D daily whether breast fed or artificially fed. This amount prevents rickets and permits excellent growth and retention. Up to 800 units daily has no observable ill effects but no increased good effects. At 1,500–1,800 units and more, daily growth of the baby is slowed and the appetite wanes. These effects become more marked with increasing dosage. Excess intake should therefore be avoided, because it may be as harmful as too low an intake.

Most preparations of vitamin D also contain vitamin A in amounts usually 5 to 10 times the total amount of vitamin D. The milk provides adequate vitamin A for the artificially fed infant and ample for the breast-fed infant, but up to 5,000 I.U. daily cause no observable damage. Overdosage with vitamin A, like that of vitamin D, can be toxic, for neither vitamin is excreted readily by the body. Both are broken down slowly; so excessive intake results in a piling

up of the vitamin to the point of toxicity, which is mild at first, and shows only by a slowing of growth. Severe toxicity is acute and dangerous.

Because most preparations contain both vitamins D and A, with the latter in greater concentration, acute vitamin A toxicity is seen more often than acute D toxicity. Overdosage can occur more easily when concentrated preparations with a drop dosage are used than when 1 teaspoonful is needed for the day's dosage. Slowing of growth often goes unobserved but is far too common. Great care should be observed to give only the prescribed dosage of these vitamins.

Babies fed human milk or cow's milk of good quality get enough thiamine, but the amount in either as fed is close to the minimum. The mothers whose intakes of thiamine are low may not provide sufficient thiamine for their infants; such deficient human milks have been reported in several countries. Orange juice provides some added thiamine. It is customary to use foods in early supplemental feedings that contain thiamine as well as iron.

When refrigeration is not available in the home and the baby must be formula fed, special precautions are needed. The best formulas under such conditions are the acid milks developed for use in an era when refrigeration was uncommon. Disease-producing bacteria do not grow in sour milk. Either fresh or evaporated milk may be used. The formula is soured by the use of an organic acid, such as lactic, citric, or acetic acids; or citrus fruit juice, such as lemon or orange juice. Vinegar also may be used.

THE ACTUAL FORMULA made from cow's milk will be prescribed by a physician, who will take into account the baby's condition. The number of formulas which can be devised and with which the normal infant will thrive is almost endless. The cheapest formula in this country is one made from evaporated milk and corn sirup or granulated sugar.

The baby born 6 to 8 weeks prematurely has a very small capacity for food and no storage of nutrients, yet he grows rapidly if he maintains the growth he would have made had he waited until full term to be born. He has no excess energy and little strength. Human milk, excellent as it is for the full-term baby, does not have enough nutrients per ounce to permit the baby to make the rapid growth normal for his stage of development. Therefore it has become customary to add dried or fresh cow's skim milk to the human milk given him. If human milk is not available, he will thrive on a cow's milk formula made with skim or half-skim milk with added milk sugar or other easily digested carbohydrate.

Feeding of the premature infant is usually adjusted to allow 2 to 2.5 grams of protein and 60 Calories per pound of baby. The added cow's milk gives an increase in protein and sufficient minerals to permit the rate of mineralization of bone normal for his age and provides adequate vitamins for his rapid growth with the exception of vitamins C, D, and A, which must be given separately.

Physicians recommend different amounts of vitamin D for premature infants. If adequate minerals are provided, 400 to 800 I.U. of vitamin D daily seem ample. When only human milk is given, even very large doses of vitamin D may not prevent the development of rickets, because the skeleton grows too fast for the amount of mineral available, and rickets is insufficient mineralization of growing bone. Too much vitamin D is toxic and slows the rate of growth.

The requirements of vitamin A will be covered if 2,500 I.U. of A are given daily. Both overdosage and underdosage with vitamins D and A are to be avoided for the premature as for the full-term baby.

The prematurely born baby will need added vitamin C in the amount of 30 to 50 milligrams daily, which is more than the young full-term baby needs. It is best given as the crystalline vitamin dissolved in a small amount of water and added directly to the feeding.

As the infant grows, his ability to take in and to digest food increases. When he reaches normal birth weight, he can be fed as any young infant past the newborn period is fed.

The feeding schedule for the baby should be somewhat flexible. The infant is to be fitted into family life and become a real member of the family. A regular life is as good for the baby as for older children. At first, he will become hungry at irregular intervals.

A watchful mother soon discerns a pattern in his hunger period and will adjust to it and adjust it to the family pattern. Too much rigidity in maintenance of a schedule and too rigid permissiveness, as feeding the infant at each cry, are equally bad. Babies cry for many reasons, and some crying spells are common even among young well babies. A baby should always be held while fed. He swallows less air when he is held than if the bottle is propped near him. Besides, he needs the comfort and the sociability of being held.

The breast-fed baby may want more food than his mother can give. Complemental feedings of a cow's milk formula have the big disadvantage that (even though the nipple holes are kept small) it is easier for the baby to get milk from a bottle than from the breast. Babies are as lazy as the rest of mankind; they are apt to refuse the breast and demand the bottle. Even under 3 months of age it often is easier to maintain breast feeding if supplemental foods, such as cereal and milk or custard, are given from the spoon.

SUPPLEMENTAL or spoon-fed foods for the infant are given soon after the baby is 3 months old. All babies by then should be receiving either breast milk or cow's milk formula, an added source of vitamin D and probably vitamin A, and orange juice or a substitute containing vitamin C. The formula-fed baby should receive 2 to 4 ounces of orange juice or 4 or more ounces of tomato juice after 3 months; the breast-fed baby may be given this much but does not require the additional vitamin C if his mother's intake is good.

Up to this time the baby's food has been liquid. Some babies can be trained at an earlier age to accept food from a spoon. Others become feeding problems if they are spoon fed too early. When the baby is formula fed, it seems wiser to wait until the nervous control of the swallowing reflex has developed sufficiently that the baby can swallow soft or semisolid foods. Most babies achieve this status by the time they are 3 or 4 months old.

At 2.5 to 3 months, the baby will have broken down the excess hemoglobin he had at birth and will have started to use the iron he had saved and stored from it. This stored iron will last only until he is 6 months old unless food iron is given. If the baby's birth supply of iron was less than normal, he should be given iron to prevent anemia.

It seems wise to give as the healthy baby's first solid food one that contains iron. Egg yolk may be hard boiled, mashed, and mixed with some of the formula or given as a soft custard made with one egg yolk and one-fourth to one-third cup of milk. An average yolk provides 1.2 milligrams of iron, 0.050 milligram of thiamine, and some vitamin A. Egg white is not used for young infants, as it may produce allergy to egg white unless every particle is thoroughly cooked. Sieved meats and pinto beans (sieved or mashed with a fork after the skins are removed) also are good sources of iron. Other types of beans common in Latin America and other countries are good sources and may be fed young babies.

Cereals prepared especially for infant feeding usually have iron added to them. These are mixed with four to five volumes of warm milk when fed. Oatmeal-containing cereals for infants contain more thiamine than other cereals.

After the baby is well accustomed to his first spoon feeding—when he is about 4 months old—sieved, cooked fruit or vegetables can be given daily. A somewhat unusual but effective procedure is to start with highly flavored fruit and vegetables.

At 4 months, a baby's taste habits are not developed enough that he will object to strong flavors. If he has been given only bland foods to about 6 months, he may refuse any food with perceptible flavor. We have used sieved apricots, peaches, and tomatoes for early supplemental feeding for many years. Let the baby have the same food 2 or 3 days; then a different one can be given him.

At about 5 months, both sieved fruit and vegetables are given daily. As soon as the baby is accustomed to the different tastes, the mother begins to accustom him to different textures. Squash and sieved peas are smooth, but sieved carrots and green beans have a coarser texture and make a transition to the chopped foods that he will learn to chew later in the year. Vegetables and fruit prepared for the family table may be sieved or mashed; they usually are as nutritious as the specially canned baby foods.

Babies nearing 6 months when the supply of breast milk begins to fail can be weaned directly to the cup. An infant gets confused if he has to learn to drink from a cup soon after he has had to learn to take a bottle.

By 6 months of age, the baby will be getting enough carbohydrate from supplemental foods and he needs less in his formula. During the next few weeks, the amount of carbohydrate in the formula can be decreased gradually until the baby takes milk with no added carbohydrate. A part of the milk or formula can be given from a cup, beginning at about 6 months.

In addition to his sources of vitamins D, C, and A, a 6-month-old infant usually is getting one serving each of sieved fruits and vegetables, one serving of egg yolk in some form, sieved meat, or baby cereal with milk. He can be fed sieved or mashed stewed peaches, apricots, apples, pears, and prunes and mashed raw, ripe banana. Potatoes, baked or mashed, can be given occasionally, especially after the carbohydrate is removed from the formula and the baby receives undiluted pasteurized milk. Squash, sieved or mashed peas, beans, greens, and tomatoes are useful. These can be bought or canned or prepared from the family table. Vegetable soup and pureed soups and simple puddings can be added from the family table.

Sample schedules intended only as rough guides are as follows: An infant 4 to 5 months old will waken early and demand his first feeding of milk. After the family breakfast, he is given his orange juice and other vitamins, and about 10 o'clock, his sieved fruit and a milk feeding. After family lunchtime is over, the baby's afternoon lunch of sieved vegetable and a feeding is served. At 5 or 6 o'clock he gets custard and a feeding. The last feeding of the day is just before the parents retire.

The 6-month-old baby has a similar schedule, except that his formula contains little or no added sugar or sirup. He can be given his fruit and cereal at the family breakfast table. His customary feeding follows. He can be given two different spoon foods at a time and part of his milk from a cup.

Babies differ in the time of day they are hungriest. A schedule can be adopted that fits the particular baby and his family. When teething has started, the use of hard crackers or teething biscuits often is helpful. The baby can hold these himself.

By 9 or 10 months, the baby should be eating three meals a day, with midmorning and midafternoon snacks. His breakfast consists of cereal or poached, coddled, or soft-scrambled whole egg and milk. Fruit juice and the vitamin D, with toast, hard cracker or zwieback, are given in midmorning. At noon he has sieved or chopped vegetable or soup, strained meat or creamed mashed fish, a breadstuff to be eaten in the hand (such as graham cracker, zwieback, rusk, or toast), and milk. Midafternoon lunch is milk and a cracker or cookie. The evening meal can consist of egg (if not given for breakfast) or peas or red or pinto beans (which are mashed or sieved), sieved or chopped fruit, toast or suitable breadstuff, baked or mashed potato or rice or corn grits, and milk.

The 9-month-old baby may have sieved or thinly sliced liver; chicken or other fowl; beef, veal, or well-cooked lean pork; and thoroughly boned fish. Well-cooked meat can be put through the food grinder and mixed with the potato or other mashed vegetable.

The baby will soon want to feed himself and should be given a spoon and helped to learn. Foods like cooked carrots, beets, and string beans can be chopped or diced instead of sieved. Cooked peas can be given whole for the baby to eat with his fingers.

It is important that the early experiences with self-feeding should be pleasant and unhurried. Awkwardness and messiness are to be expected and usually should be ignored.

THE YEAR-OLD TODDLER, if he has been healthy, well nourished, and well cared for during infancy, is sturdy, active, happy, and friendly. His weight is about three times his birth weight. His height is at least one and one-half times his birth length. He has 6 teeth, maybe 8. His blood has about 13 grams of hemoglobin per 100 milliliters, and its protein content will be about the same as an adult's. He can stand, at least with support; some one-year-olds walk alone. He tries to talk, although usually only his parents consider his attempts successful.

The period between 1 and 3 years is characteristically one of conspicuous physical and mental change. The changes in rate and type of body growth and in body composition are as striking as is the development of personality in the young child. The rate of growth, both in height and weight, has been slowing for several months. The slowing becomes obvious soon after the first birthday and may alarm the parents, but it is normal.

The pattern of growth changes also. The rate of growth of the legs and arms becomes noticeably greater than the growth of the trunk. Mothers observe that the child's clothes become too short, long before they become too narrow for his shoulders. At about 18 months, if the child's diet provides sufficient protein, a sudden surge of growth occurs in the skeletal musculature. Up to that time the muscles have remained at the infant proportion of about one-fourth the total body weight. From 1.5 to 3 years, growth of muscle accounts for about one-half of the child's total weight gain. The child is on his feet and active a good share of his waking hours. As his legs grow longer, his center of gravity is farther from the floor, and more muscle is needed to hold his body upright. The muscles so needed are chiefly the big muscles of the back, buttocks, and thighs.

The toddler age is primarily the age of rapid muscle growth. The skeleton, the next largest tissue, grows at the same rate as the total body growth; therefore it is slowing its rate of growth. Mineral is being deposited in the skeleton, however, at a rate faster than the bone growth. Thus the skeleton grows slowly but becomes stronger to support the greater weight on the legs when the child is standing or walking.

Other changes occur. The child begins to lose his baby fat and gets larger amounts of muscle. His water content becomes less, and more of the water is inside the cells. He begins to look and feel less like a baby and more like a child.

The changes that occur in his body are preparatory to the type of growth he will have in midchildhood, continuing growth of the legs and arms at a greater rate than growth of the trunk. Growth of muscle is more rapid than growth of other tissues until the child is 9 or 10 years old, when he will reach the adult proportion of muscle— nearly half the total body weight.

Unless the child is so fed that he can maintain the rate of growth of each tissue normal for his age, he arrives at the next age period with a deficit.

Primary considerations for the toddler are the need of ample protein for the rapid growth of muscle normal to this age period plus enough for growth of the other body tissues. He also needs sufficient calcium and phosphorus to provide for increased mineralization of bone, so that bone strength keeps pace with growth of muscle and the child's increasing activity. Yet his total caloric need is not high, and it increases very slowly.

As the child becomes more active, he needs more calories for activity but relatively fewer calories for general body growth than in early infancy. A few children will not eat as many calories during the second year as they did during the second half of infancy.

This drop in appetite is alarming to a mother who has not been forewarned. Often mothers try to increase the child's food intake, with results harmful both nutritionally and psychologically. The child learns that refusal to eat is a wonderful weapon, and the battle is on.

The Colorado Child Research Council has observed that 75 percent of one-year-olds ate 1,075 to 1,400 Calories a day; by 3 years, they were getting 1,150 to 1,450 Calories a day. A few large, active children eat 2,000 or more Calories daily as 2-year-olds. A few small, quiet children may ingest less than 1,000 Calories a day. Average caloric intake increases slowly from 1,025 at the first birthday to 1,300 by the third.

Though the need for calories increases slowly, the need for protein is high. A gram and a half of protein should be allowed for each pound of body weight, or about 35 grams daily at 1 year, 40 grams by 2 years, and 45 grams a day at 3 years. Half the total should be protein of animal origin, as milk, cheese, eggs, fish, or meat. Each glass (half pint) of whole milk provides 8 grams of protein. Cheese provides 5 to 6 grams, and lean meat about 6 grams per ounce. Cooked peas and beans yield 1 to 2 grams per ounce. Bread has about 2 grams a slice, and cereals 0.5 to 2 grams per serving.

The high-protein foods also carry many of the important vitamins and minerals. Whole milk provides all the minerals (except iron and copper) needed for bones and body fluids; it also provides large amounts of vitamin A and riboflavin and sizable amounts of most of the other B vitamins. Eggs provide iron, vitamin A, thiamine, and protein. Lean meat, peas, beans, and whole-grain cereals provide iron and many of the B vitamins. Potatoes, especially if baked or boiled with the skin on, carry thiamine, niacin, and vitamin C in appreciable amounts.

The year-old child will get ample protein from a pint (preferably a pint and a half) of milk, an egg, 1 to 2 tablespoonsful of ground meat, 3 slices of bread or a serving of whole-grain cereal and 2 slices of bread, together with the smaller amounts of protein furnished by fruit and vegetables. One or 1.5 pints of milk daily together with 300–400 units of vitamin D will insure sufficient retention of calcium and phosphorus for the increased strength of bone needed when his body is held upright. Three glasses (1.5 pints) of vitamin D milk (fresh or reconstituted evaporated) provide 300 units.

Sometimes the year-old child prefers solid foods to liquids and refuses milk. Milk can be given him in thickened soups, custards, and other milk puddings. Dried skim milk can be added to cooked cereal or mashed potato. If the older infant or year-old child refuses solid foods, the fluid milk can be skimmed, and the intake may be cut to a pint a day for a short time until he learns to eat other foods. The solid foods may be diluted somewhat with milk, or they can be fortified with dried skim milk.

A well-fed year-old child thus may receive during the day 1 to 1.5 pints of milk, two or more kinds of fruit (one of which is a good source of vitamin C), two or more vegetables, lean meat, an egg, and cereals (as bread or breakfast cereal), some table fat (butter or margarine), a simple dessert, and a source of vitamin D. One to two tablespoonsful of any solid comprise a serving at this age. His food should be in three meals and three lighter lunches.

That regimen is common in the Northern States. In the South, beans and the many kinds of greens families eat also provide iron; the beans provide good protein. Corn and other breads fed the toddler should be made with enriched flour or meal. Milk is an important part of the diet everywhere. Eggs should be given about five times weekly.

Many other diet patterns can be worked out for the child, depending on food habits of the family and, within reason, the baby's own preferences. The year-old child needs about 35 grams of protein and 1,000 to 1,200 Calories daily. The vitamin and mineral needs must also be met—the means can vary widely.

At 18 months to 2 years, 1.5 pints or more of milk daily can be taken easily. The child will still need 300 to 400 units of vitamin D daily to insure good absorption of calcium and phosphorus.

The diets of children 2 and 3 years old are generally like those of the one-year-old, but the variety is greater and the quantities fed are larger. The pulp of fresh ripe fruit, as watermelon, cantaloup, peaches, apricots, plums, pears, pineapple, strawberries, and blueberries, may be fed. Orange sections may be given instead of juice. Crisp foods are introduced gradually: Bacon, raw celery, lettuce, and strips of carrot are finger foods, which children enjoy and can feel and see.

Foods to be avoided are corn, peanuts, nuts, large seeds, cherry pits, bits of tough fruit skin (as from plums), and the gristle around bones, especially chicken bones. Any of them can easily be inhaled into the windpipe and cause serious trouble. Seeds and pits of fruit should be removed. Plums and peaches should be peeled.

Sugar, candy, jams, jellies, cake frosting, and bottled soft drinks, which provide only calories, should be avoided. Their sweetness cloys the palate quickly, and the child is not hungry for other foods. Such foods should be given only on special occasions and then at the end of a meal.

PSYCHOLOGICAL FACTORS are as important in the nutrition of toddlers as they are in the nutrition of infants and adults. As the child becomes able to move about independently, his independence increases toward other things. He wishes to do more and more for himself. Yet he is easily discouraged. It helps, of course, if the parents have good eating habits and manners, for young children tend to imitate them. Imitation, however, is not so reliable a guide for the young child who is learning to eat as is a constant, patient effort to help him to develop his own eating skills and habits.

When the child first wishes to feed himself, he should be given a spoon and helped to learn to use it. A large bib is essential. The spoon will often be turned upside down before it reaches the child's mouth. Mother, with her spoon, rescues the mouthful and feeds it. The toddler should never be scolded for unsuccessful attempts.

Infants are great dawdlers. Their attention is easily distracted. They need repeated assistance to bring their attention back to eating. The child may become exhausted with the effort of feeding himself and need to be aided to ingest sufficient food for his needs. On the other hand, deliberate playing with the food or throwing it on the floor means that he is not hungry. The food should be removed quietly.

New foods are introduced in small amounts at first. It is helpful if the young child sees the rest of the family eating the new food with enjoyment. Small children often will eat even highly flavored foods if they see others enjoying them; they often refuse bland foods if a member of the family comments unfavorably.

The family table is not the place to teach manners by scolding, but by imitation. It is a place for pleasant conversation and the enjoyment of good food. Good eating habits and good manners in eating are most easily achieved at this age. The time to train is while the child is interested and proud of his achievements.

Often a mother gets overconcerned because her child's appetite seems inadequate to meet his nutritional needs. His servings seem so small. Children 2 to 3 years old also may eat very little for several days and then make up for it by eating heartily for a while. Other children seem hungry only once a day and eat little at other meals. If the adults of the family checked themselves as carefully as they do the young child, they would find their own eating patterns variable. A healthy child permitted adequate exercise rarely will undereat consistently.

Most children, if permitted to do so, can feed themselves almost entirely by 18 months of age. The child should be comfortably seated at proper height from the table. Proper food should be set before him, and he should not be constantly urged to eat.

On the other hand, eating is an exhausting process. He may tire before he has eaten sufficient for his needs, and mother must aid him. Such aid can be given quietly.

In short, calm and sympathetic interest on the parents' part, without either overprotection or excessive rigidity of regimen, will give the best results in training the child to eat alone, as it does in other phases of child training.

GENEVIEVE STEARNS *was research professor in the Department of Pediatrics, State University of Iowa, for many years. She is now research professor emerita in the Department of Orthopedic Surgery of that institution.*

Between Infancy and Adolescence

MIRIAM E. LOWENBERG

A CHILD'S growth in height and weight comes in spurts. Other kinds of growth take place between those spurts. The growth also is vital in the building of a sturdy, healthy body: The child is learning to live in his world. He is having mental and emotional experiences. He is forming patterns of eating and attitudes toward food that will influence him throughout his life.

Mothers and fathers recognize the importance of the diet in the first years and often worry therefore when their child does not eat what they think he should.

Or just the opposite: In times of frustration, they adopt the attitude, "Let him entirely alone, and he will eat what he wants," believing that in some strange way the child will begin to eat the food he needs.

Neither leads to success. Rather, one has to take a close look at the demands for growth and—even more important—to study children and to understand their drives and needs.

We then come to the point of view that happy, hungry children will eat

296

and grow. As we study the child, we also recognize that he has many things to learn in order to eat acceptably. Limits there certainly are on how one eats, be he 8 or 80.

Adults set the stage for children's eating for good or ill, and parents do have a function to perform in regard to children's eating.

Dr. and Mrs. C. Anderson Aldrich, in *Feeding Our Old-Fashioned Children*, stated the functions of parents thus: "Parents are meant to enter the feeding situation for three reasons: First, to provide food; second, to support a child's progress from simple to mature methods of eating; and, third, to make it easy for him to establish his own satisfying feeding habits."

First, the foods that the growing bodies need.

We have only to follow a 2-year-old around for a few hours to know that his needs for energy are high. Children of all ages running, jumping, and playing hard in a playground often tire adults just to think of the energy being used up.

The child 1 to 3 years old, according

to the recommended daily allowances of the National Academy of Sciences-National Research Council, needs 1,300 Calories a day. That is twice as many Calories as the normal, moderately active man needs or uses in relation to the relative body weight of each of these ages.

Boys 13 to 15 years old, whose average weight is listed as 108 pounds, use almost as many Calories (3,100 Calories) as the normal, moderately active man (3,200) whose average weight at 25 years is considered to be 154 pounds.

Children also need proteins, vitamins, and minerals in amounts that are greater in relation to body weight. The National Research Council recommends that children 1 to 3 years old have daily 40 grams of protein; at 4 to 6 years, 50 grams; at 7 to 9 years, 60 grams; and 10 to 12 years, 70 grams.

A man weighing approximately 6 times as much as the child of 1 to 3 years needs only about 1.7 times as much protein.

The adolescent of 10 to 12 years needs as much protein as the man, whose average weight is about one and one-half times as much.

It is recommended that children 1 to 9 years old have 1.0 gram of calcium a day and 1.2 grams a day at 10 to 12 years. The adult body, however, may be kept in positive balance with 0.8 gram of calcium a day.

For iron, the daily recommendation for the child of 1 to 3 years old is 7 milligrams. The grown man and woman are listed as needing 10 milligrams and 12 milligrams, respectively. If we again compare the relative size of the average child of this age to an adult man or woman, we see that the need for iron also is relatively high.

Storage of some nutrients, such as iron and calcium, should be taking place during the period of growth. This storage cannot take place on inadequate diets—a matter of concern to those who guide the feeding of young children.

ALTHOUGH NUTRITIONISTS must reckon with the needs for nutrients in terms of grams and milligrams, the translation of these quantitative needs into the actual foods eaten daily is much more meaningful to those of us who are not technicians.

How, then, can we check growing children's diets to make certain that they are getting the materials they need for growth? To do this, we need to look at groups of foods that together furnish all the needed essentials in the total day's food.

Important to remember is that a good way to be sure of having an adequate diet is to provide a wide variety of foods.

Protein-high foods, including milk, meat, eggs, fish, and poultry, must bulk large in the child's diet.

Besides milk, the child needs at least one good serving of meat, poultry, or fish at one meal each day. The amount may vary from a 2-ounce portion for children 1 to 4 years old to a man-size serving of at least one-fourth pound for the hungry child of 6 to 13 years.

Eggs, which contribute a goodly share of iron as well as protein, should be considered in planning the child's diet.

Because milk and milk products contain more calcium than other foods, the child should have 3 to 4 cups of milk a day. Later I discuss ways of getting children to drink milk.

Fruit and vegetables are important for children because they furnish minerals, such as iron, vitamins A and C, and a goodly amount of several of the B vitamins.

Because children in the United States get less vitamin A than they need, we must direct special attention to including in their meals dark-green and yellow vegetables, such as broccoli, leaf lettuce, collards, kale, spinach, escarole, curly endive, carrots, sweetpotatoes, yams, and winter squash.

Tomatoes, cream, butter, and fortified margarine also add a goodly amount to the vitamin A in the diet. Liver is especially high in vitamin A.

A 2-ounce portion yields more than twice the average daily recommendation for the growing child.

Many investigations have disclosed that American children do not get enough vitamin C, largely because they do not eat enough citrus fruit, tomatoes, raw cabbage, raw fruit, and vegetables.

In planning meals for children, parents ought to give special attention to including the following each day:

Milk in each meal, as a drink, if possible;

Another protein-high food, such as meat, fish, poultry, cheese, or an egg, in each meal;

At least one serving of a raw fruit and a raw vegetable in each meal. Special attention should be given to citrus fruit and juices (canned, fresh, or frozen) and tomato juice;

At least two good servings of cooked vegetables, especially dark-green and bright-yellow vegetables;

Three to four servings of enriched or whole-grain cereals and breads;

Mildly sweet desserts, which mostly contain either milk and eggs or fruit or a combination of them;

A vitamin D preparation.

We need to know how to help children to eat happily the foods they need. I mention here only the foods that are hard to get children to eat enough of.

MANY CHILDREN do not like all vegetables. If we are to do something about it, we need to understand what children do like and why.

Children generally like crisp, raw vegetables better than cooked vegetables. If young children develop a habit of eating raw vegetables and if their parents eat salads with at least the appearance of enjoyment, the child usually will eat raw vegetables well.

As soon as children can chew pieces of raw carrots or celery, leaves of green lettuce, wedges of raw cabbage, and other crisp foods, they should appear in at least one meal a day—preferably two.

Even if young children may prefer raw vegetables, however, they cannot eat enough of them to get the nutrients we expect from vegetables.

As we study the eating patterns of children, we get clues as to what they do and do not like about cooked vegetables.

I have observed that the most important factor probably is flavor. Children in general have keener senses of taste and smell than adults. Strong flavors and odors in some of the vegetables may be really obnoxious to young children. The sulfurous vegetables, such as cabbage, onions, and turnips, become more popular with children when they are cooked in an excess of water, so that much of the strong flavor is washed away. Some valuable food nutrients are lost in doing this, but that loss may be less important than that children eat them.

Texture of vegetables is important. A child prefers celery or green beans that do not have tough strings on them and carrots that are tender. He finds tough parts difficult to manage, and he will not bother with them. When he first encounters sticks of raw celery and finds part of it inedible, he has no past memory of the food to tell him that some celery does not have tough strings on it. It requires only a small amount of effort by the parent to choose frozen or canned green beans that do not have strings in them or to remove them from fresh beans. It is easy to break a piece of celery in two and remove the strings.

The consistency of vegetables is another point. Many children refuse dry or gummy mashed potatoes and dry baked potatoes. Because they prefer their food lukewarm in temperature, mashed potatoes that were soft and fluffy when hot may become too dry or gummy when the child lets them cool to lukewarm.

The combination of vegetables also should be thought of in planning meals for children. They find it hard to eat at one time two vegetables that are not well liked.

Cooked, dried lima beans and beets, for instance, make a poor combination from this standpoint—but a child may eat willingly even a large serving of fluffy mashed potatoes with a small serving of tender, cubed, buttered beets.

NOT ALL children dislike all vegetables. There are some cooked vegetables that even a finicky child does like, and because we have such an array of dark-green, bright-yellow, and other vegetables, it is always possible to find some that any child likes.

Adults should not become discouraged and stop serving vegetables because some are unpopular, because that leads to inadequacies in children's diets. At times, however, when the mother does become discouraged, she can give her children fruit in place of vegetables: Waning young appetites often perk up when only fruit appears on the child's dinner plate.

FRUIT generally is popular with young children, although for some children 2 to 4 years old some fruit, especially orange and grapefruit juices, may be too acid in flavor. Dilution with water or even blending in a small amount of some sweetening, such as honey, may take off this sting.

Children seem to prefer combinations of fruit that include some mild, sweet fruits, like cooked or raw peaches or pears and fresh, tart fruit, like oranges, pineapple, and grapefruit.

A young child likes to choose what he wants for his dessert from a plate of pieces of raw apple, sections of oranges, slices of banana, wedges of fresh pineapple, and pieces of other fruit, such as peaches.

The child also appreciates being able to choose from a plate of raw vegetable pieces or even the color he wants in a fruited gelatin.

SOME CHILDREN find drinking even 2 cups of milk a day too much. Adults who can manage to make the child feel successful when he drinks only an ounce of milk from a tiny glass find that success leads to further success as it does in so many other segments of life and among so many of us.

Among a group of children up to 5 years old who were physically healthy and those whose patterns of drinking milk were observed, the amount of milk taken daily declined after age 2. When the children became of school age, they again increased their consumption of milk. We can expect that many children of these ages will drink less milk than they did earlier. If mothers expect such a development and allow them to drink as much as they want, with neither direct nor indirect forcing, the children will not become unfriendly toward milk as a food.

IN MY OBSERVATIONS of the milk-drinking tendencies of thousands of children in nursery schools, I have found that the amount a child takes is related directly to the temperature of the milk. The child of 2, 3, or often 4 years prefers his milk lukewarm and not icy cold.

In two large nursery schools conducted for the children of workers in a shipyard during the war, the milk sometimes was served ice cold when the kitchen workers had not followed directions. Far less milk was drunk on those days. On days the supervisor checked carefully to be sure that the milk was at room temperature, each child drank 8 ounces of milk at a meal without any urging.

I have verified this in my work with mothers and in feeding children in their homes. I believe, therefore, that attention to temperature is important in giving milk to children 2 to 6 years old. I found that children had come to appreciate cold milk at about 5 or 6 years (sometimes even at 4 years).

Another factor of seeming importance in serving milk to children in groups is the way in which the milk is offered to them. Small glasses that hold about three-fourths of a measuring cup of milk when full have been found to be best. These can be poured about two-thirds full. This gives only 4 ounces, or about one-half of a measuring cup of milk in the serving. One glass presented with the main part of the meal and one given with dessert may be taken readily by most of the children in a group. The small glasses are easily handled by small hands, and the goal looks possible to the young child.

The child who cannot drink milk easily can be given Cheddar-type cheese and cottage cheese and extra portions of meat, eggs, fish, and poultry. Certainly he should not be forced to drink milk, and the mother should not transfer to him her concern or worry about the lack of milk.

With this, as with other foods (and other people), it is not unusual for a young child to ride a food hobby. Some days he wants several eggs. Some days or weeks he may want a lot of meat.

If the family diet is varied and is built on milk and dairy products, meat, eggs, fish, poultry, vegetables, and fruit, and enriched and whole-grain cereals, the child cannot go far wrong as he goes on food jags. Only when highly sweetened foods are chosen as the exclusive food by a young child do we have to be concerned about him as an erratic eater.

When the child is served slightly less than the adult thinks he will eat, he has a chance to be successful. This rule also holds for all foods for most children. Children also like to set their own goals by pouring their milk from small pitchers, and they often drink more when they pour it themselves.

Forced feeding is or should be a dead issue. It leads nowhere. Yet the adult who sets the stage for children's eating must always have future goals in mind, as does a high school football coach when he compliments an inexperienced freshman candidate for the team.

Some milk can be "eaten" in drinkable soups, custards, puddings, and cereals or vegetables cooked in milk.

Nonfat dried milk can be added to many cooked foods. We may count about 4 tablespoons of dried milk as equal in nutritive value to a cup of skim milk. It can be used to fortify many foods, such as gravies, sauces, puddings, and cooked starchy vegetables. Cheddar cheese and cottage cheese, often eaten by children who refuse to drink milk, add to the protein, calcium, and riboflavin content of the day's food. Many times interruptions in drinking milk are just a temporary whim; if other foods are substituted for milk and no special attention is called to it, the child comes back to liking it again.

Children usually like meats, fish, and poultry that are tender and mild in flavor and do not require much chewing. Ground meats, which need little chewing, are the most popular. Next in popularity are small strips of meat, which the child can pick up in his fingers and eat.

Children in general, be they 2 or 12 years of age, prefer light seasonings, especially of spices, in meat dishes.

CHILDREN differ in their patterns of hunger. Some are satisfied with three meals, yet many young children need a midmorning and midafternoon meal. Well-spaced and regular meals satisfy the child physically and emotionally and prevent fatigue.

Of all the factors involved, tiredness is the most defeating to a good appetite. Often the child who seems not to be hungry is a tired child. Meals so spaced that food is given when he is hungry help prevent emotional upsets that follow fatigue. Many preschool and most school children therefore need a food, such as milk or fruit, at midmorning and a substantial lunch, such as a protein-loaded sandwich with milk or fruit, in midafternoon.

Children often consume as much as 10 to 17 percent of their total day's calories in snacks. Milk drunk 2 hours before a meal does not usually interfere with the appetite at mealtime. It is wise, therefore, to consider the foods eaten between the three regular meals as important.

Children choose as snacks the foods that are readily available and freely offered. A mother, as the gatekeeper of her family's food, has in snacks an excellent opportunity to influence her children's eating habits.

Any snack food that can be proudly placed by a conscientious adult on a child's table in an attractive cover will satisfy the requirements of a good snack. Snacks eaten outside the home with the gang are less nutritious foods than those eaten in the home. From them a mother can get a clue as to how to handle snacks. Children whose hunger is satisfied at home with good food have less drive to buy the so-called empty-calorie foods—the ones that supply calories and nothing else.

Children thrive on regularity and rhythm of routines. This applies to regular meals and food between meals. The child who knows that he will have a meal at 11:30 a.m. or 5:30 p.m., when he is usually hungry, has a basis for the sense of security he needs. Because he is dependent on adults, he needs to know what to expect.

Adults can help children by setting mealtimes when children are really hungry, insofar as all members of a family can fit into the schedule. That does not mean meals at all hours. Rather, it means that the 2- or 3-year-old needs special consideration when other family members must have meals 4 or 5 hours apart. Many young children cannot go that long without food. Snacks or between-meal foods therefore are necessary for many children.

BREAKFAST commonly is the day's poorest meal. Children who skip breakfasts are less well fed than those who regularly eat breakfasts. In other words, children do not generally make up at other meals the nutrients which they miss in skipped breakfasts. We have indications from research studies that the children who do not eat breakfast do less well in school, perform physical tasks less well, and may be more irritable and emotionally unstable.

The breakfast pattern (as well as total nutritive intake) tends to become progressively worse from the early elementary school years to adolescence. Girls in general eat less well than boys.

Poor breakfasts often have been blamed on lack of hunger, rushing to get to school, no regular family breakfast time, and dislike of the foods commonly served at breakfast. Young children give the same reasons as do their parents. Only by placing the blame where it belongs and by removing the underlying causes can we solve the problem.

Nutritionists who have compared groups of children who eat nutritionally adequate breakfasts with those who do not find that the former feel less rushed, enjoy eating breakfast with their families, and appreciate the fact that their mother prepares an appealing breakfast.

Efforts to lessen the tensions of the overorganized life of the young child and to serve the breakfasts that appeal to him are positive ways in which to improve his breakfast habits.

Our breakfasts have become too trite in pattern. No one needs to eat an egg and toast or cooked cereal for breakfast every day to be well nourished. A ham sandwich, a hamburger in a bun made of enriched flour, or a toasted cheese sandwich are excellent foods, which many children seem to prefer.

To be adequate, breakfast need only contain a protein-high food, at least one food for energy, some milk, and a piece of fruit or a serving of fruit juice. Many families find that the habit of having fruit high in vitamin C or fruit juice at breakfast insures that such a food is included in the day's meals. Children who regularly have a vitamin C fruit at breakfast very likely have good diets in general, perhaps because the informed and conscientious mother who includes such a fruit in the breakfast is giving greater care to the planning of adequate meals for her family. If the fruit is preferred at another time and is eaten regularly some time or other every day, there is no need to include it in the breakfast.

Some nutritionists believe that breakfast served at school is an answer. Some schools that have tried this plan report that the children and the teachers are enthusiastic about the idea.

THE NOON MEAL should receive its full share of attention.

An adequate lunch for a child must have a protein-high food, some foods for energy, and some mineral and vitamin-high foods.

Time to eat without hurry at school or at home and a dining area or lunchroom suited to the tempo and needs of children of different ages are important considerations. Everyone knows that foods hastily purchased over the counter to be eaten without sitting down, or grabbed at home, do not often furnish the needed nutrients.

THE EVENING MEAL often is the best one of the day, but even so food prejudices and dislikes sometimes keep it from being adequate. Meals planned for nutritional adequacy, time to eat and enjoy food at meals, a chance to choose a varied diet from the many foods available, and absence of stress and anxiety are well worth striving for.

Children vary in the amounts of food which they can take comfortably at one time. As I said, children are happier and eat better when they are served slightly less than they are expected to eat and are given a chance to ask for seconds.

To follow the principles of the self-regulation of diet by infants, one should allow a child 2 to 13 years old to determine how much of a food he will eat at a certain time.

This advice must of course be tempered with reason. In one research study we learned of children who, unguided, ate nine hard-cooked eggs at a meal. Of course, mothers or lunch supervisors cannot provide unusual amounts of a given food at a time. Children can learn that circumstances set reasonable limits.

A parent's attitudes are important. The parent who expects the child to eat fosters good eating habits—probably because the child is relaxed when he knows that meals are happy occasions. The child also is allowed to continue to regard food as good, because it eases the pain of hunger. He learns this from the time of the first hunger pains after he is born.

If every time he is hungry, an understanding adult, usually his mother, gives him food and shows warmth and affection as she does it, he learns that food is good.

Only when the sequence is broken do other ideas concerning food enter his mind. If he and the other members of his family enjoy and expect to enjoy food, good food habits are fostered. It takes thought, knowledge, and the desire to give all members of the family lastingly good attitudes about eating.

Children from families of higher economic levels may have better diets than children of poorer families. It is true, though, that the mother's experience and knowledge is more important than the economic level of the family in this regard.

More consideration may well be given to making children comfortable at the family table and in the school lunchroom. Also, if children are to learn to be acceptable members of a group at meals, they need to be included in the conversation for at least a part of the time. At about the age of 6 years, a child can be helped to learn how to fit into the group at the table. He can be helped to understand how to handle food dislikes so that he does not make an unpleasant display of them. Many children at this age are becoming socially conscious and want to be acceptable to the group.

MIRIAM E. LOWENBERG *is Head, Department of Foods and Nutrition, College of Home Economics, The Pennsylvania State University, University Park, Pa.*

Adolescents and Young Adults

CLARA A. STORVICK AND MARGARET L. FINCKE

THE girl and boy in adolescence grow at a faster rate than at any other time except in infancy. A boy's nutritional requirements during the time he is becoming a man are higher than at any other time in his life. Those of a girl are exceeded only during pregnancy and lactation.

Preparation begins a little before adolescence. The child stores energy in the form of body fat—the most concentrated form of fuel. The coming spurt of growth will take enormous amounts of energy—too much to take in while the most active growth is going on.

The year after that, the boy suddenly shoots up and may gain as much as 4 inches in height and 15 pounds in weight in a year. The girl also grows fast, but her total gain in height may not be quite so large.

The girl generally experiences this spurt in growth before the boy and usually is taller than he is at about 12 to 14 years. Then the more mature boy begins to surpass the girl in height, and by 15 years the average boy is taller than the average girl. She starts her increased rate of growth sooner, but she does not attain so great a final height or continue to grow for so many years.

This pattern of growth is an individual matter. Some adolescents start increased growth early and stop soon. Others do not show the real increase in height until 2 or 3 years after others of the same chronological age. Chronological age and physiological age thus may not always coincide.

Growth is more complex than increase in height alone. While fat is lost, bones increase in density and muscles in size and strength, especially among boys.

Endocrine systems—the glands that secrete internally—are growing and developing also, perhaps at their own rates, which may be somewhat different from the rate of growth of bone and muscle.

The whole body takes on additional size and development—except the nervous system (including the brain) and the lymphatic system.

Adolescence, then, is a period of stress—physical, physiological, psychological, emotional, and social. Rapid growth alone causes strain and stress. But the period of rapid growth is relatively short—2 or 3 years—while the other maturing developments go on for 8 years or more. Gain in weight continues as growth of muscle and greater hardness of bone occur.

INTEREST in adequate nutrition of adolescents and young adults is reflected in the number and kind of studies to determine their nutritional requirements.

Research workers in universities and colleges, hospitals, health agencies, the United States Public Health Service, and the Department of Agriculture have used various methods in their investigations. Surveys of large numbers of children have been designed to obtain information on nutritional status based on food habits and the intake of nutrients and calories. Some of the surveys have included biochemical tests to determine the concentration of nutrients in blood and urine.

More detailed studies have been made of smaller groups, who have been maintained for definite periods on diets of known nutrient content to determine the actual requirements of specific nutrients for various age groups.

The nutrient requirements thus determined include those for protein and the constituent amino acids, calcium, iron, vitamin A, vitamin C (ascorbic acid), vitamin B_1 (thiamine), vitamin B_2 (riboflavin), niacin, and calories.

Not all nutrient requirements have been established for all age groups, because generally it is not possible or feasible to determine the requirement for more than one nutrient at a time.

FUNDAMENTAL to the understanding of what constitutes an adequate diet is the recognition of the physiological role of various nutrients in the body.

Energy requirement is expressed in calories, and our need for them is affected by age, size, activity, rate of growth, and such physiological stress as recovery from certain severe illnesses.

Protein is a constituent of all body cells. The nutritional value of a protein is determined by the amino acids that compose it, for from them we must build all of the proteins required for the growth and maintenance of our various tissues.

Fat is our most concentrated source of calories and is essential to the transport and absorption of the fat-soluble vitamins. Many fats are rich sources of these vitamins and of the nutritionally essential fatty acids, linoleic and arachidonic.

Carbohydrate may furnish 50 percent or more of the calories. In general, it provides energy in a form quickly available to the body and is essential for the complete metabolism of fat.

Fruit and vegetables, which we generally classify by carbohydrate content, and breads and cereals, which are among our richest and cheapest sources of carbohydrate, also provide some minerals and vitamins.

In planning the adolescent's diet, attention should be given to the needs for calcium, iron, and iodine, since they are the ones most likely to be present in insufficient amounts. If the diet is planned to provide adequate amounts of them, the same foods will provide enough of the other minerals.

THE RECOMMENDED dietary allowances are guides to the maintenance of good nutrition. You can calculate your own intakes of the different nutrients by referring to the tables of composition of foods that begin on page 243.

We must remember in using the table of recommended allowances that all of these nutrients can be stored in the body, at least for a short time. It is therefore not necessary to ingest quite all these amounts every day. Sometimes it is possible to average several days' intakes to reach the recommended daily amounts. For instance, one day we may eat a serving of turnip greens, which provide 10 thousand I.U. (International Units) of vitamin A; the next day, a serving of peas with 900 I.U.; and the third day, green beans, which have 800 I.U. These, together with other vegetables and fruit, milk fat, and eggs easily can provide the 5 thousand I.U. recommended.

Likewise the adolescent girl who is predisposed to simple iron-deficiency anemia and needs to be especially concerned about her iron intake may find that if she eats liver occasionally, along with eggs and green vegetables, she will increase her average intake of iron to the amount recommended.

BOYS 13 TO 15 YEARS OLD need no more calories than they will as moderately active young men and no more vitamin A, thiamine, or niacin.

They do need more protein, calcium, iron, riboflavin, and ascorbic acid.

The boy who is between 16 and 19 years old needs somewhat more calories than his older or younger brother, but his needs for protein, thiamine, riboflavin, niacin, and ascorbic acid are considerably greater.

The teen-age girl likewise has increased nutritional needs over her moderately active older sister. As the girl starts her growth spurt earlier than the boy and stops sooner, she needs more calories when she is 13 to 15 and fewer in the later teens as she approaches the adult level. Her requirements for protein, calcium, iron, riboflavin, and ascorbic acid all through the teens continue to stay well above the adult level.

The diet has to be planned carefully then, for both boys and girls. Both have such great needs for protein, the B vitamins, and vitamin C that they cannot afford to let many of their calories come from foods that do not contribute those three.

A boy usually manages to make a better selection of food than a girl, probably because his appetite is so great that if the food is available he will eat it. He may be inclined to neglect the foods containing vitamin C, however.

A girl's appetite is more capricious and varies from day to day. She is more likely to get enough vitamin C because of her liking for salads and fruit, but her protein and iron intakes may be low.

Foods containing calcium, vitamin A, and riboflavin often are neglected by both boys and girls.

SOME SORT OF FOOD PLAN seems necessary in order to avoid the haphazardness of blind choice.

The younger child who eats all his meals at home is influenced by the family's habits.

The adolescent, however, usually eats at least one meal a day away from home. He must now exercise his own choice, and his good choice or bad choice will have far-reaching effects on his good health, stamina, and mental stability.

The girl who exercises her choice wisely gains in attractiveness and the good looks that come from an inner glow that we can attribute to a healthy body and mind. Even at home, differences in choice are possible and often are made.

Adolescents need more than three meals a day, especially while the greatest growth is taking place.

Much of this food is eaten as snacks, away from home or at home after school, while preparing the next day's lessons, or before bedtime. The snacks can contribute to the overall nutritive needs, or they can provide empty calories with little else in the way of nutrients.

There is no one set of menus which will suit everybody. Certain general guides can be offered, however. If the adolescent chooses from the following food groups, his choices will probably add up to a good whole.

For the teen-age boy or girl, the following are suggested:

Milk group—four or more cups a day;

meat group—two or more servings a day;

vegetable-fruit group—four or more servings a day—including a dark-green or a deep-yellow vegetable at least every other day; a citrus fruit or other fruit or vegetable important for vitamin C—one or more every day; other fruits and vegetables, including potatoes;

bread-cereals group—four or more servings each day.

The milk group consists of whole milk, skim milk, buttermilk, cheese, ice cream, milk sherbet, and milkshakes. Milk contributes liberal amounts of riboflavin and good-quality protein and a large share of the calcium.

The meat group contains meats of all kinds, poultry, fish, eggs, dry beans, peas, and nuts. It is well to use pork in some form, including sausage or ham, two or three times a week because it is an outstanding source of thiamine. All meats are good sources of iron, niacin, and riboflavin, but the organ meats— liver, heart, kidney—supply much more of these nutrients than muscle meats and can well be used sometimes. Pea soup, baked beans, peanuts or pea-nut butter, chili and lima beans, gar-banzos, black-eyed peas, and other legumes belong in this group, too, even though they do not supply quite so much protein or protein of as good quality as meat, poultry, fish, and eggs.

The vegetable-fruit group includes a wide variety of foods, and one that cannot be neglected if good nutrition is to be attained. The deep green of spinach, kale, chard, turnip, and mus-tard greens and the dark yellow of car-rots, winter squash, and yams indicate their value as sources of vitamin A.

Besides the citrus fruits, strawberries, cantaloup and other melons, guavas, and generous servings of tomato, cer-tain vegetables, such as broccoli, greens, and red and green peppers, give us our largest amounts of vitamin C. The vegetables can lose their vita-min C much more easily than the fruits, especially if they are partly wilted or are cooked a long time.

The adolescent will get some of his vitamin C from potatoes and other fruits and vegetables, but his require-ments for ascorbic acid are so high that it is hard to get enough of the vita-min without liberal choices from this whole group of fruits and vegetables, with major emphasis on citrus fruit and tomatoes.

The bread and cereals group empha-sizes whole-grain and enriched prod-ucts. They may be yeast breads of various kinds, quick breads, pancakes and waffles, cooked and dry cereals, hominy, tortillas, noodles, macaroni, or anything else made from wheat, rye, corn, or rice. The package should tell whether it is 100-percent whole wheat, enriched flour or bread, or an enriched corn product.

Of course, many adolescent boys— and girls, too—may eat much more than the four servings recommended in the foregoing plan. The older girl who is more sedentary may not wish quite that much. It should be remem-bered, however, that this food group constitutes one of our best sources of thiamine and iron. It also adds much protein and niacin.

Other foods to make up the rest of the calories can be chosen partly from these four groups and partly from other foods. Some fat is needed.

Sugar makes some foods more pal-atable. If too much sugar and fat are used, though, they crowd out some of the other foods.

It does not matter how the foods are used during the day. Some people feel that the day has not started right un-less there are eggs for breakfast. Other people like eggs better for lunch or as custards and other cooked dishes.

Snacks can also follow the needs and preferences of the individual boy or girl. A cheese sandwich may satisfy the boy after school. A glass of milk may be enough for the girl. Fruit be-tween meals rarely spoils the appetite for the next meal, but chocolate cake might. The important thing is to rec-ognize snacks as real meals and see that they fit into the overall plan.

Breakfast is an important meal and needs a little thought. It need not be hot, but it should contain some of the protein foods and usually some form of fruit. Some bread and butter, milk, and an apple make a better breakfast than unenriched pancakes with sirup and coffee, although there is nothing wrong with the latter plan if you add some milk and egg or meat to get good-quality protein. Many families serve the main source of vitamin C in the morning; if it is not eaten then, it may be neglected for the day. But there is no reason why we should not have oranges at lunch or peppers with the evening meal.

Weekends are times when food habits are often different. The adolescent may sleep late on Saturday. The family's Sunday meals may be quite different from the rest of the week. Therefore we need to make our choices carefully.

We once knew a junior ski champion of the Northwest. During the skiing season, which lasted from Thanksgiving through April, she went to the mountains every Saturday and Sunday and skied so hard she did not take time for meals. Then from Monday to Friday each week she tried to gain back the weight she had lost, but it was always a losing battle. By the end of the season she was painfully thin and needed the summer to recover. She was 18 at the time and was not storing up the nutrients she needed for the future.

THE YOUNG ADULT, 20 to 25 years old, very likely has stopped growing in height, although his muscles, bones, and other tissues are still growing in size and function. He is setting his adult eating habits, which probably will last him throughout life.

The recommended food plan for the young man and the nonpregnant young woman consists of the same food groups as we have given, but with smaller amounts of milk. Two or more cups a day are recommended for the young adult in place of the four or more for the teen-ager.

Activity often drops markedly when the young man begins his professional life. His need for calories also declines, and the need for the other nutrients

reaches a plateau. The boy who plays football in high school does not always change his food habits as quickly as his occupation, however, and an excess of energy-producing foods leads to overweight.

The girl may continue her general regime of bodily activity as she enters the twenties, or she may become more active as she assumes more responsibility for a home and family. In either event, the young man or woman can tell whether total calories are right by watching body weight.

The young man often gains a few pounds up to the age of 25.

The young woman is more likely to be underweight during adolescence and can well add a few pounds to give her the necessary vigor for the responsibilities of adult life.

In neither case should the gains in weight take the young adult beyond the desirable point of optimum weight for himself or herself.

THE SAME GENERAL meal plans as those used by adolescents meet the requirements and desires of young adults, except that their need for snacks in addition to the three meals is considerably less.

Food patterns for many young men and women have changed in the past few years with the establishment of the coffee break as a part of the workday. No longer must the workers last until lunchtime if they have left home without breakfast. They stay hungry only until 10 o'clock, when they can get a sweet roll or doughnut. Here is an example of changing food habits for the worse, as they now eat the "empty calories" of sweet bakery goods in place of fruit, milk, and other foods of high nutritive value.

The coffee break is advantageous from the standpoint of lessening fatigue and increasing production, but it will not take the place of a regular, good breakfast. It might be well, then, to make the coffee break consist just of coffee or to have the fruit juice then instead of at breakfast.

Heights and Weights of Adolescents Arranged According to Percentiles [1]

	Percentiles							
	10		*30*		*70*		*90*	
Age (years)	*Height, inches*	*Weight, pounds*	*Height, inches*	*Weight, pounds*	*Height, inches*	*Weight, pounds*	*Height, inches*	*Weight, pounds*
				BOYS				
12	55. 7	71. 9	57. 5	79. 6	60. 0	92. 4	62. 1	109. 0
13	57. 6	77. 4	59. 7	86. 5	62. 6	103. 8	65. 0	122. 3
14	59. 8	86. 5	62. 3	98. 2	65. 6	118. 3	68. 0	137. 7
15	62. 2	99. 7	64. 7	111. 1	67. 8	132. 2	70. 0	149. 6
16	64. 1	111. 0	66. 2	121. 4	69. 0	141. 6	71. 2	158. 0
17	65. 1	117. 4	67. 0	127. 2	69. 7	148. 1	72. 0	164. 4
18	65. 5	120. 0	67. 3	129. 9	70. 0	152. 2	72. 2	169. 0
				GIRLS				
12	56. 2	69. 7	58. 2	80. 2	61. 2	95. 9	63. 3	111. 5
13	58. 6	80. 1	60. 7	91. 5	63. 3	108. 3	65. 1	124. 5
14	60. 2	91. 0	61. 9	101. 5	64. 2	116. 9	65. 8	133. 3
15	60. 9	97. 4	62. 6	106. 8	64. 6	121. 2	66. 3	138. 1
16	61. 3	100. 9	62. 8	110. 2	64. 8	124. 3	66. 6	141. 1
17	61. 4	102. 8	62. 9	112. 2	64. 9	126. 4	66. 7	143. 3
18	61. 5	103. 5	63. 0	113. 0	65. 0	127. 5	66. 7	144. 5

[1] Adapted from E. A. Martin: Roberts' Nutrition Work With Children, University of Chicago Press, 1954. For method of calculation, see American Journal of Public Health, vol. 39, pages 878–885, 1949. Heights were measured without shoes and weights without shoes, jackets, or sweaters.

PARTIES are an enjoyable and necessary part of living.

The food should be planned for its palatability and general attractiveness and for its nutritive value as well. Fruit punch is a better drink nutritionally than one made from sugar, acid, and artificial flavoring. Ice cream, homemade ice cream sodas, and milkshakes are popular and make use of the foods in the daily food plan. Hamburgers and frankfurters on a picnic can become a well-rounded meal if one adds vegetable relishes, fruit, and milk.

TOOTH DECAY is an important problem of adolescents and young adults. It has been estimated that 98 percent of us have some decayed teeth.

We do not know to what extent each nutrient of the diet affects the soundness of the teeth, but we do know something about the composition of the teeth and some of the factors that may have a bearing on the maintenance of sound teeth or which may reduce or inhibit tooth decay.

WE KNOW that sticky, sweet foods tend to accumulate between the teeth and on the tooth surfaces and provide materials for the growth of the acid-producing bacteria that lead to the destruction of the teeth through decay. It is well therefore to consider the quality and texture of desserts and between-meal items when it may not be convenient to brush the teeth immediately after eating. Such foods as carrots, apples, pears, melons, and berries have high nutritive value and tend to cleanse the teeth rather than adhere to them.

MARRIAGE may add further responsibilities—financial, emotional, and nutritional—to those the teen-ager already has.

The National Office of Vital Statistics reported that 31 percent of all first-born children in the United States in 1955 were born to women less than 20 years old. In the same year, 43 percent of all children were born to women under 25. Further physiological, psychological, and nutritional stress thus is added at a time when the strain of growth is already present.

Pregnancy adds considerably to the nutritive requirements. Larger amounts of protein, calcium, iron, and each of the vitamins are needed.

The amount and quality of the food the mother eats before her baby is born affects her own health during and after pregnancy. It also affects the condition of the baby at birth. The mother must supply all the nutrients in good amounts for good tissue to be produced.

If the mother does not provide them, the fetus can draw on the maternal reserves to a limited extent only, and the infant comes into the world handicapped by poor tissue formation, inadequate reserves, and less than a fair chance of growing into a healthy, happy child.

We know less about the influence of the state of nutrition of the father on the condition of the infant at birth, although we believe that there is a relationship. There are additional reasons why he should be in a good nutritive state, however. He is responsible for keeping himself in top physical condition while he assumes these added cares of wife and child. He must try to avoid illness, mental depression, and lack of zest. Good nutrition contributes enormously to good health in all its aspects.

As we know that it takes some time to build up reserves of nutrients that may have been depleted previously, the adolescent girl and boy need to stay in a good state of nutrition in order to be ready for these greater physiological demands of parenthood.

SEVERAL CONDITIONS interfere with our achieving good nutrition.

First, food habits are hard to change. Food is more than nourishment. It is related to sociability and the traditions of home. A certain kind of cake for birthdays, roast turkey for Thanksgiving, baked beans for Saturday night, or grits for breakfast all become part of living and represent something more than just food.

Not all food habits are bad and need to be broken. Some need just to be changed a little or timed a little better. Fudge may be made in the evening—after and not before dinner. Determination is required to overcome the habits of skipping breakfast or omitting vegetables or eating irregularly.

A modern form of belief in magic also may interfere with good nutrition. Advertisements are persuasive and attractive and give promise of great rewards: If you want to become strong, be thin, be good looking and magnetic, or attain any other desirable state, you need only read the advertisements to find some product that apparently will guarantee results. Reliable knowledge of what food can and cannot do for you is necessary. Even then, you must have a certain amount of resistance to help guard against promises of easy rewards.

Sometimes a chronic state of overweight interferes with the attainment of good nutrition, especially for a girl. She perceives her mother's consciousness of weight gain and resolves not to follow that pattern. Or else she is overweight and tries desperately to reduce. So she deliberately undereats.

This reduction of food intake needs to be done with care and under the advice of a physician. Her needs for protein, minerals, and vitamins are as high as they are for the girl who is of desirable weight. Three good meals a day with milk, meat, eggs, vegetables, fruits, and some bread and cereals are as important as ever. Foods high in calories are the ones to restrict.

UNDERWEIGHT is perhaps even more discouraging than overweight. Appetite is usually poor, and it is hard to eat. It is wise to consult a physician. An unrecognized infection or more serious condition may interfere with normal food intake or body functions.

Gaining weight calls for continuous effort. The only way to gain weight is to eat more than you need to maintain weight. Regular meals are most important. Between-meal food is important, too, but it must be of a kind that will not spoil the appetite for the next meal. Some fruit or a glass of milk taken after school will be digested quickly, but a rich dessert, although providing more calories, stays in the stomach longer and keeps you from eating enough at the next meal. Because milk drunk during or at the beginning of a meal may fill you up, you eat little else. You may find it is better for you to drink your milk between meals.

For those who do eat regularly and choose all the foods in the recommended plan, an extra piece of bread and butter at each meal may be all that is needed to start the gain in weight. Outdoor exercise and rest often give appetite. So does a calm frame of mind.

When you gain some weight, you will have more energy to carry out a full day's work and have some left over for social affairs. It is worth the real effort it takes.

Sometimes the economic status interferes with the attainment of good nutrition. There is a point in the expenditure of money below which we cannot go and still have a good food supply. It is possible, however, to choose within a food group and still attain a good diet.

As YET, we do not know all about nutrition and our nutritive needs. Studies are going on all over the world, and it is perfectly possible that more nutrients are still waiting to be discovered. Therefore we eat foods and not just vitamin capsules, for example, because the foods are more likely to contain the unknown substances than are mixtures of individual vitamins, valuable as these mixtures are under certain circumstances. In other words, oranges and peppers are something more than vitamin C dissolved in water and held together by cell structure.

CLARA A. STORVICK *joined the staff of the School of Home Economics and of the Oregon Agricultural Experiment Station, Oregon State College, Corvallis, Oreg., in 1945. In 1948 she was appointed professor of foods and nutrition and in 1955 was made chairman of Home Economics Research. Dr. Storvick has degrees from St. Olaf College, Iowa State College, and Cornell University. She has published a number of research papers on human metabolism of the various B vitamins and ascorbic acid.*

MARGARET L. FINCKE *joined the staff of the School of Home Economics, Oregon State College, in 1935. She was appointed professor of foods and nutrition in 1943 and became head of that department in 1944. Dr. Fincke has degrees from Mount Holyoke College and Columbia University.*

Some publications for teenagers:

"A Girl and Her Figure," by Ruth M. Leverton, National Dairy Council, Chicago, Ill., 1956.

"Food and You," by Edmund Sigurd Nassett, Barnes & Noble, Springfield, Ill., 1951.

"Nutrition for Health," by Holger Frederick Kilander, McGraw-Hill Book Co., Inc., New York, 1951.

Nutritional Needs After 25

PEARL SWANSON

MANY of us are aware of the changes in appearance, mental outlook, and body functions that occur as we pass from youth into middle age and then into old age.

Behind the outer changes we see in people as they grow older are changes in the body and in its workings. We know now that some of the adverse changes are due not to aging as such but to impaired nutrition of body cells so they cannot do the job they have to do.

We have to think therefore of an adult's nutrition in terms of the past, the present, and the future. His nutritional state at any specific age reflects his current food practices and all his previous dietary history. Poor eating habits in early life leave their imprints—some correctable, some noncorrectable in later years.

And, conversely, the nutritional state at any one interval foretells what kind of individual a person will be, nutritionally speaking, 10 or 25 or 40 years hence.

A good diet throughout one's life consequently is an insurance that carries many benefits. Good eating habits in early life will bring us a vigorous maturity. A continuance of them will extend our years of usefulness and delay—and, in some instances, even prevent—the appearance of many of the so-called characteristics of old age.

The older a person grows, the longer and more complex is his dietary history. The variations in nutritional status and dietary needs of a group of adults thus are bound to be greater than corresponding variations in a group of young people. Recommendations for the food needs of this age group must be pointed especially to the needs of individuals.

The same nutritional principles that describe adequate diets for earlier periods of life apply to the diets of adults. Even though the adult has grown up—matured—his basic food supply still must provide all the nutrients necessary for maintaining body structure and for operating its machinery.

The difference between these processes in the mature and the young

311

person is largely one of intensity. Preserving the integrity of body tissue replaces the more active processes of growth and maintenance characteristic of youth. Some metabolic activities are slowed, and food needs decrease. There may be less demand for nutrients used in the manufacture of important substances in the body that control and regulate metabolism.

The adult's diet nevertheless must still supply all the energy-producing foods, the protein-rich foods, and the vitamin- and mineral-carrying foods.

The approximate amounts of food energy and nutrients essential to adult well-being in the United States have been estimated by the National Academy of Sciences-National Research Council for persons of different ages and activity. The recommendations apply to the needs of groups of people and take into account the variations among people in any group. They are generally higher than average requirements, for they include a margin of safety.

For that reason we must use these dietary allowances carefully when we try to assess an individual's nutrition. A diet pattern that provides over a period of time a substantially lower amount of any nutrient than recommended, however, is likely to be inadequate for many individuals.

ESTIMATES of how well people are eating are based on knowledge of what they are eating. This information has been obtained from surveys of food intakes of various groups of adults.

A food survey is a research device designed to get a comprehensive picture of what a number of persons, typical of a special group, eat.

Sometimes they were interviewed by the investigator and reported the kind and quantity of food they had eaten during the 24-hour period just preceding the interview. Sometimes the individuals kept records of the food they ate for a week or 10 days. Sometimes they weighed all food they ate for a definite period. Or again, they provided information in terms of a "diet history," in which the investigator established the kind and amounts of food customarily eaten over a period of time.

The data describing the food intakes of individuals participating in a survey are averaged, and mean figures are obtained of the amounts of food eaten and the nutrients supplied by the day's diet. A mean value always represents a central tendency and is made up of many values, some of which are high, some are low, and many are intermediate.

The results of eight surveys—some statewide in scope, others representative of specific groups—in which about 5 thousand persons in various parts of the United States cooperated afford a base for estimating the quality of diets chosen by adults. Mean values for food energy and the various nutrients furnished by the diets of men and women living in different places are remarkably similar, however, when the activity, sex, and age of the persons are taken into account.

In general, men choose diets that furnish nutrients (with the possible exception of calories) in amounts close to the recommended allowances of the National Research Council. The mean nutritive value of men's diets is higher than that of women's diets. All surveys reveal that mean values for calories and calcium fall short of the allowances in diets commonly chosen by women.

Mean data, however, because they are based on a collection of high, low, and middle values, may hide important facts and fail to disclose the real issue—in this instance, the number of people having poor diets. Estimates of the proportions of dietaries with specific nutrients lower than the recommended allowances may serve as a first approximation of the extent to which people choose inadequate diets. Data from a survey of food intakes of women in the North Central States in 1948 illustrate this point.

In the five States represented in the survey (2,085 women), the percentages of diets that provided less than the recommended allowances for calories, protein, calcium, ascorbic acid (vitamin C), and vitamin A were 75, 45, 80, 60, and 70, respectively.

The definition of the recommended allowances, however, does not permit us to assume that all individuals whose food contains less than 100 percent of the allowance of any nutrient are eating inadequate diets.

Nutritionists differ in what they consider poor diets. Some feel that the diets that furnish less than three-fourths of a recommended allowance may be very close to inadequacy. Others evaluate them in terms of two-thirds of the recommendations, or even one-half. In the north-central survey, nutritionists used 80 percent of the recommended allowances as the criterion.

On that basis they found that the diets of 68 percent of the 1,072 women interviewed in Iowa furnished less than 80 percent of the recommended daily allowance for calcium. The average daily calcium value of their diets was only 0.32 gram of calcium. The allowance is 0.8 gram a day.

The mean value for the protein content of the diets reported by the women appeared adequate—but we found that 29 percent of the diets provided less than 80 percent of the recommended allowance. The women whose diets fell in this group were getting an average of only 33 grams of protein a day.

Similar figures for ascorbic acid were 49 percent and 30 milligrams, respectively; for vitamin A, 63 percent and 2,350 I.U. (International Units).

Data from the other surveys, analyzed in a similar fashion, yield approximately the same figures. They show that the nutrients in which the largest percentage of diets of men and women are likely to be deficient in respect to the allowances are calcium, vitamin A, and ascorbic acid. Thiamine, or riboflavin, or iron may be poorly represented among the diets of some groups. Another analysis, based on a survey

in Iowa, suggests that even in this land of plenty a large segment of our adult population may be undernourished, and thousands and thousands of individuals—both men and women, but especially women—are short changing themselves by eating inadequate diets.

We estimated, for example, that in Iowa in 1948 about 388 thousand women were choosing diets providing less than 0.6 gram of calcium; 129,500 were getting less than 45 grams of protein daily; 333 thousand had less than 55 milligrams of ascorbic acid; and 530 thousand had less than 4 thousand I.U. of vitamin A a day.

The general nature of the inadequacies points up some of the nutritional problems of adults. The more important relate to the energy, protein, calcium, and vitamin requirements.

THE ENERGY VALUE of the food we eat determines to a large extent the good we derive from it.

The diet must provide calories to support the work that the heart and other organs in our bodies always are doing. It also must provide energy for all the chemical reactions going on in our tissues continuously. The number of calories needed for these jobs determines the basal metabolic requirement.

In addition, food also must supply enough energy to cover the calories expended in customary work and play.

A phrase I like very much has been used to describe these needs—"the calorie cost of life." This cost varies from person to person and is determined by age, body size, sex, physical activity, and specific dynamic action of food eaten.

How much energy do diets customarily eaten by men and women in our country provide?

The mean energy values of the diets chosen by men in the eight surveys range from 2,600 to 3,400 Calories a day. These intakes are close to the recommended allowances.

The recommendation for a moderately active woman 45 years old weighing 128 pounds is 2,200 Calories.

A definitely low caloric value is one of the most striking features of the diets of women. The diets of women under age 70 average about 1,700–1,800 Calories a day.

Energy values of this order are of real concern to the nutritionist. Are the low-calorie diets of women associated with a state of undernutrition?

This possibility is suggested by the observation that the diets of many women—in some groups, in the neighborhood of 45 percent—provide less than two-thirds of the recommended energy allowance. The energy intakes, therefore, in many instances may be only slightly greater than the basal energy requirement, which constitutes one-half to two-thirds of the total need. Daily energy intakes of 1,500 Calories scarcely can cover the basal metabolism and the activities of the day.

That many women may be reducing their calories by too wide a margin is indicated by their comments when they try to tell you how they feel: "I tire so easily." "I am tired all the time." "I have no pep." "I have many headaches."

But we cannot assume that undernutrition is a condition that commonly prevails among adults, for the data disclose a situation that is indeed paradoxical. One would expect persons eating the low-calorie diets characteristic of women in these surveys to be underweight. But despite the pattern of low calorie intake, overweight is characteristic of a large proportion of the women interviewed.

Probably 20 percent of the individuals in our adult population are 10 to 20 percent above desirable weight—that is, average weight at age 25. Another 20 to 25 percent are more than 20 percent above desirable weight. Undoubtedly many persons in this latter group are obese.

But we must remember that overweight is not the same thing as obesity or fatness. Other things besides fat may contribute to overweight—an accumulation of water in the tissues, or a heavy bony structure, or a large muscle mass. We would not, for example, call a 210-pound football player with a lean, well-developed musculature obese. It seems normal for women to have more fat in their bodies than men; active muscle tissue forms a smaller proportion of their bodies.

We can explain in several ways the overweight that seems to occur among people who eat food of relatively low caloric value. In the first place, they may be eating more food than they need even on these low-calorie diets.

The energy cost of an average day's activities probably has dropped some 400 or 500 Calories since the turn of the century, when many of our estimates of the energy costs of work and activities were made. The automatic washer and drier have replaced the tub, washboard, and clothesline; the power machine, the old lawnmower; and the tractor, the plow.

Possibly the recommended energy allowances represent too high values for the activities in which we engage in this modern world. How many calories are needed by adults today?

Maintenance of a desirable body weight is an index that the calorie value of the diet is adequate. Daily diets of women of normal weight in Iowa suggest that 1,800 Calories a day, on the average, will cover the basal metabolism and the calories needed for the work and play of women over age 30 under present-day conditions.

This value must be broken down, however, because the energy requirement is related to age. Women of normal weight in their thirties reported dietaries with a mean daily energy value of 1,940 Calories; women 70 years old and older, 1,580 Calories. Thus approximately 1,600 to 2,000 Calories a day seem to meet the energy needs of women today.

In the second place, the "creeping" overweight that is characteristic of people as they grow older may explain incidence of overweight on low-calorie diets.

Whereas 17 percent of one group of women 30 to 39 years old were excessively overweight, 35 percent of those who were 50 to 59 years old were excessively overweight.

People in early adulthood may adjust to planes of calorie intake more or less in line with their activities at that time and establish eating patterns that continue throughout life. But not only is the basal metabolism requirement lower as time goes on, total activity also is lower, and, therefore, the need for calories is less.

A person who oversteps his decreasing requirements by continuing to eat the habitual diet of earlier life slips into positive caloric balance: The food that furnishes the extra calories is transformed into body fat, and he takes on weight. Twenty of these extra calories a day theoretically mean adding 2 pounds of weight in a year. Eighty unwanted pounds may be accumulated between the ages of 25 and 65.

Whatever the cause, we cannot lose sight of the fact that overweight represents poor nutrition—the nutrition of excesses. It probably is the chief dietary hazard of modern living. Physically and mentally, overweight persons feel the oppression of carrying around extra poundage. They are prone to accident. They are poor surgical risks.

The greater the degree of overweight, the greater is the threat of an early death from heart and kidney diseases. Among overweight men, mortality from these diseases is approximately 1½ to 4 times the mortality among men of desirable weight, according to a statement by Dr. Fredrick J. Stare, of the Harvard School of Public Health.

Even though diets of low calorie value may be necessary to avoid the development of overweight, we cannot afford to forget that certain problems will arise in connection with their use. Diets that provide fewer than 2,000 Calories a day must be chosen carefully if needs for nutrients other than food energy are to be met. They provide little cushion for mistakes in food selection.

The protein content of the diet of Americans, for example, tends to follow its caloric value. A diet providing 1,900–2,000 Calories daily generally can be depended upon to furnish about 60 grams of protein. And foods like milk, meat, and eggs, all rich in protein, are apt to be rich in other nutrients too—notably certain minerals and vitamins. For this reason, an intake of about 60 grams of protein appears to guarantee that about two-thirds of the recommended allowances for iron, thiamine, riboflavin, and niacin will be met. Diets furnishing 1,500 Calories can be expected to average around only 45 grams of protein and are likely to fall short in other nutrients.

The easiest way to bring the total nutritive value of the low-calorie diet up to the place it needs to be is to select foods that carry more than one nutrient rather than those that furnish calories only—orange juice, which provides vitamin C along with its calories instead of a soft drink for the midmorning pickup; a plate of fresh fruit instead of a rich pastry for dessert. Empty calories have a dubious place in an adult's diet.

THIS PRINCIPLE of making sure that the bulk of the foods making up the day's meals carry nutrients in addition to calories has important implications in the formulation of reducing diets and explains why indiscriminate reduction regimes should not be undertaken. The guidance of a physician and of a dietitian are needed.

We found, for example, in the survey in Iowa that the mean energy value of the diets of a group of women trying to reduce, more or less on their own, was 1,200 Calories—some 500 Calories less than the energy value of the diets of overweight women who were not reducing. The diets, on the average, did not provide enough protein to prevent breakdown of body tissue, were markedly short in calcium, and did not supply recommended amounts of most of the other nutrients.

Diets like these may endanger health and sense of well-being. Certainly their use is associated with the development of states of frustration, irritability, and anxiety. The reducing campaigns of the individuals in this group, on the whole, did not appear to have been very successful; these women were tipping the scales at an average weight of 187 pounds.

This observation makes one wonder whether nutritional inadequacy may not offset the reducing value of a low-calorie diet, and actually predispose, instead, to the accumulation of body fat. Ercel S. Eppright, of Iowa State College, has observed that some overweight children consumed fewer calories than children of normal weight and had diets of low nutritive value.

A poorly chosen low-calorie diet may introduce still another problem by reducing the effectiveness with which other food nutrients are utilized.

Let us take protein as an example. If calories are low, negative nitrogen balances—in other words, losses of body nitrogen—may occur on intakes of protein that are considered satisfactory. Diets of a group of women 40 to 60 years old were arranged according to their caloric values. All provided close to 60 grams of protein a day. The average nitrogen balances for groups eating food that furnished fewer than 1,800 Calories were negative. On the other hand, women whose diets furnished more than 1,800 Calories did not lose body protein on the average, and we believe their nutrition was better than that of the women eating low-calorie food.

Thus, even though the actual protein intake theoretically is adequate, it may not meet body requirements for nitrogen if the intake of energy-producing food is low. This is a point that needs special consideration in evaluating low-calorie patterns of eating.

THE CONTRIBUTION that fat should make to the total energy value of the diet of the adult is a matter of concern to nutritionists, dietitians, and physicians. And to the lay public!

Fats are an important kind of food for all of us. They should not be omitted from the diet. They add variety and flavor to many foods, are concentrated sources of energy, carry vitamins A and D, and supply fatty acids that are essential for growth and health.

Linoleic acid is of special importance in maintaining growth and health. It is an essential unsaturated fatty acid and is a constituent of many fats.

Linoleic acid must be supplied in foods we eat, because the body cannot manufacture it. Common foods that contain appreciable amounts are the natural oils from corn, cottonseed, and soybean. Peanut oil and poultry fat have less linoleic acid. Olive oil and pork fat have still less. The fats of beef, lamb, milk, veal, and coconut oil contain very little linoleic acid. Margarines and shortenings differ widely in content of linoleic acid. Amounts present depend on the raw materials used and extent to which they are hydrogenated.

One of the leading causes of death in our country today is coronary heart disease. In many countries where the fat intake is low, there is less coronary heart disease than in the United States.

Cholesterol is a substance that is associated with fats in many natural foods. The body also can build it from fats, carbohydrates, and proteins, and does so continuously. It is one of the normal constituents of the blood stream. There are some indications, however, that when levels of blood cholesterol are high, fatty materials may be deposited along the inner linings of artery walls. Certain degenerative changes in the wall accompany such depositions, and the artery wall thickens and loses its elasticity and contractibility: The condition known as hardening of the arteries develops.

Observations that kinds and amounts of fat in the diet affect the amount of cholesterol in the blood suggest that a relation may exist between the fat in our diets and coronary heart disease. But experimental studies suggest that other nutrients, including certain minerals and vitamins, carbohydrates, and protein also may be involved.

We have evidence that fats with a high content of linoleic acid may lower the levels of blood cholesterol. It has not yet been proved, however, that lowering the blood cholesterol reduces the occurrence of heart disease.

Thus we do not have the answers today to questions about adult requirements for fat or about its metabolism. Neither do we know the specific nutritive values of different kinds of fat. So we feel that the time has not yet come to recommend drastic changes in the amounts or kinds of fat that should be consumed by the general public.

THE PROTEINS of the diet have a major role in establishing a good state of nutrition in the adult.

Proteins are essential constituents of both the protoplasm and the nucleus of cells. They are the chief organic constituents of muscle and glandular tissues in the body.

Food proteins after digestion and absorption also are used for building many body proteins that have special functions—hemoglobin, plasma proteins, antibodies, hormones, and enzymes. These proteins are highly important. They help keep the body healthy and the body machinery running as it should.

When diets contain ample amounts of protein, the body can store some of it in its tissues. In the case of an emergency in which dietary protein for some reason must be restricted, the reserves in the body are used to supplement food protein in meeting body needs. Under other conditions, they may be drawn on to help meet the energy requirements if the diet has too low a caloric value. Should the diet fail to provide adequate protein over a period of time, the protein stores will be used up. Then we say that protein reserves are low or that there has been a depletion of the body reserves. Because these stores of body protein ebb and flow in relation to the amount provided by the diet, we speak of them as labile.

Well-filled body stores of protein give a person a definite advantage in meeting the stresses of daily living—a greater ability to cope with infection and to withstand the shock of accident, hemorrhage, wounding, fracture, burns, or surgery. Among women, besides any sudden strains of this kind, are those associated with increased physiological stress—bearing and nursing children and menstruation. Each creates a demand for more dietary protein.

The day's meals should provide enough protein to meet the body's needs for maintaining and repairing all of its substances and to provide for building reserves of body protein in its tissues.

The body, however, has a remarkable ability to adapt itself to a low intake of protein. It guards its protein supply carefully and throws away the smallest possible amounts in the excretions. Adjustment may be so good that the body maintains itself in a state of equilibrium—that is, it excretes the equivalent of just about the same amount of protein that it receives from its food each day. But, if the supply of food protein is short, depletion of the body reservoirs must occur as time goes on.

This fact suggests that even though an individual, after adaptation to a low-protein diet, can live without losing much body protein, we cannot assume that he is well nourished.

When we increase the protein content of the diet of an experimental animal depleted of its body reserves, an immediate and efficient utilization of the protein fed occurs. It is a more efficient utilization than that which takes place when a well-fed animal is given an equivalent amount of extra protein.

We have observed in our laboratory at Iowa State College that some adult human subjects utilize supplementary protein added to their regular self-chosen diets in an extremely efficient manner. We interpret these observations to mean that these subjects have low body reserves.

One way of evaluating the protein needs of people is by means of an experimental procedure called the balance test. The food eaten, the urine, and the stools are analyzed for nitrogen, an element present in all proteins.

Results of tests of this kind depict the relationship that food nitrogen bears to nitrogen used by the body. One of three things may occur: The nitrogen in the excretions may be greater than that provided by the food; the nitrogen in the excretions may be less than that in the food; or the nitrogen in the excretions may be about equal to that in the food.

The first situation is interpreted as a protein deficiency if it is characteristic of an individual over a considerable period of time. The excess nitrogen in the excretions can come only from the body and represents body losses. This "negative" nitrogen balance can be compared to a bank balance, in which withdrawals exceed deposits. Eventually, the bank balance will go "in the red."

The second situation shows that food protein is being deposited in body tissues. Growth in children represents such retention as does deposition of protein in body stores.

In general, the third situation (when the body is in nitrogen equilibrium and is losing no more nitrogen than it is taking in) has been thought to describe a satisfactory state of protein nutrition in adults. But research work-ers have raised questions as to whether a diet just capable of maintaining nitrogen equilibrium in the adult is associated with well-filled tissue reservoirs and potential attendant nutritional benefits.

Scientists in the Midwest have studied the nitrogen retentions of 136 women, 30 to 80 years old, who lived on their regular self-selected diets.

Data in the accompanying table show that only women 30 to 39 years old chose diets that on the average supplied enough protein to maintain nitrogen equilibrium.

About 50 percent of the 136 women were in negative nitrogen balance. Some investigators believe that this is the picture that can be expected in groups consuming their usual diets—individuals being in positive balance about one-half of the time and in negative balance the other half. The overall retention over a period of time therefore would be essentially equilibrium.

What actually constitutes the nature of protein retention in women over 30 living on their customary diets seemed a problem worth pursuing to the research workers.

A group of nutritionists in Iowa, Minnesota, Nebraska, and South Dakota carried the initial research project a step further. We determined nitrogen balances day by day for consecutive intervals ranging in different persons from 30 to 280 days. One woman cooperated for a total of 797 days over 4 years. We compiled records for more than 30 women.

The study revealed that some subjects were in a continuous state of nitrogen deficit. Others fluctuated in rhythmic cycles above and below

Women in these age groups	Chose food that supplied an average of this much protein each day (grams)	But they needed an average of this much protein each day (grams)	Their need was this much greater on the average than their supply
30–39 years......	67	66	....
40–59 years......	64	70	9 percent.
60–69 years......	57	67	18 percent.
70–79 years......	51	57	12 percent.

nitrogen equilibrium, the total retention for the entire period approaching equilibrium. Still others stored nitrogen continuously for long periods over a period of years.

Further investigation suggested that nitrogen equilibrium may represent borderline nutrition. Women in this condition retained protein we added to their customary diet—an indication of depleted protein reserves. There also were indications that nutritional benefits were associated with the positive retentions of protein.

Thus it is evident that the adult's protein needs are not understood fully and are complicated by the influence of many factors. We cannot think in terms of protein alone. Protein requirements must be referred to the nutritional adequacy of the diet as a whole.

As I have pointed out, the energy value of the diet is related to the effectiveness of protein utilization.

But other items likewise need to be considered: The distribution of animal sources of protein over the three meals of the day; the nutritional value of the proteins provided; the balance between the amino acids supplied by these proteins; and the vitamin content of the diet.

Finally, protein needs must be assessed in respect to the relative nutritional state of the individual, especially in relation to body reserves.

CALCIUM is present in the body in far larger amounts than any other mineral element. Ninety-nine percent of the body calcium is in the skeleton. Calcium gives bone its strength and rigidity.

The small fraction in other tissues is of great physiological significance. This calcium helps maintain the ability of the nerves to transmit impulses. It takes part in enzyme reactions. It assists in the coagulation of blood when bleeding occurs. It keeps the membranes of cells permeable, so that substances necessary for their life and health can pass to and fro.

The amount of calcium in the blood is fairly constant under normal situations. Changes are associated with special disorders. Too low a level of blood calcium will produce convulsion-like conditions. Too high a level will cause disturbances in the work of certain organs like the heart.

The amount of calcium that the diet of an adult should furnish is one of the most debated nutrition problems of the present day.

In terms of the recommended allowance, it is the nutrient most likely to be short in the food of American adults. Does this mean that people are less healthy than they ought to be because their diets are inadequate in calcium? Or does it mean that we have set the requirement too high—that 0.8 gram of calcium a day is out of line with our actual requirements?

Obviously the food of adults should supply enough calcium for the maintenance of strong bony structures and of a satisfactory amount of calcium in the blood.

In the child, as part of the process of growth, active deposition of calcium in the skeleton goes on. If one judges from weights of average skeletons, this growth continues in human beings through age 35.

But we cannot consider bony tissue in the adult as static material. It is a dynamic substance, which constantly remodels itself. Formation of new bone and destruction of old bone go on simultaneously.

These processes approximately balance each other in the healthy adult. Thus, despite constant remodeling, the total calcium concentration in the matured skeleton remains about constant if the bone cells are healthy and functioning.

As a person grows older, however, the process of bone destruction may overbalance that of bone building. That this occurs is suggested by observations that the average weight of the skeleton decreases gradually after age 35.

The extent to which such decalcification may proceed without injury is not known. We do know that it does not always occur in all individuals. Persons may die at advanced ages with little demineralization of the skeleton, as shown by X-ray and autopsy examinations.

But we cannot ignore the fact that osteoporosis, or deficient bone substance, certainly is not uncommon in later life. The frequency with which it occurs, however, is not known. It is commoner among older women than among men. Persons with marked osteoporosis tend to eat food poor in a number of nutrients, including calcium. They also tend to improve in health and to store calcium when the diet is improved.

Many racial groups have lived for generations on diets furnishing less than 0.5 gram of calcium a day. They appear to be reasonably healthy, but in general these groups are short in stature. Skeletal growth of children 5 to 10 years old may be as much as 3 years behind that of children living on diets more liberal in calcium. However, dietary inadequacies other than calcium also may influence bone growth.

As with protein, the animal organism can adapt itself to various levels of calcium intake. D. M. Hegsted, of the School of Public Health, Harvard University, showed that a group of men in Lima, Peru, required an average of only 0.2 to 0.3 gram of calcium a day to prevent body losses of calcium. These men had lived on a low calcium diet for many years.

No evidence has been produced showing that the accumulation of large stores of calcium by the adult is desirable. Indeed, the opposite may be true. For example, K. M. Henry and S. K. Kon, of the University of Reading, learned that rats adapted to low intakes of calcium were more resistant, as old animals, to calcium depletion than were rats that had lived on diets high in calcium all of their lives.

Observations like these have led some scientists to believe that the recommended allowance for calcium has been set at too high a level.

It is exceedingly difficult to prove that the adult human being benefits from high levels of dietary calcium. The most concrete evidence is indirect evidence and comes from the long-term studies with rats conducted by Dr. Henry C. Sherman and his associates at Columbia University. Increased intakes of calcium were associated with increased body size, improved reproductive performance, and lengthened lifespan of the animals.

We must keep in mind, however, that the better performance may reflect improvement of the diet in early youth. Be this as it may, the results of Dr. Sherman's experiments cannot be translated directly into human experience. But should longer life and retention of youthful characteristics be associated with the level of calcium in the diet, calcium is indeed an important nutrient.

Estimations of the calcium requirement to date have been based largely on the balance test because of difficulties involved in following changes in bone. In the process of calcium turnover that takes place in the bone of the healthy adult, some calcium is lost from the body by excretion into the intestine and in urine. Usually a state is reached in which calcium intake and outgo of calcium are approximately equal. When that occurs, the individual theoretically is satisfying his needs for calcium and he is "in balance."

The National Academy of Sciences-National Research Council has used the results of many such balance experiments in arriving at the recommended allowance for calcium for adults.

It has recognized that adults vary widely in their need for calcium, and has attempted to specify an intake that will contribute to the good health of the majority of the population.

It believes that in our society about 0.8 gram of calcium a day will meet the calcium needs of most men and of nonpregnant, nonlactating women. There always will be a few who can maintain good nutrition on considerably less than this amount, however. A few will need more.

We must recognize that the 1958 allowances are based on the best evidence we have. Most scientists believe that these allowances are reasonable and should not be modified until we have more adequate evidence than we have now that low intakes of calcium are compatible with good nutrition.

In this connection, it is of interest that Dr. Ole J. Malm, in reporting studies from the University of Oslo, has presented evidence that indicates that male adults may adapt satisfactorily when the amount of calcium provided by the diet is reduced from 0.9 to 0.45 gram a day.

The problem of the calcium requirement has caught the interest of investigators anew. They are using new approaches and techniques for evaluating our present concepts of calcium metabolism.

The extent to which calcium undernutrition may exist in presumably well-fed and in less well-fed populations and the degree to which adaptive mechanisms enter into the picture in regard to health are questions that need answers. Also, many factors— some physiological, some dietary— affect the absorption, utilization, and retention of calcium.

All must be taken into account in evaluating the calcium requirement.

Research during the next decade undoubtedly will clarify the problem.

VITAMINS may be low in the food usually selected by adults. Vitamins most likely to be deficient are ascorbic acid, thiamine, and vitamin A.

Diagnosis of frank deficiency diseases like scurvy or pellagra among Americans now is rare, but mild states of deficiency continue to exist. They are not diagnosed easily, however, for symptoms are not the specific ones usually associated with any one deficiency disease.

Dr. T. D. Spies, of the Department of Nutrition and Metabolism, Northwestern University Medical School, has pointed out that many common ailments and manifestations of low-grade health are related to the quality of the diet and, in many instances, to a lack of a specific vitamin.

He tells us that certain symptoms, like mental confusion, easy fatigability, and anxiety, disappear with nicotinic acid therapy.

Irritation of the eyes with abnormal sensitivity to light and soreness of the corners of the mouth respond to treatment with riboflavin.

Severe body weakness and large areas of hemorrhage under the skin of the arms and legs disappear upon the administration of ascorbic acid.

Dr. Spies tells also of the effectiveness of folic acid in treating a man suffering from a disabling weakness accented by loss of appetite and diarrhea, and of the effectiveness of vitamin B_{12} in improving the condition of a sore, inflamed, and infected tongue.

The pattern of food intake in the United States suggests that diets are likely to be low in more than one vitamin. Disorders like those described by Dr. Spies may have their origin in diets that are too low in ascorbic acid, vitamin A, or the B vitamins (thiamine, riboflavin, nicotinic acid, pyridoxine, vitamin B_{12}, and folic acid), and may represent mixed deficiency diseases.

It is not difficult to understand why symptoms like these may develop when the diet falls short in its vitamin content. Vitamins serve as parts of enzyme systems that control the biochemical reactions that go on in the body and keep the cells performing their special functions.

If materials are not available for the manufacture of all the enzymes upon which the life and work of the body depend, the whole system of metabolic fires and transformations will clog, and unnatural products will accumulate in the cells and tissues. These chemical upsets then are reflected in the way an individual looks, or acts, or feels. But when they are properly replenished with the food chemicals they need for their functioning, body cells can fight back to an amazing degree. And with this will come a feeling of a return to better health.

Probably the chief reason for the incidence of disorders stemming from vitamin shortage is the fact that the American public is apt to choose its diets from a limited array of foods. We believe that the use of a varied diet containing all the essential food groups will help prevent the appearance of conditions associated with decreased strength and vitality. When such conditions do develop, the use of a varied diet becomes even more important.

Sometimes a person may need a vitamin preparation as a dietary supplement to trigger lagging body reactions, but he should consult his physician before he takes it. Too many people buy preparations of vitamins they do not need. They might better get them from an intelligently selected diet.

AGING PERSONS are an important unit in the group of adult persons whose nutritional problems we are considering.

Just as adolescence is a critical period, so are the years between 60 and 70. Associated with the transition from late maturity are emotional and physical stresses, which often are complicated by changes in external living conditions. Patterns of food intake may be altered by changes in income, housing, living arrangements, or even by the composition of the family in which an individual lives. Food likes and dislikes acquired over years of living may become progressively serious barriers to the attainment of good nutrition. Sometimes a disinterest in food— any kind of food—may develop, stemming from loneliness, lack of activity, or worry.

Much remains to be learned, however, as to how changing capacities of aging men and women affect their nutritional needs and requirements. A diet that meets the requirements of the mature person may not necessarily be the best as he grows older.

Dietary requirements in later life are influenced by the extent to which physiological changes have occurred that affect food intake and metabolism— like difficulties in chewing, inability to digest or absorb food efficiently, and less effective use of nutrients by the tissues.

Also, a person at 70 is an historical record of all that has happened to him—his injuries, infections, nutritional imbalances, fatigues, and emotional upsets. Old people, therefore, differ from each other much more than do younger folk. All this needs to be considered in food planning for any old person. Each one is an individual, quite unlike anyone else.

We do not know all we need to know about food requirements during the latter part of the life cycle. But we are sure that an old person can derive benefits from a good and varied diet.

We are sure also that he does not need so many calories as he did when he was 20. This means that special attention must be given in the selection of food if the day's meals are to provide the important proteins, minerals, and vitamins.

How are older people eating? How well do their diets furnish the nutrients we believe they need?

Studies of the diets of adults disclose that intakes of the various nutrients decrease with advancing age.

Among women in Iowa, on the average, each 10-year increase in age brought a drop in the energy intake of 85 Calories a day; in protein, of 4 grams a day; and in calcium, of 0.03 gram. Within each age group, however, use of diets of widely varying nutritive value occurred.

The pattern of food intake remained fairly consistent until age 60. As the years added up, the women continued to eat about the same kind of food, only somewhat less of it. The average number of calories furnished by most food groups dropped in proportion to the decrease in total energy value of the diets.

The eating habits of women over 60, however, were qualitatively as well as quantitatively different from those of younger women. Cereal products furnished a larger percentage of the total energy than in earlier life, and meat, fish, and poultry a somewhat smaller proportion.

IMPROVEMENT OF THE DIETS of American adults will come when more of them realize than do now that some changes in our patterns of eating are needed.

An analysis of the kinds of foods Americans like to include in their meals tells why so many diets are inadequate.

Foods in a typical day's meals are bread and butter, meat and potatoes, some one vegetable or salad or fruit, dessert, and coffee. Although meals made up of these foods may furnish adequate amounts of energy, protein, iron, and the B vitamins, they are likely to be low in calcium, vitamin A, and ascorbic acid—the nutrients in which the largest percentages of diets in many groups of adults throughout the country are deficient.

But the popular basic diet can be made adequate in all nutrients fairly easily by the daily use of milk and milk products; yellow fruits and vegetables; deep-green, leafy vegetables; and citrus fruit, tomatoes, and foods belonging to the cabbage family.

Some persons also will benefit by increasing the amounts of meat, fish, poultry, eggs, cheese, and legumes they eat and by replacing refined breads and cereals with whole-grain or enriched products.

At the same time, it is important that the calorie value of food eaten be kept at that level where desirable body weight is maintained.

The wider the variety of wholesome foods we eat, the better the chances that we shall be well nourished. Many neglected foods are outstandingly good sources of the nutrients likely to be supplied inadequately by average diets.

Especially noteworthy in this respect are the organ meats (liver, kidney, and heart) and the dark-green, leafy vegetables, like broccoli, chard, kale, and mustard and turnip greens.

In planning or choosing meals, some of us do not realize how important it is that each meal include some of all the essential food groups and that the day's quota of energy foods be distributed pretty evenly among the three meals of the day.

We are apt especially to limit the foods we eat for breakfast. It is a vulnerable spot in the American food pattern. Many of us start the day with fruit juice, toast, and coffee. We found in one group of 1,072 women, that 152 ate a breakfast consisting of coffee and toast, and 68 had no breakfast at all or coffee only.

After the fast of the night, everyone needs to replenish body fuel to get the energy that the morning's tasks will demand. Breakfasts are needed. People are more alert, efficient, and resistant to fatigue when they eat breakfasts than when they do not.

Furthermore, this breakfast needs to provide proteins, vitamins, and minerals, as well as food energy.

For example, a given daily allotment of protein will count for more if it is divided among three meals than if it is concentrated in one or two meals. Therefore some of the day's quota of milk or meat or eggs should reinforce the basic breakfast of toast, or cereal, fruit juice, and coffee.

Some people "never hungry at breakfast." But breakfast is so important that such people might do well to have a light evening meal and no snacks at bedtime. Or, perhaps, persons not in the habit of eating breakfast should try starting out with small servings, and gradually work up to eating breakfasts of ordinary size.

Snacks are an important part of the eating pattern in America—of adults as well as of adolescents and children. Indeed, the kind of snacks we eat may determine whether our overall nutrition is good or bad.

Snacks of fruit, juice, or milk have a definite protective value. Snacks of soft drinks, cookies, candy, and many popular high-calorie foods, on the other hand, furnish little except energy. Most adults have no need for extra energy and, after a day of such snacking, may have no appetite for nutritionally important foods.

IMPROVEMENT OF NUTRITION is something that can be achieved—not merely dreamed of. We have seen it happen in our country over the past quarter century. It can happen among our friends and neighbors. We can bring it about in ourselves. The difficult thing for people to realize is that it is their privilege to enjoy buoyant health.

What one person working with us in our nutrition laboratory has accomplished may be an example for others.

This woman, 48 years old when we first knew her 10 years ago, was living on a diet limited in variety. Her meals consisted of meat, potatoes, breads and rich rolls, pastries, cakes, and desserts. She used relatively few fresh fruits and vegetables. This diet, on the average, furnished 52 grams of protein and 0.4 gram of calcium a day. Balance tests at intervals from 1948 to 1953 showed that she consistently was losing body protein and body calcium.

She was about 30 pounds overweight. We were glad to help her when she expressed a desire to lose some of these extra pounds. We acquainted her with the low- and high-calorie foods, and stressed the importance of using liberal amounts of milk and foods rich in proteins and vitamins.

She took the job seriously and modified her eating practices around the dietary recommendations. She stepped up her intake of proteins to approximately 90 grams daily and the intake of calcium to about 1.4 grams daily, while stabilizing the energy value of her diet at about 1,800 Calories a day.

As a result, she lost 30 pounds. She has maintained a body weight of 135 pounds for the past 3 years on diets providing about 2,000 Calories.

As our part of the job, we followed retentions of nitrogen and calcium, day by day, for periods ranging from 3 to 9 months over an interval of 4 years. On her self-directed dietary regime, she consistently has stored both protein and calcium over the years. Protein probably replaced fat in tissue cells, and calcium enriched skeletal reserves.

A gratifying change occurred in her appearance—apparent to us in the laboratory and to all who know her. She has new animation and zest. Her friends say she looks 10 years younger. Her physician says she appears 3 years younger. He also has recorded the improvement in the color and texture of the flesh and skin and in the luster of the hair. He has noted a firmed-up musculature, a spinal curve more flexible than it was initially, and improved eyesight. All items in the medical examination are favorable.

She herself is aware of the changes that have occurred. She has never felt better. She has increased the scope of her activities. She says she can do "so much more now so much more easily." Also there is her pride in being able to wear a size 14 dress!

PEARL SWANSON *became professor of nutrition in 1936 and was appointed Assistant Director of the Iowa Agricultural and Home Economics Experiment Station in charge of home economics research in 1944 at Iowa State College, Ames, Iowa.*

Food

QUALITY

Quality in Animal Products

SAM R. HOOVER

I ate my fill of a whale that died
And stranded after a month at sea,
There is a pain in my inside.
Why have the Gods afflicted me?

THIS lament of the South Sea native in Kipling's "Natural Theology" bears directly on the first point of quality we require in animal products. They must be fresh.

The leg fresh severed from the animal, the milk fresh from the udder, and the fish fresh from rivers or seas were foods that even the simplest primitive believed to be good. This belief has come down to us because it is soundly based on fact.

Another important element of quality in animal products is our realization of their high nutritive value. No man could see the rapid growth of young animals under mother's milk, or drive an ox, or catch a bird, without knowing that the strength and agility these animals possess would make their muscles good food for his muscles. This was borne out by observations that the meat eaters were tall and powerful men. Our American

Indians took the names of the swiftest and strongest animals for their names.

One way in which man early learned to judge quality in foods was by its color. Meat that is exposed to the air darkens as the red pigments are oxidized. Other foods have distinctive colors that we associate with high quality. Today we use this judgment as a primary criterion. It is, on the whole, a valid one, but not always. For example, the desired yellow color of egg yolks and butter is due to carotene, which is a source of vitamin A. Yet we devalue meat that has a yellow color in the fat—a completely irrelevant judgment.

Similarly, the preference for brown-shelled eggs in the Boston market and for white eggs in other eastern markets has no basis in the quality of the eggs, yet for many years buyers have paid about 2 cents a dozen more for the color they desired.

Whether Lamb's delightful "Dissertation Upon Roast Pig" is historically correct or not, man came early to the conclusion that he would like his food better if it were cooked. Cooking produced new flavors, and the piquant touches of salt, pepper, and herbs could be incorporated. It was good to have the animal product brought to the table in a form that could be easily recognized as roast, a boiled leg of mutton, and the like, for then both the eye and the palate could tell that the food was good and wholesome.

Fine cookery in the modern sense was a further development. It came about with the increasing complexity of civilization. Throughout the world, wherever there have been city populations that were fed by farms in a large surrounding area, a more complicated situation has resulted. Farmers sold their products to hucksters, and markets were established in the city. The housewife or her servants could buy a wide range of animal and vegetable foods. The sophisticated foods of the Chinese and French cuisine became an art wherein the different parts of animals and cream, vinegar, wine, and herbs were combined to produce exquisite dishes. Such foods could only arise in an urban area, fed by a nearby agrarian population.

The incessant battle against decay, coupled with the feast-and-famine food supply of early man, brought about several types of processed foods.

It truly must have been a great day when the first man realized he did not have to eat on the spot as the animals did. From this fact developed our pattern of culture, in which the search for food takes up little of our time.

Because the nomadic tribes of the plains that existed on all major continents needed concentrated rations for their journeys, they developed dried meat and cheese before the time of which we have any record.

Lewis and Clark tell of the Indians along the Columbia River drying salmon for a full winter's supply.

Today the Laplanders of northern Europe prepare dried reindeer meat for their annual journey to the coast. The Indians in northern Canada prepare pemmican in the same way their ancestors did. The Chinese dry eggs in the sun in small earthenware dishes.

Food was dried to preserve it from bacterial action thousands of years before bacteria were first seen and studied. Essentially the same principles are used in our modern plants today. New drying techniques for meat products are an active field of research for the future.

Similarly, the preservative effects of smoking and salting the meat and cheese as they were dried were recognized thousands of years ago. A whole group of cured meat products was developed in this way. Parts of the animal carcass, such as the hams and shoulders, were cured, and sausages were concocted from the tasty fragments. In each tribe or community there developed special types of sausages, each with its distinctive flavor, brought about by the skillful use of herbs and curing conditions.

Canning, the preservation of foods by heat sterilization, is a modern development—one that has come about almost completely within the past hundred years. Our canned meat products have been developed by the technologists in our packinghouses.

The necessary heat treatment to sterilize such products is more than that needed to cook the food. For example, a medium well-done roast reaches an internal temperature of only 160° F., and a well-done turkey is heated to 190°. But canned meats that are fully sterilized must be heated well above the boiling point of water (212°). Commercial practice uses 240° for 20 minutes. Canned meats, with their distinctive flavors, therefore, do not have many of the qualities that make fresh meat the first item of food for American families.

The canning of milk as evaporated milk, concentrated to one-half its volume and sterilized, was a great contribution of the canned food industry. It has been especially valuable in the nutrition of infants and will continue to be a boon to future generations.

The story of cheese is a fascinating

one. In prehistoric times a legendary itinerant trader from Arabia was crossing a mountainous section of Asia. He paused to refresh himself with dried dates and goat's milk. Out of the canteen made from a dried sheep's stomach, only a thin watery liquid trickled. Cutting the skin to see what had happened, he found a soft mass of curd not at all distasteful to a hungry man. The "rennin" in the partially dried sheep's stomach had curdled the milk, and the result was cheese. Today we make cheese in exactly the same way—by curdling the milk with rennet prepared from a calf's stomach.

Cheese was introduced into Europe by Asiatic traders more than 2,000 years before the birth of Christ. The Greeks and Egyptians sang of its virtues. David presented 10 cheeses to his captain as the finest of delicacies. Distinctive types of cheese are developed all over the world. More than 400 types are described in Handbook No. 54 of the Department of Agriculture. Many of these are minor variants of the major types, of which there are considered to be about 18. An almost unbelievable range of flavors and textures is produced by skillful fermentation and control of conditions, so that there is certainly a cheese to fit any individual's taste.

The astounding growth of the food industry over the past 150 years, in which our population shifted from 85 percent on the farm to 85 percent in cities and towns, is a remarkable technological achievement. The food-handling and processing practices handed down by our forefathers were subjected to careful research. Rigorous controls of sanitary standards were imposed on both the processing plant and the various food products. The results of all of this research and development can be seen in the fine products in our food stores and on our tables.

This application of science to the food industry is a continuing study. New food products appear at an increasing rate. Standards of uniformity and quality must be established in each of them by the manufacturer. If they are not, the product will not remain long on the market.

IN SUMMARY: There are three quality factors that the consumer looks for in fresh and processed foods. They are color, flavor, and texture.

They are personal and subjective evaluations. Each person is his own judge of quality. Much research has been done on the development of objective physical and chemical tests for quality, and color can be successfully measured.

But the delicate shadings of flavor and texture which the tongue and the nose can distinguish are extremely complicated. They still defy measurement because they are such subtle combinations of satisfaction and enjoyment.

SAM R. HOOVER *in 1957 became Chief of the Dairy and Meat Laboratory, Eastern Utilization Research and Development Division, Agricultural Research Service. He has been engaged in chemical research in the Department since 1931. He received his training at Davis and Elkins College, George Washington University, and Georgetown University. Dr. Hoover received the Borden Award in the Chemistry of Milk in 1956.*

*If some superdietitian could hand everyone a simple, perfectly balanced menu and get them to use it, much as a farmer feeds his cows, it would be a comparatively simple matter to have everyone well nourished. But it would be an unfortunate state of affairs, because we would then be cows or robots instead of human beings. As human beings, we expect to get emotional satisfactions from food as well as to meet our physical needs. These emotional satisfactions are often tied up with our habits, and we resist changes that we think might interfere with them. This is one reason why the problem of nutrition is complicated, as every mother knows if she has tried to teach a child to eat properly.—*GOVE HAMBIDGE. From Food and Life, the 1939 Yearbook of Agriculture.

Livestock Production in Transition

R. E. HODGSON

GREAT changes and progress in the production of livestock in the United States have given us more food from animals and improved its quality and food value.

Two-thirds of the protein consumed by Americans and two-fifths of their intake in calories come from animals. These nutrients—in meat, milk and other dairy products, and in eggs and other poultry products—round out the well-balanced American diet.

Farm practices that affect the quality and nutritive value of animal food begin with the soil and its management. They include raising and using such crops as corn, barley, oats, sorghums, forage grasses, and legumes. They involve breeding, feeding, and managing the livestock.

The impact of widespread research and experimentation on the efficiency of livestock production is illustrated in a table, which shows the amounts of feed units needed to produce specified amounts of animal food. The trend has been toward more pounds of product for less feed consumed.

As an example, it took 18 percent

fewer feed units to produce 100 pounds of milk in 1956 than it did on the average during 1940–1944. It took 12 percent fewer feed units to produce 100 pounds of meat as cattle and calves, 13 percent fewer feed units to produce 100 pounds of eggs, 32 percent fewer feed units to produce 100 pounds of broilers, and 4 percent fewer feed units to produce 100 pounds of pork.

Such improvements came about mainly through the development of better livestock, better feed supplies, and improved management skills.

Let us examine the details of some of these developments.

OVERSHADOWING all other developments in the production of poultry meat has been the evolution of the fast-growing broiler bird through breeding experiments conducted by poultry scientists of the Department of Agriculture, State agricultural experiment stations, and private research institutions.

The effect has been to raise greatly the efficiency of converting feed to meat. Today's birds grow faster whether they are fed a 1930 broiler-feed formula or a 1956 formula.

Birds also have been bred to achieve an improvement in the appearance of dressed poultry. That involves such factors as body conformation, skin color, and rate of feathering.

No special effort has been made yet to breed for better texture, tenderness, flavor, and juiciness of the meat, but scientists say this could be done if the demand for such improvement arises.

The yield of edible meat per bird has been improved slightly by breeding, and more work to that end may be undertaken.

The crowning triumph of poultry breeding research is the Beltsville white turkey, named for the Agricultural Research Center of the Department of Agriculture at Beltsville, Md., where the bird was developed. With this bird, scientists achieved a goal they had previously determined to be desirable. They got what they set out to get—a small, meaty bird that would be useful to small families.

The results have been impressive. About 18 percent of all turkeys grown in the United States now are the small Beltsville whites. Turkey is becoming a year-round staple food, and the annual consumption of turkey meat has risen from 2.9 pounds per capita in 1940 to 5.1 pounds.

The fast-growing broiler has had a similar effect on the consumption of chicken, which rose from 14.1 pounds per capita in 1940 to 24.3 pounds in 1956.

RESEARCH in breeding, feeding, and managing swine also has influenced strongly the production of hogs.

An important result is an animal with a higher percentage of lean meat than the fat-type hog previously available to farmers. The meat-type hog came into being because of a steady drop in the consumption of lard and an insistence by consumers on nutritious, lean pork cuts.

The meat-type hog carries less back fat and a higher proportion of lean to fat, has good flavor and eating texture, and on the average is heavier per 100 pounds of feed consumed than the fatback hog.

A study done at the Ohio Evaluation Station, for example, showed that 334 pounds of feed are required per 100 pounds of gain for U.S. No. 1 meat-type hogs, compared with 358 pounds of feed per 100 pounds of gain for U.S. Nos. 2 and 3 fat-type hogs.

Carcass studies show that the value of hog carcasses goes down as the thickness of the back fat increases. Individual meat-type hogs have shown differences in carcass value of as much as 2 to 3 dollars per hundredweight over fat hogs of similar weight. Meat-type hogs at the Ohio Evaluation Station yielded 50 percent of their live weight in primal cuts, compared with 46.34 percent for fat hogs.

Swine breeding is destined to go further.

Scientists think improvements in carcass quality will result from selection from pure breeds on the basis of accurate performance records combined with some form of crossing inbred lines. The result is a kind of "hybrid vigor." Men at the Iowa Agricultural Experiment Station have estimated that crossbreeding gives an increase of 5 to 8 percent in growth rate and economy and even more in fertility.

The economically important characteristics that determine the value of swine, besides carcass value in general, are sow productivity (as measured by litter weight at various stages between birth and weaning), viability of pigs, freedom from defects and weaknesses, speed of gain in weight, and efficiency of conversion of feed.

Not all traits are equally heritable or equally important. Some, like carcass quality, require more complicated techniques to achieve improvement than others, like size of litter and gain in weight.

Such carcass traits as depth of back fat, marbling, length, quality of loin muscle, juiciness, and tenderness are

Trends in Feed Units of All Feeds Consumed per Unit of Production by Different Classes of Livestock [1]

	Milk cows per 100 pounds of milk	Cattle and calves per 100 pounds produced	Hens and pullets per 100 eggs produced	Broilers per 100 pounds produced	Hogs per 100 pounds produced
	Pounds	*Pounds*	*Pounds*	*Pounds*	*Pounds*
1940–1944.........	114	1,015	63	470	538
1945–1949.........	112	967	62	427	535
1950–1955.........	108	924	58	358	520
1956.............	104	897	55	317	519

[1] A feed unit is the equivalent in feeding value of a pound of corn.

Adapted from table 11, p. 27, *Changes in Farm Production and Efficiency*, 1956. Summary ARS 43–55, Agricultural Research Service, Department of Agriculture, August 1957.

Improvement in Broiler Production Brought About Through Improved Breeding and Improvement in Diet—1930 and 1956

Comparison	Weight at 9 weeks	Feed consumed per pound of body-weight gain	Improvement in efficiency of feed conversion
1956—Fast-growing type of broiler	*Pounds*	*Pounds*	*Percentage of 1930 broiler and diet*
Fed 1956-type diet.................	2. 64	2. 5	0. 78
Fed 1930-type diet.................	2. 08	2. 9	.91
1930—Slow-growing type of broiler			
Fed 1956-type diet.................	2. 38	2. 8	. 88
Fed 1930-type diet.................	1. 66	3. 2	1. 00

Production per Capita of Red Meat and Poultry and Eggs in the United States

Year	Red meat					Poultry meat [1]			Eggs
	Beef	Veal	Lamb and mutton	Pork	Total	Chicken	Turkey	Total	
	Lbs.	*Lbs.*	*Lbs.*	*Lbs.*	*Lbs.*	*Lbs.*	*Lbs.*	*Lbs.*	*No.*
1930........	48. 1	6. 4	6. 7	68. 9	130. 1	[2] 15. 7	[2] 1. 5	[2] 17. 2	349
1940........	54. 3	7. 4	6. 6	76. 1	144. 4	[2] 14. 1	[2] 2. 9	[2] 17. 0	331
1950........	62. 9	8. 1	3. 9	70. 6	145. 5	20. 9	4. 1	25. 0	427
1956........	86. 0	9. 7	4. 4	66. 7	166. 8	25. 2	5. 7	30. 9	391
1957........	83. 0	8. 9	4. 1	61. 3	157. 3	25. 8	6. 1	31. 9	378

[1] Ready-to-cook basis.

[2] Per capita consumption. Production is essentially the same.

Effect of Method of Harvesting Hay on Yield of Nutrients of a Forage Crop

| Methods of harvest | Yield of nutrients per acre | | Amount of 24 percent protein concentrate to be equivalent in nutrient content compared to field curing |
	Digestible protein	Total digestible nutrients	
	Pounds	Pounds	Pounds
Field curing.............	450	2,066	...
Field curing plus barn finishing.............	536	2,347	375
Grass silage.............	568	2,517	600
Artificial dehydration......	547	2,703	850

Retail Price per Unit of Product for Major Animal and Crop Food Products

Product	1946	1956	Increase 1956 over 1946
	Cents	Cents	Percent
Beef, choice grade.....................pound..	42.5	66.0	55.3
Lamb, choice grade.....................pound..	44.0	64.7	47.0
Pork....................................pound..	41.3	52.1	26.1
Milk, fluid..............................quart..	17.0	23.3	37.0
Butter..................................pound..	70.5	72.1	2.3
Eggs...................................dozen..	55.3	57.7	4.3
Bread, white...........................pound..	10.4	17.9	72.1
Cornflakes...................12 ounce package..	11.4	22.0	93.0
Cornmeal..............................pound..	8.9	12.6	41.5
Flour, white..........................5 pounds..	35.4	53.3	50.6
Rolled oats...................20 ounce package..	13.1	19.3	47.3
Oranges................................dozen..	50.0	58.2	16.4
Apples.................................pound..	12.9	15.1	17.0
Beans, green...........................pound..	19.6	25.0	22.4
Carrots................................pound..	9.0	13.7	52.2
Lettuce.................................head..	11.6	16.4	41.4
Potatoes............................10 pounds..	45.4	67.7	49.1
Sugar, beet..........................5 pounds..	39.0	52.8	35.4

Adapted from tables in part 3, Misc. Pub. 741, Agricultural Marketing Service, 1957.

highly heritable, however, and breeding programs will be aimed increasingly at getting them.

INCREASED EFFICIENCY in the production of lamb meat has been directed toward improving breeds and strains for better production and in crossing various breeds with increased production from "hybrid vigor." Better conformation and gains of 10 to 20 percent

in pounds of lamb weaned for market per ewe bred have resulted.

Selection seems to be particularly promising for making future improvements in efficiency of production in the various breeds. Selection of mating lambs is based on production records, rapid turnover of generations on the ram side, use of highly selected top flocks for sire production, and efficiency of gain.

An example of what has been accomplished is shown in results obtained at the U.S. Sheep Experiment Station at Dubois, Idaho, where individually fed rams varied in their feed requirements from 7.4 pounds of feed to 10.9 pounds of feed per pound of gain.

In studies of the improvement of lamb meat through breeding, cross-bred lambs have shown improvement in such attributes as yield of preferred cuts, the physical composition of the meat, and the dressing yield over the parent purebreds. Improvement seems to be especially marked where Merinos were used.

RESEARCHERS hope to do with beef cattle what swine breeders did to achieve a meat-type hog.

Their aim is a meat-type beef animal that yields good counter meat, has less fat, and gains rapidly on less feed than is now required.

Some progress has been made. Experiments at the Miles City Livestock Experiment Station in Montana revealed that the progeny of a high-performance sire made a 24-percent greater gain from birth to weaning age than progeny of a low-performance sire.

Ability to gain and efficiency in utilizing feed are heritable and genetically related. Other research has shown that the area of the rib eye in beef cattle is highly heritable, and the way is open for selection to improve this valuable area of the carcass.

With dairy cows, the aim of breeding research in the past was to develop animals giving high-fat milk and more milk. The scientists have turned to producing selective strains that produce milk containing more nonfat solids, especially protein, in proportion to the fat content. This factor apparently is heritable enough so that success can be achieved.

ANOTHER important explanation for improved livestock production is better feed supplies.

With a few exceptions, the composi-tion of the feed in itself does not have a powerful influence on the composition of milk and meat. The composition and nutritive value of feeds have this result, however: By improving the nutritional welfare of an animal, they raise the efficiency with which animal products are made.

Investigations at Michigan State University to compare the composition and feeding value of the same crops grown on fertilized and nonfertilized soil and the quality of milk from cows fed those crops illustrate this general truth about the role of feeds in livestock production.

One finding was that there is little or no difference in the chemical composition of crops grown under conditions of high and low fertility, although there are important differences in crop yield favoring high soil fertility.

The exception is timothy hay grown on fertilized soil. It is significantly higher in protein, carbohydrates, and ash, and lower in crude fiber than timothy grown on unfertilized soil.

The study also showed that these crops have essentially the same nutritional value when fed to dairy cows. The cows did as well and remained in good health whether their ration was from either fertilized or unfertilized soil. Their milk showed no differences in chemical composition. When this milk was fed to rats, no developmental differences were noted that could be attributed to the rations. The milks were low in carotene and vitamin A, but we can attribute that almost entirely to the low content of carotene of the hays fed.

Cows have a tendency to secrete milk of uniform composition. If the rations are markedly low in nutrients, the first defense mechanism is to reduce the amount of milk rather than alter the composition of the milk. This same principle holds in the production of meat and eggs. Farmers therefore aim to get big crops and to feed animals adequate amounts of a balanced ration.

We know also that the vitamin A value of milk and milk products that contain butterfat varies. Studies at Beltsville show a direct relationship between the vitamin A value of butterfat and the amount of carotene in a cow's ration.

Forages are the main source of carotene, which is associated with greenness of the herbage. Lush green pasturage is an excellent source of carotene and explains the high vitamin A content of milk in summer. Carotene is easily lost during harvesting and preservation of forage for winter feed unless special precautions are taken. Methods of harvesting and preserving the forage have been developed to reduce this loss of carotene. The result is that the vitamin A value of the milk supply today is being improved steadily.

The amount of vitamin D in milk is low and variable, but it can be increased by using feeds high in vitamin D. Techniques for fortifying milk with vitamin D during processing mean that fluid milk and concentrated milk now on the market contain significant amounts of added vitamin D.

Milk is a good source of water-soluble vitamins, especially riboflavin and vitamin B_{12}. Micro-organisms in the cow's rumen synthesize them. They are absorbed and secreted in the milk. The amount of these nutrients in the ration therefore influences but little the amount that appears in the milk.

Because eggs are a good source of vitamin A, poultrymen use rations that are relatively rich in vitamin A.

Alfalfa leaf meal is a good, economical source of carotene for poultry feeds, but the amount used must be regulated because too much will cause dark-colored yolks. Yolk color is sometimes regulated to consumers' tastes. Other materials are used to build up the vitamin A content of the egg and at the same time to meet the hen's need for vitamin A. As the other vitamins and vitamin factors, minerals, and fatty acids in eggs can be influenced somewhat by the amounts of them in the ration, most laying rations now are composed to provide eggs with high content of vitamins.

Feeding practices strongly influence the quality of beef. Tests conducted cooperatively by the Department of Agriculture and the Michigan Agricultural Experiment Station indicated that limited finish feeding of cattle increases total weight and quality of meat. Although paired calves receiving the limited diet required 112 more days to be finished than full-fed calves, the limited-fed animals weighed 12.8 percent more than the full-fed animals at slaughtertime. The limited-fed animals also contained 25 percent more intramuscular fat.

Four experiments at the North Carolina Agricultural Experiment Station showed that the use of corn as a roughage supplement to lespedeza hay resulted in heavier cattle at slaughter, with a higher dressing percentage and carcass grade and more intramuscular fat, than animals eating the hay alone. The steers fed roughage alone had more lean meat in their rib samples, but the corn-supplement group had a higher ratio of lean to bone. Another test showed that the addition of corn to the roughage increased the tenderness of meat by 30 percent.

Another set of experiments at the North Carolina station indicated that beef acceptable to consumers can be produced by feeding relatively low amounts of feed concentrates if a full feed of good roughage is supplied. Full-fed steers did not produce more dressed carcass in relation to live weight than steers fed at an intermediate grain level, nor were they higher in carcass quality or market grade. Limiting the grain ration to two-thirds of full feed resulted in a saving of 128 pounds of concentrate feeds per 100 pounds of gain over concentrate requirements of full-fed steers.

At the South Carolina Agricultural Experiment Station, steers consuming 0.9 pound of concentrated feeds a day per 100 pounds of live weight, with cottonseed hulls as roughage, had a higher percentage of tender meat and more of it than similar steers fed an equal amount of corn with lespedeza hay as roughage. The difference in the proportions of fat and lean was small. When the concentrate ration was increased to 1.1 pounds, the steers differed little in dressing percentage, tenderness, and other factors of meat palatability, but those getting the concentrates had higher proportions of fat and total edible meat. Steers that got 1.5 pounds more of the concentrated feed had higher proportions of fat and edible meat and more tender meat than the corn-fed steers.

Efficiency in feeding is important in raising hogs because feed may account for 80 percent of all production costs. Good progress has been made. The feed needed to produce a pound of gain in hogs dropped from 5.1 pounds in 1920–1924 to 4.5 pounds in 1950–1954.

The first concern in feeding is to provide a nutritionally adequate gestation diet for the bred gilt or sow in order to get the maximum number of strong pigs at birth. Abundant green grazing insures against nutritional deficiencies and also cuts feed costs.

A survey of 1,419 hog farms in Minnesota showed that net returns over the cost of feed were 39 percent greater on farms where good pasture was provided than where hogs were raised in dry lots. Feeding corn silage to bred sows also saves money. Where neither good pasture nor silage is available, the use of good legume hay or alfalfa meal is recommended.

The number of strong pigs born per litter has an important effect on production costs. Each litter represents an investment of about 40 dollars. If only 6 pigs are born alive, each costs 6.67 dollars; but if 10 pigs are born, each costs only 4 dollars. As an example of good production efficiency, 25 farmers named Master Swine Producers in Iowa in 1957 had 517 sows that averaged 10.8 pigs farrowed, 10 pigs weaned, and 9.4 pigs marketed per litter.

To get the best results, it has been shown that starter rations for suckling pigs are advisable. It is next necessary for farmers to push for high gains at early ages when feed efficiency is highest. The use of a good starter ration to supplement the milk of the dam will increase the 56-day weight of young pigs by about 10 pounds, or 30 to 35 percent.

Rations for fattening swine for market and the protein-mineral concentrates for feeding with grain now usually contain antibiotic-vitamin B_{12}. Feeding these supplements can increase gains by as much as 15 percent and reduce feed required per unit of gain 2 to 5 percent.

Protein is probably the most limiting factor currently in swine rations, because the grains most commonly used are low in protein, protein concentrates are more costly than the grains, and the protein in the grains and plant protein concentrates tends to be deficient in some essential amino acids.

Recently, however, it has been found that lower levels of protein can be fed to hogs if consideration is given to the quality of protein used and the proportions of essential amino acids provided.

Forced production and increased growth rate in hogs increased their mineral needs. Costly deficiencies do occur in swine rations, although mineral supplements are relatively cheap. Calcium and phosphorus requirements have been carefully investigated, and the importance of a suitable ratio of calcium and adequate vitamin D is well known.

Supplementing a calcium deficiency can be overdone. It predisposes young pigs to an apparent zinc deficiency, which results in parakeratosis and depressed growth. The use of supplementary zinc has been studied.

The feeding of lambs is best met by the use of good pasturage and harvested forage. Sheep, like other ruminants, are able to synthesize vitamins of the B complex and to alter proteins so that these nutritive requirements may be obtained from these two sources.

Roughage of a good grade also provides all the mineral requirements of sheep, except salt. Although sheep are able to use different types of pasture and browse plants, profitable lamb production depends on the feeding of good legume or mixed hay with or without silage to the ewes during gestation. Supplemental concentrates also must be supplied to ewes during late gestation and early lactation. This is the only time grain needs to be fed to ewes.

The use of pelleted rations has increased. They allow self-feeding of the lambs and bring greater feed efficiency and a more rapid gain rate.

Vitamin A is stored in the fat of beef cattle. Most of the carotene consumed by beef cattle comes from forages. Carotene and other forage pigments increase the yellow color in meat fat. Consumers sometimes object to highly yellow-colored fat. Feeders therefore try to limit the carotene consumption of steers being readied for market.

Not much vitamin A or yellow color collects in the fat of sheep and hogs. Red meat, of course, is an excellent source of protein, and it is high in iron. Pork is rich in two important water-soluble vitamins, thiamine and niacin.

Feeding vitamin and mineral supplements, other than carotene, to meat animals does not materially increase the amounts of these nutrients in the meat, but their inclusion in rations often prevents deficiencies, improves feed conversion efficiency, and so lowers the cost of production.

Feeding practices have a great influence with all types of livestock, on the rate of growth, and the amount and efficiency of production.

The amount of feed available is most important of all. The balance of nutrients in the feed supply in terms of the requirements of the individual animal is also important.

The factor that contributes most to the current high cost of production— and hence to the seemingly high cost of animal foods—is a feed supply on too many farms that is both limited,

unbalanced, and of poor quality. The large and varied supply of feedstuffs in the United States makes it possible to have balanced rations that provide essential nutrients at low cost.

Feed costs (and also total costs) of livestock production are low for a single animal when the production per animal is high. This is illustrated in a table, which shows the relation between milk production per cow, feed costs, and the returns over feed costs. If all cows were in the 10,000-pound class, dairy farmers would make more money and would be able to sell milk at lower prices than if their cows were in the 6,000-pound class, which was about average for dairy cows in the United States in 1958.

Because much livestock feed is produced on the home farm, production and harvesting practices as well as the way feed is used affect the nutritional quality of feed. Producing and using nutritious forages is a good way to feed livestock economically for high production. Rich forage means that relatively less costly supplementary feeds are needed to provide an adequate ration. Inefficient harvesting of forage for hay may result in high losses of protein, which must be made up by nutrients from other sources. The extent of the losses and how they are reduced by better methods of harvesting and preservation is shown in a table.

Various hormones or hormonelike products, antibiotics, minerals, vitamins, and chemicals are known to increase weight gains, increase milk and egg production, and in some instances improve efficiency of feed utilization. Some antibiotics also have protective advantages. These drugs have not changed the quality or value of the product. Before they are allowed for commercial use, it must be demonstrated that they or their residues are not contained in harmful amounts in the product the consumer eats.

FINALLY, livestock production has improved because of the development of better management skills. Good

Relation of Level of Milk Production to Feed Cost and Feed Cost per 100 Pounds of Milk Produced

Level of milk production	Value of product	Feed cost	Feed cost of 100 pounds milk
Pounds	Dollars	Dollars	Dollars
4,000......	199	109	2. 73
6,000......	301	146	2. 43
8,000......	377	168	2. 10
10,000.....	415	182	1. 82

management reduces production costs and in some instances improves the quality of animal products. Statistical studies show that the amount of labor required per animal and per unit of livestock production has decreased steadily in the past five decades.

Part of this saving is the result of substituting mechanical equipment for hand labor, but much of it is also attributable to more efficient use of labor and to improved animal performance.

Management changes have been extremely important in improving the production of eggs. As an important example, the use of artificial lights to alter the laying cycle has practically eliminated the spring glut of eggs that once flooded the egg market. Consumers now can have fresh eggs the whole year, and cold-storage eggs have virtually disappeared. Eggs are cleaner, too, because of the practice of keeping laying hens confined within wire-floored cages.

Several management improvements in handling hogs are worth noting. One is the experiments with administering male hormones to castrated hogs to increase the percentage of lean meat in them. Castration is necessary, to begin with, for male pigs to improve meat quality. It does, however, cause the animal to become fat. Although hormones have not come

into general use in hog production, some hormones are beneficial.

Feeding iodinated casein to lactating sows enables them to give more milk at a critical time in the development of the young pigs, and the practice contributes to lower mortality as well as higher growth rates among them.

Synchronization of rutting periods is being tried to make artificial insemination possible, thus reducing the need for keeping a large number of boars for natural service. Improvements in shelter arrangements for hogs constitute an indirect regulator of endocrine secretions by warding off the effects of extreme temperatures. Both extreme heat and cold have the effect on pigs of slowing growth rate and reducing feed conversion efficiency.

The most profitable management practices now being followed in the sheep industry include breeding selection for fast-growing and efficient animals, adequate and economical rations, and good control of diseases and parasites.

Two trends have been noticeable in the finishing of range lambs. More lambs are being marketed for slaughter directly from the range as a result of improved breeding. Some producers in the Southeast have been buying western feeder lambs for finishing on winter pastures.

The use of antibiotics as feed adjuncts has been successfully applied to sheep production. These drugs have reduced losses from enterotoxemia and increased gains and efficiency of feeder lambs receiving large amounts of feed concentrates. The value of antibiotics is limited mostly to feedlot operations involving large amounts of concentrates, however.

Improved control of diseases and parasites has helped sheep production considerably. Control of internal parasites, especially troublesome in humid areas, has been improved by pasture rotation together with the use of phenothiazine salt mixtures and drenching the sheep with phenothiazine or a mixture of drugs. The early use of

Farm Value and Marketing Bill as Percentage of Retail Costs for Farm Food Products Purchased for Domestic Consumption

	1946		1956	
Commodity group	Farm value	Market- ing bill	Farm value	Market- ing bill
	Percent	Percent	Percent	Percent
Meat products..................................	67. 1	32. 9	51. 6	48. 4
Dairy products.................................	55. 6	44. 4	46. 1	53. 9
Poultry and eggs...............................	70. 6	29. 4	62. 0	38. 0
Bakery and cereal products......................	28. 6	71. 4	19. 4	80. 6
Fruits and vegetables...........................	34. 7	65. 3	27. 2	72. 8

Adapted from table 33, Misc. Pub. 741, Agricultural Marketing Service.

antibiotics can substantially reduce losses from such disorders as pneumonia and foot rot. External parasites are controlled by improved insecticides in spray, dust, and dip form.

In the management of beef production, one of the outstanding recent improvements has been the adoption of diethylstilbestrol, a hormone, as a feed adjunct. Seventy-five percent of the cattle in feedlots received stilbestrol in 1957. The effect of the substance is to stimulate growth (19 percent on the average), with an average decrease in feed costs of 11 percent.

Feeding experiments at the Fort Reno Research Station in Oklahoma indicate that wintering cows may be fed a low-level supplemental ration with no drastic weight losses and that the cows may be bred to calve as 2-year-olds without lowering production.

The importance of providing beef with an adequate source of vitamin A has been proved by work at Beltsville. A deficiency of vitamin A caused a degeneration of testicular tissues in bulls and made them impotent. A vitamin A-deficient cow will come into heat and conceive, but will produce weak or stillborn calves.

The introduction of bulk storage of milk on the farm has resulted in lower labor requirements, lower transpor-

tation cost, and improved quality of milk.

The savings realized by improvements in livestock production practices are especially difficult to show in a period of rapidly rising prices such as the last decade. Nevertheless, a glance at the facts tells us that these savings are real.

A comparison of the retail prices of various food items between 1946 and 1956 shows that an increase in the prices of animal foods has been no greater than for other classes of foods. The cost of processing and marketing animal food products is actually less than the cost of processing and marketing other major classes of foods.

Livestock farmers received a larger share of the consumer dollar than other food producers. At the same time, however, livestock producers are more productive than they have been in the past. The total supply of food they have provided (at lower processing and marketing costs) is more liberal than it was previously.

R. E. HODGSON *became Director of the Animal Husbandry Research Division, Agricultural Research Service, Beltsville, Md., in March 1957. Dr. Hodgson, a graduate of the University of Wisconsin, surveyed dairying in seven Latin-American countries in 1942–1943.*

To Assure Good, Clean Meat

A. R. MILLER

THE meat inspection law makes it illegal to ship meat in interstate or foreign commerce unless the meat has been prepared and processed under the inspection provisions of the law and carries the mark of Federal inspection.

The meatpacker who wants to ship his products interstate or in export trade applies for the inspection, places his plant in compliance with requirements as to structural equipment and sanitation, receives a grant of inspection, and thereafter operates under the inspection supervision of the Federal program.

The law applies to the meat and edible products derived from cattle, sheep, swine, and goats. These include fresh and frozen carcasses and fresh and frozen cuts of them.

The inspection applies also to processed and manufactured meat and meat food products (like smoked ham and bacon) and cooked meats of all kinds (such as sausage and canned products) that are prepared from meat. Among the canned products are corned beef, cooked ham, corned-beef

hash, chile con carne, and spaghetti with meatballs.

The inspection begins with the live animal and continues through the slaughtering operation. It applies to the meat during its many stages of processing and manufacture and to the many ingredients that are used and the processes that are employed in its processing and manufacturing.

The purpose of the meat inspection law, which is administered by the Agricultural Research Service, and the inspection program, which is organized under the authority contained in the law, is to assure that the consumer obtains that protection to which he is entitled.

History and experience demonstrate that to provide the protection there must be an official inspection system integrated in the production line of the packing plants.

The consumer expects safety in his meat supply. He expects that there will be a strict regard for cleanliness in the production and handling of the meat. There should be no impairment of the nutritive value of meat or a

340

meat product. Its composition and labeling must be honest.

When a meatpacker applies for Federal meat inspection, he sends in with his application a plan that usually is a blueprint of his plant. The plan describes his premises, the structural features of the plant, the various operating departments, the kind and location of equipment in the slaughtering and processing departments, and the water, sewage, and lighting systems.

The plan is reviewed and compared with the standards that are essential to the effective functioning of the inspection program.

Should the applicant's plan fail to meet the standards in any respect, he is told how he can correct the shortcoming. When the applicant sends in the corrected set of plans, they are again reviewed. If they are found to be in compliance, they are marked with the stamp of approval.

The applicant then proceeds to place his plant and premises in conformance with the approved plan.

When that is done, he notifies the Meat Inspection Office, and a survey is made of the plant and its premises. They are compared with the specifications contained in the approved plan. When the plant and its premises are found to conform with the approved plan, a grant of inspection is issued to the packer and the inspection program is inaugurated in his plant.

As the animals intended for slaughter are assembled in the pens at the meatpacking plant, the inspector circulates among them to detect and eliminate any that are unfit for slaughter. An employee of the packer accompanies the inspector.

The animals that he designates as unfit for slaughter are pointed out to the plant employee, who moves them to a special pen, where they are kept until they can be given a more thorough examination. Following his examination, the veterinarian decides which are to be condemned and removed directly to the fertilizer department.

Others are classed as suspected of being affected with a condition that might require the condemnation of the carcass on post mortem examination. These suspects, so called, are handled separately from the regular kill when they are given a thorough post mortem examination. In disposing of the carcasses, the veterinarian considers both the symptoms demonstrated by the live animal and the post mortem findings.

Each carcass passed for regular kill receives a thorough post mortem examination. The inspectors take their positions right in the processing lines in the slaughtering department, where they are provided with space and facilities to perform their work.

The sanitation controls in the slaughtering departments are strict. Inedible parts of the animal are separated from the edible parts in a way that will assure against contamination. For example, the hide, the contents of the sinuses, gastrointestinal tract, and the urogenital organs may contaminate other parts unless care is exercised.

Slaughtering performed with facilities that meet the inspection standards and under the inspection control is a smooth, clean operation.

The inspector has the power to destroy a condemned product or correct an unsanitary condition. When he sees an unfit carcass or part of carcass, he removes it immediately from the production line. It is stamped many times with the word "condemned" and is removed promptly in a watertight container to the fertilizer department, which is completely separate from the slaughtering department. The condemned material is under the inspector's constant control until it has been converted into a nonfood article.

Should an unsanitary condition develop along the production line, the inspector presses a button and stops the line until the condition is corrected. Usually, however, it is an unclean article that requires additional attention and can be handled without stopping the production. The inspector affixes a "retained" notice to such an article. It may not be removed from the inspector's supervision until the condition requiring the retention has been corrected and he has removed the notice.

The inspector stops the use of unclean equipment, to which he affixes a "rejected" notice. Such equipment may be used again for handling edible products only after it has been placed in a clean condition and the "rejected" notice is removed by the inspector.

The inspection control does not end with the production of clean, disease-free meat in the slaughtering department. The product-control inspectors then take over. They see that the clean meat stays wholesome and that it is handled under sanitary conditions. Their control extends to the formulation, manufacture, and labeling of the many products that contain meat.

MANY INGREDIENTS or additives are combined with meat. They include flavorings, spices, water, curing materials, and other foods, such as flour, beans, pickles, spaghetti, and dairy products. The inspector sees that these are clean and fit materials to be used in a food product. Rejections of materials are made by the inspector for reasons ranging from insect infestation to filth and chemical contamination.

Many things can happen in the manufacturing process that might contaminate or affect adversely the wholesomeness of the product. Processing temperatures are frequently critical.

The prevention of adulteration requires constant vigilance. As investigations are conducted by food technologists in their efforts to improve foods, improve methods of food processing, and effect economies in the processing of foods, a great many food additives are developed.

Examples are agents that serve to prevent foaming, accelerate color fixation, develop flavor, retard flavor reversion, inhibit rancidity, prevent coagulation, enhance color, improve emulsification, improve tenderness, re-

duce the amount of cooked-out juices, and clarify the product.

All of them serve useful purposes and help the processor to provide the consumer with improved products. But this is true only if the product can be eaten safely, there is no concealment of inferiority, and the nutritive value of the food is not lowered.

When an inspected meatpacker wants to use a newly developed additive or wants to make a new use of a previously approved additive, he asks approval for such use. His request, addressed to the Meat Inspection Office, contains full information concerning the additive.

In handling the request, the first consideration is safety. The packer is required to show that the proposed additive is nontoxic and when used as proposed will not create an unsafe condition in the food of which it is an intended ingredient.

New chemical additives usually require considerable investigation and carefully planned feeding tests with animals to demonstrate their safety. Anyone who wants to introduce a new chemical additive has to prove it is safe, using methods that are acceptable to the inspection program.

There are also indirect additives. For example, packaging materials must be safe to be in contact with the meat without transferring toxic materials to it. Also, foods must be kept safe from pesticide residues and those that might result from treating animals with estrogenic compounds, antibiotics, and similar agents.

The use of plastic materials as packaging materials for food products has prompted the development of nontoxic synthetic resins, plasticizers, stabilizers, lubricants, and pigments. Plastic packaging materials and others intended for use at an inspected meatpacking plant are reviewed to make sure they contain nothing toxic.

Labels on meat products must not be misleading concerning the composition of the product. Statements of ingredients must identify the actual ingredients, which must not be worded in a way that will mislead the purchaser concerning the relative amounts of the various ingredients used. Illustrations on labels must not be misleading as to the composition or character of the product they pertain to.

Terms denoting quality must truthfully represent the product to which they refer. The statement of the quantity of contents must actually represent the product and it must be stated in familiar terms. Labels must not misrepresent nutritive value.

Definitions and standards of identity are developed for the various meats and meat products to assure that the inspected meat or product will conform with the purchaser's expectancy for the article labeled with a particular name of product.

These definitions and standards place maximum limits on the use of such additives as moisture, flour, and many other inexpensive ingredients. They also identify minimum meat levels to assure that the product contains at least the full amount of meat that the purchaser is entitled to expect under a particular name.

Sausage is an example of the kind of food that lends itself to adulteration through substitutions of other ingredients for meat. Limited amounts of moisture, certain cereals, and nonfat dry milk contribute flavor and texture to certain classes of cooked sausage; excessive amounts of them violate the standard, and the result is an adulterated product.

When the inspection program undertakes to promulgate a standard of identity for a particular meat food, it must first ascertain just what the purchaser expects to receive when he buys such food.

This so-called consumer expectancy is sort of a factual composite of information gleaned from cookbooks, chefs, questionnaires, and current and historical merchandising practices. In frankfurters and bologna, for example, the added moisture must not exceed 10 percent, and the use of fillers is limited to 3.5 percent. When a filler is used, its presence is declared in the name of product, as, for example, "Frankfurters, cereal added." The statement of ingredients on the label for such a product includes, of course, a declaration of all ingredients.

Corned-beef hash must contain at least 35 percent of cooked beef. Meat stews are required to contain not less than 25 percent of meat; chile con carne, not less than 40 percent of meat; chile con carne with beans, not less than 25 percent of meat—all computed on the weight of the fresh meat.

Similar requirements apply to such meat foods as spaghetti with meatballs and sauce, scrapple, hamburger, ham spread, tongue spread, pork sausage, and pork with barbecue sauce, to mention a few.

THE MEATPACKER whose plant is inspected cooperates in the producing of meat foods that conform with the prescribed standard.

He realizes that meat inspection standards that protect the consumer also protect his market. He knows that an expanding livestock and meat industry will prosper in this country only when the purchaser will buy the products of this industry with confidence knowing that they are clean, wholesome, free from adulteration, and truthfully labeled.

Each meatpacker insists, however, that the controls that are necessary to accomplish this be applied also to his competitors. Competition and economic pressure being what they are, these objectives cannot be attained without the servicing of industry by an official meat inspection system. The Federal meat inspection program is organized to accomplish this effectively in the 1,300 plants in the States.

A. R. MILLER *became Director of the Meat Inspection Division, Agricultural Research Service in 1944. He is a graduate (in veterinary medicine) of Iowa State College and of the Georgetown University Law School.*

What Grades Mean

ROY W. LENNARTSON

THE Agricultural Marketing Service administers extensive inspection and grading programs that have much to do with the quality and wholesomeness of foods we eat.

They help consumers, producers, distributors, and retailers.

They have become essential in our complex distribution system. Just as pounds, dozens, and quarts are accepted as measurements of quantity, the terms *U.S. Grade A, U.S. Fancy, U.S. Choice,* and *U.S. Inspected for Wholesomeness* are accepted as official measurements of quality.

Federal grade standards and specifications have been established as nationally uniform measures of quality for more than 100 foods, including meat, dairy and poultry products, fruit and vegetables, and grain and grain products.

Programs that provide inspection of the wholesomeness of ready-to-cook poultry and continuous inspection services for plants processing fruit and vegetables also are available.

The use of Federal grade standards and the inspection service for processed fruit and vegetables are on a voluntary—not mandatory—basis.

Beginning in January 1959, all poultry and poultry products shipped in interstate commerce must be officially inspected for wholesomeness. This development placed poultry products on the same basis as red meat in this respect.

The First World War created the setting for official Federal inspection services. Standards for grades of beef for military procurement were developed, and a system of reporting market prices and supply conditions was established.

Then followed standards for fruit and vegetables, butter, and Cheddar cheese immediately after the war and for poultry and eggs in 1923.

The first mandatory Federal inspection program came with the Meat Inspection Act of 1906, which required that all meat in interstate commerce be federally inspected. It is administered by the Agricultural Research Service.

The Poultry Products Inspection Act was adopted in 1957 and became fully effective January 1, 1959. The act requires that all poultry and poultry products sold, shipped, or handled in interstate or foreign commerce be federally inspected and approved for wholesomeness.

The most comprehensive legislation concerning inspection and grading of agricultural products is Title II of Public Law 733, known as the Agricultural Marketing Act of 1946. This act directed the Secretary of Agriculture: "To develop and improve standards of quality. . . . To inspect, certify, and identify the class, quality, quantity, and condition of agricultural products when shipped or received in interstate commerce, under such rules and regulations as the Secretary of Agriculture may prescribe . . . to the end that agricultural products may be marketed to the best advantage, that trading may be facilitated, and that consumers may be able to obtain the quality product which they desire. . . ."

Official standards of quality have been promulgated since 1918 for all major commodities and others of minor importance.

Originally they were developed for use by producers in preparing their product for markets and by distributors for trading in wholesale quantities and terminal market transactions. They continue to be of major importance in this respect.

More recently they have become increasingly useful to retailers in buying and selling and to consumers in buying.

The official grade standards reflect the opinions and needs of broad segments of the industry. No standard is promulgated or modified in any significant respect without giving the public a chance to express opinions about it. That is required by law under the Administrative Procedures Act. It also is essential to the development of objective and practical standards usable by interested persons and groups.

Official standards of quality are correlated closely with the standards of identity promulgated by the Federal Food and Drug Administration.

The use of official standards, with a few exceptions, is not mandatory. Their main value is to be a marketing aid to be used by producers, dealers, wholesale commission merchants, and retailers as they see fit. They provide a common language among producers and dealers for trading purposes for a commodity. They facilitate the development of standardization in buying procedures for many organizations. They have provided a merchandising instrument or technique in numerous food retailing establishments.

Official grade standards by themselves would have limited use or value in our distributive system. The Department of Agriculture, when grade standards were being developed, therefore began to establish an official system of inspection and grading.

Originally limited in scope, it has become nationwide and now is available at practically all major shipping points and major and secondary markets in all States.

Today the Agricultural Marketing Service employs some 4,500 Federal inspectors and graders. They inspect or grade or supervise the activities of some 8,500 State employees or individuals officially licensed by the Agricultural Marketing Service to inspect or grade food products.

The Department from the outset has followed a policy of encouraging cooperative activity with States and market agencies in the inspection and grading service. Some 296 cooperative agreements were in effect in 1959 for this purpose, mostly with State departments of agriculture. This policy has been effective in making the services readily and conveniently available to producers and dealers. It has done much to stimulate and maintain greater interest among those responsible for developing efficient marketing programs in States and communities.

The law requires that the permissive Federal inspection and grading services be supported by fees and charges to the user to cover as nearly as possible the cost of the service. This is not true generally with respect to the inspection or grading services that are mandatory.

As a voluntary program, for example, the poultry inspection service was practically self-supporting through fees and charges assessed the users. In 1957 these charges totaled nearly 3 million dollars, and about 50 percent of all poultry shipped in interstate commerce was inspected under the program. After January 1, 1959, all plants processing poultry for interstate shipment must have inspection, but the cost of the service will be paid by Federal appropriation. The annual cost of the service will likely exceed 10 million dollars.

The inspection and grading services performed by the Agricultural Marketing Service involved expenditures of about 25 million dollars in 1957. Of this, about 18 million dollars were paid by users of the service under the permissive programs. In addition, an estimated 17.5 million dollars, derived primarily from fees and charges, were expended by local cooperating agencies.

The amount of fees and charges collected under the permissive programs gives some indication of the importance of official standards of quality in our marketing system.

Thus far we have dealt with the overall aspect of quality standards and their application and use. In order to present a more detailed picture of their application in terms of specific commodities, the rest of this chapter deals with these activities as they are administered in the Fruit and Vegetable, Livestock, Poultry, and Dairy Divisions of the Agricultural Marketing Service. These commodities are the main ones that consumers buy in the form or state in which they are certified as to quality or wholesomeness.

For example, although meat is graded in carcass or wholesale cut quantities, the grade stamp is applied in such a way as to carry through to the consumer. Butter similarly is graded in churn lots, but the pound print generally carries the grade designation for the consumer's benefit. In contrast, a bushel of U.S. No. 1 wheat loses its identity when it is processed into flour or breakfast food, for which there are no official grade standards.

THE FRUIT and Vegetable Division is responsible for the inspection of fresh fruit, vegetables, and related products (including such items as tree nuts and peanuts) and of processed fruit, vegetables, and a group of other products, such as honey, maple sirup, coffee, and spices.

The use of the inspection services (like the use of the U.S. grades) is not compulsory, except in instances in which Federal or State marketing agreements and orders may require that marketings of a commodity be limited to specified grades and in which inspection for compliance with the prescribed grades is compulsory.

Most of the grade standards for fresh fruit and vegetables are designed for wholesale trading. With the more widespread use of prepackaged fresh fruit and vegetables, however, there has been a need for grade standards that are adapted especially to the retail level of trading. Several retail grades have been developed, as for potatoes, carrots, spinach, tomatoes, broccoli, celery, and corn on the cob.

Only a few vegetables and fruit are marked as to U.S. grade when displayed at retail, however, even though most of the transactions up to the retail level may have been made on the basis of these grades and the wholesale containers may have carried the mark.

The grades for fresh fruit and vegetables generally are designated by numbers, names, or a combination of the two. The basic trading grade is U.S. No. 1. Premium grades are established for some commodities, as U.S. Extra No. 1, U.S. Fancy, and U.S. Extra Fancy. Also, there are lower grades, as U.S. Commercial or U.S. Combination, U.S. No. 2, and U.S. No. 3.

Any product not meeting the lowest grade is designated as "unclassified." The basic grade designation in the series of consumer standards is U.S. Grade A, the premium grade is U.S. Grade AA, and the lower grade is U.S. Grade B. "Unclassified" products in the trading standards become "Off-grade" in consumer standards.

About 85 percent of the fruit and vegetable crop was packed in 1958, in accordance with Federal standards, and the equivalent of 1.4 million carloads was officially inspected.

The inspection service for fresh fruit and vegetables is organized and operated on a somewhat different basis from the service for processed products.

The inspection of fresh fruit and vegetables at shipping points is performed in cooperation with State agencies, usually the State department of agriculture. Inspectors are State employees, but are trained, licensed, and supervised for technical competence by the United States Department of Agriculture. Practically all inspections at shipping point are on a lot basis, usually railroad carloads or motortruck loads.

A second type of inspection of fresh fruit and vegetables is available on a Federal-State basis—the inspection of raw products to be used for processing against special Federal grade standards. It was developed with emphasis on the quality factors that processors pay most attention to. This inspection assures the grower that he receives full value for the quality of the raw material he delivers. It protects the processor against the delivery of produce of unacceptable quality and gives him information he can use in his processing operations: When he knows the quality of his raw material, he can better plan his operations to produce the type and quality of finished products that consumers want.

A third type of service is inspection in terminal markets. It usually is made to determine compliance with Federal or State grades claimed by shippers or to determine the condition of the produce, which may have deteriorated in transit to market.

Three types of official inspection service are available for processed products. The first is lot inspection, in which at the request of seller or buyer specific lots are inspected and certified as to U.S. grade or as meeting the applicant's specifications.

Continuous inspection is available to processors who meet high standards of sanitation for plant and equipment. Inspectors are stationed in the plant at all times it is operating. The inspector checks sanitation, observes preparation of all raw materials, selects samples of the product at random, and issues daily reports. When final inspection of the finished product is completed, he issues certificates, as requested, showing the final grade of each lot packed. All products packed are eligible for labeling with the U.S. grade and a statement as to continuous inspection.

Pack certification also is available to processors whose plants meet the sanitary standards and use acceptable raw material. An inspector is assigned to the plant during the processing season to inspect and certify each lot of the product as it is packed. He also observes preparation of the raw material and checks the cleanliness of the plant. He need not be present at all times during the processing operations, as is required under continuous inspection.

Grade designations for processed fruit appear as a combination of letter and name. The top grade is U.S. Grade A or U.S. Fancy. The lower grades are U.S. Grade B or U.S. Choice and U.S. Grade C or U.S. Standard. Any product not meeting the lowest grade is designated as substandard.

Processed vegetables carry the same designation, except that the second grade is U.S. Grade B or U.S. Extra Standard. About 60 percent of the canned and 90 percent of the frozen production were packed in accordance with Federal standards in 1958, and 300 million cases of processed products were officially inspected.

THE LIVESTOCK DIVISION administers programs to develop grade standards and purchase specifications and to grade livestock and meat.

Safeguards providing for the purity and wholesomeness of meat entering interstate commerce is a responsibility of the Agricultural Research Service under the Meat Inspection Act. Similar protection is provided by requirements as to minimum sanitation and inspection of the Agricultural Marketing Service as a prerequisite for the grading of meat that is not inspected federally.

Federal grade standards are used in the grading of meat and in the livestock and meat market reporting services of the Agricultural Marketing Service. In addition, the official grade standards are used as references in all trading and so form a common language for identifying characteristics of quality in private transactions throughout the entire process of converting livestock to meat. They serve as guides to producers in planning production to meet particular desires of the market and in determining the best time and place to market livestock.

Grade is an important part of the evaluation of animals by buyers and sellers at the livestock market. Packers are concerned with grade in many of their operations—buying livestock, selecting a product for a particular use, and selling meat. In meat distribution at wholesale and retail, Federal grades also are a uniform designation of quality. Thereby they facilitate transactions.

Consumers have placed increasing reliance on grade as an assurance of the quality of meat they desire and as a guide in the selection of the cooking method and use for various cuts. Federal grades thus serve the function of reflecting consumers' desires to producers at all stages of marketing.

Purchase specifications also provide a device by which to evaluate specific factors. Specifications for use in meat procurement, however, normally prescribe requirements for several factors besides grade. As an example, weight selections, cutting and trimming methods, details of processing, ingredient formulas, packaging, and similar requirements often are included. They provide safeguards for the buyers and sellers and contribute

These are the Federal grade marks for beef that may be found in retail stores. Two other grades of beef—Cutter and Canner—are ordinarily used in processed meat products and are rarely, if ever, sold as cuts in retail stores.

to more orderly and satisfactory relationship in purchase programs.

Three types of purchase specifications for meat and related products are developed for different purposes. Federal specifications are designed for Federal Government procurement. Department of Agriculture (USDA) specifications are designed for use in special purchase programs of the Department, such as surplus removal, school lunch, and similar purchases. Other specifications are designed for use by private agencies and State and local governments as a part of an Acceptance Service provided by the Department for assuring large-scale meat purchasers that products they buy comply with their specifications.

Approximately 50 percent of the beef, 16 percent of the veal and calf, and 36 percent of the lamb and mutton produced by commercial slaughterers were federally graded in 1958.

Meat grading is limited to plants operated under the Federal Meat Inspection Act or to the nonfederally inspected establishments that have facilities and an officially approved system of inspection. Periodic surveys are made of approved plants to insure that the minimum requirements are maintained always.

The grades that may be bought in retail stores are identified with one of six stamps: USDA Prime, USDA Choice, USDA Good, USDA Stndrd, USDA Comrcl, and USDA Utility.

For veal, calf, yearling mutton, and mutton, the kind of meat is indicated in addition to the grade stamp. Only the grade stamp appears on beef and lamb. Products accepted as conforming with purchase specifications are identified by stamping each piece of meat or sealed package with a stamp with the words, "USDA Accepted as Specified AC."

THE POULTRY DIVISION of the Agricultural Marketing Service develops standards for quality of poultry, eggs, and egg products; a standard for facilities; and operating procedures for the processing of poultry and egg products.

The standards are used widely and are a basis for purchase specifications of Government agencies, including the Department of Defense.

Plant sanitation is a prerequisite of the Department's program for inspection and grade certification of processed poultry and eggs.

The sanitation standards are divided into three main parts to cover building and plant facilities, equipment and utensils, and maintenance of sanitary conditions and precautions against contamination of products. The sanitary provisions set forth are considered as the minimum necessary to produce clean and sanitary food products.

Poultry processed under the inspection service is eviscerated only at the time of inspection. Standards cover the method of presentation of the carcass and viscera and the condemnation of parts of carcasses. Each carcass is opened on the production line so as to present the internal organs and body cavity for examination. The inspector examines each carcass by viewing both the external and internal surfaces. Consumers can have confidence that poultry products bearing the inspection mark are clean and wholesome.

Factors considered in grading for quality of ready-to-cook poultry include: Conformation; fleshing; fat; freedom from pinfeathers; freedom from cuts, tears, and disjointed and broken bones; and freedom from discolorations of skin and flesh blemishes and bruises.

The factors that determine the quality of shell eggs are shape, texture, and condition of shell; shape and condition of yolk; and firmness and clarity of the white.

Quality of poultry is designated as A, B, and C. Quality of shell eggs is designated as AA, A, B, and C.

The Poultry Inspection Service examines poultry, poultry products, and rabbits to determine whether they are sound, healthful, clean, and fit for human food. Carcasses found to be satisfactory are passed and certified as wholesome and eligible to be labeled with the official inspection mark. Unwholesome carcasses are rejected and condemned.

Inspection procedures include six operations:

The supervision of the sanitation of the entire plant; sanitation of the various phases of the processing operation, such as defeathering, eviscerating, chilling, packaging, and labeling; and sanitation, maintenance, and use of equipment and utensils.

An ante mortem inspection of the birds at the plant when it is deemed necessary.

A post mortem inspection of each carcass at the time of evisceration. This procedure consists of a careful examination of both external and internal surfaces as well as the lungs, kidneys, air sacs, livers, spleen, and visceral organs.

The supervision of further processing of products, such as poultry pies, dinners ready to heat and serve, and canned products. Only poultry that

This official inspection mark may be used on egg products processed under Government supervision.

This Federal inspection mark is used on tags or packages denoting that ready-to-cook poultry and poultry products so marked have been processed under sanitary conditions and found to be clean, healthy food. The round mark, formerly associated with the voluntary inspection program, is now used only on poultry and poultry products inspected under the compulsory inspection law, which went into effect January 1, 1959. The hexagonal mark is used in conjunction with the voluntary inspection program.

has been inspected previously for wholesomeness may be used in these processing plants.

The supervision of the marking and labeling to see that each package bears a label that includes the true name of the product, net weight, name of packer or distributor, official inspection mark, and the ingredients used in prepared poultry products.

The disposal of condemned carcasses or parts thereof that are found at the time of inspection to be unsound, unwholesome, or otherwise unfit for human consumption. The condemned products are treated in a way that will prevent their use for food and prevent the spread of disease if animals eat them.

Poultry is inspected by a veterinarian or by another trained person who is supervised by a veterinarian.

The grading programs provide for the cooperation of various State departments of agriculture and the extension services of the State colleges. Grade identification or grade labels in cooperating States may use the phrase, "Federal-State Graded."

Resident graders classify eggs as consumer grades, procurement grades, and wholesale grades, or according to contract specifications. When eggs are classified as consumer grades to be packaged with official identification, each egg is candled for quality and sorted for weight by a licensed grader or by a candler who has a limited license and whose work is checked by a grader.

Officially graded eggs may be marketed in cases or cartons. When cartoned eggs are officially graded, the grade mark is printed on the carton or on a label used to seal the carton. The U.S. grade, weight or size, date of grading, and plant number are indicated within the grade mark, on the tape used to seal the carton, or on the carton. The name and address of the packer or distributor must also be shown.

Ready-to-cook poultry must have been officially inspected for condition and wholesomeness and must be properly identified as an inspected product to be eligible for grading, whether the grading is done in an official plant or elsewhere.

Resident or continuous grading is done by Federal or State graders, who are stationed in the applicant's processing plant and are available at all times for grading work at the plant.

FEDERAL-STATE GRADED

This Federal grade mark for poultry may be used with the statement "Federal-State Graded" in conjunction with Federal-State grading programs.

This grade mark used on egg cartons, or on tapes sealing egg cartons, shows that the eggs have been graded in accordance with Federal standards for quality and size.

Processing plants operating under the Department of Agriculture poultry grading services may use the official grade mark on individually labeled poultry products.

The grade mark tells the quality (U.S. Grade A, B, or C). The shield design used as the official grade mark contains the letters "USDA" and the U.S. grade of the product.

When plants manufacture and pack-age egg products under the continuous supervision of a Federal or State grader or inspector, the entire processing operation is checked for adequacy of facilities, sanitation of equipment and operating procedures, selection of the raw material used, and handling and condition of the finished egg product.

Plants operating on a voluntary basis as official plants under Government supervision may have their product identified with the official inspection mark.

THE DAIRY DIVISION of the Agricultural Marketing Service offers voluntary inspection and grading services for many of the manufactured dairy products.

They include butter; Cheddar, Swiss, process, and cottage cheese; nonfat dry milk; dry whole milk; evaporated milk; sweetened condensed milk; sterilized whole milk; ghee; anhydrous milkfat; and miscellaneous dairy products.

These services are designed to provide a nationwide impartial and uniform system of quality evaluation of dairy products based on established and well-recognized U.S. standards for grades. Their widespread use encourages standardization and improvement of quality in dairy products and tends to promote more orderly marketing.

The grades generally are designated by letters or by names. For butter, however, both letters and numerical scores are used. Butter grade designations are U.S. Grade AA or U.S. 93 score; U.S. Grade A or U.S. 92 score; U.S. Grade B or U.S. 90 score; and U.S. Grade C or U.S. 89 score.

Four letter-grade classifications are used for Cheddar cheese (U.S. Grade AA, U.S. Grade A, U.S. Grade B, and U.S. Grade C) and for Swiss cheese (U.S. Grade A, U.S. Grade B, U.S. Grade C, and U.S. Grade D).

Name grades are used for all of the dry milk. Dry whole milk is classified as U.S. Premium, U.S. Extra, and U.S. Standard Grade. Dry buttermilk has two grades—the same as nonfat dry milk. Dry whey has only one grade, U.S. Extra.

Grade standards for dairy products encompass the full range of marketable quality and reflect differences in essential commodity characteristics for the benefit of producers, processors, and consumers of the product. They reflect, as far as possible, differences in quality of the raw material and hygiene of manufacture. There is no overlapping of quality between grades of a given dairy product, but a certain range or latitude in quality is allowed within each grade. As the grade decreases, the latitude in quality within each grade widens progressively.

Quality and stability of product depend largely on sound raw material and good manufacturing practices. The quality of a finished product can be no better than the raw material from which it is made. The value of good raw material can be nullified through poor processing facilities, improper processing methods, lack of sanitation, and improper packaging and handling.

Three major types of service are available to the dairy industry: Grading of products on a lot basis; "resident" grading and quality control service in processing plants on a contract basis; and plant inspection.

Grading on a lot basis is conducted at assembling, receiving, and shipping points and at terminal markets. This service enables buyers and sellers at distant locations to conduct transactions with confidence, relying on U.S. grade certificates as the basis for trading.

"Resident" grading and quality control service is designed to provide "in processing" inspection, including checks on quality of raw material used, effectiveness of processing methods and procedures, quality control laboratory testing for compliance with minimum specifications of the Department of Agriculture, and grading of the finished products in accordance with U.S. standards.

"Plant inspection" service is performed as a check at dairy plants to assist the management in improving operations wherever necessary. It aids in locating any deficiencies in equipment and facilities, processing methods and procedures, and encourages management to make corrections when necessary to produce dairy products of a stable character and of a quality commensurate with the quality of raw material used. More than 1,100 dairy plant inspections were performed in 1957 by graders licensed by the Department of Agriculture.

USE OF THE SERVICE has grown from a total of about 73 million pounds of dairy products graded in 1927 to more than 3 billion pounds in 1958.

This widespread use of the grading services has stimulated interest in quality and encouraged dairy processors to grade the milk and cream properly and to improve continually their manufacturing methods and procedures. This has brought about increased incentive to the producer in improving quality of milk and cream and has resulted in better returns to those who produce better quality.

ROY W. LENNARTSON *is Deputy Administrator for Marketing Services of the Agricultural Marketing Service, the Department of Agriculture. He is a native of Minnesota, a graduate of the School of Agriculture of Minnesota, and the College of Agriculture, University of Maryland.*

Because the science of nutrition is a relatively new science we cannot afford to crystallize our opinions and become resistant to change. We must recognize individual variability and attempt to learn more about it.—DENA CEDERQUIST, in Journal of Home Economics, February 1957.

Fish and the Fishing Industry

ANDREW W. ANDERSON

FISH is about 18 percent protein, which is complete, well balanced, and not easily affected by the usual cooking methods. It is 85 percent to 95 percent digestible.

An average serving furnishes more than enough animal protein to meet the usual daily need for protein. Fish supply 5 percent to 10 percent of the Nation's supply of animal protein for human food requirements.

The amount of fat in fish is less than 1 percent (in cod, haddock, whiting, rockfish, and sole) to 20 percent (in salmon, mackerel, lake trout, and butterfish). The fat is easily digested and is used readily by the body tissues.

Continuing research has established the nutritive value of some of the unsaturated fatty acids peculiar to some fish.

These fatty acids are unstable and reactive compounds. They are designated as unsaturated because some of the possible chemical bonds holding the constituent atoms together are not filled. Their inclusion in animal diets promotes growth and reduces the level of cholesterol in the blood serum. Cho-

lesterol, a waxy alcohol, may be deposited on the inner walls of arteries when it is present in too high concentrations in the blood serum. Some researchers believe there is a connection between the presence of excess cholesterol in the blood and the occurrence of atherosclerosis, a common form of heart disease.

The vitamin content of fish varies. An average serving of 3.5 ounces of cooked salmon and mackerel, which are fat fish, provides about 10 percent of the daily requirements of vitamins A and D. A similar serving of either fat or lean fish would satisfy about 10 percent of the thiamine, 15 percent of the riboflavin, and 50 percent of the niacin requirements.

The mineral content of the edible part of most fish includes satisfactory sources of magnesium, phosphorus, iron, copper, and iodine.

Shellfish (clams, crabs, lobsters, oysters, scallops, and shrimp) has an abundance of these minerals—about as much as milk. The softened bones in canned fish, which are good to eat, are good sources of calcium and phosphorus. An

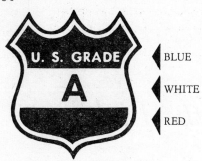

Shield using red, white, and blue background or other colors appropriate for label.

Shield with plain background.

Statement enclosed within a shield.

U. S. GRADE A

These symbols appear on many fishery product labels. They indicate that the product has been processed under supervision of a Government inspector.

average serving of six oysters supplies more than the daily need of iron and copper.

Many species have sodium values well within prescribed dietary limits of 100 milligrams per 100 grams of fish and are suitable for use in diets in which the amount of sodium is kept low.

Standards for the fishery products in the United States became available to the domestic fishing industry in 1956 on a voluntary basis. They were a significant development and a useful marketing aid.

Standardization of products and the accompanying inspection and certification improve processing; make buying, selling, and distributing more efficient; aid in settling disputes as to prices, quality, storage, and transportation; permit better comparison of market supplies and prices; make possible the sale and purchase of fishery products in commodity exchanges for future delivery; furnish a more reliable basis for bank loans; make possible more adequate production-control programs; and achieve premium prices for certified premium products.

The first standards were for grades for frozen fried fish sticks, a new product that had zoomed in 2 years to a production of 50 million pounds annually. But great variations in quality and prices resulted in unprofitable operations and a sharp decline in the number of processing plants.

The remaining processors accepted the standards without delay. They promptly asked for continuous plant inspection, rather than only certification of one lot at a time. They thereby confirmed the value of prior research as to weight changes in cooking, losses in cutting the sticks from the blocks, detecting bones by X-ray, and developing a method for determining the amount of breading.

The first program had to do with the development of the standards by the Department of the Interior and promulgation, inspection, and certification by the Department of Agriculture. The entire program became a responsibility in 1958 of the Department of the Interior.

The fishery products that meet the official standards can carry the United States shields on their labels. These symbols indicate the grade of the product and show that it was packed under the continuous supervision of a trained Government inspector. They assure the consumer that he is buying a good product.

When it is more efficient to do so (because of geographical location or the production of both fishery and agricultural products in one plant) the Department of Agriculture and the Department of the Interior have agreed to arrange for a single inspector from either agency to certify the grade and condition of either agricultural or fishery products.

The fee for the voluntary inspection and grading is paid by the buyer or seller who requests the service.

Three kinds of inspection and grading services were available in 1959.

One is continuous inspection by an inspector stationed in the plant during the operating hours. He makes daily reports to the management on plant operations, inspects the product, and issues certificates showing the grades.

Another is the sampling of specific lots by an inspector. He takes representative samples of the product, examines them as requested or for compliance with the appropriate standard, and issues an official certificate.

The third is inspection of unofficially drawn samples. Samples submitted by a processor or a buyer are inspected, and a certificate as to the quality of those particular samples is issued.

Standards for grades were effective or were being developed in 1959 for frozen fried sticks, frozen blocks from which the sticks are cut, frozen raw breaded shrimp, salmon and halibut steaks, frozen breaded and unbreaded portions, and one or more varieties of frozen fillets. More and more processors are accepting the voluntary program, and the promulgation of three standards a year probably will be required. Consumers thus can look forward to an increasingly greater variety of foods of known quality.

Federal specifications for food products aid Government buyers and industry suppliers by standardizing items and packaging; reducing the numbers of sizes, kinds, and types; permitting competitive bidding on an equitable basis; and serving as part of a legal contractual document.

Catch of Fish and Shellfish, 1921–1957

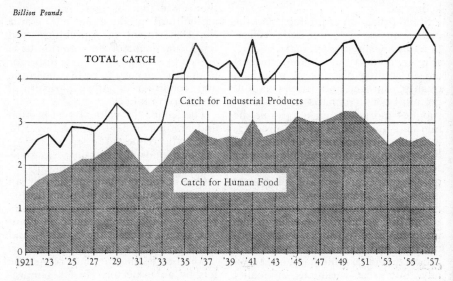

Billion Pounds

TOTAL CATCH

Catch for Industrial Products

Catch for Human Food

World Catch of Fish, Crustaceans, Mollusks, Etc.

By Countries, 1957

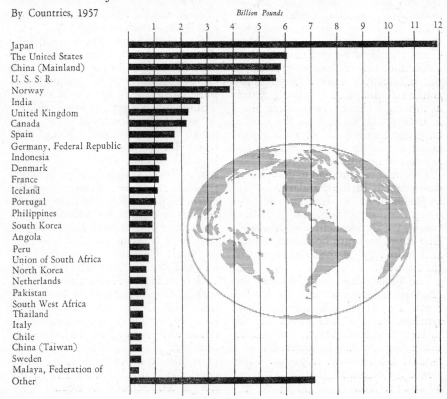

Billion Pounds

Japan
The United States
China (Mainland)
U. S. S. R.
Norway
India
United Kingdom
Canada
Spain
Germany, Federal Republic
Indonesia
Denmark
France
Iceland
Portugal
Philippines
South Korea
Angola
Peru
Union of South Africa
North Korea
Netherlands
Pakistan
South West Africa
Thailand
Italy
Chile
China (Taiwan)
Sweden
Malaya, Federation of
Other

The Bureau of Commercial Fisheries of the Department of the Interior has assigned to its laboratory in East Boston its responsibilities in this field.

Men at the laboratory determine needs of agencies, evaluate the products, conduct research, and prepare the specifications. Fifteen specifications for various forms of clams, crabmeat, fresh and frozen fish, oysters, salmon, sardines, scallops, shrimp, and tuna were in effect or were proposed in 1959.

THE STATISTICAL DATA available on the operations of the fishing industry are less comprehensive than those for most other industries. The Branch of Statistics of the Bureau of Commercial Fisheries must collect and disseminate most of the needed information because only a few States keep close track of the activities in their fishing ports and marketing centers. This is a sizable task, because American fishermen take 10 percent of the world's catch.

Field agents supplement the available State data with their own interviews to determine each year the number of fishermen (145,300 in 1957), the value of their catch (almost 1 million dollars daily), and the number of fishing craft of all kinds (84,050). They reported there were 100 thousand shoreworkers in 4,225 plants and, in all, 555 thousand persons engaged directly or indirectly in the catching, processing, and merchandising of fish and in such allied industries as shipbuilding, gear manufacture, and servicing.

Only 53 percent of the catch was used for human food. The rest became meal for chickens, fish oil for industrial use or export to Western Europe for use in margarine, canned food for pets, or bait to catch still more fish.

Of the catch for human food, 57 percent was utilized fresh or frozen, 40 percent was canned, and 3 percent was marketed as cured products—salted, smoked, or otherwise preserved.

At least 5 percent of the catch of fish for food is taken each month of the year, but almost 40 percent is taken in June, July, and August.

California caught the most fish—mostly tuna, mackerel, and sardines.

The fish taken in greatest volume—more than 35 percent of the total catch—was menhaden, a herringlike fish of the Atlantic and Gulf coastal waters. It is never seen on a dinner plate in recognizable form. Most consumers have never heard its name. Yet, processed into fishmeal, it is a small but important item in feed for chickens and hogs.

Shrimp has become the most valuable fishery product at the fisherman's level. Salmon and tuna, the former leaders, alternate in second and third places.

Fishermen fish mostly in the territorial waters or the high seas, directly off our coasts. Ten percent of our total catch was taken by the United States fishing fleet off Canada, Mexico, Panama, Ecuador, and Peru. Tuna brought back to southern California from Peru and Ecuador involve a round trip of about 8 thousand miles for the famous tuna clippers. A still smaller catch—5 percent—comes from our lakes and rivers, mainly the Great Lakes and the Mississippi River and its tributaries.

Nearly 10 million baited hooks awaited hungry or curious fish in 1957, but took only 9 percent of the catch, as compared to the 46 percent captured in purse seines. A purse seine encircles whole schools and entraps the fish when the bottom of the net is pursed, or closed.

The average person in the United States in 1958 ate 10.4 pounds of fish. (Japanese and Scandinavians average well over 40 pounds each; consumers in the United Kingdom eat about 22 pounds of fish each. A Canadian eats more than 13 pounds.)

Of the 10.4 pounds, fresh and frozen fish accounted for 5.6 pounds, and canned fish for 4.2 pounds. Only 0.6 pound was cured products. The consumption of tuna, the most popular canned fish among Americans, more

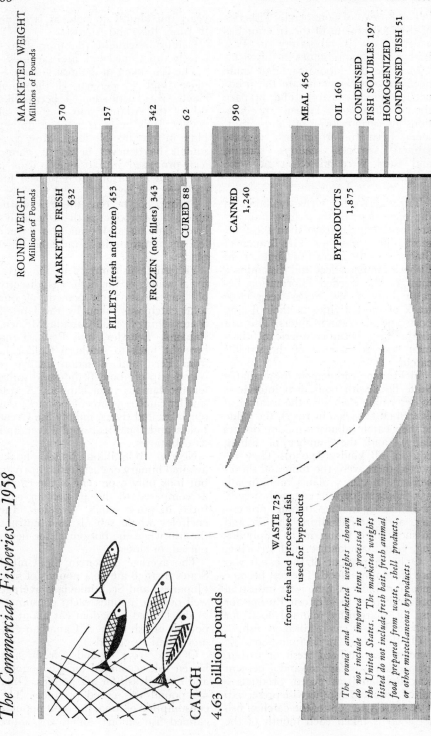

The Commercial Fisheries—1958

CATCH
4.63 billion pounds

ROUND WEIGHT
Millions of Pounds

MARKETED FRESH
632

FILLETS (fresh and frozen) 453

FROZEN (not fillets) 343

CURED 88

CANNED
1,240

BYPRODUCTS
1,875

WASTE 725
from fresh and processed fish
used for byproducts

MARKETED WEIGHT
Millions of Pounds

570

157

342

62

950

MEAL 456

OIL 160

CONDENSED
FISH SOLUBLES 197

HOMOGENIZED
CONDENSED FISH 51

The round and marketed weights shown
do not include imported items processed in
the United States. The marketed weights
listed do not include fresh bait, fresh animal
food prepared from waste, shell products,
or other miscellaneous byproducts.

than tripled since 1937—to 1.79 pounds per capita.

The use of canned salmon dropped from 2.43 pounds in 1937 to 1.07 pounds in 1958. Shrimp in all forms (0.95 pound) and fillets of cod, haddock, and ocean perch (1.49 pounds) each doubled its per capita consumption in the same period.

A preliminary review of the catch, employment of equipment and men, consumption, prices, the manufactured fishery products, values and investments, foreign trade, market patterns, and the world catch is published in April of each year. It is Fishery Leaflet 393—"Fisheries of the United States and Alaska." Free copies may be had by writing to the Bureau of Commercial Fisheries, Department of the Interior, Washington 25, D.C.

Market news service offices are maintained in seven of the country's main fishing ports and marketing centers. What these office staffs and their reporters in neighboring ports see and hear is reported the same day in "Fishery Products Reports." Copies are mailed to more than 9 thousand persons in the fishing industry, banks, insurance companies, transportation agencies, research organizations, service industries, and others who follow the detailed daily operations of the industry. Information is given about landings of vessels, fish exchange and wholesale prices, rail and truck shipments, imports, cold storage movements, frozen and canned packs, and prices. Conditions in other ports and markets are summarized.

The reports help stabilize the market, because the current factual information they present kills rumors. Such an equitable basis for trading has been established that buyers and sellers, even though in different cities, can use the current daily quotation as the contractual price when deliveries are made.

Complete information on the daily market news reports, monthly and annual summaries, and the monthly periodical, Commercial Fisheries Review, may be obtained by requesting from the Bureau of Commercial Fisheries a free copy of Fishery Leaflet 432—"Fishery Statistical Publications of the Bureau of Commercial Fisheries."

Programs to develop markets for fish seek to lift the domestic consumption of fishery products closer to the level of such direct competitors as poultry products.

The work of the Branch of Market Development includes efforts to encourage the use of fishery products in school lunch, institutional, and consumer menus; forecast marketing conditions; develop foreign markets; find new uses for underutilized species; and prepare such educational materials as recipes and motion pictures.

Gluts of some fishery products occur, but they are more readily avoided than surpluses of agricultural products. Often the fishermen can cease harvesting one kind of fish and shift to catching another variety. When surpluses do occur, market-development specialists work with industry to try to increase consumption. Cooperation is sought from large users of fishery products, such as groups of food stores and restaurant associations. Fish in oversupply are listed among the plentiful food products.

Foreign markets have been surveyed on a spot basis. Fishery attachés have been established by the Department of State in Mexico City and Tokyo, and others may be sent elsewhere.

Finding new ideas for underutilized species is difficult, because launching a new product is costly. The first economic uses consequently often are industrial or for animal feeding rather than for human food. Every technological and marketing technique nevertheless is tried to find a place for the product on the consumer's table, because it usually promises greater returns to the producer and processor and more variety and lower prices to the user.

Recipes are developed by home economists in modern laboratory kitchens. The recipes that score highest in palat-

Estimated Value of Fish and Fishery Products, 1957

At Production, Processing, and Distribution Levels

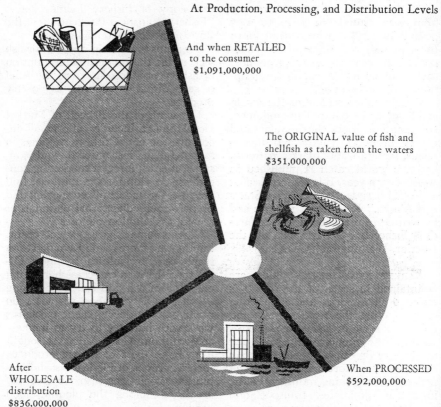

And when RETAILED
to the consumer
$1,091,000,000

The ORIGINAL value of fish and
shellfish as taken from the waters
$351,000,000

After
WHOLESALE
distribution
$836,000,000

When PROCESSED
$592,000,000

ability tests are issued in the "How To Cook——" series. Individual cookbooks cover the more important species, basic fish cookery, and fish cookery for groups of 100 persons. Most of the booklets give hints about buying and information on nutritive values. There is an illustrated publication on how to eat lobsters. Copies of the publications can be had from the Superintendent of Documents, Government Printing Office, Washington 25, D.C. They cost little.

The two major groups of fish—the finfish and shellfish—have enough variety to suit every taste and meet every need. There are about 200 commercial species of fish, but most people are familiar with fewer than 20 and recognize even fewer than that on a dinner plate.

Those with fins range in size from the diminutive silversides and white bait, which enjoy a good demand in New York's Fulton Fish Market around Christmastime, to the whales harpooned on the high seas. The tiny silversides end up fried in deep fat in batter in typical Mediterranean dishes. The best portions of the whales are imported as steaks, which are not unlike beef. Whales, although mammals, are responsibilities of the Bureau of Commercial Fisheries, because the term "fish" is usually construed to include all aquatic creatures.

Mollusks, in the shellfish category, include the minute coquina clams, which are found on the Florida beaches and are a main constituent of a delicious coquina broth. They

United States Supply of Edible Fishery Products
1947–1957, and Estimated Requirements, 1958–1975

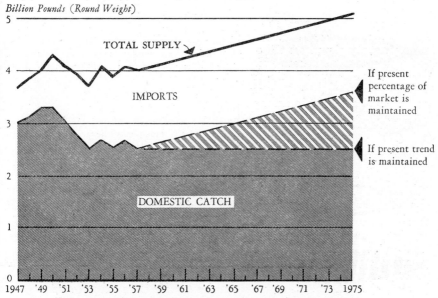

Billion Pounds (Round Weight)

TOTAL SUPPLY

IMPORTS

If present percentage of market is maintained

If present trend is maintained

DOMESTIC CATCH

1947 '49 '51 '53 '55 '57 '59 '61 '63 '65 '67 '69 '71 '73 1975

Estimated fishery requirements for 1975 are based on an estimated 30 percent increase in population (approximately 220,000,000 persons) and a corresponding 30 percent increase in consumption of fishery products (approximately 5,900,000,000 pounds). It was estimated that the increase in requirements from 1957 to 1975 would be a straight line progression.

include also a 10-pound bivalve, the goeduck, which is hunted for sport and food with a special shovel at low tide in Puget Sound.

Crustaceans include the tiny oyster crab, which lives inside its namesake. It often is eaten with raw oysters on the half shell. Sometimes partakers are unaware, but connoisseurs deem the experience a treat. Oyster crabs also are the basis for a delicious bisque, although assembling enough for a meal is a job.

At the other extreme is the small-bodied, long-legged Alaskan king crab, with a spread of as much as 5 feet and a weight of 7 to 10 pounds.

Also among the "shellfish" are frog legs, turtle steaks, octopus, and squid. Then there are the less common

foods. Sea urchins, a spiny brittle-shelled organism, is usually eaten raw. Sea cucumbers are found in Puget Sound but are better known as the dried and smoked "trepang" or *beche de mer* of the South Seas.

Consideration of quality, religion, or custom are met by the marketing of many shellfish—oysters, clams, blue crabs, and lobsters—alive in the shell, if desired. A few restaurants have live trout. Some markets sell live eels and carp.

The oyster, gulped from its shell, reaches the consumer with no preparation other than a possible last-second dunking in a sauce. The anchovy represents the other extreme. It has spent months resting in casks, while slowly aging to the taste, texture,

Purchasing Guide | Fresh and frozen fish are marketed in various forms for different uses. Knowing these forms or "cuts" is important in buying fish. The best known are:

WHOLE
As they come from the water. Before cooking, must be scaled, and the insides removed, and usually the head, tail, and fins removed. Ask your dealer to do this for you.

DRAWN
Whole fish with insides removed. Generally scaled before cooking, and usually the head, tail, and fins removed. Ask your dealer to do this.

DRESSED OR PAN-DRESSED
Whole fish with scales and insides removed, usually with head, tail, and fins removed. Ready to cook as purchased.

STEAKS
Cross-section slices from large dressed fish. Ready to cook as purchased.

FILLETS
Sides of the fish, cut lengthwise away from the backbone. Ready to cook as purchased. Practically boneless.

STICKS
Pieces of fish cut from blocks of frozen fillets into portions of uniform dimensions, usually about one-half inch wide, 3 inches long, and three-eighths inch deep, and weigh approximately 1 ounce.

CANNED FISH
Ready for use and includes many varieties of both fish and shellfish.

Ask your dealer's help.
When ordering fresh or frozen fish or shellfish tell your dealer how you plan to serve it. If you wish the head, tail, and fins removed from whole or drawn fish—or the fish cut in serving-size portions, ask your dealer to do it. He will also open oysters or clams ready for serving—or shuck them ready for cooking.

Amounts to buy.
A serving of fish is generally one-third to one-half pound of edible flesh. There-fore, for whole fish allow about one pound per person. For dressed fish allow one-half pound per person or three pounds for six people. For steaks, fillets, or sticks, allow one-third pound per person or two pounds for six people.

How to know good fish.
In selecting whole fresh fish, look for bright, clear, bulging eyes; gills reddish pink, free from slime or odor; firm elastic flesh—springing back when pressed.

and saltiness that have made it a popular tidbit.

Fish can be bought in the market in many forms—drawn for baking or steaked or spread in butterfly fashion for pan-frying or broiling. This minimum amount of dressing satisfies those who contend that bones left in add to the flavor. Then there are fillets for those who do not want to pick bones and for children who seem to prefer their fish portions to be completely edible.

Fish sticks, small pieces about finger size and an ounce in weight, need no preparation other than heating and serving. They were prepared first from cod and haddock, but their success brought forth sticks that use other species. The production of fish portions has been equally successful because the exact portions enable users to exercise the close control of the components of a meal required for profitable operations. They are supplied in uniform shapes, weights, and sizes to restaurants, industrial cafeterias, hospitals, and various other institutions that serve large numbers of meals. Newer developments are complete entrees or fish dinners, which need only heating and serving.

About 40 percent of the food fish is canned. Canned fish require no special handling, and canning gives fish a special flavor. For some fish, like tuna, canning is the most satisfactory means of preparation.

For those who like cured foods, there are smoked, salted, dried, and marinated products, for which fish and shellfish seem especially suited. Typical are kippered salmon, boneless salted cod, herring in vinegar or creamed sauce, and caviar.

Complete purchasing information is included in the Bureau's Circular 20— "Fresh and Frozen Fish Buying Manual." Copies can be obtained from the Superintendent of Documents, Government Printing Office.

ECONOMIC ANALYSES of the operations of the fishing industry have been less numerous and thoroughgoing than those of other industries.

The Bureau of Commercial Fisheries has begun to increase its studies of the economic position of the fishing industry within the national economy—the production, distribution, and consumption of fishery products; the economic effect of technological and biological developments in the industry; price levels, marketing, competitive products, and transportation rates; and tariff and trade problems.

Economists have calculated that fishery products increase threefold in value from fishermen to retailer—in 1958 from 370 million dollars to 1,150 million dollars. They have calculated that if we in the United States had no fishery resources, 11.4 billion dollars would have to be invested at 4 percent to equal the 1957 earnings of the industry's fishermen, vessel owners, processors, wholesalers, and the retailers.

Surveys of consumers' preferences have revealed that 9 of 10 households serve canned fish—the higher the income, the greater is the use.

Of special interest to packers of tuna and salmon was the finding that most tuna was eaten by persons 15 to 24 years old. The group that ate the most salmon was 55 to 59 years old.

Tuna packers were encouraged because so many consumers of their products were youthful and therefore were prospective customers for years ahead. Salmon packers realized that their future markets were endangered by major dependence on elderly consumers. Presumably this group had remained faithful to salmon over the years despite higher prices and the lessened availability that resulted from diminished salmon runs in Alaska and the diversion of most of the salmon pack to our Allies during the Second World War. The younger group had less canned salmon then, and they bought less of it.

Another survey revealed that fish is served in most households on any day of the week. Only in New England does the preference for Friday still prevail. On the other hand, it was found that one-half of the eating places in this country do not list fish on the menu.

The relationship of the prices paid to fishermen for their fish to the prices they pay for items they must buy to carry on their activities determines their ultimate profit. They have not been eligible for Government subsidies to close the gap between low returns and high operating costs. Bureau economists have worked out these ratios and found that most fish prices in 1958 were at levels that yielded the fishermen less profit than in the normal base year of 1942.

The average ad valorem equivalent of duties on all fishery imports was 5.5 percent in 1956, compared to 5.6 percent for all imports. Thirty-seven percent of the imported fishery products are on the free list. There are no domestic marketing programs or other plans that permit exclusion of competitive imports when they affect adversely program operations.

Imports furnish an important proportion of our fishery foods. They made up 38 percent of the total supply available for consumption in 1958, having more than doubled in volume in 10 years. Imports of fish have been increasing. They supply 62 percent of groundfish (mostly haddock, cod, and ocean perch) fillets, which come mostly from Canada, Iceland, and Norway.

Sixty-eight percent of our canned crabmeat was imported, primarily from Japan. About half of the canned tuna supply came from overseas, most of it from Japan. The Maine lobster competes with its Canadian neighbor, which enjoyed 44 percent of the market in 1958. Shrimp producers have yielded 41 percent of the domestic market to imports, mainly Mexican. Our sardines are produced in Maine and California; one-sixth of the sardine supply comes from Norway, Portugal, Spain, South Africa, and Japan.

We estimate that Americans in 1975 will eat the edible products from a catch of more than 5 billion pounds of fish if the present per capita consumption is maintained. A projection of the trend of imports in 1947–1957 suggests that foreign-produced fish will furnish almost 70 percent of our fishery food supply in 1975.

THE FISH AND WILDLIFE ACT of 1956 is the basic legislation under which the Bureau of Commercial Fisheries functions. The act established a national policy with respect to fish, which declared that the fishing industry could fulfill its proper function in the Nation's life only if its fundamental needs were satisfied consistent with public interest and in accord with the constitutional functions of Government.

The significant needs were spelled out as—

Freedom to develop new areas, methods, products, and markets in accordance with sound economic principles, as well as freedom from unnecessary administrative or legal restrictions that unreasonably conflict with or ignore economic needs;

Maintenance of an economic atmosphere in which domestic production and processing can prosper; protection from subsidized competing products; protection of opportunity to fish on the high seas in accordance with international law;

Assistance consistent with that provided by the Government for industry generally, such as is involved in promoting good industrial relations, fair trade standards, harmonious labor relations, and better standards of health and sanitation.

The act provided for the most efficient implementation of its functional provisions by providing further for the centralization of all primary Federal fishery activities in the Department of the Interior. A newly established United States Fish and Wildlife Service, consisting of a Bureau of Commercial Fisheries and a Bureau of Sport Fisheries and Wildlife, replaced the former Fish and Wildlife Service.

The fishery food industry that the Bureau of Commercial Fisheries is charged with watching over seeks its raw material from our waters rather than our land. It is based on a natural renewable resource that, with good management, can be expected to produce well far into the future. For example, the Grand Banks off Newfoundland have yielded good catches of cod to the vessels of a dozen countries for nearly five centuries.

Food fish usually are hunted—not farmed. Except for oyster farming and farm ponds, the fish-producing industry is still in the pursuit stage that the food-producing farmer evolved from centuries ago. Fishermen thus reap without sowing; their major attention is on their harvest. The equivalent of the farmer's efforts before the harvest is Nature's responsibility. This necessary dependence on natural phenomena—weather, water temperatures, ocean currents—to renew the fishery resources often results in great variations in supply. These in turn have significant effects on the volume and value of fish.

Our fishing industry is unusually independent. It prefers to pursue its course with a minimum of governmental assistance or the exercise of Federal or State authority. There is no Federal legislation authorizing subsidies or price supports or similar programs for fishery foods. The producers and consumers do benefit, however, from the research and similar services that the Government provides for most industries.

Financial support for the Bureau's food fish activities comes from the regular annual appropriations and Public Law 466, known as the Saltonstall-Kennedy Act. It was approved on July 1, 1954, to promote the free flow of domestically produced fishery products in commerce and to develop an increased market for fishery products of domestic origin. These purposes were to be achieved by conducting an educational service and technological, biological, and related research.

I give a few examples of the work done.

Research workers discovered the mechanism of discoloration in canned tuna and a method for preventing it. Substances in tuna flesh are subject to changes in color. Under different conditions, they may appear to be pink, brown, tan, or green. The condition apparently reflects a lack of vitamins in the flesh, as the addition of ascorbic acid (vitamin C) and nicotinamide, a B vitamin, is effective in returning the discolored flesh to its normal pink color.

New shrimp fishing grounds off the Alaska Peninsula were discovered by adapting a shrimp trawl brought from the Gulf of Mexico. Potential production around Kodiak Island is expected to reach 10 million pounds a year. The larger part of the catches consists of tiny pink Pacific shrimp, prized for their flavor. The remaining part is made up of equally desirable larger species.

Successful methods were developed for hatching channel catfish in commercial quantities for future growing in rice paddies and other inland waters. The cost of labor, chemicals, and facilities for rearing catfish in hatcheries is no greater than for trout. An annual production of 2 billion pounds of buffalofish, catfish, carp, bass, and crappie is possible if these or similar fish are raised in the nearly 2 million acres of rice lands in the five major rice-producing States.

An index of the numbers of downstream migrating pink salmon was established as a means of predicting the size of the returning adult runs. Fish traps placed in key streams in southeastern Alaska permitted the counting of the young salmon as they migrated to the sea. These counts form the basis for estimates that guide the industry in its plans for canning operations two seasons later.

Workers isolated various species of minute plants and demonstrated that they were satisfactory foods for oysters and clams. This discovery makes pos-

Monthly Catch and Utilization of Fish and Shellfish, 1957

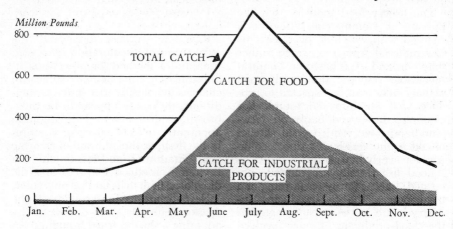

sible artificial propagation of these shellfish and the development of desirable market characteristics by selective breeding.

A wide variety of fishery products that can be preserved for food by nuclear radiation was screened to determine those which could be preserved by this process. The partial sterilization (radiopasteurization) of a large variety of fishery products (blue crabmeat, fresh and processed shrimp, fish fillets and steaks, and breaded fish sticks and portions) is practical. These findings, when applied by industry, will lengthen the storage life of fishery products held at 32° F.

The first authoritative tabulations of chemical compositions of many species of fish and shellfish were assembled for use by industry in marketing and for dietitians and other food specialists. Average figures were developed for the content of protein, fat, ash, moisture, sodium, and potassium in haddock, cod, salmon, shrimp, oysters, pollock, halibut, some species of sole, and many lesser known varieties.

Contracts for research and other projects are made with private research and educational organizations in an effort to utilize the best talents and facilities available, to expedite accomplishments, and to build up and sup-

port fishery research and service centers to supplement the activities of Federal and State groups.

During the first 5 years of the act, 196 contracts were let to 81 outside organizations. Of these, 99 were in technological research, 63 in biological research, 29 for marketing studies, and 5 for educational exhibits and films.

Three operating divisions conduct the food fish activities of the Bureau of Commercial Fisheries. Management, resource research, and industrial research and services are the major fields.

THE DIVISION OF RESOURCE MANAGEMENT manages the commercial fisheries resources in Alaska as its principal function. Formulation and enforcement of the Alaska fisheries regulations is an allied activity. In the Pacific Northwest, it represents the Bureau on the Columbia River Fisheries Development Program, a cooperative effort with Washington, Oregon, and Idaho that is designed to lessen the adverse effects of multiple-purpose water projects on salmon runs in that river and its tributaries.

Under this program, it determines the volume, variety, and distribution of species to be produced in the salmon hatcheries. It also is responsible for the design of fish ladders, weirs, louvers, and other devices that aid the adult salmon heading upstream to bypass dams and the salmon fry migrating downstream to avoid plunging over a high dam or being fatally diverted into an irrigation canal or a turbine. These efforts help to preserve the Columbia River salmon.

Management of the salmon resource in Alaska is a short-term activity compressed into a few short weeks in the summer. Salmon are unusual. They are orphans when born and die childless. A food industry, worth as much as 100 million dollars annually, has been built upon this peculiarity. The commercial catch of salmon is taken from the hordes of mature fish as they return to their native streams to spawn after spending 1 to 5 years in the open sea. Seeking their destiny, the salmon migrate up the rivers of their youth to deposit the fertilized eggs in nests in the gravel bottom. A few days later they die. Many weeks later the tiny salmon fry emerge from the eggs and the gravel bed.

Managing a resource like the red salmon runs that flood into the rivers of Alaska's Bristol Bay in late June each year is a hectic operation during the short season. Millions of dollars are risked by cannery operators for supplies, facilities, and personnel to handle a brief but highly variable run of fish. During the season of a month or less, the local Federal administrator must gage the take against the probable run and open and close the season accordingly. In 1958, for example, only about 2.5 days of fishing were permitted each week—a total of only 8 to 10 days of fishing to complete a pack to supply consumers of Bristol Bay red salmon for the ensuing year.

THE DIVISION OF BIOLOGICAL RESEARCH investigates the nature, extent, and causes of variations in the abundance of important food fishes and recommends measures for conserving and managing them. Its laboratories on shore and research vessels at sea

are engaged in learning as much as possible about our waters and the fish that frequent them—all in the interest of their ultimate use by the fishing industry.

The research vessels follow the cod, haddock, and ocean perch far to sea on the banks off New England. In this area their research has resulted in the introduction of a trawl net with larger meshes, which release the younger haddock for another year of growth, before eventually bringing them to the deck of a vessel and finally to market. Fishermen get better prices, and processors get larger and more desirable market sizes.

In the far north, the biologists are unraveling the knotty problem of where the salmon—born in Alaskan rivers—spend the ocean part of their life cycle. Outstanding research in the North Pacific and the Bering Sea has demonstrated there is a large area, above and below the Aleutian Islands, where salmon originating in Alaskan rivers and salmon spawned in Siberian streams congregate to feed. Approaching maturity, they head east and west, respectively, to spawn in the rivers and streams where they were born.

The existence of this mixing bowl has been confirmed by a five-part research study. Bureau biologists have proved this by tagging salmon in the area and recovering the tagged salmon in or near their native streams. Then they have shown that the pattern of rings on the scales differs for Siberian and Alaskan salmon. They have adapted a blood serum test, which readily distinguishes salmon from the two sides of the Pacific. They have demonstrated differences in the bodily characteristics of the fish from the "mixing" area, and they have even found that parasites in the flesh and viscera differ and are a further means of separating Siberian and Alaskan salmon.

This research is aiding the International North Pacific Fisheries Commission, which is charged with

How the Large Mesh Works

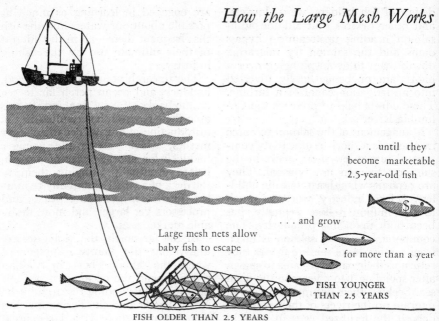

. . . until they become marketable 2.5-year-old fish

. . . and grow

for more than a year

Large mesh nets allow baby fish to escape

FISH YOUNGER THAN 2.5 YEARS

FISH OLDER THAN 2.5 YEARS

determining how far to the east the Japanese high seas vessels may fish without taking an undue proportion of Alaskan salmon. Thus the runs are not depleted.

Many fish can be tagged, but shrimp present a problem because they shed their shells periodically. Biologists have met this problem by injecting a dye, which colors the head portion of shrimp a bright blue, green, or red. It marks a significant step in charting the migration of shrimp in our Gulf of Mexico and South Atlantic fishing grounds and in the conservation of this valuable resource.

Sometimes the Bureau biologists are called on to kill fish, rather than to conserve them. This is their task in the upper Great Lakes, where the sea lamprey—a primitive, eel-like fish—has found the habitat to its liking and the inhabitants (especially lake trout) well suited to its parasitic nature.

The sea lamprey overcame natural obstacles between the lakes in its journey from the sea by passing through the manmade canals. In Lake Huron and Lake Michigan, the sea lampreys, which have rasplike mouths, attached themselves to lake trout and fed upon them. As the lake trout declined catastrophically in these lakes, the sea lampreys migrated to Lake Superior and began the final onslaught on the lake trout there.

Biologists placed electric barriers in the streams in which the lampreys spawned, thus providing an effective but costly killer or deterrent to reproduction. Meanwhile the search for a chemical killer (a lampreycide) was carried on. Experiments indicated that after testing 6 thousand different chemicals, scientists found one with the desired characteristics. Placed in the streams in small amounts—a few parts per million—it is lethal to lamprey adults, young, and—most important—to the larval forms, which remain in the mud of the stream bed up to 5 years.

Kills of more than 99 percent have

Main United States Fisheries

been obtained in test operations with practically no damage to desirable fish and animals or to useful organisms in the streams. Biologists are optimistic that the sea lampreys in Lake Michigan and Lake Superior can be brought under control in 10 years. Restocking of the lakes with lake trout can go forward meanwhile in anticipation of gradual restoration of the trout and its ultimate return,

in oldtime volume, to the tables of the Midwest.

THE DIVISION of Industrial Research and Services, the Bureau's third operating unit, is directly concerned with fish as food. Catching the fish is its primary interest. Seeing that the resulting fishery products are served to the consumer in a way that merits confidence in the product and future purchases is its final task. In all, it functions as a scout (exploratory fishing), researcher (technology), judge (standards and inspection), accountant (statistics), reporter (market news), salesman (market development), teacher (films and exhibits), analyst (economics), and cook (home economics).

EXPLORATORY FISHING vessels locate new fishing grounds, determine the extent and character of the fish available, and decide on the most effective gear for commercial use.

The vessels and the research staff have a long line of successes behind them. They discovered commercial quantities of yellowfin tuna in the Gulf of Mexico and deep water red shrimp in the Gulf and off the south Atlantic coast of Florida. They also found the Pacific shrimp off Alaska.

Their investigations have indicated that shrimp and shrimplike crustaceans may be one of the largest untapped fishery food resources in the sea. But exploitation of midwater and deep sea shrimp depends on technological improvements to fishing gear and the slow acquisition of knowledge about how to fish in very deep water.

TECHNOLOGICAL RESEARCH in the Bureau consists of chemical, bacteriological, nutritional, and engineering investigations. These studies are directed toward general problems of handling, processing, and distributing fishery products, which the industry finds it difficult or impossible to solve with its own resources. The composition, properties, and nutritive values of fishery products are determined. Sanitation practices are studied. A voluntary inspection and grading program is administered, in addition to conducting the research and carrying out the development required for establishing the standards for the grades.

The five regional technological laboratories usually specialize on certain problems, in addition to handling local phases of programs of national interest. The Seattle laboratory, for example, has done much fundamental work on fish proteins, oils, and irradiation.

The Boston laboratory has spearheaded the standards project and worked out the problems created by the new technique of freezing fish at sea, rather than bringing them back in ice, as is the usual practice.

The laboratory at College Park, Md., has concentrated on nutritional studies. At Ketchikan, Alaska, solutions have been sought to the processing problems of the local fishery products, such as king crabs, butter clams, pink salmon, and shrimp.

A new laboratory has been established at Pascagoula, Miss., to aid the shrimp, oyster, and other fishery food industries in the Gulf States.

ANDREW W. ANDERSON *is Assistant Director of the Bureau of Commercial Fisheries. He has been with this Bureau since 1930 in technological research, statistical and market news activities, and as Chief of the former Branch of Commercial Fisheries. He also is the representative of the Department of the Interior on the Food and Agriculture Organization Interagency Committee.*

How to bring to all our people the benefits of the newer knowledge of nutrition as promptly as possible is both an educational and an economic problem. The teaching of the principles of nutrition, of the relation of nutrition to health, and of the nutritive values of foods should go on constantly both as a regular part of the work of schools of all grades, and through the various means of adult education.—HENRY C. SHERMAN.

What Makes Fruit and Vegetables Good?

VICTOR R. BOSWELL

QUALITY has many meanings, but usually when we speak of quality of food we mean high quality, or excellence.

We ask, "What is the basis of quality in a fruit or vegetable?" What we usually mean is, "What specific characteristics make a fruit or a vegetable most desirable?"

But which fruit? Which vegetable? Most desirable from what standpoint—its nutrient content? Its marketability? Marketability where? Its attractiveness when eaten? Eaten by whom, and under what circumstances?

I cannot, therefore, give one answer to the question, "What specific characteristics make a fruit or a vegetable most desirable?" Like my farmer uncle, in response to almost every question, I have to answer, "Well, now, that depends."

We all can agree, though, that in order to have high quality, fruit and vegetables must be unspoiled by diseases, insects, mechanical injury, or contamination with foreign matter.

We can agree that most fruits must be ripe.

We can also agree that products must be fresh or properly stored or preserved if they are to possess their respective desirable properties.

Beyond these requirements and regarding details of properties, we begin to differ.

It is partly because of differences in tastes or desires of consumers that farmers and gardeners grow so many different kinds of fruit and vegetables. Preferences in taste also underlie some of the different practices in harvesting and handling certain products.

SOME PERSONS say Americans eat with their eyes instead of with their palates. That is an overstatement, but certainly appearance is the basis of our first judgment of excellence. Appearance is important, but often we depend too much on appearance alone as an index of what is best.

Color catches the eye first. We do not taste color or the substances that are responsible for it, but we associate color with flavor, texture, nutritive value, and wholesomeness. Color in itself may have some pertinence because it contributes to the attractiveness of a food as served, and attractiveness adds to enjoyment.

TEXTURE AND CONSISTENCY, the structural features of fruits and vegetables, are attributes of top importance. Much of our satisfaction in eating fruits and vegetables we get from the structural features of each one.

These features must conform to what our experience has taught us about the goodness of each. A physical makeup that we want most in one product might repel us in another. Thus we apparently do not like crispness—or juiciness or a buttery texture—just for itself; it must be associated with the specific food we are eating.

We want crispness in apples and cucumbers but not in avocados and muskmelons. We want to be able to squeeze the juice from an orange or a lemon, but not from an apple. Most people want white potatoes to be dry and mealy when they are baked, but sweetpotatoes should be moist and plastic.

Texture, fiber, and consistency are greatly affected by stage of maturity. Vegetative tissues and pods generally become more fibrous and tough, some to the point of inedibility, as they age and mature. Most fleshy fruits become softer, less crisp, as they mature. Some become juicier and softer with overmaturity. Others become soft or mealy and less juicy.

FLAVOR is another main attribute. Most flavors are due mainly to aromatic substances that we detect through our sense of smell.

There are only four primary components of taste—sweet, sour, salt, and bitter. The number of flavors and aromas and sensations—such as hot, biting, and burning—is infinite. Again, as with texture and consistency, and even with color, "desirable" properties, like sweetness, are not necessarily desirable in themselves, but only when we associate them with a particular product.

We do not want sweetness in white potatoes. We like the flavor and aroma of onion in some salads and in scores of foods. The flavor of onion and chives is delightful in some cheese preparations—but not in milk from which cheese is made. Endive in a salad is not objectionable to those of us who like endive, but we dislike a similar bitterness in a lettuce salad. Cucumbers taste fine when we are eating cucumbers, but a poorly developed muskmelon that tastes like cucumber is thrown away as unfit to eat. Japanese horticulturists have told me that they consider the flavor and odor of the Jonathan apple "offensive"! They prefer Rawls Janet, a variety which, as grown in Japan, strikes me as drab and uninteresting.

We say that the color, texture, consistency, flavor and aroma of fruit and vegetables make them good. But I have tried to make it clear that as long as a product is truly edible and wholesome there is nothing inherently good—or bad—about any of these normally accepted properties in themselves.

What, then, makes a fruit or a vegetable "good"?

We associate certain combinations of characteristics with whatever we learn to like (or dislike) through custom, habit, or design. People say, "We do not eat what we like, but we like what we eat." In general, we develop preferences for what we have become accustomed to.

Enormous differences exist in composition (and therefore in nutritive values) among the many kinds of fruits and vegetables, among varieties within a single kind, and even among lots within single varieties of many kinds.

The stage at which a fruit or vegetable is harvested, how it is handled between harvesting and serving it, and the time between harvesting and serving all affect nutritive values.

Deep-yellow- or orange-colored flesh generally contains more provitamin A than pale-colored or white flesh. Deep-green leaves and stalks are richer in provitamin A than pale green, yellow, or white.

Succulent fruits, seeds, and tubers that are high in total solids at the eating stage generally contain more stored-up total food value, pound for pound, than the respective kinds that are low in total solids. They contain more total nutrients as they approach maturity than at immature stages, although the proportion of each changes. On the other hand, many edible leaves and fleshy pods become fibrous and woody as their total dry matter increases, and there is a decline in the digestible carbohydrates and proteins, minerals, and vitamins that make them valuable.

THE NUTRITIVE PROPERTIES of fruits and vegetables determine how good for us they are, but those attributes often bear little relation to how good we consider one product or another to be.

Your prejudices regarding color, texture, or flavor may cause you to choose the less nutritious rather than the more nutritious variety or stage of development. Choice of the less nutritious item may or may not be of significance in your diet. As in all these considerations of goodness of food, "it depends."

Significance of an item of low nutritive value depends on how much of it is eaten, what else the individual eats, and how much of what else. After all, we eat some foods purely for the pleasure of eating them, not solely for the purpose of "participating in a nutrition program," as the late Bob Burns once put it.

It is hard to say whether we Americans automatically or unconsciously choose the more nutritious kinds (and states) of fruit and vegetables in preference to those less so.

We may, however, incidentally prefer the more nutritious form if high nutritive value happens to be associated with one or more other features that we find attractive. Likewise, we may prefer the less nutritious unless we are educated to prefer the more nutritious forms.

Ethnologists have discovered some food choices of great nutritional significance that apparently have evolved among some peoples as the results of unrecorded trial and error, coupled with keen discernment. An example is certain flours of mixed grains instead of wheat alone, in the Orient. Another is the corn and bean mixtures of the Indians.

In lands having an abundance or superabundance of foods, both in diversity and quantity, a pronounced automatic preference for the more nutritious fruits and vegetables is unlikely. Many of our past preferences have been to the contrary. Some still are. With few exceptions (baby foods are a notable exception), the consumer pays little attention to the nutritive value of the fruits and vegetables he chooses.

Our nutritionists, with their newer knowledge of nutritional values, have induced us to eat more yellow fruits and more yellow, green, and leafy vegetables. It is difficult, however, to change long-established food habits of people.

We eat more yellow sweet corn and less white sweet corn, and more green asparagus, celery, and cabbage, and less of the white than formerly. We generally prefer our sweetpotatoes to have deep-yellow rather than pale-yellow flesh and high rather than low solids. We eat more carrots and broccoli than people did a generation ago.

We still insist, however, that our Irish potatoes must be white-fleshed, not yellow, as many Europeans use. Some people still prefer white corn, blanched celery, and pale sweetpotatoes. If a white-fleshed variety of peach happens to taste better than a yellow-fleshed one that is equally available at the time, we Americans probably would choose the yellow-fleshed one because of a prejudice against white-fleshed peaches. White-fleshed peaches are preferred in northern Europe.

We have increased our use of yellow- and orange-colored varieties of the fruit and vegetables that we have been accustomed to using and that have both white and colored sorts.

It appears, however, that we do not readily change to a colored variety of a kind of fruit or vegetable if we have long been accustomed to using only white varieties of that kind. Habit or custom sometimes outweighs our knowledge of nutrition.

Often, too, we insist on colors—or lack of them—that have no nutritional importance. The root of beet, for example, must be red, preferably purplish-red, and as deeply colored as possible, but we want no trace of that same beautiful color in the root of sweetpotato or carrot. White-fleshed beets may taste just as good as red ones, but we think they must be red to be good.

We in the United States spend about 20 percent of our food money for fruit and vegetables, including nuts, beans, peas, potatoes, and sweetpotatoes. They supply only about 11 percent of our energy and protein intake and a negligible amount of fat. In total, however, they are important sources of carbohydrates and major sources of minerals and vitamins.

Therefore, if we are to be concerned about "what is good for us"—as well as with what is merely "good"— we need to give attention to the properties in these foods that are associated with high vitamin content—the degree of yellow or orange and green color and their freshness or state of preservation.

WE HAVE SAID that people's preferences for one combination of properties over another in a food are largely determined by habit or custom. We tend to prefer what is familiar to us and to retain the food habits, likes, and dislikes we had when we were children.

Geography has determined largely what people like and why they choose specific qualities in preference to others.

The climate and soil of a region determine what fruits and vegetables can be grown there, and the horticultural varieties of each. The climate affects the properties the harvested product will have by the time it is prepared for the table. Varieties that are unsuited to a region and properties that are difficult to obtain and to retain there are unlikely to find special favor in that region.

Varieties and properties are, however, usually highly prized in regions where they are common. From time to time I get letters asking where seed (or trees) of some old variety—often a mediocre or poor one—can be obtained. Each writer tells me that he has never eaten any variety so good as that one he knew back home or when he was a boy.

Geography likewise influences our preference for degree of maturity in each fruit and vegetable. For example, in warm regions where corn develops fast and the sugar content of the kernels decreases fast during development and after harvest, lower sweetness and higher starchiness of roasting ears are acceptable than in much cooler climates—they may even be preferred.

People who live too far north to grow peaches may have had no chance to learn how good a fully tree-ripened peach can be. Their ideas of acceptable quality probably will be quite different from those of people who are accustomed to fully tree-ripened fruit of good varieties.

Circumstances cause our standards of quality to change, although we may have had opportunity to know the very best. Certain fruits and vegetables shipped long distances to us may appear in late winter to be quite good enough, perhaps a special treat. During the season of plentiful local production, however, that same degree of quality may appear barely acceptable. Our degree of hunger for, or the scarcity of, a particular fruit or vegetable definitely affects our standards of quality.

Price, too, affects what we may consider to be good, better, or fair. The less expensive grades of these commodities generally have properties that are somewhat different from the fancy-priced ones. These lower priced grades of many products may be no less nutritious and wholesome but more plentiful and available to buyers of limited means. Many people brought up on certain foods of such wholesome but less expensive properties actually prefer those properties. That should not surprise us.

Some of us may overlook an important fact regarding quality that is obvious to the housewife, chef, and the food processor.

A critical individual judges the goodness of fruit and vegetables in the raw state according to how they are to be used. The very properties that make an item good for one purpose or manner of serving may make it poor for another.

We pay fancy prices for the first new potatoes of the season because we like them that way—their characteristic waxiness is suited to preparation in specific ways, but such potatoes would be rated as of very poor quality if they were to be baked.

Some of the best oranges for the squeezing of juice may be of far less desirable quality for eating out of hand. For slicing and for some kinds of pickles, cucumbers must be dark green; for other kinds of pickles greenish-yellow cucumbers are wanted. Apples that are excellent for sauce may be undesirable for baking. Cabbage containing much green color is excellent for boiling but would not be used for making kraut. It is not clear to me why some green color in pickled cabbage leaves (kraut) should be considered bad, while dark green in most pickled cucumbers is considered not only good but essential.

It might seem that our regional preferences in quality in this country should be fast disappearing now, since we ship the produce of all regions to all other regions and since people from most parts of the country have moved more or less extensively to all other parts. The food customs and standards of single regions are becoming blended somewhat with some of those of other regions.

Regional preferences, however, continue to persist largely for the geographic reasons I mentioned earlier and also for cultural reasons. Newcomers to a region, district or neighborhood bring their ideas and customs with them, but they also tend to adopt many of the ideas and customs of the natives. We still have "Southern cooking," "New England cooking," "French cooking," and food preferences characteristic of other geographical areas and ethnic and cultural groups.

We use in processed form an ever-increasing proportion of our total consumption of fruit and vegetables. Many American youngsters are being brought up on factory-canned or frozen products rather than on home-prepared fresh produce. Some of them are so unfamiliar with the properties of home-prepared fruit and vegetables from the orchard and garden or from the fresh market that they definitely dislike them, preferring the respective processed products. Many adults, for that matter, have become more accustomed to certain processed products than to the original nonprocessed commodities and so have ideas of quality that differ from those of persons who are more familiar with fresh foods.

This preference for certain processed products does not necessarily represent a corruption or distortion of taste. Some commodities are highly perishable. The good eating qualities of some such items actually can be preserved better by proper processing than by the usual long-distance shipping and wholesale-retail marketing procedures. Sweet corn and peas in the pod are notoriously difficult to maintain in true garden-fresh condition during marketing. Over long distances and duration of many days it is hardly feasible to do so. A good canned or frozen sweet corn or a good package of frozen peas may very well have eating qualities closer to those prepared from garden-fresh goods than most of the sweet corn and peas carried home from the fresh market.

We can hardly quarrel with one who prefers a very good processed product to a merely good to fair (or worse) nonprocessed commodity, even though the processed product, when served, is unavoidably somewhat different from the same fruit or vegetable that has been prepared for the table very promptly after harvest at the proper stage.

Although geography, cultural background, and economic conditions influence our ideas about what is good, we have no reason to believe that race, as such, has any effect. True enough, there are marked differences in ideas about goodness of fruit and vegetables among different races in their native lands and in other lands where they may be.

I believe, however, that these differences can be accounted for by geographic, cultural, and economic factors. Preferences for properties in foods are learned just as language, religion, and social customs are learned—they are not inherited.

We do not know how to evaluate the effects of advertising and propaganda, as distinct from all other factors, upon people's ideas of what is good in a specific raw food or food product. Most advertising of foods is devoted to manufactured products marketed under specific brand and company names. To the extent that such advertising induces a shift in buying, from fresh to processed foods, there may be an incidental change in what we become accustomed to and therefore a change in what we consider to be good.

The educational campaigns of our nutritionists without doubt have helped increase our consumption per capita of fruits and vegetables. They have induced some people to use certain fruits or vegetables with which they had been unacquainted and therefore affected the preferences of those people to some degree. Certainly the modern knowledge of the importance of minerals and vitamins in the diet has stimulated the use of more leafy vegetables and a shift from white to green edible vegetative parts of plants and to more use of fruits and vegetables with high content of carotene.

Despite available knowledge, we continue to perpetuate innumerable prejudices and self-deceptions about food "quality."

Just why, for example, should growers, dealers, and others be so insistent that new and better varieties of potatoes to be bred for one part of the country must have red skins; for another part, smooth, cream skins; and for still another, russet skins? As far as we know, skin color has nothing to do with the eating quality of the flesh. All these skin properties are possessed by one or another of several excellent varieties.

Many processors and sellers of canned snap beans these days insist that they want only white-seeded varieties—varieties that will show no tinge of dark color in the liquor of the canned product. What is so bad about a little color in the liquor in a can of snap beans? Nothing.

Radishes must be just the right shape—not olive shaped, but globular; or not globular, but olive shaped, as the case may be. The red color must be just the right shade of red.

Canners object to the use of varieties of tomatoes that have colorless skin. They want only varieties having yellow skin. The skins, of course, are completely removed in processing, and there is no connection between skin color and flesh color or flesh properties—but still, tomatoes for canning must have yellow skins!

Many of these unfounded prejudices or outmoded prejudices for specific colors, lack of color, specific shapes, and pattern can be overcome.

Our plant breeders were told that in our production of new disease-resistant watermelon varieties we must not try to introduce a variety with a light-green skin, no matter how good it might be— light green just would not be acceptable on the market. The most popular watermelon in the eastern United

States today is a light-green one, Charleston Gray, released by the Department of Agriculture in 1954.

Despite the same kind of prejudice against white-skinned potatoes some years ago in an important potato-growing district of the South, the principal and most profitable variety now grown there is white—not red, as many thought necessary.

If the productivity, texture, consistency, flavor, odor, juiciness, nutritive value, and other respective appropriate properties of a new variety of fruit or vegetable are all superior, colors and many shapes may appear quite unimportant. Shapes of many fruits and vegetables are, however, actually important because of the way shape affects the amount of waste in the product or the efficiency with which it can be harvested, handled, shipped, or run through food processing machinery.

We do, nevertheless, have many prejudices about foods that are only prejudices and bear little or no relationship to nutritive, economic, or esthetic values.

VICTOR R. BOSWELL, *Chief, Vegetables and Ornamentals Research Branch, Agricultural Research Service, studied horticulture in the Universities of Missouri and Maryland. Dr. Boswell taught and did research in the latter institution before joining the Department of Agriculture in 1928. He has published many papers and articles for farmers and gardeners.*

Home Production and Canning
Farm Families, 1941 and 1954
Amount canned per family in the year, processed weight

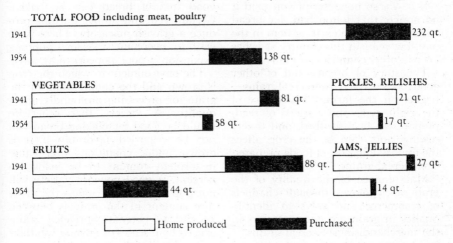

TOTAL FOOD including meat, poultry
1941 — 232 qt.
1954 — 138 qt.

VEGETABLES
1941 — 81 qt.
1954 — 58 qt.

PICKLES, RELISHES
1941 — 21 qt.
1954 — 17 qt.

FRUITS
1941 — 88 qt.
1954 — 44 qt.

JAMS, JELLIES
1941 — 27 qt.
1954 — 14 qt.

☐ Home produced   ■ Purchased

The Quality of Cereal Grains

L. P. REITZ AND M. A. BARMORE

THE bread you ate as toast this morning, as a sandwich this noon, and bread this evening—was it good or just average?

If it was so nondescript you paid it no notice, that is too bad, for bread has come to be an exciting item in the past few years in this country as it has been in other countries for many years.

The story of bread—and of other good foods derived from cereal grains—begins on the farm. The choice of the right type and variety of seed, preparation of a seedbed, and timely sowing and care of the crop affect the quality and cost of foods prepared from cereal grains.

Maintenance of the quality of the grain as it moves through channels of commerce and ways to identify quality in grain are unseen factors in the merchandising of cereal grains.

THE KIND OF SEED the farmer sows places definite limits on the quality of the crop. If he plants a variety suitable only for animal feed, the crop will compete in the coarse-grain market—not in the food market.

Processors and consumers are particular about the quality of products they buy. For example, we know of no red durum wheat from which a good loaf of bread can be baked. Certain red and amber durums produce a grayish macaroni. There is no way to overcome the low popping expansion a poor popcorn may have.

The environment in which the crop is grown and the conditioning of the grain for processing profoundly affect quality. A variety that otherwise would be good for making bread will not be regarded favorably if it is grown under conditions that cause its protein content to be below 10 percent. A good popcorn variety will not pop satisfactorily unless the moisture content in the grain is between 13 and 15 percent. Shriveled grain, caused by diseases or adverse weather, will not mill well.

High quality depends also on other factors: Choice of land, tillage and rotation practices, fertilizers, control of weeds and insects, time of sowing, treatment of seed to control seedborne diseases, timely harvesting, proper

378

threshing or shelling, and drying and storage conditions.

Farmers strive to obtain high yields and high quality at the same time, and they succeed for the most part. They do a remarkably effective job in safeguarding their crops from the major hazards.

Protein content is a varietal characteristic in most cereals, but it is influenced even more by the environment. Early preparation of the seedbed, the use of legumes in the rotation, summer fallow, and applications of nitrogenous fertilizer and manure tend to raise the protein content of the grain.

An application of nitrogenous fertilizer relatively late in the season almost always results in higher protein content. Higher protein means changes in the grain. Usually it will be harder in texture and darker in color. Phosphate fertilizer tends to hasten maturity, increase the plumpness of the grain, and raise the starch content more than the protein.

Abundant moisture tends to produce a more starchy grain. Dry weather, especially during the filling period, is conducive to hard grain of a high content of protein.

Weed control conserves moisture, allows the crop access to the nutrients in the soil, eliminates adverse effects of shading, and otherwise enables the desired crop to produce satisfactorily.

Tillage provides conditions for the elaboration of plant foods and a weed-free medium in which crops may grow and find the nutrients and moisture they need.

WEATHER CONDITIONS affect quality in various ways.

High temperatures during the time the kernels of rice are being formed may cause chalky kernels that mill poorly and are less good in cooking quality than kernels formed during cooler weather. Dry, hot weather during kernel formation induces hardness and shriveling in other grains. Shriveling leads to poor milling quality and low yield of mill products in all grains.

Temperatures above 90° F. during the last 15 days of kernel formation are detrimental to gluten quality in wheat. The result is shorter dough development time and smaller loaves of bread.

Barley grown in dry regions tends to be steely, or hard, slender, and too high in protein and too low in starch for best malting quality.

Only a small percentage of defective seeds can be tolerated in good malting barley because the release of diastase and other enzymes will be reduced or altered, the starch may not be fully converted, or the aroma and flavor of the malt will be adversely affected.

Grain should have less than 25 percent moisture when it is ripe and harvestable. It cannot be stored safely until the moisture is reduced to about half that amount. Wheat, barley, and oats generally are left standing in the field until the grain is dry enough to store. Corn and rice may be left also, but they are generally harvested when much higher in moisture and dried subsequently. Ear corn cures well in a ventilated crib, or it may be dried with forced unheated or heated air. Rice that is to be dried is subjected to warm (100° to 130°), dry air to bring the moisture content down to 13 or 14 percent within 12 to 36 hours. The heated air is applied intermittently for a total time of 90 minutes to 3 hours.

Drying temperatures that are too high (above 100°) for a long time may destroy the germination of cereal grains. The quality may be damaged by temperatures above 130°. Temperatures above 90° are unfavorable for drying popcorn.

Insects may damage the growing plant and thereby cause the kernels to be shrunken. Stored grain is much more subject to insect damage. Dry, cool, sound grain is more resistant to insect invasion, but often it is necessary to fumigate the grain to preserve its quality.

Diseases may adversely affect the growing plant and developing kernels, or they may be directly associated with the grain that is marketed.

Rusts, mildew, root rots, and virus diseases are examples of diseases that weaken or kill the plant, indirectly reduce kernel plumpness, and alter the chemical composition of the grain.

Stem rust of wheat may cause so much shriveling that the grain is worthless for milling.

Stalk rots of corn may kill the plant before the grain is mature; that results in badly shrunken grain.

Barley stripe, stinking smut, and some molds reduce yield and quality on the farm and, when they are in or on the grains, make them unsuitable for processing or suitable only after special treatment, such as washing wheat to remove the smut.

Stem rot and blast of rice cause shrunken and chalky kernels.

White tip causes the grains to be deformed and low in milling quality.

Control of diseases therefore is of extreme importance not only in obtaining a large volume of food but in maintaining the quality. Chemical seed treatments are relatively effective in controlling smut, stripe, and some root rots. Breeding resistant varieties is the best control, and the only practical control for diseases such as stalk rot, rust, and mildew.

WEED SEEDS sometimes become a part of the grain that is marketed from the farm. Some of the seeds are so near the shape and size of cereal grains that separation is difficult. Garlic bulblets in wheat cause difficulties in milling and taint the flour. Some seeds impart colored specks to the flour; they are harmless, but they detract from the appearance. Red rice, black barley, and black oats detract from the appearance of the whole-grain cereal product.

Farm producers and commercial handlers and processors of grain take elaborate pains to deliver weed-free, insect-free, clean food products. In doing so they use a number of tested chemical weedkillers, insecticides, and rodenticides. Federal laws, administered by the Food and Drug Admin-

istration, and State laws are strict about tolerable residues of any poisonous chemical that is used. Severe penalties are provided for marketing products that exceed the established tolerances, and the grain or product in question must be removed from food and feed channels.

THE CEREAL GRAINS are the edible seeds produced by certain plants of the grass family. They provide 20 to 80 percent of the food energy in different countries of the world.

The per capita consumption of cereal grains in the United States is: Wheat, 121 pounds; corn, 25.8 pounds; rice, 5.3 pounds; oats, 3.4 pounds; rye, 1.4 pounds; and barley, 1.3 pounds.

Cereal grains have many natural advantages as foods. They are nutritious. One or another can be grown almost anywhere on earth. The grains are not bulky. They can be stored for long periods and transported cheaply over long distances. They are readily processed to give highly refined raw foods. They are bland foods that skilled and unskilled cooks can use in thousands of recipes.

Four general groups of foods are prepared from the cereal grains, and these must be kept in mind by the grower and processor when quality is considered.

Baked products, made from flour or meal, include pan breads, loaf breads, pastries, pancakes, and flatbreads.

Milled grain products, made by removing the bran and usually the germ (or embryo of the seed), include white rice, farina, wheat flour, cornmeal, hominy, corn grits, pearled barley, bulgor (from wheat), semolina for making macaroni products, prepared breakfast cereals, and soup, gravy, and other thickenings.

Whole-grain products include rolled oats, brown rice, popcorn, shredded and puffed grain, breakfast foods, and home-ground meals made from wheat, corn, sorghum, and millet.

Beverages are made from fermented grain products (distilled or undistilled) and from boiled, roasted grains. Beverages made from cereals are as old as recorded history.

Preference for a cereal depends on the form and flavor of the food made from it, its amount of nourishment and contribution to health, cost, its general availability, and the food habits of a people.

Wheat flour and milled rice are the leaders the world over. Only limited and local substitution of the other grains occurs, but impressive amounts of them are eaten nevertheless.

Large quantities of wheat are produced and consumed in China. The Indians of North America and South America did very well on corn for 40 centuries and still regard it highly. Rye is used by millions of northern Europeans as the principal cereal grain; barley and oats also contribute to the diet. Millets and sorghum are important components of the diet of some groups in China, India, and Africa.

ALL CEREAL GRAINS have high energy value, mainly from the starch fraction but also from the protein and fat. The fiber content of the edible portion is low—1 percent or less in most milled products.

The mineral and vitamin composition varies considerably among the cereals and among varieties within species. It reflects the places where they are grown, the conditions of storage, and the portion of the kernel that is utilized.

Enriched cereal foods of today very nearly supply their share of nutrients in the diet in proportion to their caloric content. The main exceptions are the amino acids lysine, threonine, and methionine; vitamins A, C, and D; and the minerals phosphorus and calcium. But there is no reason why cereals should be complete foods. They are seldom eaten alone. They should be eaten—and are—with meat, fish, vegetables, milk, and other foods.

The food value of cereals depends on their chemical composition and the availability of the constituents for use by the human body.

But there is more to quality than that. Acceptability, ease of processing, adaptability, and value to the user also are important. The terms "high quality" or "low quality" may be meaningless.

High quality exists only as an attribute that prevails after a certain level has been reached and in a recipe where it may find expression. For example, the amount of protein in wheat is a quality factor, but it is not ordinarily a mark of high quality in the usual range of 10 to 12 percent of protein. Somewhat higher levels are desired for bread flour production, and lower levels are desired for pastry flour. Some aspects of quality thus become contradictory because of the diverse uses.

Quality testing therefore may be largely a matter of determining whether a variety of grain qualifies for a particular use and gives attractiveness to the end product. Chemical composition, digestibility, and other measurable attributes of varieties and grains can be ascertained, however, and are useful to producers, tradesmen, home economists, and consumers.

QUALITY STANDARDS in cereal grains have to do with the nature of the raw product, the ease of processing a wholesome food from it, and the intended use. Some standards of quality are observed in all countries, albeit some are the simple requirement that grain should be "clean, sound, and dry."

Official grain standards have been established in the United States and Canada for most of the cereals. A sample of grain that passes inspection is certified as meeting certain limits of cleanliness, purity, plumpness, and soundness.

Consideration is given to the moisture content, color and texture, shriveled kernels, cracked kernels, weight per bushel, foreign material and dockage, mixtures of other classes, heat damage, red and chalky kernels (rice only), skinned and broken kernels (barley only), garlic, smut, ergot, blight, stones and cinders, weevil or other insects, animal filth, objectionable odors, and chemical treatment.

Each class or subclass of grain is divided into several grades, which are based primarily on the minimum allowable weight per bushel and maximum limits of moisture, mixtures of various kinds, and damaged kernels.

Wheat is divided into seven market classes according to the botanical type, the area where it is grown, or the major use. They are hard red spring (the usual protein content is 12–14 percent) and hard red winter (9–13 percent protein), the bread wheats; durum (about 11–14 percent protein), for macaroni products; soft red winter (10 percent protein) and white (8–11 percent protein), the pastry wheats; red durum (any others on an optional basis), used as feed; and mixed wheat, the use of which depends on its composition.

Wheat in some countries is made into a coarse flour that includes most of the bran. White wheat is preferred for such coarse flour, as the bran is lighter in color than from the red wheats and the flour and chapatties are more attractive.

Corn is classed as yellow, white, and mixed. There are special grades for flint corn. Both yellow and white corn are utilized for cornmeal. White corn is favored for hominy and breakfast foods. Starch, sirup, sugar, and oil made from the different classes are similar in quality.

Popcorn is graded on the basis of popping expansion, uniformity, and degree of maturity. Popcorn to be caramelized should pop into a smooth, mushroom-shaped grain in contrast to the larger "butterfly" type most popular for buttering. Yellow popcorn has become more popular than white.

Barley classes distinguish among eastern- and western-grown six-rowed barley. Subclasses for malting barley and special grades for two-rowed barley further specify market samples for uses requiring special qualities.

Oats are classified by color of the hull as white, red, gray, black, and mixed oats. White oats are preferred for milling, but yellow and red oats also are used. The grain should have heavy weight per bushel, high purity, and soundness.

Plump, clean rye of uniform kernel size is desired for milling as well as for making distilled liquors.

Rice is graded as rough rice (50 percent or more of the grains in the hulls); brown or cargo (more than 50 percent of the hulls removed); and milled rice (the hulls and practically all of the embryos and bran layers are removed).

There are special grades for unpolished milled rice, sometimes called undermilled rice; the parboiled milled rice, which was processed before milling by soaking, steaming, and drying; and coated milled rice, which receives a coating of glucose and talc. Four grain types can be clearly identified—the long, slender-grain Rexoro and Patna varieties; the Bluebonnet long-grain type; the medium-grain Magnolia and Zenith types; and the short-grain Pearl or Caloro type. Most long-grain varieties break more readily in the milling process than do short- and medium-grain varieties. The grain standards of the United States have made the merchandising of rice highly specific; usually there is only one variety in a market class.

Grain quality, then, has two general meanings—physical quality, which pertains to cleanliness and freedom from foreign seeds and trash, and processing quality, which means suitability for the use for which the grain is intended.

Physical quality sometimes partly describes the processing quality. Certain market classes are more suitable for the production of consumer foods than others.

Grain that has been stored for many years, or for a shorter period under poor conditions, may be less suitable for food. A reduction in yield of products manufactured from this grain, slightly objectionable flavor or odor, and high fat acidity commonly occur.

The fat in such grain begins to break up into simpler compounds, fatty acids and glycerol. The free fatty acids can be measured by chemical methods, and the amount contained is a measure of the deterioration or biochemical age of the grain.

A short maturing period after harvest is considered by some users to be beneficial in rice, wheat, and other grains, because important changes in enzymatic activity occur then.

FLOUR is made from the endosperm, the central part of the wheat kernel. Seventy to 75 pounds of flour are commonly obtained from 100 pounds of wheat. The amount of flour depends on the percentage of flour-forming material in the grain and on the ability of the milling machines to separate it from the bran and shorts.

The miller is concerned about the amount of flour he obtains, because flour sells for 6 to 8 cents a pound, depending on the grade, and bran and shorts for 2 to 3 cents a pound. As his cost per hour of milling is constant, he is concerned about the rate at which he can process the grain. Therefore he considers the yield of flour, its grade and composition, and the number of bushels that can be milled per hour to be most important.

Varieties of wheat may differ markedly in millability. The white club wheats as a group are perhaps the easiest to mill, and they produce a high yield of flour. This quality may be determined readily in a laboratory mill from a few pounds of grain.

Ease of separation of the endosperm from the bran is related to the thickness of the walls of the endosperm cells, especially those near the bran layer, which hold the endosperm in place. Since the cell wall material is made up of pentosans (a polysac-charide composed of five-carbon sugar molecules), a determination of the pentosan content indicates milling quality.

White flour may be divided into two major classes—bread flour and pastry flour. Bread flour is used to make rolls and vienna bread, as well as the common sliced, wrapped white bread. Pastry flour is used for cakes, cookies, piecrusts, doughnuts, crackers, and biscuits.

Bread flours are made from hard red or hard white wheats that contain at least 11.5 percent protein. Pastry flours are made from soft wheats of a protein content of 10 percent or less. Bread flours are known as strong types. Pastry flours are weak by comparison.

Flours for crackers, general purposes, and biscuits are intermediate in strength. Their protein content also is intermediate, commonly 9 to 10.5 percent.

Flours made from the hard or bread wheats give a coarser, or more granular, flour than pastry flour. The strength of bread flour is measured by its ability to develop into a dough as the water and other constituents are mixed with the flour. The changes in resistance to mixing as the dough is being formed and further mixed is one of the best measures of strength. The best bread flours can absorb a high percentage of water in making a dough.

Another measure is its ability as a dough to hold the carbon dioxide gas liberated by the yeast during fermentation. The gas-retaining ability is probably best measured by the size of the loaf of bread produced. Fine structure and an elastic, soft texture of the bread slice are good measures of the gas-holding properties of the dough.

The protein content can be measured easily—but not the quality—by standard laboratory methods. Some varieties of wheat may yield flour that looks good and is high in protein, but the flour is unsuited for bread production, even when the varieties are grown under favorable conditions. The only explanation we have is that such flour

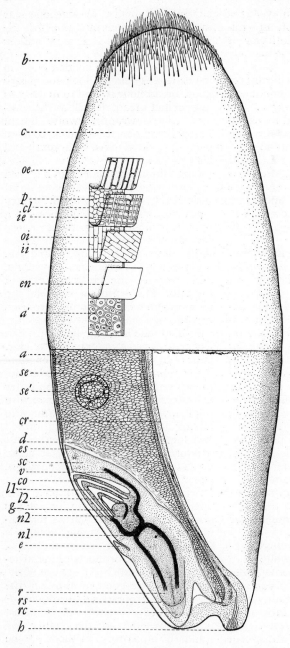

A Grain of Wheat

Bran—Coat of the grain and associated tissues and usually the aleurone:
    b—brush
    c—cuticle
    oe—outer epidermis
    p—parenchyma
    cl—crosslayer
    ie—inner epidermis
    oi—outer integument
    ii—inner integument
    en—epidermis of nucellus
    a and *a'*—aleurone

Endosperm—The starchy interior of
the grain:
    se and *se'*—starch and gluten
                  parenchyma
    cr—exposed endosperm section
    d—crushed endosperm cells

Germ—Embryo or seedling plant
within the grain:
    sc—scutellum
    es—epithelium of scutellum
    v—vascular bundle of scutellum
    co—coleoptile
    l1—first foliage leaf
    l2—second foliage leaf
    g—growing point
    n2—second node
    n1—first node
    e—epiblast
    r—primary root
    rs—coleorhiza or root sheath
    rc—root cap

Point of attachment:
    h—placenta

(*Drawn by M. N. Pope*)

lacks strength—and that is no real explanation at all. The deficiency seems
to be due to some difference in the
proteins.

Pastry flours have almost the opposite
characteristics of bread flours. They are
low in protein, fine, soft and smooth,
and very weak, compared to bread
flours. They have about 6 percent to 9
percent of protein. They are made

from softer wheats compared to those used for bread flours. They generally are made from soft wheats in order to obtain the low-protein type necessary to make pastries and rich cakes.

The strength of the soft-wheat flours may be measured by the amount of water they absorb in a slightly acid or weakly alkaline solution. Strength appears to be proportional to the amount absorbed. There is little resistance to mixing at any stage when soft-wheat flour and water are mixed. Quality of pastry flours may be judged by the feel of a flour-water dough. A good pastry flour dough will be short—one whose dough will stretch relatively little but breaks instead.

The cookie baking test is a reliable test to measure strength of pastry flours. Good quality in a cookie flour is measured by (and is directly proportional to) the diameter of the cookies produced.

Cake baking tests are used for testing cake flours, but they are less standardized, and the cakes must also be judged or scored for grain and texture. Grain and texture appear to be of about equal importance to ability of a cake to rise.

Semolina, a granular middlings or meal, is used to make spaghetti and macaroni products and noodles. It is made from a very hard wheat (durum), which is suitable mainly for this purpose. Its desired protein level is at least 11.5 percent. Macaroni quality is measured by mixing and kneading the semolina with water, forming the shape of a typical macaroni, or a flat thin sheet, and drying it slowly. Acceptability is judged photometrically—utilizing a color analyzer—or by visual means according to the transparency and general color. The best semolinas produce a translucent, golden, or amber product. The yellow color is not known to be important nutritionally, however.

QUALITY IN RICE is evaluated according to kernel shape and uniformity, milling loss (broken kernels), and cooking characteristics.

Cooking quality is judged by the water uptake, volume of cooked rice, starch and other solids in the residual liquid, degree of cohesiveness, cooking time, color, flavor, and aroma.

Tests are being developed to measure the swelling characteristics, the temperature at which rapid absorption of water begins, type of disintegration that takes place after cooking, the amount of undissolved solids or starch lost in the cooking water, and the content of the amylose starch (the straight-chain type of molecule).

Americans generally seem to prefer the fluffy, long-grain types, which are dry when cooked and do not tend to stick together.

The rice kernel in unprocessed rough rice is enclosed in a tough, fibrous hull. The product when the hull is removed is called brown rice. Part of the germ and bran is removed in undermilled or unpolished rice. Further milling removes the bran and germ, and the product is marketed as white or polished rice. Many kernels may be broken in the vigorous milling process. The broken pieces may lower the grade. The smaller pieces sometimes are separated and marketed as screenings or brewer's rice.

Varieties of rice and conditions of growing them affect the amount of breakage and so determine market quality. The amount of head rice and total milled rice is determined with a laboratory milling machine, and the percentage of each is used to determine the market value of the rough rice.

Rice fresh from the combine harvester usually is high in moisture and requires prompt and careful drying. A few hours in a truck or bin in a damp condition may cause souring or fermentation.

Processors of rice prefer different textures for different products. Those who package quick-cook rice and who produce canned products prefer the fluffy, dry, whole-grain cooking types. Manufacturers of breakfast and baby foods prefer the firm, or chewy, cooking types, in which the grains tend to stick together. Near-perfect kernels are needed for puffed rice.

Parboiled rice is produced by soaking rough rice, steaming or cooking it, and drying and hulling and milling. For this rice, vitamin and mineral content are factors of quality, because 70 to 90 percent of such nutrients in the rough rice are retained in the parboiled rice after milling.

The selection of the most suitable new commercial varieties by rice breeders used to be based on such factors as adaptation to climatic conditions, disease resistance, yield, harvestability, and drying properties. Plant breeders now also apply standardized cooking, processing, and taste-panel tests to judge the possible value of new varieties.

CORN is processed by the wet milling process to make oil, starch, and sirup for food purposes. Considerable amounts also are dry milled for the production of cornmeal, hominy, grits, and ready-to-eat breakfast foods. The most important quality characteristics of the grain are full maturity; freedom from any type of mold, spoilage, and animal or insect contamination; and, if dried artificially, drying at temperatures below 135°. Yellow corn contains appreciable amounts of vitamin A. White corn contains only a trace.

Immature, heat-damaged, or frosted corn yields less starch and oil, requires more processing to produce high quality products, and increases the amount of byproducts to be sold at reduced prices and for animal feeds. Moldy or soured corn increases the percentage of fatty acids in the oil, which, in turn, requires additional processing.

Moldy or sour corn cannot be permitted in any grain processed into breakfast cereals or cornmeal, because the resulting products have an objectionable flavor. Improperly dried corn is also undesirable for this purpose, as it exhibits considerable cracking and checking, which lead to an increase in bacterial contamination and prevents the production of large, uniform grits. Animal and insect contamination cannot be removed completely and is therefore intolerable.

The changes that occur during high-temperature drying reduce the solubility of the protein and probably cause other changes that cannot be determined readily by laboratory tests. This type of damage has become a serious problem for the manufacturers of cornstarch, oil, and sirup. More and more corn is artificially dried, partly because mechanical picker-shellers may be used to harvest corn when it is too high in moisture content for safe storage.

HIGH-QUALITY OATS is mature, ungerminated, unweathered, free from foreign material and other grains, and of high weight per bushel. Manufacturers of rolled oats believe that grain high in protein and low in fat makes the best product. Rolled oats with a high fat content are chunky, become rancid easily, and produce pasty, watery porridge when cooked.

RYE FLOUR, generally mixed with relatively large amounts of wheat flour, is used to make specialty bread.

The starch-liquefying enzyme (*a* amylase) must be present in the proper amount, especially when relatively pure rye bread is baked. Too little results in a dry, brittle crumb and a cracked, torn crust. Too much results in a wet, soggy crumb and large hollow spaces. It is determined by measuring the thickness or viscosity of hot flour-water pastes.

Small-scale bread-baking tests may be used to evaluate the flour. The bread is scored for general appearance, size, and crust color of the loaf and grain and texture of the crumb.

CHANGES IN THE QUALITY of cereals can be made to some degree if consumers demand it. Several illustrations have already been given, such as content of protein and vitamin A, in which diverse forms of the same cereal grain are available. Further genetic changes in content and quality

A Kernel of Corn

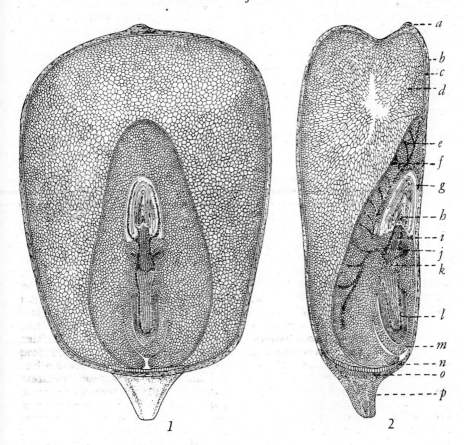

(a) *Silk scar—point where silk was attached;* (b) *Pericarp—the modified and matured ovary wall, part of the seedcoat;* (c) *Aleurone—outer cells of the endosperm, often pigmented;* (d) *Endosperm—the starchy interior of the grain;* (e) *Scutellum—an organ in the germ;* (f) *Glandular layer of scutellum;* (g) *Coleoptile—a sheath covering the plumule;* (h) *Plumule—first leaf bud;* (i) *First internode—parts found between two joints of the stem;* (j) *Lateral seminal root—first root;* (k) *Scutellar node—the first node, joining the scutellum, root, and plumule;* (l) *Primary root;* (m) *Coleorhiza—a sheath covering the first root;* (n) *Basal conducting cells of endosperm;* (o) *Abscission layer—a protective and closing tissue near the base of the seed;* (p) *Pedicel or flower stalk.* (From Nebraska Research Bulletin 161)

of protein can be brought about in oats, wheat, barley, and rice.

The amount of oil and protein in corn can be lowered or raised by breeding varieties high and low in oil.

The starch in cereals is of two types—amylose, made up of long, unbranched molecules, and amylopectin,

composed of large branched molecules. The usual ratio of these starches is about 27 percent of amylose and 73 percent of amylopectin. That ratio is altered to approximately 100 percent amylopectin in the waxy endosperms of corn, sorghum, barley, and rice.

A newly developed form of corn

has more than 70 percent of amylose. Waxy starch has cooking properties resembling tapioca, but the high-amylose starch is especially suited for industrial films and fibers.

The vitamin content of cereal grains may be modified also by breeding. Research has begun to develop a sorghum grain with high levels of vitamin A and to raise the amount of vitamin A in corn. Likewise, niacin, thiamine, and some other vitamins can be increased in oats.

Grain producers can modify the chemical content (except protein) of grain only slightly. Experiments have demonstrated that protein in wheat can be increased 4 to 5 percent by a single spray application of nitrogen fertilizer at flowering time. Several spray applications have increased protein as much as 10 percent. Such spraying is not considered practical,

but it is an example of one possibility.

Grain processors modify the grain and divide it into fractions to suit various outlets. Many products can be produced in a wide variety to suit customer needs—within limits. A new process enables millers to produce flours from a single lot of wheat that range from 6 to 20 percent in protein content. More kinds of food products with different properties can be made from wheat as a result of this discovery.

L. P. REITZ *is agronomist in charge of wheat investigations in the United States, Cereal Crops Research Branch, Crops Research Division, Agricultural Research Service, Beltsville, Md.*

M. A. BARMORE *is a chemist and director of the Western Wheat Quality Laboratory, Cereal Crops Research Branch, Crops Research Division, Agricultural Research Service, Pullman, Wash.*

Food Purchased

By Farm Families, North Central Region

Families buying in a week

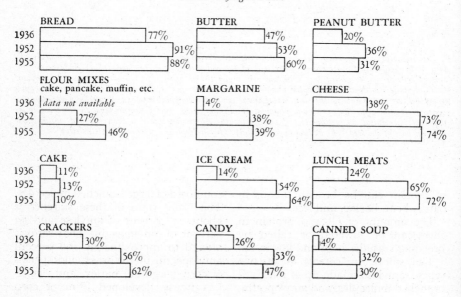

Factors That Affect the Nutrients in Plants

LOUISE F. GRAY

WIDE variations exist in the amounts of nutrients in the fruit and vegetables we eat. One sample of a particular food, like the potato, may have much more of a mineral or vitamin than another.

Such differences occur in the composition of all the edible parts of the plant—the seed, the leaf, and the root. Peas grown one year at the New York Agricultural Experiment Station at Geneva contained 19 to 40 milligrams of vitamin C per 100 grams of fresh peas. The iron content of turnip greens grown at several locations in the South ranged from 0.01 to 0.06 percent and the carotene in sweetpotatoes from 0.5 to 44 milligrams percent on a dry basis.

The differences in the content of vitamin C in the peas and of carotene in the sweetpotatoes were due primarily to differences among varieties of the vegetables. Since only one variety of turnip was studied, the levels of iron in the turnip greens were associated with the different locations where they were grown.

These examples indicate also the three classes of factors that have been found to affect the composition of plants—factors of soil, climate, and genetics.

The first two constitute the overall environment of the plant—the root environment and the top environment.

One of the most important of the many variables in the soil is the supply of available mineral nutrients the plants need for growth. Some of the others are moisture supply, aeration, and temperature of the soil.

Some of the easily recognized climatic variables are rainfall, sunlight, humidity, and temperature. The sum total of all these environmental components constitutes a location effect.

The influence of soil and climate on the nutritive value of foods for man and animals—the soil-plant-animal relationship—has been recognized for some time. The Department of Agriculture established the U.S. Plant, Soil and Nutrition Laboratory at Ithaca, N.Y., to study the many facets of this relationship. Many of the studies considered here were conducted at the laboratory or by members of the staff in collaboration with scientists at other institutions.

THE SOIL is the source of all the minerals the plant contains. With these and with water, carbon dioxide from the air, and energy from the sunlight, the plant synthesizes the organic components—the carbohydrates, fats, proteins, and vitamins— that man and animals need for life.

The regional differences in the mineral content of soils may or may not be reflected in the levels of the minerals in plants.

The calcium level of the soil increases as one goes from the southeastern part of the country toward the Northwest and the Colorado area. The calcium contents of the vegetables and forage grown in these regions reflect these differences in soil calcium.

The climates of these regions also are quite different, ranging from the warm, humid Southeast to the cool, dry Colorado area. Because weather factors, such as temperature and rainfall, affect soil formation and mineral availability, climate affects plant composition indirectly through its influence on root environment.

While the mineral contents of soils and vegetables have often been positively correlated, examples can be cited in which no correlation was to be found.

Investigators at Rutgers University studied the relationship of manganese and iodine in several soils in New Jersey to the amount of manganese and iodine in plants. They found wide variations in the concentrations of these minerals in both wild and cultivated plants, but they obtained no relationship between the iodine or manganese content of the soil and that of the vegetation growing in it.

The absence of such a relationship raises many questions as to why plants often do not contain mineral nutrients in proportion to the amounts of the nutrients in the soil.

The absorption of mineral ions by plant roots is a complicated process.

All of the facts needed for an adequate explanation are not yet known. Soil structure, pH (acidity), soil microorganisms, and moisture exert an influence on this process.

Raising the level of one mineral ion in the soil may depress the uptake or movement within the plant of another. The following are examples of some antagonisms that have been observed: Nitrogen depresses phosphorus and calcium; magnesium depresses calcium; manganese, copper, zinc, and cobalt depress iron.

Calcium, through its effect on soil pH, also depresses the uptake of certain ions, notably those of cobalt, copper, iron, and manganese.

Beneficial or sparing effects (the ability of one mineral ion to increase the effective concentration of another) have likewise been observed. Nitrogen spares magnesium, potassium spares iron, and magnesium spares phosphorus. These effects on the mineral contents of plants are more pronounced when the levels of the two elements differ greatly.

These are some of the findings that help explain why the mineral content of plants varies markedly and why apparently contradictory results occur when similar fertilizer treatments are used in different studies.

K. C. Hamner and his associates at the Plant, Soil and Nutrition Laboratory studied the effects of various fertilizers and concluded from their experiments that if a change in the mineral content of a plant does occur with fertilization, the change is small.

The effect of the different fertilizer treatments on the contents of vitamin C and carotene of tomatoes and turnip greens also was studied in these experiments. No treatment influenced the levels of these vitamins in either of the foods.

Some places in this country are deficient in minerals. The mineral content of the soil there is reflected in a low mineral level in the plants. Thus, copper-deficiency areas exist in the Southeast, notably Florida, and cattle pastured there must receive additional copper.

Too much molybdenum intensifies a copper deficiency in animals. A high level of sulfate in the diet further accentuates this "conditioned" copper deficiency in ruminants. We do not know why.

High levels of zinc also increase the amount of copper required to prevent symptoms of the deficiency in animals.

Such observations as these emphasize the importance of understanding that too much of a mineral nutrient can be as detrimental to optimum performance as too little. Such excesses, however, are not likely to occur in human diets.

Because copper, iron, manganese, zinc, cobalt, and iodine are required in relatively small amounts for the proper nutrition of animals, they have been called trace elements, or micronutrient elements.

Iron, copper, and iodine (and cobalt, as a part of the vitamin B_{12} molecule) are essential for man. In all probability people also require zinc and manganese, which animals need.

Molybdenum and fluorine have a function in animal metabolism, but the criterion for essentiality—the inability of an animal to survive without its presence in the diet—has not yet been demonstrated. Fluorine has been shown to decrease the incidence of dental caries in human beings.

A deficiency of micronutrient elements is seldom a problem in human nutrition. One reason is that transportation and refrigeration enable most people in industrial countries to include foods from different areas in their diets. Furthermore, procedures used to prepare and package foods for marketing often contribute several of these minerals to foods. Copper, iron, and zinc, for example, may be added by processing machinery and cans and by cooking utensils in the home. Iodized salt provides iodine.

The effects of deficiencies of several mineral elements—calcium, potassium, magnesium, phosphorus, nitrogen, and sulfur—on the amino acid composition of turnip greens were investigated by J. F. Thompson at our laboratory.

He assayed the amino acid contents of both the protein fraction and the free amino acid fraction (amino acids not combined in protein). He noted no differences in the amino acid composition of the protein fraction, but several changes in the amounts of free amino acids were associated with the different mineral deficiencies.

As most plant proteins are low in the sulfur amino acids, methionine and cysteine, a change in the levels of these amino acids is of interest. Nitrogen deficiency raised and sulfur deficiency lowered the levels of both amino acids.

Since amino acids must be present in certain proportions if protein is to be synthesized, such changes in the relative amounts of the free amino acids in the plant may be important. The percentage of the total amino acids in this fraction is small, however, and the probability that this affects the protein nutrition of man is slight.

Two STUDIES that demonstrate a positive effect of fertilization on the protein content of corn are noteworthy.

The first, reported by H. H. Mitchell and his colleagues, gives the results of a part of long-continued research at the University of Illinois. They grew both hybrid corn and Illinois High Protein corn on two kinds of plots—unfertilized plots, from which corn had been cropped for nearly 25 years with nothing returned to the soil; and plots that received applications of lime, manure, and rock phosphate. Crop rotation also had been practiced on the fertilized plots for about 45 years.

The protein content of the hybrid corn from the unfertilized plots was 7.32 percent, and that from the fertilized, well-managed plots was 10.73 percent. The protein content of the Illinois High Protein corn from the same two plots was 13.47 and 20.04 percent, respectively. Thus the fertilization and crop-rotation program increased the protein content of both varieties of corn.

Feeding trials with rats were conducted to test the nutritive value of the corn samples from the fertilized and unfertilized plots. The corn protein content of the diets and the amount of food consumed by the two groups of rats were equalized. The results showed that the biological value of the corn protein decreased as the protein content increased. Supplementation with lysine and tryptophan—two of the essential amino acids—raised the biological value so that it was comparable with that of meat protein.

The protein content of corn has been increased by both fertilization and breeding experiments. Most of the increase in protein has been due in all instances to the increase in zein, one of the proteins in corn. Because zein is low in lysine and tryptophan, the proportion of them in the total corn protein decreases as the protein increases. This explains the lower biological value obtained when the corn protein was equalized in the diets.

A second study of the relative nutritive value of high- and low-protein corn was made by H. E. Sauberlich and his associates at the Alabama Agricultural Experiment Station. They compared low-protein corn (7.7 percent) obtained from plots receiving a suboptimum level of nitrogen with high-protein corn (11.0 to 12.5 percent) from plots receiving 3.5 times as much nitrogen.

The high-protein corn supported better growth of chicks and rats when equal amounts of corn were included in the diets. As in the experiments in Illinois, however, when the amount of corn protein in the diets was equalized, the high-protein corn was somewhat inferior to the low-protein corn—a reflection of the greater proportion of zein in the protein.

CLIMATE, the aboveground environment of the plant, also is a composite of many interacting variables. Most important from the viewpoint of plant growth and composition are light, water, and temperature. Climate also affects the soil by the so-called weathering processes, but its main effect is on the aboveground part of the plant.

Variations in several of the organic constituents of the plant—vitamins, carbohydrates, proteins—often have been linked with variations in climate.

Mary Elizabeth Reid, of the Department of Agriculture, observed in 1938 that 11-day-old cowpea seedlings grown in the light contained about nine times more vitamin C than did similar seedlings grown in the dark. She pointed out the importance of light in the production of fruit and vegetables high in vitamin C.

Some of the early work in our laboratory was directed toward obtaining a better understanding of this relationship between light and vitamin C in plants.

K. C. Hamner, G. F. Somers, and their colleagues found that the amount of vitamin C in tomatoes and turnip greens was directly correlated with the exposure of the tomato fruit or the turnip leaf to sunlight during the period just before harvesting. The content of vitamin C (per 100 grams of fresh weight) of turnip leaves was shown to be directly related to the light intensity to which they were exposed, ranging from 28.2 milligrams at the lowest intensity to 235.5 milligrams at the highest.

Shading the tomato leaves did not reduce the amount of vitamin C in the nearby fruit; the fruit itself had to be shaded. Thus heavy foliation that shades the fruit will reduce the vitamin C content of tomatoes. Any fertilization treatment (like nitrogen) that produces extensive vegetative growth has been associated with reduced levels of vitamin C in the fruits.

The carotene content of plants may vary from season to season at a given location. Attempts to explain these seasonal differences have resulted in divergent conclusions.

G. F. Somers and W. C. Kelly observed that the carotene content of turnip greens, like the amount of vitamin C, was affected by sunlight. In contrast to the findings with vitamin C, however, exposure to sunlight lowered the carotene content. These scientists pointed out that light conditions favoring high levels of vitamin C in the plant are unfavorable for high levels of carotene, and vice versa.

The influence of light on the thiamine and riboflavin contents of tomato, corn, pea, bean, spinach, and potato plants was investigated by F. G. Gustafson, of the University of Michigan. He found that the concentration of thiamine is higher in plants that are exposed to higher light intensities. The same relationship held for riboflavin, but the effect was much less pronounced.

The relationship between climate and the protein content of grain has been of special interest to many investigators because of the importance of protein in the selection of grains for various uses in the milling industries.

The protein in small grains is higher in hot, dry climates and lower in moist, cool climates. The nitrogen content of the soil in dry, hot regions generally is higher, and less leaching of the nitrogen present occurs than in moist, humid regions. A limited moisture supply means that less vegetative growth takes place, and more nitrogen is available for grain production. High-protein grain is produced in dry years and low-protein grain in wet years.

By examining the protein content of wheat produced at 13 locations in Kansas from 1943 to 1945, we can draw a north-south line through the approximate middle of the State. It divides the high-protein locations of the drier western part from the lower protein locations in the eastern part, where the average rainfall was approximately twice that in western Kansas. The average content of protein of the three varieties of wheat from the locations in the western half of Kansas was 14.8 to 17.7 percent on a dry basis; that for samples from the eastern half was 11.7 to 13.0 percent.

I HAVE BEEN concerned thus far with various factors of soil and climate that affect the nutritive value of plants. A recent project at our laboratory was planned to compare the relative nutritive value of corn, cowpeas, and turnip greens grown at different places in the South. We measured the overall "location effects" by the response of experimental animals to diets containing these foods.

Only the turnip greens differed in nutritive value for the rat. Microbiological analyses indicated that some of the difference between these greens could be the content of vitamin B_{12}. Experiments with chicks showed that vitamin B_{12} was present in the sample of the superior turnip greens. This finding caused considerable surprise, because it is generally agreed that vitamin B_{12} is not present in plants, certainly not in significant amounts.

The origin of the vitamin B_{12} in turnip greens was an intriguing question. Perhaps certain soil micro-organisms make vitamin B_{12} and release it to the soil. Plants growing there may be able to absorb some of it, as is the case with tomato plants grown in water solutions containing riboflavin. Or, perhaps soil containing vitamin B_{12} may have been present on the leaves even after careful washing. Whatever the explanation, the results suggest the importance of the contribution of soil micro-organisms to the nutrient content of plants.

An extensive study of the effects of both soil and climate on the composition of turnip greens was made by the Southern Cooperative Group, which comprised scientists associated with several agricultural experiment stations in the South. Five stations—one of them in Puerto Rico—participated in the 3-year project. A single variety of turnip greens was grown in both spring and fall at all locations. Records were kept of the climatic and soil variables. The levels of most of the nutritionally important constituents in the turnip greens were determined, and statistical analyses were made of all data.

Differences in the composition of the greens were found which were related to the location where they were grown. The levels of some nutrients varied greatly—carotene, as much as 60 percent, and iron, more than 100 percent. Others, including total nitrogen, differed only slightly among locations.

The levels of some nutrients, however, differed more when crops grown at two separated sites at a single location were compared than when a similar comparison was made between locations. The same was true for crops grown in the spring or fall at a single location. At one site in North Carolina, for example, the calcium content was 35 percent and the ascorbic acid content 39 percent higher in the spring than in the fall. The latter results can be attributed principally to differences in weather.

Many of the conclusions drawn by this group were possible only because of the extensive measurements and analyses that were made. The scientists pointed out that a single environmental factor never varies by itself and that joint variation between two or more factors must always be expected in a natural environment. They found that large variations in weather can result in small differences in the plant if certain factors vary together and cancel one another. On the other hand, small variations may result in a large response if factors act without such "canceling-out" effects.

They found that the greater the content of organic matter in the soil, the higher the content of iron in the plant. On the other hand, high levels of sunlight were associated with smaller quantities of iron in the plant than were low levels. These two factors, working in opposite directions, would therefore tend to have a canceling effect with respect to the iron level in the plant.

Viewing the overall environmental influences on the plant, they concluded that weather played the dominant role in influencing the organic composition but that the soil was more important in affecting the inorganic composition of the plant.

THE DEVELOPMENT of varieties of food crops with qualities that make them commercially and economically attractive has received much attention from plant breeders.

Disease resistance, high yield, color, texture, and flavor are important, because consumers want those qualities. The amount of a nutrient a food contains is also a major point to the consumer and should be considered in the development of commercial varieties.

Varietal differences in the plant's content of nutrients have been observed. B. D. Ezell and his associates, of the Department of Agriculture, found a threefold difference in the average vitamin C content among several varieties and strains of strawberries. They stated that the amount of vitamin C in strawberries can be increased by a third by breeding.

W. C. Kelly, working at our laboratory, conducted a potato-breeding study in cooperation with F. J. Stevenson of the National Potato Breeding Project of the Department of Agriculture. The objective was the development of a strain of potatoes that would have a high content of vitamin C. The level of vitamin C in the potatoes is not high compared with the amount in citrus fruit, but potatoes account for about one-third of the vitamin C intake in this country because of the quantities consumed.

Dr. Kelly tested more than 100 commercial varieties of potatoes. Some contained twice as much vitamin C as others. It was possible by breeding to produce a potato that contained double the amount in the highest commercial variety tested. The problem is not only the production of a strain with a high vitamin C content. The task is to combine high vitamin content and desirable commercial characteristics in a variety.

An illustration of what can be done by selective breeding to produce large changes in two nutrients of corn is the program started by C. G. Hopkins in 1896 at the Illinois Agricultural Experiment Station. Starting with a corn variety which contained 4.7 percent oil and 10.92 percent protein, Dr. Hopkins and his coworkers produced what are now known as Illinois High Oil, Low Oil, High Protein, and Low Protein corns. In 1949, when the program was completed, the contents of the four strains were: High Oil, 15.36, and Low Oil, 1.01 percent of oil; High Protein, 19.45, and Low Protein, 4.91 percent of protein.

New varieties must possess characteristics that will benefit the farmer economically if he is to accept them. Either the protein yield per acre, which he obtains by the use of a high-protein corn, must be equal to that obtained from other commercial varieties, or a premium price must be paid for such high-protein corn, as is the case with high-protein wheat.

The yield of the Illinois High Protein strain was only half that obtained from a commercial hybrid. On the basis of yield of protein per acre, the High Protein corn produced about 100 pounds less protein per acre than the commercial variety. The Illinois High Oil strain, however, produced more pounds of oil per acre than the commercial variety, although the yield of the hybrid was about 50 percent greater than that of the High Oil strain. This breeding program exemplifies the possibilities for altering the levels of nutrients in foods, but it also illustrates some of the problems encountered.

Some of the differences in the concentration of nutrients in plants that result from variations in the environment or varieties may appear small. A small increase in the amount of a vitamin, mineral, or other essential nutrient, however, may mean the difference between an adequate or inadequate level of that nutrient in a diet.

Thus both environment and heredity affect the nutrients in plants that are essential for the proper nutrition of man and animals. A part of the environment of the plant—climate—is not yet subject to control by the farmer, but he can do much to improve the root environment—the soil—by proper fertilizer and management practices. The hereditary characteristics of the plant that determine the nutrient composition certainly deserve more of the attention of the plant breeder than they have received in the past.

Louise F. Gray, *a biochemist, has been a member of the staff of the U.S. Plant, Soil and Nutrition Laboratory in Ithaca, N.Y., since 1943. She has conducted research in biochemistry and nutrition with special emphasis on mineral interrelationships in animal nutrition and on differences in the nutritive value of foods associated with differing sites of production.*

In the past, science has conferred on those peoples who availed themselves of the newer knowledge of infectious diseases better health and a greater average length of life. In the future it promises to those races who will take advantage of the newer knowledge of nutrition a larger stature, greater vigor, increased longevity, and a higher level of cultural attainment. To a measurable degree, man is now master of his own destiny where once he was subject only to the grim hand of Fate.—James S. McLester. From his presidential address to the American Medical Association, 1935. Quoted in Food and Life, the 1939 Yearbook of Agriculture.

Farm Practices, Quality, and Cost

VICTOR R. BOSWELL

SOME people have erroneous ideas about what the scientists, industrial technicians, and farmers are doing to the quality of the fruits and vegetables we are getting.

They seem to think that the plant breeders, shippers, processors, and merchants care only about the yield, looks, and shipping and market properties and that they are indifferent to eating quality.

On the contrary, most people in the food industry try to supply produce that both tastes good and looks good.

I would be the first to agree that there is room for improvement in the quality of most of the fruit and vegetables we buy. That has always been so. It is also true that not everyone will ever be satisfied and that more attention is being devoted now to growing and delivering good produce than ever before—not because quality is lower than before but because consumers keep raising their standards.

The general level of food quality is certainly higher than a generation ago.

We should understand what has happened as our people have moved from the country to town and from town and country to the city: Fewer of us have the chance to eat fruit and vegetables immediately after they are harvested from the home garden or orchard. As the cities have expanded, growers of fruits and vegetables have had to move farther and farther from the centers of consumption. Most of the fresh produce, which used to be plentiful for only a short time during the local harvest season, now is shipped (perhaps 2 thousand miles or more) to our markets most of the year. Modern refrigeration and transportation make possible this great improvement in our supply of fresh food.

Still, it may not be fair to compare certain fruits and vegetables that can be shipped a long distance to our retail food markets with the best that can be obtained fresh from our own home gardens or from neighboring farms.

Some of the complaints about "poor quality" involve our faulty recollection and our own failure to realize how much our individual reactions to foods can change with the years.

396

Many people believe that high yields of most products are obtained only by methods that impair quality.

Actually, however, high yield and high quality generally go together. Poor crops, even when harvested at the proper time, generally give mediocre or poor products. Plants that are runty, starved, or damaged by pests cannot develop edible parts of the size, shape, succulence, sweetness, tenderness, and richness that develop in pest-free, vigorous plants. It is possible to push some plants too fast with too much manure, too much fertilizer, or too much water, but it is not commonly done because overgrowing to the point of impairing eating quality also impairs other economic properties and is expensive, inefficient, and less profitable than proper growing.

The use of specific varieties, pesticides, fertilizers and soil amendments, growth-regulating substances, machines, and specific methods of propagation and field management all have a bearing on the costs as well as the quality of fruit and vegetables.

Time of harvest and speed and method of handling these foods from the field onward have enormous effect on quality. The finest product can be seriously impaired by harvesting it too soon or too late and failing to handle it properly from field to consumer.

What, then, are the facts, favorable and unfavorable, about "what is being done to" our fruits and vegetables?

One complaint is, "Our new varieties don't have the quality of the old ones."

We must ask which new varieties— and which old ones. Some old varieties of the highest quality have had to be displaced by new varieties, some of which are hardly the equal of specific old ones in all points of quality. But some old ones have been displaced by superior new ones, too.

Potato varieties are examples.

The Green Mountain variety accounted for 25 to 40 percent of all certified potatoes produced in the United States for planting purposes in the 1930's. It accounted for hardly 1 percent in 1959. It became impracticable to produce Green Mountain potatoes in most potato-growing districts because many serious diseases impair their quality and reduce yields to unprofitable levels. The quality of many new disease-resistant varieties is definitely superior to the quality of diseased Green Mountain. If a third of our potatoes today were of the Green Mountain variety, the complaints about potato quality would be far louder than they are. Furthermore, the quality of many new sorts is equal or superior to that of many once-popular old varieties, whether the latter are diseased or not.

Two-thirds of our potatoes now consist of varieties that were unknown in 1930. Kennebec, first available commercially in 1948, is a good, disease-resistant, high-yielding variety. It has rocketed into fifth place in production of certified seed in less than 10 years. Red Pontiac, first available commercially in 1947, shot into third place among varieties of certified seed. It has high quality as an early-season potato, although others surpass it for storage and late-potato uses. Both these varieties, among other new ones, have high quality when they are properly handled.

Consumers generally do not understand that the quality of a variety is affected by the region or district and sometimes by the manner in which it is grown. Even growers who do understand this are impelled to try out the new varieties on the chance that they will yield well and have the desired quality. Varieties are often grown in districts where they are not adapted, sometimes against sound advice and sometimes in the absence of definite information. Then everyone learns the hard way in what places a variety fails to have the high quality it can develop elsewhere or how it must be handled in order to develop its best features.

You may wonder why such hard experience is necessary at your expense as a consumer and the grower's expense. Cannot steps be taken to insure that growers will produce only the varieties that develop high qualities on their respective farms?

The Department of Agriculture and cooperating agencies conduct extensive evaluations of yield and quality before they release a new sort for commercial use. If there are certain regions or districts where the new variety appears very good, it is recommended to growers in those places. Otherwise a potential new variety is not released by critical plant breeders and evaluators, who are mindful of their reputations for good work.

But it is clearly impracticable to test each new sort for more than several years under all probable growing conditions before it is released. That would take too long. The cost would be prohibitive. Growers and consumers might be deprived of a good variety for an unreasonable time. Rather, a thorough knowledge of all the adaptabilities, limitations, and qualities of a variety can be gained only through extensive commercial production and continuing research.

Those who work with problems of improving varieties recognize that every new variety has its limitations although it may have many superiorities. Some weaknesses may not become evident until a new sort has been in commercial production for some time. The weaknesses cannot all be uncovered during experimental and early commercial evaluations.

We find sometimes that a new variety that is highly productive, attractive, profitable, and even popular, may not live up to its original promise of superior quality under a wide range of conditions. When that happens, breeders try to produce a better variety to take its place as soon as possible, and horticulturists try to find ways of growing it and handling it that will overcome, or minimize, its weak points.

Some of the vigorous, productive, old varieties of potatoes, such as White Rose and Red McClure, are still grown on a large scale even though they never have been notable for their high quality anywhere. They are acceptable, but not outstanding in quality by common standards.

Still other old kinds are notable for their high quality as grown and prepared for market in certain districts or regions. The Russet Burbank as grown in the West is an example. Many growers and dealers in some of the Eastern States, to which Russet Burbank is less well adapted, would like to be able to take advantage of the popularity of Russet Burbank as it is shipped from the West. It grows reasonably well in some eastern districts, but usually it develops a smaller percentage of total solids in the East than in the West and does not exhibit quite the same properties. That is the good fortune of western growers and shippers but not necessarily the ill fortune of those in the East, who can grow other excellent varieties that produce excellent quality when they are grown in the East.

No one district and no one variety has all the advantages. Indeed, the days of Russet Burbank may be numbered. It is highly susceptible to diseases that are serious in the West and elsewhere. Sooner or later it probably will become generally so unprofitable to grow that it may have to be displaced in many places. Plant breeders are striving to produce a worthy disease-resistant successor.

Some people believe that the new, disease-resistant, highly productive varieties of many fruit and vegetable crops are consistently, even necessarily, of mediocre quality, or no better than good.

That is not true. It is more difficult, however, to produce a new disease-resistant variety of very good to high quality than one of only good, fair, or poor quality. It is true that some new, disease-resistant, highly productive varieties are no better in some elements of quality than many of the old standard sorts. Some are not quite so good as certain excellent old sorts used to be—old sorts that no longer can be grown successfully or profitably. In general, however, the new sorts are as good as those formerly available.

Examples are the early sweet corns that are resistant to bacterial wilt, wilt-resistant peas, mosaic-resistant snap beans, mildew-resistant cucumbers, wilt-resistant cabbages, anthracnose-resistant watermelons, wilt-resistant tomatoes, mildew-resistant and root knot-resistant lima beans, and strawberries resistant to leaf spot and red stele. All of them include varieties that are productive and very good to excellent in quality.

High quality in new varieties exists especially in the crops that are processed extensively. Requirements for processing are generally more exacting than those for the fresh market. The processed-food business is highly competitive. Processors therefore strive for high quality in the products marketed under their names or brands, and persistently urge research agencies and seedsmen to produce varieties of ever better quality.

Color, texture, consistency, composition, flavor, odor, and adaptability of a variety to the specific machines and procedures used in producing and processing a commodity have important bearing on the quality of product that can be profitably prepared. Strawberries that darken or soften too much on freezing, snap beans that slough, peas that are too starchy or lacking in flavor, sweet corn with tough pericarp, and peaches that break up in the can may indicate that wrong varieties are used for processing.

New bush varieties of snap beans for processing must develop their pods to reach harvest nearly all at one time. The pods must be so located on the plant that they can be effectively harvested by a machine that passes over the field just once. The pods must have ends neither too thick nor too slim, so they can be snipped off just right by the snipping machines. They must be resistant to mosaic and other diseases and must have high quality and productivity.

Makers of potato chips have exacting requirements that many varieties cannot meet. For example, all varieties become "sweet" in cool storage; some of the starch in the tubers changes to sugar at low temperature.

That sugar in some varieties will return to starch when the potatoes are moved to room temperature for several days; the sugar content stays high in others. High sugar causes excessive browning even at a proper frying temperature; such potatoes are unfit for chipping. Several of the new varieties are excellent for chips.

Certain varieties of some crops having the very highest eating qualities are too perishable to be shipped very far. Such sorts can be obtained at moderate cost only in our own gardens or close to point of production. Bibb lettuce is an example.

Some varieties of excellent quality are notoriously poor in yield and therefore cost much more to produce than others. Too few consumers will pay enough more for such varieties to enable a farmer to grow them profitably. It is understandable that the farmer will not voluntarily grow one variety at a loss or very small profit when he can grow others more profitably. Some varieties of high quality are too perishable and are too unproductive to be widely available.

There are still other very good varieties that are productive and could be shipped successfully, but we rarely find them on the market because the demand is too small.

Some yellow-fleshed tomatoes and watermelons, for example, are of truly excellent quality, but the prejudices against their color have restricted their production largely to home gardens. Market demands and consumers' tastes, however, are sometimes fickle. There is no way to predict when popular demands may change.

THE WORD "PESTS" I use here to include all diseases, insects, nematodes, and weeds that interfere with crop production. Pesticides are chemicals used to control them.

Nobody likes to use pesticides. Spraying, dusting, fumigating, or otherwise using fungicides, insecticides, nematocides, and herbicides in crop production are troublesome and expensive. Gardeners, orchardists, and farmers would stop using them if they could produce adequate yields and quality without them. Very likely, however, we would not have enough fruits and vegetables if we did not have fungicides, insecticides, and nematocides with which to combat the enemies of those crops. Production costs would be higher if we did not have herbicides to help reduce costs of fighting weeds.

Pesticides help insure that we have enough fruit and vegetables and that the quality is better than if pests were permitted to damage the produce. Insect infestation may destroy parts of the edible products, increase loss from spoilage organisms, and lower usefulness and attractiveness in other ways. Plant diseases impair the appearance of edible products, destroy parts of them, increase waste, and produce bad flavors or lack of good flavor. The wholesomeness of many of our foods would be seriously damaged without pesticides.

Efforts to control various diseases and insects of fruit and vegetables in the United States are estimated to cost more than 75 million dollars a year. Control, however, is far from complete. No satisfactory controls are known for many diseases and some insects. We live with those troubles as best we can until controls can be developed. Losses in yield and value of product from pests represent about a fourth of our total production of fruit, nuts, and vegetables.

If we had no pests to contend with, we could produce our present marketable supplies of fruit and vegetables on about 2 million fewer acres and at much lower cost. The estimated losses and costs of control amount to more than 500 million dollars a year. Farmers and consumers share these losses and costs of fighting pests.

Most pesticides are poisons. Poisonous or not, they are used to kill or to prevent development of various forms of life that are directly or indirectly harmful to man. Certain insecticides have helped virtually to eliminate some serious diseases and parasites of man and domestic animals in this and other countries. The health of tens of millions of men and animals is improved and safeguarded by them.

Our laws are exact and strict in regard to the use of pesticides and their presence in or on foods and feedstuffs.

Excessively heavy or too frequent application, or improper timing, or improper formulation may lead to trouble. If no truly safe method of use is established, a new pesticide cannot legally be sold for use on crops or soils. If, under the law, harmless limits are not established and stated for the presence of a pesticide in or on the fruit or the vegetable, no detectable amount of the substance is permitted legally to occur. Fruits or vegetables that carry more than the approved harmless quantity of a pesticide cannot legally be sold.

Thus we are between two fires: If no pesticides are used, the quantity and quality of food are substantially reduced. If pesticides are used improperly, the quality and safety of the foods may be in question. Fortunately, a safe and narrow course is possible and practical.

In considering here the effects of pesticides on the quality and costs of fruits and vegetables, we assume that the requirements of the law are met so that no harmful amount of any pesticidal substance occurs as a contaminant of the food. We also assume that where the various pesticides are used, they are reasonably effective with no direct injury to the quality of the product either by pests or by the pesticides. Now, what indirect and direct effects of other kinds are likely to be produced on quality by various pesticides?

We have long known that arsenical insecticides applied to foliage of citrus trees lower the acid content of the fruit. Properly used arsenicals produce a desirable reduction in the acidity of grapefruit, but they reduce both sugar and acid content of oranges and tend to produce a flat, undesirable flavor. The use of arsenicals on orange trees is prohibited therefore in Florida. Arsenicals have been observed experimentally to depress slightly the sugar, acid, and overall quality of some varieties of apples. Arsenicals are now used less than formerly. Oil-emulsion sprays interfere with the behavior of citrus leaves and tend to lower fruit quality. Other types of sprays that produce no such effect are therefore preferred.

Soon after the Second World War, when the use of BHC (benzene hexachloride) as an insecticide was new, several instances occurred where its musty, unpleasant odor and flavor contaminated various fruits and vegetables, especially potatoes. Consumers now encounter little or no trouble from BHC because its hazards to quality are generally well understood. It is used in such small amounts and in such form and manner as to avoid its potentially bad effects. It is no longer used for control of soil insects in growing tuber and root crops.

Toxaphene, when it was experimentally used in soil at moderately heavy rates, tended to lower the score of acceptability of potatoes, but the other common recommended insecticides did not. Toxaphene is not now recommended for mixing into the soil to control potato insects.

Extensive studies on the residual effects of DDT and chlordane in soil over a period of 4 years at the New Jersey Agricultural Experiment Station indicated a slight lowering of the scores on flavor and odor in several vegetables. Differences were too small to be significant in any year, but their persistence through the 4 years indicates a possible small effect. In no case could the effect of these two substances

on quality be considered appreciable when used as recommended, but the results indicate the need for strict adherence to recommendations. No trouble from soil residues is anticipated with tree fruits, because the tree roots mostly lie below the zone where persistent pesticides can accumulate.

Several experiments indicate possible impairment of quality of vegetables following substantial accumulation of certain pesticidal residues in the soil. The trend in 1959, however, was to use smaller dosages of various pesticides than were used a few years earlier. We realize that accumulations of residues of highly stable pesticides in soils may become a problem. Consequently we favor the use of pesticidal substances that do not accumulate in the soil enough to affect the eating quality of the food product or to result in the presence of a contaminating substance in it, when properly used.

Leaf diseases—chiefly mildews—seriously reduce the flavor, aroma, and sweetness of muskmelons, even though the fruits appear excellent. Control of the diseases by fungicides is expensive but essential if the fruit quality of most varieties is to be satisfactory. Most commercial varieties of muskmelons are susceptible to powdery mildew and downy mildew, so that a fungicide is generally necessary for one or both of them.

The direct effects of weedkillers on the quality of crops are not yet well known. It is safe to say, however, that no adverse effects are known when approved herbicides are used according to recommendations, no harmful amount of the substances is left in or on the edible product, and no harm is done to the growth of the crop plants.

Soon after it was learned that kerosenelike "oils" were good for killing weeds in fields of young carrots, some errors were made. Petroleum fractions that did not evaporate soon enough after application sometimes were used. They caused the carrots to retain a tinge of kerosene or paraffin flavor after harvest.

Now we know how to use the more volatile petroleum fractions such as Stoddard solvent (a dry-cleaning fluid) when the carrot plants are young, so that no suggestion of oily flavor occurs in the harvested carrots. This solvent, sprayed on a weedy field of young carrots, kills the weeds but leaves the carrots unharmed.

Forward-looking research has forecast the potential hazards involved in unwise use of pesticides. Present law helps greatly to insure against unwise use. It thus appears unlikely that pesticidal use will get out of hand, to the detriment of the wholesomeness or the eating quality of our fruits and vegetables.

Scientists have expanded research on controlling pests by biological methods, such as fostering development of parasites and predators of insects, finding insect and disease enemies of certain weeds, breeding insect- and disease-resistant crop plants, and developing soil- and crop-management systems that may suppress various disease and insect enemies of crops. They may reduce further the need for certain pesticides.

SCIENTIFIC and popular interest has grown since the 1930's in the possible agricultural uses of so-called hormone-like, or growth-regulating, substances and of vitamins on crop plants.

The application of vitamins in plant production has not been proved to have any value and is not recommended.

Many studies have been conducted with other substances that produce marked effects in growth or development when applied in tiny amounts. Some of the substances that were found to encourage rooting of plants were found later to induce fruit setting, with or without seeds. There was a short-lived fad of producing seedless tomatoes, melons, and other fruits by this means.

Some substances affect the stems of some fruits so they do not drop from the tree as they become ripe. Now we have not only root-promoters, fruit-setters, drop-preventers, and growth-stretchers but growth-stoppers and plant-killers among these fantastically potent substances.

Interest continues unabated in the quest for such substances, which may give us better control over our crops and reduce costs, increase yields, and improve quality.

The use of root-inducing compounds and weedkillers has become a highly successful, standard practice in many horticultural enterprises. The stop-drop sprays have won a place in the production of apples, pears, and citrus fruits. Some thinning out of excess small fruits in fruit trees is done by chemical means. The size and early maturity of some varieties of plums and apricots are promoted by such substances. Otherwise, profitable uses of the fruit-setters and other regulators have not developed to an important degree in fruit and vegetable production.

Fruit-setting substances were used in many commercial greenhouses for several years as a substitute for hand pollination of tomatoes. Satisfactory yields of largely seedless fruits were economically obtained, but continued commercial experience showed that such tomatoes tend to be less firm, more fragile, and of a little less desirable all-round quality than fruits set by hand pollination. The practice therefore lost favor and is even prohibited among the members of some tomato-producers' organizations. Buyers in some markets discriminate against such tomatoes.

The stop-drop sprays are used extensively with late apples and pears and with some varieties of oranges. The grower who uses them must, however, guard against the error of letting the apples and pears get too ripe before he picks them and puts them into cold storage or markets them. The stop-drop sprays fasten the fruit on the tree so it will not fall off too soon, but they do not slow down the maturity process. If the grower is too slow about harvesting he will not lose fruits by their dropping to the ground, but he will lose quality from overripeness. The stop-drop sprays do not directly impair quality, but if the grower is not alert he may let the fruit hang on too long.

Interest was high in 1959 in the potentialities of a group of substances called gibberellins, which certain fungi of the genus *Gibberella* produce. These substances produce effects that differ greatly among species.

Gibberellins greatly increase stem growth in many plants and in some may hasten time of harvest. Tests with vegetables, however, have indicated that undesirable effects on quality are involved. It is therefore not at all certain that gibberellins will find a place in commercial food production or will become a factor in the quality of our produce.

Quite aside from the use of growth-promoting substances, something needs to be said against an ill-advised interest in gigantic specimens. Consumers in general and exhibitors at fairs and harvest shows should realize that the biggest specimen is not necessarily the best. In fact, specimens of any fruit or vegetable that are very much larger than is typical for its variety are likely to be inferior in eating and other qualities. Gigantic specimens are undesirable for other practical reasons, and the production of such monstrosities should not be encouraged.

A FEW PERSONS believe that no amount of any manufactured fertilizer should ever be applied to the soil. They believe fertilizer is "poisonous" to plants and to the microlife of the soil and harmful to man and animals that eat plant products so fertilized. They believe it is all right to use ground limestone and raw phosphate rock, but not anything that has been processed. They believe that all other additions to soil must be from such organic sources as animal manures, garbage, crop residues, green manures, sawdust, leaves, and lawn clippings.

We have plenty of evidence that most soils need additions of organic matter and respond to them—a point that agricultural research and teaching in this country have emphasized from the beginning.

But we have no evidence that fertilizers, as such, are necessarily harmful to the soil itself, to plants growing therein, to microlife of the soil, or to man or animals that eat plants grown on fertilized soil. Fertilizers can be improperly used, of course, and the organic aspects of soils can be—and generally are—badly neglected in this country.

The "organic" extremists, however, seem to overlook the great body of evidence that shows that organic matter plus fertilizer gives long-range results on most soils that are superior to either one alone. The use of fertilizer on soils that are badly deficient in organic matter may indeed result in unsatisfactory soil properties and crop yields and quality. Exhaustion of soil organic matter is bad, even if no fertilizer is used, but the judicious use of fertilizer and organic matter together on most soils leads to better yields and quality than the use of organic matter alone.

Many of our fields and gardens will produce good crops of high quality when nothing but manure is added. Some fields produce good crops of high quality when only fertilizer is used or even when nothing at all is applied for a time. (Crop residues and green manures should, of course, be turned into the soil to help maintain it.)

Other fields need both additional organic matter and fertilizer. The claim that organic matter alone is a cure-all and produces the pinnacle of quality is neither borne out by common observation nor demonstrated by adequate experiments. Muck and peat soils are organic soils; they are so high in organic matter that they will burn when dry. It is common knowledge, however, that they are so low in mineral elements that they do not produce the best quality of many crops.

Manures are unbalanced as sources of plant nutrients. They are low in phosphorus in proportion to the nitrogen and potash they contain. Heavy use of manure alone may result in disappointing yields of some crops under many conditions and a too rapid, soft growth and low quality. The more manure is applied, the more phosphorus-bearing fertilizer needs to be applied.

Even if the organic enthusiasts were partly right about fertilizers, we still would have to use them. It appears impossible economically to produce the amounts of the crops we need without fertilizers, without at the same time pauperizing our farmers and nonfarmers alike.

All this does not in the least deny the need for improving the organic matter status of our soils. Organic matter has benefits beyond the mere addition of the chemical elements therein. It is vital to a favorable balance of soil micro-organisms. Known methods of improvement of organic matter content must be more generally applied and more economical ones devised to accomplish much further improvement. High organic matter contributes to high yields on mineral soils, and high yields and high quality generally go together.

Although rarely is the eating quality of a fruit or a vegetable impaired through misuse of fertilizer, that is sometimes possible. Too heavy applications of nitrogen to apple trees may make the foliage so dense as to shade the fruits too much and impair the development of the desired bright color. Careful studies have failed to prove that nitrate of soda fertilizer impairs the quality of watermelons.

We have some evidence, however, that we can overdo efforts to get maximum yields and quality under some conditions. These effects are rarely due to fertilizers alone, but rather to a combination of factors.

Potatoes commonly are kept growing vigorously so late in the season that the tops have to be killed mechanically or with flame or chemicals in order to harvest the crop efficiently. Fertilizers probably contribute to this situation, but so does the control of insects and diseases that formerly killed the plants well before harvesttime. We believe pest control contributes most to this lengthened life of the potato plant. The result is that the crop is not mature when growth is suddenly terminated. Although the tubers are left in the ground to mature for several days after killing the tops, they may be a little less mature and a little lower in solids than after the tops are killed by pests gradually and somewhat longer before harvest. Compensating for some of this immaturity feature of such potatoes, however, is the lower degree of certain insect and disease damage to the potatoes than was generally encountered in the past.

If consumers want potatoes as they formerly were grown, they must be prepared to pay more for them because the lower yields obtainable by old methods make the potatoes cost more per bushel to grow than by present methods.

Muck soils tend generally to produce crops having a little more water and succulence, a little lower content of solids, and less firmness than those grown on mineral soils. This is no disadvantage in leafy crops, celery, and onions for most purposes, but processors prefer that potatoes and carrots be grown on mineral soils.

One should not infer that the quality of these muck-land products is necessarily poor. It is not. The quality can be highly satisfactory for most purposes, although not satisfactory for some uses or most pleasing to some critical consumers.

There is a significant demand for high quality within trade channels as well as by the ultimate consumer. Competition for good markets and good customers stimulates efforts to produce and to maintain high quality in fruit and in vegetables, especially during periods of ample supply. The seller of produce of low quality can expect penalties in the prices he receives. Economic pressures in favor of high quality work to the advantage of the consumer.

THE STAGE OF DEVELOPMENT at which a fruit or vegetable is harvested has much to do with its eating quality; its shipping, storing, market, and processing qualities; and yields and profits. The grower and his crews may have good judgment in harvesting to obtain the best quality, but bad weather or other factors beyond their control may interfere with timely and proper work.

There often is temptation to delay harvest past the stage of best quality in order to get higher yields or to harvest too early in order to take advantage of favorable prices. Either error often may backfire to the disadvantage of the growers, especially when the supplies of the product are ample.

Most berries and tree fruits must be harvested before full ripeness if they are to be shipped long distances to market. They otherwise become so overripe as to deteriorate somewhat before they can be used. For the local market and home use, they can be harvested fully ripe and used before their high quality is lost.

Tomatoes are commonly harvested mature-green for shipment long distances. If they are never chilled or overheated, thoroughly mature-green tomatoes develop acceptable color and other qualities. When tomatoes are picked before they turn pink, it is difficult to avoid picking some that are too immature, so that they never ripen to good quality. Chilling mature-green tomatoes in the field or after harvest also interferes with satisfactory ripening. In fact, the green-harvested tomatoes do not equal vine-ripened tomatoes from one's own garden (or another nearby source) even under good conditions of harvesting and handling.

Consumers are now demanding better quality in fresh tomatoes. It is known how to harvest and ship them after they start to turn pink, but the necessary care and speed of handling ripe tomatoes makes them cost more than those harvested mature-green. Since vine-ripened tomatoes are worth more because of their better quality, vine-ripened greenhouse tomatoes can compete on many markets with the less costly field-grown, mature-green product.

Watermelons and muskmelons do not improve in flavor and sweetness after they are harvested. Premature harvest impairs their quality. The stems of cantaloups and closely related varieties of muskmelons begin to separate from the fruits as they approach maturity. When the fruits are fully ripe, the stems slip off very easily with no broken or torn tissues of stem or fruit. Broken tissue or pieces of stem at the stem scar reveals that a fruit was harvested before full ripeness. Harvest at "half-slip" gives acceptable quality for long-distance shipment, but not as good quality as harvest at "full-slip." In the "winter" type of muskmelons, such as the Honey Dew and the Casaba, the stem does not start to separate from the fruit until well after the fruit is fully ripe. Such fruits therefore are harvested by cutting the stems. Maturity must be judged by subtle changes in color and surface characteristics. This is an art; it takes experience and practice.

Summer squash and cucumbers must be harvested when quite immature, before the rinds and seeds become tough. Winter squash and pumpkin must be fully mature, with hard rinds and seeds.

Okra pods must be harvested when only 4 to 6 days old to avoid unpleasant fibrousness.

Plantings of summer squash, cucumbers, and okra need to be harvested every 2 or 3 days to insure that the fruits do not develop too far.

Peas in the pod and sweet corn can mature too far in a few hours on a hot day.

Harvesting snap beans and peas a little too soon may be very costly to the grower because of the low yield; waiting a little too long for high yield to develop may harm quality and price.

Maximum yield and maximum quality coincide in sweet corn. After the best eating quality of sweet corn is reached, the ear loses moisture so fast in the maturing process that the weight of an ear actually decreases.

Although potatoes and sweetpotatoes do not mature in the sense that fruits and pods do, they undergo changes as they develop that make them progressively more desirable.

If sweetpotatoes are harvested much too soon, the yields will be low and the content of carotene and total solids will be lower than from later and more timely harvest. Still, sweetpotatoes must be harvested before freezing weather. Leaving the roots in the cold, wet soil or harvesting in very chilly weather or when the soil is cold and wet impairs their keeping quality and eating quality.

Asparagus, leafy vegetables, and those such as celery that are grown for other vegetative parts must be harvested before the tissues become tough or fibrous with age.

Heads of such plants as cabbage and head lettuce should be allowed to become well filled and firm, but they should not be left in the field so long that the heads burst or become misshapen by the elongation of the core, or main stem. Too late harvest of such leafy crops as lettuce, spinach, and mustard may result in the presence of flower stalks or their beginnings. Those structures are coarse and result in considerable waste in plants grown for their leaves.

In broccoli and cauliflower, however, those structures develop so they can be eaten. Broccoli should be harvested before the yellow petals show in the flower buds. Cauliflower should be harvested before the curd begins to separate or toughen.

Radishes become pithy and too strongly flavored very soon after they reach the harvest stage.

Parsnips develop sweetness and best quality only after exposure for a few weeks to very cool or cold weather. They are unharmed by freezing in the ground, but they must not be frozen after harvesting.

Most root vegetables can be harvested over a rather wide range of development and time. If they have been well grown and are neither too small nor too large to suit the consumer, the exact stage of development has relatively little effect on quality. Of course, no one wants old, rough, "woody" roots of any size or roots of biennials that have remained in the field until they have started to produce flower stalks.

Overwintered roots that have started to go to seed do not thereby become poisonous, as some believe, but have poor texture and flavor.

WE IN THE UNITED STATES derive about 11 percent of our energy intake and the major part of our vitamin A and vitamin C requirements from fruit and vegetables at the cost of about 20 percent of our food dollar. Fruits and vegetables thus cost relatively more than other foods as sources of energy, but are less expensive as sources of vitamins.

Most fruits and vegetables cost more to produce and to market than many of our staple crops because their production is more complex and less highly mechanized and because they are relatively perishable and subject to high rates of loss before use. They therefore require expensive protection and methods of handling.

To grow fruits and vegetables generally takes more different field operations, more kinds of machines, more hand labor, and costlier pest control than most staple crops.

Bringing an orchard into profitable production takes several years of expensive work and use of capital before any income is realized. Three years are needed to bring an asparagus field into normal production.

Propagation costs of some annual

vegetable crops, too, are high. Costs of seed potatoes, of propagating sweet-potatoes, and of pea seed are large items in the total cost of growing those crops. Growing and transplanting young plants of such crops as tomatoes, cabbage, celery, and onions are relatively expensive. Supporting such plants as tomatoes and beans on stakes, poles, or trellises and providing temporary frost protection by plant covers, windbreaks for each row, heaters, and motor-driven fans involve great expenditures for materials, equipment, and labor.

Even operations that are mechanized, although less expensive than handwork, may hardly be called cheap when costs of machinery, supplies, and materials are noted.

Soil preparation, fertilizer placement, planting, transplanting, cultivating, and spraying and dusting for pest control have become widely mechanized for growing fruits and vegetables. The harvesting of some vegetables that will be moved at once to the processing plant is largely mechanized.

Peas, bush snap and lima beans, sweet corn, beets, carrots, spinach and some other greens for processing, as examples, can be harvested and delivered to the factory entirely by machine, ready for further machine handling in the factory.

Potatoes can be handled mechanically, but some hand sorting on the harvester or at the point of washing and bagging may be needed.

Fruits, most vegetables for fresh market, and those that require repeated selective harvesting must be harvested by hand. Machines for cutting asparagus, picking cucumbers, and picking pole beans for processing were being developed in 1959 but were not in common use.

Some machines are satisfactory for harvesting vegetables for processing, but do not do the job satisfactorily if the vegetables are to be sold as fresh produce. Peas and lima beans, for example, are shelled out of the pods directly from the harvested plants. They do not keep well after shelling. Snap beans and sweet corn unavoidably receive a degree of bruising that does not impair quality when promptly followed by processing but impairs appearance and keeping quality for shipping.

Various aids to harvesting have been developed to reduce costs with crops that must be harvested by hand. Mobile platforms and conveyors for tree workers and mobile conveyors for ground workers or for handling the produce are in use. Mobile packing houses are used in fields of some crops.

Research agencies, farmers, and industrial units alike are constantly trying to lower costs of producing and delivering produce of high quality, as a matter of good business.

Some major objectives that seem to hold promise are increased mechanization and simplification of farm operations; increased yields and decreased cost of pest control through use of superior new resistant varieties; and increased yields and decreased costs of fertilizers and pest control measures through new knowledge and management of the interrelationships of soil organic matter, soil micro-organisms, and crop plants.

We can expect progressive improvements in quality of commercial fruits and vegetables, but perfection is an elusive ideal rarely attainable on a very large scale—if ever.

VICTOR R. BOSWELL *is Chief of the Vegetables and Ornamentals Research Branch, Agricultural Research Service. He has conducted research with vegetables since 1928 in the Department of Agriculture. He became president of the American Society for Horticultural Science in 1939 and was a member of the Division of Biology and Agriculture of the National Research Council in 1954–1957. Dr. Boswell received his degrees from the University of Missouri and the University of Maryland. Prior to joining the Department of Agriculture, he taught at the University of Maryland and did research in vegetables at the Maryland Agricultural Experiment Station.*

Marketing, Quality, and Cost

W. T. PENTZER

SUPERMARKETS, which comprise about 8 percent of the number of retail stores, do about 60 percent of the retail food business in the United States.

Many supermarkets are grouped together in local, regional, or national chains. Their requirements for food are large and often take most of the output of several canning, freezing, and meatpacking plants and the fruit and vegetables produced on thousands of acres.

Their need for a large volume of goods of uniform quality has led them to contract directly with processors and deal directly with shippers of fresh produce. They make direct purchases by the carload for delivery to warehouses for distribution to the supermarkets— almost a direct line from producers to the consumers.

The supermarkets make specifications as to quality that the processors, the packinghouses, the shippers, and growers must meet.

The buyers exercise a great deal of control of quality. They usually inspect fruit and vegetables in the orchards and fields before they buy. They may

also specify the kind of package to be used, the amount of precooling, special treatments against decay, refrigeration in transit, and other requirements they consider important.

Often local representatives of a food chain supervise the packing and preparation of fruit and vegetables. They have the opportunity to control, under one management, quality from the shipping point to the retail store.

Also important is the direct communication from the retailer to the shipping point or processing plant. A change can be made quickly if quality is not acceptable to the customers of the supermarket.

THE RETAILER always has had this chance to make known his satisfaction or dissatisfaction. Usually he did it indirectly through the wholesaler, auction or carlot broker, and the shipper, and it took time. The supermarket system is sensitive to the retailers' needs, and it commands enough business to make its needs felt quickly all the way back to the producer.

I can cite many improvements in

handling and shipping practices that have come about through the joint efforts of receivers and shippers.

One example involves the shipping and handling of tomatoes, about which many, many notions exist. The ice bunkers of refrigerator cars may be filled to capacity at the beginning of the journey; they may be refilled every day; or the ice may be removed after a few days and the ventilators opened to let in warm air.

Many used to believe that refrigerator cars loaded with tomatoes must never be closed completely—that the ventilator hatches must be opened a little to prevent suffocation of the tomatoes. Most shippers and handlers of tomatoes knew in a general way that mature-green tomatoes behaved like bananas and that they could be chilled by too cold temperatures so that they would not ripen satisfactorily. This knowledge was not applied very well in the selection of icing practices.

Heavy losses from decay of California tomatoes in the ripening rooms of a food chain disclosed that something was wrong with the tomatoes or the way they were handled. Previous research had shown that long exposure to temperatures below 55° F. predisposed mature-green tomatoes to abnormal ripening and development of decay. A critical review of icing practices gave reason to believe that fall shipments of tomatoes from California were getting too much refrigeration.

An investigation was started of the temperatures provided by the refrigeration methods then in use, beginning at the shipping point and extending through the ripening rooms. Pack-out percentages and icing and temperature records were compared.

As the research work expanded, workers from the California Agricultural Experiment Station obtained field temperatures that showed that chilling may be started by low temperatures in the field. The early results demonstrated that many shipments were overrefrigerated. Trial shipments with less refrigeration were made. To-matoes in those shipments ripened in less time and developed less decay than those from cars receiving more refrigeration. The trials were extended to shipments originating in Texas, Florida, Mexico, and other places.

Out of this work came recommendations for icing practices that will not cool the tomatoes to temperatures lower than 55°. These recommendations have been adopted by shippers and many receivers—especially receivers who see the bad effects of too much refrigeration on the quality of tomatoes.

Decay is less prevalent. Color and edible quality are better because of the more favorable temperatures for tomatoes. Savings have also been possible by the reduction of decay and ripening failures, the lower cost in ripening and handling, and lower charges for refrigeration. The savings permitted one receiver to reduce the retail price 3 to 4 cents a pound. We estimate for the fresh tomato industry the savings amount to about 1 million dollars a year.

FAULTY PRACTICES in refrigeration sometimes become established in the perishable food industry. During the Second World War, when freight schedules were uncertain and the costs of refrigeration in transit could be added to the delivered price, maximum refrigeration for many fruits and vegetables was used commonly.

During the tougher times of the early 1930's, shippers had learned that refrigeration costs could be reduced by re-icing in transit only once or twice, or sometimes not at all, if the commodity was cool and the weather was not warm. The amount of ice needed depends mainly on the temperature of the produce when it is loaded, the outside temperatures expected in transit, and the distance to be shipped. Some in the industry, particularly the California citrus industry, tried to keep refrigeration charges to the minimum needed for the commodity. Generally, however, the shippers used as much refrigeration as the buyers asked, and that often called for the ridiculous extreme of re-icing cars every day in transit in winter on shipments moving out of cold storage.

Reconsideration of refrigeration in the light of actual needs of the commodity seemed desirable to food chains that had often been paying for unnecessary charges on thousands of cars of fruit and vegetables. With full cooperation from the carriers, shippers, and receivers, the practices in use and possible alternative methods of lower cost were investigated.

Particular attention was given to Florida citrus fruit. More than 500 test cars were shipped in 3 years. The results of this research reduced refrigeration costs as much as 25 to 50 dollars a carload. For a receiver handling 2 thousand cars a year, the savings amounted to more than 50 thousand dollars. These efforts to reduce marketing costs covered many other crops.

Irish potatoes shipped from California are an example of how better results were obtained with less money spent on refrigeration. New potatoes are skinned and scuffed during digging, but they can heal if temperatures are moderately warm, say 55° to 75°. Tests demonstrated that skinned potatoes, given the chance to heal, do not turn brown in the warm, dry stores and are less subject to decay than potatoes that did not heal because they were overrefrigerated. Use of less refrigeration for California early potatoes improved appearance, reduced decay, and saved money.

California grapes, honeydew melons, lettuce, and Bartlett pears also have been studied. Current practices were compared with alternative ones. Shippers and receivers were shown how to reduce refrigeration costs. It is hard to say whether the savings have been passed on to the consumer, but in the long run they probably have lowered retail prices. Better quality is an advantage the consumer has received.

PRECOOLING, a common practice for many perishable foods, quickly lowers temperature so that spoilage by micro-bial activity will be lessened and the loss of edible quality and nutritive value will be held to a minimum. Quick chilling of milk by milk coolers to 50° or lower after milking is an example. Putting dressed poultry through a chill tank removes body heat quickly, and slows down microbial activity. Chilling beef to 40° soon after slaughter is desirable.

Precooling of many fruits and vegetables is an old practice. It is done a lot in California, where many fruits and vegetables are grown, the distance to market is great, and field temperatures during much of the shipping season are high. Methods of precooling loaded refrigerator cars and trucks have been developed, and many precooling rooms have been built.

Some commodities—head lettuce, for example—would not be available the year round if it were not for quick cooling.

Lettuce for almost 6 months of the year is produced chiefly in the Salinas-Watsonville district of California, some 3 thousand miles from the large eastern markets. Before the lettuce industry could grow, a method of getting this perishable crop to market had to be found. This was accomplished by packing it in crushed ice, loading the icepacked lettuce into preiced refrigerator cars, and covering the top of the load with 12 thousand to 18 thousand pounds of ice. Icepacked crates contained about 30 pounds of ice and 60 pounds of lettuce. A carload consisting of 20 thousand pounds of lettuce was usually refrigerated with a total of 40 thousand pounds of ice. This method of refrigeration quickly reduces the temperature of the lettuce to 32° to 34° and keeps those temperatures for the 9 to 10 days it is en route to the market.

The lettuce industry grew until by 1946 more than 200 thousand acres were in production. Production now amounts to more than 3.25 billion pounds annually.

After some 30 years of shipping lettuce by the icepack method, a change occurred. Dry-pack, using no ice in the crate, and packing in the field began to grow in volume for local and Pacific coast shipments. More lettuce and less ice were shipped; field packing cost less; and the mechanical damage done by ice in the package was reduced.

The problem remained of refrigerating a highly respiring vegetable, like lettuce, without using package ice. Various methods were tried, such as precooling in the car or in precooling rooms, but they were slow and inadequate if the lettuce was warm. Use of the dry-pack seemed limited to local and Pacific coast shipments unless refrigeration could be improved.

Then came vacuum cooling. The first cooler was constructed in a warehouse at Salinas, Calif., in 1948. It consisted of a steel tank that would hold about one-half carload of lettuce, a steam ejector vacuum pump, and a condenser. The packed crates of lettuce were loaded into the tank, the door was sealed tightly, and a high enough vacuum was created to cause the water in the lettuce to boil at a temperature of about 32°. Evaporation of the water cooled the lettuce quickly and rather uniformly throughout the crate. A half carload of lettuce could be cooled in 20 to 30 minutes to 35° to 36° from field temperatures of 65° to 70°. It could then be loaded into a refrigerator car and shipped with ice-bunker refrigeration and air-circulating fans as far as icepacked lettuce.

The idea caught on slowly, for there were doubts about shipping lettuce without package ice and top ice, but lower costs of packing, refrigeration, and freight more than offset the cost of vacuum cooling, and the practice grew.

The fiberboard carton of half-crate size was introduced for lettuce soon after vacuum cooling got underway. Vacuum cooling then grew fast as a demand was established for carton-pack, vacuum-cooled lettuce. More than 90 percent of the shipments of lettuce from Western States now are vacuum cooled. Some vacuum-cooling plants are large enough to hold the loaded refrigerator car or truck. Installations have been made in most vegetable districts, and portable coolers are available for short-season use.

Consumers gain because the mechanical damage to the lettuce itself is less and economies are effected in refrigeration and packing. One disadvantage is more careless trimming and packing than when close supervision was possible in packinghouses.

Packages of salad mixes can be cooled quickly by the vacuum cooling method before distribution to retail stores. Leafy vegetables, like spinach, lettuce, and cabbage, are well adapted to vacuum cooling.

Commodities that present little surface for evaporation in respect to mass, such as potatoes, apples, and oranges, are not cooled well by this method.

Sweet corn has been successfully cooled commercially. Evaporation from the husks and porous cob probably accounts for the ease with which green corn can be cooled. Vacuum cooling is faster than cooling by cold water (hydrocooling) and could be a way to improve the quality of corn in the market.

A vegetable like sweet corn loses sweetness so fast at 70° to 80° that in a few hours it no longer tastes like fresh sweet corn. It will have acceptable quality for several days if it is cooled to 40°. At 32° it will hold quality even longer. That is true also for green peas, asparagus, broccoli, celery, cauliflower, lima beans, and other vegetables.

Hydrocooling is widely used for celery, asparagus, sweet corn, and several other vegetables. Hydrocooling of peaches has become a commercial practice in many places. Its purpose is to cool the fruit so quickly that ripening and decay development will be checked and riper fruit can be shipped. The goal is improved quality for the consumer, but sometimes the goal is not reached because the product was of poor quality to start with, precooling was inadequate, or refrigeration was lacking at the market.

A great change in the marketing of poultry is the expanded use of broilers and cut-up, ready-to-cook fryers and the diminished use of New York dressed chickens and the shipment of live birds to market. Shipments are made from Georgia to markets as far away as Los Angeles.

Quick handling, shortening the time between slaughter and use, quick cooling, and good refrigeration have made possible the expansion of the poultry meat industry. Broiler production in 1940 amounted to 413 million pounds, with a value of 71.6 million dollars. Production in 1955 was almost three times as much, 1,078 million pounds, and the value was 834 million dollars. The consumption per capita of broilers has jumped from 2 pounds in 1940 to 16 pounds in 1956. High efficiency in the production of poultry meat, preparation for marketing, and distribution kept the price down.

PACKAGING is an important part of the self-service supermarket system. Most of the staples, such as beans, rice, sugar, and flour used to be displayed in barrels or 100-pound sacks. Few commodities are offered for sale in bulk today.

The perishable commodities were the last to be consumer packaged. Large commercial trials were made with fruits and vegetables, and debate grew warm as to whether the produce should be packaged at the receiving point or at the shipping point. The question is still not settled. Some produce is so perishable—salad mixes and coleslaw, for example—that it should be packaged as close to the retail point as possible. Other hardier items, like potatoes, oranges, and carrots, offer few problems in packaging at the shipping point.

About 25 percent of all fruits and vegetables in 1959 were prepackaged before they reached the retail store. Some vegetables, such as carrots, tomatoes, spinach, kale, mustard and other greens, are predominantly prepackaged. Prepackaged carrots increased from 1 percent of retail sales in 1951 to 85 percent in 1956 and to practically 100 percent today. Potatoes and oranges are also prepackaged in large volume.

Packaging of meats for consumer display is common practice in most supermarkets. The same is true for poultry and other items on the meat counter. Packaging of these commodities is usually done at the retail store.

Packaging into consumer units saves the time of retail clerks and the purchaser. What does it do for the commodity?

When fruits and vegetables were first packaged in plastic films, claims were made that refrigeration could be dispensed with. Commercial experience and controlled tests soon showed this was not so—that prepackaged produce needed just as much refrigeration as produce not in film packages.

A major advantage in prepackaging fruits and vegetables is the retardation of moisture loss, thereby keeping the produce fresh and attractive. Another advantage is that prepackaging keeps women customers from pawing over and damaging the produce.

An important function of retail packaging is to protect the food from contamination by dirt and insects and to preserve the wholesomeness of the product.

A hope that the film package could be sealed tightly, thereby excluding oxygen and extending shelf life, has not materialized. Fruits and vegetables are alive and require oxygen to keep life processes going. They also must get rid of the products of respiration, chiefly carbon dioxide. The film bag in which spinach, apples, and potatoes are packaged have tiny holes in the film. They are there to let in oxygen and let out carbon dioxide. The holes are so small and few in number that they do not permit excessive loss of moisture.

The use of plastic films in retail packaging of meat, poultry, cheese, and other foods helps to retain quality by retarding moisture loss (as it does for fruits and vegetables), but these commodities are not alive and do not respire. Perforation of the films therefore is not necessary.

Often the cost of packaging foods is offset by lower costs in selling at retail and in savings because less trimming and handling are required.

Studies of carrots showed that retail sales costs were 2 cents per dollar for prepackaged carrots and 14 cents per dollar for bunched carrots with tops on. Waste and spoilage were 8 percent for bunched carrots and 1 percent for prepackaged carrots. Packinghouse costs were reduced 37 percent by prepackaging. Plastic films, especially the polyethylene films, have become competitive in price with paper bags.

Storage and shipping containers for foods have changed for reasons of economy and protection of quality. One of the hazards in the storage of frozen poultry is freezer burn, caused by drying out of the surface area of the bird. Packaging in films, which almost stop moisture loss, has helped to solve the problem.

A marked change from wooden shipping containers to fiberboard has come about because of savings in cost and weight. The change to fiberboard took place many years ago for canned goods, dried fruit, and staple grocery items, and in later years for fresh fruit and vegetables.

Fiberboard boxes for lemons are half the size of the former wooden boxes. They cost less, weigh less, and are cheaper to pack. Hand wrapping and packing of lemons has given way to fill-pack, which requires little hand labor. Savings amount to about 50 cents a standard box of lemons—about 1 to 2 cents a dozen, depending on the size of the lemons.

Oranges and grapefruit have followed lemons in the change to carton pack, but the changeover is not so general. More fiberboard containers for apples have been used because of savings in the cost of containers and in labor for packing.

A fiberboard container for tomatoes has been developed that can be formed into two containers at the market for use in distributing the ripened tomatoes to retail stores.

Even more drastic changes are underway to save handling and packaging charges. For example, bins that hold about 2 thousand pounds of potatoes are in use for shipments from Maine to Washington, D.C., where the potatoes are repacked in bags for consumers. The empty bins are returned to the shipping point for reuse. The saving of labor in loading and unloading cars and trucks is one of the big advantages. Less mechanical damage is another possible advantage, because produce can be handled by power equipment more gently than by hand.

Bins are used for handling fruits and vegetables from the field to the processing plant, packinghouses, or cold storage. They also serve as storage containers for onions, potatoes, apples, and other produce.

The elimination of shipping containers by shipping in bulk is about as far as we can go in saving container costs. Bulk shipment is under commercial trial for Florida oranges moving to terminal markets in trucks for retail packaging and for California pears shipped in rail cars to canneries in the Midwest. The shipment of milk from the farm to market in tank trucks, instead of milk cans, is a growing practice. These changes are making it possible to cut marketing costs for foods.

FAST, EFFICIENT transportation is the lifeline of the food-marketing system.

It is doubtful if there is much over a week's supply of food on hand in our large cities. A disruption of transportation would be disastrous within a few days. More and more we depend on motor vehicles for our transportation needs. Over the network of farm roads and highways move the products of the farm to market and, within the towns and cities, foods are transported to the retail stores by truck and trailer. The family automobile is now the delivery vehicle from store to home.

Foods move faster to market by truck

than they do by rail. For example, shipments of citrus from Florida to New York usually require 3 days by rail and 36 hours by truck. A reason for the difference in time is that trucks do not have to wait, as refrigerator cars do, for assembly into trains before starting to market. Trucks do not stop to change crews at division points or stand on sidings to let faster traffic go by. Truck shipments often move directly to the retail store. The fast direct service from point of production to retailer means a quick turnover and economies in operation. Speed also gives opportunity for delivery of perishable goods in a fresh condition.

Refrigerator trucks and trailers have been developed for special purposes. For frozen foods, temperatures of 0° F. can be maintained, and this has helped to preserve their quality during shipment. For other perishables, mechanically refrigerated trucks and trailers are in service in which temperatures can be held at almost any level.

Many trucks are refrigerated with ice placed in bunkers in the front end of the truck. Air is circulated through the ice bunker with a fan operated by a gasoline engine. Crushed ice may be blown over the top of the load. Facilities for re-icing the bunkers and top icing again are available en route to market.

Refrigeration in trucks and trailers is usually adequate for keeping the product cool but not for removing heat quickly from a warm load. Precooling the commodity before loading is necessary for good transit temperatures. Refrigerated transport by truck has made possible the development of some of our new agricultural enterprises. The icepack broiler and frier industry is a good example.

RAILROADS still move a large quantity of perishable foods, however. About 40 percent of the fruit and vegetable shipments move by rail. It is higher than this for the Pacific coast and other shipping areas far from market.

Transportation by rail has been improved in a number of ways.

Rail schedules have been shortened as much as a day in shipments from the Pacific coast to Chicago and New York. Improvements have been made in refrigerator cars through installation of air-circulating fans, heavier insulation, larger doors adapted to mechanized loading, and improvements in ice bunkers.

About 72 thousand fan-equipped refrigerator cars were available in 1959 out of a fleet of about 122 thousand refrigerator cars of all types. Fan-equipped cars have helped in the job of delivering to market perishables that are high in quality and nutritive value. The fans can be operated by electric motors or gasoline engines while the car is standing, and in this way fan cars can be used to precool the load or to keep it cool after reaching the market. While the car is in motion, the fans are driven by the car wheels. Air circulation by the fans in transit assures uniform temperatures in summer and winter and increases the efficiency of refrigeration from ice bunkers and the delivery of warm air in the winter from portable heaters placed in the bunkers.

I mentioned that vacuum-cooled, dry-packed lettuce must move in fan cars. The newest development in fan cars is a continuous operation and thermostatic control.

Mechanical refrigeration is a new development in railroad transportation. Refrigerator cars with a self-contained refrigeration system were built about 1945 on an experimental basis for citrus concentrate and other frozen foods. They can hold temperatures of 0° and are in wide use for frozen foods. They are also used for such other perishable foods as meat and fresh fruits and vegetables. There were 3,382 mechanically refrigerated cars in service in January 1959, and a fleet of 3,500 cars of this type is likely soon.

An innovation in rail transport is the piggyback transportation of mechanically refrigerated trailer loads of perishables on specially built flatcars. The trailer is unloaded from the flatcar at the destination, the power is attached, and away it goes to the purchaser. Advantages are the economy of moving a large number of trailers on one train and delivery of the foodstuffs directly to the retail stores, instead of having to unload them at a warehouse and transfer to delivery trucks.

STORAGE of farm products is a part of marketing. Storage permits food to be available the whole year. Peaks of high production are used to build up a reserve to draw on for later consumption. Storage is valuable for processed foods, because production is usually seasonal and must be at a high volume to be economical.

Storage is equally important in the marketing of fresh foods, like apples and potatoes, which are produced most heavily during a few months of the year.

Great improvements have been made in the storage of most commodities. Wheat, corn, and rice, for example, are now force dried to get them to a safe moisture content as soon as possible. This has helped to prevent spoilage from molds and yeasts and to make it more difficult for insects to attack the stored grain. The air-circulating system used for drying has helped to cool the grain to safe storage temperatures and has made it possible to fumigate the stored grain with insecticides more efficiently than previously.

The improved storage of grain has given us a raw commodity of higher quality and has reduced losses in storage.

Much has been learned about the preservation of the nutritive value and quality of frozen foods. Researchers have found that at temperatures from 0° to 30°, changes in the vitamin C content of strawberries were pretty much in proportion to the temperature and its duration. Color and flavor

losses went along with the loss in ascorbic acid. Each increase of 5° in temperature above 0° caused deterioration to increase 2 to 3 times. Many commodities have been studied, and the results have given great impetus to an industrywide program to stop the mishandling of frozen foods. The temperature advocated for frozen foods in storage, in transit, and in the wholesale and retail trade is 0°.

Controlled-atmosphere storage of McIntosh apples is a notable achievement. Research workers at Cornell University helped the growers of this variety to store them under atmospheres consisting of 5 percent carbon dioxide and 3 percent oxygen at temperatures of 36° to 38°. The fruit through its own respiration depletes oxygen and builds up carbon dioxide in the airtight rooms. By scrubbing the air with caustic solution and by ventilation, the desired concentration of CO_2 and O_2 are maintained. Under these conditions the apples keep in good condition until April and have excellent market life. The high concentration of CO_2 acts like a mild anesthetic; it slows down the living processes in the fruit. Before this method was developed, storage at 32° was possible for only a few months because of a functional disease known as brown-core. At 40°, where it is less serious, storage life is short.

This method of storage, called gas storage in England, where it was first developed, is useful for varieties of apples which do not tolerate 32°. Several varieties in this country are in this category. Controlled atmosphere storage costs more, but it returns more than it costs in apples of better quality for marketing in late spring.

We had storage capacity for about 2.5 million bushels of apples under controlled atmospheres in 1959. Most of this was in the Hudson Valley of New York. An increase to about 3 million bushels is expected—not a large part of the total, for about 35 million bushels are stored annually.

A new development in the storage

of pears has improved their quality. Pears gradually lose quality in storage. They may lose their capacity to ripen if they are kept long enough. The loss of ripening capacity can be delayed by gas storage. Research workers sought a plastic film in which the fruit might be sealed that would let CO_2 build up and oxygen diminish to safe levels. Polyethylene films of 0.015-inch thickness met those requirements. Commercial application took the form of lining the pear box with a bag made of polyethylene, packing with pears, exhausting the air, and sealing the bag and closing the box in the usual fashion.

The storage life of Anjou pears was extended 6 to 8 weeks. Other varieties also showed benefit. The fruit ripened with better flavor, and it stayed crisp and fresh longer. The added cost of about 10 cents a box was more than compensated for by the higher value of pears marketed late in the season. About 80 percent of the Northwest pears are now stored in this kind of film. The film must be torn as the pears move out of storage to allow air to enter, so ripening will proceed normally. Sometimes the sealed liners have retained too much CO_2, and the pears have been damaged. As a precaution against this, a few small perforations have been made in the polyethylene liner at the time of packing. Eventually, when rooms become available in pear districts, pears will probably be stored under controlled atmospheres.

These are just a few examples of improvements in the storage of foods. For the long list of commodities, there has been refinement in storage practices as knowledge pointed up errors in former practices.

The consumer is seldom aware of these changes. Many people know that care is taken in transporting and ripening bananas to avoid temperatures lower than about 55° that will chill them or high temperatures that will impair ripening. Few people know that many other fruits and vegetables do not tolerate for long the usual storage temperature of 32°. Sweetpotatoes, mature-green tomatoes, peppers, and lemons have a lower limit of 55°. Melons, okra, squash, avocados, mangoes, and other subtropical fruits are easily chilled. Humidity is also a factor in successful storage of most foods, and improvements have been made in its control in storage.

REFRIGERATION in retail stores is another development. It has helped to keep perishable foods fresh, wholesome, and nutritious during marketing.

Anyone who shops at a modern market is aware of the amount of refrigeration in use. The display cases for frozen foods, fresh fruits and vegetables, seafood, milk, cheese, eggs, dairy products, and meat may line the two sides and back of the store. Most stores have a refrigerated room in which supplies are held in replenishing those on display. The front part of the store at least is air conditioned. The reason for all this expenditure for refrigeration is that there is no substitute for refrigeration as a means of keeping fresh or frozen food from losing quality.

The statement that an apple ages as much in a day at 70° as it does in a week at 32° is a way of expressing the value of refrigeration. Meat spoils quickly without refrigeration. Milk loses flavor, and the bacterial content rises if the milk is not cold. Eggs lose quality unless they are well refrigerated.

The retail store is no place to break the chain of refrigeration. Here the perishable food, which has been kept refrigerated from the time it is harvested, is most vulnerable to spoilage and loss. Much improvement has been made—but not enough.

Retail display cases are not cold enough for fresh or frozen produce. Food that requires refrigeration often waits to be put into a cold storage room or placed on the refrigerated retail stand.

We have evidence that the warm

temperatures cause losses of vitamins. Spinach loses about 50 percent of its vitamin C in 3 days at ordinary room temperature, but there is very little loss in 3 days when it is kept at 34° to 37°. Other leafy vegetables behave much the same. Acid fruits may retain their vitamin C better, but there is usually a loss from exposure to warm temperatures. Other vitamins contained in sizable amounts in fruits and vegetables are not lost so readily as vitamin C, but retention is best at cool temperatures.

We have come to the general conclusion that the conditions that keep fruits and vegetables fresh and attractive usually help them retain their nutritive value.

SUPPLEMENTAL TREATMENTS and practices may be useful as adjuncts to refrigeration in the preservation of perishable foods.

The pasteurization of milk is a generally accepted practice.

Sanitation in food plants has long been preached and practiced as an effective method of reducing the danger of spoilage.

Chlorine and other antiseptic washes are commonly used for cleaning the commodity and the equipment used in the plant.

Two antibiotics, oxytetracycline (Terramycin) and chlortetracycline (Aureomycin), have been approved by food authorities for use under closely controlled conditions as antiseptic washes for poultry meat. The antibiotics are destroyed by heat when the poultry is cooked.

Oiling the shells of eggs is a useful supplement to their refrigeration when done properly. The beneficial effect of oiling eggs comes from retaining carbon dioxide within the egg. If the carbon dioxide is held high enough, chemical and physical changes in the albumen and yolk are retarded. Oiling also retards loss of moisture.

Carbon dioxide, placed in the loaded refrigerator car, is used in the shipment of strawberries and cherries. As

I indicated before, apples and pears keep longer when stored in atmospheres somewhat higher in CO_2 and lowered in oxygen.

A NUMBER of fungicidal treatments are applied to fruit and vegetables to aid in control of decay. They must meet the requirements of the Food and Drug Act in regard to acceptability and in method of use. The fumigation of grapes with sulfur dioxide before shipment and in storage helps to control decay and keep the fruit in an attractive sound condition. Fungicidal washes are used for pears, apples, citrus fruit, and several other fruits and vegetables.

Much has been said about the use of radiation as a means of preservation of perishable food without refrigeration. It does not appear possible to preserve fresh fruit, vegetables, meat, poultry, fish, milk, and dairy products simply by irradiation. Dosages that sterilize the product, making refrigeration unnecessary, usually damage flavor, appearance, or the texture. A combination of heat treatment and irradiation shows promise with a number of foods, but the changes that are brought about in the food make it no longer a fresh product. Irradiation at lower dosages that give a pasteurizing effect may provide a practical means of preventing spoilage if used in conjunction with refrigeration. Even lighter dosages are required to inhibit the sprouting of potatoes, but a complicating factor of increasing decay susceptibility must be solved before irradiation can be recommended.

W. T. PENTZER *has done extensive research in the field of handling, transportation, and storage of fruits and vegetables in the Department of Agriculture, beginning in 1926. He is an officer in the International Institute of Refrigeration, past president of the American Society for Horticultural Science, and a member of the Scientific Advisory Council of the Refrigeration Research Foundation.*

Modern Food Processing

MILDRED M. BOGGS AND CLYDE L. RASMUSSEN

A FEW of the 5 thousand-odd food items sold in a modern supermarket are fresh, but most of them are processed—canned, waxed, dried, frozen, bottled, pickled, packaged, wrapped, baked, changed in one way or another.

Stabilization of foods, which keeps them from spoiling, is a main purpose of processing.

Micro-organisms are the first thing we think of in connection with deterioration of food. Yeasts and molds work primarily on acid fruits and cause them to become soured, yeasty, or moldy. Bacteria, the main trouble-makers in most other foods, cause changes all the way from lower quality to putrefaction.

Other chemical changes go on all the time—before, during, and after processing and when there is no processing. Enzymes, present in every living cell, speed up some of the chemical reactions.

When food is canned, heat destroys the micro-organisms that cause food to spoil. Hermetic sealing of the cans prevents later contamination.

Preservation by dehydrating and freezing deprives the organisms of some condition they need for growth—water or warmth. Both processes destroy some organisms but not all. The organisms grow again if water or warmth is restored.

Some common ways to slow down chemical changes are to keep foods cool, protect them from light, add chemicals that interfere with reactions, and minimize contact of the food with air—by driving the air off with heat, removing it with vacuum, or replacing the air of the package with an inert gas, such as nitrogen, which does not combine with foods.

To cut down the loss of vitamins and minerals, a processor has to keep in mind that all B vitamins, vitamin C, and some of the minerals dissolve in water and may be thrown away in the water. Vitamins A and D dissolve in fat—for example, in the oil on canned fish. Contact with air is damaging to vitamins A, C, and D. Vitamin B_1 is destroyed by heat in nonacid foods, even in the absence of air. Light is bad for vitamin B_2 and perhaps also for A and C. All these losses occur faster in warm foods than in cold foods.

The first limitation on the quality of a processed food is the raw material from which it was made.

If a turkey to be frozen has eaten

418

food that produces the kind of fat that becomes rancid rapidly, or if the peas are starchy, the fruit is green, the variety of strawberries is low in flavor and color, the final product will be no better.

Just as not all apples are good for eating and not all potatoes are good for baking, not all types of raw material are good for processing. Fresh-market potatoes are produced in nearly all States, but a few varieties grown only in special areas are best for drying and freezing.

Different processes for the same food may have different requirements.

Mealy potatoes with a low water content are best for dried mashed potatoes. The waxy type is best for canning. These two types can be separated with salt brines, because the mealy potatoes sink in it and the others float.

Economic considerations sometimes dictate the use of varieties other than those known to be best. Less desirable varieties may be included in the total pack in a year in order to extend the processing season beyond the short time the best variety is available.

Having decided what raw material to buy, the processor must next make sure it arrives at the plant in good condition—as quickly and as cool as possible.

Fish and shellfish used to be subject to long delays, but the situation has improved. Much fish is packed heavily with crushed ice immediately after it is caught. Large quantities are frozen on ships and are thawed and eviscerated in plants on shore. Some is completely processed—canned or frozen—aboard ship. These procedures help preserve flavor and quality.

Rapid cooling and refrigeration of milk, eggs, meat, and poultry are necessary whether they are used in fresh form or in processing.

Asparagus, sweet corn, peas, and lima beans are the most perishable of the processed vegetables. They rapidly lose flavor, sweetness, general excellence, and vitamins B_2 and C unless they are processed promptly or kept cool.

Peas present a special problem because some are vined (threshed from vines and pods) at stations some distance from the plant. An objectionable flavor develops quickly in bruised, warm peas. The trend has been to vine at the plant or to water-cool the peas at the vining stations.

The first procedures in the processing plant are cleaning, sorting, grading, and preparing the foods as for table use—eviscerating the poultry, peeling the fruit, straining the milk, and so on.

The foods must be clean. An inspector can easily see whether a plant is clean. Standards of cleanliness usually are high.

Sorting and grading have a good deal to do with the uniformity of packs. The extent to which a processor can afford to separate material into sublots adapted to different uses depends largely on the diversity of his line of products. Some persons believe that separations based on appearance have been carried too far and those on flavor not far enough.

Many foods are transported in the plant in a trough—a flume—of water. Some of the flavoring constituents and vitamin C, the B vitamins, and minerals are lost thereby. Some processors have replaced flumes with conveyor belts.

After they are prepared for table use, most foods receive some kind of treatment, such as blanching, pasteurizing, concentrating, or sulfiting. (Each of these terms we explain later.)

Many liquid products—milk, cream, eggs, fruit juices—are pasteurized. Pasteurization is mild heating, which destroys all or most micro-organisms, depending on the product. It also inactivates enzymes and so helps in retention of flavor and color of the foods. Pasteurization of orange juice that is to be concentrated and frozen reduces the amount of separation into pulp and clear layers during storage but tends to take away the fresh flavor.

Batch pasteurization, which involves heating liquids at about 165° F. for 15 or 30 minutes, is giving way to continuous high-temperature, short-time procedures, in which the fluid is rapidly heated and then cooled as it flows through a series of coiled tubes. It may take only a fraction of a second and gives better flavor and color.

Most vegetables and some fruits are blanched. Blanching consists of cooking pieces of food for a short time in water or steam. Small pieces, such as peas, are cooked for about a minute at the boiling temperature or for a slightly longer time at lower temperatures. Larger pieces are cooked longer. The purpose of blanching is to inactivate enzymes and thus enhance the retention of color and flavor during storage.

Blanching procedures are not standardized. Some processors have a leaching loss of 5 to 10 percent of each water-soluble vitamin or other constituent. Others have losses of 40 to 50 percent—or even higher with the same food.

Losses are larger in water blanching than in steam blanching and larger with long-low temperature treatment than with quick-high temperature treatment. Industry has changed largely to quick-high temperature blanching for frozen green beans, and the color of the product has been greatly improved.

Considerable research has been conducted to develop electronic blanching, which would avoid losses through leaching, but a satisfactory procedure had not been worked out in 1959.

Some dehydrated and frozen fruits and vegetables are sulfited instead of blanched. A few are both blanched and sulfited. Sulfiting consists of exposing the food to sulfur dioxide gas or dipping the food in a liquid containing a similar substance. Either way, the sulfite protects color and flavor of the food by combining with the enzymes and thus inhibiting them. The chemical may disappear gradually during storage at the temperatures used for dehydrated foods. The protection then

is lost. Sulfite aids in the retention of vitamin C, but it destroys vitamin B_1. Too much sulfite gives a flavor that most persons consider objectionable.

Because we want berries, peaches, apricots, and cherries for dessert to taste as uncooked as possible, they are not blanched, but are covered with sugar sirup, which shuts out air and gives them some protection from oxidation.

Vitamin C sometimes is added to the sirup for apricots, peaches, and cherries to increase their stability. Oxygen combines with the added vitamin instead of with the fruit constituents. The vitamin may be used up during storage.

Soups, milk, fruit juice, and other liquids sometimes are partly concentrated before they are canned and frozen in order to reduce the amount of material to be packaged, shipped, and stored. The water is removed at a reduced temperature by means of a vacuum. There is little impairment of quality or nutritive value in this step.

The recovery of fruit essence is a special application of concentrating. It saves the components of flavor. The flavorful vapors that boil off during the early cooking of jelly and other fruit products are collected, condensed, and concentrated. The essence may be added to jelly in the final cooking stage, to fruit beverages and juices, fruit-flavored ice creams, and other fruit products.

IRRADIATION is a potential processing method for foods. Although no irradiated food was on the market in 1958—in fact, the law did not permit it—millions of dollars have been spent on research on irradiation.

Just as X-rays can be used to destroy cancer cells in the human body, gamma rays or high-speed electrons can be used to kill micro-organisms and insects in foods. Irradiation does not make the foods radioactive.

The first patent related to irradiated foods was taken out in France in 1930 by Otto Wüst, but extensive research did not start until 1947. Hundreds of papers have been published since then by universities, Government agencies, and private industries.

Small exposures to radiation (less than 100 thousand rads) have been used experimentally to prevent sprouting of potatoes, destroy insects in flour and spices, and delay the ripening of fruit. Such low levels usually have little or no effect on the flavor or color of foods. Radiation dosages in foods are now almost always expressed in rads. The rad represents 100 ergs of energy per gram of the irradiated material.

In the range of 100 thousand to 1 million rads, a medium level, a sort of "pasteurization" takes place—that is, nearly all the micro-organisms are destroyed, but the product is not made completely sterile. After exposure in this range, meats, fish, and certain other foods can be kept longer under refrigeration, and the shelf life of fruits and vegetables is extended.

Many products suffer a serious loss of quality at 1 million rads, but a lower level can often be found which will improve keeping quality without substantial changes in flavor, color, or texture. Irradiation at these levels may be used in conjunction with other methods of preservation, such as canning, freezing, or dehydrating.

Large exposure to radiation (a few million rads) sterilizes foods so that they can be stored like canned foods when they are suitably packaged. Such levels, however, often cause serious off-flavor, especially in meat and fat, and marked softening of vegetables.

Research is being continued to try to achieve stability without damaging foods and to reduce the rather high cost of the method.

Research results as to the safety of continued eating of irradiated foods are encouraging, but safety had not been proved in 1959.

MANY CHEMICALS are added to foods. They include coloring agents; flavoring materials; mold inhibitors, such as the propionates in bread; antioxidants, which delay development of one kind of fat rancidity; emulsifiers, such as the ones used to prevent separation of french dressing; bleaching agents, as for flour; thickening agents; and substances to prevent caking of powders. They are called additives.

Relatively few additives were used in 1938. The Federal Food, Drug, and Cosmetic Act passed that year protected the consumer at the time. But technologists learned soon thereafter that additives can help food processing in many ways. Hundreds of chemicals not used in 1938 and many not then known came into use. People became concerned about the safety of some of the substances. After much controversy and study, the Congress passed in 1958 the Federal Food, Drug, and Cosmetic Act, as amended.

Let us look at these developments in more detail.

The 1938 law did not provide for advance clearance of safety of food additives. It left it up to the Food and Drug Administration to discover their use in foods already on the grocers' shelves and to make tests to prove them "poisonous or deleterious" to the satisfaction of the court in order to remove them from the market.

So many additives came into use that it was impossible for the Food and Drug Administration to keep up. Even those for which testing could be undertaken could stay on the market while the lengthy tests (usually 2 years of feeding tests with animals) were being conducted. A congressional committee investigated chemicals in foods and reported that only 428 of the 704 chemicals used in foods were definitely known to be safe.

Many sponsors of new food additives made the necessary tests and checked with the Food and Drug Administration before using the additives. But some did not—and the law did not require it.

The 1958 amendment to the food and drug law provides that industry must prove the safety of chemicals used

Variety in Foods, from Processing

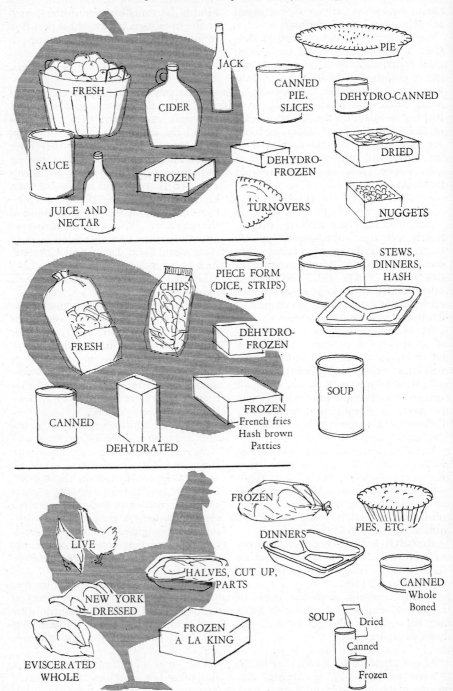

FRESH

JACK

CIDER

PIE

CANNED PIE. SLICES

DEHYDRO-CANNED

SAUCE

DEHYDRO-FROZEN

DRIED

FROZEN

JUICE AND NECTAR

TURNOVERS

NUGGETS

PIECE FORM (DICE, STRIPS)

STEWS, DINNERS, HASH

CHIPS

DEHYDRO-FROZEN

FRESH

SOUP

CANNED

FROZEN
French fries
Hash brown
Patties

DEHYDRATED

FROZEN

PIES, ETC.

DINNERS

LIVE

HALVES, CUT UP, PARTS

CANNED
Whole
Boned

NEW YORK DRESSED

SOUP   Dried

FROZEN A LA KING

Canned

EVISCERATED WHOLE

Frozen

in the processing of foods before the chemicals can be sold for use in foods. The promoter of the additive has to test it for safety on animals and submit the test results to the Food and Drug Administration. If the evidence seems satisfactory under proper conditions of use, the Food and Drug Administration issues a regulation specifying the amount that may be used, the foods in which it may be used, and any other necessary conditions of use.

If the safety of the additive is not established, the petition is denied. A promoter who is not satisfied with the decision can ask for a public hearing and court review.

WE ALL KNOW the advantages and limitations of canned foods.

They are convenient to use, reasonably stable during storage at room temperature, and as safe as we can expect any food to be. No case of illness traceable to microbial spoilage of commercially canned foods has been reported since the late 1920's.

The color, flavor, and texture of many canned foods are different (because of the long cooking required to make them safe) from those of home-cooked fresh foods. Some people like the canned foods and simply think of them as different from the fresh foods.

Canners worked for a long time to develop a safe heat process that would not overcook foods. Now they have one that keeps the good quality of many products. It involves heating the food for only a few seconds—at most, a few minutes—at about 285° F. These times and temperatures are approximate. Many factors determine the exact conditions for a particular food.

The new process is called high-temperature, short-time, or high-short processing. Its principle is that destruction of bacteria increases about tenfold for each 18 degrees of rise in processing temperature, while the chemical reactions responsible for the deterioration of the product are only doubled. Thus the food is made safe without being overcooked.

Aseptic canning uses these principles. The food is processed under conditions that provide rapid heat penetration. Then it is filled into cans and sealed in an aseptic chamber to avoid contamination during these operations.

Products prepared by the new process in 1959 included several milk, fruit juice, and creamed-soup goods. Many other foods have been successfully prepared experimentally—baby foods, corn, peas, diced vegetables, tomato juice, and several kinds of fruit. Very likely almost any liquid, puree, or small-piece food can be canned successfully by the new process. Foods that are packed in chunks, such as meat and fish, will have to wait for developments in other processes, such as high frequency electronic heating.

Another new way to reduce the heat damage in canning involves adding substances that increase the killing effect of heat on bacterial spores (the form in which bacteria are hardest to kill). The substances make it possible to destroy the bacteria with less heat than the usual canning process requires.

Of the 650 substances tested up to 1958, 26 speeded up the killing of spores, but some of them are unsuitable for use with food because of odor or toxicity. Among the most promising are two antibiotics, subtilin and nisin. Nisin occurs naturally in some types of cheese. Other effective substances are propylene oxide (which is now used in dried fruit), diepoxybutane, dodecylguanidine, and hydrogen peroxide.

Before any of them can be added to commercially canned food, it must be demonstrated that they kill the spores that have been put in experimentally canned food. Some canning tests have given favorable results. It must be proved by feeding tests with animals that any substance proposed for commercial application is not toxic under prolonged use. The tests may take 2 years.

DEHYDRATED FOODS usually are economical. Most of them are relatively easy to prepare. Their small weight and volume make them convenient to store. They are well adapted to use whenever transportation is a problem.

Much has been done to improve the quality of dehydrated food. Among the things that have led to improvement are the use of raw material that is better adapted to the requirements of dehydration; new processing technology; more careful application of known processing procedures; less dependence on sulfiting for vegetables; improved equipment, especially dryers; lower moisture content in the finished product; and packaging with inert gas.

The aim in dehydrating is to remove most of the water from food—sometimes 99 percent of it—without damaging the product. Heat damage causes a brown color, scorched flavor, and changes in texture. The first portion of water is removed rapidly, with little impairment of quality. Most of the damage occurs when the food is almost dry and water is removed slowly.

Better equipment for spray drying, which gives less heat damage during drying, has improved the quality of dried eggs. A treatment applied to the egg mix before drying also has helped. An important cause of deterioration of dried eggs in storage is that the natural sugar and a protein constituent of the egg combine to make a substance that is objectionable. The new treatment adds substances that change the sugar so it cannot combine with the protein.

Better spray dryers also have improved the drying of milk. The quick rehydrating quality of the new skim milk powder, however, is due to a second drying step, which gives the particles a fluffy, porous, spongelike structure. It took 30 years of research to achieve the powdered—instant—skim milk that came on the market in 1954.

Many piece foods are dried on trays in a forced-draft tunnel, where air circulates past them. Often part of the material is damaged by heat before the rest is dry enough to store.

Several new dryers provide more uniform and better results than the one we described. With the fluidized-bed dryer, enough hot air is blown into granular-type food so that it flows like a liquid and is kept in suspension in air throughout the drying time. This equipment is used commercially in the final drying stage for dried mashed potatoes in the form called granules.

The new belt-trough continuous dryer tumbles the food on the belt to give uniform drying. Another dryer gets uniform heating by turning the food from one conveyor belt to another at intervals.

In prospect is dehydration under high vacuum—thus at very low drying temperature and in the absence of air. The drying step can then be done with little or no loss in the overall quality of the original, unprocessed product. High-vacuum drying also makes it possible to remove practically all of the water from foods so that, suitably packaged, they store well.

The high-vacuum process works well for the dehydration of fruit juices, which are difficult to handle by conventional drying procedures because their high sugar content causes caking and sticking. Besides, some fruit juices, especially citrus juice, develop off-flavors quickly in the presence of air.

Considerable quantities of orange and grapefruit juice powders produced by the method were sold in 1958. It was expected that blended orange-grapefruit juice powder and tomato juice powder would be available before long. The latter can be reconstituted to single-strength juice or (with less water) to a puree or paste. The tomato powder can be used in dry mixes for tomato aspic, spaghetti sauce, and similar products.

Vacuum can be used with both shelf and continuous-belt drying of beverages, eggs, and fruit and vegetables in piece or juice form. The process is rather expensive, however, and was not widely used commercially in 1959.

Freeze drying, another low-temperature drying method, has produced excellent products, especially meats, which are hard to dry satisfactorily.

In-package desiccation sometimes is used to remove the last small amount of water from dehydrated foods. A small envelope containing a chemical (activated lime) is put into the final package. It absorbs water from the food during storage. The procedure avoids the damage to quality that occurs in the late stage of usual dehydration, but it raises the cost a little.

Many dehydrated foods—including many experimental packs produced by the newest techniques—were used in the ration for Antarctic explorers during the International Geophysical Year. A typical meal, weighing a pound, consisted of two dehydrated beef steaks, dehydrated onions, mashed potatoes, green beans, crackers, canned butter, canned fruit cake, and dried, instant chocolate milk.

CEREALS we may not think of as dried foods, but their stability is due largely to their dryness. The cereal grains are dried partly or completely in the field.

The first thing a consumer wants to know about a cereal food is whether the whole seed or only the endosperm—the inner portions of the kernel—was used in it. The outer bran layer of the seed and the oily germ contain important nutrients, but they may be discarded because they do not keep well or because people do not like them.

The miller of white flour reduces the endosperm part of the seed to the particle size of flour, blends different lots to get the properties he wants for particular uses, and adds chemicals to speed up the normal bleaching and maturing of the flour.

A new procedure in milling involves separating batches of flour into smaller lots, each of which is adapted to a particular use. Streams of air at different speeds separate the heavy particles from the light ones.

Bakers and manufacturers of dry bakery mixes often buy flour that meets a specified performance standard in a given formula. Thus bakery products—those the homemaker buys and those she makes—are likely to be better and more uniform.

Cereal foods are enriched to compensate for the nutrients lost in processing to make them stable. A finely powdered mixture of vitamin B_1, niacin, iron, and vitamin B_2 is added to wheat flour during milling. Standards of enrichment have been established for a number of staple foods.

The National Academy of Sciences-National Research Council has endorsed the enrichment of flour, bread, cornmeal, and white rice. The other chemicals used in flour, as well as those in bread, have been evaluated, and specified amounts of each have been approved by the Food and Drug Administration.

The protein quality of breakfast cereals—both the prepared cereals and the ones you cook—is improved in two ways. Sometimes several cereals, such as wheat, oats, barley, and even flaxseed, are combined to provide a better balance of proteins. Sometimes proteins from other foods—wheat gluten, soybean protein, or casein from milk—are added.

A growing proportion of cereals reaches the consumer as ready-to-serve breakfast foods—flaked, shredded, granular, puffed, and toasted cereals. Some have sugar coating. The consumer usually pays more for the prepared cereals than for equal nutrients obtained from cereals she cooks herself.

Cereals and foods made from cereals account for more than 20 percent of our food calories, and they furnish nearly all of our vitamin B_1.

WE BUY much white flour in the form of dry bakery mixes, which one can prepare for the oven in a few minutes. They are scientifically prepared and yield uniform quality time after time when they are finished at home. There are mixes for angel-cake, butter and fruit cakes, cookies, piecrust, rolls, muffins, and others.

The mixes are prepared in the plant primarily by mixing automatically the weighed dry ingredients together by hoppers, feeders, and conveyors. Then oil is incorporated into it by spraying it on the dry ingredients or by cutting fat into the mix by machines.

A big problem has been the development of rancidity in the mixes. It gives an objectionable flavor and impairs baking quality. Another problem concerns the leavening agents. Sometimes they react before baking time and cause the finished product to have poor volume. Both difficulties have been lessened by drying the flour to a water content of 6 to 7 percent instead of the usual 13 or 14 percent. A strong taste of baking powder in the baked product means the processor has been apprehensive about having enough leavening agent left by baking time.

Other combinations of several dried ingredients in one package are the dried soups. Each ingredient is dried separately. The beef extract may be dried on a drum dryer, the vegetables in a belt-trough dryer, and noodles on trays in a tunnel. Finally the dried spices and seasonings are mixed with the other ingredients, and the complete mix is redried.

The finished soup is no better than its ingredients. The manufacturers are looking always for better ingredients and a more convenient product—soup that rehydrates instantly with boiling water, for instance.

PRODUCTION of frozen foods increased from 275 million pounds of edible weight in 1932 to 7,329 million pounds in 1955. Ice cream, cream, eggs, poultry, and wholesale cuts of meat are not included in the figures. When they are added, the production was about 10 billion pounds in 1955.

Flavor, color, and nutritive value of most foods change little or not at all during the freezing step itself by present commercial procedures. If a frozen food is poor in these respects, we usually find that poor raw material was used, or it was handled poorly prior to freezing, or the frozen food was stored too long at too high a temperature.

It is possible to freeze so slowly that flavor, color, and nutritive value are impaired, but that is not a common cause of trouble.

The texture of frozen food is something else. The texture of several is changed by the freezing itself. Raw salad vegetables, such as lettuce and tomatoes, become too limp for use. Most fruit is softened. Raw egg yolk—but not egg white—jells and does not regain fluidity after thawing unless salt or sugar or glycerine is added. These additives limit the later use of the frozen eggs.

Packages for frozen foods have undergone many changes. Many frozen foods would retain high quality longer if they were packaged in hermetic containers—in the absence of air—instead of in paperboard or other non-hermetic materials. Only a few foods are so packaged, mainly because hermetic containers cost more.

Poultry is especially vulnerable to drying out, which causes discolored skin. To minimize this effect, birds may be wrapped in moisture-impermeable materials, such as polyethylene.

DEHYDROFREEZING of fruits and vegetables aims to combine the best features of both drying and freezing. Dehydrated fruits and vegetables offer the economies of greatly reduced weight and volume, but quality may be impaired in the late stages of drying. Freezing has advantages, but costs of storage and transportation are relatively high.

Dehydrofreezing consists of drying the fruit or vegetable to about 50 percent of its original weight and volume—but not to the stage where quality impairment occurs—and then freezing the food to preserve it.

The quality of dehydrofrozen fruit and vegetables is equal to that of the frozen products, but they cost less (because of smaller weight and bulk) to package, freeze, store, and ship.

The foods that have been satisfactorily dehydrofrozen include peas, carrots, potatoes, apricots, cherries, boysenberries, and apples. The homemaker buys dehydrofrozen foods now only in remanufactured foods—vegetables in soup, for example, and fruits in bakery pies.

FROZEN PRECOOKED foods have developed mostly since the late 1940's.

Today almost a billion pounds of 200 kinds of these foods are sold.

They include almost every food prepared in the home—soups, meat, poultry, fish dishes, nationality foods, bakery products, desserts, and complete dinners.

A number of frozen precooked foods can be made in almost the same way as the unfrozen foods. They include most breads, rolls, cakes, pies, other pastries, and waffles. They have essentially the same quality after relatively long storage as the product before freezing. They require wrappings that keep the food surfaces from being soaked with the moisture that condenses on the package during thawing.

A good many products are relatively unstable. Sometimes the storage life can be lengthened by adding sauces and gravies, which displace the air of the package. The absence of air retards the change in flavor that oxidation would cause—a common cause of warmed-over and other undesirable flavors in precooked dishes.

The sauces that contain egg or the usual starchy thickeners—gravies, white sauces, puddings, and fillings for cream puffs—separate or curdle on freezing. Curdling can be overcome commercially by the use of special thickening agents and stabilizers that are not readily available to homemakers.

As FROZEN foods are not sterile, they must be handled as perishables from the time they are processed until they are eaten.

Many micro-organisms are destroyed during processing, but some almost always remain in the food. They begin to multiply when the food thaws. If the food is held too long after defrosting, off-odors and off-flavors develop, consistency and appearance change, and finally the food spoils completely. Some frozen foods spoil faster than similar fresh foods, and so they should be eaten reasonably soon after they are defrosted.

The bacteriologist carries out two kinds of tests on frozen foods—tests to determine the number of organisms and tests to determine whether the food is likely to contain the kind of organisms that might make people ill.

Frozen foods produced under highly sanitary conditions contain only a small number of bacteria. They are less likely than foods with a high bacterial count to contain food-poisoning or disease-producing bacteria. Furthermore, foods prepared under conditions that give low bacterial count also are likely to be more nutritious and, in general, higher in quality.

Although we want frozen foods of low total count of bacteria, we are more concerned about the possible presence of even a few bacteria of the kind that could cause illness.

The possible sources of disease-producing bacteria are the soil on which foods grow, people who handle foods in processing plants, and, in the case of animals, the foods themselves.

Most specialists believe that the frozen foods we cook in the same way as fresh foods are as safe as similar fresh foods. Examples of such foods are frozen vegetables and frozen raw meats. Both are cooked—not just warmed—before they are eaten.

The situation with frozen precooked foods is quite different. They present several special problems and require extra precautions in the processing plant and at all stages until the food is eaten.

Precooked foods offer more chances for contamination before freezing than do the simpler frozen foods. Most of them contain several ingredients, each of which may be contaminated. Operations often are carried out by hand, such as hand boning of chicken.

Some of the preparations take time, and bacteria may increase during delays—especially when various foods for one package are cooked separately. The gravy for a plate dinner might be ready before the french-fried potatoes, for example.

Another reason some precooked foods require special precautions is that they are not cooked so long at serving time as the similar home-prepared foods. Many of the frozen precooked foods are not really cooked in the home. They are just warmed. We need therefore to keep such foods frozen until we are ready to cook them so that any bacteria in them cannot multiply.

There have been few authenticated cases of illness traceable to frozen foods. But new processors and new products enter the field all the time, and great care must be taken to insure the production of wholesome products.

The food industries that produce and distribute frozen foods, as well as homemakers and regulatory agencies, have responsibilities for the sanitary conditions of foods. Early in 1956 representatives of industry and food and drug officials started a large project of great interest. The purpose is to establish sanitary codes for frozen foods from producing plant through warehousing and transportation to handling at the retail level. The code, a voluntary one, would be used as a guide by the various States and municipal food and drug enforcement agencies. The first draft of the code for frozen precooked foods was expected to be ready in 1959.

When we consider all the processes a food goes through, we realize how hard it is to produce a high-quality food, even with all our scientific controls. Quality can be lost at almost every step in processing.

Most processed foods therefore are not fully equal to strictly farm-fresh foods or freshly caught fish or home-baked cake. But when we cannot get the farm-fresh foods and do not have time to bake the cake we are glad to have the processed foods.

BEFORE CONSIDERING the effects of the specific processes on costs of foods, let us look at total costs of food.

Americans spent about 20 billion dollars for food products in 1941. They spent nearly 70 billion dollars in 1958. They spent 25 percent of their cash income on foods in 1958. For the same kinds and quantities of food that consumers bought in 1935–1939, they would have spent only 16 percent of their income in 1958. It is obvious that our food does cost more. Many factors contribute to this increase besides the additional costs that might be attributed to processing. Consumption of more expensive food items, higher marketing margins, and more food eaten in restaurants are other factors.

The Census of Manufactures gives some indication of the total bill for processing. The value added by manufacturing in food and kindred products amounted to 3.5 billion dollars in 1939. The comparable figure in 1954 was 13.5 billion dollars.

The figure for 1939, adjusted to 1954 prices and for increased population, becomes 9.5 billion dollars. This, then, is evidence that our homemakers are now paying 4 billion dollars a year more than they did in 1939 for the convenience of having some of the work of food preparation transferred to the factory.

This figure, however, does not represent the net cost for this transfer of functions. Having foods in prepared form instead of raw form necessarily affects the costs of transportation and distribution. In some instances, these costs are less; in others, they are more, mainly because of such factors as weight, bulk, and type of storage required. While the total food processing bill has increased on a comparable basis, processing has lowered costs in many instances.

The first factor that affects proc-

Effect of Processing on Cost of Food

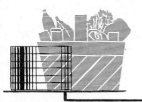

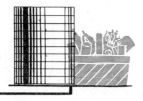

	COST DECREASE	COST INCREASE	

COST DECREASE	COST INCREASE
Lower purchase price for raw material	
Decreased waste	Upgrading
Complete utilization of all grades and portions	Processing labor, equipment, and supplies
Reduced bulk and weight	Additives
Efficiency	Quality maintenance
Portion control	Packaging
Storage stability	Refrigeration
Reduced preparation time and cost by user	

essing costs is the cost of the raw material.

Factory purchases of raw material often are made under contracts with farmers. Prices so agreed on usually are lower than prices farmers get from fresh-market sales, because farmers may prefer the security of a fixed price contract over the insecurity of possibly higher but greatly variable prices received from the fresh market. Thus, asparagus for processing in 1957 averaged 168 dollars a ton in California; fresh-market asparagus averaged 272 dollars.

Another factor that helps reduce costs associated with processing is that factories can use grades of raw material that would not be suitable for fresh-market sales. The factories can use poorly colored apples, misshapen potatoes, jumbo sweetpotatoes, small oranges, and eggs having discolored shells, all of which are available at much lower prices. These imperfections are meaningless in some processes, because the raw material is peeled and cut into pieces, or made into juice, or handled in some such way.

Processing converts perishable raw material to a stable form, of which very little is lost before it reaches the consumer. The shipment of raw material in fresh form and the subsequent distribution often result in considerable wastage and spoilage. Perhaps this loss is most obvious in retail stores, where often much raw produce is discarded. One source estimates this loss to total 125 million dollars a year for fresh eggs alone.

Elimination of waste parts of the material in processing offers substantial savings in the costs of packaging, storing, and transporting food products from farm to market. The pod, representing more than half the weight of green peas and lima beans, is eliminated in processed products.

Cut sweet corn is only one-third the weight of the corn in the husk. Thirty percent of the weight of the wheat kernel is removed in the production of flour. Canned orange juice represents about 60 percent of the weight of fresh oranges.

A part of these savings in weight is offset if brine, sirup, or sugar is added as in canning. A No. 2½ can of peaches may contain 11 or 12 ounces of sirup and 18 ounces of peach halves. The total weight of the canned product shipped thus is likely to be greater than the weight of fresh peaches used in making the pack.

Food Costs in Dollars and Hours

Expenditures per day for a family of four

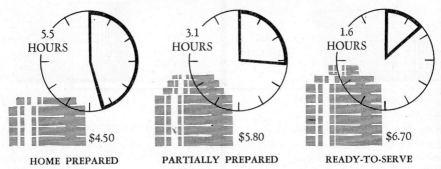

5.5 HOURS	3.1 HOURS	1.6 HOURS
$4.50	$5.80	$6.70
HOME PREPARED	PARTIALLY PREPARED	READY-TO-SERVE

Processing makes savings possible by complete utilization of a crop or animal. Most meats are sold in fresh form, but complete utilization of the carcass is possible only because parts not sold fresh are processed into canned-meat products and byproducts. Peel from citrus-fruit processes is made into feed products. Processing of milk makes possible a wide range of products, each utilizing a fraction of the original—for example, butter, cheese, skim milk, milk powders, and whey. Apples that are rejected from fresh-market packinghouses may be made into juice; the peel may be processed for pectin; and the remaining cake made into cattle feed.

Processing can also, in effect, increase costs of raw materials and produce a product for a special market. By selecting a high-quality part of the original material, a processor can upgrade the product considerably. Perfect peach halves, packed in heavy sirup, can be sold at premium prices. Other examples of this upgrading include artichoke hearts, tiny peas (petits pois), and white flour.

RECOGNITION of additional costs involved in handling and storing unnecessary weight prompts research into ways of reducing these costs.

We now have canned vacuum-packed cut corn containing only a small amount of liquid and canned packs of apples and apricots containing no added liquid at all. Concentrated products eliminate even more weight. A can of frozen orange juice concentrate represents the equivalent of four cans of juice. Dehydrofreezing reduces the weight and bulk of fruits and vegetables by 50 percent before freezing. Condensed canned soups represent a 50-percent reduction in weight and bulk.

These savings make possible sizable reductions in the cost of packaging, storing, and shipping. Dehydrofrozen peas packed for restaurants could save the user more than 2 cents a pound, compared with conventional frozen peas. Frozen orange juice concentrate generally sells at prices that are lower than those for equivalent amounts of canned juice.

A complete list of technological advances would be impossible to make, but we mention some notable ones.

DEVELOPMENTS that have made important reductions in costs are those concerned with materials handling and with continuous processing.

One materials handling method, called hydroconveying, carries the product in a stream of water, either in open troughs or flumes or in pipes. The canning and freezing industries widely use hydroconveying for moving such items as fruit and vegetables. Vegetables of small uniform size, such as green peas, lima beans, and cut corn, often are conveyed in water through pipes. Specially designed water pumps are used to elevate the mixture to higher levels.

Continuous or excessive contact with water often lowers the quality of the product mainly because soluble solid components leach into the water. Products having exposed surfaces resulting from peeling or cutting of the material are especially susceptible to leaching losses. Hydroconveying does have some advantages, however, which may offset somewhat its disadvantages. It results in transport of material at a minimum of time and labor cost. It reduces desiccation or drying of the product. It partly cools the product, an advantage in the freezing process.

Bulk transport also leads to savings. The material is hauled in large containers, trucks, and tanks without being packaged in small units. A tank car, an example of a bulk transporter, can carry dry or liquid materials. Sugar in liquid form, which many factories use, can be delivered in tank cars or trucks and transported within the plant through a pumping system. More and more milk is handled right from the farm in bulk in tank cars or trucks.

Bulk transport also is used for grain, peanuts, and soybeans. Many fruits and vegetables for processing are carried in bulk. Large containers, called tote boxes, each carrying as much as a ton or more, are used for hauling raw material to the plant. Within processing plants, large bins are used to carry dry ingredients, such as flour. Lift trucks are finding an ever-increasing application. These efficient machines can lift a tote box or a pallet load of cases or boxes weighing several tons to heights above 20 feet and can carry the loads quickly throughout the plants and loading yards.

Pneumatic conveying, or carrying materials in a stream of air, is finding increasing application in handling products in powdered, ground, or flaked form. Pneumatic conveyors carry flour, milk powder, sugar, beans, cocoa, coffee, peanuts, malt, and rice. Powerful blowers force air at high speed through a duct into which the product is fed. The duct may run from one machine or storage container to another within a building, or it may run many hundreds of feet between buildings. The product is separated from the air in a collector, which permits the flow of air greatly to decrease, dropping the product at the bottom while the air slowly rises to an exhaust vent.

These large-scale and continuous transport methods greatly reduce handling costs. Older methods use considerable hand labor. The result is a lower cost per unit of finished product. One man can now move hundreds of tons of product in a large, well-organized processing plant.

Factory preparation of food offers cost advantages to be gained from the large-scale and scientific processing. Newer types of cookers in canneries are continuous. The batch type was used previously. Even butter, cheese, and ice cream can now be made in continuous processes. Continuous diffusers give an improved extraction of sugar from beets and drastically reduce labor costs. Continuous ovens, automatic bread depanners, and band slicers that can slice 50 to 60 loaves a minute have become common.

A piece of equipment usually is classified as continuous if the items it handles are fed to it and discharged without interrupting its operation, with little if any requirement for labor. An oven in the home is a good example of a batch machine. It cooks one loaf, cake, pie, or load at a time. A continuous oven may consist of a very long chamber through which a belt moves continuously. The burners within the chamber are so located and regulated that items of bakery goods can be fed continuously into one end and emerge completely cooked.

Citrus fruits are squeezed for juice automatically. Peaches, pears, and apricots are automatically filled into cans in contrast to costly hand filling previously used. Exhaust boxes have given way to vacuum closing, which saves processing time. High-vacuum, low-temperature, continuous evaporators are used extensively in producing citrus juice concentrates, tomato pastes, and other concentrates.

New continuous types of dehydrators find increasing application. The belt-trough dryer dries fruit and vegetables uniformly with a minimum of labor. The investment cost per unit of drying capacity is low.

All of these advances have brought about important reductions in processing costs, despite large investments generally required to set up factories. Low unit costs are made possible by the large volumes of food that are efficiently put through the plants.

Costs of packages for processed foods vary greatly. Sometimes the package may cost as much as the food itself. Hermetic containers, such as are necessary for canned products, are relatively expensive. So are containers for liquids or products that become liquid.

The container cost is reduced if a product can be held so that it does not need a hermetic seal. Thus the paperboard package for frozen peas and the cellophane bag for dried fruits are less costly than the tin can for these canned foods. Some of the new materials, such as foil and a plastic film laminated together, are nearly hermetic and intermediate in price between tin cans and simple films. Aerosol, or bomb-type, packages are expensive.

Packaging costs can be reduced by reducing the amount of water included in or with the food to be packaged. Dehydrated mashed potatoes represent about one-fifth the weight of peeled raw potatoes. Orange concentrate represents one-fourth of the weight of the juice.

Portion control has been receiving much attention. A package of meat may contain four equal-sized servings. A package of dried mashed potatoes may contain two envelopes, each holding enough material for serving four persons. Individual servings of jam and chocolate-beverage powder are other examples. Portion packaging increases container costs, but it may avoid waste in the kitchen.

Frozen, canned, and dehydrated foods have advantages and disadvantages as to costs.

As a group, dehydrated foods generally offer the greatest cost savings to the consumer. They are greatly reduced in bulk and weight. They do not require costly storage temperatures. Packaging requirements generally are not critical. Dehydrated foods are not always the least costly, however. Dehydrated foods become more expensive if vacuum drying is necessary and if the output is small in relation to size and cost of equipment. Two examples: Ordinary dried apples are usually the lowest in cost of all processed apples. A new product, vacuum-dried orange juice powder, however, is likely to be quite costly, even more than the equivalent quantity of frozen or canned juice. Not only must dehydration be carried out under a high vacuum, a relatively costly process, but the product must be hermetically sealed to prevent a gain in moisture content.

Canned and frozen foods offer advantages and disadvantages in costs. The higher cost of the tin can is a disadvantage. The higher cost of freezing temperatures for transportation and storage of frozen foods also is a disadvantage. The relative importance of these factors differs with each product and situation. We might say that frozen peas should usually be sold at a lower price than the equivalent canned, but that canned condensed soups not requiring refrigeration should be cheaper than frozen soups of the same degree of concentration, because both are packaged in tins.

One question that naturally arises in any discussion of changes in processing costs is whether the increases in costs and the savings have been passed on to the consumer. The answer is obviously yes, but it would be difficult to determine the exact effect on retail selling prices. Any such changes have been masked by other changes, such as changes in the cost of farming, increased marketing margins, changes in package size and types, and even changes in process formulas. For some items that can be directly compared over a period of 20 years, for example, frozen peas, data can be assembled that show retail prices have not increased proportionally as much as the general price level.

A study conducted by the Department of Agriculture in 1953 provides comparison of cost of actual meals from home prepared, partially prepared, and ready-to-serve foods. The study included an evaluation of quality and time to prepare the comparable meals from different types of foods. It included meals for 2 days for a family of four, including two teen-age children. The meals were described as being a little more varied and expensive than the everyday meals of most families.

It took the homemaker 5.5 hours a day to make home-prepared foods, in which bakery bread was about the only prepared food. When she used partly prepared foods, which included such things as apple pie from canned apple and bakery mix, about 3.1 hours were required for preparation. When ready-to-serve meals were used, 1.6 hours were involved. The latter included frozen apple and beef pies but not a frozen complete dinner. The meals cost 4.50 dollars for the home-prepared foods, 5.80 dollars for the partly prepared foods, and 6.70 dollars for the ready-to-serve foods for the family of four for a day.

The home-prepared meals were liked best, but those from partly prepared products were considered nearly as acceptable. Meals from ready-to-serve foods were less acceptable. Individual foods within each group, of course, differed in acceptability. The quality of home-cooked foods would certainly depend on the cook. In this

study, trained home economists were the cooks. Some homemakers might not do so well, but most homemakers have the knack of preparing foods the way their families like them.

THE RAPID RISE of convenience and variety foods leads us to expect more of them, if the general economic situation is favorable. Consumers have demonstrated that they place convenience high in their choice of foods.

Processors will probably pack an increasing percentage of foods in concentrated or semiconcentrated form in order to offset as much as possible mounting costs of labor, supplies, and distribution.

Many processors and food researchers expect expansion of what they call combination processes—the use of processing steps that have especially good features. Dehydrofreezing is an example. The excellent container for canned foods might be more widely used for dehydrated and frozen foods. Canned and dehydrated foods might be stored at reduced temperatures (40° to 60° F.), but not at freezing temperature. Irradiation might serve as a supplementary step for any of the usual preservation methods. Perhaps more fresh foods will be pasteurized. We cannot exclude the possibility of radically new processes.

MILDRED M. BOGGS *has worked in food technology research since 1936 at the State College of Washington Experiment Station and (since 1942) in the Western Utilization Research and Development Division of Agricultural Research Service, Albany, Calif. She studied at the University of Wisconsin, Columbia University, and Cornell University.*

CLYDE L. RASMUSSEN *is in charge of Industrial Analysis Investigations in the laboratory in Albany, Calif., and makes studies concerning the economic feasibility of processes and market potential of products under study in the Division. He has worked in economic and cost analysis in several Government agencies and has had experience in various food-processing plants.*

The Development of New Foods

JOHN R. MATCHETT

CONVENIENCE is a fine thing in a new food product, but, as we have made clear by our buying, it alone is not enough.

Convenience has to do with easy preparation; reduction in weight and bulk for economy in transportation, storage, and display; and stability in storage.

We look for something more than that, however, when the grocer offers us a new kind, or type, or package of food. Orange juice concentrate was available—but stayed on grocery shelves—long before the frozen product was developed. Potato flour and dehydrated riced potatoes antedate potato granules and flakes. The first dried egg found little favor.

If many of us are to buy it, a food product must look right. It must taste right. It must have the texture we want.

Because we are becoming increasingly aware of the nutritive value of our foods, research workers that envision new or improved products maintain programs to learn the basic chemical and physical makeup of

foods. Knowing the individual chemical substances and all the changes they undergo under various conditions of temperature, contact with oxygen, and so on, they can choose conditions for processing that will preserve the characteristics we like and modify those we wish changed.

A thorough understanding of the chemical constituents and the function of each in the final product makes it possible to evaluate raw and processed foods. Evaluation now is based mostly on appearance and other subjective—personal—reactions.

The research has yielded a great deal of information, although it has not been underway very long. Perhaps we can relate some of it to several of the important factors of quality and see how it is taken into account in developing a new food product.

COLOR is a major aspect of quality; it makes food look good.

The so-called anthocyanin pigments lend their brilliant colors to grapes, cherries, plums, strawberries, and other deciduous fruit. The pigments are soluble in water. They are relatively stable in juices, canned fruit, jellies, jams, and the like if the acidity is kept high and the temperature is not too high.

Another class of pigments known as carotenoids colors citrus fruits and a number of vegetables, including carrots, sweetpotatoes, and rutabagas. They account for the color of butter, poultry, and meat fat. They are present in all dark-green, leafy vegetables, although chlorophyll may mask them. Among them are beta-carotene and alpha-carotene, precursors of vitamin A. They are yellow, except lycopene, the characteristic coloring matter of tomatoes and pink grapefruit.

These pigments do not dissolve in water, and care must be taken to keep them in suspension if brightly colored juices are to be had. They are not greatly affected by high temperatures of processing or storage, but they must be protected carefully from oxygen. They are quickly lost through oxidation, especially in such dehydrated products as carrots and sweetpotatoes and powdered citrus juices.

Not only is their color lost in the presence of air; off-flavors and odors result. An odor like that of violets, sometimes observed in dehydrated carrots not adequately protected, results from the oxidation of carotene.

The most familiar green pigment is chlorophyll, the universal coloring matter in plants, which we prize in peas, beans, and green vegetables. Chlorophyll does not dissolve in water. It is not highly susceptible to oxidation, but it changes rapidly to the unattractive olive-colored pigment pheophytin at high temperatures and even more quickly if the acidity increases. Therefore we keep the time of blanching and heat processing green vegetables as short as thorough treatment allows.

Many other classes of pigment occur naturally in foods. Among them are the polyphenols, some of which may have important physiological functions. They are of special concern to the food technologist, because they may give rise to discoloration if control measures are inadequate.

They have little color or none at all until they are exposed to air in the presence of an enzyme of the kind called polyphenol oxidases. Then they soon become the unattractive brown or gray of the cut surface of an apple or potato that is left standing too long.

Enzymatic reactions like this one do not proceed in the raw fruit or vegetable because the cell structure is so arranged as to keep enzyme and substrate—the pigment in this instance—separate. It proceeds rapidly when the cells are damaged, as in peeling or cutting. Cells generally are damaged in food freezing. Inadequately protected frozen fruit therefore turns brown quickly after it thaws in the air.

This discoloration poses a serious problem during processing and sometimes afterward, as in frozen fruit.

A common method of control is blanching—or scalding—which inactivates the enzyme that is accountable for it. Frozen fruit often is packed in an ascorbic acid (vitamin C) solution. Oxygen then attacks the ascorbic acid in preference to the polyphenol, and the fruit color is spared until the ascorbic acid is depleted.

Enzymatic browning can be controlled also by treating the cut surface with sulfur dioxide, applied as the gas or in the form of sulfite dissolved in water. It combines with the enzyme and makes it inactive in some fashion that we do not wholly understand. Because, like ascorbic acid, it is attacked by oxygen, its protective action may be lost in time.

A number of other chemical substances control enzymatic browning but are not used in food technology. Some have not been proved unequivocally to be safe. Some can be tasted when they are present in amounts sufficient to be useful. Sulfur dioxide can readily be tasted. Many persons do not find it seriously objectionable in the amounts that are needed.

Research ultimately will explain the mechanism of enzymatic discoloration completely, and improved methods for its control very likely will be developed.

Perhaps the most serious problem of color in concentrated and dehydrated foods is posed by nonenzymatic browning. We have known for a long time that highly concentrated foods stored in warm places for long periods gradually develop a brown color, which is accompanied generally by some off-flavor. This unattractive color generally is the limiting factor in shelf life of dry vegetables, especially when stored under adverse conditions—that is to say, their appearance deteriorates faster than their flavor. It deteriorates faster than their gross nutritive value, too, but the rate is roughly proportional to the rate of loss of vitamin C.

Vigorous research looking toward understanding and control of nonenzymatic browning has shown that the chemical reaction between those naturally occurring sugars known as reducing sugars with proteins and perhaps other nitrogen-containing constituents (the so-called Maillard reaction) is a major factor. Its rate is not materially affected by the presence or absence of oxygen. Temperature and moisture content are the critical factors. It is always best, of course, to keep foods as cool as possible.

The observation that lowering the moisture content slows the rate led to the development of "in-package desiccation" or "lime packing." Dry lime or another drying agent is put in a package through which moisture can pass as vapor. This package is then placed in the moisture-tight package that contains the food. The drying agent absorbs the moisture vapor given up by the food. Thus its moisture content is reduced slowly. The method avoids the extended high-temperature treatment, which may cause damage, that would be required to achieve the same moisture content in the dehydrator. Surprisingly, sulfur dioxide controls the rate of nonenzymatic browning as well as browning of the enzymatic type, and it has substantial

use in protecting the color of many products through the dehydration step as well as later in the storage of the product.

One should remember that the "browning reaction" is not always a factor of deterioration. We like it in some cases—for instance, bread crust, pancakes, toast, and steaks.

So deeply ingrained in us is our association of color with quality in foods that we color many of them artificially to correspond with our views of what they should be.

Pale butter is colored with annato or dyes known as yellow 3 or yellow 4. The green of mint jelly is supplied by a mixture of blue No. 1 and yellow No. 5. Maraschino cherries must be the correct shade of red, and this is accomplished by red No. 1.

I could give many other examples. The certified colors and the protective chemicals I have discussed exemplify our approval of the employment of additives that researchers have proved to be safe in order to give foods an attractive color. We are equally receptive to additives—similarly tested—which serve other useful purposes. The food technologist must consider their possibilities from many points of view when he is engaged in the development of a new product.

RESEARCHERS find it particularly hard to understand and evaluate flavors. All of us respond differently to flavor stimuli. We vary in acuteness of taste. Individuals respond differently at different times when tasting products known to be identical.

The ability to assay flavors differs among flavors, too. A person who readily differentiates degrees of sweetness may be much less sensitive to variation in saltiness. These differences in people do not necessarily correspond with their preferences.

The flavor complex with which the food technologist must deal in contemplating a new process is further complicated by various preferences.

In view of all these factors he must

first think of the flavor his product should have. Then, in turn, he must devise ways to measure progress toward its attainment and test his judgment by seeking the opinion of a sampling of potential consumers.

Although some progress toward successful chemical assay of flavor has been made (I refer to it later), we must depend on taste panels for guidance. We cannot yet foresee the day when these subjective—personal—methods will be wholly replaced. So we proceed with care to select panel members suitably qualified for the task at hand. Their results are integrated and constantly checked through the indispensable methods of statistical analysis. It is really astonishing how confidently the results can be relied on when all the significant variables have been brought under control.

Taste panels are set up for at least three separate, specific purposes, which must be kept in mind when we design research and when we interpret results, although panels may well overlap the boundaries a little in actual practice.

One type of panel is composed of experts on a given food. Its members are chosen on the basis of demonstrated ability to differentiate the natural flavors and the off-flavors and have been trained to recognize and evaluate them. Such a group can score food flavors with consistent results. Its members know the food thoroughly and are prepared to interpret their taste results in quality terms. Generally they are expert also in understanding the preferences of consumers of the food and the extent of flavor departure from the norm that consumers will accept.

A second type of panel is chosen on the basis of demonstrated and consistent ability to distinguish among degrees of differences in flavor. Its members need not be expert in respect to the food itself. Their job is to detect differences between samples set before them. Such a panel does not assign a quality score. It determines, for instance, whether a given varia-

tion in processing has affected flavor detectably or not or at what point two samples originally alike but stored under different conditions become distinguishable.

The third type of panel is chosen as a cross-section sample of all potential consumers of a new product. These panels must ordinarily consist of several hundred members. Products must be used by them in the home just as they would be if bought in the store. The opinion of such a panel regarding the market outlook for a new product is very persuasive, and great care is devoted by industry to its evaluation.

So complex are the chemistry and psychology of a person's response to taste that we once regarded it as impossible to define and measure in objective, nonpersonal terms. This view is being modified.

We have learned to differentiate the relatively simple sweet, sour, salt, and bitter from the more subtle but more characteristic volatile flavors.

We link sweet, sour, and salt tastes with the amount of sugar, acid, and salt in a food. We can assay them reasonably well by relatively simple chemical means. A bitter taste is less readily measured objectively, but we have made progress in isolating and characterizing the substances to which it is due. Some day we shall have analytical methods by which to measure it.

But the volatile flavors are the ones that announce what's cooking at mealtime or jellytime and give individuality to each of our foods. They are the ones, too, that pose the most difficult problems for researchers. They are complex chemical mixtures, and until a few years ago we had little hope of knowing exactly what they are.

Now we have new techniques for separating and identifying chemical entities, which have given new impetus to the search.

The same phenomenon by which a drop of ink on soft paper is separated into colored and colorless zones has become the basis for a keen analytical tool. Known as chromatography, it has been applied successfully to the separation of extremely complex materials into single constituents or simpler mixtures.

It and other procedures have helped us to separate and to label 90-odd separate constituents in the flavorful oils of orange and grapefruit and 26 in apple volatiles. Strawberry, fresh bread, meat, poultry, and certain vegetables are being studied.

None of these researches has yet given us complete specification of a flavor. Good progress is being made, and complete understanding will be had in due course. When unequivocal measures of flavor and other quality factors can be made by rapid laboratory methods, development of new and superior varieties of fruit, vegetables, and other agricultural products will be facilitated.

Rational choice of protective processing and storage conditions will be made possible through a knowledge of the chemical constituents that have to be retained intact and those which must be altered to serve our purpose.

New procedures in preparing foods will be suggested through precise knowledge of the effect of various conditions on the important chemical entities concerned.

Quality evaluation will be simplified, and flavor will become a factor that we can determine and use in grading fruit and vegetables and other foods. Flavor as assayed by taste testing has heretofore been entirely too subjective for such use, except in instances that involve an obviously objectionable flavor.

TREATMENTS during processing generally cause changes in flavor.

The "cooked" flavors differ from those of the raw product. Long storage under unfavorable conditions generally brings about gradual deterioration of flavor accompanied by accumulation of off-flavors. These usually are ascribed to oxidative reactions and generally are controlled by excluding oxygen or using an antioxidant, a chemical substance that interferes with oxidation of food constituents. Many antioxidants occur naturally in foods. Others have been prepared and put into commercial use after thorough testing to assure their suitability for use in foods.

Oxidative rancidity is a widely recognized kind of off-flavor. Pork or fish kept too long in a freezer suffer in this way. Stale flavors that sometimes appear in foods stored too long may belong to this class also. Oxidative reactions generally are favored by extreme lowering of moisture content, a point to be considered by processors who are developing a new dehydrated product, particularly one containing even a small amount of fat.

Enzymatic activity affects the flavors of some foods. Frozen and dried vegetables develop off-flavors rapidly in storage if they have not been blanched adequately. We do not know the exact nature of these reactions.

We know of some enzymes—not necessarily troublemakers—that can serve as indicators, however. As a general rule, for example, we know that vegetables have been scalded enough when the peroxidase system in them has been inactivated. This can be determined by simple laboratory testing.

TEXTURE is an important aspect of quality in food: Think of soggy pie crust, lumpy mashed potatoes, tough meat, mealy apples, overmature peas and corn, fruit juice that has lost its cloud, dry milk that will not dissolve.

Research has given us some insight into the control of texture, but much remains obscure.

The natural expediters known as enzymes again seem to be vital. The aging of meat is thought to be enzymatic, although the chemistry is far from clear. Enzymatic destruction of pectin appears related to loss of cloud in fruit juices and concentrates. Heat treatment, properly timed, usually controls it.

Thorough scalding is required for

acceptable rehydration of dehydrated vegetables. Forewarming—initial heat treatment, that is—has an essential but little understood part in the physical stability of concentrated milk.

Conditions of processing affect texture, too. The effects of cooking and overcooking are well known. Vacuum- or freeze-dried products generally retain their size and shape during dehydration in piece. Liquiform products (juice, purees, milk) when vacuum dried generally are more bulky than their spray-dried counterparts. Cubed vegetables shrink less when they are dried in hot, dry air than when they are dried more slowly in humid air. The rehydration rate is roughly proportional to the bulk of the product. Whether this is necessarily so has not been demonstrated.

THE CONDITIONS that favor retention of the other qualities favor the retention of nutrients in foods.

Storage at a low temperature and a low content of moisture protects against loss of ascorbic acid as it does against the browning reaction. Anaerobic atmosphere—without free oxygen—guards carotene, as it prevents rancidity. Protection from light conserves riboflavin, as it protects against rancidity.

Research thus far has given only a glimpse into the vast science of food constituents, their identity, their interactions under all conditions, and their effects on human nutrition.

The food technologist, though, can work to develop a new product with a considerable background of fact.

To be commercially successful, his new product must have the maximum of convenience in preparation for the table. Its bulk must be the minimum, consistent with the intended use, for economy in packaging, storage, and distribution. It must be stabilized by the least costly means that will assure retention of acceptable quality until consumed.

His task might pertain to some popular food that requires much time and effort to prepare. His first step is to consider the work that can be handled by mass methods in the factory better than in the home—such operations as washing and peeling fruits and vegetables, plucking and eviscerating poultry, mixing of ingredients, and cooking.

He chooses the method of preservation, taking account of how each kind of processing affects the quality and weight, bulk, packaging, and storage temperature requirements.

His primary aim is to prevent the depredations of micro-organisms. He can do that by creating an environment in which they cannot multiply—by holding it at low temperatures or by bringing the moisture below growth requirements, or by canning processes to destroy the organisms present and prevent others from entering. Salting and fermentation create unfavorable chemical environments and also are sometimes used to develop desirable flavors.

We have been discussing the quality factors that consumers demand in our processed foods. These generally are color, flavor, texture, and nutritive value. Each must be acceptable in a new product if it is to find a large market. Each is determined by the presence and proportion of definite chemical substances.

We have reviewed very sketchily the little that is as yet known about these and have outlined broadly the changes they undergo under various conditions and precautions that must be observed to retain those characteristics we desire and to avoid changes we do not want.

The principles developed must be observed in any new product development. But it is interesting to note that in addition there seems always to be one or more key steps that make a new product practical. Of course, these always turn out to be consistent with the general principles but they demonstrate that new food design is by no means reduced to a routine procedure.

Frozen orange concentrate is an example. For years it had been known that evaporation under high vacuum would produce a concentrate having no off-flavor or darkened color induced by heating. The vital volatile flavors evaporated along with the unwanted water, however. The concentrate when diluted with water to the original strength had a flat and nondescript flavor. It was not disagreeable, but was not attractive enough to find large markets. Some of it was canned or barreled and exported during the war for use principally as vitamin C concentrate. But researchers never lost sight of the advantage of economy in transportation, storage, and convenience in use, and the key to the situation was developed when it occurred to one of them to add a portion of fresh juice to the flat but otherwise excellent vacuum concentrate. The resulting product was nearly like the fresh juice, which contains enough volatiles to flavor the whole product. Freezing and storage at zero temperatures preserve its good quality.

There were three keys to the development of citrus juice powders. The flavorful volatile oil of orange lends itself to entrapment in molten sorbitol, or sugar, to form a stable granular substance, which releases the flavor instantly upon being dissolved in water. When incorporated with dry orange juice it supplies flavor quite comparable to that of fresh juice.

The second key was the observation that a film of juice concentrate could be made to puff under controlled conditions of temperature and pressure in a vacuum dehydrator. This puff then dries to a friable powder, readily dissolved in water. Before the puffing process, citrus juice dried to a taffylike mass, which was impractical to dry and hard to reconstitute. Flavorful puff-dried powder was readily prepared by these processes, but it would soon cake and discolor on storage and at a rate greatly accelerated by increasing temperature or moisture.

The third key to a successful citrus powder was in-package desiccation. By this means the moisture content is reduced slowly and without exposure to high temperature. The resulting pack is amply stable for commercial distribution. It makes available without refrigeration citrus juices of excellent quality.

Dried egg was one of the dehydrated foods most urgently needed in wartime. Intensive programs of excellent research demonstrated the necessity of low moisture content, inert gas pack, and minimum storage temperature. Darkening and off-flavor development were delayed, but the shelf life remained quite unsatisfactory until investigators engaged in basic research on the problem observed an apparent advantage in removal of the 1 percent or so of sugar in the mixture. Within a short time the stability of dried eggs had been increased ten times. The product today is commercially feasible. Research continues, for problems remain to be solved.

Research workers also tried a long time to develop a dry whole milk that could be transported and stored at minimum cost, would retain its fresh quality under all reasonable conditions, and could be reconstituted in a jiffy. Through their efforts we have learned to make powders that suffer very little by comparison with the milk from which they were prepared. Their reconstitution is the work of a few seconds. But despite the careful application of every known principle to improve stability, this problem had not been solved in 1959.

The search for new knowledge of foods and their constituents goes on at an ever-increasing rate in university, Government, and industrial laboratories. As it accumulates, improvement in commercial food products will follow. So will the development of new ones.

JOHN R. MATCHETT *is Assistant to the Administrator of the Agricultural Research Service for Utilization Research and Development. His principal field has been for many years the development of new or improved foods and industrial products to expand and stabilize the market for agricultural commodities.*

The Federal Trade Commission

S. F. STOWE

AT a free dinner for a ladies' club, which was staged by a demonstrator on behalf of a large distributor of stainless-steel cookware, the salesman held up an aluminum cooking utensil and sternly warned his audience that the use of aluminum utensils would result in cancer and other illness.

Aluminum is a porous metal, he maintained, and when food is cooked in it, some food is retained in the pores and becomes poisonous.

This is one type of sales trickery the Federal Trade Commission is greatly concerned with and is trying to eliminate from the food industry.

Aluminum is not a porous metal in the sense that some of the food cooked in it will be retained, and food so cooked will not become poisonous or cause illness.

As a result of these false claims, the Federal Trade Commission instituted proceedings against this distributor, which resulted in an order that stopped the use of these scare-selling techniques.

In the advertising and marketing of food, the Federal Trade Commission plays a part as important as it is inconspicuous.

To most people, the Commission is little known, and its work remote from the subject of nutrition. Producers, wholesalers, and distributors of food and retail outlets are under no such illusion, however. They are quite aware of the Commission's power to promote free and fair competition as it applies to the food industry.

One of the Commission's principal concerns here is to assure that prices will not be discriminatory at any point in the line of distribution from manufacturer to retailer. Under authority of the Clayton Act, as amended by the Robinson-Patman Act, the Commission moves against monopolistic practices that threaten the free and fair play of the forces that give consumers a fair competitive price for food.

The Commission also is empowered to move against false and misleading acts and practices in commerce. While its own jurisdiction is generally limited to businesses that advertise and sell in interstate commerce, the Commission works closely with State and local organizations, such as better business bureaus and chambers of commerce, to suppress improper business methods. This teamwork has been effective.

The fact that the Commission's actions are directed at sellers usually one or two steps removed from the ultimate consumer belies the effect they have on him. To pay an exorbitant price for a pound of coffee, for example, is a consumer problem, whether the high price is set by the corner grocery store or by the wholesaler supplier or, indeed, the actual producer of the coffee.

Because the local grocer is likely to be engaged only in intrastate commerce, the Commission's actions are rarely directed against him. They are directed instead against illegal restraints in the interstate supply line and extend to those who supply raw material to the manufacturers.

For example, a few years ago the price of coffee spiraled to an unprecedented point, and the Commission investigated. After an economic study, which led all the way back to the producing regions of Central and South America, the Commission found that a major cause of the abnormal price was a restrictive contract used by the New York Coffee and Sugar Exchange. The Commission ordered the contract broadened to permit wider trading in coffee for future delivery. As a consequence, the price of coffee could be reduced sharply by local grocery stores. The ultimate consumer knew not of the Federal Trade Commission, but he knew that once again coffee was obtainable at a more reasonable price.

More commonplace are the Commission's actions to maintain competition when it is threatened by monopolistic practices.

Particularly important are actions to prevent giants in the food industry from driving out competition by such illegal means as discriminatory pricing. A number of actions in 1958 were aimed at the practice whereby certain suppliers gave their biggest customers

favored prices, directly or indirectly, for food products, and so enabled them to undersell their competitors and force them out of business. With competition gone, the favored stores could set whatever price the traffic would bear.

Such illegal discrimination often takes indirect forms, such as the granting of illegal brokerage, which puts buyers not so favored at a competitive disadvantage that could lead eventually to their elimination as competitors.

Still another and an equally grave threat to competition in the food field are illegal mergers, the effect of which is to deprive the ultimate consumer of competitive prices and products.

An example: The Commission has been moving against alleged illegal mergers in the dairy and flour businesses. The dairy mergers challenged are those in which large, national dairies have been buying small local competitors, with the result that milk producers are deprived of as wide a market for their milk as existed formerly and retail outlets are denied the advantage of being able to buy from competing sellers.

The Commission has challenged the purchase of an important manufacturer of dried food seasonings by one of the country's principal food processors and chain retailers. The Commission charged that this merger would deprive many food suppliers of the competitive market formerly available to them.

Of more direct impact on the consumer are the Commission's actions against false and misleading advertising of food products. The Commission has brought actions to stop manufacturers of food supplements, particularly vitamins, from misrepresenting that their products are more nutritious than rival products. In addition, these actions have challenged claims that the vitamins provide wider and greater benefits than they do. The Commission has been halting false claims that the vitamin preparations are "cures" for a number of human ailments. Not only have these advertisements enumerated a fictitious number of ailments for which the vitamins are of benefit but they also impute to them greater effect than is the fact. In one case, for example, the Commission challenged the claim that "red blood can all be yours with just one tablet daily." The Commission's complaint said the tablets have no value for reddening blood or anything else.

The Commission's work in the field of false advertising also is apparent in actions taken to prevent the sale of oleomargarine as butter. Acting in the belief that a purchaser is entitled to know what he is buying, the Commission has challenged direct misrepresentations of oleomargarine as butter and also advertising that suggests that it is. Typical of the latter are cases in which oleomargarine was advertised under names suggestive of butter or phrases having to do with dairy products, such as "country-fresh" and "richer in milk minerals than most expensive spreads."

Not only in food products themselves does the Commission cock a wary eye at false nutrition claims.

It takes action to stop false advertising of cooking utensils by sellers who make unjustified claims for their own products and falsely disparage competing utensils. It seems to make little difference what the cooking utensils are made of, according to recent cases challenged by the Commission. A maker of stainless-steel utensils was charged with promising that his product would assure good health while aluminum ware would cause food to become tainted. A maker of aluminum ware had advertised the reverse of this.

Still another manufacturer touted his cookers by advertising that boiling food causes nutritional deficiencies leading to heart disease, arthritis, kidney trouble, and diabetes. The Commission issued orders requiring the firms truthfully to represent their own products and to stop falsely disparaging others.

Besides taking action against individual food companies, the Commission began a broad-scale economic investigation of competitive methods and practices used in marketing food. Here the purpose was not to single out violators of the law but to shed light on developments that affect competition among food sellers. The period chosen for the study was 1948–1958.

Questionnaires were sent to more than 1 thousand food sellers, including food chains, voluntary groups of wholesale grocers, and retailer-owned food distributing groups. The Commission sought to find out just how much concentration has taken place and its pattern. Have the chain stores been growing faster than independent stores which have banded together into cooperative groups for the purpose of cooperative advertising, purchasing, warehousing, and other activities? The answer to this and many other questions would give an idea of the concentration trend and how competitive free enterprise in the food industry might best be preserved.

Another broad-scale effort by the Commission was aimed at price trickery in retail sales, including food products. This campaign, launched in October 1958, would put a stop to the advertising of a product as being reduced from a "regular" price at which it never had sold, thus making the actual selling price appear to be a bargain. The Commission holds this to be a deception of the buyer—who is entitled not to be lied to in forming a judgment on whether the price he pays is advantageous to him. This fight against fictitious pricing was supported by better business bureaus and other groups devoted to honest business, with the result that by early 1959 in many areas of the country housewives could again believe that a marked-down price really was a genuine reduction.

S. F. STOWE *is Director of Information, Federal Trade Commission, Washington, D.C.*

The Pure Food Law

GEORGE P. LARRICK

MANY consumers are worried about the safety and nutritive value of our foods. They ask if the chemicals used in them are harmless, whether modern processing methods rob foods of their natural vitamins, and whether there is any basis for the information peddled by nutrition cultists and quacks with "health foods" to sell.

The public does not know enough about the workings of food standards and the other instruments for protecting consumers under Federal law.

Federal food laws for more than half a century have been dedicated to safety, wholesomeness, and the type of labeling that will permit citizens to make intelligent selections in their purchases. Telling people what to eat is attempted by education rather than by regulation. Their choice affects the whole food industry, for in the long run the practices of manufacturers reflect consumers' wishes.

The Federal Food, Drug, and Cosmetic Act (our national pure food and drug law) prohibits the movement in interstate commerce of adulterated or misbranded food. It broadly defines adulteration and misbranding and directs the Secretary of Health, Education, and Welfare to supplement some provisions of the law with more detailed and technical specifications by administrative regulations.

These supplementary regulations for foods include definitions and standards, selection and certification of safe and suitable coal tar colors, labeling requirements for special dietary foods, and tolerances for safe amounts of pesticidal residues that may remain on raw agricultural commodities and for safe amounts of additives in food.

The Food and Drug Administration is the agency named to enforce this law and the regulations implementing it for products other than meat and poultry.

A small organization as Government agencies go, the Food and Drug Administration has a staff of about 1,400 to cover not only foods but drugs, devices, and cosmetics as well. About 60 percent of its employees are assigned to the 17 district offices throughout the country, from which factory and warehouse inspections are made and samples are collected for testing in district laboratories or in Washington staff laboratories when special analyses are required.

Adulterated and misbranded products may be removed from the market by Federal court seizures. Persons and firms responsible for the violations may be prosecuted under criminal court proceedings, and potential violators may be restrained by the court from unlawful practices.

The Food and Drug Administration in 1958 seized 824 shipments of food, filed 91 criminal prosecutions against alleged violators of the food provisions of the act, and requested 17 injunctions to restrain manufacturers and storers of food from further violative practices.

Filth or decomposition accounted for most of the actions and for 78 percent (5,466 tons) of the total volume seized. An additional 19 percent (1,333 tons) resulted from contamination by deleterious ingredients, mainly excessive residues of pesticides.

Most manufacturers have the will and the knowledge to produce clean, safe, and accurately labeled foods and voluntarily consult with the Food and Drug Administration when new problems develop. In general, court proceedings are needed only to protect the public from the ignorant, the heedless, and the greedy.

The many skills needed to administer the law call for a scientific organization. New manufacturing processes require new methods of inspection and analysis and may require long studies of safety and effects on nutrient values. Normal composition of foods must be established before debasement can be detected and proved to the satisfaction of the court. Proof that claims in adroitly phrased labeling are misleading may require the help of experts in public opinion analysis to determine the impression prospective purchasers may gain from the label.

It is becoming easier to conceal substitution or inferiority from ordinary observation in today's processed, compounded, packaged foods. The housewife is becoming more and more dependent on the enforcement of labeling requirements.

No official standards have been promulgated to specify the proportion of the more desirable ingredients such products as ready mixes and heat-and-serve items must contain, and price competition frequently leads to lowering of quality. The law comes into play, however, to require the labeling of unstandardized foods to be truthful and to avoid sins of omission.

Failure to reveal material facts on the label constitutes misbranding if it may lead to deception of the consumer. Valuable constituents may not be omitted or abstracted without appropriate declaration on the label.

FOOD STANDARDS promote honesty and nutritional advances.

The definitions and standards of identity that have been established for many of our staple foods have been called the Nation's most important cookbook. They specify the normal composition of the food—the required ingredients and certain permissible ingredients that may be added at the option of the manufacturer.

Once a standard goes into effect, only the products that meet the specifications may bear the name of that food.

The standards are issued to promote honesty and fair dealing in the interest of consumers. Although the housewife may not know the details of the specifications, she knows what to expect when she buys a standardized food by name. The label need not list the required ingredients, but some optional ingredients, such as the type of sirup used in canned fruit, are stated.

The manufacturer knows the specifications. He knows that he and his competitors must follow them. They are a protection for the honest manufacturer against the chiselers.

The enforcement officer uses them as a yardstick to determine whether a food is adulterated or misbranded. Trial courts do not have to determine, as they did under the 1906 law, what the standard should be for a product charged to be in violation but only whether it meets the official standard.

Originally the law provided that public hearings be held for interested parties to present their views on new standards or amendments to existing ones and that the final regulation be based entirely on the evidence recorded. Many of the hearings were long and costly to all concerned under this procedure.

The law was amended in 1954 to require hearings only when genuine controversy arises concerning specific proposals. All interested parties have the opportunity, as before, to comment on the proposed regulations, which are published in the Federal Register.

Definitions and standards of identity cover plain and enriched foods, with no middle ground for the type of partial enrichment that may mislead the purchaser. Leading nutritionists of the country have assisted in formulating the criteria for supplementing foods to meet the country's nutritional needs.

Basically, this policy is aimed at maintaining good nutrition as well as correcting deficiencies in the diets of significant segments of the general population. If a particular nutrient is to be added to a specific food, there should be clear indications of probable advantage from increased intake of the nutrient, assurance that the food concerned will be an effective vehicle for distributing the nutrient to be added, and evidence that such an addition will not interfere with the achievement of a diet that is good in other respects.

These principles were originally formulated by the Food and Nutrition Board of the National Academy of Sciences-National Research Council in response to a request of the Commissioner of Food and Drugs in 1941. The Council on Foods and Nutrition of the American Medical Association joined the Food and Nutrition Board in issuing a revision of the statement in 1953. They have been invaluable guides to the Food and Drug Administration.

Legal standards for the following staple foods containing added nutritive ingredients have been established: Enriched flour, enriched cornmeal and grits, enriched rice, enriched macaroni and noodles, enriched bread and rolls, evaporated milk with vitamin D, and margarine with added vitamin A. Standards for the same kind of foods without vitamin and mineral addition have also been established. This gives the public a freedom of choice, except in States that require that all items in certain classes be enriched. Even in other States, public preference for enriched foods has virtually eliminated plain foods in some of these classes from the retail market.

Our present knowledge of nutrition has developed, to a large degree, since the passage of the Food and Drugs Act of 1906.

The word "vitamin" was coined in 1912, but not until 1926 were regulatory examinations made of products for their vitamin content. Cod-liver oil was the first. Discoveries between 1910 and 1930 that established that vitamins A, B, C, and D are essential to man resulted in commercial production during the next decade.

The commercial application of the rapidly increasing knowledge of nutrition was still in its infancy, however, when the Food, Drug, and Cosmetic Act of 1938 was passed. This revised law gave broad authority to regulate the labeling of foods claiming special nutritive benefits.

In recognition of the difficult labeling problems for foods for special dietary uses, the Secretary of the Department of Health, Education, and Welfare is given administrative power to prescribe the type of labeling necessary to inform purchasers of the value of such foods for their intended uses.

SPECIAL DIETARY FOODS must be informatively labeled.

Public hearings were conducted in 1940 to establish regulations for the labeling of foods for special dietary uses, and the regulations published in November 1941 were based on the evidence recorded at the hearings.

The unit of measurement adopted for vitamins and minerals and the products enriched with them is based on Minimum Daily Requirements for them, called MDR for short. The percentage of the MDR that will be supplied by the quantity of the dietary item normally consumed in a day must be declared on the label. If the article contains vitamins and minerals other than those for which the MDR has been established, that fact must be stated on the label.

Apart from vitamin or mineral content, some foods for special dietary purposes are used in the management of diseases, such as diabetes and certain types of heart conditions. Others are used for infants, the aged, the obese, the allergic, and the pregnant.

Without going into details about the labeling of each, which are available in Food, Drug, and Cosmetic Regulations, Part 125, let us consider the problems and resulting regulations for low-sodium foods. These products became important a few years ago when it was shown that a low intake of sodium was important in the control of certain types of high blood pressure.

Many consumers started to demand unsalted foods, and processors promptly responded. Some had the false impression that foods with "no salt added" would accomplish the results scientists had announced. They did not know that sodium is a natural constituent of many foods and that others are increased in sodium content by the addition of monosodium glutamate seasoning, or of sodium propionate to prevent mold, or from other processing practices.

A survey of "low-salt" and "low-sodium" foods on the market disclosed this lack of uniformity and frequently the misleading nature of the composition and labeling of such products. The Food and Drug Administration formulated new regulations on the basis of the survey, and a public hearing was held.

The regulations, announced on June 30, 1954, require that if a food is offered as a means of regulating the intake of sodium or salt, the label shall state the number of milligrams of sodium in 100 grams of the product and in the quantity constituting an average serving of it. Declaration of the sodium content of average servings is needed particularly in dealing with condiments, crackers, and other items ordinarily consumed in small amounts. A relatively small number of seizures have been necessary because of failure to label low-sodium products as required or to measure the sodium content accurately. Some of the early producers of such items, who did not have the equipment or expert skills required, have turned to other fields that require less precision.

NUTRITIONAL QUACKERY is a health problem as well as an economic one.

In the wake of scientific advances there often follows a host of persons who will misinterpret them and exploit them for private gain.

That has been true in the field of nutrition. The nutritionist studies the long-range benefits to the public health from new scientific findings, withholds premature endorsement, and has confidence that future research holds great promise. For example, the 1939 Yearbook of Agriculture, in the chapter, "Are There More Vitamins?" said that studies of the use of milk in deficiency diseases have added much to practical knowledge, and added: "But it is obvious that this knowledge is very rapidly changing and still incomplete, and that it must be consistently reappraised in the light of more recent developments."

The exploiting promoter of food supplements, on the other hand, does not wait for the facts or the possibility of different findings in the future. He hastens to cash in before all the facts are known.

Those interested only in profits employ clever copywriters to promote products by pseudoscientific statements, using half-truths, innuendo, and gross exaggeration to build up a scare psychology that will persuade people to buy nutritional supplements. Some of these sold on a "contract basis" cost as much as 20 dollars a month for each adult in the family and about half that for each child. This cost is often taken from the family food budget, which would supply an adequate diet if used for foods readily available throughout the country.

The American Medical Association estimates that nutritional quackery is costing 10 million Americans more than 500 million dollars a year.

Misleading promotion of food supplements relies heavily on the false theory that today's food supply does not provide essential nutrients.

An extensive mythology of nutrition has been built up through pseudo-scientific periodicals, books, magazine articles, and other media, as well as product advertising. Much of this is highly critical of modern commercial foods; at the same time it promotes various so-called natural or organically grown food items. Many readers of such literature accept it blindly with great faith and zeal. Always ready to believe every new idea and to buy every new "health food" that is suggested to them, they keep the promoters of diet fads in business.

The latter occasionally misjudge, and break, the law. Two such went to jail in 1957 for making "medicine man" claims in selling simple food supplements. One was a lecture-hall promoter. The other sold his vitamin products through door-to-door agents.

It is estimated that approximately 50 thousand canvassers now sell vitamin and mineral food supplements in the United States. These agents are not qualified to advise the public on matters of diet and health, yet many of them are in a sense "practicing medicine without a license." To make sales, they do not hesitate, in the privacy of the home, to recommend their products for the treatment of any disease condition. When this leads to delay in obtaining competent medical treatment, it is very serious.

Sales agents for vitamins are a fertile source of misinformation about food. To pave the way for sales, they commonly utilize a number of false theories that are calculated to undermine confidence in the food supply.

This type of false and misleading information was involved in the second of the two cases I mentioned. The manufacturer was convicted for supplying sales literature to agents, which falsely represented that "Nearly everyone in this country is suffering from malnutrition or in danger of such suffering because of the demineralization and depletion of soils and the refining and processing of foods. . . . All illnesses and diseases of mankind are due to improper nutrition. . . . Said articles would be effective in the cure, treatment, and prevention of the ills and diseases of mankind."

It was also claimed that certain specific diseases would be effectively treated or prevented, including diabetes, polio, tuberculosis, and cancer— all conditions that are not subject to treatment with vitamins or food supplements.

Each of these charges was contested and litigated in the trial. Testimony of outstanding medical and nutrition experts was introduced by the Government to disprove not only the claims for treatment of disease but also the false statements concerning the effects of soil depletion and food processing. The jury found the defendant guilty, and he was sentenced to a year in prison. The court of appeals upheld the conviction in a detailed opinion, which the Supreme Court declined to review.

Regarding soil depletion as a cause of malnutrition, there is no scientific basis for the theory that crops grown on poor soil or with the help of chemical fertilizers are nutritionally inferior in any way. On the contrary, research has shown that while soils may be so depleted that they will no longer yield good crops, the nutritional values of such crops are not affected by the soil or the fertilizer.

L. A. Maynard, who testified for the Government at the trial, summarized these findings in the Journal of the American Medical Association, August 11, 1956, page 1478. The only disease of man that is known to be associated with any deficiency of soil or water is simple goiter due to the lack of iodine in some areas. This disease has become quite rare as a result of the widespread use of iodized salt.

It is true that some methods of food processing and cooking do result in removing or reducing some vitamins and minerals contained in foods. But this is routinely exaggerated by food quacks, who conveniently overlook the fact that modern food-processing methods have been devised to preserve nutritional values or to restore them to foods. Also ignored is the great variety of the American food supply, which in itself is a protection against deficiencies in diet.

The other man jailed for such claims in 1957 is a "health lecturer" with a number of prior convictions in both State and Federal courts. He invited the public to introductory free lectures, during which he sold tickets for a paid series. The lecture tuition was less than 10 percent of the cost of the products his pupils purchased. He recommended his own proprietary brand of such items as whole-wheat flour, peppermint tea, wheat germ, and honey for the prevention and cure of arthritis, cancer, liver trouble, heart trouble, and most other ills, and to "put off death to the very last minute." He repeatedly told his audiences not to buy other brands of these products; only his own (sold at several times their normal price) would achieve the promised results, he said.

After a month-long trial, the jury brought in a verdict of guilty. While on bail, pending appeal, he conducted another extensive lecture tour, during which he successfully solicited contributions from his audiences to continue his struggle against "persecu-

tion" by the "medical trust," the Better Business Bureau, and the Food and Drug Administration.

He was sentenced to a year and a day in the penitentiary. He appealed the sentence and filed suit against the Federal judge who sentenced him. The appeals court upheld the conviction.

Operators of this type, and there have been many others who followed similar patterns, are virtual successors to the medicine men who blatantly promoted patent medicines at the turn of the century. Their attempts to build up a fanatic zeal in their followers are too often successful. To combat it will require increased efforts to teach the public the facts about good nutrition, and that even the best nutrition is not a substitute for competent medical care.

The Food and Drug Administration each year seizes numerous products with exaggerated claims made by promoters who take advantage of developments of current interest in medicine and science.

A good example is the exploitation of research seeking to determine the relationship, if any, between certain heart ailments and the type of fats consumed in the diet. Food-fad promoters did not wait for the additional research needed on this question, but promptly started to market products supposed to protect the public against heart disease, for which they were worthless. A number of products containing vegetable oils and unsaturated fatty acids combined with vitamins were seized in 1958 for such claims.

Increased interest in the problems of the aging has brought forth numerous nostrums falsely claiming to benefit older people. Royal jelly in various diluted forms, offered at exorbitant prices, has been seized for rejuvenation claims on the labeling. Royal jelly is the bee food that makes queen bees productive and long lived, but is of no practical value for human beings. So much misleading information about this material appeared in certain periodicals that many people were led to buy it by name, without the direct labeling claims which would have made it subject to regulatory action.

Other items seized for false representations for chronic diseases of the aging include powdered grapefruit, lecithin, honey, kelp, and mixtures of vitamins and minerals with other ingredients such as oyster and egg shell, seaweed, parsley, alfalfa, rose hips, lemon peel, chlorophyll, powdered bone, and clay.

The public should distrust any suggestion of self-medication with vitamins or minerals to cure diseases of the nerves, bones, blood, liver, kidneys, heart, or digestive tract. Although a physician may employ these products in certain cases, such conditions require competent medical diagnosis and treatment.

Also to be distrusted is the claim that anyone who has "that tired feeling," or an ache or pain in almost any part of the body, is probably suffering from a "subclinical deficiency" and needs to supplement his diet with some concoction. A "subclinical vitamin deficiency" is defined as a condition in which it is not possible to obtain any observable evidence of a vitamin deficiency, but a deficiency is suspected.

Of course, no normal person can go through even a small part of his life without experiencing some of these symptoms. There is no basis for believing that they are usually due to subclinical deficiencies. Such symptoms may be caused by many other conditions than vitamin or mineral deficiencies. Advice of a competent physician is needed to identify vitamin or mineral deficiencies and to prescribe their proper treatment. The competent physician will not overlook such "musts" as calcium during pregnancy and vitamins C and D for babies and young children.

FOOD ADDITIVES present a problem that is very old. Dr. Harvey W. Wiley's campaign for the pure food law of 1906 was to a large extent a fight against chemical preservatives.

The too-common misconception that all chemicals are harmful fails to take into account salt, baking soda, vinegar, and other common chemicals used in every kitchen. Only those that may be harmful require regulation.

The law as written in 1938 protected the public against food additives that could be clearly proved to be injurious. It did not, however, require that chemicals be adequately tested and shown to be safe before they are marketed, except for coal tar colors.

Lists have been established of coal tar colors that may be used in foods, drugs, and cosmetics. Each batch of color must be tested in the Washington laboratories of the Food and Drug Administration to determine that it is of satisfactory quality and purity. Several colors were removed from the permitted list in 1955 because modern testing procedures showed that they did not meet the law's requirements.

When we talk about chemical food additives, people often bring up the use of insecticides on our fruit and vegetable crops. There are more than a hundred of these pesticide chemicals. Some are relatively harmless to people. Some are highly toxic. Some quickly disappear before the crop is harvested. Many leave traces of residue which might be harmful if the residue were excessive.

The law now contains a requirement that these materials be tested for safety before they are submitted to the Government with a request that residue tolerances be established. Under the Miller pesticide amendment, passed in 1954, safe tolerances are required to be set up limiting the amount of residue that may remain on the food crop after it is harvested. If these tolerances are exceeded, the foods can be seized and taken off the market.

The 1938 act restricted the use of most chemicals in food—even in safe quantities—unless they were required in good manufacturing practices or could not be avoided. This philosophy was unscientific because it deprived consumers of the benefits to be derived safely from modern scientific research.

Another, more serious, defect of the 1938 law was that it did not require a manufacturer to test a new chemical before using it in food. If a manufacturer decided to use a new substance without testing it, the public was exposed unnecessarily during the 2 or 3 years required for adequate tests by the Government.

This deficiency of the 1938 act was studied by the Congress from 1950, when it formed a Select Committee to Investigate the Use of Chemicals in Food, until 1958, when it passed the food additives amendment.

The substances covered by this amendment are those additives not recognized by competent experts as having been shown to be safe under the conditions of their intended use. Antioxidants, mold inhibitors, rancidity prevention agents and other preservatives, emulsifiers, and stabilizers are examples of the types of additives that are covered.

Substances commonly used in food before January 1, 1958, and generally recognized as safe because of experience based on such use, are exempt from the law. Thus a great many ingredients do not have to go through the clearance procedures of the bill.

Substances that get into food accidentally, such as lead ores, for example, are not covered by the legislation. These substances, if proper precautions are taken, would not reasonably be expected to get into food, and if they do get in, the food is illegal under the basic 1938 law.

Other additives not covered by the new amendment are pesticide chemicals, which, as I mentioned, are already taken care of under the pesticide chemicals amendment, and substances that have already been approved by the Government for use in food under the Food, Drug, and Cosmetic Act, the Meat Inspection Act, or the Poultry Products Inspection Act.

The person who wants to promote a new food additive will have to test it for safety on animals and submit the results of the safety tests to the Food and Drug Administration.

Scientists of the Food and Drug Administration will study the safety data and reach an independent decision as to the suitability of the new ingredient for use in our food supply. If the evidence clearly demonstrates that the material is a suitable component of food, then the Department of Health, Education, and Welfare will issue a regulation stating safe permissible uses for the material. But if there is a question as to the safety of the additive, it will not be permitted, and the public health will be safeguarded in a way that was not possible before.

Use of an additive that promotes deception of consumers is not sanctioned. If the additive can only be used in a limited amount, to safeguard health, only the quantity needed to accomplish the intended technical or physical effect will be allowed, and this amount will be allowed only if it is safe. In case the Government and industry are unable to agree about the contemplated use of food additives, industry has a right to a public hearing on the suitability of a proposed additive and the right to appeal an adverse Government decision to the circuit court of appeals.

With this amendment, the country has the best safeguards it has been possible to develop. It provides for advances in food technology without risk to human health. The additives that go into food are there to improve the food and bring it to the housewife in better condition and in a more convenient form. The 1958 amendment is a significant advance in the protection of the welfare of consumers—all of us.

GEORGE P. LARRICK *has been Commissioner of Food and Drugs, Department of Health, Education, and Welfare, since 1954. He has been continuously engaged in Federal food and drug law enforcement since he entered the service in 1923.*

The Public Health Service

LEROY E. BURNEY

THE Public Health Service, the principal health agency of the Federal Government, is concerned with all the factors, including nutrition, that influence the health of people.

Americans continue to enjoy good health because of advances in medical science and public health, the application of disease control and sanitary procedures, education, a high standard of living, and growth of the science of nutrition and food technology.

Improvement in the average diet has built stronger Americans, saved lives, and virtually eliminated such once-prevalent deficiency diseases as pellagra, rickets, and infant scurvy. It has played an important part, along with other public health measures, in the decline of tuberculosis. Improved milk and food sanitation has helped conquer typhoid fever and other infectious diseases. Better nutrition has contributed to the development of a generation of children who are taller and heavier than children were 20 or 30 years ago.

Such progress has brought public

health to the point where the science of nutrition can be brought to bear in an early attack on some of our most devastating disease problems in the United States. Public health and related agencies throughout the country are therefore turning increasing attention to research, services, and education in the field of nutrition.

Many organizations, groups, and individuals have a hand in protecting and advancing the Nation's health— State and local agencies, voluntary organizations, universities and medical schools, hospitals, research institutions, and citizens' groups.

Within this partnership, the Public Health Service conducts programs in research and training, medical care for designated beneficiaries, and the protection of public health. Its responsibilities are specifically designated by the Congress in matters relating to national health, but its programs have been developed in cooperation with agencies and groups having an interest in health.

From the national standpoint, the Public Health Service helps to develop health resources and to improve health services. For nearly a third of its 160-year history, for example, the Service has conducted research and perfected procedures to combat milkborne and foodborne diseases.

THE RELATIONSHIP between contaminated milk and the spread of typhoid fever and other communicable diseases was determined as early as 1908. At the same time, studies in Public Health Service laboratories established the thermal death time for the organism that causes tuberculosis. This formed the basis for the development of standards of pasteurization. Yet, additional work on the pasteurization process is still being done— in relation to new disease problems. In 1955 the Public Health Service and the University of California completed a series of joint studies on the thermal inactivation of the organisms that cause Q-fever. The findings indicated a need to increase the temperature for vat-type pasteurization to protect the milk consumers from this new disease.

State and local agencies are responsible for protecting the public against foodborne diseases except when specific problems of an interstate nature are involved. All States and most municipalities now have milk and food sanitation programs. They look to the Public Health Service, however, for the technical assistance, scientific data, and the recommended standards on which to base effective programs. The Service also receives many requests from industry, particularly in developing uniform standards and evaluating new processes.

COOPERATIVE PROGRAMS with the States and with industry have been successful in improving sanitation in the handling of milk and food. Only under the direct statutory requirements covering milk, food, and water served on interstate carriers, such as trains, buses, vessels, and airplanes, does the Service exercise legal authority. Even here, however, the rules of enforcement are grounded in consultant and cooperative relationships.

The Public Health Service has prepared sanitary ordinances and codes for voluntary adoption by State and local governments for milk, shellfish, frozen desserts, eating and drinking establishments, and poultry. First published in 1924, the Milk Ordinance and Code served as a basis of regulations in 1959 in 36 States, 479 counties, and more than 1,420 municipalities.

An activity that affects millions of Americans is the cooperative State-Public Health Service program for the certification of interstate milk shippers. This program, which is endorsed by health agencies, shippers, and producers, enables milk-shortage areas to obtain milk of high sanitary quality from distant sources. Begun in 1951 with 160 milk shippers, the list in 1959 included 614 interstate shippers certified by the States, and comprising the production of about 80 thousand dairy farms.

A SIMILAR cooperative program is in effect for the certification of interstate shippers of shellfish. A list of such State-certified shippers is published by the Service for use by health authorities in controlling shellfish sold within their States. All of the 22 coastal States participate in the program, as does Canada, through an agreement negotiated between the United States and the Canadian Government.

The Ordinance and Code Regulating Eating and Drinking Establishments, developed by the Service for voluntary adoption by States and municipalities, has been in existence since 1938. A revision was undertaken in 1958 to keep pace with technological advances in the food service industry. In 1959, it served as a basis of restaurant regulations in 36 States, the District of Columbia, 772 municipalities, and 377 counties—which have a combined population of more than 95 million.

TECHNOLOGICAL ADVANCES are creating revolutionary changes in the processing and merchandising of food. Thus public health agencies are faced with new problems in the sanitary control of food.

One such change is the increasing mechanization of parts of the food industry. Standards, developed in 1957, are designed to prevent the transmission of disease through food and drink dispensed by vending machines. This new industry had a volume in excess of 2 billion dollars in 1957, about half of which was in sales of food and beverages. The swift growth of this industry underscored the need for public health protection involving both the machines and the products.

As a result of all these activities, food reaching American consumers today is safer than in almost any other part of the world. Nonetheless, outbreaks of foodborne disease, totaling thousands of cases each year, continue to be reported. In 1956, 241 outbreaks, involving 11,906 cases and 16 deaths, occurred. Moreover, these statistics represent but a fraction of the cases because many outbreaks result in minor illnesses and because reporting by the States is incomplete.

When outbreaks of "food poisoning" occur, State health departments frequently call on specialists from the Communicable Disease Center of the Public Health Service for help in epidemiological investigation—or "disease detective" work. By prompt inquiry into the circumstances, epidemiologists are often able to pin down the particular disease organism that caused the outbreak, the food involved, and the way in which the food became contaminated. Such investigations help prevent other outbreaks.

Increases have been noted in the number of reported foodborne infections due to certain species of *Salmonella*. Bacteriologists of the Communicable Disease Center have demonstrated the presence of *Salmonella* organisms in animal feeds, in the places where food is processed for the market, among people who prepare and handle food, and in other situations where the presence of these organisms invites the spread of disease.

One way to keep free from contamination—in food production, processing, preparation, and serving—is to eliminate flies. Flies breed in all kinds of organic filth and can carry disease organisms to any food they alight upon. Entomologists and sanitarians constantly seek better ways to cut down fly populations and thereby reduce the incidence of diarrhea, dysentery, and other flyborne diseases. In many places these insects have developed resistance to DDT, malathion, and other insecticides. The Communicable Disease Center studies the nature and extent of this resistance and tries to find ways to counteract it.

Toxicologists also evaluate insecticides used to kill agricultural pests to make sure thay are not harmful to consumers. In studies with DDT, a commonly used insecticide, investigators have found that about 200 times the amount of DDT contained in the average person's daily food can be consumed every day for as long as a year with no ill effect.

RESEARCH is also conducted on toxic agents in food and on chemical and radiological contaminants, particularly at the Sanitary Engineering Center in Cincinnati, Ohio. Synthetics and other chemical substances are increasingly used in food production and processing. Radiation contamination in food supplies presents a potential hazard to the public health. In 1958 the Service began a nationwide pilot study to determine the amount of radioactivity in milk. Milk samples are collected in various sections of the country and analyzed in the laboratories of the Sanitary Engineering Center.

Both the Sanitary Engineering Center and the Communicable Disease Center offer training in fields related to the purity and wholesomeness of food. State and local sanitary engineers, health officers, and other health workers are invited to these courses.

Training is given in the control of diseases carried in water, milk, and food and in laboratory diagnosis, epidemiology, disease vector control, and general environmental sanitation. Through its regional offices, the Service also provides technical assistance and consultative services to State and local health agencies on milk, food, and shellfish sanitation problems.

Such services are also made available in nutrition and diet problems related to disease. Careful supervision of the diet, for example, is particularly important for people with diabetes and heart disease and for patients in institutions. Nutrition consultants from the Public Health Service help plan and set up, in cooperation with health agencies and educational institutions, special diets required in these situations. They also help develop educational materials pertaining to diets and nutritional services.

The growth of an aging population has resulted in a great increase in the number of nursing homes, homes for the aged, and similar facilities. Sound nutritional practice is an important factor in health maintenance for these older patients. Health agencies, as well as the proprietors of nursing homes and homes for the aged, are turning to the Public Health Service for advice on these problems. The Service in 1958 developed a new program of consultation on the nutritional problems of patients in nursing homes throughout the country.

THE SERVICE participates in nutrition surveys conducted in foreign countries. The surveys are organized by the Interdepartmental Committee on Nutrition for National Defense and are supported by the Departments of State, Defense, Agriculture, and Health, Education, and Welfare and the International Cooperation Administration.

Upon the request for assistance from a country under the Mutual Defense Assistance Program, the Committee organizes a nutrition team composed of specialists in medicine, nutrition, sanitation, food technology, and agriculture. The team studies a country's food and nutrition problems and sets up a nutrition program designed to remain in effect after the team departs. Surveys have been conducted in Korea, Iran, Pakistan, the Philippines, Turkey, Libya, and Spain.

A SERIOUS problem in some countries is the lack of enough food, especially food that contains high-quality protein. In countries where rice is a staple food, the rice is usually polished at the mills for preservation and storage, but the polishing process removes valuable vitamins and mineral elements.

As a result of the nutrition surveys, two new mills for the enrichment of rice were built in the United States and shipped to Taiwan. They make it possible to coat the rice with vitamins and minerals at low cost and to provide the people with adequate amounts of thiamine, riboflavin, niacin, and iron.

The Public Health Service also helps other countries improve nutrition by participating in other international health work and through cooperation with the World Health Organization.

IN ITS RESEARCH PROGRAMS, the Public Health Service gives grants and fellowships to support a wide variety of research projects in nutrition in universities, medical schools, and institutions throughout the country. Most of this work is centered in the National Institutes of Health in Bethesda, Md., the main research arm of the Public Health Service.

Nutrition research by the Public Health Service had an impressive beginning with the discovery by Dr. Joseph Goldberger that pellagra was caused by a dietary deficiency and not by infection. An outgrowth of this early work was the discovery of another vitamin-deficiency disease, ariboflavinosis, caused by a lack of riboflavin in the diet.

The emphasis in nutrition research has shifted considerably. Because deficiency diseases have dwindled considerably, attention has focused on some of the less well recognized nutritional disturbances.

From fundamental research we have learned, for example, that the trace element selenium is the essential active ingredient in the dietary substance known as factor 3, which protects experimental animals against fatal deficiency diseases. This discovery represents a major step forward in the study of experimental nutritional liver disease.

RESEARCH programs of the Service thus reflect the increasing emphasis on biochemistry—the basic discipline of nutritional science—in the studies conducted at the National Institutes of Health and in many research projects supported by grants.

Biochemical research is the entering wedge for the solution of many basic problems in such diverse fields as cancer, the cardiovascular, neurological, mental, and infectious diseases, and the major metabolic disorders.

Atherosclerosis, the commonest form of arteriosclerosis, is the primary cause of 97 percent of all cases of coronary artery disease and a high percentage of mental disorders in older people. Scientists have been pressing forward to identify the specific biochemical and physiological causes of atherosclerosis. The widespread scientific interest in blood cholesterol level and its relation to heart disease has spurred a tremendous amount of research on nutritional factors that may have some influence on the cardiovascular system. Although the exact relationships between dietary factors and atherosclerosis are not yet known, we have reason to believe that dietary changes will have a part in its prevention. The National Institutes of Health is supporting a wide range of research projects related to atherosclerosis, including studies of dietary factors. Among the many factors under study are fatty acids, vitamins, minerals, amino acids, and trace minerals.

Nutrition research is also directed toward other cardiovascular diseases. Epidemiological studies of selected and general population groups are being carried out to determine the possible relationship of dietary factors to coronary heart disease and hypertension. Several such projects are underway in the United States and elsewhere.

OBESITY is a major nutritional problem in the United States. Overweight is believed to be closely related to such chronic diseases as diabetes, hypertension, gout, and some types of arthritis.

Scientists at the National Institutes of Health are studying the problem of obesity in fundamental and clinical research. In one laboratory study, for example, they have produced some of the largest experimental rats ever recorded, by feeding a special diet to otherwise normal animals. The obesity results solely from the consumption of a diet containing 60 percent of fat along with adequate amounts of vitamins, minerals, and protein. The giant rats can then be reduced to normal size and studied to see whether obesity has permanently affected their metabolism. The development of this method for producing obesity by dietary changes alone makes it possible to study the disorder when it is uncomplicated by other physiological changes.

SCIENTISTS at the Public Health Service's Clinical Center started a long-term research project in 1954 to establish baselines on energy metabolism for definitive studies of obesity. They are using a special metabolic chamber where the energy expenditure of subjects can be measured, calorie by calorie, for periods of 24 to 48 hours.

Patients under study in this specially constructed respiratory chamber can live comfortably inside the chamber for several days. They eat and drink precisely measured amounts of food and liquid prepared in a special metabolic kitchen and engage in planned exercises. The composition of the air they breathe is controlled, and all exhaled air and other waste products are captured and analyzed. The studies conducted inside this chamber may provide answers to physiological problems that are not now understood.

NUTRITION STUDIES are also becoming more important in cancer research. For a number of years, antifolic acid compounds have been the most effective treatment for leukemia. Although these compounds initially suppress the symptoms of the disease, patients finally become resistant to them or develop toxic symptoms. Many leukemia patients are now under study to determine if their disease is associated with altered folic acid metabolism.

Other studies at the National Institutes of Health are throwing light on certain dietary problems of rheumatoid arthritis patients, who are being treated with synthetic steroids, such as cortisone and prednisone. The studies are concerned with the inflammatory and metabolic effects of these drugs. It has been found, for example, that the synthetics tend to increase the excretion of nitrogen. As a result, a diet fairly high in proteins is indicated for patients on these drugs.

The nutritional problems of old age are commanding increasing research attention. In addition to its research programs in the chronic diseases, the Public Health Service is conducting and supporting a number of studies on the processes of aging. In the area of calcium metabolism, for example, laboratory and clinical investigations are underway to determine the level of calcium intake required for the maintenance of healthy bone structure as the individual ages. These basic studies are an outgrowth of interest in osteoporosis, a condition that results in serious disability in many older people. The purpose is to learn whether the level of calcium intake plays an important role in this fundamental bone defect.

At the other end of the lifespan, scientists at the National Institutes of Health have demonstrated the specific biochemical defect in galactosemia, a fatal hereditary disease of infants. The investigators discovered that the disease is caused by the lack of a specific enzyme in normal red blood cells, which is needed to catalyze the conversion of galactose (one of the principal sugars in milk) into the common sugar of the blood, glucose. When the enzyme is missing, the infant is unable to metabolize the galactose in the milk and will become extremely ill if he continues to receive it.

This disease has been difficult to diagnose in the past because the early symptoms, such as diarrhea, resemble those of other, less serious afflictions. A relatively simple blood test has been developed. It indicates the presence or absence of the necessary enzyme. It is thus possible to establish a diagnosis of galactosemia in earliest infancy and—by prescribing milk-free diets—to prevent its devastating effects.

Work with germ-free animals is a new field of nutrition research. The animals are born and reared in an atmosphere completely free of all bacterial contamination. They also receive germ-free food and water. Studies with them help to determine how intestinal bacteria influence the production and metabolism of certain nutrients within the body.

THROUGH WORK such as the foregoing, the Public Health Service hopes to speed the march of health progress. Food technology, diet, and the science of nutrition will undoubtedly play important parts in this progress. As in all health fields, the key to success is the discovery and prompt application of new knowledge.

LEROY BURNEY *was appointed Surgeon General, Public Health Service, Department of Health, Education, and Welfare, in 1956. A native of Burney, Ind., he holds degrees of bachelor of science and doctor of medicine from Indiana University.*

It is now seventy-nine years since Mother and I started a cooperative feeding study which revealed two important facts. Both were already known to others. One was that an infant fed breast milk may thrive as I did until seven months old or longer. At that age Mother was informed by my little brother that he was coming to live with us. She was in a quandary about what course she should take, but concluded it was best to wean me early and conserve her strength for the next baby.

She told me that the women in Kansas at that time were convinced that if a baby were fed cow's milk it should surely die. Their belief was fully justified. If you could go back with me and see our cows, or barn, the milk pails and cans, and our lack of facilities for keeping milk cold, you would doubtless have been convinced that no baby could survive such unsanitary milk. It is my belief that I could have survived being fed on milk contaminated with stable filth. It was the cloth strainer which a baby could not compete with by his defense mechanisms. We rinsed the strainer after pouring the morning's milk through it, and hung it up to dry. In summer, fifty or more flies would alight on it within a minute and feed upon the milk residues, speckling it with flyspecks. In the evening the fresh milk was poured through this fly-excrement-laden cloth. A baby could scarcely ever fail, when fed such contaminated milk, to suffer from diarrheal infection and die.

Mother decided to feed me potato soup made from mashed potatoes boiled in milk. For the sake of variety she also gave me daily chicken broth. This too was strongly heated. So the second point we demonstrated was that a baby could not survive on foods which have been strongly heated. I developed scurvy. Nobody knew what was wrong with me so nothing was done to help me. Mother despaired of my survival because of extensive hemorrhages in my skin and mouth, swollen joints and exquisite sensitiveness to handling. I owe my survival to the chance occurrence that we had, about my first birthday, March 3rd, a stock of overwintered apples; that Mother peeled some to make pies; that she held me on her lap the while to try to comfort me while I puled in misery. By chance she gave me some scraped apple and observing

that I liked it, she gave me a considerable amount, and did so the following and successive days. She said that within two days I was noticeably improved, so she kept on with giving me scraped apple. I recovered. . . .

In 1907 I began laboratory work as assistant to Professor E. B. Hart, at the Wisconsin Agricultural Experiment Station, to try to discover why cows failed to thrive on certain single-plant rations. It was a famous nutrition study in its period. In the course of a few months I became convinced that we lacked techniques for finding why cows fed only the parts of the wheat plant were seriously mal-nourished. It was while reflecting on our project, and reading widely in the literature describing past studies with simplified diets composed of purified food substances, that I became convinced that the most important problem in animal nutrition was to discover why animals restricted to diets composed only of protein, carbohydrate, fat and mineral salts, speedily failed nutritionally and died. This conclusion led to my setting up a rat colony late in 1907 for the purpose of trying to solve the problem of what was lacking in these purified mixtures . . . .

With the assistance of Marguerite Davis I conducted many experiments to determine combinations of natural foods, each of which was, when fed alone, inadequate to nourish young rats and promote growth. Certain combinations were good because one component supplied what was lacking in another. In other words, we found that there were important supplementary relations between certain foods but not in other combinations. The most effective food for making good what other common foods lacked from the nutritional standpoint was milk. This was a very important observation, and led me, about 1915, to do my best to sell milk. I criticized the typical American diet of that period, which was in great measure composed of refined cereals, muscle meats, potatoes and sugar, as being of inferior quality, and asserted that the best way to improve it was by including more milk in the daily menus. The idea took hold and milk consumption steadily rose during the years following.— ELMER V. McCOLLUM. *From an address on receiving the Borden Centennial Award. Printed in Proceedings of The Borden Centennial Symposium on Nutrition.*

Food

PREPARATION

Food

PREPARATION

Freezing Food at Home

GLADYS L. GILPIN

IN THE freezing of food, extreme cold is used to slow down the changes that affect quality or cause spoilage in food.

Spoilage in frozen foods (as in canned food) is due to micro-organisms that cause fermentation and decay.

Among them are bacteria, yeasts, and molds, which live everywhere—in air, soil, water, and food and on people. The micro-organisms grow and multiply least easily in extreme heat, cold, or dryness. They do not grow well in high concentrations of salt, vinegar, or sugar. Smoking limits their growth. Acid foods are less subject than others to spoilage by micro-organisms.

Oxygen in the air reacts chemically with fruits and vegetables by a process called oxidation, which changes their color and flavor and reduces their content of certain vitamins. Oxygen can cause fat foods to become rancid.

Action of enzymes is a third cause of change. Enzymes—chemical substances that are in all plants and animals—help them grow and mature and may improve or impair their quality after harvest or slaughter. Heat, drying, and thorough smoking stop or slow enzyme action. Vinegar and other acids and cold reduce enzyme activity.

Preservation by freezing is based on the principle that extreme cold retards growth of micro-organisms and slows down enzyme activity and oxidation. Freezing does not sterilize food—the number of micro-organisms on the food must be reduced and kept at a minimum. Cleanliness in the food, utensils, surroundings, and the person doing the work is essential.

Acid and the low temperature slow enzyme activity enough in acid foods like fruit, but one has to use some additional means in low-acid foods like vegetables. Brief heating, sometimes called blanching or scalding, before freezing accomplishes this purpose and also reduces the number of micro-organisms. Enzymes make poultry and meat more tender, and the amount of activity going on during frozen storage has no bad effect on eating quality.

Oxidation goes on at a fast enough rate to impair color, flavor, and texture of food during frozen storage. The best ways to eliminate or reduce oxidation are to select packaging that will allow little if any air to get into the sealed package and to reduce in every way possible the amount of air left in the package when packing and sealing. Tight packing, covering food with

461

sirup, water, or gravy, and a tight seal help to do this.

The browning of some fruits in the air during preparation is due to oxidation; that is, oxygen combines with substances in the fruit to produce dark-colored compounds. It helps to use antioxidants, such as ascorbic acid or lemon juice, which combine with the oxygen so it cannot change the color of the food.

The quality of frozen foods may be changed because the moisture in them forms ice crystals, which may damage their cells or fibers. The effects on different foods vary, because foods vary greatly in composition and structure.

SEVERAL TYPES of prepared frozen foods present problems because of changes that take place during freezing. Gravies and cream sauces may separate or curdle because water in them separates as ice crystals and causes the starch emulsion to break down. The sauce often can be reblended in foods that can be stirred during heating for serving. Waxy rice flour and waxy corn flour, which contain a certain type of starch found in waxy varieties of cereals, have been used to stabilize these products in commercial freezing and are suggested for home use if they are available. A uniformly low storage temperature also helps.

Custards break down during freezing, because water changes to ice crystals and separates out and because the coagulated protein of the eggs is altered so that it is no longer soluble. A similar change in the protein of cooked egg white makes it tough and rubbery when eggs are frozen.

In french dressings and mayonnaise, the water that has been emulsified with the oil separates on freezing.

Graininess of ice cream and sherbet is due to large ice crystals, which get larger when the temperature is not low enough.

Frozen jams, which have most of the color and flavor of the fresh fruit, sometimes form white crystals during storage. The crystals look like mold and may spread through the mixture once they have started to form. They are formed when the sugar combines with the water in the jam. They spoil the appearance and texture but are not harmful.

Some leavening power is lost in frozen batters when ice crystals form. Too little liquid is left then to hold the carbon dioxide in solution. Cakes made from the batter have slightly less volume than cakes made from fresh batter. The kind of baking powder used affects the amount of carbon dioxide that is lost. The least loss occurs with the slow-acting sulfate-phosphate baking powder and more with phosphate and tartrate baking powders.

Angelfood cake freezes more successfully than cakes that contain egg yolk and fat. Egg-yolk sponge cake (especially when the batter is stored) develops rancid off-flavors, probably because the fat in the egg yolk oxidizes. Cakes that have a higher proportion of egg yolks deteriorate faster than those with less. Lemon juice or another antioxidant added to the batter retards the development of off-flavor.

Yeast doughs sometimes do not rise properly after freezing, because the yeasts lose their ability to form the carbon dioxide needed or because that formed before freezing has been lost, as in the batters.

Some frozen meat fats become rancid in a short time even though the meat is protected from oxidation by superior packaging and low temperatures. The fat from turkey and pork gives more trouble than that from most other meats. The stability of fat—its ability to withstand the chemical changes that cause rancidity—is due to its chemical composition. Some fats are so formed that oxygen can react with them easily to change the structure or break the molecule into smaller parts, thus leading to rancidity.

Frozen cooked poultry often fails to retain the flavor and texture of the freshly cooked products. In 4 to 6 months at 0° F., fried chicken develops a stale or warmed-over flavor and is less juicy. Off-flavors develop faster in frozen fried chicken than in uncooked frozen fryers. The flavor changes occur in the meat of the precooked chickens as well as in the skin. They are not related to the cooking fat taken up in the flour coating during precooking.

Another kind of change in freezing may be due to the gellike protein material in some foods, including meat and poultry. We do not understand fully the precise effect of freezing on this colloidal material. "Drip" or "leakage" in the thawed food is sometimes one effect.

Sometimes the bone and adjacent meat of young frozen poultry darken in the knee joint, leg, thigh, back, and wing. Bloody marrow leaching through the bone during freezing, thawing, and cooking is the cause. It is seldom observed on the surface of the bird. The color changes to a deep gray or brown during cooking. This darkening is not associated with bacterial spoilage and does not affect the eating quality of the meat.

THE RATE OF FREEZING has a bearing on the size of the ice crystals in the food. The crystals are smaller when food is frozen quickly than when the freezing takes place slowly. Even the smallest crystals are larger than the individual cells of fruit and vegetables. There is a minimum of tearing or breaking of the cell walls when small crystals form.

If freezing is fast enough to check the growth of micro-organisms, the differences in freezing rates have little bearing on palatability and nutritive value of vegetables.

When meat is frozen quickly at o° F. or lower, the cells in the fiber retain their normal places. Slower freezing causes moisture from the fibers to form ice crystals between the groups of fibers, and the meat may darken and lose liquid. Except for appearance, freezing rate has little effect on poultry—less with fat than lean birds.

With home equipment that can freeze at o° F. or lower, good frozen food can be produced if the equipment is used properly.

The amount of food frozen at one time should be limited in order to get as quick and efficient freezing as possible. Only the amount of unfrozen food that will freeze within 24 hours should be put into the freezer. Usually that will be about 2 or 3 pounds to each cubic foot of freezer capacity. The speed of freezing will be lower if the freezer is overloaded with unfrozen food.

Some packaging, particularly extra layers of material, cuts the freezing rate.

Packages of food should not be packed too closely when food is being frozen because those in the center may freeze too slowly. Bacterial growth can then occur.

Proper storage conditions for frozen foods are important. We recommend that the temperature should be o° F. or lower for home storage of frozen foods.

The changes in eating quality and nutritive value that take place very slowly at o° or below increase in rate rapidly as the temperature increases. The loss of quality from storage temperatures above o° is directly related to the temperature and the length of time the food is held at that temperature.

Frozen uncooked poultry deteriorates about two or three times faster at 10° than at o° and four to six times faster at 20° than at o°. Serious damage can result from poor storage for several short periods, because the bad effects accumulate.

It is not possible to undo damage from poor storage. It is possible only to check the change and prevent further deterioration. The amount of loss in quality from poor storage differs with the food.

Also important is the packaging. Food to be frozen is put in packages to keep it from drying out and to prevent air from entering the closed package and causing oxidation.

Moisture-vapor-proof packaging materials that permit no moisture to leave or air to enter the package are best in these respects. Glass, pottery, aluminum, tin, and rigid plastic are moisture-vapor-proof materials.

Many other materials are resistant enough to maintain satisfactory quality in the food packed in them. Among them are freezer papers coated with Cellophane, polyethylene, or wax; laminated freezer paper; various types of plastic bags; and waxed cartons.

Ordinary waxed papers, household aluminum foil, and cartons in which ice cream and cottage cheese are bought are not moisture-vapor-resistant enough for packaging foods for freezing.

The type of packaging best suited to a particular food depends somewhat on the size and shape of the food, its consistency, and whether the pack is solid or liquid.

Rigid containers are needed for liquid packs of fruit and for combination dishes of semiliquid consistency. Bags are most satisfactory with dry packs, like vegetables and raw poultry and meat.

The various freezer papers and other materials that come as rolls or sheets also are suitable for poultry and meats and for corn on the cob.

Aluminum freezer foil is particularly useful for wrapping foods having an irregular shape, like poultry, because it can be molded close to the food to exclude air.

Baked goods and prepared foods, like casserole dishes, sometimes are frozen in the baking pans or casseroles ready for reheating before use. Or some may be removed from the pans they were baked in, wrapped, and boxed if necessary to protect them. You may wish to try lining a casserole with aluminum foil so you can remove the casserole after the food is frozen. The foil then is the container.

Freezing cannot improve food, but it can preserve much of the original quality of the fresh food if the food, packaging, and processing procedures are well selected and proper storage conditions are maintained.

Raw materials must be of high quality. They should be fresh and of the maturity required for eating immediately. Some varieties of fruits and vegetables are better than others for freezing. Your State extension service can give you information about the best locally grown varieties.

PREPARATION OF FRUIT for freezing involves cleaning it thoroughly to reduce the bacterial count, removing any material that is inedible, and getting it into the desired form.

Small fruits and berries can be frozen whole. Large fruits are usually halved or sliced. Most fruits and berries also can be frozen crushed or as puree for use as fruit toppings or fillings. Juice pressed from fruit or berries may be sweetened slightly before freezing.

Whether to pack fruit in sugar or sirup or to leave it unsweetened depends partly on how you intend to use the fruit.

Fruit packed in sirup is generally best for dessert use. Fruit in dry sugar or unsweetened is best for cooking, because less liquid is in the pack. Unsweetened packs are useful especially for jams and jellies or in baking, in which you have to know how much sugar the ingredients contain.

Most fruits are satisfactory when packed in either sugar or sirup. The best proportion of sugar to fruit or best sirup concentration varies with the sweetness of the fruit.

Sour cherries and strawberries take three-fourths cup of sugar to a quart of fruit. Apples and apricots take only one-half cup of sugar.

In sugar packs, the sugar is sprinkled over the prepared fruit and mixed in gently before the fruit is packed in the containers. Ascorbic acid (vitamin C) is sprinkled over the fruit just before the sugar is added. Ascorbic acid in crystalline or powdered form can be purchased at drugstores and at some locker plants.

For sirup packs, you put the fruit in

the containers and cover it with cold sirup. Fruits that darken easily are best sliced directly into the sirup. Any ascorbic acid or other antidarkening agent is mixed with the sirup.

Blackberries, blueberries, cranberries, currants, figs, gooseberries, grapes, pineapple, plums, raspberries, rhubarb, and strawberries and purees of avocado, dates, and persimmon are satisfactory packed into containers with no sweetening, sealed, and frozen.

Apple slices may be packed unsweetened after they have been steamed to prevent darkening. If apples are not firm and crisp, holding in a calcium chloride solution before steaming will firm them. To make the solution, use 1 teaspoon U.S. Pharmacopoeia grade calcium chloride (available in drugstores) to each quart of water. Hold apple slices in the solution 5 to 20 minutes—the longer time is for the softest apples.

Peaches may be frozen without sweetening but should be packed in water to which ascorbic acid has been added.

Some fully ripe fruits when used with commercial fruit pectins gel without cooking to make jams or jellies of fresh flavor and bright, natural color. Mix 3 cups of crushed blackberries, blueberries, raspberries, strawberries, or peaches with 5 cups of sugar; let this stand 20 minutes, stirring occasionally. Dissolve 1 package of powdered pectin in 1 cup of water, heat to boiling and boil for 1 minute. Pour pectin solution into fruit mixture and stir for 2 minutes. Put into jelly glasses or freezer containers. Seal. These uncooked products are highly perishable and must be refrigerated or frozen.

Vegetables should be thoroughly cleaned, the edible parts cut into pieces (if desired), and then heated to stop or slow down enzyme action. You should do this as soon as possible after the vegetables are picked.

If vegetables are not preheated sufficiently, enough enzyme action will continue during storage to lower the quality of the food. Vegetables usually are

preheated in boiling water—a gallon of water to a pound of vegetable. The times required for heating different vegetables in boiling water in a covered kettle are given in the table. When a time range is given, use the shortest time for small vegetables and the longer times for large vegetables. Start counting time as soon as you put the vegetable in the water.

Vegetable	*Minutes*
Asparagus stalks	2 to 4.
Beans, lima (or pods)	2 to 4.
Beans, green or wax (1- or 2-inch pieces or frenched).	3.
Beets	25 to 50 (until tender).
Broccoli stalks (split)	3.
Brussels sprouts	3 to 5.
Carrots (small, whole)	5.
Carrots (diced, sliced, or lengthwise strips).	2.
Cauliflower (1-inch flowerets).	3.
Corn on the cob	7 to 11.
Corn (whole-kernel and cream-style—cut corn from the cob after heating and cooling).	4.
Peas, green	1.5.
Spinach	2.
Squash, summer	3.

Steaming may be used for some vegetables. Split broccoli and whole mushrooms take 5 minutes; button mushrooms, 3.5 minutes; and sliced mushrooms, 3 minutes. Pieces of pumpkin and winter squash and whole sweetpotatoes may be steamed until soft or they may be heated in a pressure cooker or an oven set at 400° F. until they are soft.

Quick, thorough cooling is necessary to stop the cooking. Vegetables should be plunged in cold water below 60°. The water should be changed often. It is best to use ice water or cold running water.

The cooled vegetables should be tightly packed immediately into suitable containers, leaving ½-inch headspace, except for vegetables like asparagus and broccoli that pack loosely and require no headspace. The containers then are closed and put in the freezer.

MEAT should be of high quality, properly chilled, and frozen in amounts suitable for cooking at one time. All meat should be clean and ready to be cooked before wrapping it for freezing.

Most kinds of raw poultry can be frozen satisfactorily at home. The birds should be well fleshed with well-distributed fat and few, if any, skin blemishes. Freshly killed poultry is best for home freezing. A low scalding temperature should be used when removing the feathers so that the outer layer of skin is left intact. This helps prevent loss of moisture and darkening of the poultry. If you do not know how the bird was scalded, we recommend immediate tight packaging in a material that is moisture resistant.

You should age fryers and broilers in the refrigerator for 12 hours before cooking, either before freezing or during thawing in order to insure tender meat.

Poultry may be frozen whole, in halves, or in pieces in order to provide variety and to make it suitable for different uses.

Turkeys and chickens for roasting are frozen whole, unstuffed.

Poultry for broiling and frying takes less space in a freezer and is more convenient to use if it is cut into serving pieces and then frozen. Poultry should be wrapped tightly to prevent discoloration of the skin by drying. It should be frozen immediately.

When you cook the family meal, plan to prepare a double amount of some food—an extra casserole or a second pie or cake, for instance. Cool the extra food immediately and package and freeze it as soon as possible.

Leftovers often can be frozen satisfactorily if cooled and frozen as soon as the meal is over. Sometimes slight undercooking before freezing will prevent a warmed-over flavor and too soft a texture when you reheat the food for serving.

HOME ECONOMISTS have studied the freezing of baked goods—breads, cakes, pies—a great deal. They have been interested primarily in ingredients and whether to bake the products before or after freezing.

With yeast breads, the question is whether to freeze the dough or bake it before freezing or partly bake it to have brown-and-serve products.

We think yeast breads are better if they are prebaked before freezing. Yeast breads and rolls may be frozen as dough, however, if they are to be stored no longer than 6 weeks. Results are better with unshaped dough than with shaped frozen rolls. Frozen brown-and-serve rolls are another way to hold yeast rolls successfully.

We have not decided whether it is better to freeze cakes before or after baking. Most kinds can be frozen either way fairly satisfactorily if the storage time is no more than 3 or 4 months. Cakes frozen as batter may have less volume and a more compact texture than prebaked cakes because of the loss in carbon dioxide.

Spice cake is better prebaked than baked from frozen batter. Results with frozen batter are best when the batter is thawed before the cake is baked and when the storage period is short.

Most fruit pies may be frozen baked or unbaked, but the quality seems to be better when they are not baked before freezing.

The lower crust of prebaked pies may become soggy during reheating. To counteract this tendency, it may help to roll the crust thinner than usual, brush the crust with melted fat or egg white before adding the filling, or bake the pies in a very hot oven (450°). Or, for a change, you might make a deep-dish fruit pie with only an upper crust.

Fruits that discolor easily in the air need the same treatment in pies as they do when frozen alone.

Single-crust pies should be frozen without meringue, which becomes tough when it is frozen.

Pastry shells can be made in advance and frozen either baked or unbaked. Lard shortenings make more tender pastry than vegetable shortenings, although there may be a problem of ran-

Storage-Life Recommendations for Home-Frozen Foods at 0° F.

Food	Maximum storage period (months)
Fruit........................	8 to 12.
Vegetables..................	8 to 12.
French-fried potatoes— parfried.	2 to 6.
Meats:	
Beef....................	6 to 12.
Lamb and veal...........	6 to 9.
Pork....................	3 to 6.
Sausage and ground meat..	1 to 3.
•Cooked meat—not covered with gravy or other sauces.	1.
Meat sandwiches.........	1.
Poultry:	
Chickens................	6 to 12.
Turkeys.................	3 to 6.
Giblets..................	3.
Cooked poultry meat......	1.
Cooked poultry dishes.....	3 to 6.
Precooked combination dishes...	2 to 6.
Baked goods:	
Cakes:	
Prebaked............	4 to 9.
Batters.............	3 to 4.
Fruit pies, baked or unbaked	3 to 4.
Pie shells, baked or unbaked	1½ to 2.
Cookies.................	6 to 12.
Yeast bread and rolls:	
Prebaked............	3 to 9.
Dough..............	1 to 1½.

cidity with lard unless antioxidants have been added. Freezing and storage also seem to make pastry tenderer.

Many types of cookies can be frozen after baking or as dough. Those baked from dough are usually crisper than prebaked cookies and take less space during storage in the freezer. Macaroon and other meringue-type cookies have poor texture when frozen, regardless of whether they were frozen before or after baking.

Frozen fruit salad with a whipped cream base is best when eaten before it is completely thawed. Because spoilage organisms thrive in it, everything should be fresh and clean.

Fruit or meat-gelatin salads also are satisfactory, particularly if the liquid called for in the recipe is reduced about one-fourth. If too much liquid is used, it separates when the salad is defrosted. Mayonnaise, which separates during freezing, should be used sparingly in frozen salads.

The fillings largely determine the quality of frozen sandwiches. Only freshly made fillings should be used. Sandwiches should be frozen as soon as they are made and eaten soon after they have thawed. These precautions are necessary because bacteria grow easily in many of the ingredients used for fillings, and sandwich making involves much handling of the food and provides chances for contamination.

Suitable for freezing are fillings made of meat and poultry, hard-cooked egg yolk, cheese, peanut butter, pickles, or olives. Anything should be omitted that may soak into the bread, as jelly or salad dressings, cooked egg white, which toughens, and vegetables, which will wilt. There will be less sogginess if the bread is spread to the edges with butter or margarine.

You know that a long-time food plan is more economical than planning from day to day or by the week. Food for meals on busy days you can freeze in quantity on slack days so as to balance time and effort. When you assemble the ingredients and equipment, it is often worth while to increase the amount of food usually prepared at one time.

The management plan should include a schedule for using the food you have frozen. The amounts of different foods frozen should be based on the actual family needs.

The time food should be held in the freezer depends on its kind and form, its initial quality, the packaging you use, and the storage temperature.

From the standpoint of quality and economy, it is a good practice to keep foods moving in and out of the freezer, rather than holding them.

GLADYS L. GILPIN *has been a project leader in the Food Quality Laboratory of the Human Nutrition Research Division, Agricultural Research Service, since 1945.*

Canning Food at Home

GLADYS L. GILPIN

IN CANNING, prepared food is packed in containers, which are heated to destroy spoilage organisms and sealed to keep out other organisms and air. The heat inactivates the micro-organisms and enzymes present in the food.

Most of the air in the container and in the food itself is driven out during heating and is kept out thereafter by the tight seal that is formed. If air is left in, the top layers of the food may darken gradually because of oxidation. Such food is not dangerous, but it does not look good.

The temperatures required to sterilize different foods vary. For safety, the heat treatment must be right for the particular food.

Acid foods, like fruit, tomatoes, and pickled vegetables, can be processed safely at the boiling point, because the types of organisms that cause spoilage in acid foods usually have low resistance to heat.

Low-acid foods—most vegetables, meat, and poultry—are hard to sterilize. Preheating (or blanching) them may reduce the number of micro-organisms on the food, but it will not lower the temperature required for the destruction of those that remain.

Low-acid foods often contain bacteria, which form heat-resistant spores.

Some anaerobic micro-organisms (these grow in the absence of air) will grow and spoil food in sealed containers. One of them, *Clostridium botulinum*, is dangerous because it can produce an extremely potent poison in the food. This poison can be present in food when there is no evident sign of spoilage. Acid foods—fruit and tomatoes—usually have not been problems in this respect, but the low-acid foods—vegetables and meats—have caused serious problems when the heat treatment has been insufficient.

We can determine the processing times required at specific temperatures to destroy the micro-organisms in foods by inoculating packs with known numbers of test bacteria and determining the heat treatment required to sterilize the pack. The amount of heat during the whole period while the food is brought to the processing temperature, processed, and cooled is considered.

The low-acid foods require a temperature higher than that of boiling water for processing safely in a reasonable time. A pressure canner is used for processing them to obtain the necessary high temperature. Water in the canner is converted to steam. The steam, when held under pressure, raises the temperature according to the amount of pressure maintained. Pressure saucepans that have gages or indicators for controlling the pressure at 10 pounds can be used for processing. The processing times required are longer than with the pressure canner because saucepans heat and cool more quickly.

The open-kettle method of packing hot food into jars and sealing them without processing (further heating) should be used only for jellied fruit products and for pickles that do not rely on heat processing alone for their keeping quality. The high content of sugar of the jellied products helps to preserve them. Also, the temperatures reached when cooking them are well above boiling. The high acid content of pickles retards the growth of spoilage organisms.

Open-kettle canning is not recommended for fruit. It is dangerous for vegetables, meats, and poultry.

Oven canning also is dangerous. The temperature in the jars is not high enough to make certain the bacteria are destroyed in a reasonable time, and the jars may explode during processing.

One should not depend on aspirin, canning powders, or other chemical preservatives that are supposed to prevent spoilage without high heat. They may be harmful in themselves.

Only fruits and vegetables of the best quality should be used, because processing cannot make a good food out of a poor one. Your State extension service will tell you which varieties grown in your State are best for canning.

Fruits should be fresh, firm, ripe, and sound. Vegetables must be freshly harvested—young, tender, firm, and unwilted.

You can use slightly imperfect and less uniform—but sound—fruit and surpluses of fully ripe fruit to make jelly if you add pectin to them to help form the gel.

Juices are another way to use large, small, or misshapen produce. Moldy or spoiled material lowers quality, however, and makes sterilization much harder.

CLEANLINESS is necessary in every step to keep the bacterial count low, so that the processing will be enough to sterilize the product. Thorough washing with running water or several changes of water is essential, because dirt contains some spoilage organisms that are hardest to kill. The food should be lifted out of the water, so that the soil will be left in the pan— not drained back into the food.

Meat and poultry that is to be canned should be fresh killed, chilled at once, and kept chilled until canned. You can use either young or mature poultry, as the processing will make the meat tender. Meat and poultry should be thoroughly clean and ready for cooking. Large pieces of fat should be trimmed off, because fat may react with the rubber or composition in the jar closure and prevent a good seal on the jar.

Some foods may be canned in different forms—whole, cut up, strained, and as juice—or, in the case of poultry and meat, with or without bone.

Sorting or cutting to provide pieces of similar size and maturity in each pack improves the quality because they process uniformly.

Peeling is done primarily to remove inedible parts. It also eliminates some of the organisms. Some foods, like peaches and tomatoes, peel more easily if the food has been dipped for a few seconds in boiling water.

Many foods can be packed either raw or after heating. The raw pack is simpler to make, and the product is as good or better than the precooked pack. On the other hand, more precooked than raw food can be packed into a jar, a point to consider if storage space is limited or the family is large.

Most foods can be packed tightly into the containers. A few—lima beans, black-eyed peas, green peas, spinach, raw-packed corn, hot-packed summer squash, and snap beans—should be packed loosely. Sweetpotatoes may be pressed down to make a dry pack or may be packed less tightly and boiling sirup or water added for a wet pack.

Different containers and different foods take different amounts of headspace—the space left at the top of the jar or can when the food is packed.

Most fruits need one-half inch of space at the top of the jars. In cans, pack fruit to one-fourth inch of the top; then fill to the top with hot sirup or boiling water. Fruit juices, purees, and tomato juice are packed to one-fourth inch of the top of jars, to the top of cans.

Most vegetables are packed to one-half inch of the top of jars and covered with liquid, leaving one-half inch of headspace. They are packed to one-fourth inch of the top of the cans; then the cans are filled to the top with hot liquid.

Starchy vegetables need more headspace because they swell during processing. Leave an inch at the top of jars when packing corn, peas, lima beans (hot-packed), and the sweetpotatoes. Leave one-half inch at the top of cans for corn and hot-packed lima beans and black-eyed peas; then fill the cans to the top with liquid. Raw-packed lima beans take even more headspace. Black-eyed peas also take more headspace when packed in jars and when packed raw in tin cans.

The meat and poultry products are packed in jars and covered with liquid. An inch of space is left at the top. In cans, these foods are packed to one-half inch from the top. The cans are filled to the top with liquid. Raw ground beef is packed to the top of the cans, exhausted, and pressed down to one-half inch from the top.

Safety demands that the processing time recommended for the particular pack be used, because the time varies with the size of pieces, the consistency of the food, and the type of pack. Starchy vegetables and strained foods heat more slowly than liquids or foods packed in liquid. Correct processing times also mean better quality. Darkening of canned foods at the top of the jar may result from too little processing, so that the air is not expelled properly. Overprocessing—overcooking—may cause discoloration of foods throughout the container.

Fruit prepared for canning can be packed raw into containers and covered with a boiling-hot sugar sirup, juice, or water. The fruit also can be heated in dry sugar, a sugar sirup, water, steam, or extracted fruit juice before packing.

Juice or water packs can be used when unsweetened packs are needed, as for special diets.

Sugar sirup is made by boiling sugar and water together for 5 minutes. The proportions of sugar to water depend on the sweetness of the fruit. A medium sirup requires 3 cups of sugar to a quart of water.

Vegetables may also be packed raw into containers and covered with boiling water or preheated in water or steam. When packing preheated vegetables, the cooking liquid should be used (unless it is dark, gritty, or strong flavored) because it may contain valuable nutrients dissolved out of the vegetable.

Corn may be canned as cream-style or whole-kernel corn. Cut the corn from the cob at about the center of the kernel; then scrape the cob for cream-style corn. Cut the kernels closer to the cob—about two-thirds the depth of the kernel—for whole-kernel corn.

Salt may be added or not. It is used only for flavor. If desired, put one-half teaspoon salt into pint jars and No. 2 cans of vegetables and a teaspoon of salt in quart jars and No. 2½ cans. Spinach takes only one-fourth teaspoon of salt per pint of vegetable.

Mushrooms and some of the light-colored fruits have better color if ascorbic acid (vitamin C) is added to the pack before processing. Ascorbic acid helps prevent the formation of dark-colored compounds by oxida-

Processing Times for Fruits in Water-Bath Canner

| | | Process in water-bath canner [1] | | |
| | | In glass jars | | In tin cans | |
Fruit		Pints	Quarts	No. 2 cans	No. 2½ cans
Raw pack:		Minutes	Minutes	Minutes	Minutes
Apricots ⎫					
Peaches ⎬ halves or slices.....................		25	30	30	35
Pears ⎭					
Berries (except strawberries).................		10	15	15	20
Cherries....................................		20	25	20	25
Plums, whole with skins pricked, freestone halves..		20	25	15	20
Tomatoes, whole, halves, or quarters...........		35	45	45	55
Hot pack:					
Apples, pieces—boil 5 minutes...............		15	20	10	10
Applesauce—heat through...................		10	10	10	10
Apricots ⎫					
Peaches ⎬ halves or slices—heat through.........		20	25	25	30
Pears ⎭					
Berries ⎫ (except strawberries)—add ½ cup sugar					
Cherries ⎭ to 1 quart fruit, bring to boil........		10	15	15	20
Fruit juices, heat to simmering...............		5	5	5	5
Fruit purees, heat to simmering..............		10	10	10	10
Plums, whole with skins pricked or freestone halves, heat to boiling..........................		20	25	15	20
Rhubarb, ½-inch pieces—add ½ cup sugar to 1 quart fruit, bring to boiling.................		10	10	10	10
Tomatoes, quarters—heat to boiling...........		10	10	10	10
Tomato juice—heat to boiling................		10	10	15	15

[1] These times are for altitudes less than 1,000 feet above sea level. When processing time is 20 minutes or less, add 1 minute if you live 1,000 feet above sea level; add 1 minute for each added thousand feet altitude. If processing time is more than 20 minutes, add 2 minutes if at 1,000 feet and 2 minutes for each added thousand feet altitude.

tion. Use one-eighth teaspoon of crystalline ascorbic acid (available at drugstores) for the pint jars and No. 2 cans and one-fourth teaspoon for quarts and No. 2½ cans.

Meat and poultry may also be packed raw or after preheating. Simplest for poultry is to pack it raw in quart jars with no added liquid. Quick and easy also is beef-vegetable stew, made of raw beef, potatoes, carrots, celery, and onions with no added liquid.

Another way is to pack raw meat or poultry in glass jars or tin cans. The containers are set in a kettle of warm water; the kettle is covered, and the food is heated until it is steaming hot (170° F.)—a procedure known as exhausting. If the food shrinks, you should cover it with boiling water, then adjust the lids, and process the containers.

Meat and poultry may also be partly cooked and packed hot. Cook meat until medium done in a covered pan with enough water to keep it from sticking. Cover poultry with hot water or broth made from the bony pieces and cook until medium done. Corned beef is covered with cold water, brought to boiling, and drained. It may be necessary to repeat this parboiling to remove most of the salt. When packed, these should be covered with hot broth or boiling water. Salt may be used if desired for flavor—one-half teaspoon for pint jars or

No. 2 cans; three-fourths teaspoon for No. 2½ cans; and a teaspoon for quart jars and No. 3 cans. For ground meat, use a teaspoon of salt to each pound of meat.

If you use tin containers, the food must be at a temperature of 170° at the center of the can before the can is sealed. Sometimes hot-packed food requires no further heating before sealing. If preheated food is not at 170° when it is packed, it is necessary to heat the packed cans until that temperature is reached.

Raw-packed food in tin cans should always be heated in this way before the cans are sealed. This heating shrinks the food, makes for a well-filled can, helps assure the needed vacuum in the can after processing, and prevents buckling of the ends of the cans.

GLASS JARS for home canning, jar closures, and tin cans are well standardized and generally give good results if they are in good condition and used properly.

The containers must seal perfectly to keep bacteria from getting in after processing and to prevent leakage.

Manufacturers of canning jars, closures, and tin cans provide good directions which one should follow precisely for the best results.

The size and type of container depend largely on family needs and preferences. Wide-mouth jars are handy for packing large whole fruits or vegetables and for meat and poultry. Pieces of food can be removed easily from them without breaking.

To make good seals, jars must be free from cracks or chips, and the lids must be without dents. Jars need only be washed in hot soapy water, rinsed, and heated before being packed with hot foods. It is not necessary to boil jars before filling them. Any harmful bacteria will be destroyed during the processing.

Tin cans for home canning are of three types: Plain tin, which are suitable for most foods; R-enamel, best for red-colored foods and for pumpkin and squash; and C-enamel, for corn and hominy.

Tin cans require a mechanical instrument for sealing.

Any large container can be used as a water bath canner if it is deep enough to have an inch or two of water over the tops of the jars. A rack to keep the jars from touching the bottom and a cover are needed to complete the canner.

A pressure canner must have an accurate gage to register the pressure in the canner. This is important, because processing times are based on a given pressure that must be maintained to provide adequate heat treatment. The manufacturer can tell you how the gage can be checked. Some can be checked at home. Others need special servicing. If the gage is off 5 pounds or more, it is best to get a new one.

Every pressure canner has a safety device that lets out the steam in case of emergency. Be certain that this device is in working order. You may need to take it apart to see that it is clean.

A pressure canner is easy to use and safe if you follow the directions of its manufacturer. All canners require 2 to 3 inches of boiling water in the bottom before the food is put in to make sure the canner will not boil dry during use.

Containers of food should not touch each other, because the steam must reach all sides.

When the canner is loaded and the lid adjusted, the vent should be open to let the air escape as the steam forms. Let steam escape through the vent for 10 minutes. Then close the vent, and the pressure will start to rise. Count processing time after the pressure has reached 10 pounds. The pressure must be steady; you should try out the canner ahead of time to learn how to control the heating unit.

When the processing is over, if glass jars are used, the canner should stand until the gage reaches zero. If you use tin cans, the canner should be opened immediately. This is done by slowly

Processing Times for Vegetables in Pressure Canner

| | Process in pressure canner at 10 pounds pressure [1] | | | |
| | In glass jars | | In tin cans | |
Vegetables	Pints	Quarts	No. 2 cans	No. 2½ cans
	Minutes	Minutes	Minutes	Minutes
Raw pack:				
Asparagus, 1-inch pieces.....................	25	30	20	20
Beans, fresh lima...........................	40	50	40	40
Beans, snap, 1-inch pieces...................	20	25	25	30
Carrots, slices or cubes.....................	25	30	25	30
Corn, cream-style..........................	95	......	105	......
Corn, whole-kernel.........................	55	85	60	60
Peas, fresh black-eyed......................	35	40	35	40
Peas, fresh green...........................	40	40	30	35
Squash, summer, ½-inch slices halved or quartered..................................	25	30	20	20
Hot pack:				
Asparagus, 1-inch pieces—boil 2 or 3 minutes....	25	30	20	20
Beans, fresh lima—bring to boil................	40	50	40	40
Beans, snap, 1-inch pieces—boil 5 minutes.......	20	25	25	30
Beets—boil until skin slips (15–25 minutes); can small beets whole, slice or cube large beets.....	30	35	30	30
Carrots, slices or cubes—bring to boil	25	30	20	25
Corn, cream-style—heat to boiling (1 quart corn and 1 pint boiling water)....................	85	......	105	......
Corn, whole-kernel—heat to boiling (1 quart corn and 1 pint boiling water)....................	55	85	60	60
Hominy—heat through.......................	60	70	60	70
Mushrooms, whole, halves or quarters—steam 4 minutes or heat gently 15 minutes............	30	......	30	......
Okra—boil 1 minute, cut into 1-inch slices or leave whole.....................................	25	40	25	35
Peas, fresh black-eyed—bring to boil...........	35	40	30	35
Peas, fresh green—bring to boil................	40	40	30	35
Potatoes, ½-inch cubes—boil 2 minutes.........	35	40	35	40
Potatoes, whole (1 to 2½ inches diameter)—boil 10 minutes.................................	30	40	35	40
Pumpkin ⎫ 1-inch cubes—bring to boil...... Winter squash⎰	55	90	50	75
Pumpkin ⎫ strained—heat through.......... Winter squash⎰	65	80	75	90
Spinach (and other greens)—steam for 10 minutes or until wilted............................	70	90	65	75
Squash, summer, ½-inch slices, quartered or halved—bring to boil.......................	30	40	20	20
Sweetpotatoes, dry pack—boil or steam until partially soft (20–30 minutes); skin, cut in uniform pieces....................................	65	95	80	95
Sweetpotatoes, wet pack—boil or steam until skins slip easily; cut in uniform pieces.............	55	90	70	90

[1] For each 2,000 feet above sea level, add 1 pound pressure. With pressure saucepans, add 20 minutes to these processing times.

opening the vent to release the steam. When all the steam has escaped, the cover should be removed carefully. The cover should always be tilted away from you when you remove it so the steam will be directed away from the face.

When glass containers of food are removed from the water bath or pressure canner, they should be cooled on racks away from drafts. With some closures, it is necessary to complete the seal. Others are self-sealing as they cool and should not be touched. The next day, jar seals should be tested by turning the jar part way over to make sure it does not leak.

Tin cans are put into cold water as soon as they are removed from the canner. Water should be changed often to cool the food quickly and prevent unnecessary further cooking. When still warm, the cans should be placed on racks so the air can dry them.

Storage places for canned foods should be dry and cool. Warm storage may lower eating quality, and dampness can corrode metals and eventually cause leaks.

ANOTHER WAY to preserve fruit for future use is to make jellied fruit products—jelly, jam, conserve, marmalade, preserves, and fruit butter.

Many—apples, crabapples, grapes, blackberries, plums, currants, quince— contain enough pectin to make a gel if about one-fourth of the fruit is underripe.

As the fruit ripens, the pectin changes to a form that does not aid in gel formation, but added fruit pectin can be used with fully ripe fruit.

Fruit, sugar, pectin, and acid have to be present in the proper proportions to make a gel possible. Besides giving its characteristic flavor to the gel, the fruit furnishes some of the required pectin and acid. Lemon juice or citric acid are added sometimes to less tart fruit.

Commercial fruit pectins come in liquid and powdered forms. They should be used with suitable recipes that take into account their jellying power. These pectins are made from apples or citrus fruit.

For jelly, juice is extracted from crushed, raw fruit or from crushed fruit that is heated in a small amount of water. The prepared fruit is put in a cloth bag, and the juice is allowed to drain out. Juice will come much faster if you press the bag. Juice pressed out will not be so clear as juice allowed to drip through the bag. It will make clear jelly, however, if it is strained again through several thicknesses of cheesecloth or a clean bag.

Jelly also can be made from commercially canned and frozen concentrated juices if pectin is added. For quick and easy grape jelly with fresh-fruit flavor, heat 6½ cups of sugar and 2½ cups of water to a full rolling boil. Boil 1 minute. Remove from heat. Add 1 bottle of liquid pectin. Stir in three 6-ounce cans of frozen concentrated grape juice (thawed) and mix well. Pour into hot containers and seal.

Jams, conserves, and marmalades are made from crushed or cut fruit. Preserves are whole small fruits or berries or pieces of large fruit cooked in a sirup to retain their shape.

Jellied products made without added pectin are usually made from equal amounts (or slightly less) of sugar to fruit or juice. These must be cooked long enough to obtain the needed sugar concentration for gel formation. Make small batches of these products for best flavor.

Recipes for products made with added pectin and those made in an electronic range call for a larger proportion of sugar to fruit. They therefore cook quickly to the required concentration.

To make jellies or jams without added pectin, mix the fruit juice or crushed fruit with the sugar in a large pan. Boil over high heat.

The best way to tell when these products are done is to use a temperature test. Cook jellies to a temperature 8° F. and jams to 9° above the boiling point of water. Place the thermometer

Processing Times for Meat and Poultry in Pressure Canner

| | Process in pressure canner at 10 pounds pressure [1] | | | |
| | In glass jars | | In tin cans | |
Meat or poultry	Pints	Quarts	No. 2 cans	No. 2½ and No. 3 cans
Hot pack:	*Minutes*	*Minutes*	*Minutes*	*Minutes*
Beef, veal, pork, lamb—cut to fit jars or cans....	75	90	65	90
Ground meat or sausage—form into thin cakes (omit sage from sausage)....................	75	90	65	90
Corned beef—cut to fit jars or cans.............	75	90	65	90
Poultry—with bone—remove breastbone only....	65	75	55	75
Poultry—without bone—remove bones either before or after precooking....................	75	90	65	90
Giblets—can livers separately.................	75	......	65	....
Raw pack—exhaust before processing:				
Beef, veal, pork, lamb—cut to fit jars or cans....	75	90	65	90
Ground meat—pack into cans.................	......	......	100	135
Poultry—with bone—remove breastbone only....	65	75	55	75
Poultry—without bone.....................	75	90	65	90
Cold pack—do not exhaust:				
Poultry—with bone—do not use those with excessive fat (use quart jars only)................	......	80	......	....
Beef-vegetable stew—2 quarts cubed potatoes, 2 quarts cubed carrots, 3 cups diced celery, 1¾ quarts small onions, and 2 quarts 1½-inch cubes of beef..................................	60	75	40	45

[1] For each 2,000 feet above sea level, add 1 pound pressure. With pressure saucepans, add 20 minutes to these processing times.

straight down into the mixture. The thermometer bulb must be completely covered with the mixture but must not touch the bottom of the kettle. Stand so you can read the thermometer at eye level.

A commonly used but less dependable test is the spoon or sheet test. The jelly mixture should drop from the side of a spoon as one sheet—the last few drops will run together—when the jelly stage is reached.

Another test is to put a small amount of the boiling mixture on a cold plate in the ice compartment of a refrigerator for a few minutes. If it gels, the jelly is done. The jelly mixture should be removed from the heat while this test is being made.

Cooking time, rather than these tests, determines when jellied products made with added pectin are done. The order of combining ingredients is different with liquid than with powdered pectin and is not the same for jams and jellies. Powdered pectin must be dissolved in order to help form a gel. It dissolves better when it is added to the fruit or juice and the mixture is brought to a full rolling boil before the sugar is added. You will know when it reaches this point, because the mixture increases in volume and almost fills the kettle. Even vigorous stirring will not make it return to the original volume as long as it is left on the heat. The mixture is again heated to a full rolling boil and boiled for 1 minute.

WITH LIQUID pectin, the fruit or juice and the sugar are mixed and brought to a rolling boil. For jellies, the pectin then is added; the mixture is heated again to a full rolling boil and boiled for 1 minute. Jam is made by boiling the fruit and sugar together for 1 minute and stirring in the pectin after the mixture has been removed from the heat.

Fruit pieces in jams are less likely to rise to the surface if the mixture is stirred several times during a 5-minute period before it is poured into the glasses.

All jellied products are poured hot into hot glasses or jars and are covered with paraffin or jar lids immediately to make a seal. They should stand overnight and then should be stored in a cool, dry place. Jellied products

have best color and flavor when held only a few months.

Jelly should be clear and tender. It should hold its shape when it is removed from the container. The other jellied fruit products generally are less firm than jelly.

GLADYS L. GILPIN, *a member of the Institute of Home Economics in the Department of Agriculture, has conducted extensive research on canning and freezing food and has written a number of publications about quality in food. A graduate and former faculty member of the University of Minnesota, she joined the Department of Agriculture after working in agricultural extension in California.*

Food Purchased

By Farm Families, North Central Region

Food used in a week, percentage purchased

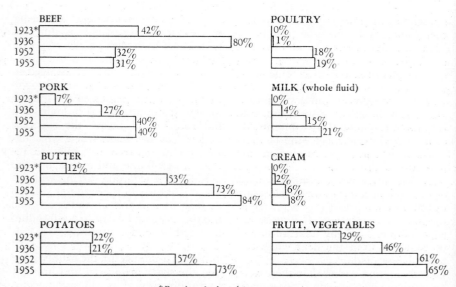

Based on food used in a year.

Storing Perishable Foods at Home

RUTH REDSTROM

FOOD spoils because of the action of the enzymes, molds, yeasts, or bacteria in it. Actual spoilage usually is pretty evident—the rancid odor and flavor of fats caused by oxidation, the fermented odor of fruit juices due to yeast growth, the appearance of a moldy slice of bread. These kinds of spoilage are undesirable, but they are not health hazards.

Food spoiled by bacterial action can cause illness, however. Not all bacteria are harmful, but most consumers cannot tell which are harmful and which are harmless. Slime on the surface of meats, off odors in foods, or a sour taste in bland foods are danger signals that indicate bacterial spoilage.

Low temperatures retard spoilage and other changes in the quality of perishable foods. They slow the action of enzymes and the growth of organisms of spoilage.

Foods vary in the degree of cold best suited for maintaining good quality, however. Too-low temperatures may be as detrimental to some foods as too-high temperatures. Some fruits and vegetables decay faster if they are held too long at even moderately low temperatures. Bananas are among them. Some apples and root vegetables keep well in a cool basement or outdoor cellar or storage pit.

Too much moisture on some foods or in the air around them can lead to early spoilage. Wet berries and cherries are susceptible to mold and rot. Molds grow quickly on breads or uncovered cheese in moist air.

On the other hand, water evaporates from the living cells of some foods and causes wilting, drying, and sometimes loss of nutrients. These foods need a high relative humidity to reduce loss of moisture. Control of moisture in the air in storage containers therefore is important, but it may be difficult to obtain such control in most homes. Some control of temperature and relative humidity is possible in cellars or storage pits by opening windows or ventilators at night when the outside temperature is not freezing and the air is not too dry.

A refrigerated food that tends to become unpalatable through drying or shriveling should be kept covered to

477

retard evaporation. Most refrigerators provide at least one covered container for holding fruit and vegetables. The plastic bags in which fruit and vegetables sometimes are packaged retard the evaporation of moisture from food stored in them.

Temperatures in refrigerators vary with the location of the storage compartments. The temperature in most refrigerators is lowest just below the freezing unit at the top of the cabinet. The temperature at the bottom of the cabinet is highest. Air within the cabinet circulates; the cooler air falls and forces warmer air near the bottom upward along the sides. The moving air tends to dry out uncovered and unwrapped food.

One should check the setting of the temperature control by placing a thermometer in different places in the refrigerator. With the control set for normal operation, the temperature in the center storage section usually is between 38° and 42° F. The temperature below the freezing unit is lower—often between 30° and 35°. The bottom of the cabinet is somewhat warmer than the center. An accumulation of thick frost on the freezing unit or frequent openings of the refrigerator door, especially on humid days, raises the temperature inside.

Many refrigerators have a freezer compartment in which frozen foods are kept for short periods. All frozen foods need a storage temperature of 0° or lower to maintain high quality. Frozen foods should be held for only a few days if the temperature in the freezer compartment is above zero.

HOME-GROWN FOODS present few problems as to storage. They need only be placed in the proper place as soon as possible after harvest or slaughter. They may be selected and used at the best stage of ripeness.

Foods bought in retail markets are harder to select at their peak in quality. A purchaser has no way of knowing how much of a food's high-quality life remains when it is bought.

It is wise to shop at clean markets and places where foods are properly refrigerated and handled.

FRESH DAIRY PRODUCTS should be kept cold and tightly wrapped or covered so that they do not absorb odors and flavors of other foods. A storage temperature of 40° is most desirable in protecting flavor and food value of milk and cream.

As soon after purchase or delivery as possible, the glass bottle or carton should be rinsed under cold running water, dried, and refrigerated promptly. Exposure to sunlight is harmful to the flavor and riboflavin of milk.

Evaporated and condensed milk may be stored at room temperature until the container is opened. Then it should be refrigerated in the same way as fresh fluid milk.

Dry milks will keep for several months at room temperatures of 75° or lower, or they may be kept in the refrigerator. Nonfat dry milk is somewhat more stable than whole dry milk because of its lack of fat. Both should be stored in tightly covered containers to prevent moisture absorption, which causes off-flavors to develop and makes reconstitution difficult.

The flavor of cottage cheese deteriorates rapidly. It (and the other soft cheeses) should be stored—tightly covered—in the coldest part of the refrigerator.

Hard cheeses should be wrapped tightly before refrigerating to protect them from exposure to air. The original wrapping often is satisfactory, or any of the wide variety of wrapping materials available to consumers may be used. Hard cheeses will keep indefinitely at refrigerator temperatures; exclusion of air is the important factor. Any mold that forms on the surface of hard cheeses may be trimmed off before using.

Cheese spreads and cheese foods keep well without refrigeration until the container is opened. Refrigeration is advisable for the unused portion in an opened container.

To protect its flavor, butter should be stored tightly wrapped or covered in the coldest part of the refrigerator—preferably at 40° or lower. Exclusion of air will protect the fat from reacting with oxygen to produce a rancid flavor and odor. Only enough butter for immediate use should be held in the butter conditioners featured in some refrigerators. Exposure to warmth or light hastens the development of rancidity, and long periods of exposure should be avoided.

Most other fats and oils need the same protection from air, heat, and light as butter does to prevent rancidity.

Margarine and fat drippings, like butter, tend to become rancid more quickly than other fats and oils because they contain more moisture. They should be covered or wrapped and refrigerated promptly. Lard will keep longer at refrigerator temperature than these fats.

Some cooking and salad oils may become cloudy and solidify at refrigerator temperature, but this is not harmful. If allowed to warm to room temperature before use, they will liquefy and become clear again. The less surface area of these fats exposed to the air, the less chance there is for rancidity to occur. Fats and oils in partly filled containers will keep longer if they are transferred to smaller containers that have little or no air space.

Mayonnaise, other salad dressings, and foods with a high content of fat, such as peanut butter, keep better in the refrigerator after the container is opened.

The oils in some of the firm shortenings have been stabilized by hydrogenation; therefore they can be kept at room temperature without damage to flavor.

SHELL EGGS should be refrigerated promptly. Flavor changes quickly if eggs are held at room temperature but much more slowly at refrigerator temperature. Other quality changes occur if eggs are held too long. The thick white gets thin, and the yolk membrane weakens and may break when the shell is opened. The shell is porous and allows passage of moisture, bacteria, and molds. A covered container is recommended therefore if eggs are kept for several weeks. Eggs are not kept very long in most homes, and they do not require special handling. The carton in which eggs are sold is a good container, or the eggs may be transferred to another covered container.

Dried egg should be kept in the refrigerator. After a package is opened, the unused portion keeps best in an airtight container with a close-fitting lid.

FRAGILE FRUIT needs special handling to protect it from bruising and crushing. The softened tissues of bruised or crushed fruit make them susceptible to faster quality breakdown and the entrance of spoilage organisms.

Fruits should be sorted before storing. Injured fruit should be removed for immediate use or discarded if decay is present. This will protect firm, sound fruit from contamination.

Berries are perishable. The sorted fruit needs to be kept dry and refrigerated until ready for use. Preparation such as washing before refrigerating results in loss of food value and a greater chance of spoilage.

Ripe tomatoes, eating-ripe apples, peaches, apricots, cherries, grapes, pears, plums, and rhubarb all keep better under refrigeration. To minimize wilting and drying, they may be held in a covered container or in perforated plastic bags on the refrigerator shelf.

Even moderately low temperatures can harm some fruits and vegetables, especially if they are kept for a long time.

If grapefruit and lemons are held for several weeks at temperatures lower than 50° to 55°, pitting of the skin and discoloration of the flesh may result. Bananas, both ripe and green, suffer chilling injury at temperatures below 56°. These fruits and melons, avocados, and pineapples are best stored at a cool

Approximate High-Quality Life of Some Perishable Foods Held in a Home Refrigerator

1 or 2 days

Fruit:
  Berries
  Ripe tomatoes

Meats, poultry, fish:
  Ground meats
  Variety meats (liver, kidney, brains)
  Poultry, cut-up and whole
  Fish
  Leftover cooked meats and meat dishes

Vegetables:
  Sweet corn
  Asparagus
  Broccoli
  Lima beans, shelled
  Brussels sprouts
  Spinach and other green, leafy vegetables
  Lettuce
  Green onions
  Green peas

3 to 5 days

Dairy products:
  Milk and cream
  Cottage cheese

Fruit:
  Cherries
  Grapes
  Peaches
  Apricots

Meats:
  Fresh meat cuts
  Hearts
  Cold cuts
  Corned beef
  Ham slice
  Ham, half

Vegetables:
  Cabbage
  Cauliflower
  Lima beans, unshelled
  Snap beans
  Celery
  Carrots, tops removed

1 week

Fruit:
  Apples, eating-ripe
  Oranges
  Grapefruit
  Lemons

Poultry products:
  Shell eggs

Meats:
  Bacon, sliced

2 weeks

Dairy products:
  Soft cheeses (other than cottage cheese)
  Butter

Meats:
  Cured ham, whole
  Dried beef, sliced

---

room temperature. Keeping citrus fruits in the refrigerator for as long as a week or chilling of any of these fruits to a desired serving temperature will not be harmful.

Because temperature is an important factor in ripening, unripe fruit should not be placed in the refrigerator. Slightly underripe fruits that are fresh and sound will ripen in open air at room temperature, but they should not be placed in the sun. Tomatoes, peaches, bananas, avocados, pears, and plums may be ripened. Cantaloups will soften but will not improve in flavor on holding.

Refrigerator temperatures delay the development of rancidity in nuts that have a high content of fat. Nuts should be stored in airtight containers to protect them from contact with oxygen. Unshelled nuts keep better than shelled ones. As salt hastens rancidity, unsalted nuts keep their quality longer than salted nuts.

Opened jars of preserved fruit products such as jellies, jams, and preserves and opened cans of fruits and fruit juices need refrigeration to keep the food from spoiling. Any of them may be stored safely in its original container, glass or tin, but it is advisable to cover the container. Reconstituted frozen juice concentrates should also be covered and refrigerated. Glass or plastic containers are preferred over tin because tin cans may impart a metallic flavor.

Dried fruits should be stored in the refrigerator in humid weather. At other times they keep well in tightly closed containers at room temperature.

Fresh vegetables have better flavor and nutritive value if they are eaten soon after harvest. The aging of foods goes on after harvest. The sweetness of corn, asparagus, beans, and green peas disappears therefore as sugar is changed to starch. The crispness and flavor of green, leafy vegetables deteriorate as water evaporates from vegetable tissues. Because low temperatures delay the aging process, most vegetables keep better in the icebox.

The exceptions—white potatoes, sweetpotatoes, dry onions, hard-shell squash, eggplant, cucumbers—need only cool storage.

White potatoes keep best in a cool, dry, dark place with good ventilation. Light causes greening. High temperatures hasten sprouting. Temperatures of 45° to 50° are best for white potatoes. Lower temperatures may convert some of the starch to sugar, giving the potatoes an undesirable sweet taste. If potatoes have become excessively sweet in too-cold storage, their flavor can be improved by holding them at room temperature for a week or two.

High temperatures and high humidity cause sprouting and decay of dry onions.

If onions are purchased in airtight, unperforated bags, it is important to transfer them to a loosely woven bag or container with good circulation of air for home storage.

Others of these vegetables may suffer chilling injury if held at temperatures much below 50° to 55°.

Lettuce, celery, other raw salad vegetables, green onions, and green, leafy vegetables need to be kept cold and moist in the refrigerator after washing and draining. Storing them in plastic bags helps to reduce the evaporation of moisture from them. Asparagus and vegetables of the cabbage family should also be covered or wrapped and refrigerated.

Carrots, beets, and radishes keep best in the refrigerator when the tops and root tips are removed. Sweet corn remains fresher if unhusked. Beans and peas stay better in the pod if they need to be kept a day or two in the refrigerator.

Bruised or soft vegetables should be used immediately or discarded—not stored with sound, firm vegetables.

FRESH MEAT, poultry, and fish and cured and table-ready meat may be held for short periods at temperatures just above freezing. Ground meat and meat that has been mechanically tenderized are more susceptible to spoilage than roasts, steaks, and chops, because a larger surface area of the meat has been exposed to potential contamination from the air, from handlers, and from equipment. Such meat as livers, kidneys, and brains also are especially perishable.

Meat becomes rancid because of the oxidation of unsaturated fats. The oxidation of pigments in meat causes discoloration. Since low temperatures retard these changes and inhibit bacterial growth, meat should always be held in the coldest part of the refrigerator.

Some animal fats, especially those of pork and poultry, are more easily oxidized than others. Shorter holding periods are recommended for them.

Since smoking of meat makes it more resistant to the development of rancidity, smoked pork may be kept slightly longer than fresh meats. There is very little penetration of the smoke to the center of a smoked ham, however; while uncut hams are protected from oxidative changes, ham slices may be unprotected over much of their area.

Some circulation of air is beneficial to fresh meat cuts in a home refrigerator. The transparent film wrappings and cardboard trays used in prepackaging should be removed from fresh meat, poultry, and fish, and the foods should be loosely wrapped before they are put in the refrigerator. The tight packaging, which is convenient and sanitary in handling in markets, keeps fresh meat in a moist atmosphere in a home refrigerator, and the growth of micro-organisms on the surface of the meat is encouraged. Poultry giblets are often packed in a separate bag placed inside of a whole bird or under cut-up pieces. They, too, keep best if removed from the bag and covered loosely before refrigerating.

In packaging cured meats, the exclusion of oxygen and light, which hasten rancidity, is a main consideration. They may be kept in the refrigerator in their original packaging. If only part of the cured meat is used when the package is opened, the unused part should be rewrapped in the original packaging or in any of the various home wrapping materials.

Leftover cooked meat and meat dishes need to be cooled and refrigerated promptly if they are to be held safely. The stuffing should be removed from a turkey or chicken and both cooled separately. After cooked foods have cooled, they may be covered or wrapped loosely to prevent drying in the refrigerator.

DRY FOODS, such as flour, cereals, sugar, and spices, are less demanding in storage requirements than other foods. They keep well at room temperatures in tight containers that keep out dust, moisture, and insects.

In summer, flour and cereals should be stored only in small amounts and inspected often to detect weevils. Dry mixes may also be held at room temperatures, but they last longer and better in the refrigerator.

Bread that must be kept for several days is better protected from mold in the refrigerator than in the breadbox, especially in hot and humid weather. At refrigerator temperature, however, it will lose the softness many people

like. Keeping the breadbox thoroughly clean, well aired, and dry discourages growth of mold. Bread will retain its original freshness for a week or two if frozen in its original waxed-paper wrapping and stored in a freezer.

Honey and sirup in unopened containers keep well at a cool room temperature. When the containers have been opened, they have more protection from mold formation in the refrigerator. If crystals form, the honey and sirup may be warmed by placing the container in a pan of hot water to dissolve the crystals.

RUTH REDSTROM is a food specialist in the Food Quality Laboratory, Human Nutrition Research Division, Agricultural Research Service, Beltsville, Md. A graduate of the University of Wisconsin, she joined the Department of Agriculture in 1949.

A new concept in food processing has been introduced with the preservation and sterilization of foods by ionizing radiations. Technologically, considerable research is still to be pursued toward the improvement of certain radiation-sterilized products in regard to color, texture, flavor, and odor. Irradiation in combination with heat, or treatment under vacuum and inert atmosphere may hold some promise in the resolution of these problems. Radiopasteurization or preservation of foods with lower than sterilization doses of 500,000 rads to increase shelf life is of considerable current economic and market interest. The destructive effect of radiation on insects (50,000 rads), the inhibition of sprouting of tubers (potatoes and onions at 10,000 rads), and the destruction of trichina in pork (30,000 rads) offer some promise in food technology. There has been no evidence thus far that radiation processing of foods induces carcinogens. Similarly, irradiated foods have not been found to be toxic on the basis of animal or human feeding experiments. While there is some destruction of the vitamins in processing, this is no greater, and in most cases less so, than that observed in heat processing of foods.—
H. F. KRAYBILL in Journal of Home Economics, November 1958.

Conserving Nutritive Values

BERNICE KUNERTH WATT AND WOOT-TSUEN WU LEUNG

WE GET many letters from people who ask whether foods lose much of their nutritive value in the stages between the farm and the table and how their nutrients can be conserved. The answers vary with the food in question.

Losses begin to occur after harvest or slaughter and are of two kinds.

The first is the obvious physical loss that comes when edible parts, like the outer leaves of plants and the fat of meat, are removed.

The second is the chemical loss that follows the changes in the structure of plant or animal tissue. Because respiration and activity of enzymes continue after production, the texture and vitamin content of some foods deteriorate rapidly, especially if the temperature around them is not right.

The importance of the loss depends partly on its extent and partly on the value of a food as a source of the nutrient in question. For example, pasteurization causes the loss of a large proportion of the ascorbic acid in milk. The loss can be ignored, however, because milk has relatively little ascorbic acid, and we do not depend on it for that vitamin as we do on fresh fruit and vegetables, which contribute about 90 percent of ascorbic acid (vitamin C) to our diets.

Ascorbic acid is lost more easily from most foods than other important nutrients are. It is subject to chemical destruction, and it is soluble in water.

In research on changes in nutrient composition of foods, ascorbic acid is the vitamin frequently studied, because measures that protect it usually also protect other water-soluble and heat-sensitive nutrients.

Some vegetables retain ascorbic acid very well for several days after harvest if they are chilled rapidly under vacuum and packed in crushed ice. Other vegetables have excellent retention at higher temperatures and lower humidity. These seemingly simple facts have had far-reaching implications in the handling of foods for the market and in the care of foods in the home.

The temperature, percentage of humidity, length of the storage period, method of handling to prevent physical injury, method of preparation for serving, and (in some foods) exposure to light are among the factors to keep in mind in considering losses and retentions of nutritive value of foods.

FRESH VEGETABLES, such as kale, spinach, turnip greens, chard, broccoli, and salad greens, need to be refrigerated as soon as possible. They keep their nutrients best near freezing and at high humidity.

Leafy, dark-green vegetables and broccoli keep practically all of their ascorbic acid for several days if they are packed in crushed ice. They retain about half of it after 5 days in the refrigerator at 40° to 50° F. Although this represents a large proportional loss, deep-green leaves have such high initial values that they remain excellent sources of ascorbic acid and vitamin A even after this substantial loss. They could be expected to provide more vitamins C and A than freshly harvested snap beans and head lettuce—perhaps more even than tomatoes.

Cabbage is a more stable source of ascorbic acid than most leafy vegetables. Kept in cold storage under 40°, it retains three-fourths or more of its vitamin C as long as 2 months.

Cabbage should not be allowed to dry out. If it is to be held at home for a few days, it should be wrapped or put in a special compartment where the humidity is high. Cabbage holds its vitamin C well for a few days even at room temperature (usually considered to be 65° to 80°).

Among other vegetables that also retain their ascorbic acid well at room temperature and do not require high humidity are a number that stem from tropical plants, like peppers (a rich source of vitamin C), snap beans, lima beans, and tomatoes.

The ascorbic acid in tomatoes vine ripened out of doors in summer sunlight is double that in those grown in greenhouses in winter. Green tomatoes just beginning to turn color also are a good source if they have been exposed to full sun; they may have more vitamin C than red tomatoes from the same plant that ripened under foliage.

Tomatoes picked before they turn red do not reach their best in appearance and nutritive value either on a hot window sill or in the refrigerator. The bright-red color does not develop when the temperature goes above 85° for very long. A temperature between 60° and 75° is desirable. Tomatoes become soft, watery, and easily subject to decay when they are ripened in the refrigerator.

Firm, ripe tomatoes can be held at room temperature several days, probably a week, without loss of ascorbic acid. They lose their value rapidly as soon as they become overripe.

Fresh strawberries are such a good source of ascorbic acid that a handful direct from the patch would supply a man his entire day's need of vitamin C.

Berries generally are highly perishable and lose much of their ascorbic acid quickly if capped or stemmed or if their tissue becomes bruised. Berries to be held a few days must be kept cold, dry, and whole to retain their maximum values.

Oranges, grapefruit, lemons, limes, and tangerines have a high initial content of vitamin C, and it is well retained under many conditions. Citrus fruits when whole keep well several days without refrigeration.

Orange juice, whether it is freshly squeezed, or canned, or reconstituted from frozen concentrate or dehydrated crystals, retains most of its ascorbic acid for several days in the refrigerator. A few hours outside the refrigerator will not result in serious loss. A change in flavor would occur before much of the vitamin value is lost.

For practical purposes, foods usually are kept covered, but a lid on the orange juice container makes no important difference in the retention of vitamin C. There is no harm in keeping canned juice in the can until it is used up.

There is a loss of edible material—and therefore nutritive value—when oranges are squeezed and the juice is strained. The edible yield of the orange as strained juice is only about two-thirds to three-fourths that of the orange eaten by sections. Babies need the juice strained, but others get much more value from the orange used in other ways.

Carrots, sweetpotatoes, potatoes, and other roots and tubers retain their most important nutrients reasonably well outside the refrigerator if kept cool and moist enough to prevent withering. They spoil quickly when they are in direct contact with water. Condensation moisture should not be allowed to drop on them. They may be kept in a root cellar; a cool, well-ventilated basement in summer; or an unheated pantry or garage. Information on building simple storage facilities for maintaining good eating qualities of specific fruits and vegetables is available in publications that can be had by addressing the Office of Information, the United States Department of Agriculture.

Carrots and sweetpotatoes are unique among these roots and tubers for their high content of carotene.

Carotene, often referred to as provitamin A, is a substance in plant foods that the body can convert to vitamin A. Hence, we speak of vitamin A value. This term, "vitamin A value," may refer to vitamin A itself or to its precursors, among them beta carotene.

Carrots have carotene as their most important nutrient. Removing the tops does not affect their vitamin A value.

Sweetpotatoes of the deep orange-colored varieties are important sources of carotene. The content is high initially; it increases during the usual period of storage before sweetpotatoes reach the retail market. The carotene content drops gradually after 6 months. Few sweetpotatoes are stored that long.

Potatoes, parsnips, turnips, and sweetpotatoes are not rich in ascorbic acid but nonetheless may be vital sources of it.

Freshly dug potatoes are highest in ascorbic acid. Immature potatoes have more than those left to mature. The loss of ascorbic acid is progressive throughout the storage period, but is most rapid during the early weeks. About half is left after 3 months of storage. Potatoes still retain about one-third of their original content after 6 months.

Potatoes develop an undesirable sweet flavor when held a long time at a few degrees above freezing. Such chilling does not impair their nutrient content, and their bland flavor returns if they are brought to room temperature or just below for a few days.

Potatoes exposed to strong light may develop green spots. Since there is some question of toxicity associated with the pigmented area, it is advisable to discard the green-colored parts.

Ascorbic acid behavior in sweetpotatoes follows the pattern of greater losses in the early months of storage and more gradual loss later. At the end of 3 months in storage, when about 75 percent of the crop has reached the consumer, 30 to 50 percent of the original content of ascorbic acid is lost. Another 10 percent is lost by the end of 6 months.

CANNING is one of the most familiar forms of food preservation. This means of preserving fruits, vegetables, and meats by partial cooking or another process and sealing them in tin cans, glass jars, and other containers originated more than 150 years ago.

Foods lose some value during the canning process and afterward throughout the storage period.

Newer techniques have succeeded in reducing losses of nutrients in canning and improving the quality of canned food. A short-time, high-temperature process, followed by rapid cooling, is superior to the conventional method of holding the foods at lower temperatures for longer periods.

Expulsion of air before sealing and processing reduces oxidative losses of vitamins at high temperatures.

Continuous agitation of cans reduces processing time and prevents overcooking of food near the can wall; thus the additional losses of vitamins, inevitable in the older method, are avoided.

Canned meats lose some of their thiamine during storage. Pork luncheon meat may lose about 20 percent by the end of 3 months and 30 percent by the end of 6 months when it is stored at 70°. Losses of thiamine increase at higher temperatures. Riboflavin, another vitamin of which meat is a good source, is not affected by ordinary storage temperatures.

Canned vegetables stored at 65° lose up to 15 percent of their thiamine in a year; stored at 80°, the losses increase to about 25 percent.

Canned fruits and vegetables have small losses of ascorbic acid when stored at 65°. Losses are about 2 to 7 percent after 4 months and increase gradually to about 10 percent by the end of the year. When, however, the storage temperature is 80°, losses range up to 15 percent after 4 months; up to 20 percent after 8 months; and up to 25 percent after a year.

Carotene is retained well in canned fruits and vegetables. Losses average about 10 percent in a year when stored at 80°. Tomato juice is a particularly stable, year-round source of carotene.

Usually the drained solids in canned vegetables make up about two-thirds of the total contents of the can. Soon after canning, the nutrients in the vegetable that are soluble in water distribute themselves evenly throughout the solids and the liquid. The solids thus retain about two-thirds of the soluble nutrients, and the other third may be in the liquid.

FREEZING, a relatively new way to preserve food, offers much in the way of retaining nutrients and eating qualities of foods.

Frozen foods undergo some nutritive losses. The ascorbic acid in the freshly gathered vegetable is reduced during the blanching process before freezing. There is small loss of other water-soluble vitamins and some minerals as well if the blanching is done in water.

Frozen foods should be transferred to the home freezer or freezing unit of the refrigerator as quickly as possible after they are bought at the market. Thawing and refreezing adversely affect the content of ascorbic acid and the flavor.

Most frozen foods should be held well below the freezing point for best retention of ascorbic acid. Acid foods hold their vitamin C remarkably well. Frozen concentrated orange juice, for example, held only to freezing, 32°, loses no more than 5 percent in a year.

Most frozen foods, however, when held only at the freezing point, show progressive loss. At zero, frozen beans, broccoli, cauliflower, and spinach lose one-third to three-fourths of their ascorbic acid in a year but only a little at −20°.

To obtain the best ascorbic acid value and highest quality in commercially frozen foods, it may be necessary to buy in smaller quantities and replenish supplies oftener unless the home freezer can be maintained below zero.

Frozen foods on hand after several months of storage may have lost a considerable part of their ascorbic acid. If they were such excellent sources as broccoli, kale, and cauliflower to begin with, however, they would still be good sources.

The nutrients other than ascorbic acid in frozen foods probably are not adversely affected by temperatures only as low as freezing. Therefore home-frozen supplies that cannot be held at the low temperatures most desirable for retaining the maximum content of ascorbic acid should not be overly discounted.

PASTEURIZATION of raw milk is a necessary safeguard. It does not free milk entirely of bacteria, but it destroys those that cause diphtheria, tuberculosis, typhoid, undulant fever, and other diseases. Loss of nutrients through pasteurization is insignificant compared to the safety it provides.

Pasteurization does not affect materially the main contribution of milk and milk products to the diet—that is, the calcium, protein, riboflavin, and vitamin A. The losses induced by heating are chiefly in the vitamins ascorbic acid and thiamine—losses that easily can be made up in a diet composed of a good variety from several other groups of food.

Milk and milk products provide about two-thirds of the total calcium in our diets, nearly half the riboflavin, and more than a fifth of the protein. Calcium and protein are well retained in milk.

Riboflavin in milk is reduced by exposure to direct sunlight, daylight, or artificial light. The rate of destruction is affected by the intensity of the light, length of the exposure, and the temperature of the milk.

The total loss of riboflavin from the time of production until the milk is served need not be large if it is handled properly—if it is kept clean and cold and out of direct sunlight.

Milk under artificial light in refrigerated showcases loses little of its riboflavin. The milk there is cold, and the light bulbs usually are of low intensity. If the showcase is near a window so that the milk is exposed to considerable daylight, however, losses could increase enough to be important.

Milk delivered on the doorstep should be protected from light quickly. Within the first 5 minutes there is little loss of riboflavin from milk exposed to the sun in clear-glass quart bottles. By the end of 30 minutes, losses are about 10 percent. They reach about 40 percent after 2 hours, even when the temperature of the milk does not rise above 70°. The loss increases as the milk warms.

The size and type of container are related to retention of riboflavin. Milk in half-pint bottles loses about twice as much as milk in 2-quart bottles. Paper containers and brown glass provide several times as much protection to the riboflavin as clear glass.

Fresh eggs can be kept in cold storage or in the refrigerator for long periods without serious loss of nutritive value—although cold storage of eggs has become an uncommon practice.

Some transfer of water and nutrients may take place between white and yolk during storage, but eggs tested after 18 months of cold storage showed no loss of protein. Changes in flavor and in cooking properties probably occur before the eggs lose their more important nutrients—riboflavin, iron, and vitamin A.

Dried eggs are a good source of the same nutrients important in shell eggs. Dehydration itself does not reduce the values for protein, vitamin A, or riboflavin, but loss of vitamin A value occurs under some conditions of storage.

Dried eggs should be kept cold, preferably below refrigerator temperatures, and in a tightly closed container that gives protection against air and moisture. Dehydrated eggs lose about a third of their vitamin A value in 6 months and about two-thirds in 9 months when stored at ordinary room temperature. The losses are accelerated at higher temperatures. Nearly two-thirds of the vitamin A value is lost after 3 months of storage near 100°.

Small progressive losses in riboflavin occur in dehydrated eggs. They amount to about 10 percent after 9 months at room temperature and 15 percent when stored near 100°.

PROTEIN, iron, and the B vitamins, notably thiamine and niacin, are among the chief contributions of cereals to the diet. The minerals and vitamins are more highly concentrated in the germ and outer layers than in the inner portions of the grain.

Cereal grains undergo fairly sizable physical losses when they are processed into the forms we use most. The nutritive losses are directly related to the physical losses. The kind and extent of processing determine the proportions of nutrients remaining in the finished product.

Milling wheat for white flour for

breadmaking and for general home use involves removing some 28 to 37 percent of the weight of the kernel. Even more is removed for very highly refined cake flours. About 72 pounds of straight-grade white flour are obtained from 100 pounds of cleaned hard wheat. This amount of flour has about a third of the amount of iron in the unmilled kernel, about a fourth of the thiamine and niacin, and about a third of the pantothenic acid, another important B vitamin in cereals.

Losses in milling are even higher for some less familiar nutrients. For example, vitamin E is present in high concentrations in the oil of wheat germ. Nearly all of this vitamin is removed with the germ and outer layers of the wheat kernel in the milling of white flour. The importance of the loss cannot be estimated until more is known about the role of vitamin E in human metabolism.

Rice and other cereal grains also lose much of their nutrients in milling.

The highly milled, polished rice commonly referred to as white rice contains smaller amounts of iron and the B vitamins than either parboiled or brown rice. Brown rice has the value of the whole grain.

Parboiled rice, also called converted rice, is prepared by a special adaptation of the milling process whereby it retains much more iron and vitamins than ordinary white rice, although it looks like white rice. The nutritive value of parboiled rice is intermediate between regular white rice and brown rice.

Whole-grain or nearly whole-grain forms of cereals are available generally. Among them are whole-wheat flour, sometimes called graham flour, brown rice, dark rye flour, and whole-ground cornmeal. They retain the germ and outer layers and thus the high nutritive values of these portions. They are preferred by many for their flavor and the roughage they provide.

CRAFTSMANSHIP in the kitchen transforms the food at hand into meals the family enjoys and keeps nutritive values in the food.

Foods must be trimmed or otherwise prepared. Many must be cooked. Surplus portions must be properly cared for. Leftovers must be made use of. Such skills in the home determine whether a family is well fed or only well filled.

Trimming is necessary for damaged leaves, bruised spots, infected portions, and other inedible material. Trimming may be desirable to discard parts like coarse leaves or excess fat. Discarding any amount of food, however, reduces the nutrients originally present.

Vegetables almost always need a little trimming. Different parts of the plant differ in nutrient content. Stems are more fibrous than the leaf blades they support. The blade is rich in many nutrients. The outer leaves are coarser and contain higher concentrations of vitamins and minerals than the more tender leaves and buds they protect.

The leafy part of collard greens has about 30 times more vitamin A value than the midrib. Turnip greens have more than 20 times as much vitamin A value in the leafy part as in the midrib. The pale color of the stems and midribs of kale and of various other leafy vegetables in comparison with the dark-green color of the leaf indicates that these vegetables also have most of their vitamin A value in the thin part of the leaf, which often contains many times more vitamin C than the stems and two to four times more iron.

Stems and midribs account for nearly half the weight of the leafy vegetable. They may be discarded with little loss of nutrients. If these fibrous parts are removed from turnip greens, less than 5 percent of the vitamin A value of the whole leaf is removed. Such trimming is worth while if it increases acceptability of the more nutritious parts.

Trimming broccoli, head lettuce, and cabbage usually involves discarding the more nutritious parts. Dark-green outer leaves of lettuce are as much as 30 times higher in vitamin A value than the inner bleached leaves. The darker leaves might make up 10 percent of the weight of a particular head of lettuce. If those leaves are not used, more than three-fourths of the vitamin A value of the whole head would be lost.

Broccoli leaves are edible and have about 20 times as much vitamin A value as the stalks and several times as much as the flower bud. If these outer parts are tender enough to use when the vegetable is brought home, they should be chilled and kept moist until they can be used. Losses of vitamins and minerals are disproportionately higher if the outer leaves wilt and toughen and must be discarded. They may appear to revive if they are put in cold water for a time, but vitamins already destroyed cannot be regained.

Meat, poultry, and fish provide protein, fat, minerals, and many soluble nutrients, including the B vitamins, riboflavin, thiamine, and niacin.

Washing or long soaking of meats and poultry may result in significant loss of nutritive value and flavor. Wiping with a damp cloth is sufficient. Water should not be used directly on frozen forms of these foods to hasten thawing.

COOKING is a refinement that has many advantages and some hazards in keeping the values in foods.

Cooking improves the palatability of some foods, improves the digestibility of fibrous foods, and sometimes is a safeguard against disease-producing organisms. Pork, for example, should always be well cooked to avoid the danger of trichinosis. Beef should be cooked at least to the rare-done stage (140°) to avoid danger of cysticercosis.

Cooking speeds the loss of some nutrients. It concentrates others—mainly by removing moisture and fat.

Ascorbic acid, all the B vitamins, and some of the mineral compounds are soluble in water.

The amount of water used, the length of the cooking period, and the amount of surface area exposed are of special importance in retaining these nutrients.

The three R's of cooking to conserve nutrients are: Reduce the amount of water used; reduce the length of cooking period; reduce the amount of surface area exposed.

The volume of water used in cooking is most important.

If vegetables are cooked in a large amount of water—more water than vegetable—the loss of nutrients through solubility will be greater than when the volume of water is small. Cabbage cooked quickly in about one-third as much water as cabbage retains nearly 90 percent of its vitamin C; cooked in four times as much water as cabbage, it retains less than half. Broccoli, frozen or raw, cooked quickly in a small amount of water, loses only half as much vitamin C as when cooked in excess water.

Much of the vitamin C loss can be recovered if the cooking liquid (pot liquor) is used along with the vegetables. If served at a later meal, the liquid contributes the minerals it has in solution, but some of the ascorbic acid and thiamine in the liquid are destroyed on standing and reheating.

The longer a food is cooked, the greater is the destruction of nutrients in it. If a vegetable is started in cold water, fairly large losses of ascorbic acid occur before the water begins to boil. This loss is attributed to enzyme activity, which perhaps is increased during the first part of the heating period and stopped when the heat reaches the temperature, below boiling, at which the enzymes are destroyed. This critical period and the total cooking time are shortened if the water is boiling when the vegetable is added.

Cutting or shredding foods permits greater oxidative destruction at the cut surface. It also permits greater extraction of nutrients in the cooking water. Because cut pieces cook more quickly than if left whole, the adverse effects of extra surface exposure may be offset, at least partly, by the shortened cooking period.

Methods for cooking vegetables to conserve their nutrients are steaming, pressure cooking, and cooking quickly in a tightly covered pan with only enough water to prevent scorching. Ascorbic acid losses can be held to a minimum if the vegetable is cooked by any of these methods only until done.

Baking is satisfactory for potatoes and sweetpotatoes and for a few other vegetables that require long cooking. We do not discuss it with the other methods here because it is seldom used for most vegetables and quite probably would cause considerable nutritive destruction.

Waterless cooking is not necessarily superior to other methods. The term is a misnomer, as the method depends on juice extracted from vegetables and on any clinging rinse water. The method does not permit quick cooking, and the advantage of using little or no added water may be canceled by the longer cooking period.

Expensive equipment is not essential for cooking foods to conserve their nutrients. Any utensil that has a lid that fits the top and is heavy enough to prevent vapor and steam from escaping to any extent is suitable for cooking with a minimum amount of added water.

The material (aluminum, enamel, glass, stainless steel) used in the construction of the cooking utensil is not important. Copper in direct contact with food would hasten the oxidation of ascorbic acid, but copper pans have practically become collectors' items. Modern pans having copper-plated bottoms have another metal covering the inside surface.

There is no scientific basis for the idea that aluminum pans are injurious to health.

Meats shrink in weight and volume as they cook, and they become more concentrated sources of some nutrients. They also lose some nutrients.

Much of the total loss is water, which goes off mainly through evaporation, although some usually is in the drippings. The greater the water loss, the drier the meat will be and the greater the concentration of nutrients that remain.

The fat that is lost becomes part of the drippings and would be eaten if the drippings were used in gravy or for other food purposes. Fat spatters and burns easily, and some fat may be completely lost if the meat is cooked at high temperatures.

Protein in meat is not destroyed by cooking, and only small amounts go into the drippings. The loss of protein is unimportant when meat is cooked without added water. Even when meats are stewed or cooked otherwise in large amounts of water, only about 10 percent of the protein goes from the meat into the broth.

The caloric value and the protein and fat content of any piece of meat depend first on the composition of the raw meat and then on such factors as the degree of doneness at which the cooking is stopped, the temperature at which the cooking is done, and the method (roasting, braising, stewing) that is used.

A roast of beef can be used for illustration. Let us say that this particular one is without bone and has about 20 percent (one-fifth) fat, which could be trimmed off but is still on the roast. If the roast is cooked to a medium stage of doneness at moderate oven temperatures, it would be expected to lose about one-fourth of its weight when raw. A 2-ounce slice of the cooked roast would have about 14 grams of protein and 13 grams of fat and would furnish about 175 Calories.

If the same roast before cooking had all the fat removed that could be cut off with a knife and were cooked at the same temperature also to medium doneness, a 2-ounce slice would have about 16 grams of protein and only 3 grams of fat and would furnish about 95 Calories.

If the roast had been cooked only to the rare-done stage, the water content would be higher than at medium doneness, and there would be less protein and fewer Calories in a 2-ounce slice.

Vitamin losses in meat are related to cooking conditions. The B vitamins (thiamine, riboflavin, and niacin) are soluble. The meat juices carry some of them into the drippings as the meat cooks.

Riboflavin losses are usually 10 to 15 percent. Niacin losses are 10 to 40 percent.

An additional loss of thiamine is due to destruction by heat. A braised roast may lose more than half its thiamine content, but a medium-done oven roast may lose only about a third to half of its original content.

Searing or browning of meat, often practiced at the beginning of the cooking period, induces some thiamine loss. Well-done roasts appear to lose more thiamine than those cooked rare or medium done.

It is difficult to generalize about nutrient retentions by various cooking methods.

On one point there is general agreement. Meat drippings contain significant amounts of the water-soluble nutrients—the drippings from thawing frozen meat; the drippings from cooking meat, particularly in braising and stewing; and the juices released by slicing meat. If the water portions of the drippings cannot be served with the foods, they could be saved for flavoring or used in other ways.

Since about one-third of the water-soluble nutrients in canned vegetables are in the liquid, it is desirable that the liquid be used. This may be done in various ways. Some boil down the liquid before adding the vegetable. Others consume the liquid hot as an appetizer, particularly in winter. Others save it to use in soups and gravies. In any case, it should be used as quickly as possible to avoid the losses of holding.

LEFTOVERS and food cooked in advance for later meals may save time, but this saving is at the expense of nutrients.

Cooked vegetables show losses of ascorbic acid that progress with the length of time that they are kept. They have about three-fourths as much ascorbic acid after 1 day in the refrigerator as when freshly cooked. They have about two-thirds as much after 2 days.

Reheating takes another toll of ascorbic acid, so that cooked vegetables reheated after 2 or 3 days in the refrigerator can be counted on for only one-third to one-half as much ascorbic acid as when freshly prepared.

Smaller but significant losses of thiamine occur in meats that are held and reheated. Probably there is no thiamine or other nutrient loss from the roast if it is served cold.

Eggs should be cooked. Raw eggs are not sterile and occasionally carry *Salmonella*, one of the pathogenic bacteria. Raw eggs contain avidin, a protein material that can combine with the B vitamin, biotin, causing the vitamin to be unavailable to the body. Cooking renders avidin inactive.

Eggs do not lose much nutritive value when they are cooked, probably because the cooking period is short and fairly low temperatures are used.

Poached and fried eggs may lose about 15 percent of the riboflavin in the raw egg. Prepared other ways, they lose less. Thiamine losses—15 percent— are about the same for all methods of preparation.

Cereals, by way of their flours and meals, lend themselves to a greater variety of cooking uses than perhaps any other type of food. Wheat, corn, rice, oats, and rye become myriad food items.

We have breakfast foods, macaroni and other pastes, cakes, doughnuts, puddings, pastries, cornbread, mush, hoecake, griddlecakes, loaves, rolls, biscuits (to name but a few) and that great American institution, hot toast.

Cereal products as a group are good sources of several nutrients, especially protein, iron, and the B vitamins.

Cereals and their products are has an adverse effect on thiamine re-
cooked in many different ways. Nu- tention. As with other baked goods,
tritive losses probably occur in all the the thiamine retention is higher when
methods, but some are small. The most the proportion of crumb to crust is
important loss is in thiamine, which is greater. Baking cornbread in a loaf
subject to destruction by heat and is pan results in higher retention than
also soluble in water. baking in corn sticks because of the

A characteristic of cereal cooking is greater proportion of crumb to crust
absorption of water, which has the in the loaf than in the sticks.
effect of dilution of the nutrients. This A study at the Texas Agricultural
is not a loss, however, as the nutrients Experiment Station showed the aver-
are simply distributed in the greater age retentions in corn loaves, muffins,
volume and weight of the cooked and sticks as 85 percent, 79 percent,
product. and 66 percent, respectively, when the

Baking is one of the commonest proportion of crust was 30 percent,
forms of cooking cereal products. 40 percent, and 68 percent.

In baking, the retention of thiamine Toasting reduces the thiamine con-
varies with the product, but is affected tent of bread about 15 to 20 percent.
generally by the length of the cooking The thinner the slice, the greater the
period, the temperature, the amount heat penetration and the greater the
of surface area exposed, and the destruction. One comparison showed
amount of baking powder or soda. a toasted thin slice as losing 31 percent

Bread baked to medium brownness and a thick slice losing only 13 percent.
loses about 20 percent of the thiamine Riboflavin is not greatly affected by
in the ingredients. Bread removed heat but is sensitive to light.
when the crust is light loses less, about Usual good housekeeping practices
17 percent; when quite dark, it loses for keeping cereals include covering
about 25 percent. them to prevent either drying out or

Rolls baked to the usual degree of taking up moisture. Such protection
brownness lose only about 15 percent would ordinarily reduce the exposure
of thiamine — somewhat less than to light and thus prevent the loss of
bread. The shorter baking time re- riboflavin.
quired for rolls more than compen- Clear Cellophane and translucent
sates for the greater surface area wax papers are used for packaging
exposed to heat. many items. Some products, as vienna

Quick breads, like biscuits and bread, do not usually have a wrapper.
muffins, made with baking powder as A large percentage loss of riboflavin
the leavening agent, lose about 20 to in these products could be important,
25 percent of the thiamine in their especially in enriched products, be-
ingredients. Increasing the amount of cause they are particularly good
the baking powder by half increases sources of this light-sensitive vitamin.
the loss of thiamine to about 25 to Experimental studies have been
30 percent. made of the loss of riboflavin in such

Cakes made at home lose about 20 commercial products as bread, unto 30 percent of the thiamine of the wrapped and wrapped in translucent
original ingredients. Cakes may lose and in opaque coverings; and par-
as little as 10 percent and as much as tially baked rolls, some unwrapped
35 percent, depending on the bulk and some covered with clear Cello-
and the temperature and length of phane. The rolls used in these studies
the baking period. had not been baked long enough to

Cornbread made with soda and develop any surface color or any ap-
sour milk retains thiamine reasonably preciable amount of crust.
well, unless more soda than necessary The experiments showed that 1-
is used. Excess alkali from the soda pound loaves of the enriched bread

wrapped in heavy wax paper retained riboflavin well for as long as a week when exposed to artificial light or to bright sunlight in winter. Losses did not occur in unwrapped bread until 3 days when the bread was exposed to strong artificial light. By the end of the first day in the sun, however, there was a loss of about 10 percent.

The riboflavin losses in the partly baked rolls, unwrapped or covered with Cellophane, were somewhat higher than in the baked breads. Strong artificial light induced small losses by the end of the first day. Sunlight induced losses of about 30 percent or more.

These studies indicate that reasonable protection from light, such as that afforded by a translucent covering like heavy wax paper, permits excellent retention of riboflavin in bread.

Bakery products wrapped in clear Cellophane and distributed commercially probably do not undergo the larger losses of the more drastic experimental conditions. The light that reaches the products stacked on the grocer's shelves may be subdued enough to cause no serious loss of riboflavin during the time the products are there.

Cereals cooked in only enough water to be absorbed lose only small amounts of thiamine—probably 5 to 10 percent.

Such products as macaroni, other Italian pastes, and rice lose some of their thiamine by heat destruction in cooking. When they are cooked in an excessive amount of water, they also lose fairly large portions of the remaining thiamine and other water-soluble nutrients when the cooking water is thrown away.

The handling of rice has changed considerably in recent years. It was once sold from bins in the stores, and it had to be washed. Some people still wash rice, although for the cleaned packaged rice of today washing is unnecessary and nutritionally expensive.

Washing once before cooking can cause a thiamine loss of 10 percent in brown and converted white rice and 25 percent in regular white rice. After changing water three times, the loss of thiamine may increase to 55 percent in white rice, 20 percent in brown rice, and 10 percent in parboiled rice. The loss of riboflavin and niacin is not so great—10 to 15 percent.

Cooking rice by boiling in an excessive amount of water and discarding the cooking water leads to high losses of nutrients in all types of rice. The loss of B vitamins is roughly proportional to the volume of water used and the amount of water drained off.

If a poor cooking method is used, such as cooking 1 cup in 8 to 10 cups of water and draining the cooking water and rinsing afterward, the loss is about one-third of the original thiamine in the white and enriched rice. Rice cooked in the top of a double boiler with a minimum amount of water, until all the water is absorbed, with no rinsing afterward, loses 10 to 20 percent of the thiamine and less than 10 percent of the riboflavin and niacin. The use of a double boiler is desirable to avoid the high temperatures at the bottom surface of the cooking utensil, which tend to accelerate losses of vitamins.

Another good method is to bake the rice after just enough water is added to it in a casserole to produce a palatable but not too soft rice by the time the cooking water is absorbed. The loss of thiamine then is 10 to 30 percent, depending on whether the rice is washed once or not at all.

The label on some packages of rice says, "To retain vitamins, do not rinse before or drain after cooking." If that principle is followed in the preparation of rice for eating and if the amount of water used is just enough for absorption, the values will be well retained.

WE HAVE DISCUSSED some of the factors that affect the nutritive value of foods before and after they come into the home. Foods do indeed undergo nutritive losses, but all the time we are learning better ways to retain their original values.

Food crops and livestock products available throughout the year are abundant for the nutritive needs of all our population. With reasonable care all along the line from farm and ranch to the family meal, foods will retain much of their quality, flavor, and nutritive value.

Revolutionary changes are at hand in the processing and preparation of foods. The electronic oven, for example, is in use in some institutions and homes with a performance that is almost fantastic. Food is cooked by microwaves. A plate of food put into the oven is cooked in a few minutes. The food becomes hot, but the plate remains cool, except as it is heated by the food itself.

The effect on nutrients of this short-time cooking process is under study in many research laboratories. We cannot say what the findings will be, but it is certain that among the peacetime applications of energy in the atomic age will come methods for better retention of nutrients than our present good practices provide.

BERNICE KUNERTH WATT *is a member of the Household Economics Research Branch, Agricultural Research Service. She has responsibility for compiling and evaluating worldwide research findings on the nutritive value of foods and for the preparation of tables of food composition. Dr. Watt is a graduate of Iowa State College and received her doctorate from Columbia University. Before coming to Washington, D.C., in 1941, she was a member of the faculty and research staff of Kansas State College at Manhattan.*

WOOT-TSUEN WU LEUNG *is a nutrition analyst with the Household Economics Research Branch. Formerly she served on the staff of the Foreign Economic Administration and the National Research Council. Dr. Leung has a degree from Lingnan University, Canton, China, and her doctorate from The Pennsylvania State University.*

Home Freezers on Farms

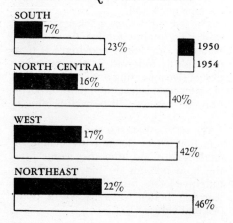

SOUTH
7%
23%
■ 1950
□ 1954

NORTH CENTRAL
16%
40%

WEST
17%
42%

NORTHEAST
22%
46%

Food Baked at Home

Southern Farm Families,
1948 and 1955

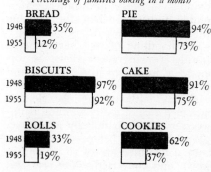

Percentage of families baking in a month

BREAD
1948 35%
1955 12%

PIE
94%
73%

BISCUITS
1948 97%
1955 92%

CAKE
91%
75%

ROLLS
1948 33%
1955 19%

COOKIES
62%
37%

When You Cook

ELSIE H. DAWSON

YOU can prepare better food if you know what goes on in the food you are preparing and why things happen as they do.

Foods change physically and chemically during cooking. If you know their composition and structure you can control these changes and have superior products from your efforts.

Proteins, fats, and carbohydrates are your major allies (and maybe problems) in cooking.

Protein in egg white, for example, serves as a stabilizer for foams and makes possible such products as meringues, angelfood cakes, souffles, and so on. Proteins help emulsify, thicken, and bind together other food materials.

Fats give flavor and richness to foods in which they occur naturally, as in milk, eggs, and meat, and the foods to which they are added, as in vegetables, baked products, and salad dressings. They are used to fry or to cook foods and to add tenderness to breads, cakes, and pastry.

Carbohydrates have a part in thickening, tenderizing, or sweetening cakes, breads, candies, ice cream, and other foods.

Each group of foods has its own chemical and physical properties that determine the best method of preparing or cooking it. These properties I discuss in relation to their application in the preparation of food. They are the secrets of good cooking.

EGGS are highly useful in cooking. They give color and flavor and hold other ingredients together. The proteins in the white and yolk coagulate on heating and thicken the liquids they are mixed with, as in custards. The proteins can encase air, and so provide leavening power, or lightness, as in cakes. Eggs bind ingredients together, as liquids in mayonnaise and solids in croquettes, and help to form an elastic framework, as in cream puffs and popovers.

Eggs often are sold by grade. Grade AA and Grade A eggs are of top best quality. They have a large proportion of thick white, which stands up well around the firm, high yolk. High-quality eggs are good for all uses, but their appearance and fine flavor are especially appreciated for poaching, frying, and cooking in the shell.

Because most of the white of Grade B and Grade C eggs is thin, it spreads when the egg is broken out on a flat surface. The yolk is rather flat and may break easily. In hard-cooked eggs of B or C quality, the yolk is offcenter because the white is too thin to hold the yolk in place. B and C eggs have dozens of uses in which appearance and delicate flavor are less important. They are good to use for scrambling, baking breads and layer cakes, thickening sauces and salad dressings, and combining with other foods.

Grade AA and Grade A eggs make larger and better flavored angelfood cakes than Grade B or Grade C eggs.

The ability to coagulate—to change from liquid to solid form—is an important characteristic of the proteins in egg. The change is largely physical, from soluble to less soluble protein or from liquid to solid form. The commonest method of coagulating protein is by heat.

Proteins have no definite temperature for coagulation, because it may be raised or lowered by a number of conditions, such as the presence of varying amounts of salt, sugar, acid, alkali, or alcohol. Sugar raises the temperature of coagulation of egg protein. Acids and salts usually lower it. Eggs can coagulate faster in the presence of salts or acids, such as those in milk and fruit juices, and the alcohol in wines that are sometimes used in cooking.

The texture of eggs cooked in the shell is affected by the heat. The white is firm but tender, and the yolk is smooth when eggs are cooked at simmering temperatures below the boiling point of water. Cooked at the boiling point of water, the white is firm but somewhat tough and the yolk is mealy.

Cooking eggs at high temperatures for a long time causes hydrogen sulfide gas to form from the sulfur present in egg white. The gas comes into contact with the iron in the yolk and forms ferrous sulfide, which causes a green discoloration on the surface of the yolk. The green color is harmless, but it looks less appetizing than a yellow yolk. The hydrogen sulfide diffuses to the outer surface and less discoloration takes place if the eggs are cooled quickly in cold water immediately after cooking.

For the same reason, a green color sometimes develops on the bottom of a foamy omelet during cooking. It happens oftenest when the omelet is cooked in the oven, because a longer cooking time is needed, and some of the yolk may separate from the white and drain to the bottom of the pan. You can prevent it in omelets by beating the white thoroughly, mixing well with the yolk, and cooking promptly.

The coagulation temperature of an egg-milk mixture is higher than that of egg alone. It depends on the proportion of such ingredients as egg and sugar. If you use more sugar, the coagulation temperature of the egg is higher and there is less chance of overcooking. The egg in baked custard thickens more readily when less sugar or more eggs are used.

Custards separate or curdle because they are cooked at too high a temperature or too long a time. Then the proteins shrink, and the mixture becomes watery. The safest way to keep the liquid from separating is to control the temperature and time of cooking custards by placing them in a pan of hot water and cooking in a moderate oven to maintain a uniformly low temperature. They should be removed from the heat as soon as coagulation takes place. A knife blade inserted in the center of the custard will come out clean when the egg has coagulated. Soft custards must be removed from the heat when the mixture coats the spoon and has the thickness and smoothness of cream.

When you make pie fillings and use egg in combination with starch as a thickening agent, you have to cook the starch with the liquid before you add the egg, since each thickening agent requires a different temperature and time of cooking. The mixture must be heated enough to coagulate the egg after you add it, or the filling will be thin. The coagulation temperature of the egg in pie fillings is generally higher than in custards, as more sugar is used, and there is more danger of undercooking than overcooking the egg. The filling may have a grainy texture if the egg is overcooked.

Eggs help two liquids—such as oil and vinegar in mayonnaise dressing—to form stable emulsions. Oil and vinegar mixed together by beating tend to separate quickly unless the oil droplets are coated with thin layers of some substance such as egg yolk. The yolk is better for this than the white or whole egg because it contains fat as well as proteins. Adding salt, paprika, mustard, sugar, or other seasonings to the yolk before the oil is added makes a more stable emulsion.

In cream puffs and some types of cakes, other emulsions are formed, which eggs help to stabilize. The stability in cream puffs is important, and cakes made from stable emulsions are better than those made from batters containing broken emulsions. Egg brings about an intimate mixing of fat and liquid with each other and with other ingredients in batters and doughs. This gives cake fineness of grain, particularly in a mixture containing fat, and makes it lighter. If a cake is not rich enough, yet falls when more fat is added, the addition of another egg permits the use of more fat. The same rule holds if you want richer muffins; egg as well as fat may need to be added if the product is to retain its lightness.

A foam is formed when egg white is beaten. It is due to its albumin, a tenacious and viscous protein that stretches and holds the air beaten into it. The foam consists of many tiny bubbles surrounded by a film of coagulated protein. The coagulation of the protein, caused by the whipping, makes the foam rigid. The yolk does not increase in volume when it is beaten as much as the white, and the foam is much finer. If the white and yolk are beaten together, a frothy foam is formed after long beating. The emulsified fat in the yolk ap-

parently cuts the foaming power of the proteins of the white. That is why you should not permit any of the yolk to get into the white when you separate eggs if the white is to be beaten stiff.

A little sugar added to beaten egg white increases the stability of the foam. There is less danger of overbeating egg whites when sugar is added at the start of beating, because the beating time is increased. This is an advantage with electric beaters and a disadvantage with hand beaters. Overbeating the egg white before adding the sugar increases the tendency of liquid to separate from the foam (leakage). You get a more stable meringue if you add the sugar at the start or during beating. Salts or acids in the form of cream of tartar or lemon juice also increase the stability of beaten egg white for meringues and angelfood cake.

Many cooks encounter leakage and beading (droplets of sugar sirup on the surface) in soft meringues for toppings of pies and puddings. The degree of coagulation of the egg white is important in controlling the amount of beading and leakage in a soft meringue. Too little coagulation leads to leakage. Too much leads to beading.

The temperature of the filling has a lot to do with it. When the filling is cold at the start of baking, the meringue is apt to leak. When the filling is warm, it is more apt to form beads of sugar sirup on top. Less leakage occurs on cold fillings when meringues are baked at 325° F. for 10 minutes than at 425° for 4½ minutes. On warm fillings, where leakage is at a minimum, less beading occurs when meringues are baked at 425° than at 325°. On either filling, meringues baked at 425° are more tender and less sticky when cut than those baked at lower temperatures.

The grade of the egg makes little difference in the extent of beading, but the addition of cream of tartar (an acid salt), especially to eggs of lower grades, tends to increase the beading because acids coagulate egg protein. Hard meringues are usually crisp and puffy. They are used for dessert, alone or with fruit and ice cream. You make them by drying foams of sweetened whites in the oven. The sugar crystallizes as the water evaporates. Because you use a large amount of sugar, 4 to 6 tablespoons for each egg white, you have to beat the whites a long time to form a stable foam. Acid or cream of tartar is sometimes added to produce a more stable foam and to increase the tenderness of hard meringues.

A crisp, tender meringue, however, depends largely on the baking. The oven is set at as low a temperature as possible, and the moisture is evaporated slowly. High temperatures cause browning before the water has a chance to escape from the inside, because the heat penetrates slowly through the foam. To get a meringue that cuts and eats well, the sugar must crystallize in small crystals during the drying-out process in the oven. Many sugar crystals give a product that is easily broken apart; few or no crystals make it chewy.

On a moist or rainy day, the sugar in the meringues attracts water from the atmosphere, and the meringues may become wet and sticky if the sugar crystals take on water.

MILK AND milk products are available in many forms. Fresh fluid milk is almost always pasteurized. It may be homogenized—treated under pressure to reduce the size and increase the number of tiny fat globules so they will not rise to the top as cream. Sometimes vitamins A and D are added to it. Sometimes nearly all of its fat may be removed. Evaporated, dry, frozen, condensed, and fermented milk (buttermilk and yoghurt) are used in the preparation of food.

Low cooking temperatures are recommended when milk is a main ingredient of a recipe. Long cooking at high temperatures coagulates some protein, causes an off-flavor in the milk, and caramelizes the lactose—that is, it decomposes or breaks it down into simpler compounds. The milk gets a brown color.

Milk soups and sauces therefore are cooked usually in a double boiler, and custards are cooked in a baking dish set in a pan of hot water.

You can use most forms of milk in place of fresh, whole milk in a recipe. Exceptions are buttermilk and yoghurt, which might give an unwanted flavor, and sweetened condensed milk, which contains such a high percentage of added sugar that it is used almost entirely in making candy, cookies, and desserts.

Homogenized milk may be used interchangeably with nonhomogenized milk in a number of dishes. You may, however, find slight differences in texture of the finished products or variations in cooking times with some recipes. Sauces made from homogenized milk are stiffer and show more fat separation than those made from nonhomogenized milk.

Cornstarch puddings made with homogenized milk are more granular. Homogenized milk tends to curdle more readily than nonhomogenized milk in soups, gravies, scalloped potatoes, cooked cereals, and custards.

Baked and soft custards made with homogenized milk take 15 to 20 minutes longer to cook than custards made with nonhomogenized milk because the rate of heat penetration is slower.

Evaporated milk is homogenized whole milk concentrated to double strength by evaporating part of the water from the milk. If you use equal parts of evaporated milk and water, you can use evaporated milk as you would any other fluid milk. It produces excellent results in making cream soups and other foods where a fine, smooth consistency is desired.

Evaporated skim milk, one of the newer forms of milk, may be diluted with an equal amount of water and used like fresh skim milk.

Dry whole milk and nonfat dry milk, made by removing all the water from milk, may be used in any recipe calling for whole or skim fluid milk, respectively. The dry milk mixes readily with water to make fluid milk, or it can be sifted with dry ingredients for cakes and breads, stirred into flour for gravy and sauce, or mixed with cornstarch and sugar for puddings.

You can use dry milk in addition to fluid milk to increase the nutritive value of many foods. The proper amount of dry milk to use depends on the effect the added milk has upon the palatability and physical qualities of the product.

Cream must contain at least 20 percent of butterfat to whip easily—25 to 40 percent is better. Both the fat particles and the air bubbles are stabilized by films of protein in whipped cream. For a stiff, stable foam, there must be enough protein to form the stabilizing film around the air bubbles, and the fat particles must clump. Larger fat particles clump more readily and thus give more structural support, but too much clumping causes butter to form.

Higher viscosity increases the whipping properties of cream. Aging increases the acidity and viscosity of the cream and hence its whipping properties. Warm cream does not whip well, because the fat particles are oilier and thinner. The fat stiffens and the cream thickens as cream is chilled. The best temperature for whipping cream is between 35° and 40°.

The addition of sugar to cream, before or after whipping, reduces its stiffness and stability by preventing coagulation of the protein around the air bubbles. Adding the sugar before whipping the cream increases the whipping time and reduces the volume.

Evaporated whole milk has about one-fifth of the amount of fat of whipping cream, but it has more whole milk solids. Undiluted evaporated milk may be whipped if it is first chilled to about 32° or lower until fine ice crystals form. Bowl and beater should also be chilled. Lemon juice or vinegar in the proportion of 2 tablespoons for each cup of milk may be added for greater

stiffness and stability when the flavor is suitable to the food with which the whipped milk is to be combined. The volume of evaporated milk increases two to three times when it is whipped. The foam produced is smooth, thick, and glossy, and will be stable for 45 minutes to an hour if it is chilled.

The foaming ability of nonfat dry milk varies widely. In the best brands, the volume increases about four times, and the foam may be stable for several hours. The foam is more stable if the mixture of nonfat dry milk and water, 1 cup of each, is chilled first and if 2 tablespoons of lemon juice and 4 tablespoons of sugar are added before whipping. Nonfat dry milk then makes an acceptable, light-bodied topping.

MEAT is made up of bundles of fibers or cells that contain a solution of proteins, nitrogenous substances, salts, carbohydrates, pigments, enzymes, and vitamins.

The fibers are surrounded by fluids of similar composition. The muscle fibers are surrounded and bound together by protein membranes, called connective tissue. Collagen and elastin are two proteins in connective tissue.

Among the muscle fibers are globules of fat. In general, the less connective tissue and the more widely distributed the fat, the tenderer the meat. The size of the muscle fibers, which depends on the exercise and age of the animal, also influences the quality of the meat. Tough meat usually has a coarser grain than tender meat.

Tender and less tender cuts of meat are obtained from the same animal because the muscles are not exercised or used equally. The muscles in the animal that get the most movement develop the most connective tissue, and so are less tender. Cuts from the leg, shoulder, and neck generally are not so tender as those from the middle back. From the middle back come steaks and roasts from the loin and sirloin, and rib roasts, which are considered tender cuts of beef.

All cuts of pork are generally tender

because of age and fatness. Most lamb cuts are tender because of age.

Aging or ripening of meat permits its natural enzymes to become active and induce tenderness by making some of the proteins more soluble. An animal's muscles become stiff or rigid soon after slaughtering. If the muscles are cooked soon thereafter, they are apt to be tough. After some time, they become pliant again. With longer storage, enzymes and chemical changes produce ripened meat.

Various treatments before cooking have been recommended for tenderizing meat. Grinding, cubing, slicing, and pounding break up the muscle and connective tissue and make meat tenderer.

Several commercial preparations containing an enzyme are available. The enzyme often used is papain, which is obtained from the papaya plant. You sprinkle the enzyme powder over the meat and pierce it with a fork to aid in getting the enzyme into the meat. A solution of the enzyme is used commercially. The enzyme softens the connective tissue as well as the muscle protein. The maximum activity of the enzyme seems to occur at higher temperatures during the early cooking process, as the best temperature for papain activity is about 176°. If the meat is not well done, the continued activity of the enzyme in the warm meat after cooking would break down the muscle tissue to an unpalatable stage.

Heat causes the coagulation of proteins, melting of the fat, and change in color of red meat to pink and finally brown or gray. In the presence of water or moisture naturally present in meat, collagen hydrolyzes to gelatin when heated.

Heat affects tenderness of meat. The coagulation of proteins causes a toughening of the meat and the hydrolysis of collagen to gelatin makes it tender. The total effect of heat depends on which reaction predominates. The changes in flavor caused by heat are due partly to the loss of

volatile matter, caramelization of carbohydrates, decomposition of proteins and fats, and coagulation of protein. More and more changes in flavor take place the longer the meat is cooked.

The shrinkage of meat during cooking is due mainly to the loss of water, which escapes as steam, and to the loss of the water and fat, which are released from the meat and collect at the bottom of the cooking pan.

Losses due to cooking increase as the roasting temperature is increased with all varieties of cuts—ribs, chuck, rump, sirloin tip, or heel of round.

Searing at a high temperature for a short time followed by a low cooking temperature may cause greater shrinkage than if the meat is not seared. For a minimum amount of shrinkage and the most servings per pound of meat, low oven temperatures are recommended for as short a time as possible.

Some kinds and cuts of meat (chops, steaks, rib and loin roasts of beef, veal, pork, and lamb) are most palatable when cooked by dry-heat methods—baking or roasting, broiling, pan-broiling or pan-frying. Other cuts (pot roast, round steak, stew meat, heart, kidney, and tongue) are best cooked by moist-heat methods—braising, stewing, or simmering. Dry-heat cooking generally is successful with naturally tender meats that have little connective tissue. They need only to be heated to the desired temperature for eating. Moist-heat cooking is required by meats with much connective tissue, which is tenderized by long, slow cooking in a moist atmosphere.

For oven roasting, you put the meat on a low rack in a shallow pan at about 325°, with fat side up so it will be self-basting. You add no water and do not cover the pan. The heat moves freely around the meat. The rack in the bottom of the pan keeps the meat from sticking. The bones of some cuts form a natural rack to keep the meat out of the drippings.

You do not need to flour, sear, or baste the roast during cooking. Good-quality meat holds its juices and cooks perfectly in an open pan if you use a constant low heat.

Roasting directions are similar for beef, lamb, and pork.

Many cuts of beef, including rib, loin, chuck, round, and rump, are tender and flavorful when cooked by the dry-heat method. Actually, the meat has enough natural moisture to soften small amounts of connective tissue and produce tender meat in the time required to cook by low heat.

Leg of lamb retains its shape, cooks in less time, and is juicier when the fell—a thin, paperlike, tasteless membrane or skin covering—is left on the leg of lamb roast until after cooking.

A meat thermometer shows the temperature inside the meat and is the most accurate measure of doneness. You insert it so that the bulb is at the center of the thickest part of the meat and does not touch bone or fat.

Beef may be cooked to the degree of doneness you desire—rare (140°), medium (160°), or well done (170°). If beef is cooked so that it is still pink on the inside, shrinkage will be less and the meat will be juicier than if it is well done.

Veal is usually cooked well done to soften the connective tissue and to develop good flavor. Veal is young beef (calf) and is, therefore, lacking in fat. It is cooked by roasting, braising, or stewing until it is thoroughly done.

Lamb can be either medium or well done. Lamb chops are juicier if they are not overcooked.

Fresh pork needs to be cooked all the way through to bring out its flavor and to make it safe to eat. For best eating quality, it is usually cooked until the temperature inside the meat is 185° (well done) as indicated by a meat thermometer. At this temperature, no traces of pink color in the juice or meat are present.

Tender turkeys, chickens, and ducks can be roasted in the same way as tender cuts of beef, lamb, and pork—in an oven at 325° on a rack in a shallow uncovered pan. Ducks have a lower yield of cooked meat and more fat than tur-

keys and chickens roasted at the same temperature. Four-pound ducks have 22 percent of edible cooked meat; chickens and turkeys have 41 to 47 percent, respectively, of edible meat.

Cooking losses for roasted duck are exceptionally high, 42 percent, compared to 29 percent for roasted chicken and 27 percent for roasted turkey. The yield of meat from chicken and turkey compares favorably with that from beef, pork, and lamb cuts with bone in.

The cooking time for young turkeys can be shortened by covering the turkey and cooking it at the higher temperature of 450°, but the cooked bird does not look quite so good as when it is roasted uncovered at 325°. When the pan is covered, the steam is held around the bird and the collagen is solubilized to gelatin faster than by roasting in dry heat. The roasted turkeys have less splitting, the skin is less blistered and shriveled, and the browning is richer and more even.

The meat from turkeys cooked covered or uncovered is equally as tender, juicy, and flavorful, although thigh meat is juicier than breast meat in both cooking methods.

Most persons like poultry well done for full development of flavor, but you must be careful to cook poultry no longer than necessary for adequate doneness, because a few minutes of extra cooking results in considerable loss in juiciness. An internal temperature of 185° to 195°, with the thermometer bulb inserted in the center of the thickest part of the thigh muscles or into the breast muscles, usually indicates that the meat is adequately cooked. The muscles are at a higher temperature than the stuffing inside, which is less exposed to the heat. Sometimes therefore the stuffing is undercooked; then it spoils easily.

For broiling tender meat or young poultry under direct heat, you can adjust the temperature by the distance between the meat and the source of the heat. When the broiler rack is placed so that the top of the meat is

2 to 3 inches from heat, the temperature at the surface of the meat is about 350°.

For pan-broiling tender meats with a naturally high content of fat, you use a heavy frying pan and pour the fat off as it accumulates. For pan-frying leaner meats and chicken, you add a small amount of fat to prevent sticking.

Young chickens cut in halves or quarters are easy to cook in an oven set at 400°. The chicken pieces are brushed with soft fat and seasoned with salt and pepper as desired, before you place pieces, skin side down, in a shallow pan. After 30 minutes in the oven, the pieces are turned and basted with fat. The chicken should be done in an hour or less, depending on the thickness of the pieces. They come out brown, plump, and juicy.

You cook less tender cuts of meat and older turkeys and chickens longer, add moisture, and cover the roaster. They can be cooked also by braising and stewing or in steam under pressure.

Braising consists of browning the meat in fat, then cooking it in a covered pan, with or without added liquid, over low heat on top of the range or in the oven. The meat is cooked slowly until the meat is tender when pierced with a fork. Pot roasts and swiss steaks are examples of meats cooked by braising.

The meat for stews and soups is cooked slowly in a small amount of water until the meat is tender. A pressure saucepan may be used to shorten the cooking time of meats cooked by moist heat. Some of the flavor of the meat is lost to the liquid in braising. It is important therefore to use the liquid as gravy or sauce to be served with the meat. The fat may be skimmed off. The meat juices that are left may be poured over the meat or extended by adding more liquid and thickening with flour after the meat has been removed.

Cooking time for rib roasts of beef in the electronic range is less than in the conventional oven. The cooking is done by microwaves, a particular type of high-frequency radio energy. Microwave cooking is the application of this type of energy for producing heat within foods. When microwave energy comes into contact with a food, it is absorbed by the food and converted into heat. The only heat produced is in the food. The air in the range, the range itself, and the utensils remain at room temperature, except for the small amounts of heat they may pick up from the food.

A 4-pound roast cooked to well done in the electronic range takes 25 minutes instead of 3 hours—but roasts cooked electronically have 10 percent higher shrinkage than roasts cooked conventionally. Microwaves at this high frequency fail to penetrate a roast deeply and uniformly. The outer portions are heated rapidly by microwave energy, but the center is heated slowly by conduction. In a roast cooked to rare, there are distinct areas of well done, medium, and rare from outside to inside. When cooked to rare, the roasts in the conventional oven are tenderer than those cooked in the electronic oven. The difference in tenderness is less in medium-done and well-done roasts.

The amount of food to be cooked and its arrangement in the electronic oven affects the time and evenness of cooking. Four bacon slices will cook quickly and evenly to a golden brown. A little more time is needed for each additional slice. Quartered fryers cooked one at a time in an electronic oven take only 16 minutes to cook. Fryers cooked two at a time take about 24 minutes in an electronic oven and 1 to 2 hours in a conventional oven.

Beefsteaks and lamb chops require a combination of electronic cooking and conventional broiling. Thus there is little saving in time for steaks and chops cooked in this way.

Most frozen meat may be thawed before cooking or cooked without thawing with equally good results. The usual cooking methods and times are used for thawed meat.

If frozen meat is not thawed, extra cooking time is required to allow for thawing during cooking. Large frozen roasts may take as much as one and one-half times as long to cook as the unfrozen roasts of the same size and shape. Small roasts and thin cuts cooked without thawing require less extra cooking time, depending on the size and shape of the cut.

Thawing frozen meat in the refrigerator results in the most uniform thawing and the most attractive appearance, but it takes longer. The time for the interior temperature of frozen meat to reach the temperature at which ice crystals start to melt (28°) is two to three times as long in the refrigerator as in the room; two times as long at room temperature as in running water; and two to three times as long in running water as during cooking.

Commercially frozen stuffed turkeys and chickens usually are roasted without thawing first. A minimum temperature of 165° must be reached in the center of the stuffing of frozen turkeys during the roasting period to assure adequate destruction of microorganisms. The lower the initial temperature and the larger the turkey, the longer is the roasting period required.

The roasting of a turkey should not be interrupted until the temperature of 165° is reached in the middle of the stuffing. Roasting a turkey partly and holding it to complete the roasting the next day is not advised.

Electronic cooking of frozen stuffed turkey is not recommended, because the meat is done before the temperature of the stuffing reaches 165°.

It is usually best to thaw frozen unstuffed poultry until it is pliable before cooking. The recommended method is to thaw frozen poultry in the refrigerator in the original wrapper. To shorten the thawing time, birds sealed in watertight wrappings may be thawed in cold water. After they are thawed, they can be cooked in the same ways as fresh poultry.

Frozen poultry parts may be cooked without thawing first, if desired.

THE FATS AND OILS we use include corn, cottonseed, olive, peanut, and soybean oils and lard, butter, and other semisolid fats from animal and vegetable sources. To make solid vegetable fats, vegetable oils (like cottonseed, corn, and soybean) are partly solidified by hydrogenation, which gives certain characteristics of both the original oil and the solid fats.

We use fats and oils for shortening, as in pastry, biscuits, muffins, and cakes; for frying and cooking foods; in mayonnaise and salad dressing; and to give richness and flavor to such cooked foods as vegetables and meats.

The primary purpose of shortening in pastry, biscuits, muffins, and cakes is to make a tender product. This effect may arise because a thin film of fat forms around the particles of other ingredients and the gluten cannot form.

The tenderness and flakiness of the pastry reflect the way the fat is distributed. Flakiness is determined by the layers of fat that separate layers of dough but melt during baking and allow steam to collect and maintain the open spaces between pastry flakes. Hard or plastic fats form layers more readily than soft fat or oil.

A tender pastry results when the flour particles are well coated by films of fat. Oil or melted fat therefore tends to give a tender, mealy pastry, and a solid fat gives a flaky pastry, although the way the ingredients are mixed and the dough is handled will make a difference in results.

To make pastry with liquid oil, you mix the oil with ice water until thick and creamy and then add all at once to the flour. You roll the dough between two pieces of waxed paper to the desired thickness and bake in the same way as other pastry.

Workers in experimental kitchens use an instrument, called the shortometer, to determine the shortening power of a fat. It measures the force needed to break crackers, cookies, or pastry made from the fat. Research workers found that pastry becomes tenderer if the fat is mixed well with the flour. Soft fats require less mixing than hard fats to be equally tender. After the water is added, longer mixing develops gluten, and pastry is not so tender. Dough that is held in the refrigerator for a few hours or overnight is tougher than it was at first.

Day-to-day variations in tenderness are due to temperature, humidity, atmospheric pressure, and perhaps the way you handle the dough. If you use more water than is called for in a recipe for piecrust, you get less tender pastry, because the water develops the gluten in the flour. Kneading and rerolling also increase toughness of pastry because of gluten development. Pastry flour gives a more tender pastry than bread flour, because it makes less gluten when it is mixed with water.

When fat and sugar are creamed—mixed by hand or in an electric mixer—for cake, the fat is adsorbed on the crystalline sugar and air is incorporated. The addition of egg dissolves some of the sugar, but the fat remains widely distributed. The liquid appears to be emulsified by the fat.

The temperature of the fat to be creamed is important, because neither liquid fat nor hard fat can form effective fat films around the sugar crystals.

In order to distribute oils successfully in cakemaking, you add the oil, egg yolks, water, and flavoring in that order to a mixture of the flour, sugar, baking powder, and salt; mix them well; and then fold the mixture into stiffly beaten egg whites. In some quick-mix cakes, solid fats are first blended with the flour to distribute them evenly before the other ingredients are added.

If you use too little fat, the cake will be tough. Too much fat means the cake will be excessively fine, compact, and moist. Extra beating will improve the volume, but it will never be quite so large as a cake with less fat.

The amount of heating a fat or oil can stand before it smokes is impor-tant in the selection of a fat for frying. Deep-fat frying may require a temperature as high as 400°.

A heated fat is breaking down chemically when it smokes. Its fumes have a sharp odor and irritate the mucous lining of the nose and throat. The fumes give the fried food an unpleasant flavor and may be irritating to the digestive tract or a burden in metabolism. Once a fat is heated to the smoking point, its period of usefulness is limited; it becomes rancid sooner.

Only fats that have high smoking temperatures therefore are suitable for deep-fat frying. They include most of the vegetable oils and hydrogenated shortenings. Olive oil is not desirable for this purpose because of its low smoking point.

Shortenings vary as to the basic fats used and as to the additives that may affect the frying quality.

Because of its high percentage of free fatty acids, lard tends to smoke at a lower temperature, but many people like the flavor of food fried in lard.

The emulsifier type of shortenings (those that contain monoglycerides to make quick-mix cakes possible) sometimes appear to smoke even before they have reached deep-frying temperature. This bluish "smoke" is actually the vapor given off as the emulsifiers are broken down by heating.

Each time a fat is used, its smoking temperature will become lower. If fat used in frying is not overheated and if it is clarified frequently, you can use it over and over again. You should strain it carefully after use to remove crumbs and other foreign matter that escape from the food into the fat.

Solid fats are clarified by pouring hot water over the fat, using 1 cup of water for each cup of fat, and heating this mixture slowly for 10 minutes. The fat and water mixture is strained through a cloth. The cloth filters out the small, charred food particles, which contribute to fat breakdown. Then the fat and water mixture is chilled. When the layer of fat that comes to the top is hard, the water is drained off.

To clarify oils and fats that are soft at room temperature, thin slices of raw potato, 4 or 5 slices to a cup of fat, are added and cooked slowly over low heat for 20 minutes. The fat is then strained through a clean cloth and cooled. Strainers containing copper or iron damage fat and speed its breakdown.

THE CHOICE of fats for pan-frying is not limited to those with a high smoking point, because the cooking may be done at lower temperatures than is possible for deep-fat frying. Fats for pan-frying should not be heated high enough to smoke or burn, however.

The cooking time for french-fried foods is very short at the right fat temperature. Croquettes and all previously cooked foods are fried only 2 to 5 minutes at 375°; fritters and raw batter and dough mixtures, 2 to 3 minutes at 350° to 375°; and chicken, 15 to 20 minutes at 350°. Breaded chops or cutlets are cooked 5 to 8 minutes at 375° to 400°.

A thermometer helps you check the temperature of the fat. Fat that is too hot scorches the food and may not cook it through. Fat that is too cool soaks the food before a crust is formed, and the food must be cooked a longer time at the lower temperature. The amount of fat absorbed by fried foods affects their palatability and calorie value; checking the temperature of the fat therefore is doubly important.

The kind and proportion of ingredients used in the food for french frying influences the amount of fat that is absorbed. In doughnuts a rich dough, high in sugar, fat, and eggs, tends to absorb more fat than a lean formula. Longer mixing of the dough, however, develops the gluten and tends to lessen the amount of fat absorbed, but the product will be less tender. Increasing the amount of flour in the recipe or using bread flour instead of cake flour lessens the absorption of fat during cooking.

CEREAL PRODUCTS are cooked to absorb water, soften the texture, modify the starch and protein, and develop full flavor.

Proper preparation depends on an understanding of the type and form of the product to be cooked. Some are relatively unprocessed whole kernels. Others are processed so that they require little or no cooking. Modern packaged whole-kernel cereals, such as rice, need no washing before use. Indeed, washing enriched rice removes some of the nutrients.

When you boil rice, you should use the smallest possible amount of water so that none is left over when the rice is tender. Proportions of 1 cup of rice and 2 cups of boiling water are used for regular white rice. The rice is sprinkled into the boiling water, a cover is placed on the pan to hold in the steam, and the rice is cooked over low heat until the water is absorbed (about 20 minutes). The pan then is removed from direct heat and allowed to stand for 10 minutes for the rice to finish cooking in its own steam. The cooked rice will be tender, firm, and dry. For a softer cooked rice, the water is increased to 2¼ cups, and the cooking time is extended to 25 minutes.

Another convenient method of cooking regular white or parboiled rice is in the oven. Boiling water is poured over the rice in a pan not more than 2 inches deep, the pan is tightly covered with a lid or aluminum foil, and placed in a moderate oven (350°). The rice will be tender, and not soft and sticky, in about 30 minutes.

A precooked enriched rice product is quickly and easily prepared. Boiling water is added in the proportions recommended on the package, and in 5 minutes the rice is ready to serve.

A canned white rice developed by the Department of Agriculture is partly rehydrated in the can. After the can is opened, the rice is heated for a few minutes in a little water to finish the rehydration while the rice is heated for serving.

FRUIT AND VEGETABLES are made up chiefly of cellulose, hemicellulose, and pectic substances that give them texture and form. Starch, sugar, acids, minerals, and vitamins are present in varying amounts.

Many changes take place when a fruit or vegetable is cooked. The flesh is softened by alteration of the cell structure. In starchy vegetables, like potatoes, the starch gelatinizes during cooking; pectins, proteins, and hemicellulose also change. In frying potatoes and other vegetables, some of the sugar is caramelized. Coloring pigments also undergo chemical change when heat is applied.

The color of a fruit or vegetable has much to do with its attractiveness when it is served.

Green vegetables, such as spinach, chard, green snap beans, peas, broccoli, and green cabbage, cooked to the crisply done stage, have a better color than those that are cooked until soft. Alkaline water helps keep the color of green vegetables.

Red vegetables, such as beets and red cabbage, retain their color better when vinegar or some other acid is added to the cooking water. Hard water, which is alkaline, turns red cabbage violet or blue.

Yellow vegetables—carrots, corn, squash, pumpkin, rutabagas—keep their attractive color well during cooking. The yellow color is stable to heat, acids, and alkalies used in food preparation.

The white color of potatoes, cauliflower, white cabbage, celery, turnips, and white onions turns yellow in hard water. Adding a teaspoon of lemon juice, cream of tartar, or white vinegar to the cooking water helps to retain the white color of vegetables cooked in hard water.

Raw apple and other light-colored fruits often darken from exposure to air when they are cut. Some nuts also make raw apple darken, especially if the fruit has come in contact with iron in a knife blade or chopper. Apples cut for salads can be mixed with acid fruit juice—lemon, orange, grapefruit, or pineapple—to protect

them from darkening. Salad dressing also acts as a protective coating.

Both acids and alkalies influence the texture of vegetables and fruits. The vegetable softens in a shorter time when sodium bicarbonate, an alkali, is added to the water in which the vegetable is cooked. Quick-cooking vegetables may become too soft and mushy when sodium bicarbonate is added; excess soda lowers nutritive value. If an acid like vinegar is added, a firmer, more solid structure is obtained, and the vegetable takes a longer time to soften.

Calcium chloride is a salt used to increase the firmness of food. It combines with pectic acid present in vegetables and fruit to form an insoluble substance that acts as a binding material between the cells and helps to prevent the breakdown of the structure during cooking.

The flesh of some fruit, like apple slices, can be made crisp and firm when soaked in a water solution of calcium chloride. The sloughing, or breaking up, of the outer layers of a potato during boiling can be controlled by calcium salts in the water.

Sodium chloride, or common salt, on the other hand, softens the structure by replacing the calcium and magnesium naturally present. Cucumber slices soaked in salt solution lose their crispness.

Fruits tend to keep their shape better in a sugar sirup because the sirup attracts water from cells through osmotic pressure and leaves a more dehydrated cell structure. Sugar is absorbed into the fruit only after the tissues are softened by cooking.

Many fruits, like apples, plums, peaches, and apricots, can be cooked directly in a sugar sirup. Others, like Kieffer pears, that have sturdy cell walls become shriveled and hard if cooked directly in a sirup. It is necessary to soften them by cooking before the sugar is added. For making purees, the fruit is cooked in water to soften it, and then the sugar is added to the fruit puree.

Vegetables are more vulnerable to mistreatment in cooking than many other foods. For the best in color, texture, and flavor, one should cook all vegetables the shortest time possible because they are less palatable when they are overcooked. Most vegetables have a mild, sweet flavor when cooked just right. Overcooking causes strong, undesirable flavors to develop.

The commonest method of cooking fresh or frozen vegetables is in a small amount of water in a tightly covered saucepan. After the vegetable is added to boiling water, the water is brought quickly back to a boil over high heat. Then it is turned to low heat to maintain gentle boiling until the vegetable is tender and crisp, not mushy. For many leafy vegetables, like spinach and shredded cabbage, the cooking time is less than 5 minutes.

Rapid boiling does not cook vegetables any more quickly than slow boiling because the highest temperature attainable under atmospheric pressure is 212°, the boiling point of water at sea level. At the higher temperatures and pressures obtained in a pressure saucepan, the tendering process is speeded up, and the cooking process is short for most vegetables.

Other methods of cooking vegetables include baking, braising, steaming, and frying. Baking whole in the skin is commonly used for potatoes, sweetpotatoes, and squash. Carrots, onions, turnips, young beets, parsnips, and cucumbers can also be baked successfully in a covered casserole. A moderate oven (350°–400°), which allows for gradual penetration of heat, is best, although a temperature of 450° is preferred for potatoes.

Braising, or panning as it is sometimes called, is a method of cooking with very little water or with the steam formed from the vegetable's own juices. The liquid used becomes a part of the flavorful sauce, which is served with the vegetable. Braising works well with a number of vegetables and is thrifty of color, flavor, and food values. Shredded cabbage,

kale, spinach, okra, and snap beans are a few of the vegetables cooked successfully by this method. The vegetable is cut into small pieces and cooked in a heavy pan on top of the range. A little fat is added to prevent sticking, and a tight cover is used to hold in the steam. The vegetable is cooked over low heat until just tender.

Steaming vegetables in a home-type steamer, consisting of a perforated pan placed over rapidly boiling water, may take slightly longer than by boiling. There may be some loss of color in certain vegetables, particularly the green vegetables. Others, like beets, carrots, parsnips, sweetpotatoes, squash, and pumpkin, have a good flavor when steamed, and their color is retained well.

MICROWAVE cooking of vegetables in an electronic range is new. The color of fresh and frozen broccoli is similar when cooked by microwave and by the conventional method of boiling on top of the range. The flavor of the broccoli is about the same cooked by either method. It is best to pare the broccoli stems because the tough outer layers do not cook to the desired tenderness in the same length of time as the rest of the broccoli.

Frozen vegetables usually require a shorter cooking time than do fresh ones, because they have been blanched before freezing. Most packers give detailed directions for cooking frozen foods, including exact cooking times, and these you should follow carefully, since even slight overcooking adversely affects the quality.

Canned vegetables are quick and easy to prepare for serving because they are already cooked. To serve canned vegetables with the most flavor and food value, the liquid in which they are packed should not be discarded. Sometimes, as for whole-kernel corn, which has only a small amount of liquid, the vegetable may be heated and served in the juice. For some other vegetables, such as peas, beans, and carrots, which are packed with more liquid than is desirable to serve on them, the liquid is drained off and boiled down to a third of its original volume, and then the vegetable is heated in the concentrated liquid. This conserves all the minerals, although some of the vitamins are lost.

Dry beans and peas require a longer cooking period than fresh vegetables to replace the water lost during drying and to soften the cell structure. To shorten the cooking time, dry beans and peas are soaked to absorb some of this water before cooking.

The rate of rehydration is faster in hot water than at room temperature. Dry beans absorb as much water in 1 hour when soaking is started by boiling them in water for 2 minutes as they do in 15 hours in cold water. When the beans are cooked in the liquid used for soaking, they are as pleasing as those prepared by the standard practice of soaking overnight. Dry beans cooked without soaking take longer to cook and are not so tender as those soaked before cooking.

The minerals naturally occurring in hard water, such as the salts of calcium and magnesium and sometimes iron, affect the softening of dry beans during cooking. The beans will be hard and tough if the water is very hard. The time required for cooking dry beans in softened water is much shorter than in hard water. The addition of small amounts of sodium bicarbonate softens hard water and has a softening effect on dry beans and consequently will shorten the cooking time considerably. Excesses of soda will increase the loss of the B vitamins during cooking.

Dry beans and peas that have been soaked can be cooked quickly in a pressure saucepan. After bringing the pressure up slowly to 15 pounds, only 3 to 10 minutes at this pressure is needed for different varieties of beans and peas, and then the pressure is brought slowly back to zero. Certain precautions are necessary—have the beans soaked, fill the cooker no more than one-third full, including the water, and add a little fat to prevent foaming and possible clogging of the vent tube of the cooker.

Baking is recommended for split peas, unless they are to be pureed, because they break up easily during cooking if other methods are used. After the 2-minute boil and a half-hour soak, the split peas are placed in a baking dish and baked at 350° for 25 minutes. The color and the flavor are good.

Mealiness is an important cooking characteristic generally desired in potatoes selected for mashing, baking, and french frying. Waxy or nonmealy potatoes are good for salads and hash browning and casserole dishes because they hold their shape. One key to the degree of mealiness of a cooked potato is the specific gravity of the raw tubers. This can be measured by placing the potatoes in salt solutions of different concentrations. Those that are heaviest for their size have high specific gravity and are mealy when cooked. It is possible to separate potatoes according to specific gravity and send them to market labeled as to the cooking method for which they are best suited.

For high-quality, french-fried potatoes, the two-stage method is recommended. Raw potato strips are partly fried (parfried) until tender but not browned, taken out of the fat, and browned later in a second frying. The best temperature and time for parfrying ⅜-inch potato strips is in fat at 360° for 4 minutes. For finishing, the parfried potatoes are cooked in 375° fat until golden brown.

With the two-stage method, potatoes may be prepared and parfried ahead of time during less busy hours, then finished quickly just before serving time. Parfries may be held as long as 4 hours at room temperature or 24 hours in the refrigerator. For longer storage, parfries can be frozen and stored at 0°. Frozen parfries may be thawed, then browned in fat; unthawed parfries may be browned in an extremely hot oven (500°). Parfries browned in the oven are less oily and slightly less tender than those that are browned in fat.

Potatoes are wrapped in a double thickness of aluminum foil for barbecuing on the grill. Other fresh vegetables that can be cooked in foil on the outdoor or indoor grill are sweetpotatoes, herb-seasoned carrots, applestuffed acorn squash, small beets, and young sweet corn in the husks.

You can also cook frozen or canned vegetables (like peas and snap beans) on the grill or over hot coals. For this, individual portions, seasoned with salt and pepper and a little butter or margarine, are wrapped tightly in aluminum foil and cooked for 10 to 15 minutes.

When vegetables lose their gardenfresh flavor, the addition of a little sugar to the cooking water restores the desirable sweetness and masks the starchy taste, especially in green peas, carrots, and sweet corn. The addition of salt, pepper, and butter reduces even more the differences in flavor of fresh and aged vegetables. Tomato flavor also responds favorably to the addition of a little sugar.

Monosodium glutamate also is thought to enhance the flavor of fresh, canned, dehydrated, and frozen food products, including meats, poultry, vegetables, and many specialty items. Additions of glutamate seem to lessen saltiness in some foods and increase it in others. A great deal of the effect depends on the other flavor factors of the food product. It also accentuates low levels of sugar when they are near optimal value. Small amounts of glutamate reduce the sour taste of tomato juice, catsup, and other tomato products. It acts as a blender of flavors in meats, seafood, and vegetables, especially when these foods have been prepared with other seasonings. The imaginative use of seasonings, spices, herbs, and condiments can lead to highly palatable and interesting flavors.

Cooking can be fun with all the new ideas to try in your own kitchen. You can experiment with new ways of cooking familiar foods, and use garnishes and sauces to make plain cooked foods look and taste better. You can dress up frankfurters with a barbecue sauce, mild or hot as you like. Hollandaise sauce and chopped nuts go well on asparagus or broccoli, a cheese sauce on cauliflower or cubed potatoes. White sauce can be varied by seasoning with onion salt, mace or nutmeg, cayenne, or paprika. You can change the flavor of beef stew or pot roast by adding allspice, cloves, or whole black peppers and a bay leaf or two. Sage, garlic salt, or dry mustard give new flavor to meat loaf.

Frankfurters are served not only as hotdogs in a bun with mustard, onion, and pickle relish. "New England hotdogs" are stuffed with baked beans. "Dutch dogs" are slit lengthwise and filled with sauerkraut.

Kabobs—appetizer, main course, or dessert on a skewer—are popular because so many different foods can be used together. To prepare kabobs, cubes of meat are placed alternately with fruit or vegetables on skewers. Meats to use include beef, lamb, pork and veal, chicken or turkey, fish and seafood. Fruits and vegetables for kabobs are selected for the right flavor and color combination. You can use such vegetables as red or green peppers, tomatoes, small white onions, mushroom caps, eggplant, cucumber, ripe or green pitted olives, or zucchini squash. Fruits to use on kabobs are many—raw or canned peaches, cooked or dried apricots, dried prunes, raw bananas, apples or avocados, peeled oranges, and canned or fresh pineapple chunks. You should choose foods that take about the same time to cook, or cut long-cooking items into smaller pieces.

ELSIE H. DAWSON *is Chief of the Food Quality Laboratory of the Human Nutrition Research Division, Agricultural Research Service. She is a native of California and was educated at the University of California at Berkeley. She was an instructor and took graduate work at Syracuse University and at Cornell University before joining the Department in 1941.*

Planning Meals for the Family

BETH BAILEY MCLEAN

YOU do not have to be a scientist to serve good meals, but you cannot trust to chance or a spur-of-the-moment selection of foods.

A plan is needed. It can be flexible to take advantage of lower prices of seasonal foods and to meet the changing needs and desires of your family, but it has to be a plan. Any job or undertaking needs planning, foresight, and schedules, which are especially necessary in a task as important as feeding a family.

The first step is to decide which foods and amounts of foods are needed to make a nutritionally adequate and pleasant diet for each person.

The basis of the plan is the selection of the amount of food needed from each of the food groups: Milk and milk products; meat and poultry, fish, eggs, and dried legumes; vegetables and fruit; and bread and cereals. The plan should include all the meals and the between-meal items eaten at home and elsewhere.

I know of no physiological reason for the convention of three meals a day. There may be some advantage, in fact, to eating smaller meals at shorter intervals if the total amount of food satisfies the body's needs. The mid-morning crackers and milk or apples at school, the fruit juice or doughnut and coffee at work, and the cookies at the neighborhood kaffeeklatsch are part of the overall meal plan. Counted, too, must be the afterschool milk and sandwich and the refreshments at tea. What the refrigerator yields in the evening also is to be considered.

Planning for these extra items—or at least awareness of them—makes it easier for the family to pick the foods that are best for them. For example, a cupboard and a section of the refrigerator might be labeled "snacks," and stocked with fruit, crackers, cheese, milk, and a surprise or special for the day.

A general plan for all the meals for a week can save you time, work, and money. It will help you avoid humdrum meals.

A GOOD BREAKFAST is a good way to start the day.

In many homes, the family can eat

breakfast together, and minor adjustments to suit an individual can be made by serving more of some food or by adding a food. To a breakfast of orange juice, whole-grain cereal, milk, toast, and jam can be added bacon and eggs for those who will have the noon meal away from home.

Breakfast is the time to serve foods that awaken the appetite and appeal to the sight, smell, and taste. Colorful foods and table settings and fragrant, tart foods and a change from day to day in the menu help start the day right.

A basic breakfast plan of fruit, cereal, milk, bread, and eggs can be varied by using a different kind or form of fruit, cereal, and bread and by changing the method of cooking the eggs or by adding a breakfast meat to the eggs.

Although a variety in the breakfast menu is desirable, the family may not like a radical change in foods or the introduction of a strange flavor. At this first meal, most of us want familiar foods that do not require too great an adjustment in our eating habits.

Foods for breakfast should be quick and easy to prepare and serve.

The rising hour of different members of the family may make one breakfast time impractical. In a family of four children 4 to 15 years old, the father left for work at 7 o'clock. The children had to leave for school at 8 and 9 o'clock. The mother solved her problem by serving breakfast informally from 6:30 to 8 o'clock and so adjusted the basic breakfast menu to suit each one, including herself. She had time, too, as they worked together to prepare the food, to chat with each one about plans for the day.

Sunday breakfast may be a special occasion for which the weekday plan is changed, the method of service is different, and the hour is fitted in with the day's schedule. Sunday breakfast may retain the traditional foods with modifications to make less work.

SOME KIND OF SANDWICH—with hamburger, frankfurter, cheese, peanut butter, or one of many other fillings— open faced or closed, hot or cold, with milk, a vegetable, and fruit is popular for many noon meals.

A substantial soup with toast, a fruit salad, and a beverage make a good lunch. Meat, fish, poultry, or cheese salad with bread or crackers and fruit is another suggestion. A vegetable or fruit salad with cottage cheese, bread and butter, and a beverage may be appetizing on a warm day. A combination of two or three vegetables served with a cheese sauce needs a tart fruit and a bit of sweet to complete a good menu. A big serving of strawberry shortcake with whipped cream or hot mincemeat pie with hard sauce could be the main feature of the lunch.

If a lunch is packed to be eaten at school, work, or play, the meal planner can select the packed foods to fit into the total scheme.

If the packed lunch contains an egg-salad sandwich, slices of carrot, milk, a cupcake, and an apple, the lunch served at home could be creamed eggs on toast, carrot and apple salad, milk, and cupcakes.

Or, if eggs are served at breakfast, the packed lunch can include a meat sandwich and a peanut butter and jelly sandwich, milk, celery stalks, and an orange. The home lunch may be baked beans, brown bread and jelly, milk, and an orange and celery salad.

When a member of the family selects a meal away from home, the problem of carrying out the food plan requires family consultation and agreement in the selection of food for the meal.

The adult who buys a meal away from home can choose a light or substantial meal according to his need to supplement the meals served at home. This is not too difficult if everyone in the family takes an interest in the plan for meals and understands the place of food in a good health program.

DINNER TIME is family time. The hour of service for dinner may be adjusted to suit the family schedule. Perhaps a television program calls for a dinner 15 minutes earlier or later than usual. Perhaps an early evening meeting suggests an easy-to-serve buffet or tray meal.

The social custom of eating with others has an important psychological effect on the enjoyment of food. The emotional stimulation of pleasant companions influences the appetite and may improve the physiological utilization of food. The person who eats alone may develop poor eating habits.

The dinner menu often is planned around a main dish. A special dessert or salad may be the focal point, however, and the other foods can be selected to complement this choice. If planning begins with the main dish, the vegetables, bread, salad, and dessert should make a harmonious combination that rounds out the nutrients needed for the day.

Sameness in the breakfast and luncheon menus may be all right, but variety and change in the dinner foods is desirable. Monotony often causes discontent and lack of appetite.

Some of us, however, are victims of our prejudices: We are reluctant to try something different and cling to a dinner of meat, gravy, potatoes, bread, and pie. A repetition of a limited number of foods may result in an omission of some of the essential nutrients.

To break a habit of narrow choice requires ingenuity in introducing a slight change to create a desire to explore the pleasures of new flavors.

Many kinds and forms of meat, poultry, and fish at the markets make it easy to serve a different main dish for every dinner for 2 weeks or more. There is no excuse for repeating the same kind or cut of meat each week or for serving the same main dish on the same day week after week. Such lack of imagination takes the challenge out of planning and reduces the anticipation for the meal.

The main dish should be planned to fit into the work schedule. Some meat dishes, such as roasts, pot roasts, stews, and boiling pieces, require more than an hour for preparation. Many cuts of meat, fish, and poultry require less than an hour or perhaps no time at all for preparation.

When planning a main dish, consider the desirability of leftovers for another meal. With a roast, serve oven-browned potatoes, scalloped tomatoes, a green salad, hot rolls, and apple pudding. For a busy second-day dinner, plan a meat pie with biscuit topping, buttered peas, carrot salad, biscuits, and a fruit gelatin dessert.

Dinner is the time for vegetables. The great variety of fresh, canned, dried, and frozen vegetables suggests two or more of these foods for the dinner meal. The many methods of preparing vegetables suggest a rule to serve a different vegetable and combination of vegetables every day for a week or two. When seasonal vegetables, such as asparagus, corn on the cob, tomatoes, and other semiperishable vegetables are plentiful in garden or market, considerable repetition for a short period may be all right.

Salad greens we can get at all seasons. A green salad may be served as a first course for dinner. A salad of greens, with or without other vegetables, often is served with the main course. The salad should fit the meal. A light salad of greens or citrus fruit with a tart, light dressing makes a good appetizer. A hearty salad of meat, poultry, fish, egg, or cheese with mayonnaise or cooked salad dressing becomes a good main course for a dinner or supper. A fruit salad with cream dressing may be right for dessert.

The dessert for dinner can be a substantial one, such as pie, cake, or pudding, following a light main course, or it may be a simpler dessert of fruit, gelatin, cookies, sherbet, or cheese and crackers after a high-calorie main course.

Usually the dessert is sweet. If the main course has included a number of foods that are sweet and rich in fat, however, sherbet, grapefruit, or other sour dessert may be more agreeable.

The dessert may be reserved for later in the evening so that there can be fuller enjoyment of it. Such postponement may be especially desirable after a festive dinner.

Whatever the dinner menu for the day, a few well-chosen, good foods make a more satisfactory dinner than a large collection of indifferently prepared foods. Key the meal to the time available for preparation and to your ability to cook and serve the food at the peak of perfection.

THE LOWER THE ALLOWANCE for food, the more important it is to plan meals carefully and to shop to get the right foods to meet the nutritional needs of each member of the family.

The amount of money spent for food does not indicate how well the food has supplied the nutritional needs of the family. The economics of food purchasing is a broad subject, and the importance of a wise expenditure of the money must not be underestimated.

If the money spent for food is more than 25 percent of the total income, some essential of living must suffer.

In figuring the cost of food, however, do not confuse the amount spent at the food store with the actual amount spent for food. The price of cleaning supplies, equipment, and other nonfood items may appear on the same cash register slip with that of the food items and may lead to a false idea of the money spent for food. On the other hand, money spent for food eaten away from home is rightly included in the cost of food for the family.

When you set up a meal pattern, you must decide how much you can afford to pay for prepared and partly prepared food. Women who have heavy demands on their time and energy, outside and inside the home, may find the use of prepared foods a reason for paying a higher price for some food.

Time available for meal preparation and service becomes a factor in adjusting meal patterns and food purchases for a family. Questions must be answered as to what food to buy, what qualities of food are desirable, what amounts make a good unit of purchase, and what stores offer the best value for the time and money spent. Each question must be answered in terms of the physiological and psychological needs of a family as well as what the family can afford.

When starting to plan meals for the week ahead, it is wise to check the supplies of staples as well as the perishable foods. The refrigerator and the cupboards may contain foods that should be used before new supplies are bought. Packages of crackers, partly used containers of pickles, sirup, jellies, cheese spreads, meat sauces, and similar items may lose quality when opened and so prove an expensive waste. Packaged, frozen, and canned foods lost in the confusion of storage often prove that the original purchase was not a wise or economical choice.

A tentative food plan and a shopping list for the week ahead will be helpful in buying food. At the store, the plan may be revised to take advantage of a good buy as long as the substitution is made within the same food group. A lamb roast might be a better bargain than the planned pork roast. There may be a sale on apples which could be used in place of the canned fruit on the shopping list.

While shopping, consider the supply of food for unexpected or unplanned guests. It is wise to have two or three menus in mind for quick preparation or a trick or two for extending a family meal to include an extra person.

Canned and frozen foods, prepared mixes, and other convenience foods can be part of the meal extender plan. It is not wise to keep food just for an emergency, and so delay overlong the use of the food. It is better to use, vary, and replenish the stock of foods for unexpected guests.

A GOOD WAY to keep away from stereotyped meals is to include in the meal plan at least one different food or one new recipe each week.

How can a liking for food flavors be

broadened and menus diversified? Foreign foods may prove to be part of the answer.

Modified foreign foods suggest new combinations for menus. The friendly exchange of recipes between neighbors, the many recipe books, food articles in magazines and newspapers, food advertisements, packaged and frozen foreign foods, and restaurants featuring foreign foods offer unlimited opportunities to bring more variety to the family meals.

The curry of India, the pizza of Italy, the chili of Mexico, and the different breads and desserts of many lands are intriguing. New experiences in using seasonings, spices, herbs, and wine come from these adventures. Foreign recipes make meal planning more interesting and accustom the family to accepting a greater variety of flavors.

The regional differences in food in the United States have developed from nationality habits of the settlers and from the supply of foods characteristic of each section. The Creole dishes of New Orleans are a blend of French and Spanish cuisines adapted to a plentiful supply of shrimp, oysters, crab, fish, poultry, rice, yams, and other foods. Californians have developed a regional style of cooking to make the most of the abundance of fresh vegetables and fruits. Herbs and wine cookery are typical of this western fare.

Originality and creative ability can be expressed in planning meals. The new recipe can be developed by giving a familiar food dish a new flavor or appearance. Veal chops are good when seasoned with dill, thyme, or sour cream instead of tomatoes. Baking-powder biscuits seem different when cut in diamonds or squares. A beef stew with a sprinkling of chives looks different when it is served in individual ramekins.

Originality should not lead to freakish, elaborate, or inedible garnishes or time-consuming overmanipulation of foods. A food creation must taste good.

Food should look good to eat. The sight of food, including the color, shape, size and surface of the food, should tempt a person to eat.

A meal of mashed potatoes, creamed onions, fried liver, celery, white bread, and rice pudding needs color to be appetizing. An improvement is made by serving buttered peas, pickled beets, and brown-crusted rolls in place of the onions, celery, and bread. A spoonful of red jelly enlivens the rice pudding. Raw and cooked vegetables and fruit, jellies, and relishes should be chosen to make a harmonious color picture.

Clashing colors are unpleasant. The purple-red of beets and red cabbage, the pinkish red of radishes, the orange-red of tomatoes and pimientos, and the intense red of maraschino cherries are not attractive together.

Colors naturally associated with foods have more appeal than unfamiliar colors. Green, yellow, orange, red, and brown are appetizing colors. Unusual colors may arouse suspicion. Green bread suggests mold, and red chicken loaf is alarming.

Blue and purple foods are usually not tempting unless experience has taught that these are natural colors for good-tasting foods. Orange juice in a blue glass is not so tempting as when served in a clear glass.

Black is associated with burnt flavors. Dark-colored foods are usually less appealing than light-colored foods.

Artificial food coloring should be used sparingly and should suggest accepted food flavors, such as pink and green coloring in gelatin salads, meringues, frostings, and frozen and whipped-cream desserts.

Colored dishes, flowers, and other items may help bring color to a meal.

A variety of shapes in a meal is more tempting than a similarity of shapes. A meal of round meat patties, peas, sliced carrots, baking-powder biscuits, round gelatin salad, and cupcakes can be made more pleasing to the eye by substituting whole green beans and cubed carrots for the vegetables and by cutting the gelatin salad in squares. A tray of cold cuts is more inviting if the meats are different shapes, sizes, colors, and textures. A tray of tea sandwiches or canapes is more interesting if there is a variation in the shapes of the foods served.

Irregular shapes are often more attractive than smooth, definite shapes. It is questionable whether a smooth, round scoop of mashed potatoes is as tempting as a fluffy spoonful of the same potatoes. Swirls in the meringues on pies and the frostings on cakes are nice.

An orderly arrangement of foods is more appealing than the jumbled mingling of foods on a plate. An uncrowded plate with foods in recognizable portions is preferable to heaped, overcrowded food. A semblance of plan for the dining table, the serving dishes, the lap tray, or the picnic table can add to the appreciation.

Food should smell good and should create an anticipation of pleasurable flavors. Reactions to the smell of a food are due largely to the association of an odor with food likes or dislikes. Thus, an odor may have a pleasant or unpleasant effect on the appetite. The smoky fragrance of fresh bacon, the pungent odor of curry, the bouquet of fresh apples, the acid smell of pickles, and refreshing scent of oranges set up distinct reactions to influence a desire to eat.

When you plan a meal, consider the aromas that will greet the family at mealtime. Too many strong odors in one meal are overpowering and cause a loss of the sensitivity to smell, but a meal lacking in fragrance fails to whet or satisfy the appetite.

Avoid irritating, obnoxious, and intense nonfood odors in the dining area. The smell of disinfectant, musty air, perfume, and fumes of gasoline overpower the odor of food and seem to impart the unpleasant odor to the food.

But, after all is said and done, food must taste good, or it will not be eaten.

When someone says he likes the flavor of a food, he means he likes its odor, taste, and feel or texture, because the sensations he receives from them are so interrelated.

The word "taste" is correctly used to refer to tongue taste. In popular usage, however, taste is synonymous with flavor. The taste of food is affected by the sense of smell. In fact, when the sense of smell is lost, all food tastes the same.

The four basic tastes are sweet, sour, salt, and bitter, but most foods are blends of two or more tastes. In recipes and menus, tastes are combined, and contrasting tastes are used to give more enjoyment to eating. Salt increases the sweet taste of food, as when salt is used on grapefruit. As sweet reduces the salty taste, some form of sweet is often served with salty meat. Salt and sweet lessen sourness. A little salt added with sugar to cooked rhubarb makes a milder tasting sauce.

People differ in their liking for sweet, sour, salt, and bitter. A salt shaker is usually placed on the table for those who like more salt, but even those who use very little salt find a salt-free diet flat and tasteless. Some people crave sweets and use an excessive amount on cereal and berries and in coffee and tea. Pickles, lemon, and other sour foods are essential for some people.

In planning meals, you can take advantage of the effects of sweet, sour, salt, and bitter tastes to make foods more satisfying. Tart foods sharpen the appetite. Sweets dull it. Citrus fruit for breakfast, a tart fruit or vegetable salad for dinner, and pickles with the luncheon sandwich whet the appetite. Sweet preserves with toast, cookies for lunch, and a sweet dessert for dinner are satisfying.

Meals should contain a balance of tastes or flavors. An excessive use of an intense flavor in a meal overpowers the senses and masks the flavor of mild foods. Taste fatigue, due to overstimulation of the taste buds, diminishes the enjoyment of a taste. If the robust flavor of garlic is relished, it may be used to season one food. Use a gentle touch. If garlic is used in the soup, potatoes, veal scallopini, green beans, and tossed salad, the cumulative effect overpowers the sense of taste, so that none of the food is appreciated.

Do not serve more than one or two strong-tasting foods in one course of a meal. Green onions, chili, curry, garlic, pineapple, catsup, dill pickles, and peanut butter have distinct, strong flavors and should be used with mild-tasting foods to balance their flavors. The taste of browned hamburger patties is lost when topped with mustard, catsup, sliced onion, and pickle relish. Only the hunger of growing boys and outdoor appetites can withstand the shock of so many strong flavors.

Herbs used with discretion give identity to a dish. If you are unaccustomed to seasoning with herbs, begin with two or three of the better known herbs, such as marjoram, thyme, or sage. Leftover meats, poultry, and fish may appear in a new guise by a judicious use of the complementary flavors of herbs. An overuse of herbs in one dish or in several dishes in one meal destroys the pleasing experience of herb flavors.

A blend of seasoning and flavorings enhances the savor of a meal. Seasoning should be used to bring out natural flavors, not to cover up or destroy the enjoyment of mild-flavored foods.

Bland meals are uninteresting. Potatoes, rice, macaroni, navy beans, white sauce, and white bread need seasoning or companion foods of more flavor to satisfy the appetite. The bland foods are good equalizers and extenders for stout-flavored foods.

Combinations of certain flavors are liked because these complementing tastes are familiar. Apples with pork, mint with lamb, tomatoes with veal, lemon with fish, and cranberries with turkey are traditional companions. It is well to try different flavor combinations. There is no reason why lemon cannot be enjoyed with pork, tomatoes with lamb, mint with veal, cranberries with fish, and apples with turkey. A new experience may prove to be pleasant.

Avoid repeating the same food flavors in a meal, such as tomato soup, spaghetti with tomato sauce, and a tomato salad. Apple juice, candied apple rings with the meat, apple salad, and apple dumplings give a dominating flavor of apples to all other foods in the meal.

A new taste is accepted better if it is introduced with foods of established acceptance. In this way, a satisfactory meal can be enjoyed even if only a small portion of the new food is eaten.

The family can be conditioned to trying new food flavors by incorporating a new recipe in each weekly food plan. The recipe may not become a favorite, but the experience of trying new flavors develops a greater enjoyment of many foods.

Variations in the texture and temperature of foods give an added attraction to the meal. The sensations caused by the feel of foods have led to many food customs. Crackers are enjoyed with soup. So, too, toast with creamed foods, crisp bacon with eggs, and cake with ice cream are accepted contrasts. Most people prefer smooth to rough-textured foods, but a meal of all soft foods is unpleasant. On the other hand, a meal of coarse, scratchy foods is irritating and difficult to eat.

The pleasure derived from variations of textures in foods is appreciated when you have a cold and cannot smell or taste. Even if blindfolded, you feel the difference between mashed and riced potatoes, pureed and whole peas, and crushed and sliced strawberries.

To assure appealing texture variations in meals, check the foods for contrasts of soft and firm, pliable and crisp, smooth and rough, thin and thick, moist and dry.

Some of the pleasurable sensations of different textures are closely associated with other sensations. The crunch of celery, a crisp apple, popcorn, and hard rolls is heard and felt. The surface of a broiled steak is felt and tasted. The sizzle of a hot steak may increase the anticipated enjoyment of this food.

A contrast of hot and cold foods adds variety and attraction to a meal. Even on hot days, one hot food enhances the pleasure derived from the cold foods. On cold days, a chilled salad makes the hot soup or cocoa seem more enjoyable. Cold meals in cold weather and hot meals in hot weather tend to accentuate any physical discomfort due to the weather, however.

The flavor of foods is modified by the temperature at which the food is served. The quality of most foods is superior at a right temperature. The maximum flavor of ice cream is apparent at 16° F., but a colder temperature subdues the flavor, and a temperature of 20° or more may make the ice cream taste soured. The flavors of pineapple and bananas reach full strength at a warm rather than chilled temperature. Hot roast beef tastes different from cold roast beef. Hot mashed potatoes have a pleasing flavor; cold mashed potatoes don't.

People have different ideas as to what is hot. Some want coffee scalding hot. Others let it cool somewhat before drinking.

What is hot? What is cold? For home-served meals, aim to serve hot foods from range to table on hot plates. Cold salads and desserts are best served when chilled from refrigerator or freezer. Many foods are more flavorful at room temperature. These foods seem to increase the pleasant contrasts of hot and cold foods.

In planning meals, choose food that permits service at the most suitable temperature for fullest flavor.

Variety is the keynote of good meal planning. The lower the food budget the more ingenuity is required to cook and combine foods. A variation in cooking methods of the different foods may help. Avoid using all fried foods, boiled foods, or baked foods in the same meal. Change the method of cooking a food from meal to meal. Potatoes and eggs can be prepared in a number of ways to make them appear and taste different.

The traditional Thanksgiving and elaborate feast meals often cause discomfort because of eating many foods rich in sugar and fat. Simpler menus of well-chosen foods are more desirable and result in fewer leftovers.

Plan to use different types of food service. Surprise the family with picnic-style meals served indoors. Treat the family to the elegance of candlelight and best china for no special reason except the pleasure of a surprise.

Make birthdays an occasion. If the favorite dish is apple pie, why not put candles on the pie instead of on the traditional cake?

Recognize holidays with a bit of flourish. Valentine's Day, St. Patrick's Day, May Day, and the Fourth of July can be reason for a feature menu.

A meal plan should provide for guest meals. Make guests feel welcome to enjoy the family meals. Do not let meals for company upset the schedule or food allowance lest you limit the number of guests or make them conscious of the inconvenience they have caused. Whether the guest meal is prearranged or not, the menu and type of service should be in key with the family pattern of living. A few well-chosen, attractive, good foods served with calmness and ease are to be preferred to a display of many foods. An informal buffet, tray service, kitchen meal, or guest-participation meal may be more appreciated and enjoyed than a banquet served at a formally set table.

The success of a company meal depends on the hospitality that prevails in the home more than on the number of dishes or the elaborateness of preparation or service. Today's hostess is wise to plan her guest meals with the thought of being with her guests and enjoying their visit. The gracious hostess makes a guest feel welcome to share in a portion of the family life. No greater honor can be paid a guest.

BETH BAILEY MCLEAN *is associate professor, Foods and Nutrition Department, School of Home Economics, Oregon State College, Corvallis. Formerly she was director of home economics, Swift & Co. She is author of six books, including "Meal Planning and Table Service."*

Time was when the baker of inferior bread could be publicly whipped, or have his ears nailed to a post, or be pilloried with the offending loaf hung around his neck. In these woefully lax days, the lover of honest bread, if he can find no honest baker, takes a subtler revenge. He bakes his own.

Revenge, then, is doubly sweet, for to the prejudiced sentimental palate the least of home-baked breads seems somehow better than the finest baker's loaf, because it is home-baked. The smell of home is essentially the smell of baking, and of all the sweet and spicy, nutty and toasty, smells of the oven, the smell of baking bread is best.

Homemade breads are well worth the trouble they take, and the trouble they take grows progressively smaller with each batch. Follow directions, especially those concerning temperatures for rising, for yeast is a sensitive organism. Kneading warrants no qualms; kneading is simply the mixing by hand of a dough too stiff for spoon beating, and doughs leavened with yeast thrive on rough treatment.

> *Some hae meat and canna eat,*
> *And some wad eat that want it;*
> *But we hae meat, and we can eat,*
> *And sae the Lord be thankit.*

We have beef; the beef on which the Britons batten, the beef which traditionally wins final battles. We have beef in several languages . . . boeuf à la mode, chili con carne, New England boiled dinner. We have beef in shades of elegance from the exquisite filet to the plebeian stew.

We have veal, relative newcomer to American cuisine, favorite on the Continent; we have England's mutton; lamb from the world; the pork that made Charles Lamb's pen take wings.

And we have the joys within, les dessertes de la table, the animal innards, and last, the dishes which combine meats in happy blending.

And so the Lord be thankit.

The eminent poet-prelate, Sydney Smith, composed a salad and ate it. In the manner *of poets, he then composed a poem called "A Recipe for Salad." The punch line of that poem earned immortality for itself and for its author: "Fate cannot harm me, I have dined today."*

Sydney Smith's salad was a green salad. . . . Salads may also be composed of meat, fish, and fruit. . . .

But the gourmet's salad is the green salad, a very palatable paradox, at once the greatest and simplest of salads; and a very palatable paradox is the dressing for a green salad, at once the greatest and simplest of dressings.

Of soup and love, quoth Thomas Fuller, the first is best. And we are not disposed to quarrel with the poet. Love has its charms, but only soup so well nourishes the young, stokes the fires of manhood, and comforts the old.

There are as many different soups as can be devised by active imagination, an infinite number of variations on each delectable theme. First, there are the stocks, bouillons, and broths. These, thin in consistency but rich in flavor, differ slightly from each other, but they are essentially strong extractives of meat, fowl, fish, or vegetables; we take the liberty of using the three designations freely and interchangeably.

There are, next in the natural order of soups, the consommés, variously garnished, which sharpen the appetite.

Then comes a group of thickened soups, elaborations of the stock-broth-bouillon base. Hearty meat soups include such favorites as grande marmite, oxtail soup, and mulligatawny. By way of contrast, there is the family of meatless soups; their stock is water from the teakettle. There are soups made of fish, soups made of game, soups made of dried beans, soups made of fruits and of wines. There are soups which must be served very hot, soups which must be served very cold, jellied soups. In a word, there are soups aplenty, and all better than love— almost.—Reprinted with permission from The Gourmet Cookbook, Gourmet Distributing Corporation, New York, 1950. Earle R. MacAusland, publisher.

What and How To Cook

GEORGIA C. SCHLOSSER AND GLADYS L. GILPIN

PLANNING and preparing meals that furnish the food the family needs and enjoys are two of the homemaking responsibilities that give many women great pleasure and satisfaction.

It is not hard to plan a day's menus that contain enough of each of the different kinds of recommended foods—milk, meat, vegetables and fruit, and bread and cereals. A wide range of choices is available.

But the way foods are prepared, and the choices that are made are important in assuring nutritionally adequate meals. Food can lose much of its nutrients and much of its flavor, texture, and color if it is not cooked properly.

For help with cooking problems, many homemakers turn to recipes that describe procedures in detail.

The recipes given here have been developed in the food research laboratories of the Institute of Home Economics in the Department of Agriculture. They follow basic principles of food preparation to give the best possible results in eating quality and nutritive value.

The recipes are arranged according to the four food groups used in the daily food guide—the milk, meat, vegetable-fruit, and bread-cereal groups. This arrangement points up the most important contribution of the recipes toward meeting daily food needs and makes it easy to find different ways to use foods in each group to give variety in meals from day to day.

Many of the recipes combine foods from two or more groups and can be counted toward the day's total for each of those groups. Cream of tomato soup, for example, which is included in the milk group, furnishes not only a half cup of milk in each serving but also about a half cup of tomatoes—enough to count as half of the recommended daily serving of a vegetable or a fruit rich in vitamin C.

Suggestions for variations are given with some of the recipes, and there are many other ways to vary them.

Seasonings different from those specified can be used or others can be added. A different combination of vegetables can be used in a soup or stew. A casserole or a scalloped dish can be made sometimes with rice in place of macaroni or noodles.

Planning a different menu each time a dish is served is another way to obtain variety in daily meals.

Milk Group

Some Milk for Everyone Every Day:

CHILDREN	3 TO 4 CUPS
TEEN-AGERS	4 OR MORE CUPS
ADULTS	2 OR MORE CUPS

Part of the milk may be as cheese or ice cream

THERE ARE PLENTY of ways to get milk into meals. Many people never tire of drinking milk—plain or in flavored beverages, hot or cold. Many get some of their daily quota of milk by using it on cereals. Cooked foods and other prepared foods offer additional ways to get part of the recommended amount of milk.

In food prepared with milk each serving can provide:

½ to 1 cup of milk in soups and chowders

¼ to ½ cup of milk in scalloped or creamed vegetables, meat, fish, or eggs

¼ to ⅔ cup of milk in desserts such as ice cream, puddings, custards, and cream pies.

You can step up the milk included in many foods that contain fluid milk by adding nonfat or whole dry milk. Four tablespoons of dry milk added to each cup of fluid milk used in a recipe doubles the milk content of the dish.

Puddings and pie fillings made with evaporated milk carry more milk into meals if 2 or more parts of evaporated milk are added to 1 part of water instead of the usual 1-to-1 proportion.

Cheese, too, provides many opportunities for adding milk value to dishes served in family meals. An ounce of Cheddar-type cheese can be counted as about ¾ cup of fluid milk.

WHITE SAUCE

For the fat in the recipes below use butter or margarine for extra flavor if the sauce is to be combined with mild-flavored foods. A bland cooking fat or oil is satisfactory if the sauce is to be used with highly flavored foods.

Thin

1 cup milk
1 tablespoon flour
1 tablespoon fat

Uses: Cream soup, gravy, creamed and scalloped vegetables, eggs, fish, meat.

Medium

1 cup milk
2 tablespoons flour
1 to 2 tablespoons fat

Uses: Gravy; creamed and scalloped vegetables, eggs, fish, meat.

Thick

1 cup milk
3 to 4 tablespoons flour
2 to 3 tablespoons fat

Uses: Binder for croquettes; souffles.

To make: Melt fat and blend in the flour to make a smooth mixture. Add milk slowly and cook over very low heat, stirring constantly, until thickened. Add salt to taste—about ¼ teaspoon for each cup of milk used. Cook 3 to 5 minutes longer, stirring occasionally.

Milk gravy.—Make like thin or medium white sauce, using pan drippings for the fat.

Cheese sauce.—Add 1 cup finely grated cheese to 1 cup hot white sauce—thin or medium. Stir until cheese is melted. Do not overcook.

Egg sauce.—Stir 2 chopped hard-cooked eggs and 2 tablespoons lemon juice into 1½ cups hot white sauce—thin or medium.

Vegetable sauce.—Add ¼ cup cooked peas and 2 tablespoons of chopped pimiento to 1 cup hot medium white sauce.

CREAM OF GREEN VEGETABLE SOUP

1 tablespoon chopped onion
1 tablespoon butter or margarine
3 cups thin white sauce
¾ cup cooked spinach, broccoli, or peas, chopped or pureed
Salt and pepper to taste

Cook onion in the fat until clear but not brown.

Combine with white sauce and vegetable. Add salt and pepper.

Heat. Serve promptly. 4 servings.

CREAM OF TOMATO SOUP

3½ cups cooked or canned tomatoes
¼ cup chopped onion
2 tablespoons butter or margarine
3 tablespoons flour
1 teaspoon salt
½ teaspoon sugar, if desired
3 cups hot milk

Cook the tomatoes and onion together about 10 minutes. Press through a sieve.

Melt the fat and blend in flour, salt, and sugar.

Gradually add sieved tomatoes. Cook over low heat, stirring constantly, until thickened.

Gradually add tomato mixture to milk, stirring constantly. Heat to serving temperature. Serve at once.

6 servings.

QUICK CARROT OR TURNIP SOUP

2 tablespoons finely chopped onion
2 tablespoons butter or margarine
2 tablespoons flour
1 quart hot milk
1 cup grated raw carrots or turnips
Salt and pepper to taste

Cook the onion in the fat until lightly browned. Blend in the flour. Add milk, carrots or turnips, and salt and pepper.

Cook, stirring frequently, until the carrots or turnips are tender, about 10 minutes. 4 servings.

OYSTER STEW

1 pint oysters
2 tablespoons butter or margarine
1 quart hot milk
1 teaspoon salt
Paprika

Look over the oysters and take out any bits of shell.

Melt the fat, add the oysters and their liquid, and cook over low heat until the edges of the oysters begin to curl—about 3 minutes.

Add milk and salt, and reheat. Sprinkle each serving with paprika.

4 servings.

CORN CHOWDER

3 ounces diced salt pork
3 tablespoons chopped onion
1¼ cups diced potato
1 cup water
¾ cup cream-style corn
3½ cups hot milk
½ teaspoon salt

Place the salt pork in a heated fry pan and cook until crisp and brown. Remove the crisp pieces of pork and reserve for later use. Lightly brown onion in pork fat.

Add onion and fat to potato and water. Cook for 10 minutes. Add corn and cook 10 minutes longer.

Stir the milk and salt into vegetable mixture. Add the crisp pieces of pork and heat mixture before serving.

6 servings.

CHEESE RAREBIT

2 tablespoons butter or margarine
¼ cup flour
¼ teaspoon salt
¼ teaspoon powdered dry mustard
Few grains paprika
2 cups hot milk
3 cups shredded cheese
1 egg, beaten

Melt the fat, blend in the flour, salt, mustard, and paprika. Add to the hot milk and cook until thickened, stirring constantly.

Blend in the cheese. Remove from heat and add the egg. Reheat.

Serve on toast or cooked rice.

6 servings.

CHEESE FONDUE

4 eggs, well beaten
2 cups hot milk
2 cups soft breadcrumbs
½ pound cheese, shredded (2 cups)
¼ teaspoon salt

Combine all the ingredients. Pour into a greased baking dish and bake at 350° F. (moderate oven) for about 40 minutes—or until set and lightly browned on top. Serve at once.

6 servings.

SPOONBREAD

3 cups milk
1 cup cornmeal
1½ teaspoons salt
2 tablespoons butter or margarine
3 eggs, beaten

Combine the milk, cornmeal, salt, and fat. Cook over boiling water, stirring constantly, until thickened. Gradually add cornmeal mixture to beaten eggs.

Pour into a greased baking dish and bake at 375° F. (moderate oven) for 45 to 60 minutes or until set. Serve at once.

6 servings.

BAKED CUSTARD

¼ cup sugar
¼ teaspoon salt
3 eggs, beaten
2 cups hot milk
1 teaspoon vanilla

Combine sugar, salt, and eggs. Add milk slowly; add vanilla.

Pour into custard cups, and set in a pan of hot water.

Bake at 325° F. (slow oven) until the custard is set—30 to 40 minutes.

4 servings.

CREAM PIE

½ cup sugar
4 tablespoons flour
¼ teaspoon salt
2 cups milk
2 egg yolks, slightly beaten
2 tablespoons butter or margarine
1 teaspoon vanilla
9-inch baked pastry shell or graham cracker shell

Mix dry ingredients with a little of the milk. Add rest of milk. Cook over boiling water, stirring until thick. Cover and cook 15 minutes longer, stirring occasionally.

Add a little of the hot mixture to egg yolks. Pour back and cook a few minutes longer. Add the fat and vanilla.

Pour filling into shell, cool slightly, and cover with meringue.

Bake at 350° F. (moderate oven) 12 to 15 minutes, or until brown.

6 servings.

MERINGUE

2 egg whites
¼ teaspoon salt
4 tablespoons sugar

Beat egg whites with salt until stiff. Beat in sugar slowly until smooth and glossy.

Banana cream pie.—Slice 2 bananas into the pie shell before adding the filling.

Coconut cream pie.—Add ½ cup shredded coconut to cream filling; turn into a baked pie shell. Top with meringue and sprinkle with coconut. Bake as for cream pie.

Chocolate cream pie.—Make filling as for cream pie, adding ½ cup milk, ¼ cup sugar, and 2½ squares chocolate. Melt chocolate in milk. Top with meringue and bake, or serve plain or with whipped cream.

BANANA PUDDING

4 cups milk
½ cup sugar
⅛ teaspoon salt
4 eggs, separated
1 teaspoon vanilla
Vanilla wafers or other cookies
Bananas

Heat the milk, sugar, and salt in a double boiler. Beat the egg yolks slightly, and slowly add some of the heated milk.

Pour back into the double boiler, and stir constantly until the custard coats the spoon. Remove at once from the heat, place the pan in a bowl of cold water, and stir the custard occasionally as it cools. Add the vanilla.

In the bottom of a greased 2-quart baking dish, put a layer of vanilla wafers or cookies, slice over them a layer of banana, and add some of the custard. Repeat until the dish is about three-quarters full.

Make a meringue of the whites of the eggs, using 2 tablespoons of sugar for each egg white. Spread over the pudding and bake for about 12 minutes at 350° F. (moderate oven) until lightly browned. Chill the pudding before serving. 6 servings.

BREAD OR RICE PUDDING

2 cups milk
1½ cups soft breadcrumbs or 1 cup cooked rice
1 tablespoon butter or margarine
¼ cup sugar (increase to ⅓ cup when using rice)
¼ teaspoon salt
⅓ cup raisins or nuts
2 eggs, beaten

Heat milk; add breadcrumbs or rice, and fat. Add sugar, salt, and raisins or nuts to eggs, then slowly stir in the hot milk mixture. Pour into greased baking dish, set in pan of hot water. Bake at 350° F. (moderate oven) 1 hour, or until set. 4 servings.

SPICE MILK

Ingredients for 1 serving:

4 tablespoons dry milk
⅛ teaspoon cinnamon
⅛ teaspoon nutmeg
½ teaspoon sugar
Pinch of salt
1 cup fluid milk

Ingredients for 6 servings:

1½ cups dry milk
½ teaspoon cinnamon
½ teaspoon nutmeg
1 tablespoon sugar
¼ teaspoon salt
1½ quarts fluid milk

Add dry ingredients to milk and beat, stir, or shake until smooth.

MOLASSES MILK

Ingredients for 1 serving:

4 tablespoons dry milk
Pinch of salt
1 cup fluid milk
1 tablespoon molasses

Ingredients for 6 servings:

1½ cups dry milk
¼ teaspoon salt
1½ quarts fluid milk
⅓ cup molasses

Mix dry milk and salt; mix fluid milk with molasses. Add dry ingredients to liquid and beat, stir, or shake until smooth.

PUDDING MIXES USING NONFAT DRY MILK

Pudding mixes made with nonfat dry milk can be prepared in quantity and kept on hand to be used when needed for a quick dessert.

The quantities of ingredients given for chocolate and caramel pudding mix make enough for 24 servings of pudding.

Chocolate Pudding Mix

1½ cups sugar
2½ cups nonfat dry milk
1¼ cups flour
1 teaspoon salt
¾ cup cocoa

Caramel Pudding Mix

1½ cups brown sugar, packed
2½ cups nonfat dry milk
1 teaspoon salt
1¼ cups flour

Vanilla Pudding Mix

1½ cups sugar
2½ cups nonfat dry milk
1¼ cups flour
1 teaspoon salt

To Prepare Mix

Sift the ingredients together three times.

Store in tightly covered containers in a cool place.

To Make Pudding From Mix

1¼ cups chocolate or caramel or vanilla pudding mix
2½ cups warm water
1 tablespoon butter or margarine
1 egg, beaten
¾ teaspoon vanilla

Combine the mix with the water in top of double boiler. Place over boiling water and cook until thickened, stirring constantly.

Cover and cook 10 minutes longer. Add the fat.

Remove from heat and beat half of the hot mixture into the egg. Blend slowly into the remaining hot mixture.

Cook over hot water 1 minute longer.

Remove from heat and stir in the vanilla. 6 servings.

For Variety

Add ¼ cup chopped nuts or coconut to chocolate or caramel pudding before cooling it. Or stir in ½ cup marshmallows cut in small pieces.

Meat Group

2 or More Servings Daily

BEEF, VEAL, PORK, LAMB

POULTRY, FISH, EGGS

As alternates—dry beans, dry peas, nuts

THE MINIMUM of two daily servings of foods from the meat group is easily taken care of by our usual pattern of eating. Meat, poultry, or fish, with dry beans or peas, nuts, or eggs as an occasional alternate, is commonly the main dish at our noon and evening meals. Eggs appear often on our breakfast tables, too, sometimes with ham, bacon, or sausage.

Some of our favorite main dishes are combinations of meat, poultry, or fish with vegetables, milk, or cereals—in stews, salads, creamed or scalloped dishes, and casseroles. These combinations offer many ways to get variety into meals—and they often are frugal dishes that make good use of leftovers and help balance the food budget.

Meal planning usually starts with the main dish—meat or a meat alternate—and the rest of the meal is built around it. We have suggested foods that go well with each main dish to make appetizing and satisfying meals. Breads and beverages to complete the meals are not specified.

MEAT COOKING GUIDE

Listed below are cuts of meat grouped according to the method of cooking that is generally most suitable. Broiling, pan-frying, and roasting are recommended for tender meat only. Less tender cuts are more satisfactory if braised, pot roasted, or simmered. Broiling is not recommended for fresh pork because of the long cooking the meat requires. Veal has too little fat for satisfactory broiling.

Broiling

BEEF:
    Thick steaks: Rib, sirloin, T-bone, club, porterhouse
    Patties (ground beef)

VEAL:
    Liver

LAMB:
    Chops
    Patties (ground lamb)

PORK:
    Smoked ham slices
    Canadian bacon
    Bacon

Pan-frying

BEEF:
Thin steaks: Rib, sirloin, T-bone, club, top-round
Cube steaks
Patties (ground beef)
VEAL:
Cube steaks
Patties (ground veal)
LAMB:
Chops
Patties (ground lamb)
PORK:
Smoked ham slices
Canadian bacon
Bacon
Thin steaks
Thin chops
LIVER: (beef, veal, lamb, pork)

Roasting

BEEF:
Rib, standing or rolled
Sirloin tip
Rump
VEAL:
Large loin
Leg
Shoulder
LAMB:
Loin
Leg
Shoulder
Rib
PORK:
Fresh and smoked ham
Fresh and smoked shoulder
Loin
Spareribs

Braising, pot-roasting

BEEF:
Rump
Chuck
Heel of round
Shortribs
Round steak
Flank steak
Liver
VEAL:
Round, shoulder, and rump roasts
Loin and rib chops
Cutlets

LAMB:
Shoulder cuts
Shanks
Neck slices
Breast
Shortribs
PORK:
Ham slices
Thick chops
Thick steaks
Tenderloin
Spareribs
Hocks
Liver

Simmering, stewing

BEEF:
Heel of round
Brisket
Shank
Shortribs
Corned beef
VEAL:
Shank
Riblets
Breast
LAMB:
Shanks
Neck slices
Breast
PORK:
Smoked ham
Smoked shoulder
Spareribs

ROASTS . . . BEEF, VEAL, LAMB, PORK

Place roast, fat side up, on a rack in a shallow pan. Do not add water; do not cover. Season either before or after cooking.

A guide to cooking time is given in the table. The minutes per pound are only approximate. Quality of meat, size and shape of roast, and its temperature at the start all affect the time required. If you use a meat thermometer, insert it so the bulb is at center of thickest part of meat and does not touch bone or fat. Cook meat to the temperature given in last column of table.

Timetable for Roasting Meats

Kind and cut of meat	Ready-to-cook weight pounds	Approximate roasting time at 325° F. hours	Internal temperature of meat when done ° F.
BEEF:			
Standing ribs:			
Rare	6 to 8	2 to 2½	140
Medium	6 to 8	2½ to 3	160
Well done	6 to 8	3⅓ to 4½	170
Rolled rib:			
Rare	4 to 6	2 to 3	140
Medium	4 to 6	2½ to 3¼	160
Well done	4 to 6	3 to 4	170
Rolled rump	5	3 to 3¼	160 to 170
Sirloin tip	3	2 to 2¼	160 to 170
VEAL:			
Leg	5 to 8	2½ to 3½	170 to 180
Loin	5	3	170 to 180
Rolled shoulder	3 to 5	3 to 3½	170 to 180
LAMB:			
Leg	6 to 7	3¼ to 4	180
Shoulder	3 to 6	2¼ to 3¼	180
Rolled shoulder	3 to 5	2½ to 3	180
PORK, FRESH:			
Loin	3 to 5	3 to 4	185
Shoulder	5 to 8	3½ to 5	185
Ham, whole	10 to 14	5½ to 6	185
Ham, half	6	4	185
Spareribs	3	2	185
PORK, CURED:[1]			
Ham, whole	12 to 16	3½ to 4¼	160
Ham, half	6	2½	160
Picnic shoulder	6	3½	170

[1] For fully cooked, ready-to-eat hams and shoulders follow directions on package.

POT ROAST OF BEEF

Select 4 to 5 pounds of beef—chuck, rump, or round.

Rub the meat with salt, pepper, and flour, and brown on all sides in a little hot fat in a deep heavy pan.

Slip a low rack under meat to keep it from sticking to pan. Add ½ cup water; cover pan closely.

Cook slowly over low heat until done—about 3 hours. Add more water as needed.

During the last hour, cook vegetables with meat—quartered potatoes, onions, and whole carrots.

Make gravy with the liquid.

Menu Suggestion

Serve with the vegetables, lettuce wedges, and peach or other fruit shortcake.

BROILED STEAK

Choose a steak 1 to 2 inches thick, of high-quality beef.

Slash the fat at the edges of the meat to prevent curling.

Preheat broiler. Grease broiler rack lightly.

Place steak on rack so that top of meat is 2 to 3 inches below source of heat—3 inches if the steak is to be cooked well done. Leave oven door open when using an electric range.

Broil the steak until top side is well browned, season, then turn and brown the other side. (Stick fork into fat, not lean, when turning.)

Broiling time for steaks.—The table below is a guide to broiling time. Only approximate times can be given, because much depends on the broiler, personal preference in doneness of meat, and the meat itself.

	Total time
Steak	*(minutes)*
1 inch thick:	
Rare _____	About 10
Medium _____	About 15
Well done_____	20 to 25
1½ inches thick:	
Rare _____	About 15
Medium _____	About 20
Well done_____	25 to 30
2 inches thick:	
Rare _____	About 25
Medium _____	About 35
Well done_____	45 to 50

Menu Suggestion

Serve with baked potatoes and chopped spinach. For dessert have fruit cup and coconut-frosted cake.

PAN-BROILED LAMB CHOPS

Loin, rib, or shoulder chops may be used.

Heat a heavy fry pan very hot and grease lightly. Lay chops in pan and brown quickly on both sides. Turn thick chops on edge to brown the fat. Reduce heat and cook slowly, turning often. Do not add water and do not cover. From time to time pour off excess fat.

Chops ¾ to 1 inch thick take 10 to 15 minutes to cook.

Menu Suggestion

Serve with creamed potatoes, beets, tossed green salad, and have cupcakes for dessert.

BRAISED CHOPS

Sprinkle chops (veal, lamb, or pork) with salt, pepper, and flour. Brown in a little fat or oil in a fry pan. Cover and cook over low heat ¾ to 1 hour.

Make gravy with the drippings or pour the drippings over the chops on the platter.

Menu Suggestion

Serve with mashed potatoes or sweetpotatoes, spanish snap beans, and fruit upside-down cake.

BROWN BEEF STEW

1 pound boneless stew beef, cut in 1-inch cubes
Flour
Salt and pepper
Fat or oil
1½ cups water
3 potatoes, diced
2 onions, sliced
3 carrots, diced
1 cup raw snap beans

Roll meat in flour which has been mixed with salt and pepper. Brown in a little fat.

Add water, cover, and simmer until almost tender—2 to 3 hours.

Add vegetables and continue to simmer, covered, until vegetables are done. Stir occasionally.

4 servings.

Green-tomato stew. — Use ½ chopped onion in place of sliced ones. Brown with the meat. Use 2 medium-sized green tomatoes, quartered, instead of beans.

Lamb or veal stew.—Use breast or

neck of lamb or veal in place of beef and ½ cup diced turnips instead of beans.

Quick stew with hamburger.—Use hamburger in place of stew meat. Brown the meat, add vegetables and water and simmer. The stew will be done in half an hour or less.

Menu Suggestion

Serve with coleslaw or green salad, and a baked pear or peach for dessert.

BRAISED VEAL SHOULDER

3 to 5 pounds boned and rolled veal
    shoulder
Salt, pepper, flour
Fat or oil

Rub meat with salt, pepper, and flour. Brown on all sides in a little hot fat.

Place meat on a rack in a deep pan. Cover pan.

Cook in oven at 350° F. (moderate) about 2½ hours.

Make gravy with drippings.

Menu Suggestion

Serve with mashed potatoes and gravy, peas, jellied fruit salad, and ice cream for dessert.

MEAT LOAF

2 pounds ground beef or veal
½ pound sausage or salt pork
½ cup chopped onion
¼ cup chopped celery
¼ cup chopped parsley
1 cup soft breadcrumbs
1 cup milk or canned or cooked tomatoes
1 egg, beaten
1 teaspoon salt
Pepper

Mix all ingredients together thoroughly. If salt pork is used, cut it in small pieces and fry until lightly browned before adding to the other ingredients.

477248°—59——35

Mold mixture into a loaf. Place on tough paper or foil on rack in uncovered pan.

Bake at 350° F. (moderate oven) 1½ to 2 hours. Serve hot or cold.

8 to 10 servings.

Menu Suggestion

Serve with scalloped potatoes, tomato jelly salad, and have apricot pudding for dessert.

CURRIED MEAT

1 cup chopped celery and tops
1 tablespoon chopped onion
2 tablespoons fat or oil
2 cups chopped cooked lamb, pork, or veal
¾ cup brown gravy
⅛ to ½ teaspoon curry powder
Salt to taste

Lightly brown celery and onion in the fat.

Add meat, gravy, and seasonings. Heat, stirring to keep from sticking. If dry, add a little boiling water.

4 servings.

Menu Suggestion

Serve with rice, spinach, crisp vegetable salad, and fruit cobbler.

SWISS STEAK

1 pound beef or veal rump or round, cut
    about 1 inch thick
Salt and pepper
Flour
Fat or oil
2 cups cooked or canned tomatoes or
    tomato juice

Season meat with salt and pepper, sprinkle with flour. Pounding helps make the meat tender.

Cut meat into serving pieces and brown in a little fat.

Add tomatoes or juice, cover, and

simmer gently until meat is tender—about 1½ hours.

4 servings.

Swiss steak with brown gravy.—Use water instead of tomatoes. When done, remove meat. Add water if needed to make 1 cup total liquid, and if necessary thicken with flour blended with cold water.

Swiss steak, onion gravy.—Add 2 cups sliced onions to swiss steak with brown gravy during the last half hour of cooking.

Menu Suggestion

Serve with mashed potatoes, corn, lettuce salad, and prune whip.

HAM WITH SWEETPOTATOES

1-pound slice of ham
2 medium sweetpotatoes, pared
2 tablespoons brown sugar
1 cup hot water

Cut ham in serving pieces and brown lightly in a fry pan.

Place the ham in a baking dish. Slice the sweetpotatoes over it, and sprinkle with sugar.

Add water to drippings, pour over sweetpotatoes. Cover.

Bake at 350° F. (moderate oven) about 45 minutes, basting occasionally with the liquid. Remove cover to brown for the last 15 minutes.

4 servings.

Menu Suggestion

Serve with broccoli, crisp celery, and a fruit chiffon pie.

HAM WITH NOODLES

1½ cups cooked noodles
2 cups ground cooked ham
2 cups thin white sauce
Bread or cracker crumbs mixed with melted butter or margarine

Place half the noodles in a greased

baking dish or pan and top with half the ham. Add another layer of noodles and ham.

Pour white sauce over mixture. Top with crumbs.

Bake at 350° F. (moderate oven) 20 minutes.

4 servings.

For variety.—Use cooked macaroni or spaghetti in place of noodles.

Menu Suggestion

Serve with asparagus or snap beans, a tossed green salad, and berry pie.

HAM TIMBALE

2 cups ground cooked ham
1 cup medium white sauce
2 eggs, beaten
¼ teaspoon powdered dry mustard

Mix all ingredients and pour into shallow greased baking dish. Place dish in pan of hot water.

Bake at 350° F. (moderate oven) about 50 minutes, or until mixture is firm in center.

4 servings.

Menu Suggestion

Serve with baked squash, coleslaw, and cooked dried fruit.

FRIED LIVER AND BACON

1 pound liver, sliced (beef, calf, lamb, or pork)
Salt, pepper, flour
8 slices bacon

Remove skin and heavy blood vessels from liver. To make the flavor of lamb or pork liver more mild, you may want to scald it—that is, pour boiling water over it and drain.

Cook bacon over low heat, turning often, until brown and crisp. Drain on paper; keep hot.

Sprinkle liver with salt, pepper, and flour.

Cook in the bacon fat at moderate heat until lightly browned on one side. Turn and brown on the other side. Do not add water and do not cover. Slices ½-inch thick take about 5 minutes. Take care not to overcook.

4 servings.

Menu Suggestion

Serve with creamed potatoes, panned kale, relishes, and cherry cobbler.

LIVER LOAF

1½ pounds liver
2 tablespoons fat or oil
¼ cup chopped onion
¼ cup chopped celery
¼ pound pork sausage
1 teaspoon salt
1 cup soft breadcrumbs, mashed potatoes, or cooked rice
1 egg, beaten
About ⅔ cup milk or canned tomatoes

Brown the liver lightly in the fat. Chop fine.

Brown the onion and celery in the fat and add to the liver. Add the rest of the ingredients, using just enough milk or tomatoes to moisten the mixture well.

Pack firmly into a loaf pan. Bake at 350° F. (moderate oven) 1½ to 2 hours.

6 to 8 servings.

Menu Suggestion

Serve the loaf with spanish sauce, buttered carrots, tossed green salad, and ice cream or fruit gelatin.

SPANISH SAUCE

2 tablespoons chopped onion
2 tablespoons fat or oil
1 tablespoon flour
2 cups cooked tomatoes
½ cup chopped celery
½ cup chopped green pepper
Salt and pepper

Brown the onion in the fat and blend in the flour. Add the other ingredients and cook about 20 minutes, or until rather thick.

BRAISED STUFFED CALF'S HEART

2 calves' hearts (½ pound each)
Stuffing made with 2 or 3 cups breadcrumbs
Fat or oil
½ cup water

Wash the hearts and make a slit to the center cavities. Remove gristle and blood vessels.

Fill hearts with stuffing and sew up slit.

Brown hearts on all sides in a little fat. Place in a baking dish or pan, add water, and cover closely.

Cook in oven at 300° F. (slow) until tender—about 1½ hours.

4 servings.

Braised stuffed beef heart.—Prepare as above, but cook about 4 hours.

8 servings.

Menu Suggestion

Serve with glazed carrots, lettuce wedges, and apple crisp.

RABBIT IN BARBECUE SAUCE

Rabbit (about 3 pounds ready-to-cook) cut in serving pieces
Flour, salt, pepper
3 tablespoons fat or oil
Barbecue sauce (see recipe on next page)

Roll rabbit in mixture of flour, salt, and pepper. Heat the fat and brown rabbit on all sides over moderate heat (about 20 minutes). Pour sauce over rabbit; cover pan.

Bake at 325° F. (slow oven) about 45 minutes, or until meat is tender. Uncover pan and place under broiler. Broil 15 minutes, or until meat is brown.

6 servings.

BARBECUE SAUCE

2 tablespoons brown sugar
1 tablespoon paprika
1 teaspoon salt
1 teaspoon powdered dry mustard
1/4 teaspoon chili powder
2 tablespoons worcestershire sauce
1 cup tomato juice
1/4 cup chili sauce or catsup
1/4 cup vinegar
1/2 cup chopped onion

Combine ingredients and cook over low heat 15 minutes.

Menu Suggestion

Serve with parsley potatoes, snap beans, and blueberry cobbler.

RABBIT FRICASSEE WITH VEGETABLES

Rabbit (about 3 pounds ready-to-cook) cut in serving pieces
Flour, salt, pepper
1/3 cup fat or oil
2 cups hot water
4 cups raw vegetables—peas and coarsely chopped carrots, onions, and celery
1 teaspoon salt
1/4 cup flour

Roll rabbit in mixture of flour, salt, and pepper.

Heat fat and brown the rabbit slowly, turning often. Add water and cover pan.

Cook slowly on top of range about 1 hour, or until rabbit is almost tender. Add water if needed during cooking. Add vegetables and salt and cook about 20 minutes longer, or until vegetables are done.

Or, after browning, bake rabbit at 325° F. (slow oven) about 1½ hours, add vegetables, and bake about 30 minutes longer.

Mix the 1/4 cup flour with a little cold water, add a few tablespoons of hot liquid from the pan, and stir the mixture into the liquid in pan. Cook 15 minutes longer, or until sauce is smooth and thick.

8 servings.

To fricassee a smaller rabbit (about 2 pounds ready-to-cook), use 1/4 cup fat for browning, and half the quantity of the other ingredients in the recipe above. Cooking time on top of range before adding vegetables is about 30 minutes; in oven, about 45 minutes.

4 servings.

Menu Suggestion

Serve with avocado-grapefruit salad on lettuce, and apple pie.

ROASTING POULTRY

Prepare the bird and ingredients for the stuffing a day in advance, if you like, and keep in the refrigerator overnight, but do not stuff the bird until time to roast it.

Sprinkle inside of bird with salt. Stuff body and neck cavities loosely. Hold stuffing in at tail with cord laced across poultry pins.

Tie chicken or turkey legs to tail, legs of duck or goose close to body.

Fold loose neck skin toward back; fasten with poultry pins. Fold wing tips back of heavy wing bone.

Brush skin of chicken or turkey with soft fat. Ducks and geese do not need added fat.

Place bird breast side up on rack in shallow pan. Or start a heavy bird (18 pounds or over) breast down and turn when half done for more even cooking. Always roast a goose breast side up.

To prevent overbrowning cover bird loosely with aluminum foil or with a thin cloth moistened with melted fat. Do not cover pan; do not add water.

Salt the giblets, seal in aluminum foil, and roast along with the bird. Or simmer them in salted water until tender.

Cook at 325° F. (slow oven) according to the Roasting Guide.

Baste a chicken or turkey several times with drippings or melted fat.

Roasting Guide

Kind of bird	Ready-to-cook weight (Pounds)	Large bread-crumbs for stuffing (Quarts)	Approximate roasting time at 325° F. for stuffed chilled bird (Hours)
Chicken:			
Broilers or fryers	1½ to 2½	¼ to ½	1¼ to 2
Roasters	2½ to 4½	½ to 1¼	2 to 3½
Duck	3 to 5	½ to 1	2½ to 3
Goose	4 to 8	¾ to 1½	2¾ to 3½
	8 to 14	1½ to 2½	3½ to 5
Turkey:			
Fryers or roasters (very young birds)	4 to 8	1 to 2	3 to 4½
Roasters (fully grown young birds)	6 to 12	2 to 3	3½ to 5
	12 to 16	3 to 4	5 to 6
	16 to 20	4 to 5	6 to 7½
	20 to 24	5 to 6	7½ to 9

Ducks and geese are fat enough to need no basting.

At the half or two-thirds point of roasting, cut string to release legs of bird.

The bird is done when the leg joints move easily and the flesh on the leg feels soft and pliable when pressed with the fingers.

BREAD STUFFING

The recipe for bread stuffing given below is based on 1 quart of ½-inch crumbs cut or torn from the loaf or from sliced bread. For the number of quarts to use for a bird the size you are cooking, see the Roasting Guide. Then multiply each ingredient in the recipe by this number.

⅓ cup butter, margarine, or poultry fat
¾ cup chopped celery
3 tablespoons chopped parsley
2 tablespoons chopped onion
1 quart breadcrumbs
½ teaspoon savory seasoning
½ to ¾ teaspoon salt
Pepper to taste

Melt the fat in fry pan, add celery,

parsley, and onion, and cook a few minutes.

Add to crumbs with the seasoning. Mix lightly but well.

Oyster stuffing.—Omit celery and reduce parsley and onion to 1 tablespoon each. Add ½ pint oysters, heated in their own liquid and drained.

Nut stuffing.—Omit parsley and savory seasoning and add ½ cup chopped nut meats—pecans, roasted almonds, filberts, or cooked chestnuts.

BROILED CHICKEN

Plump young chicken, about 1½ to 2¼ pounds ready-to-cook
Melted fat or oil
Salt and pepper

Split the bird down the back and, if desired, cut into halves through the breastbone. Break joints and cut off wing tips.

Brush chicken on both sides with melted fat, sprinkle with salt and pepper.

Preheat the broiler and grease broiler rack lightly. Place chicken on the rack, skin side down, with highest part 4 to 5 inches from the heat.

Turn the bird as it browns so that

it will cook evenly. Baste often with the pan drippings or other melted fat. Cook until well done—35 to 45 minutes.

Ovenbaked chicken.—Prepare the chicken as for broiling and bake at 400° F. (hot oven) 45 minutes to 1 hour. Turn once during cooking.

Menu Suggestion

Serve it with broiled tomatoes, creamed potatoes, and lemon sponge.

For broiled tomatoes, brush cut sides of tomato halves with melted fat, season with salt and pepper, and broil with chicken for the last 10 to 15 minutes.

FRIED CHICKEN

Plump young chicken, 1½ to 3 pounds ready-to-cook
Salt, pepper, flour
Fat or oil

Cut chicken in serving pieces. Season with salt and pepper and roll in flour.

Heat fat (about ½ inch deep) in a heavy fry pan.

Put the thickest pieces of chicken in the fat first. Do not crowd—leave enough space for the fat to come up around each piece.

Cook slowly, turning often. Do not cover pan. The thickest pieces will take from 20 to 35 minutes to cook.

After the pieces have been browned, cooking may be finished in a moderate oven (350° F.) if more convenient.

French-fried chicken.—Cut a young chicken (about 1¾ pounds ready-to-cook weight) in quarters or smaller pieces. Dip in thin batter made with 1 cup sifted flour, 1 egg, ¾ cup milk, and ½ teaspoon salt.

Heat fat in a deep pan to 365° F. Fry chicken, a few pieces at a time, 10 to 15 minutes.

Serve with mashed potatoes, carrots, and green salad. For dessert have pumpkin chiffon pie.

STEWED CHICKEN WITH DUMPLINGS

Plump stewing chicken, 3 to 4 pounds ready-to-cook
Hot water
¼ cup flour
Salt and pepper

Cut chicken in serving pieces. Put in pan and add hot water just to cover. Season lightly with salt.

Cook over low heat until chicken is tender—3 to 4 hours. Remove pieces of chicken from the broth and keep them hot.

Skim fat from broth and blend ⅓ cup of it with the flour.

Measure broth and add water if needed to make 1 quart.

Stir flour mixture into broth and cook until slightly thickened. Season to taste with salt and pepper.

5 or 6 servings.

CHICKEN OR TURKEY NOODLE SCALLOP

3 cups medium white sauce
¼ cup finely minced onion
3 cups cooked noodles (6-ounce package)
½ cup cooked or canned peas
2 cups diced cooked chicken or turkey
½ cup grated cheese
Bread or cracker crumbs mixed with melted butter or margarine

Use chicken or turkey broth, if available, as part of the liquid in the white sauce. Add onion to sauce.

Place layers of noodles, peas, turkey, cheese, and sauce in a greased baking dish. Sprinkle crumbs over top.

Brown at 400° F. (hot oven) about 20 minutes or until sauce starts to bubble through crumbs.

8 servings.

For variety.—Use cooked spaghetti or macaroni in place of noodles.

Menu Suggestion

Serve with broccoli with brown butter and have cherry crisp for dessert.

DUMPLINGS

¾ cup sifted flour
2½ teaspoons baking powder
½ teaspoon salt
1 egg
⅓ cup milk

Sift flour, baking powder, and salt together.

Beat egg, add milk, and mix with the dry ingredients.

Drop by small spoonfuls on boiling chicken gravy, cover tightly, and cook 15 minutes. Do not remove the cover while the dumplings are cooking, for if the steam escapes they will not be light.

Menu Suggestion

Serve with broccoli or other green vegetable, jellied vegetable salad, date-and-nut pudding.

CREAMED CHICKEN OR TURKEY

3 tablespoons chicken or turkey fat, butter, or margarine
1 tablespoon chopped green pepper
¼ cup flour
1 cup chicken or turkey broth
1 cup milk
2 cups diced cooked chicken or turkey, or an equal amount in large pieces
¾ teaspoon salt

Heat the fat and cook the green pepper in it until tender.

Blend the flour into the fat and vegetable mixture. Stir in the broth and milk and cook to a smooth sauce, stirring constantly.

Add chicken or turkey to sauce and season with salt.

Heat the mixture thoroughly and serve on rice, toast, or biscuits.

4 servings.

For variety.—Use only 1½ cups chicken or turkey. Add ½ cup mushrooms browned in fat and ½ cup cooked celery or green peas.

BAKED TURKEY OR CHICKEN HASH

2 cups finely chopped cooked turkey or chicken
2 cups finely chopped raw potatoes
2 tablespoons chopped green pepper
¾ cup finely chopped onion
1½ teaspoons salt
Pepper
½ cup turkey or chicken broth or water

Mix all ingredients together. Place in a shallow greased baking dish or pan. Cover.

Bake at 350° F. (moderate oven) about 1 hour, removing cover during last half hour for browning.

4 servings.

Menu Suggestion

Serve with grilled tomatoes, head lettuce with Thousand Island dressing, and pineapple tapioca pudding.

TURKEY OR CHICKEN PIE

1½ cups chopped cooked turkey or chicken
¼ cup cooked diced celery
2 tablespoons finely minced onion
¾ cup cooked diced carrots
¼ cup canned or cooked peas
1½ cups turkey or chicken gravy
Unbaked pastry

Place turkey or chicken, vegetables, and sauce in layers in shallow baking dish or in four individual baking dishes.

Bake at 425° F. (hot oven) 20 minutes or until hot through. Meanwhile, cut pastry into four circles or other designs and bake 12 to 15 minutes on baking sheet.

Place baked pastries on top of pie and serve.

One cup seasoned mashed potatoes may be used in place of pastry. Add potatoes in ring around edge of pie before baking.

4 servings.

TURKEY OR CHICKEN SALAD LOAF

¼ cup vinegar
⅓ cup salad oil
¼ teaspoon salt
Pepper
Paprika
3 cups chopped cooked turkey or chicken
2 tablespoons unflavored gelatin
½ cup cold water
2½ cups hot broth
½ teaspoon salt
½ cup cooked or canned peas
6 stuffed olives, sliced
1 teaspoon onion juice
½ cup finely chopped celery

Mix first five ingredients and pour over turkey or chicken. Let stand in refrigerator 1 to 2 hours, stirring occasionally.

Sprinkle gelatin on cold water, let soak a few minutes, then dissolve it in hot broth. Add salt. Cool until partially thickened.

Combine drained turkey, peas, olives, onion juice, and celery with the gelatin mixture. Pour into a loaf pan and chill until firm.

Unmold and serve on lettuce or other salad greens.

Menu Suggestion

Serve with baked stuffed potatoes, sliced tomatoes, and fresh or frozen peaches and sugar cookies.

BROILED FISH

1 pound fish fillets or steaks or small dressed fish
Salt and pepper
3 to 4 tablespoons melted fat or oil

Preheat broiler.

Cut fillets or steaks into serving pieces; split dressed fish down the back. Sprinkle with salt and pepper.

Grease broiler rack lightly. Place fish on rack, skin side up. Brush with melted fat.

Place rack 2 to 3 inches from heat. Broil fish 5 to 8 minutes or until brown. Baste with fat. Turn, baste other side, and broil until brown.

4 servings.

Menu Suggestion

Serve with rice, spinach, grapefruit salad, and have jellyroll for dessert.

PAN-FRIED FISH

1 pound fish fillets or steaks or small dressed fish
Salt and pepper
Flour
1 tablespoon water
1 egg, beaten
Fine bread or cracker crumbs or cornmeal
Fat or oil

Cut fillets or steaks in serving pieces; leave small fish whole. Season on both sides with salt and pepper. Roll in flour.

Add water to egg. Dip fish in egg mixture, then roll in crumbs or cornmeal. (Egg helps make a crisp crust but may be omitted. If not used do not flour fish before rolling it in crumbs or cornmeal.)

Heat fat—about ⅛-inch deep—in a heavy pan. Fry the fish slowly until brown on one side; turn and brown on the other side. Cooking time will be 10 minutes or more, depending on the thickness of fish.

4 servings.

French-fried fish.—Prepare fish fillets or steaks as for pan frying. Half fill a deep kettle with melted fat or oil. Heat to 375° F. Place fish in a wire frying basket and cook in the hot fat until browned—3 to 5 minutes.

Menu Suggestion

Serve with creamed potatoes, snap beans, and cucumber slices with sour cream dressing. Have gingerbread for dessert.

OVEN-FRIED FISH

1 pound fish fillets or steaks
½ cup milk
½ tablespoon salt
½ cup fine breadcrumbs
2 tablespoons melted fat or oil

Cut fish in serving pieces. Dip it in milk, with salt added, and roll in crumbs.

Place fish in a greased baking pan and pour the fat over it.

Bake at 500° F. (extremely hot oven) until fish is tender and brown—about 10 minutes.

4 servings.

Menu Suggestion

Serve with stuffed baked potatoes, baked tomatoes, apple salad, and peach cobbler.

SALMON LOAF

2 cups flaked canned or cooked salmon
3 tablespoons fat or oil
3 tablespoons flour
1 cup milk and salmon liquid
Salt and pepper
2 tablespoons finely chopped parsley
2 cups soft bread cubes
1 egg, beaten

Drain canned salmon, saving the liquid.

Make sauce: Heat fat, blend in flour. Add enough milk to the salmon liquid to make 1 cup, and stir into the flour mixture. Cook until thickened, stirring constantly. Season.

Mix the sauce with the other ingredients. Form into loaf.

Bake in uncovered pan at 350° F. (moderate oven) about half an hour, or until brown.

4 servings.

For variety.—To give extra flavor to salmon loaf, add ½ cup coarsely chopped sweet pickle and 1 teaspoon grated onion to mixture before baking.

Use cod, haddock, or tuna in place of the salmon.

BAKED STUFFED FISH

3- or 4-pound dressed fish
1½ teaspoons salt
Bread stuffing made with 1 quart crumbs
4 tablespoons melted fat or oil
3 slices bacon, if desired

Wash and dry the fish. Sprinkle inside and out with salt.

Fill body cavity of fish loosely with stuffing. Sew the opening with needle and cord or close with skewers.

Place fish in greased pan; brush with fat. Lay bacon over top.

Bake at 350° F. (moderate oven) 40 to 60 minutes.

6 to 8 servings.

Menu Suggestion

Serve with tartar sauce, scalloped potatoes, peas and celery, and tossed green salad. Baked apples make a good dessert.

FISH SHORTCAKE

2 to 3 tablespoons chopped onion
2 tablespoons fat or oil
4 tablespoons flour
2 cups milk
⅓ cup grated cheese
1½ cups flaked cooked or canned fish
Salt and pepper to taste
Hot biscuits or cornbread

Cook onion slowly in the fat until tender. Blend in the flour. Add milk slowly, stirring constantly, and cook until the sauce is thickened.

Add cheese and fish. Season with salt and pepper.

Heat the mixture through, stirring occasionally. Serve on hot biscuits or cornbread.

4 servings.

Menu Suggestion

Serve with broccoli and stuffed tomato salad, with upside-down cake for dessert.

FISH PATTIES

1½ cups flaked cooked or canned fish
1½ cups mashed potatoes
1 tablespoon finely chopped onion
½ teaspoon salt
1 egg
Pepper
Flour
Fat or oil

Combine all ingredients except flour and fat.

Shape mixture into patties, roll in flour, and brown in fat.

4 servings.

Menu Suggestion

Serve with pickled beets, a green vegetable, celery, and for dessert molded cornstarch pudding with a sauce of cooked dried apricots.

JELLIED TUNA SALAD

1 tablespoon unflavored gelatin
¼ cup cold water
½ teaspoon salt
½ teaspoon celery seed
¼ cup vinegar
¼ cup water
2 eggs, beaten
2 cups flaked canned tuna (or other canned or cooked fish)

Sprinkle gelatin on cold water and let soak a few minutes.

Add seasonings, vinegar, and water to eggs. Cook over boiling water until thickened, stirring constantly.

Add gelatin and stir until it is dissolved.

Add fish and mix thoroughly. Pour into individual molds or large ring mold and chill.

4 servings.

Menu Suggestion

Serve with scalloped potatoes with chives, cooked carrots, and have floating island with a topping of a bright, tart jelly for dessert.

EGGS . . . IN SHELL, POACHED, FRIED, BAKED

Eggs cooked in shell.—Wash eggs, put them in a pan; cover completely with cold water.

For soft-cooked eggs, heat water slowly to simmering. Cover pan and remove from heat. Let stand 3 to 5 minutes, the longer time for larger number of eggs.

For hard-cooked eggs, bring water to simmering and simmer 20 to 25 minutes. Do not let the water boil. Serve the eggs hot or plunge them at once into cold water until cold.

Poached eggs.—Have salted water boiling gently in a shallow pan. Break eggs into a saucer, one at a time, and slip them into the water.

Reheat water to simmering, take pan from heat, and cover. Let stand 5 minutes, or until eggs are firm.

Fried eggs.—Heat fat in a fry pan. Break eggs into a saucer, then slip them into the fat. Sprinkle with salt and pepper. Cook over low heat, basting with the fat, until whites are firm.

Or, if you prefer eggs with less fat, use this "fry-poach" method. Melt a little fat in a fry pan—just enough to grease the bottom—and keep over low heat. Add eggs one at a time, pour in 2 or 3 tablespoons of water, cover pan tightly, and steam until eggs are done.

Baked eggs.—Break eggs into a shallow greased baking dish. Add 1 tablespoon milk for each egg and dot with fat. Sprinkle with salt and pepper. Cover the pan.

Bake at 325° F. (slow oven) 20 to 25 minutes, or until eggs are firm.

FRENCH OMELET

4 eggs
½ teaspoon salt
Pepper
¼ cup milk
2 tablespoons butter or margarine

Beat eggs until well mixed. Blend in salt, pepper, and milk.

Melt the fat in a hot fry pan, pour in the egg mixture, and place over moderate heat. As the omelet cooks, lift edges toward center and tip pan so that the uncooked mixture flows under the cooked portion.

When bottom is brown, fold one half over the other. Serve immediately.

For variety.—Spread tart jelly or browned mushrooms on half of the omelet just before folding.

Menu Suggestion

Serve with creamed potatoes, lettuce salad, and cherry or berry pie.

HOT DEVILED EGGS

2 tablespoons butter or margarine
½ green pepper, chopped fine
⅓ cup celery, chopped fine
1 small onion, chopped fine
1 tablespoon flour
1⅓ cups cooked or canned tomatoes
1 teaspoon salt
1 teaspoon worcestershire sauce
2 drops tabasco sauce
⅔ cup cold milk
6 hard-cooked eggs, sliced
Bread or cracker crumbs, mixed with melted butter or margarine

Heat the fat and cook chopped vegetables in it until they are tender. Blend in the flour.

Add tomatoes and seasonings and cook until thickened, stirring constantly.

Stir the hot tomato mixture into the milk and carefully add the eggs.

Turn into a greased baking dish and top with crumbs. Dot with butter or margarine and bake at 375° F. (moderate oven) until the crumbs are brown and the mixture is hot, about 10 to 15 minutes. 4 servings.

For variety.—Instead of adding crumbs and baking the deviled egg mixture, serve it on toast or in patty shells.

Menu Suggestion

Serve with spinach or other green vegetable, mashed potatoes, and have fruit pie with cheese for dessert.

EGG AND POTATO SCRAMBLE

2 slices bacon
4 medium-sized potatoes, sliced thin
1 teaspoon salt
4 eggs, beaten
¼ cup milk
Pepper

Fry bacon slices and remove from fry pan.

Fry potatoes in the fat until they are well browned, sprinkling with salt as browning starts.

Cover pan closely. Cook over low heat until potatoes are tender.

Combine eggs, milk, and pepper. Pour over potatoes in pan and cook slowly, stirring occasionally, until eggs are set.

Crumble bacon slices and add just before removing pan from heat. Serve at once.

For variety.—Bits of cooked ham, chipped beef, or any cooked meats may be used in place of the bacon in this recipe. Thin slices of sausages or chopped chicken livers are especially good. Fry the potatoes in bacon fat or other meat drippings when omitting the bacon.

Small cubes of cheese or flakes of smoked fish are other welcome additions with their own distinctive flavors.

Menu Suggestion

Serve with scalloped tomatoes or eggplant, spinach or kale, pear and cottage cheese salad, cookies.

BOSTON BAKED BEANS

2 cups navy beans
1½ quarts cold water
¼ pound salt pork
4 tablespoons molasses
1 to 2 teaspoons salt
½ teaspoon powdered dry mustard
Hot water

Boil beans in the water for 2 minutes. Remove from heat and let soak 1 hour, or overnight if more convenient.

Boil soaked beans gently in the same water for 45 minutes or until they begin to soften.

Make cuts through rind of the pork about ½ inch apart. Put half the pork in a bean pot or deep baking dish. Add beans and bury rest of the pork in them, exposing only the scored rind.

Mix molasses, salt, and mustard with a little hot water. Pour over the beans, and add enough hot water to cover beans. Cover bean pot.

Bake at 250° F. (very slow oven) 6 or 7 hours; add a little hot water from time to time. Uncover for the last hour to let the beans brown on top.

Or if you want to shorten the baking time, bake the beans at 350° F. (moderate oven). At this temperature about 2½ hours will be required.

6 to 8 servings.

Menu Suggestion

Serve with frankfurters or cold cuts, brown bread, and a vegetable relish plate, with fresh fruit for dessert.

LIMA BEANS
IN TOMATO SAUCE

1 cup dry lima beans
3 cups water
¾ teaspoon salt
4 slices bacon
½ cup chopped onion
1 cup cooked or canned tomatoes

Boil beans in the water for 2 minutes. Remove from heat and let soak 1 hour, or overnight if more convenient.

Add ½ teaspoon salt to the beans and boil gently 45 minutes. Drain.

Chop bacon and brown it with the onion in fry pan. Add beans, tomatoes, and rest of salt.

Boil gently until beans are tender— about 30 minutes, stirring occasionally to keep from sticking. Add a little more water or tomato if the mixture gets too dry.

4 servings.

Menu Suggestion

Serve with peanut butter biscuits, tossed green salad with cottage or other cheese, and ice cream.

BROILED BEAN SANDWICHES

4 slices bread
2 cups baked beans
4 large slices fresh tomato
4 strips bacon

Toast one side of bread under broiler. Spread beans on untoasted side; top with tomato and bacon.

Return to broiler for a few minutes, until bacon is crisp and beans are heated through. 4 servings.

For variety.—Omit bacon; top beans with a slice of cheese and lay slice of tomato on top. Broil until cheese melts and beans are heated.

Menu Suggestion

Serve with raw spinach salad and baked chocolate custard.

SPLIT PEA OR LENTIL SOUP

1 cup dry split peas or lentils
6 cups boiling water
Ham bone
1 small onion, chopped
Salt and pepper

Add peas or lentils to the water with ham bone and onion. Boil gently about 3 hours—until of consistency desired for soup.

Remove ham bone. If lentils are used, press soup through a coarse sieve to remove skins. Remove meat from bone; chop meat and return it to the soup. Season and reheat.

If there is little or no meat from the bone, garnish bowls of soup with thin slices of frankfurters or bologna, or add ½ cup ground peanuts before reheating the soup. 4 servings.

Menu Suggestion

Serve with fruit and cottage cheese salad and raisin-rice pudding.

PEANUT-STUFFED PEPPERS

4 green peppers
1 tablespoon melted butter or margarine
⅓ cup uncooked rice
3 tablespoons finely chopped onion
¼ cup chopped celery
1 teaspoon salt
1 cup water
1⅓ cups cooked or canned tomatoes
⅔ cup chopped salted peanuts
¼ cup fine bread or cracker crumbs mixed
with
1 tablespoon melted butter or margarine

Cut out stem ends of the peppers and take out the seeds. Cook peppers 5 minutes in boiling salted water.

Combine the fat, rice, onion, celery, and salt in a fry pan.

Add water slowly as the mixture begins to cook, and simmer covered 5 to 10 minutes. Add tomatoes and simmer 10 minutes longer or until rice is almost done, adding more liquid if needed. Stir in peanuts.

Stuff peppers with the mixture and sprinkle with crumbs. Place peppers in a baking pan with a little hot water and bake at 350° F. (moderate oven) 30 to 40 minutes.

4 servings.

Menu Suggestion

Serve with 5-minute cabbage, raw carrot sticks, and cheesecake.

BAKED LIMA BEANS IN SOUR CREAM

2 cups large dry lima beans
5 cups water
¼ cup melted butter or margarine
1½ teaspoons brown sugar
2 teaspoons salt
1½ teaspoons powdered dry mustard
2 teaspoons molasses
½ cup sour cream
3 tablespoons milk
¼ teaspoon onion juice

Boil beans in the water for 2 minutes. Remove from heat and let soak 1 hour, or overnight if more convenient.

Boil beans gently until tender—about 45 minutes. Drain.

Place the beans in a baking pan or casserole.

Combine the remaining ingredients and pour the mixture over the beans.

Bake at 350° F. (moderate oven) about 1 hour. Add a little hot water during baking if the beans become dry.

6 servings.

Menu Suggestion

Serve with tossed green salad, blueberry muffins, and for dessert have ice cream with strawberries.

BEANS AND SAUSAGE MEXICAN STYLE

1½ cups dry kidney beans
5 cups water
1 pound pork sausage
1 cup chopped onion
⅓ cup chopped green pepper
¾ teaspoon minced garlic
2¼ teaspoons salt
1½ teaspoons chili powder
2 cups tomato puree
1 cup bean liquid
2 tablespoons flour

Boil beans in the water for 2 minutes. Remove from heat and let soak 1 hour, or overnight if more convenient.

Cook beans in the same water until just tender—about 1 hour. Drain and save the liquid.

Combine sausage, onion, green pepper, and garlic. Cook until light brown.

Add beans, salt, chili powder, tomato puree, and ½ cup of the bean liquid.

Blend the flour with the remaining ½ cup of bean liquid and stir into the sausage mixture.

Simmer, stirring frequently, until thickened—about 1 hour 40 minutes.

6 servings.

Menu Suggestion

Serve with rice, relishes (celery curls, carrot sticks, radishes, dill pickles), toasted french bread, and sliced peaches.

Vegetable-Fruit Group

4 or More Servings Daily, Including—

A CITRUS FRUIT OR OTHER FRUIT OR VEGETABLE
IMPORTANT FOR VITAMIN C

A DARK-GREEN OR DEEP-YELLOW VEGETABLE FOR
VITAMIN A—AT LEAST EVERY OTHER DAY

OTHER VEGETABLES AND FRUITS, INCLUDING
POTATOES

VEGETABLES AND FRUITS— fresh, frozen, canned, dried—offer the homemaker a wide range of choice in planning for the four or more servings recommended daily.

The needed serving of vitamin C-rich food is furnished much of the time in many homes by the citrus fruit or juice that is part of the breakfast pattern customary among many families. Ample variety for a serving at least every other day of a vegetable or fruit rich in vitamin A is provided by the many dark-green and deep-yellow kinds available in our markets and gardens. And there are plenty of other vegetables and fruits to choose from to make up the two or more additional servings without frequent repetition.

A cooked vegetable is a standby for serving with the main dish at the noon or evening meal. Raw vegetables in salads or on the relish plate and vegetables in stews and other combinations all count toward the day's quota, too.

Most fruits are at their best when simply prepared. Many people prefer them raw, either whole or sliced or diced and perhaps slightly sweetened, or in fruit cups and salads. Stewed and baked fruits are popular too—at breakfast, with the main course at lunch or dinner, or as dessert. For a change, there are fruit pies and puddings in wide variety.

COOKING VEGETABLES

Here are some pointers on preparing and cooking vegetables to prevent loss of nutrients:

Trim sparingly such greens as cabbage, head lettuce, chicory. Dark-green outer leaves are rich in iron, calcium, and vitamins. When you pare vegetables keep the parings thin.

Cook potatoes in their skins to get the most food value from them.

Boil vegetables in as little water as

possible. Some vitamins and minerals cook out into the water, and losses are greater when a large amount of water is used. Whenever practicable, serve any remaining cooking liquid with the vegetable or use it in sauce, gravy, or soup.

Cook vegetables only until they are tender. Overcooking lowers nutritive value—and eating quality too. Be especially careful about cooking time when using a pressure cooker, because even an extra minute or two may result in overcooking. Follow the directions that come with your cooker. For very young and tender vegetables you may be able to cut the time. Frozen vegetables require less time to cook than fresh vegetables. Cook them according to the directions on the package.

Serve cooked vegetables promptly.

CREAMED OR SCALLOPED VEGETABLES

Asparagus, lima beans, snap beans, broccoli, cabbage, carrots, cauliflower, celery, onions, peas, potatoes, spinach

For four servings use 2 cups cooked vegetable and 1 cup thin or medium white sauce.

To cream, simply mix vegetables with white sauce and heat thoroughly. Potatoes and lima beans, because they are drier than the other vegetables, may be best with the thin sauce.

To scallop cooked vegetables, combine them with white sauce in a baking dish and top with bread or cracker crumbs mixed with melted butter or margarine. Bake at 350° F. (moderate oven) until the mixture is heated through and the crumbs are browned.

GLAZED VEGETABLES

Carrots, onions, parsnips, sweetpotatoes

Blend 2 tablespoons fat or oil with ¼ cup brown sugar and 1 tablespoon water in a heavy fry pan.

For glazed carrots, parsnips, or sweetpotatoes, use cooked vegetables cut in strips or large pieces. Put the vegetable in the pan with the fat and sugar mixture. Cook over low heat, turning several times, until the sirup is very thick and the pieces are well coated—15 to 20 minutes.

For glazed onions prepare 1 quart sliced raw onions. Add them to the fat and sugar mixture and cook over low heat, turning frequently, until tender—20 to 30 minutes.

PANNED VEGETABLES

Cabbage, kale, collards, spinach, okra, or summer squash

Finely shred cabbage, kale, collards, or spinach. Slice okra or summer squash thin.

For four servings use 2 quarts spinach; 1 quart cabbage, kale, or collards; 3 cups okra or summer squash. Measure vegetable after cutting.

Heat 2 tablespoons butter, margarine, or drippings in a heavy fry pan. Add vegetables and sprinkle with salt. Cover pan to hold in steam. Cook over low heat; stir once in a while.

Cabbage will be done in 5 to 10 minutes; other vegetables take longer.

BROCCOLI WITH TART SAUCE

1 bunch broccoli (about 1 pound)
½ teaspoon salt
1½ teaspoons sugar
½ teaspoon paprika
2 tablespoons lemon juice
2 tablespoons butter or margarine
1½ teaspoons prepared horseradish

Trim off tough outer layer of large broccoli stalks and split the stalks. Cook in lightly salted boiling water about 10 minutes. Drain.

Blend salt, sugar, and paprika. Add lemon juice, fat, and horseradish. Mix well and pour over the broccoli.

4 servings.

WILTED GREENS

Melt 2 tablespoons drippings in a heavy pan. Add a little chopped onion, and cook until soft and yellow. Stir in 1/4 cup vinegar, then add 1 quart leaf lettuce or other greens washed and cut. Cover and heat a few minutes until greens are wilted. Season with salt and pepper. Serve hot.

4 servings.

CASSEROLE OF BRUSSELS SPROUTS

1 1/2 tablespoons butter or margarine
1/2 cup chopped celery
1/4 cup chopped onion
1 1/2 tablespoons flour
1/2 teaspoon salt
Pepper
1 cup cooked or canned tomatoes
1 1/2 cups cooked brussels sprouts
Fine bread or cracker crumbs mixed with melted butter or margarine

Heat the fat in a fry pan. Add the celery and onion and cook slowly until they are yellow.

Blend in the flour, salt, and pepper, and add the tomatoes. Stir and cook until the mixture is thick.

Put the brussels sprouts into a greased baking dish and add the tomato mixture. Sprinkle the crumbs over the top.

Bake at 350° F. (moderate oven) about 30 minutes.

4 servings.

SPINACH AU GRATIN

1 pound spinach, chopped fine
3 ounces cheese, grated (about 3/4 cup)
1 cup hot medium white sauce
Slices of crisped bacon
Bread or cracker crumbs mixed with melted butter or margarine

Cook the spinach a few minutes in a covered pan without added water.

Add cheese to hot white sauce and stir until melted.

Mix spinach and sauce and pour into a baking dish. Crumble the bacon over the top and sprinkle with crumbs.

Bake at 350° F. (moderate oven) until crumbs are brown—about 20 minutes.

4 servings.

STUFFED GREEN PEPPERS

4 medium-sized green peppers
2 tablespoons fat
1/4 cup chopped celery
1 cup cooked rice
1/4 cup chili sauce
2 ounces cheese, grated (about 1/2 cup)
1/4 teaspoon salt
Bread or cracker crumbs mixed with melted butter or margarine

Cut out stem ends of peppers, and remove seeds. Boil peppers 5 minutes in salted water; drain.

Heat fat and cook celery in it until tender.

Mix all ingredients.

Fill peppers with rice mixture; top with crumbs. Place in a half inch of hot water in a baking dish.

Bake at 350° F. (moderate oven) until peppers are tender and crumbs browned—about 30 minutes.

4 servings.

BAKED SQUASH

Cut acorn squash in half, Hubbard in 3- to 4-inch squares. Remove seeds. Place squash in baking pan.

Sprinkle squash with salt and brown sugar and dot with butter or margarine. Pour a little water into the pan. Cover.

Bake at 400° F. (moderate oven) until squash is partly done—about 30 minutes for acorn, 45 minutes for Hubbard.

Uncover and continue baking until squash is soft—about 20 minutes for acorn, 30 for Hubbard.

SCALLOPED SWEETPOTATOES AND ORANGES

2 large sweetpotatoes, cooked, peeled, and
  sliced
1 large orange, peeled and sliced
1 tablespoon grated orange rind
Salt
3 tablespoons sugar
2 tablespoons butter or margarine
½ cup orange juice

Place a layer of sweetpotatoes in a greased baking dish, add a layer of orange slices. Sprinkle with orange rind, salt, and sugar, and dot with fat.

Repeat until all ingredients are used. Pour orange juice over the top. Cover.

Bake at 350° F. (moderate oven) 45 minutes to 1 hour. 4 servings.

BEETS IN HONEY SAUCE

1 tablespoon cornstarch
½ teaspoon salt
1 tablespoon water or beet juice
2 tablespoons vinegar
¼ cup honey
1 tablespoon butter or margarine
2 cups diced or sliced beets, cooked or
  canned (No. 2 can)

Mix the cornstarch and salt. Blend in the water or juice from canned beets. Add vinegar, honey, and fat. Cook slowly, stirring constantly, until thickened.

Add sauce to beets; let stand at least 10 minutes to blend flavors. Reheat.

4 servings.

CRISP 5-MINUTE CABBAGE

1½ cups milk
1 quart shredded cabbage
1½ tablespoons flour
1½ tablespoons melted butter or margarine
Salt and pepper

Heat milk and add the cabbage. Simmer about 2 minutes.

Mix the flour and melted fat and add a little of the hot milk.

Stir this mixture into the cabbage, and cook 3 or 4 minutes, or until thickened, stirring constantly.

Season to taste with salt and pepper. 4 servings.

HOT SLAW

2 eggs
¼ cup water
3 tablespoons vinegar
½ teaspoon salt
¼ teaspoon powdered dry mustard
2 tablespoons sugar
Few celery seeds
1 tablespoon butter or margarine
1 pint finely shredded cabbage

Beat the eggs, add the water, vinegar, salt, mustard, sugar, and celery seeds.

Cook, stirring frequently, until thick. Add the fat.

Stir in the cabbage, and mix thoroughly with the dressing. Cover and heat a few minutes.

4 servings.

CORN PUDDING

2½ cups cream-style corn
2 eggs, beaten
1 tablespoon melted butter or margarine
½ cup milk
1 teaspoon sugar
¼ teaspoon salt
Pepper

Mix corn, eggs, fat, and milk. Add sugar, salt, and pepper.

Pour into greased baking dish and set in a pan of hot water.

Bake at 350° F. (moderate oven) until set—50 to 60 minutes.

4 servings.

Note: 1 egg and ⅔ cup soft bread-crumbs may be used instead of 2 eggs.

SPANISH SNAP BEANS

1 tablespoon fat or oil
1 tablespoon chopped onion
⅓ cup chopped green pepper
1 cup cooked or canned tomatoes
1½ cups cooked or canned snap beans
Salt and pepper
Toasted bread cubes

Heat the fat and brown the onion and green pepper in it. Add tomatoes and cook slowly about 15 minutes.

Add beans and season to taste with salt and pepper.

Heat thoroughly. Turn into serving dish and top with bread cubes.

4 servings.

BAKED TOMATOES

Wash medium-sized tomatoes, ripe or green, and cut off the stem ends.

Place tomatoes in a baking dish. Sprinkle tops with salt and pepper and bread or cracker crumbs mixed with butter or margarine. Add just enough water to cover bottom of dish.

Cover and bake at 375° F. (moderate oven) until tomatoes are soft—about 30 minutes for ripe tomatoes, 45 minutes for green.

When tomatoes are about half done, uncover the dish to brown the crumbs.

STUFFED BAKED POTATOES OR SWEETPOTATOES

Select medium-sized potatoes or sweetpotatoes. Rub with fat if soft skin is desired.

Bake at 425° F. (hot oven) until soft—35 to 60 minutes.

Cut slice off top of potato, scoop out inside. Mash potato and season with salt and butter or margarine. Add pepper and hot milk to white potatoes, brown sugar and cinnamon to sweetpotatoes.

Stuff shells with the mashed potato and put back in oven a few minutes to brown.

POTATO STRIPS WITH CHEESE

3 cups raw potato strips (cut as for french fries)
½ cup milk
1 tablespoon butter or margarine
1 teaspoon salt
Pepper
½ cup thinly shaved process cheese
1 tablespoon finely cut parsley

Put the strips into a greased baking dish and pour the milk over them. Dot with the fat and sprinkle with salt and pepper.

Cover and bake at 425° F. (hot oven) for 40 minutes, or until the potatoes are tender.

Sprinkle with cheese and parsley and bake, covered, for 5 minutes more.

4 servings.

QUICK CREAMY POTATOES

2½ cups diced raw potatoes
1 cup milk
2 tablespoons finely chopped onion
1 teaspoon salt
Pepper
1 tablespoon finely cut parsley

Combine the potatoes with the milk, onion, salt, and pepper in a heavy fry pan.

Cover and cook slowly, stirring frequently, for 20 to 30 minutes, or until the potatoes are tender and most of the milk is absorbed. If the potatoes are very mealy, more milk may be needed.

Sprinkle with the parsley before serving.

4 servings.

SCALLOPED POTATOES

3 medium-sized potatoes, pared and sliced
1 tablespoon flour
1 teaspoon salt
Pepper
1 cup hot milk
1 tablespoon butter or margarine

Put a layer of potatoes in a greased baking dish and sprinkle with some of the flour, salt, and pepper. Repeat until all the potatoes are used.

Pour milk over potatoes and dot with the fat.

Cover and bake at 350° F. (moderate oven) 30 minutes. Remove cover and continue baking until potatoes are tender—about 30 minutes. If potatoes are not brown enough on top, place the uncovered dish under the broiler for 3 to 5 minutes.

4 servings.

HOT POTATO SALAD

3 cups diced raw potatoes
4 slices bacon
¼ cup finely chopped onion
1 tablespoon flour
1 teaspoon powdered dry mustard
1 teaspoon salt
1 tablespoon sugar
½ cup water
1 egg, beaten
¼ cup vinegar

Cook potatoes in a small amount of boiling salted water until tender. Drain.

Cook bacon in a fry pan until crisp. Remove from pan and chop.

Using 2 tablespoons of the bacon fat, cook onions until golden brown.

Blend flour, mustard, salt, and sugar into the fat. Stir in the water and boil for 2 minutes.

Add about 2 tablespoons of the hot mixture to the beaten egg, then stir this into the rest of the mixture. Add vinegar and reheat.

Pour the hot dressing over the hot diced potatoes. Mix in the chopped bacon. Serve hot.

5 or 6 servings.

VEGETABLE AND FRUIT SALADS

Chill ingredients before mixing—except for molded salads.

Provide tartness in the salad ingredients or dressing.

Use salad greens other than lettuce sometimes. Have you tried chicory, escarole, endive, kale, spinach, dandelion greens, romaine, watercress, and Chinese cabbage?

Sprinkle orange, lemon, lime, or pineapple juice on fruits that may turn dark—apples, peaches, and bananas, for instance.

For tossed green salads, tear greens in fairly large pieces or cut with scissors. Larger pieces give more body to the salad.

Prevent wilting and sogginess by drying the greens used in salads, draining canned foods well before adding to salad, using just enough salad dressing to moisten. For raw vegetable salads, add dressing at the last minute.

Vegetable Salad Combinations

Grated carrots, diced celery, cucumber slices.

Spinach, endive, or lettuce, with tomato wedges.

Sliced raw cauliflower flowerets, lettuce, chopped green pepper, celery, pimiento.

Shredded cabbage, cucumber cubes, slivers of celery.

Cooked red kidney beans, thinly sliced celery, sweet onions.

Cooked cut green beans, crisp bacon bits, sweet pickles, onion rings.

Fruit and Vegetable Salad Combinations

Shredded raw carrots, diced apples, raisins.

Sliced or ground cranberries, diced celery and apples, orange sections.

Thin cucumber slices, pineapple cubes.

Avocado and grapefruit sections, tomato slices.

Shredded cabbage, orange sections, crushed pineapple.

Fruit Salad Combinations

Sliced pineapple, apricot halves, sweet red cherries.

Watermelon balls, peach slices, orange slices.

Grapefruit sections, banana slices, berries or cherries.

Grapefruit sections, unpared apple slices.

Peach slices, pear slices, halves of red plums.

Pineapple wedges, banana slices, strawberries.

Cooked dried fruit, white cherries, pineapple chunks.

STEWED DRIED APRICOTS OR PRUNES

1 pound (about 3 cups) dried apricots or prunes
1 quart water
¼ teaspoon salt
½ cup sugar
2 slices lemon, if desired.

Cover fruit with water. Let soak for an hour or two if very dry; moist dried fruit does not require soaking.

Add salt and simmer until fruit is tender—15 to 20 minutes for apricots; 25 to 30 minutes for prunes. Add sugar and lemon slices during the last 5 minutes of cooking.

12 servings.

BAKED APPLES

Core apples without cutting through the blossom end. Pare apples one-third of the way down.

Place apples in a baking dish. Sprinkle the cavities lightly with salt. Add 1 tablespoon sugar to each apple. Pour a little water into the dish to keep apples from sticking to the bottom.

Bake uncovered at 400° F. (hot oven) about 1 hour, or until apples are tender. Baste the apples with the liquid in the pan once or twice during baking.

For Variety

Fill centers of apples with chopped fresh cranberries before baking.

Fill centers with crushed pineapple before baking.

Serve baked apples with a topping of cream cheese softened with cream and beaten until fluffy.

BAKED PEACH HALVES

6 fresh peaches
½ cup brown sugar, packed
¼ cup melted butter or margarine
1½ teaspoons lemon juice, if desired

Peel peaches, cut in halves, and place in a baking pan.

Stir brown sugar into the melted fat. Add lemon juice if desired. Spoon the mixture into the peach halves.

Cover and bake at 350° F. about 30 minutes, or until peaches are tender.

6 servings.

JELLIED ORANGE-GRAPEFRUIT-AVOCADO SALAD

1 package lemon-flavored gelatin
1½ cups hot water
½ cup grapefruit juice
¼ teaspoon salt
½ cup diced grapefruit sections
½ cup diced orange sections
1½ cups diced avocado

Dissolve gelatin in hot water. Add grapefruit juice and salt. Chill until mixture begins to thicken.

Add grapefruit, orange, and avocado. Pour into individual molds and chill until firm. Unmold on salad greens. 6 servings.

FRUIT JUICE PUNCH

2 cups cranberry juice
2 cups water
¾ cup pineapple juice
¼ cup lemon juice
1 cup orange juice
2 tablespoons sugar

Combine ingredients and chill. Pour over crushed ice and serve at once.

Makes 12 half-cup servings.

Bread-Cereal Group

4 or More Servings Daily

WHOLE GRAIN, ENRICHED, OR RESTORED

THE FOUR DAILY SERVINGS of foods from the bread-cereal group may come from many different grain products, used in many different ways.

The bread need not always be a slice of yeast bread, nor must the cereal necessarily be a breakfast cereal. For variety there are biscuits, muffins, pancakes, and many other hot breads, and quick loaf breads such as date or nut bread. All of them may be counted, provided they are made with whole-grain or enriched flour or meal. Half to three-fourths of a cup of rice, grits, spaghetti, noodles, or similar products may be counted as a serving of cereal if the product is enriched.

Part of the day's quota from the bread-cereal group may be in combination dishes. Bread is often an important ingredient in stuffings for meat, poultry, and fish, and in scalloped dishes and puddings. A serving of cereal can come from a combination such as macaroni and cheese, spaghetti with meat sauce, or spanish rice.

Enriched or whole-grain flour or cereal in cakes, cookies, pastries, and other sweet baked goods used primarily to round out meals and to satisfy the appetite also may count toward the quota.

YEAST ROLLS

1 package active dry yeast
or
1 cake compressed yeast
¼ cup lukewarm water
¼ cup sugar
¼ cup butter or margarine
1 teaspoon salt
1 cup scalded milk
1 egg, beaten
About 4 cups sifted flour

Soften yeast in water. Add ½ teaspoon sugar.

Add rest of sugar, fat, and salt to hot milk. Stir until sugar is dissolved.

Cool, then add egg. Stir in softened yeast.

Stir flour into liquid ingredients until well mixed. If using an electric mixer, mix flour into the liquids at low speed, scraping dough from the beater occasionally; then continue beating until dough has pulled cleanly away from sides of bowl several times.

Turn dough out onto a lightly floured board. If it was mixed by hand, knead it quickly until smooth and elastic. Do not knead the dough if it was machine mixed.

Form dough into a smooth ball,

549

place it in a greased bowl, and turn it over once or twice to grease the surface.

Cover and let rise in warm place (80°–85° F.) until double in bulk—about 1 hour.

Turn dough out onto board, knead well, and shape into rolls as desired. Place in a greased pan or on a baking sheet.

Cover with waxed paper or a cloth and let rise in a warm place until double in bulk.

Bake at 400° F. (hot oven) 15 to 20 minutes.

Makes 20 to 25 rolls.

Parker House rolls.—Roll the dough ½ inch thick and cut in 2-inch rounds. Brush lightly with melted butter or margarine, crease through center, fold over, and press down. Brush tops with fat if you like a soft crust.

Place rolls on greased baking sheet about ½ inch apart, or farther apart if you want them to be crusty on all sides. Let rise and bake as above.

QUICK NUT LOAF

2½ cups sifted flour
2 tablespoons sugar
3 teaspoons baking powder
½ teaspoon salt
½ teaspoon cinnamon
1 cup milk
2 eggs, beaten
4 tablespoons melted shortening or oil
1 cup chopped nuts

Sift together flour, sugar, baking powder, salt, and cinnamon.

Add milk to eggs. Stir into dry ingredients and mix just until smooth.

Stir in the shortening and nuts.

Pour into a greased loaf pan. Let stand 20 minutes.

Bake at 350° F. (moderate oven) about 1 hour.

Raisin loaf.—Use 1½ cups chopped raisins instead of nuts.

CORNBREAD

⅓ cup sifted flour
¾ cup yellow cornmeal
1½ teaspoons baking powder
1 tablespoon sugar
½ teaspoon salt
1 egg, beaten
⅔ cup milk
2 tablespoons melted shortening or oil

Sift together the flour, cornmeal, baking powder, sugar, and salt.

Combine the egg, milk, and shortening. Add to dry ingredients and stir only enough to mix.

Pour batter into a greased 8- by 8-inch baking pan.

Bake at 425° F. (hot oven) 25 minutes. 6 servings.

BISCUITS

2 cups sifted flour
2 teaspoons baking powder
¾ teaspoon salt
⅓ cup shortening
About ¾ cup milk

Sift flour, baking powder, and salt together. Cut or rub in shortening until well blended.

Slowly mix in milk, using just enough to make dough that is soft but not sticky.

Turn dough onto a lightly floured board and knead a few strokes. Roll or pat to ¾-inch thickness. Cut with a biscuit cutter or cut into squares.

Place on a baking sheet and bake at 450° F. (very hot) about 15 minutes.

Makes about sixteen 2-inch biscuits.

Cheese biscuits.—Add 1 cup grated cheese to dry ingredients.

Quick marmalade rolls.—Roll dough into a rectangle ¼ inch thick. Spread with ⅓ cup citrus marmalade. Roll as for jellyroll and slice. Place slices on a greased baking sheet and bake at 450° F. (hot oven) 15 minutes. Makes 12 to 16 rolls.

Rich biscuit dough.—Increase the fat to ½ cup, and use for shortcake.

MUFFINS

2 cups sifted flour
2 teaspoons baking powder
½ teaspoon salt
2 tablespoons sugar
1 egg, beaten
1 cup milk
¼ cup melted shortening or oil

Sift together flour, baking powder, salt, and sugar.

Combine egg, milk, and shortening. Add to the dry ingredients all at once, stirring only enough to moisten.

Fill greased muffin pans two-thirds full.

Bake at 400° F. (hot oven) about 20 minutes.

Makes about 12 muffins.

OVEN-COOKED RICE

2 cups boiling water
½ teaspoon salt
1 cup white rice

Measure boiling water into a baking dish and add salt. Stir in the rice.

Cover and bake at 350° F. (moderate oven) about 35 minutes.

PASTRY

2¼ cups sifted flour
1½ teaspoons salt
¾ cup shortening
4 to 6 tablespoons cold water

Sift flour with salt. Cut in shortening until mixture is granular.

Sprinkle water over mixture, blending lightly with fork. Add water sparingly until dough clings together but is not wet. Let stand 5 minutes before rolling. Makes two 9-inch crusts.

BAKED PASTRY SHELLS

Roll pastry thin; place in pie pan or muffin pans. Trim ¼ to ½ inch from edge. Double edge of pastry over and pinch with fingers to make an upright rim. Or shape pastry to outside of pans and trim close.

Prick bottom and sides of pastry with a fork to keep crust flat. Bake at 425° F. (hot oven) 10 to 12 minutes.

CHOCOLATE LAYER CAKE

⅔ cup shortening
1 teaspoon vanilla
1⅓ cups sugar
3 squares (3 ounces) chocolate, melted
2 eggs, separated
2 cups sifted cake flour
2 teaspoons baking powder
½ teaspoon salt
1 cup milk

Cream shortening, vanilla, and half of the sugar together until light and fluffy. Blend in chocolate and add egg yolks.

Sift together flour, baking powder, and salt.

Add to creamed mixture in three portions alternately with milk in two portions.

Beat egg whites stiff, and add the rest of the sugar slowly, beating constantly until glossy. Fold into the batter.

Turn batter into two greased 9-inch round layer pans.

Bake at 350° F. (moderate oven) 30 to 35 minutes or until cake pulls away from pan and top is springy to touch.

For Variety

Add ½ cup chopped nut meats to the batter just before pouring into pans.

Cupcakes.—Pour batter into greased muffin pans, filling them two-thirds full. Bake at 375° F. (moderate oven) 20 minutes, or until top is springy to touch.

Makes about 30 small cupcakes.

WHITE LAYER CAKE

½ cup shortening
½ teaspoon vanilla
½ teaspoon almond extract
1 cup sugar
2 cups sifted cake flour
2 teaspoons baking powder
½ teaspoon salt
¾ cup milk
3 egg whites

Cream shortening, flavorings, and half of the sugar together until very light and fluffy.

Sift together flour, baking powder, and salt.

Add to creamed mixture in three portions alternately with milk in two portions.

Beat egg whites until stiff and add the rest of the sugar slowly, beating until glossy. Fold into the batter.

Turn batter into two greased 8-inch round layer pans (or one 8-inch square loaf pan).

Bake at 375° F. (moderate oven) until cake draws away from pan and top is springy to touch—about 25 minutes. (Bake loaf 30 minutes.)

For Variety

For party cakes (petits fours) cut white cake in cubes or triangles. Make confectioner's sugar frosting, using enough liquid so that it will pour. Color frosting, if you like, and pour over cakes, covering tops and sides. The cakes may be sprinkled with coconut or chopped nuts while frosting is still soft.

CONFECTIONER'S SUGAR FROSTING

For a two-layer cake, 9-inch size, mix 2 cups confectioner's sugar, 4 tablespoons butter or margarine, and enough cream, orange juice, or strong coffee to spread well. Add flavoring—vanilla, grated orange rind, melted chocolate, or spices.

SPICED PRUNE CAKE

½ cup shortening
1 cup sugar
2 eggs, well beaten
1¼ cups finely chopped cooked prunes
2 cups sifted flour
1½ teaspoons soda
1 teaspoon cinnamon
¾ teaspoon cloves
¾ teaspoon salt
½ cup sour milk

Cream shortening and add sugar. Cream until fluffy. Add eggs and beat well. Blend in prunes.

Sift together flour, soda, spices, and salt. Add to creamed mixture in three portions alternately with the sour milk in two portions.

Turn into a greased shallow pan about 12 by 8 inches.

Bake at 350° F. (moderate oven) 35 to 40 minutes.

PEANUT BUTTER COOKIES

1 cup shortening
½ teaspoon salt
1 cup peanut butter
1 cup granulated sugar
1 cup brown sugar, firmly packed
2 eggs, well beaten
1 tablespoon milk
2 cups sifted flour
½ teaspoon soda

Combine shortening, salt, and peanut butter, and mix well.

Gradually add granulated sugar and brown sugar. Cream thoroughly after each addition.

Add eggs and milk, mixing well.

Sift together the flour and soda. Blend with first mixture.

Drop the dough by teaspoonfuls onto greased baking sheets, or roll the dough into balls ¾ to 1 inch in diameter. Press lightly with a fork to flatten. Bake at 325° F. (slow oven) 15 to 20 minutes.

Makes 10 to 12 dozen cookies.

GINGERBREAD

1½ cups sifted flour
¼ teaspoon soda
1 teaspoon baking powder
¼ cup sugar
¼ teaspoon salt
1 teaspoon ginger
1 teaspoon cinnamon
¼ teaspoon ground cloves
½ cup milk
1 egg, beaten
½ cup molasses
¼ cup melted shortening or oil

Sift together dry ingredients. Add milk to beaten egg. Pour into dry ingredients and stir until smooth.

Stir in molasses and shortening.

Pour batter into greased shallow pan (about 8 inches square).

Bake at 350° F. (moderate oven) 30 to 40 minutes.

OATMEAL COOKIES

½ cup sifted flour
⅓ cup sugar
½ teaspoon salt
1 teaspoon baking powder
¼ teaspoon cinnamon
1½ cups quick-cooking rolled oats
½ cup raisins
1 egg, slightly beaten
½ cup milk
½ teaspoon flavoring
¼ cup melted shortening or oil

Sift together flour, sugar, salt, baking powder, cinnamon. Mix in oats and raisins.

Combine egg, milk, flavoring, and shortening, and add to first mixture. Stir only until ingredients are moistened. Drop dough by teaspoonfuls onto greased baking sheets.

Bake at 375° F. (moderate oven) about 20 minutes.

Makes about 3 dozen cookies.

CRANBERRY UPSIDE-DOWN CAKE

Cranberry Mixture

1½ cups finely ground cranberries
¾ cup sugar
¼ cup orange juice

Combine the ingredients. Bring to a boil and simmer for 5 to 10 minutes.

Pour into a greased baking pan.

Cake Mixture

½ cup sifted cake flour
½ teaspoon baking powder
2 eggs
½ cup sugar
1 teaspoon lemon juice
¼ cup hot milk

Sift flour and baking powder together three times.

Beat eggs until very thick and light. Add sugar gradually, beating until well blended. Add lemon juice.

Fold in the flour-baking powder mixture gradually.

Add milk and mix quickly until the batter is smooth.

Pour batter over cranberry mixture.

Bake at 350° F. (moderate oven) about 30 minutes.

6 servings.

WAFFLES

1½ cups sifted flour
1½ teaspoons baking powder
½ teaspoon salt
1 tablespoon sugar
2 eggs, separated
1 cup milk
2 tablespoons melted shortening or oil

Sift dry ingredients together.

Beat egg yolks and whites separately.

Combine egg yolks, milk, and shortening. Mix with dry ingredients, stirring only until batter is smooth. Fold in beaten egg whites. Bake in a hot waffle baker.

Makes 4 waffles.

GINGER MUFFINS

FRENCH BREAD

⅔ cup sugar
⅔ cup dark molasses
⅓ cup melted shortening or oil
1 egg, slightly beaten
2 cups sifted flour
1½ teaspoons cinnamon
¼ teaspoon nutmeg
1½ teaspoons ginger
1½ teaspoons baking soda
⅔ cup buttermilk

Mix sugar, molasses, and shortening with the egg.

Sift together the flour, cinnamon, nutmeg, ginger, and soda.

Add dry ingredients alternately with the buttermilk to the egg mixture, stirring just enough to blend.

Pour the batter into greased muffin pans. Bake at 425° F. (hot oven) about 15 minutes.

Makes 12 medium-sized muffins.

FRUIT NUT BREAD

½ cup dried apricots
½ cup raisins
¾ cup water
½ teaspoon grated orange rind
¼ cup orange juice
1 teaspoon baking soda
¾ cup sugar
2 tablespoons melted shortening or oil
1 teaspoon vanilla
1 egg, beaten
2½ cups sifted flour
4 teaspoons baking powder
¼ teaspoon salt
½ cup chopped nuts

Soak apricots and raisins in the water for 30 minutes. Drain; save the liquid. Chop the fruit fine.

Add orange rind, juice, and drained liquid to the fruit. Stir in the soda, sugar, shortening, vanilla, and egg.

Sift together the flour, baking powder, and salt. Combine with the fruit mixture. Add the nuts and blend well.

Pour into a greased loaf pan. Bake at 350° F. (moderate oven) about 1 hour.

2 packages active dry yeast
or
2 cakes compressed yeast
½ cup warm water
2 teaspoons sugar
2 tablespoons shortening
2 teaspoons salt
2 tablespoons sugar
2 cups boiling water
About 8¾ cups sifted flour

Combine yeast, warm water, and 2 teaspoons sugar.

Add shortening, salt, and 2 tablespoons sugar to the boiling water. Cool to lukewarm; add to yeast mixture.

Stir in the flour, using just enough to make a dough that can be handled.

Turn dough out onto a lightly floured board to knead until it is smooth and elastic. Form into a smooth ball, place in a greased bowl, and turn dough to grease the top.

Cover and let rise in a warm place (80°–85° F.) until double in size.

Punch the dough down and divide it into two portions. Roll each portion into a 12- by 15-inch rectangle. Roll each rectangle up tightly as for jelly roll. Seal the edges well. Place loaves on a greased sheet pan and let rise in a warm place until double in size.

Using scissors, cut slits in each loaf every 2½ inches. Brush the loaves with a mixture of slightly beaten egg white and 1 tablespoon water.

Bake at 400° F. about 25 minutes.

GEORGIA C. SCHLOSSER *is a food specialist in the Human Nutrition Research Division of the Agricultural Research Service. She has had experience in food service management in schools and commercial cafeterias. Her major work is in the development of recipes and food management guides for use in the National School Lunch Program.*

GLADYS L. GILPIN *is a food specialist in the Human Nutrition Research Division of the Agricultural Research Service.*

Food

COSTS

What Your Food Money Buys

FREDERICK V. WAUGH AND KENNETH E. OGREN

MRS. Brown says that her food money does not buy much of anything these days. She just got back from the store, and her bill for groceries came to 23.65 dollars. She will have to buy still more food during the week for her family of four.

Mrs. Brown is right. A dollar buys less food today than it did a few years ago and much less than before the war. But still Mrs. Brown's 23.65 dollars will buy many things.

What it actually does buy depends on what she selects from among the thousands of items in today's grocery store.

"Subsistence" is a word economists once used to mean the bare necessities of life. If you ask Mrs. Brown what she bought with her food money she might say it was subsistence, although she probably will use some other word meaning the same thing. Still, she probably will admit that her family could subsist on less money than she is spending for food. They would not starve if she bought cheaper things.

Some of us hold to the notion that "we eat to live," as people very likely did a few centuries ago. Highly respectable economists, including the Rev. Dr. Robert Thomas Malthus, preached the "dismal science" that only a future shortage of food and high cost of subsistence would hold the world population in check.

As far as the United States is concerned, the Malthusian theory is not working. Almost everyone in this country has income enough to buy subsistence, and most have a lot more. Those who cannot afford a subsistence level, such as some of the aged and the sick, are cared for by relief and welfare programs.

Good nutrition means more than subsistence. It means a diet that will contribute to health and vigor.

Nutrition in the United States has improved greatly during the past generation. President Franklin D. Roosevelt's statement in the 1930's that one-third of our population was ill-fed was supported by studies by the Department of Agriculture and by many surveys, which disclosed that deficiency diseases were widespread.

The diet of the American family has

557

improved considerably since then. Diseases due to improper food have declined sharply and may almost disappear within another generation. Recent studies show that a large share of our people are buying enough of the right foods to provide nutrients that meet standards set by research workers.

Sanitation and cleanliness in foods are now taken for granted in the United States. That was not always true. It still is not true in many countries. Probably most of us, like Mrs. Brown, often forget that our food money also buys sanitation and cleanliness, things that do not come free. Farmers and food processors pay a great deal of money to keep food clean.

Enjoyment has become a big factor in our food buying. We buy food not only to live, but to enjoy. When Mrs. Brown wheeled her pushcart up to the checkout counter, it included one of the more expensive cuts of meat, some top-grade fruit, and some fancy cheese. Mrs. Brown buys these not only because she thinks they are nutritious but because she knows that her family likes them. Discrimination in taste is a good thing, both for the consumer and the farmer. The consumer gets real enjoyment from high-quality foods, and many farmers can get a good return for producing them.

Convenience has become an important requirement. American homemakers are alert to all sorts of developments aimed at saving time and work in the preparation of foods. Striking changes in processing and packaging a wide assortment of foods and the development of mixes and prepared meals attest to that. Mrs. Brown, like most of us, spends some of her money for convenience foods. Many of them cost more than the old-fashioned, simple foods we used to buy. Some may feel that the trend toward prepared food is taking away the individuality and enjoyment from eating. When losses are weighed against gains, however, many of us prefer to spend part of our money for services. Convenience therefore has become more important today than it was a few years ago.

Style maybe is less important in foods than in many other commodities. Nevertheless we sometimes buy foods partly for style. (Another economist, Thorstein Veblen, called it "conspicuous consumption.") The Romans used to show off by serving tongues of peacocks to their guests. We do much the same thing on a smaller scale when we serve out-of-season peaches or imported caviar. Probably few of us spend much of our food money for style alone, but at least occasionally we do buy expensive foods because we like them and want to impress company. Cost then usually is less important than in everyday food buying.

Unless your income is far below the American average, you, like Mrs. Brown, get more for your money than subsistence—even more than good nutrition.

What you buy with your food money is mostly up to you, however.

If you are a typical American, you will probably say at this point, "That is all very well, but I want still more for my money." Most of us feel this way, and it is good that we do. We make progress only because we are dissatisfied and look for ways to improve things.

Food production and marketing have improved greatly in the past decade or so, but there is still room for much more improvement.

To see what the possibilities are, we shall review briefly some of the main facts about food prices and costs.

FOOD IS THE LARGEST recurring item of expense that must be planned for in budgets of most families.

Food takes almost one-fourth of total consumer income in the United States. It includes money spent for meals away from home and food bought for use at home.

Because food is a basic necessity, families with low incomes and those with several children tend to spend a larger part of their income on food than families with larger incomes and those with few or no children.

A survey of household expenditures of urban families made by the Bureau of Labor Statistics in 1950 disclosed that families with incomes of more than 10 thousand dollars spent an average of 15 percent of their income for food, compared with 45 percent for those with incomes of less than 2 thousand dollars. Large families—those with six persons or more—spent an average of about 35 percent of their yearly income on food. Families of two persons spent 27 percent.

Ernst Engel a century ago studied the expenditures of Belgian workingmen's families at all income levels. He concluded, "The poorer a family, the greater the proportion of total outgo that must be used for food." Every investigation since Engel's has confirmed his conclusions, although at first glance they may seem not to.

Consumers have been able over the past several decades to buy more and more of the same kinds of items with their money. When that happens, consumers have had an increase in "real income," regardless of whether we are in an inflationary period or a recession. An increase in our incomes as well as in what money buys would seem to mean that, if "Engel's law" still applies, the share of the income going for food should decline. That has not happened. Consumers spent about 23 percent of their income for food in 1935–1939. They spent about the same share in 1958.

If American consumers had bought the same foods in 1958 as they did in the prewar period and if they had bought the same services with these foods, only about 16 percent of the 1958 incomes would have gone for food.

The proportion of income spent for food has stayed up not because consumers have been eating more food but because they have upgraded their diets and have been buying more services with their food dollars.

More meat, more dairy products, more eggs, more out-of-season fresh produce, fewer potatoes, less bread and other cereals, less beans: These changes have given consumers a more varied and attractive diet—but also a more expensive one.

More meals eaten in restaurants, more processed and ready-to-serve foods, more packaging: These changes mean more services to pay for—but less waste, fresher foods, and less time in the kitchen for millions.

ARE FOOD PRICES too high? Many homemakers may answer yes, especially if they are asked this question at a time when the cost of living and prices of food are going up.

Food prices were higher in 1958 than in 1957. They also were higher than in 1947 and much higher than in 1940. But prices of almost all goods and services are higher. Wages and incomes of city workers are higher, too. Average family income in 1958 was almost three times what it was in 1940. The average American family today has the highest level of living in history. Despite higher prices, the average American income can buy more of most things, including food.

Consider, for example, the amount of food that can be bought with average wages at different times. The average take-home pay per hour of factory workers in 1957 bought more loaves of bread, more quarts of milk—in fact, more of almost any food than in 1947 or before the war. This comparison confirms what we noted earlier—that if consumers bought the same foods and services as they did in earlier periods, they would spend a smaller part of their income for food.

Food prices in the United States are higher than in many countries. So are workers' incomes. The average American workingman's wages will buy more food than will the wages of most wage earners in other countries. The proportion of the income going for food also is lower here than in most other countries.

Foods Bought by Hour's Take-home Pay

	1940	1947	1957
STEAK lb.	1.7	1.6	2
MILK qt.	5	6	7.5
EGGS doz.	2	2	3.5
BREAD lb. loaf	8	9.5	10
ORANGES doz.	2	2.5	3
CANNED TOMATOES No. 2 can	7	6	15

Food prices generally follow overall trends. Food prices go up when prices of other items are rising. Food prices go down during periods of general price declines.

Food prices do fluctuate more than do prices of most other items. So, during periods of sharp changes in the cost of living, up or down, often it is food prices that are responsible for a large part of this change.

Declines in prices of food often bring down the overall cost of living, or at least keep it from rising as much as otherwise would have been the case. For example, between 1952 and mid-1956, there was little change in the cost of living, as measured by the Consumer Price Index of the Bureau of Labor Statistics. This was possible only because food prices went down during this time. Most other items used to estimate changes in the overall cost of living—rent, the upkeep of the family car and other travel expenses, medical and dental costs, and other expenses, like drycleaning and beauty parlor bills—went up during that period. In contrast, the sharp rise in the cost of living between mid-1956 and mid-1958 was caused by a fairly large rise in the price of food, while at the same time prices of the other items continued to go up.

Homemakers pay a lot of attention to changes in food prices, because the prices are variable, if only seasonally, and because homemakers buy food oftener than any other major item in the family budget.

Another change has started to affect the grocery bill. Part of the higher grocery bills is likely to result from increased buying of household supplies, cigarettes, drugs, clothing, and many other nonfood items in grocery stores.

As more and more food stores stock a larger and larger number of items other than food, the proportion of grocery store sales represented by nonfoods has increased steadily. A study made by home economists in Purdue University revealed that nonfoods made up an average of almost 20 percent of consumers' purchases in markets in Lafayette, Ind., and Indianapolis. A surprisingly large number of individual shoppers' purchases consisted largely or entirely of nonfoods.

YOUR FOOD DOLLARS are divided among farmers, who produce the food, and marketing agencies, which bring it from the farm to the store. Your food dollar pays for having the kind of food you want, where you want it, when you want it.

For most foods, the farmer gets less than half of the amount the consumer pays for them. The farmer receives such a small part for some foods that even if he gave them away their prices at retail would be reduced by less than a fifth. For example, the retail price of a 1-pound loaf of white bread averaged about 19 cents in 1957; the farmer got about 2.5 cents for the wheat used to make the loaf. Thus, even if the farmer had been paid nothing, the loaf of bread would still have cost 16.5 cents.

Other foods for which the farm price is a small part of the price at the grocery are items like soda crackers and many other bakery and cereal products, several kinds of canned and frozen fruits and vegetables, and other prepared and processed foods.

Even large changes in the farm prices of such products might have little effect on the price a homemaker pays at the grocery store. In 1947–1957, for instance, the average retail price of bread went up more than 6 cents, while wheat prices were going down.

Farmers receive a larger share of the retail price for foods like eggs, fresh beef, chicken, butter, and cheese—but not necessarily because the companies that market those foods are more efficient or that they make less profit than companies that handle wheat, flour, and bread.

The differences in the farmer's share depend largely on how much a particular food has to be processed before it gets to the grocery store, who does the processing, and how much it costs. For wheat, a two-stage manufacturing process takes place after the farmer sells it—first it is milled into flour and then made into bread. Buying, selling, transporting, and storing the wheat, flour, and bread bring additional outlays. On the other hand, little processing is necessary for products like fresh vegetables and eggs.

These facts explain much of the differences in the marketing costs among foods.

The share of the consumer's dollar that goes to the farmer varies among foods and also for the same foods from one time to another. The point is demonstrated by pricing the same foods at different times, as marketing researchers do each month in computing the statistics for the Department of Agriculture's "market basket." This basket includes foods that are representative of those bought for use at home in a year by an average city worker's family. It does not include food bought at restaurants. Because the purpose is to ascertain the share of the food dollar that goes to the American farmer, all imported foods, even coffee, tea, and seafoods, are excluded from the list of foods that are priced.

The farmer's share is determined by comparing how much the farmer got for producing the foods with the amount the homemakers had to pay for them at the grocery store. The comparisons show to what extent the farmer's share varies from time to

The Market Basket of Farm Foods

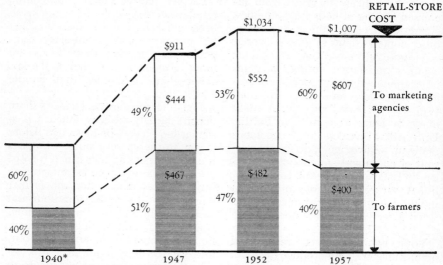

Dollar figures for 1940 not comparable

time. For example, the farmer in 1940 and in 1957 got about 40 cents out of every dollar the consumer spent for food, even though the price of food rose considerably during this period. Though this was the case, the farmer's share fluctuated between these two dates.

The farmer's share of your food dollar rose during the Second World War but has declined almost steadily since then.

A look at the cost of the market basket in 1947, 1952, and 1957 reveals the changes in the total costs and in the shares going to farmers and marketing agencies.

The retail-store cost of the market-basket foods rose from 911 dollars in 1947 to 1,034 dollars in 1952 because of higher prices to farmers and increased marketing charges. But the part going to marketing agencies went up much more than that going to farmers. As a result, the farmer's share went down from 51 percent in 1947 to 47 percent in 1952.

In the next 5-year period, between 1952 and 1957, the cost of the market-

basket foods dropped 27 dollars, but the returns to farmers dropped 82 dollars. The continued rise in returns going to marketing agencies kept food prices from going down more. The farmer's share dropped by 7 percentage points during this period because of the rise in marketing charges and the drop in farm prices of products.

Variations in the farmer's share of the consumer's food dollar do not necessarily reflect changes in either profits or efficiency of farmers or marketing agencies.

The changes we described related mainly to changing relationships between agricultural and nonagricultural prices—not to changes in farm or marketing efficiency. The ups and downs of the farmers' shares do reflect to some extent the ups and downs in farmers' net incomes.

Farmers' incomes are notoriously unstable. During the Second World War, their average returns went up much faster than for most other groups. Even so, the average income of people living on farms has generally been much less than that of nonfarmers. The farmers' incomes have gone down during much of the postwar period, while nonfarm workers have had an almost steady increase in income.

Farmers have been caught in a cost-price squeeze. Because most costs of production such as wages, fuel, fertilizers and other supplies, and taxes have gone up along with the general increase in most prices, the farmers have felt "squeezed" from both sides—lower prices for what they sell, higher prices for what they buy.

Although farmers' incomes lately have tended to lag behind incomes of other workers, their productivity has not. Even with fewer farmers, American agriculture is so productive that it is hard to find markets for surplus foods. Each worker on the farm in 1957 produced enough food for himself and 23 other people. This is an increase of 10 persons over 1947 and 13 over 1940.

With this increase in productivity, the farmer has come to rely more and more on others to provide him with the supplies and equipment he needs for farming. This increased productivity per farmworker consequently reflects in part a shift from the farmer supplying his own "horsepower" and fuel for this horsepower, to nonfarm workers supplying power and other needs.

These shifts have made the farmer less self-sufficient and have increased his out-of-pocket expenditures. He is therefore more vulnerable than formerly to changes in the retail prices of the things he now must buy.

FARMERS DO NOT SEEM to be reaping large profits at the expense of the food-buying public.

What about the food-marketing agencies—the processor, wholesaler, and retailer? They receive more than half of the consumer's food dollar and their share, in dollars and in percentages, has increased almost steadily since the end of the Second World War.

Food-marketing agencies, like farmers and other businessmen, have had to pay higher wages, higher rents, higher taxes, higher transportation costs—in fact, higher costs for almost everything used in processing and distributing food products. The result is that marketing agencies have had to charge enough for food to pay for these higher costs.

Many of these costs, like freight rates and wages, are sticky. They do not drop much or not at all in response to large food supplies and low prices. Also, food processors and distributors have more control over the prices they charge than farmers have. As a result, marketing margins (costs and profits) tend to be less flexible than farm prices, especially when prices drop.

Profits naturally receive much attention whenever consumers get concerned about higher prices. Since the war, however, the higher prices of foods seem to be caused more by the increased cost of doing business than because marketing firms are getting bigger profits. Of course, with the large volume of food being sold and with higher prices, many firms may make more profits in terms of actual dollars than they did. But when these are compared with total sales, which also are higher in terms of dollars, profits still represent about the same share as before. For processing and distributing firms, such profits make up less than 5 cents out of every dollar the consumer spends for food.

Although profits are a small part of the sales dollar for most food firms and sudden changes in price levels may cause some large changes in profits, either up or down, we should not conclude that their profits are not adequate.

Profits in relation to investment are what the stockholder looks at. Because of the rapid turnover and large dollar volume in the food industries, returns on investment in food industries are generally comparable to those in other industries but usually are no higher.

Increase in the Number of Persons Supported by One Farm Worker

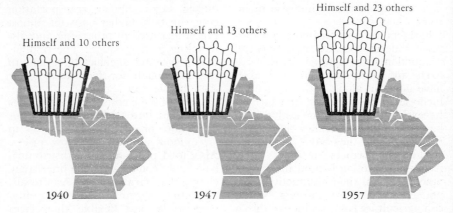

Himself and 10 others

Himself and 13 others

Himself and 23 others

1940   1947   1957

The number of workers in activities associated with the marketing of food products has increased steadily for many years. That is partly the reason why an increasing share of the food dollar goes for marketing. Most people in a primitive society are employed in agriculture, and farmers do most of the marketing. More workers in marketing and fewer workers in agriculture are part and parcel of our growing industrial economy. It reflects specialization.

Marketing is essential in our modern industrial economy—as essential as farm production. It is a vital and integral part of the entire production process. Food marketing includes storing, processing, packaging, transporting, distributing, and selling—which the commercial farmer does not do today. He is a specialist in growing potatoes or in feeding hogs. He relies on other specialists to market his products. Much of our American efficiency has come from such kinds of specialization.

Even though we recognize that we must have this marketing system and understand its many services, we still can ask if it is giving us our money's worth.

Despite the continued increases in food marketing costs in recent years,

there have been some marked gains in efficiency. Food processing and distributing companies have made large investments in their businesses to streamline their operations. They make extensive application of assembly-line procedures. Modern procedures for handling food are used in many plants, warehouses, and stores.

Not all of the increases in costs—wages and the cost of supplies and materials—have been reflected in increases in actual costs of each pound or can of food. In 1957, for example, average hourly earnings of food-marketing workers were 56 percent higher than during 1947–1949. At the same time, the actual labor costs for each unit of a product handled increased by only half as much—28 percent. This could happen only by the mechanization of plant and equipment and other improvements so that each worker can handle a large number of products in the same time.

Gains in efficiency have not offset fully the rising costs of marketing firms, but they have kept the total food-marketing bill from rising as much as it would have if there had been no improvements.

The new way in which broilers—young chickens—are being produced and marketed is an illustration of how consumers have benefited by the use of more efficient methods. Growing broilers has become a full-time occupation of some farmers. Improvements in production methods, which have reduced death loss of chicks and reduced the amount of feed needed per pound of chicken raised, have lowered production costs. Many of the broiler farms operate the year round and are located close enough together so that the chickens can be processed in large plants with assembly-line methods. Cut-up frying chickens of a uniform high quality are a large-volume seller in supermarkets rather than the specialty items they once were. As a result, costs of marketing broilers have been held down to a relatively constant level. Between 1950 and 1957, when prices of most food products increased, the retail price of frying chickens dropped an. average of 10 cents a pound.

Research has helped give consumers more for their food dollar. It has enabled farmers to adopt new methods that have increased remarkably the amount each farmworker produces.

Research has helped improve the quality of food products, has made it possible to transport foods long distances at all seasons, and has brought food in new and different forms to grocery store shelves. Five thousand or more items are commonplace in food stores today. A thousand or so items were usual a few decades ago.

Some of the new convenience foods can be bought at the same prices as foods in a less convenient form. An example is frozen concentrated orange juice. The oranges are squeezed at the plant, and the juice is shipped in concentrated form. This saves the cost of shipping a bulky, perishable product long distances.

WHAT WE HAVE DISCUSSED so far seems to say that Mrs. Brown is getting her money's worth from her food dollar. Both farmers and marketing agencies are more efficient in doing their jobs than they used to be. Each hour's

pay buys more food than it did formerly. Food generally is of higher quality. Convenience and timesaving are built into many foods. The homemaker has many more choices of food products in fresh and processed forms and in packages of different sizes and different grades. She can shop in attractive, convenient, air-conditioned markets that provide space for parking her car, carry-out services for her packages, and sometimes a playground for her children.

We have not achieved perfection in either production or marketing of food products. There are inefficiencies. There is room for improvement.

Not all farmers produce—or even know—the best varieties of crops for their production areas or the most efficient methods of feeding their livestock. Many farms are too small to make economical use of modern laborsaving equipment. Such farms produce much less per worker than do farms that use up-to-date methods and equipment. A small proportion of farmers consequently produce and market the major share of our food products.

IN MUCH THE SAME WAY, there is room for improvement in the methods used by individual companies in marketing operations. We know that specific jobs, such as loading boxes in a freight car, can be done in many ways. Some methods are better than others because they take less labor and turn out better products. For example, new loading techniques for watermelons and peaches have resulted in marked reductions of damage during shipping. Improved methods and equipment for handling and processing food products have been developed, many of which still are not in general use.

Many assembly houses, processing plants, and retail stores are too small for the most efficient operation. Many have worn or old machinery and equipment and do not have the money needed to replace it. It costs these firms relatively more to run their business and they make less efficient use of their employees than do the more efficient firms.

Other inefficiencies exist that often are beyond the control of a single marketing firm. Many large wholesale markets are located in congested parts of the city and have such inadequate facilities that excessive handling, delay, and waste results. New modern markets have been built to replace old and inefficient ones in some cities, but much still remains to be done along this line. Numerous studies show that reorganization of a marketing system could eliminate expensive overlapping and duplication in the assembly and delivery of many food products. Milk is a classical example.

Extra services add to marketing costs. Some homemakers are willing to pay a higher price to get these conveniences. Others prefer lower prices in place of some of the extra packaging and frills. Competition among food processors often results in a proliferation of brands, fancy packages, and new types of food products rather than lower prices on widely used items. Likewise, competition among supermarkets has resulted partly in a wider selection of foods and nonfoods, in fancier stores, in more advertising, trading stamps, and other promotional gimmicks.

But price is still important. It is well that this is so. The wide-awake homemaker, searching for a bargain, is the main force that drives us toward improvements in efficiency, both in farming and in marketing.

Of course, efficiency is not everything. The farmer, the food processor, and the homemaker are all interested in more than low costs. This is especially true when costs are reduced at the expense of a small business and when it cuts down competition.

Mass production has brought about great efficiencies in many manufacturing industries. Perhaps less spectacular are the gains due to the mass processing and mass distribution of foods. Yet there are many examples in the food business of lower costs as firms get bigger. Possibly there is less danger of monopoly in the case of food products than in the case of most manufactured goods, but still we must be on our guard lest a few large companies control the market and dictate prices either to the farmer or to the consumer. If that situation arises, the Government, for example, will have to take considerable responsibility for determining prices just as it now does for determining freight rates.

FREDERICK V. WAUGH *is Director of the Agricultural Economics Division, Agricultural Marketing Service.*

KENNETH E. OGREN *is Chief of the Market Organization and Costs Branch, Marketing Research Division, Agricultural Marketing Service.*

Calcium Equivalents

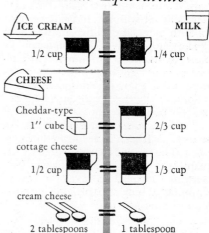

ICE CREAM — 1/2 cup ≡ MILK — 1/4 cup

CHEESE
Cheddar-type 1″ cube ≡ 2/3 cup

cottage cheese 1/2 cup ≡ 1/3 cup

cream cheese 2 tablespoons ≡ 1 tablespoon

Your Money's Worth

LOUISE PAGE AND ELOISE COFER

IF yours is a typical family, very likely more than one-half of your money for food goes for milk, meat, and eggs.

About one-fifth is spent for vegetables and fruit.

The rest is nearly equally divided among the grain products; the fats, oils, sugar, and sweets; and such miscellaneous items as spices, vinegar, leavening agents, coffee, tea, and other beverages.

Do you wonder if your money for food is spent to best advantage? A good way to determine this is to compare foods in each of the groups by their yield in food value as well as by their price.

The following examples show the kinds of foods that are apt to give the most food value for the money.

Everybody needs milk in some form because it is our best source of calcium. Milk also is an important source of protein and riboflavin.

One serving of fluid whole milk, evaporated milk, buttermilk, skim milk, or dry milk furnishes about the same amounts of those nutrients but at widely different costs.

Dry milk generally costs least and fluid whole milk the most for a serving.

Some of the products made from milk give more food value for the money than others because of differences in cost and in amounts of nutrients they furnish. Cream cheese and ice cream are apt to be more expensive for the value received than most other milk products, except butter and cream.

Cottage cheese provides good amounts of protein and riboflavin and can be counted as a bargain for them. Cheese of the Swiss and Cheddar types usually are more economical sources of calcium than cottage cheese.

Meat, poultry, fish, and eggs are important mainly for the high-quality protein, iron, and the B vitamins they provide. Dry beans, peas, and nuts are valuable for many of the same nutrients and can be used in meals some of the time in place of the animal foods.

You can make worthwhile savings when buying meats and meat alternates by choosing wisely and shopping carefully.

To rate meats, poultry, and fish as economical sources of nutrients, judge them on a comparable basis. When you buy them, you often pay for parts that are not eaten, such as bones and gristle. Part or all of the fat from the

Cost of a Day's Supply of Vitamin A Value From Vegetables and Fruit

Item	Purchase price per pound	Cost of a day's supply of vitamin A value [1]	Amount of food as eaten to give day's supply of vitamin A value
	Cents	Cents	
Carrots......................	15	2	¼ cup.
Collards....................	15	2	⅓ cup.
Sweetpotatoes................	15	2	⅓ medium.
Kale, trimmed...............	25	3	½ cup.
Spinach, trimmed............	25	3	¼ cup.
Winter squash...............	10	3	⅓ cup.
Broccoli.....................	20	9	1 cup.
Cantaloup...................	20	12	⅓ medium.
Tomato juice, canned.........	15	14	1 cup.
Apricots, canned.............	25	18	1⅓ cups.
Peaches, fresh...............	15	25	5 medium.
Tomatoes, fresh..............	25	26	3 medium.
Green snap beans.............	20	36	5 cups.
Peas, canned.................	20	36	3–4 cups.
Peaches, canned.............	20	44	4 cups.
Asparagus, fresh.............	25	48	2½ cups.
Corn, in husks...............	10	68	7 cups.

[1] For average adult.

Cost for One Serving of Food, Items Priced From 5 Cents to 150 Cents per Item

Retail price per unit (cents)	Number of servings per unit					
	2.0	3.0	4.0	6.0	12.0	16.0
	Cost per serving (cents)					
5.................	2.5	1.7	1.2	0.8	0.4	0.3
10.................	5.0	3.3	2.5	1.7	.8	.6
15.................	7.5	5.0	3.8	2.5	1.2	.9
20.................	10.0	6.7	5.0	3.3	1.7	1.2
25.................	12.5	8.3	6.2	4.2	2.1	1.6
30.................	15.0	10.0	7.5	5.0	2.5	1.9
35.................	17.5	11.7	8.8	5.8	2.9	2.2
40.................	20.0	13.3	10.0	6.7	3.3	2.5
45.................	22.5	15.0	11.2	7.5	3.8	2.8
50.................	25.0	16.7	12.5	8.3	4.2	3.1
60.................	30.0	20.0	15.0	10.0	5.0	3.8
70.................	35.0	23.3	17.5	11.7	5.8	4.4
80.................	40.0	26.7	20.0	13.3	6.7	5.0
90.................	45.0	30.0	22.5	15.0	7.5	5.6
100................	50.0	33.3	25.0	16.7	8.3	6.2
110................	55.0	36.7	27.5	18.3	9.2	6.9
120................	60.0	40.0	30.0	20.0	10.0	7.5
130................	65.0	43.3	32.5	21.7	10.8	8.1
140................	70.0	46.7	35.0	23.3	11.7	8.8
150................	75.0	50.0	37.5	25.0	12.5	9.4

meat often is discarded. A comparison therefore should be based on the cost of a serving of lean meat.

The lean parts of beef, lamb, pork, and poultry are much alike in food value, except that pork is a superior source of thiamine.

Buying the less expensive cuts of meat can mean saving money and getting about the same food value. A serving of lean meat from beef chuck roast, for instance, is likely to be quite a bit less expensive than the lean from prime ribs of beef, yet each provides about the same amounts of nutrients.

Cheaper cuts may be no bargain, however, if they contain such large amounts of bone, fat, and gristle that there is little lean meat.

Liver is exceptionally high in many nutrients. Money spent for it usually is well spent. Other variety meats, like kidney and heart, also are highly nutritious.

Dry beans give high food value for the money spent. You can cut food bills if you use dry beans and peas occasionally as the main dish in place of meat because they cost much less than most meat. Peanut butter is another good value in this group.

Eggs furnish valuable amounts of several nutrients. Eggs of the top market quality, which cost more than eggs of lower grades, are best when flavor and appearance are important, as for frying, poaching, and cooking in the shell.

You save money by buying eggs of the lower market grades when you want eggs for scrambling, baking, or combining with other foods.

Prices may vary for eggs in the same grade, depending on their size. The large eggs cost more. Small eggs often are as good buys as the larger ones.

A good rule to follow is: Small eggs are as economical as large ones when they are at least one-fourth cheaper; medium-sized eggs, when they are one-eighth cheaper. The minimum weight for the large size is 24 ounces per dozen; for the medium, 21 ounces; and for the small, 18 ounces.

Color of the shell may affect egg prices but has no bearing on food value or cooking quality. Therefore select whichever color is the less expensive, if the eggs are of comparable market quality and size.

VEGETABLES and fruit furnish a large share of the vitamin A value and most of the vitamin C that you get from food. Certain vegetables and kinds of fruit can be depended on to give good food value in return for the money spent for them, although prices vary with locality and season.

One day's supply of vitamin A can be bought—as dark-green or deep-yellow vegetables—for a few cents. Examples are carrots, collards, kale, spinach, sweetpotatoes, and winter squash. For a little more money, broccoli, cantaloup, tomatoes in season, and canned tomatoes and juice provide the needed vitamin A.

Most other common fruit and vegetables, including light-green and pale-yellow ones can be expensive sources of vitamin A because they contain such small amounts of it. You also would have to eat large amounts of them to get enough vitamin A for a day. It would take about 7 cups of corn, for instance, or 3 to 4 cups of peas to give as much vitamin A value as one-fourth cup of carrots. Those amounts of corn and peas could cost 10 or more times as much as the smaller amount of carrots.

Ordinarily you would not count on just one vegetable or fruit to supply all the vitamin A in meals. The example, however, points up that some give much more for the money than others.

Even though many vegetables provide less vitamin A value than the dark-green and deep-yellow ones do, the smaller amounts they furnish help toward the total needed for a day.

Oranges and grapefruit and their juice and raw cabbage generally supply the most vitamin C for the money. Some dark-green leaves, po-

Cost of a Day's Supply of Vitamin C From Fruit and Vegetables

Item	Purchase price per pound	Cost of a day's supply of vitamin C [1]	Amount of food as eaten to give day's supply of vitamin C
	Cents	Cents	
Cabbage.....................	10	4	1½ cups, raw.
Oranges.....................	10	4	1 medium.
Grapefruit juice and orange juice, frozen.	35	4	¾ cup.
Grapefruit juice and orange juice, canned.	10	4–5	¾ cup.
Grapefruit...................	10	6	½ medium.
Broccoli....................	20	7	⅔ cup.
Kale, trimmed...............	25	7	1⅓ cups.
Collards....................	15	9	1¼ cups.
Strawberries, fresh...........	35	10	1 cup.
Cabbage....................	10	11	2¼ cups, cooked.
Potatoes....................	10	14	4 medium cooked in jacket.
Tomato juice, canned.........	15	15	2 cups.
Strawberries, frozen..........	50	20	¾ cup.
Tomatoes, fresh..............	25	20	2½ medium.
Cantaloup..................	20	21	⅔ medium.
Potatoes....................	10	22	5 cups mashed.
Pineapple juice, canned.......	15	27	3¼ cups.
Peaches, fresh...............	15	35	9½ medium.
Bananas....................	20	50	7½ medium.
Apples.....................	15	61	12 medium.

[1] For average adult.

Cost and Nutrient Contributions of Selected Meats and Alternates

Item	Purchase price	Cost of serving	Size of serving [1]	Percent of daily allowances provided by a serving [2]				
				Protein	Iron	Thiamine	Riboflavin	Niacin
	Cents	Cents		Percent	Percent	Percent	Percent	Percent
Ham......	70/pound..	28	3 ounces.....	29	21	38	11	29
Beef rib roast.	75/pound..	25	....do......	29	22	4	9	30
Pork chops.	....do....	25	....do......	29	22	59	12	36
Beef chuck roast.	55/pound..	18	....do......	32	22	3	10	29
Halibut....	60/pound..	18	....do......	33	6	4	4	74
Beef liver..	....do....	15	....do......	30	55	18	198	105
Eggs, large.	60/dozen..	10	2 eggs.......	19	22	7	16	1
Bacon.....	60/pound..	5	2 strips......	6	4	7	3	7
Peanut butter.	55/pound..	4	2 tablespoons.	12	5	3	2	43
Dry beans..	20/pound..	2	¾ cup, cooked.	16	30	8	6	12

[1] Meat servings are cooked meat without fat, gristle, and bone.
[2] For an average adult.

tatoes, and sweetpotatoes, properly cooked, give good amounts of vitamin C at moderately low cost.

Tomatoes also are a fairly economical source of vitamin C. Tomato juice and canned tomatoes usually are cheaper for vitamin C except when fresh tomatoes are in season.

Most other common kinds of fruit and vegetables furnish little vitamin C and are seldom economical as the sole source of this nutrient.

Some vegetables and fruit are valued for both vitamins A and C. Examples are some that have dark-green leaves, tomatoes, and sweetpotatoes. Many dark-green vegetables also provide important amounts of other vitamins and minerals. Money used for them generally is well spent.

All fruit and vegetables contribute toward the daily need for several nutrients. A variety of them each day helps insure a good diet.

Canned, frozen, and fresh fruit and vegetables that have been cooked differ somewhat in food value. When properly prepared, however, the differences are small. A good way to save money is to compare the cost of a serving of food sold in different forms and to buy the cheapest.

WHOLE-GRAIN, restored, or enriched cereals and bread can mean extra food value for the money.

Natural whole grains are significant sources of iron, thiamine, riboflavin, and niacin. These nutrients are subject to some loss in the manufacture of certain cereals and in the milling of white flour.

Many breakfast cereals have nutrients added to make partial restoration of losses in milling the whole grain. Such cereals are called "restored." A product may be restored in several nutrients or in only one or two. The selection of nutrients and amounts added is determined by the manufacturer as there is no Federal standard for restored cereals.

Enriched bread is white bread with iron, thiamine, riboflavin, and niacin added in amounts within the limits specified by the Federal standard for enrichment.

Enriched white bread made with 4 percent of milk solids gives about three times more iron, one and a half times more riboflavin, four times the thiamine, and more than double the niacin than an unenriched loaf that has the same amount of milk solids. Except for the riboflavin, the differences are even greater between whole wheat bread and unenriched bread.

If breads of these types cost the same or if there is a difference of only a few cents in the price of a loaf, the whole-grain or enriched kinds will give the most value for the money.

The same is true of cereals. The best investment of money for breakfast foods is in the whole-grain and enriched or restored kinds. Cereals made from a combination of grains also are likely to give good returns in food value. Many ready-to-eat and ready-to-cook forms are available.

Sugar-coated cereals that are ready to eat cost more, per ounce, than many common unsweetened ones. Some of these sweetened cereals do not have added nutrients. Buying sugar-coated cereals, especially those that are not whole grain or enriched, can be an uneconomical use of food money.

Breakfast cereals promoted as extra high in certain nutrients also are apt to be higher priced. As a result, you may not get any more for your money than when you buy some of the cheaper whole-grain and enriched items.

A serving of cereal may cost less when the larger packages are purchased. Cereals you cook yourself, particularly the kinds that take longer to cook, are nearly always less expensive for a serving than the ready prepared ones.

BAKED GOODS usually can be made at home for less money than when bought ready baked or as mixes. A small group of homemakers in Dawson, Minn., took part in a study to see if it is more economical of time and

Cost of 100 Calories From Selected Fats and Sweets

Item	Purchase price per pound	Cost of 100 Calories	Amount to give 100 Calories
	Cents	Cents	Teaspoons
Butter......................	70	2.2	3
Salad oils....................	40	1.0	2½
Margarine...................	30	.9	3
Lard........................	25	.6	2⅓
Honey......................	35	2.6	5
Molasses....................	20	1.8	6
Sugar, brown................	15	.9	6
Sugar, white................	15	.9	6

Cost and Nutrient Contributions of Milk and Selected Milk Products

Item	Purchase price	Cost of serving	Size of serving	Percentage of daily allowances provided by a serving [1]		
				Protein	Calcium	Riboflavin
	Cents	Cents		Percent	Percent	Percent
Milk, whole, fluid....	25/quart.....	6	1 cup.......	12	36	25
Milk, skim..........	20/quart.....	5	....do......	13	38	26
Buttermilk..........	....do......	5	....do......	12	36	25
Evaporated milk.....	15/14½-ounce can.	4	1 cup diluted.	13	38	27
Nonfat dry milk......	45/pound....	2	1 cup reconstituted.	13	40	28
Ice cream..........	55/quart.....	7	½ cup.......	4	10	7
Cottage cheese.......	30/pound....	7	....do......	32	14	20
Cream cheese........	80/pound....	5	2 tablespoons.	4	2	4
Swiss cheese........	85/pound....	5	1 ounce.....	11	33	6
Cheddar-type cheese..	65/pound....	4	....do......	10	26	7

[1] For average adult.

money to make baked goods (starting with the ingredients) or to use bought mixes. They saved time using the commercial mixes, but the cake, cookies, piecrust, and biscuits cost more than those they made starting with individual ingredients.

When you compare the cost of home-baked goods with mixes and ready-to-eat items, compare those that are alike. For example, compare the cost of a cake mix for yellow cake and the extra ingredients the directions call for with what it would cost you to make a comparable plain yellow cake. The cost of a fancy or extra rich cake that might be baked at home should not be compared with that of a plain product, mix, or purchased cake.

Fats and sugars tend to be inexpensive sources of calories. The cheaper fats and refined sugars are among the most economical foods for calories only.

MORE OF THE food preparation is being taken out of the home kitchen.

We should expect that these added conveniences raise the prices of the foods. There are exceptions. Frozen and canned fruits and vegetables, for instance, may be cheaper than the fresh, especially when the fresh ones are out of season and in short supply.

Reasons for lower cost may be that fruit and vegetables are canned and frozen when supplies are large and prices low. Savings are made in transportation because only the edible parts of the foods are retained. Other savings may come because there is none of the waste that occurs in the handling and storage of perishable produce.

Money can be saved even when buying convenience foods, however.

To illustrate: Some cake mixes give more servings from a package than others. Some call for additional ingredients, such as egg or milk. To compare fairly the cost of mixes for the same type and quality of cake, we need to add the price of any extra ingredients to that of the package of mix. The next step is to determine the cost of a serving from the different mixes. By this means it is easy to see which is cheapest.

DOES YOUR MIND divide each item you wish to purchase into the number of servings it will yield? Do you often wonder if the fresh, canned, or frozen fruit is cheaper? You can calculate the relative cost of food items by dividing the number of servings yielded into the cost of the item.

You can make these calculations every time you shop, or you could make yourself a table. In the farthest column to the left, place a series of prices, for example from 5 to 50 cents. At the top of the columns list horizontally the typical number of servings for various units of retail items. Divide each number into each price. Place the appropriate price per serving opposite the price and under each number of servings. For example, opposite 10 cents and under two servings, place 5 cents as the cost of a serving, and under four servings, 2.5 cents the cost per serving. Continue in this manner for all prices and servings until the table is complete.

To use this table, you may want to compare the cost per serving of canned and frozen peas. The can gives four servings and costs 25 cents. Opposite 25 cents in the column to the left and under four servings, you will find 6.2 cents. This is the cost per serving for the canned variety. The box of frozen peas gives three servings and costs 20 cents. Opposite 20, and under three servings, the cost of the frozen peas is 6.7 cents per serving.

A guide for the number of servings to expect from market units of food you buy is a convenient tool to have in purchasing foods.

For milk, a serving size is usually 1 cup; for cheese, 1 ounce; and for ice cream, one-half cup. The servings per market unit can be easily estimated from these amounts.

The number of servings to expect from a pound of meat varies from one to two servings for bony cuts to about four servings for boneless cuts.

It is harder to estimate the number of servings per pound for fresh vegetables and fruit because of the variation in the amount that has to be trimmed in preparation for cooking. For example, lima beans in the pod or corn on the cob yield about two servings (one-half cup cooked) per pound; green snap beans or carrots yield four or five servings per pound. The trimmed, fresh greens usually purchased in packages yield a greater number of servings per pound than the bulk, untrimmed vegetables.

For cooked or ready-to-eat cereals count about 16 servings to the pound or an ounce for each serving.

LOUISE PAGE *is a nutrition analyst in the Household Economics Research Division of the Agricultural Research Service.*

ELOISE COFER *is a food economist in the Household Economics Research Division, Agricultural Research Service.*

Servings per Market Unit for Selected Foods

Food as purchased	Serving size	Market unit	Approximate number of servings per market unit
Milk, cheese, ice cream:			
Milk:			
Fluid, whole..............	1 cup.............	1 quart......	4.
Evaporated..............	1 cup diluted.......	14½-ounce can.	3½.
Nonfat dry milk solids.......	1 cup reconstituted..	1 pound.....	16 to 20.
Cheese:			
American................	¼ cup grated or 1 ounce.	....do......	16.
Cottage.................	⅓ cup.............	12-ounce package.	4½.
Cream, coffee................	2 tablespoons.......	½ pint......	8.
Ice cream...................	½ cup.............	1 quart......	8.
Meat, poultry, fish:			
Meat........................	Cooked lean meat 2½–3 ounces unless otherwise specified.		
Boned or boneless, ground...	....	1 pound.....	About 4.
With some bone, as chops, steaks, roast.	....	....do......	2 to 3.
With large amount of bone, as spareribs, shank, brisket, shortribs.	....	....do......	1 or 2.
Poultry: Fresh and frozen:			
Chickens:			
Broilers, ready-to-cook...	½ bird............	1 bird.......	2.
Fryers, ready-to-cook....	1 meaty plus 1 bony piece.	....do......	4.
Stewers, roasters........	2½–3 ounces cooked lean meat.	1 pound.....	1½ to 2½.
Turkeys, ready-to-cook......	....do.............	....do......	About 2.
Fish: Fresh or frozen:			
Fillets....................	2½–3 ounces cooked.	....do......	3 to 4.
Whole fish................	....do.............	....do......	1½ to 2.
Fish sticks, frozen..........	3–4 sticks..........	10 ounces....	2 to 2½.
Shellfish:			
Oysters, shucked..........	4 medium.........	1 pint.......	4 to 5.
Shrimp, fresh or frozen (green).	5 medium large....	1 pound.....	5 to 6.
Shrimp, fresh or frozen, cooked, peeled, cleaned.	2 ounces cooked meat.	....do......	8.
Canned:			
Luncheon meat, corned beef.	3 ounces..........	12-ounce can.	4.
Chicken, turkey, boned......	....do.............	6-ounce can..	2.
Salmon.................	2½–3 ounces.......	1-pound can.	4 to 5.
Tuna fish in oil, solid pack or chunk pack.	....do.............	6½–7-ounce can.	2.
Dried: Chipped beef..........	2 ounces cooked....	4-ounce package.	2½.
Vegetables:			
Fresh: Untrimmed unless indicated:	½ cup cooked unless otherwise indicated.		
Asparagus, lima beans in pod, broccoli, corn in husk, peas in pod.	....	1 pound.....	About 2.
Winter squash, greens, spinach, mashed sweetpotato.	....	....do......	2 to 3.

Food as purchased	Serving size	Market unit	Approximate number of servings per market unit
Vegetables—Con.			
Beets without tops, chard, cauliflower, collards, kale, potatoes, mashed or cubed, yellow summer squash, most root vegetables except carrots.	½ cup cooked unless otherwise indicated.	1 pound.....	3 to 4.
Beans, snap or wax, brussels sprouts, cabbage, carrots (without tops), eggplant, okra.	....	....do......	4 to 5.
Kale, trimmed.............	....	....do......	4 to 5.
Potatoes..................	1 baked medium....	....do......	2 to 3.
Sweetpotatoes.............	....do...........	....do......	2 to 2½.
Tomatoes................	1 small raw........	....do......	4.
Spinach, trimmed.........	....	....do......	3½.
Canned: All kinds............	½ cup heated......	8-ounce can..	2.
		16–17-ounce can.	4.
		20-ounce can.	4 to 5.
		29-ounce can.	6 to 7.
Frozen: All kinds.............	½ cup cooked......	10 ounces....	3.
Dried: Beans and peas any variety.	....do...........	1 pound.....	11.
Fruits:			
Fresh:			
Apples, bananas, oranges, pears.	1 medium.........	....do......	3.
Peaches..................	....do...........	....do......	4.
Plums...................	3 medium.........	....do......	4.
Watermelon..............	1 slice or wedge....	....do......	2½.
Berries:			
Blackberries, blueberries.	½ cup whole, raw...	1 quart......	8 to 9.
Cherries..............	....do...........	1 pound.....	5.
Cranberries...........	½ cup chopped, raw.	....do......	6.
Raspberries...........	½ cup whole, raw...	1 pint......	5 to 5½.
Canned: All fruits............	½ cup or 2 pieces of fruit and juice.	8½–8¾-ounce can.	2.
		9-ounce can..	2.
		16- to 17-ounce can.	4.
		20-ounce can.	5.
		29-ounce can.	7.
Frozen.....................	½ cup............	10 ounces....	2 to 3.
Dried: Apricots, peaches, prunes.	½ cup cooked fruit and juice.	1 pound.....	11 to 12.
Juices—Vegetable and fruit:			
Canned (single strength)........	½ cup............	18-ounce can.	4 to 5.
		46-ounce can.	11.
Frozen (concentrated 3 to 1)....	½ cup reconstituted juice.	6-ounce can..	6.
Bread, Cereal Products, Baked Goods:			
Bread.......................	1 slice............	1 pound.....	16.
Crackers:			
Graham..................	2 crackers.........	....do......	30.
Soda....................	....do...........	....do......	35.
Macaroni, noodles, spaghetti....	¾ cup cooked......	....do......	10 to 12.
Rice.......................	½ cup cooked......	....do......	16 to 17.

Food Plans at Different Costs

ELOISE COFER AND FAITH CLARK

THE food budgets of the Department of Agriculture have helped many families to estimate the money they need to set aside for food and to spend their food money prudently.

Farm families use them for planning how much food to grow at home and estimating the amount to preserve.

Nutritionists use them as a guide in counseling programs. Teachers use them in teaching food management. Many social welfare agencies base their family food allotments on the Department's budgets. Economists use the budgets as a check on estimates of potential demand for farm products.

The budgets—arranged as low-cost, moderate-cost, and liberal budgets—are plans for the amounts of different groups of foods that together supply an adequate diet.

The nutritional goal in devising the food plans is the Recommended Dietary Allowances of the Food and Nutrition Board of the National Academy of Sciences-National Research Council. The allowances are the amounts of calories and nine nutrients that are needed by children and adults.

The plans take into account the habits and practices of families in three income classes, because otherwise they would not be adaptable to family use. The guide for the low-cost plan was the food consumed weekly by families in the low-income group, as reported in surveys. For the moderate-cost plan, the amounts used by families with average income were used. The food of families with higher-than-average income served as the guide for the liberal plan.

Grouping of foods is a major aspect of a food plan or budget. In these budgets, we use 11 groupings—more than in guides for making nutritionally good selections. More groupings are needed to include all types of food that a housewife needs to provide a week's meals for her family.

The foods that have similar nutritional value or place in the menu are grouped together. For example, the dark-green and deep-yellow vegetables—broccoli, spinach, other dark greens, sweetpotatoes, pumpkin—excellent sources of vitamin A and iron, generally are used as part of the noon or evening meal.

Within each group are the many foods the family may choose to suit their own tastes and habits. A southern family may eat sweetpotatoes and turnip greens as their foods from the dark-green and the deep-yellow vegetables. The midwestern family may choose spinach for a vegetable and pumpkin for pie from the group.

THE 11 GROUPS and common foods in each are:

1. *Milk, cheese, ice cream.*

Milk—whole, skim, buttermilk, dry, evaporated, condensed; cheese; cream; ice cream.

Amounts suggested in the food plans are in terms of quarts of fluid milk. When buying cheese or ice cream, count the amount of milk as indicated: 1 pound of Cheddar-type cheese as 3 quarts of milk; 4-ounce package of cream cheese as one-fourth cup of milk; 12-ounce container of cottage cheese as about 1 cup of milk; 1 quart of ice cream as 1 pint of milk.

2. *Meat, poultry, fish, including bacon and salt pork.*

Beef, veal, lamb, pork; variety meats, such as liver, heart, tongue; luncheon meats; bacon; poultry; fish and shellfish.

In suggesting the amounts of meat for the food plans, we assume that families will buy no more than one-third pound of bacon and salt pork for each 5 pounds of other meat, poultry, and fish.

3. *Eggs.*

As eggs, or in cooking.

4. *Dry beans and peas, nuts.*

Dry beans of all kinds; dry peas, lentils, soybeans, and soya products; peanuts, peanut butter, and tree nuts.

5. *Flour, cereals, baked goods (whole grain, enriched, restored).*

Flour and meal; cereals, including ready-to-eat cereals; rice, hominy, noodles, macaroni, spaghetti; bread, cake, other baked goods.

Amounts suggested in the food plans are in terms of pounds of flour and cereal. Bread and other baked goods average two-thirds flour by weight. Therefore, count 1 pound of bread and baked goods as two-thirds pound of flour.

6. *Citrus fruit, tomatoes.*

Grapefruit, lemons, limes, oranges, tangerines; tomatoes.

7. *Dark-green and deep-yellow vegetables.*

Broccoli, chard, collards, kale, spinach, other dark greens, green peppers; carrots, pumpkin, yellow winter squash, sweetpotatoes.

8. *Potatoes.*

9. *Other vegetables and fruits.*

Asparagus, beets, brussels sprouts, cabbage, cauliflower, celery, corn, cucumbers, green lima beans, snap beans, lettuce, okra, onions, peas, rutabagas, sauerkraut, summer squash, turnips; apples, bananas, berries, dates, figs, grapes, peaches, pears, plums, prunes, raisins, rhubarb, and all vegetables and fruit not included in other groups.

10. *Fats and oils.*

Butter, margarine, mayonnaise, salad dressing, salad and cooking oils, fat drippings, lard and other shortening, suet.

11. *Sugar, sirup, preserves.*

Sugar (beet and cane), granulated, powdered, brown, maple; molasses, sirup, honey; jam, jelly, preserves.

FOR THE SAME expenditure of money, some foods give better nutritive returns than others.

Some foods that seem expensive when judged only by the cost per pound may be cheap when judged in terms of the amount of several nutrients supplied for the money spent.

Conversely, a cheap food may be expensive because it contributes so little to the nutritive value of the diet.

We can calculate the return in nutritive value from money spent for different kinds of food. The share of the total contribution that each food group makes to the supply of each

The Return in Nutritive Value From Money Spent for Different Kinds of Food by City Families in 1955

Food group	Money spent	Food energy	Pro-tein	Cal-cium	Iron	Vita-min A value	Thia-mine	Ribo-flavin	Nia-cin	Ascor-bic acid
	Pct.	Pct.	Pct.	Pct.	Pct.	Pct.	Pct.	Pct.	Pct.	Pct.
Milk, cheese, ice cream.........	14	15	22	65	3	13	13	44	3	6
Meat, poultry, fish.	33	23	40	4	34	19	25	21	50	1
Eggs.............	4	2	6	2	7	6	3	6	(1)	0
Dry beans, peas, nuts...........	1	2	3	1	4	(1)	2	1	5	(1)
Flour, cereal, baked goods..........	10	24	19	15	26	1	34	15	25	(1)
Citrus fruit, toma-toes...........	5	2	2	2	4	9	7	2	4	50
Dark-green and deep-yellow veg-etables........	2	1	1	2	3	31	2	2	1	10
Potatoes.........	2	3	2	1	4	(1)	5	2	5	8
Other vegetables and fruit.......	12	5	4	6	12	11	9	6	7	25
Fats, oils........	4	13	(1)	1	(1)	10	(1)	(1)	(1)	0
Sugar, sweets.....	5	10	1	1	2	(1)	(1)	1	(1)	(1)
Miscellaneous....	8	(1)	(1)	(1)	1	(1)	(1)	(1)	(1)	(1)
Total......	100	100	100	100	100	100	100	100	100	100

[1] Less than 1 percent.

nutrient may be compared with the share of the total money for food that was spent for that group.

An example: 14 percent of the money spent for food by a group of city families was spent for milk, cheese, and ice cream. It bought approximately 15 percent of the calories, 22 percent of the protein, 65 percent of the calcium, and 44 percent of the riboflavin.

Such comparisons enable us to see which foods give high returns in one or several nutrients and are therefore good purchases or bargains. Spending 14 percent of the food dollar for milk products and getting much more than 14 percent of the supply of four different nutrients means that milk products give good returns on the investment.

The proportion of money spent for potatoes in 1955 was only 2 percent, but the return was approximately 4 percent of the iron, 5 percent of the thiamine and niacin, and 8 percent of

the ascorbic acid furnished by all the food purchased.

The group that includes breads, cereals, and baked goods provides good amounts of several nutrients. It furnishes two to three times as large a share of the energy, iron, thiamine, and niacin in the total diet as the percentage of the total dollars spent on the group. Within this group, the enriched, restored and whole-grain items return more than three times their money value in iron and niacin and more than five times that value in thiamine.

We do not expect that all food groups will give as good returns in nutritive value as the milk, potatoes, and the grains we cited—some foods will give a high return in one or two nutrients, while a few will give high returns only in food energy (calories).

Five percent of the money spent for citrus fruit and tomatoes can buy 50 percent of the ascorbic acid in the diet—but relatively little of other nutrients. Thus it can be seen that one food group that gives excellent returns in a particular nutrient can supplement other groups that are poorer sources of the nutrient needed. Such figures can be used as a guide in choosing the most economical sources of the dietary essentials.

WITH THIS INFORMATION as a basis, we have worked out food plans—food budgets—at different cost levels.

Each plan gives the amount of food for persons of different ages for 1 week. The relative amounts of the 11 groups of food help to determine the cost level of the plans.

The low-cost plan has more potatoes, dry beans and peas, and flour, cereals, and baked goods. These are the foods that give relatively high returns in calories, protein, iron, and the B vitamins for the money.

The moderate-cost and liberal plans have more meat, eggs, and fruit and vegetables other than potatoes.

Milk is prominent in all three plans because of its high calcium content, its high-quality protein, and its other dietary essentials.

More or less expensive choices can be made within each group. This can raise or lower the cost of following the plan.

Families that must economize would expect to use more of the inexpensive foods in each of the groups. Homemakers who use the low-cost plan will prepare most dishes from basic ingredients when it is cheaper to do so.

Following a liberal plan could run food costs much higher than the estimates given here if many out-of-season foods, ready-to-eat meals, unusually expensive meats, rare cheeses, or other speciality foods are chosen frequently.

Seasonality, type of packaging, and many other factors affect the cost of the fresh, canned, and frozen product. It is economical to buy the form of the food that costs the least per serving.

Since somewhat more food must be brought into the house than will be eaten, the food plans provide for some extra poundage to cover losses and discards. Beyond the normal loss of rinds, peelings, and bones and fat of meat in preparing food for cooking, we also have allowed for some loss of calories and nutrients in the discard of plate scraps and leftovers.

The low-cost plan allows enough food to provide 5 percent more calories than the National Research Council's allowances suggest. For the moderate-cost plan, the amounts provide 15 percent more calories. The liberal plan provides 20 percent more calories.

The number of calories and amounts of 8 nutrients have been calculated for each of 19 family-member groups in the three plans. The food values used in estimating the nutritive value of the food plan quantities are from "Composition of Foods—Raw, Processed, Prepared," Agricultural Handbook 8.

Allowance was made for average loss of vitamins in cooking all foods and for loss of fat in cooking meat. Diets based on the suggested food plans are nutritionally adequate in number of calories and in eight nutrients, as judged by the National Research Council's allowances. For most of the family-member groups—and for most nutrients—there is ample margin above the recommended allowances.

The low-cost plan is just as generous in calcium, thiamine, and riboflavin as the moderate-cost and liberal plans. The more expensive plans provide a more generous margin above the allowances than the low-cost plan in protein, ascorbic acid, vitamin A, and niacin.

The vitamin D value of the plans has not been calculated. It may be supplied by some foods (milk, for example), by sunshine, or, on the advice of a physician, from a natural or synthetic vitamin D preparation.

The proportion of calories to nutrients is lower for women than for men. Women therefore should take extra care in selecting foods that are good sources of some of the nutrients, especially iron and ascorbic acid.

Cost of Food Suggested in Three Plans by Families of Selected Size, January 1959

Family type	Low-cost plan per week	Moderate-cost plan per week	Liberal plan per week
	Dollars	Dollars	Dollars
Family of 1, woman.........................	7–8	10–12	11–13
Family of 2 persons, 20–34 years of age..............	15–17	20–22	23–25
Family of 2 persons, 55–74 years of age..............	13–15	18–20	21–23
Family of 4 with preschool children (man and woman 20–34, children, 1–3 and 4–6 years)................	20–22	27–29	31–33
Family of 4 with school age children (man and woman 20–34 years, child 7–9, and boy, 10–12 years).......	23–25	32–34	36–38
Family of 6 (man and woman 35–54 years, boy 16–19, girl 13–15, children, 7–9 and 10–12 years)..........	37–39	52–54	59–60

Each family can make its own choices within the groups of food and thus adapt the plan to its own food likes and to market offerings and can prepare the food in keeping with family customs.

WHICH PLAN to follow may depend on the amount of money that can be spent for food. The total cost of food is related, of course, to the size of the family and the age of its members, as well as to the type of diet—low, moderate, or liberal.

For the family of four—a young mother, father, a boy 11 years old, and a girl 8 years old—the cost of diets selected according to the plans in January 1959 was 24 dollars a week for the low-cost plan, 33 dollars for the moderate-cost plan, and 37 dollars for the liberal plan.

These costs are based on the amounts of the food groups specified in each plan and on current average costs per pound of each of the food groups. The costs include some outlay for such miscellaneous items as salt, vinegar, and coffee, although the plans list no amounts of them.

In general, to follow the moderate-cost plan will cost about 25 to 35 percent more than to follow the low-cost plan. To follow the liberal plan will cost 10 to 20 percent or even more than to follow the moderate-cost plan.

Families of one or two members usually cannot buy and use their food as economically as can larger families. Allowance for that is made in the pricing of the plans for small families.

AFTER SELECTING the plan that seems most appropriate to your purse and tastes, the next step is to determine the total amounts of the food groups you need.

To do that you need to make a food plan for your family: List your family members by age; refer to the master plan to find the amounts of food groups for each person in the family; total the amounts for each of the food groups. You now have a family food plan.

The family of four (mother and father, about 33 years old; a boy, 11; and a girl of 8 years) using the moderate-cost plan would have a weekly food plan that would total 19 or 20 quarts of milk; 16 or 17 pounds of meat, poultry, and fish; 24 to 30 eggs; 10.5 to 11.5 pounds of cereal products; 8 or 9 pounds of potatoes; and 9.5 to 10.5 pounds of citrus fruit and tomatoes.

These amounts are only guides for keeping the groups in proper balance and for keeping an eye on the cost. A family will not buy the food listed in each group to the nearest ounce. The ranges give some idea of the leeway for buying quantities within a group. If some members of the family always eat lunch at school or work, the amounts needed for home meals will be less.

During weeks when it is most economical to buy vegetables and fruit in the fresh form, the amounts of them should be increased because there will be more than average discard of peelings, seeds, and other inedible parts than when some of them are bought in processed forms. When all the meat is bought as ground beef or other boneless cuts, a smaller amount will be needed than when many items with a lot of bone are purchased.

CERTAIN ADJUSTMENTS may be made in quantity without affecting the cost or the food value of the plans. The amounts given for the dark-green and deep-yellow vegetable groups are minimal. Additional pounds from this group may be used and a like amount subtracted from the others in the vegetables and fruit group. Replacing "dark-green and deep-yellow" vegetables with those of the "other vegetables and fruit" group, however, may unduly lower the vitamin A value of the week's food.

The amounts of foods for individuals in the plans are for persons of average height and at ideal weight for that height. To adjust the quantities for children who are taller or growing more rapidly than their age group, the plan for the next higher age level may be used.

For adults who are taller than average (69 inches for men and 64 inches for women) or who are very active physically, more calories may be added by increasing the amounts of one or more groups.

Additions to the animal-products groups (milk, meat, eggs) will add more to the cost of the plans than will the addition of other foods.

Additions to the flour and cereal group will provide calories and nutrients at relatively low cost. For persons

Preparing a Family Food Plan

Family members	Milk, cheese, ice cream (Qts.)	Meat, poultry, fish (Lb.)	(Oz.)	Eggs (No.)	Dry beans and peas, nuts (Oz.)	Flour, cereal, baked goods (Lb.)	(Oz.)	Potatoes (Lb.)	(Oz.)	Citrus fruit, tomatoes (Lb.)	(Oz.)	Green and yellow vegetables (Lb.)	(Oz.)	Other vegetables and fruit (Lb.)	(Oz.)	Fats, oils (Lb.)	(Oz.)	Sugar, sweets (Lb.)	(Oz.)
Man............	3½	5	8	7	4	4	0	3	0	2	12	0	12	6	8	1	0	1	4
Woman.........	3½	4	4	6	2	2	4	1	8	2	8	0	12	5	12	0	8	0	14
Boy, 11 years....	6½	4	0	7	4	2	12	2	4	2	8	0	12	5	8	0	10	0	14
Girl, 8 years....	6	3	0	7	2	2	0	1	12	2	4	0	8	4	12	0	10	0	14
Total........	19½	16	12	27	12	11	0	8	8	10	0	2	12	22	8	2	12	3	14
Range........	19-20 qt.	16-17 lb.		2-2½ doz.	½-1 lb.	10½-11½ lb.		8-9 lb.		9½-10½ lb.		2-3 lb.		22-23 lb.		2½-3 lb.		3½-4 lb.	

Food Plan at Low Cost: Suggested Weekly Quantities of Food (as Purchased, Assuming Average Choices Within Groups) for 19 Sex-Age Groups

Family members	Milk, cheese, ice cream Qt.	Meat, poultry, fish Lb.	Oz.	Eggs No.	Dry beans, peas, nuts Lb.	Oz.	Flour, cereal, baked goods Lb.	Oz.	Citrus fruit, tomatoes Lb.	Oz.	Dark-green and deep-yellow vegetables Lb.	Oz.	Potatoes Lb.	Oz.	Other vegetables and fruit Lb.	Oz.	Fats, oils Lb.	Oz.	Sugar, sweets Oz.
Children:																			
Under 1 year	5½	1	0	5	0	0	0	12	1	8	0	2	0	8	1	0	0	1	2
1–3 years	5½	0	4	5	0	1	1	4	1	8	0	4	0	12	2	4	0	4	4
4–6 years	5½	1	8	5	0	2	2	0	1	12	0	4	1	4	3	4	0	6	6
7–9 years	5½	2	0	6	0	4	2	4	2	0	0	8	2	0	4	4	0	8	10
10–12 years	6½	2	4	6	0	6	3	0	2	4	0	8	2	8	5	0	0	8	12
Girls:																			
13–15 years	7	2	8	6	0	4	3	0	2	4	0	12	2	8	5	0	0	10	12
16–19 years	7	2	8	6	0	4	2	12	2	4	0	12	2	4	4	12	0	6	10
Boys:																			
13–15 years	7	2	8	6	0	6	4	4	2	8	0	12	3	4	5	4	0	12	12
16–19 years	7	3	4	6	0	8	5	4	2	8	0	12	4	12	5	8	0	14	14
Women:																			
20–34 years	3½	2	8	5	0	4	2	8	2	0	0	12	2	0	5	0	0	6	10
35–54 years	3½	2	8	5	0	4	2	8	2	0	0	12	1	8	4	8	0	4	10
55–74 years	3½	2	8	5	0	4	2	4	2	0	0	12	1	4	3	8	0	4	6
75 years and over	3½	2	8	5	0	4	2	0	2	0	0	12	1	4	3	0	0	4	6
Pregnant	7	2	8	7	0	4	2	8	3	8	1	8	2	0	5	0	0	6	8
Lactating	10	3	4	7	0	4	3	0	3	8	1	8	3	4	5	8	0	8	10
Men:																			
20–34 years	3½	3	12	6	0	6	4	4	2	4	0	12	3	4	5	8	0	12	0
35–54 years	3½	3	8	6	0	6	3	12	2	4	0	12	3	0	5	0	0	10	12
55–74 years	3½	3	4	6	0	4	3	8	2	4	0	12	2	8	4	12	0	10	10
75 years and over	3½	3	4	6	0	4	3	4	2	0	0	12	2	4	4	8	0	8	10

who are small or sedentary, the amount of fats and oils, sweet foods, and bulky vegetables may be reduced but not the amounts of milk, meat, eggs, cereals, fruits, and nonbulky vegetables. This adjustment will lower the calorie intake while keeping the other food values high.

MAKING A MENU is the next step, once the type of diet and amounts of groups of food needed by the family have been estimated.

If much of the family marketing is done weekly, it is more satisfactory to make weekly menu plans.

Here are a week's menus for the moderate-cost plan used by a family of four in the Washington, D.C., area:

SUNDAY

Breakfast:

Grapefruit Halves
Waffles—Sirup
Bacon
Milk for children

Dinner:

Braised Chuck Roast and Onions
Broccoli   Browned Potatoes
Lettuce Wedges—Cheese Dressing
Rolls
Sliced Peaches   Cake
Milk for children

Supper:

Peanut Butter Sandwiches
Asparagus Salad—French Dressing
Baked Apple with Vanilla Ice Cream
Milk

MONDAY

Breakfast:

Orange Juice
Poached Eggs on Toast
Milk for children

Lunch:

Vegetable Soup
Toasted Cheese Sandwiches
Coleslaw
Milk

Dinner:

Casserole of Beef and Lima Beans
Mashed Potatoes
Cucumber-Onion Salad
Bread
Fruit Gelatin   Cake
Milk for children

TUESDAY

Breakfast:

Grapefruit Juice
Ready-To-Eat Cereal
Raisin Bread Toast
Milk for children

Lunch:

Hamburgers—Buns
Celery Sticks
Oatmeal Cookies
Milk

Dinner:

Fried Chicken—Gravy
Parsley Potatoes   Carrots
Waldorf Salad
Bread
Cherry Cobbler
Milk for children

WEDNESDAY

Breakfast:

Grapefruit-Orange Juice
Fried Eggs—Bacon
Raisin Bread Toast
Milk for children

Lunch:

Chicken-Rice Soup
Green Salad—Cheese Dressing
Jelly Sandwiches
Apples
Milk

Dinner:

Sauteed Liver
Mashed Potatoes
Marinated Green Bean Salad
Cornbread
Bananas and Raspberries
Milk for children

Food Plan at Moderate Cost: Suggested Weekly Quantities of Food (as Purchased, Assuming Average Choices Within Groups) for 19 Sex-Age Groups

Family members	Milk, cheese, ice cream	Meat, poultry, fish		Eggs	Dry beans, peas, nuts		Flour, cereal, baked goods		Citrus fruit, tomatoes		Dark-green and deep-yellow vegetables		Potatoes		Other vegetables and fruit		Fats, oils		Sugar, sweets	
	Qt.	Lb.	Oz.	No.	Lb.	Oz.	Lb.	Oz.	Lb.	Oz.	Lb.	Oz.	Lb.	Oz.	Lb.	Oz.	Lb.	Oz.	Lb.	Oz.
Children:																				
Under 1 year	6	1	4	6	0	0	0	12	1	8	0	2	0	8	1	8	0	1	0	2
1–3 years	6	1	12	6	0	1	1	0	1	8	0	4	0	12	2	12	0	4	0	4
4–6 years	6	2	4	6	0	0	1	12	2	0	1	4	1	0	4	0	0	6	0	10
7–9 years	6	3	0	7	2	2	2	0	2	4	1	8	1	12	4	12	0	10	0	14
10–12 years	6½	4	0	7	0	4	2	12	2	8	2	12	2	4	5	8	0	10	0	14
Girls:																				
13–15 years	7	4	8	7	0	0	2	12	2	8	2	12	2	4	5	12	0	12	0	14
16–19 years	7	4	4	7	0	2	2	8	2	8	2	12	2	0	5	8	0	10	0	12
Boys:																				
13–15 years	7	4	12	7	0	4	4	0	2	12	3	0	3	0	6	0	0	14	1	0
16–19 years	7	5	8	7	0	6	5	0	3	0	4	12	4	4	6	4	1	2	1	2
Women:																				
20–34 years	3½	4	4	6	0	2	2	4	2	8	2	12	1	8	5	12	0	8	0	14
35–54 years	3½	4	4	6	0	2	2	0	2	8	2	12	1	4	5	4	0	8	0	12
55–74 years	3½	4	4	6	0	2	1	12	2	4	2	12	1	4	4	4	0	6	0	8
75 years and over	3½	3	12	6	0	2	2	12	2	4	2	12	0	8	3	12	0	6	0	8
Pregnant	7	4	4	7	0	2	2	4	3	8	1	8	1	8	5	12	0	8	0	12
Lactating	10	5	0	7	0	2	2	12	5	0	1	8	2	12	6	4	0	12	0	12
Men:																				
20–34 years	3½	5	8	7	0	4	4	0	2	12	3	12	3	0	6	8	1	0	1	4
35–54 years	3½	5	4	7	0	4	3	8	2	12	2	12	2	8	5	12	0	14	1	0
55–74 years	3½	5	0	7	0	2	3	4	2	12	2	12	2	4	5	8	0	12	0	14
75 years and over	3½	5	0	7	0	2	2	12	2	8	2	12	2	0	5	4	0	10	0	12

THURSDAY

Breakfast:

Orange Slices
Oatmeal with Raisins
Toast
Milk for children

Lunch:

Scrambled Eggs
Hashed-Brown Potatoes
Toasted Cornbread
Fresh Fruit in Season
Milk

Dinner:

Swiss Steak—Gravy
Potatoes Boiled in Jackets
Greens
Raw Vegetable Relishes (Celery,
Carrots, Peppers)
Bread
Frozen Peppermint Pudding
Milk for children

FRIDAY

Breakfast:

Tomato Juice
Omelet
Toast—Jelly
Milk for children

Lunch:

Cubed Swiss Steak and Gravy
(left over)
on Toast
Green Beans
Tomato and Shredded Cheese Salad
Bread
Milk

Dinner:

Fish
Creamed Potatoes   Peas and Celery
Tossed Green Salad
Bread
Lemon Pie
Milk for children

SATURDAY

Breakfast:

Orange Juice
Ready-To-Eat Cereal
Toast
Milk for children

Lunch:

Luncheon Meat Sandwiches
(with lettuce)
Celery and Carrot Sticks
Lemon Tarts
Milk

Dinner:

Sweet-Sour Spareribs Chinese Style
Rice   Buttered Beets
Green Salad
Bread
Cookies
Milk for children

FOOD FOR THE WEEK'S MENU

Milk, Cheese, Ice Cream:
19 quarts fluid whole milk
½ pound Cheddar cheese
1 ounce blue cheese
1 pint vanilla ice cream

Meats, Poultry, Fish:
4 pounds beef chuck
2 pounds round steak
1 pound ground beef
3 pounds pork spareribs
¾ pound bacon
1 pound liver
3–4 pounds chicken
1 pound fish, fillet
½ pound luncheon meat

Eggs: 2½ dozen

Dry Beans, Peas, Nuts:
⅓ pound dried lima beans
⅓ pound peanut butter
1 ounce walnuts (pieces)

Dark-Green, Deep-Yellow Vegetables:
1 bunch broccoli
1–1½ pounds carrots
½ bunch parsley
½ pound green peppers
1 pound salad greens
2 pounds greens

Food Plan at Liberal Cost: Suggested Weekly Quantities of Food (as Purchased, Assuming Average Choices Within Groups) for 19 Sex-Age Groups

Family members	Milk, cheese, ice cream (Qt.)	Meat, poultry, fish (Lb.)	(Oz.)	Eggs (No.)	Dry beans, peas, nuts (Lb.)	(Oz.)	Flour, cereal, baked goods (Lb.)	(Oz.)	Citrus fruit, tomatoes (Lb.)	(Oz.)	Dark-green and deep-yellow vegetables (Lb.)	(Oz.)	Potatoes (Lb.)	(Oz.)	Other vegetables and fruit (Lb.)	(Oz.)	Fats, oils (Lb.)	(Oz.)	Sugar, sweets (Lb.)	(Oz.)
Children:																				
Under 1 year	6	1	4	7	0	0	0	12	1	12	0	2	0	8	1	8	0	2	0	2
1–3 years	6	2	4	7	0	1	1	0	1	12	0	4	0	12	2	12	0	4	0	4
4–6 years	6	3	0	7	0	1	1	8	2	4	0	8	0	12	4	8	0	8	0	12
7–9 years	6	3	12	7	0	2	1	12	2	12	0	8	1	8	5	4	0	10	1	0
10–12 years	6½	4	12	7	0	4	2	12	3	0	0	12	2	4	6	0	0	10	1	0
Girls:																				
13–15 years	7	5	8	7	0	2	2	8	3	0	0	12	2	4	6	0	0	12	1	2
16–19 years	7	5	4	7	0	2	2	4	3	0	0	12	1	12	5	12	0	10	1	0
Boys:																				
13–15 years	7	5	8	7	0	4	4	0	3	4	0	12	3	0	6	8	0	14	1	4
16–19 years	7	6	4	7	0	6	5	0	3	8	0	12	4	4	7	4	1	4	1	2
Women:																				
20–34 years	4	4	12	6	0	1	2	0	3	0	0	12	1	4	6	4	0	8	1	2
35–54 years	4	4	12	6	0	1	1	12	3	0	0	12	1	0	6	0	0	8	1	0
55–74 years	4	4	12	6	0	1	1	8	3	0	0	12	1	0	4	8	0	6	0	12
75 years and over	4	4	4	6	0	0	1	8	3	0	0	12	0	12	4	0	0	6	1	0
Pregnant	7	4	12	7	0	1	2	0	4	8	1	8	1	4	6	4	0	8	0	0
Lactating	10	5	12	7	0	2	2	12	5	8	1	8	2	8	6	4	0	12	1	2
Men:																				
20–34 years	4	6	0	7	0	4	3	12	3	0	0	12	2	12	7	12	1	0	1	8
35–54 years	4	5	8	7	0	4	3	8	3	0	0	12	2	4	6	8	0	14	1	4
55–74 years	4	5	4	7	0	2	3	4	3	0	0	12	2	0	6	0	0	12	1	2
75 years and over	4	5	4	7	0	2	2	12	2	12	0	12	1	12	5	12	0	10	1	0

Potatoes:
  8–9 pounds white potatoes
Fats and Oils:
  1 pound table fat
  1 pound shortening
  1 pint salad dressing
  ½ cup salad oil
Citrus Fruit, Tomatoes:
  2 grapefruit
  1–1½ pounds oranges
  ¾ pound tomatoes
  1 No. 2 can grapefruit juice
  1 No. 2 can grapefruit-orange
    juice
  1 No. 2 can tomato juice
  1 No. 303 can tomatoes
  2 6-ounce cans frozen orange juice
Other Vegetables and Fruit:
  2 pounds green beans
  1 bunch beets
  ⅓ pound cabbage
  1 bunch celery
  ½ pound cucumbers
  2 heads lettuce
  1 pound onions
  1 14½-ounce can green asparagus
  1 can condensed vegetable soup
  1 package frozen peas
  3 pounds apples
  1 pound bananas
  1–1½ pounds fresh fruit in season
  1 No. 303 can cherries
  1 No. 2½ can sliced peaches
  ½ pound raisins
  1 package raspberries (frozen)
Sugar and Sweets:
  1½–2 pounds granulated sugar
  ½ pint sirup
  ½ pound jelly
  1 package flavored gelatin
  1 package lemon filling mix
  1 ounce peppermint candy
Baked Goods, Flour, Cereals:
  2 loaves enriched white bread
  1 loaf whole wheat bread
  1 loaf cracked wheat bread
  1 loaf rye bread
  1 loaf raisin bread
  4 hamburger rolls
  6 brown-and-serve rolls
  5 ounces plain chocolate cookies
  2¼ pounds all-purpose flour

⅔ pound oatmeal
10 ounces ready-to-eat cereal
⅔ pound cornmeal
½ pound rice

After the week's menus have been made out, the foods and the amounts needed for the week to prepare them should be listed, just as we have done. Compare the totals for each food group with the quantities of the 11 food groups for the plan you choose.

Some amounts may be much higher or much lower than the suggested plan. If so, go back and revise the menus. When you get a set of menus and a corresponding list of foods that approximates the food plans, try them out for a week. The cost will be close to the costs we have estimated.

The next week you may want to make some modifications in the kind or amounts of the different foods you buy. Do not feel you have to follow the plans here slavishly. They are merely guides to help families plan.

ADAPTING THESE menus and market order to the low-cost plan will mean planning meals with more emphasis on grains, potatoes, and dry beans and peas and less emphasis on meats, eggs, and fruit. It also means choosing most of the time the less expensive foods within each food group.

The breakfast menus for the moderate-cost plan we gave generally follow a pattern of fruit, cereal, and milk, or eggs with or without bacon, toast or hot bread, and a beverage. The amounts of eggs and meat suggested for the low-cost plan are not large enough for them to be used frequently for breakfast. In their place, the low-cost menus will feature cereal oftener.

The cost of the breakfast menu can be kept low by making wise choices of fruit and cereals. Citrus fruit is a good choice as fruit for breakfast in any meal plan. Careful comparison shopping will help you choose the form—fresh, canned, or frozen—that is best to buy at a particular time.

Hot cereals, those that have to have some cooking, are usually more economical than the ready-to-serve varieties. Some like to add raisins or other fruit to cereal.

If your family likes a hot bread for breakfast, you may want to have pancakes instead of waffles. Pancakes usually take fewer eggs.

Several of the lunches in the moderate-cost menus we have given contain soup and sandwiches or sandwiches and salads with milk served to everyone. These combinations, using the less expensive foods, can be followed for low-cost menus. Potatoes and dry beans and peas can be used as a base for the soups in low-cost lunches. Soups or chowders using beans or potatoes also give opportunity for using less expensive forms of milk such as nonfat dry milk. The meat filling of sandwiches can be replaced by peanut butter, and the cheese can be extended with chopped vegetables. Left-over meat goes further as a sandwich filling if it is ground and combined with chopped raw cabbage, onions, carrots, or celery. It can also be added to macaroni, spaghetti, or rice to make economical luncheon dishes.

There is enough milk in the low-cost plan for it to be used as the beverage for everyone at lunch.

The amount of meat in the low-cost plan is large enough to give everyone a generous serving each day for dinner. Or by extending the meat served at dinner with potatoes, bread, or other cereal products, meat may sometimes be served at other meals as well. The choice of kinds of meat to serve depends on the market at a particular time. Beef, veal, lamb, pork, poultry, and fish have times when one or another is most economical.

Every housewife knows that for each kind of meat some cuts are less expensive per pound than others. They may be less tender or have a larger proportion of bone and fat to lean.

In choosing cuts for the low-cost plan, select the cheaper cuts, but consider the cost per serving as well as the cost per pound. If you have a choice between U.S. Good and U.S. Choice grades of meat, choose the U.S. Good for pot roasts, ground beef, and stews. Do not overlook liver—beef, pork, lamb—as it is a bargain in vitamins and minerals. Fish, fresh, canned or frozen, may be cheaper than meat.

Consider, too, the relative cost of poultry. Although poultry has a large proportion of bone to lean, it is often a bargain. As a general rule, frying chickens are as cheap as fairly lean ground beef (in protein) when the price per pound of the chicken is three-quarters or less the price of beef.

Many low-cost vegetables and fruits are good nutritionally. Carrots, for example, are an excellent source of vitamin A. They are available all year and usually are relatively cheap. When fresh vegetables and fruit are in season locally, they are generally cheapest. At other times the canned or frozen products may be the bargains.

Since the low-cost plan has smaller amounts of vegetables and fruit than the other plans, fruit cannot be served so often for dessert. However, grain products can be the basis for desserts, with fruit to add flavor and contrast in taste. Some of the milk, eggs, fat, and sugar may well be used in making desserts, such as cookies, puddings, gingerbread, and custards.

It doubtless takes more skill and imagination to be a good meal planner and cook when using the low-cost plan. The reward comes in having a satisfied, well-fed family.

ELOISE COFER *is a food economist in the Household Economics Research Division, Agricultural Research Service, Washington, D.C. Before joining the Department in 1955, she was a nutrition specialist with the Extension Service of West Virginia. She has a doctor's degree from the University of Chicago.*

FAITH CLARK *is Director of the Household Economics Research Division and has participated in the development of food budgets for families for many years.*

Food

TRENDS

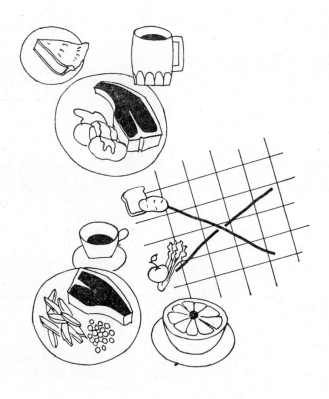

Pounds and Percentages

MARGUERITE C. BURK

AN American eats just about 100 pounds less food than an American did 50 years ago, but he eats differently. The average was about 1,600 pounds a year just before the First World War.

Americans are eating more of the foods they want and have better diets than they did 50 years ago.

The apparent inconsistency between these facts and the reduction in poundage is explained by the weaknesses of poundage as a measure of the consumption of all foods. The amount of water and cellulose affects the poundage, and the number of pounds does not reflect preferences of consumers or production or marketing costs. We use a measure based on value to reflect these aspects of demand and supply.

To develop such a measure, we multiplied the annual average number of pounds of each food consumed per capita in 1947–1949 by its average retail price in that period. We added the 78.56 dollars for meat, the 7.70 dollars for fish, and so on, and obtained 324 dollars as the average value at retail of all food a person consumed a year in 1947–1949.

Comparable calculations for each food consumed in 1909 and 1956 yielded total values for each year of 286 and 336 dollars, respectively. The 1909 value is 89 percent of the 1947–1949 average value; the value for 1956 is 104 percent.

The measure has been named the index of per capita food consumption. It has been computed for each year since 1909. The series reveals some interesting facts about overall changes in the consumption of food.

Average consumption of food in the 1920's was higher than the level before the First World War. Economic depression and droughts reduced the overall average during the mid-1930's below 90 percent of the 1947–1949 average. Thereafter a higher output of food and higher incomes meant that consumption of food began going up. It reached 97 percent in 1941.

Supplies of food for civilians could not meet consumer demand during the Second World War because of the military needs. Therefore some foods were rationed. Even so, the annual index of food consumption by civilians did not drop below 96.

When housewives were restocking their pantries and retailers their shelves at the end of the war and more people than ever were eating as they

Trends in Our Eating Habits

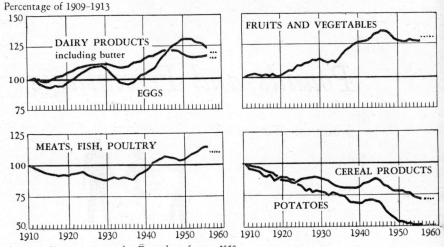

Percentage of 1909–1913

5-year moving average centered. Data shown for year 1958.
Per capita civilian consumption, U.S. (using 1947–1949 retail prices as weights).

wished, record quantities of food moved through distribution channels to civilians.

Retail prices rose sharply after decontrol in 1946 and civilian buying of food tapered off from the rather artificial 1946 peak for a few years. Real incomes per capita have gone up more than food prices since 1951, and output of food has reached new highs. Civilian food consumption consequently increased gradually to equal in 1956 the record level—104 percent of 1947–1949. But consumption of food averaged somewhat lower in 1957–1958.

Such is the broad outline of changes in the consumption of food in the United States.

How do we know such changes have occurred?

How do we know how much food is consumed each year?

To be frank, we do not know precisely how much of each food is actually eaten each year, but we can measure the total flow of food past particular points in the distribution system during a year.

For example, millers report to the Bureau of the Census how much flour

they mill. The Bureau also collects data on how much flour is exported and imported each year. From the Department of Defense we find out how much flour and baked goods it buys for the Armed Forces. By adding the amounts of flour produced and imported and subtracting the amounts exported and taken for military use, we get a good estimate of how much flour moved into distribution channels in each year for civilian use. We have to assume that millers' and distributors' stocks on hand did not change.

This measure of annual flow into civilian use, described as apparent disappearance, is the best gage of annual consumption of flour by the civilian population. By dividing the total disappearance (or consumption) figure by the number of civilians, we get an estimate of per capita consumption. For example, the flour figure for 1955 is 123 pounds per capita, compared with 217 pounds for 1909.

It is harder to measure the consumption of fresh produce. Take fresh oranges, for instance. The Crop Reporting Board of the Department of Agriculture collects from orange growers and people who deal with them information about how many oranges the growers sell to distributors for sale as fresh (not including sales to processors to make orange juice and other items) and how many they use in their own homes. Here, too, we take account of imports, exports, and military takings in estimating the total going to civilians. By dividing this total by the population figure, we obtain the per capita rates. But this calculation does not allow for oranges that spoil between the time they leave the grove and the time they are put in the shoppers' sacks. The spoilage runs about 5 percent. So we take 95 percent of the farm weight of oranges per capita as the retail weight of oranges consumed each year.

The procedures we use for every food are described in Consumption of Food in the United States, 1909–1952, Agriculture Handbook No. 62. A compilation of the data for 1909 to 1956 was published as the Supplement for 1956 to that volume in September 1957. Current data for major foods are reported each quarter in the periodical, National Food Situation.

HISTORICAL TRENDS in consumption rates for major foods are quite divergent. In general, livestock products have increased more than crops. The consumption of potatoes and sweetpotatoes and of cereal products has declined substantially.

Little change was evident between 1909–1913 and 1954–1958 in per capita consumption of fats and oils, fish, and the group that includes dry beans, peas, and nuts, but some significant shifts occurred among foods in these groups.

Now a few comments about the food groups for which consumption rates have been higher in the mid-1950's than in the years immediately before the First World War. Meat consumption has been only slightly higher than 50 years earlier, but the low level of the 1930's makes current rates seem quite high by comparison. Also, poul-

try, the consumption of which doubled, has supplemented supplies of red meat.

We have been eating a fifth more eggs per capita, but much of the increase has been in the egg content of purchased prepared foods.

The consumption of dairy products, excluding butter, has gradually increased to a level about 40 percent above that of 50 years earlier. The increases came in manufactured dairy products and in fluid whole milk. The decline in consumption of butter holds down the trend for all dairy products on the chart.

The consumption of fruit rose 10 to 15 percent between 1909–1913 and recent years. A big shift from apples to citrus fruit and from fresh to processed forms has occurred.

Consumption rates have gone up about one-third for vegetables other than potatoes and sweetpotatoes. The increase in poundage has not equaled the decline in potatoes and sweetpotatoes.

Americans have been consuming more sugar and sirup in all forms than they did 50 years ago, but less than in the 1920's.

The consumption of coffee and cocoa (but not tea) is up.

WITHIN FOOD GROUPS there have been some striking changes in the rates of consumption. The consumption of potatoes and sweetpotatoes is only about half the per capita average of 50 years ago.

Although the consumption of wheat flour in all forms is down almost 100 pounds per capita, from the 215 pounds or so before the First World War, the consumption of flour in forms of purchased bread and other bakery products has increased. This gradual shift from purchases of family flour for home cooking and baking to purchases of flour in processed foods tends to raise expenditures for cereal products. The use per capita of cornmeal, hominy, and grits has fallen drastically. Consumption rates for wheat cereals and oat food products are about the same now as 50 years ago, but less rice and barley are used per capita.

Some changes offset others. The increase in the average poundage of nuts has been about equal to the decline in dry beans and peas, including those in canned pork and beans and in soups. Similarly, the poundage declines in butter and lard, the major animal fats, have balanced the increase in margarine, shortening, and other edible fats and oils of vegetable origin.

There has been a substantial shift from salmon to other types of canned fish, and from cured fish to fresh and frozen fish since the 1920's, as supplies and marketing facilities have changed.

The overall level of consumption of fish per capita from the commercially caught supplies apparently has been about the same in recent years as 50 years ago. We know little about the catch of game fish for family use.

The types of meat we consumed have changed with the swings in the hog and cattle cycles. Economists have identified rather systematic expansions and contractions in livestock production as farmers have tried to adjust their operations and have overcompensated for changes in market prices of livestock and in feed prices.

After these swings are taken into account, the level of pork consumption per capita appears to be generally about the same now as five decades ago, that of lamb and mutton is down, and consumption of beef and veal is somewhat higher.

Americans are consuming more fluid whole milk now than they did 50 years ago, but less than the record rate in the war years. The use of fluid cream has declined markedly in the past 10 years. Consumption of fluid skim milk is apparently only half as high as several decades ago, when the farm population made up a larger part of the United States total. Farm families commonly separated the cream and skim milk, selling the cream and using the skim milk for the family and for feeding chickens and pigs. In the 1950's, however, commercial sales of fluid skim milk increased sharply. Chocolate milk has grown in popularity, and consumption of skim milk in chocolate drinks now averages about 8 pounds per capita, about two-thirds of the rate for skim milk as such.

The use of nonfat dry milk (dry skim milk) has risen gradually from none at the time of the First World War to about 5 pounds per capita. In fluid skim milk equivalent, this amount of dry powder is four or five times as large as the 11-pound decline in consumption of fluid skim milk from 1909 to recent years. Much of the powder is used in commercially prepared foods.

Remembering the gallons of homemade ice cream consumed years ago, no researcher would insist that consumption of all ice cream is anywhere near 10 times as high as it was 50 years ago—but data on commercially produced ice cream show that degree of increase. The milk and cream used in homemade ice cream is counted in the figures for fluid whole milk and cream.

The average use of condensed milk has declined in the past several decades, but the per capita consumption of evaporated milk increased manyfold from 1909 to recent years, although the average is down now from the record level of 1946–1950.

We are now consuming about twice as much whole and part-whole milk cheese of commercial manufacture as before the First World War. The consumption of cottage cheese has risen even more. The upsurge in the use of cultured buttermilk has not offset the decline in use of natural buttermilk.

The consumption per capita of apples in the mid-1950's has been running less than half of the average of 50 years ago, but the use of citrus fruit in all forms has quadrupled.

The use of oranges and other citrus fruit bought in fresh form or homegrown rose from 16 pounds per capita in 1909 to a peak of 65 pounds in 1944. Frozen concentrated juices since then have been substituted extensively for the fresh fruit. The consumption per capita of deciduous fruit (other than apples) has gone up slightly. Some major shifts from fresh to canned and frozen forms have occurred. Bananas remained the same.

The consumption of commercially produced melons has held at about the same rate per capita, but the use of home-produced melons has fallen.

The rise in commercial production of vegetables for the fresh market apparently has not equaled on a per capita basis the decline in home-produced fresh vegetables, but the increase in consumption per capita of processed vegetables has more than made up the difference.

The average use of tomatoes in all forms—fresh, canned whole, canned tomato products, catsup, frozen juice—from commercially produced supplies has doubled in the past 50 years. Home production is much less significant, primarily because of the relatively smaller farm population. The drop has offset only part of the increase in consumption of commercially produced and marketed tomatoes.

The same kinds of overall shifts have occurred among leafy, green, and yellow vegetables as among tomatoes. We eat less cabbage and more lettuce. Canned green beans and peas have gained in favor, even though frozen beans and peas are also leading items.

Frozen peas, however, apparently have made some inroads into the market for canned peas.

The consumption of vegetables (other than tomatoes, leafy, green, and yellow vegetables, potatoes, and sweetpotatoes) has declined somewhat on a per capita basis because the decline in home production apparently has been greater than the increase in commercial supplies. The only remarkable changes for items in this group of vegetables have been the increases in consumption of commercially produced celery and fresh and canned corn.

The consumption of cane and beet sugar rose from 74 pounds per capita in 1909 to a little more than 100 pounds in the 1920's. Our statistics indicate some sharp ups and downs since then in trade movements, which probably were reflected only partly in actual consumption. Consumption has run just below 100 pounds in recent years.

The use of corn sugar and sirup has varied rather widely, but has held up much better than other sirups and maple sugar.

CHANGES IN CONSUMPTION by groups within our population have brought about these changes. For example, people in the South generally are eating more and better food now than they did 25 years ago. Many families have moved off farms in all parts of the country and have raised their levels of living and eating because their incomes have gone up.

The average consumption of all food per person in farm, rural nonfarm, and urban households was higher in 1955 than in 1942, but the increase for the rural nonfarm group was greatest.

Households in all urbanization categories ate more meat and poultry, shortening and margarine, processed fruit and vegetables, and beverages, but less butter, lard, potatoes, and sweetpotatoes.

Nonfarm households cut back on fresh fruit and vegetables as they stepped up their use of processed items.

Rural nonfarm households used less flour and cereals, as did farm households, which shifted some of their total consumption of flour from flour bought as such to the flour in the bakery products they bought.

Farm households also have reduced their average use of milk and cream, probably because fewer keep cows.

Some of these changes were so widespread that they appeared among all households in cities and the country. This was true of the rises in beef, poultry, margarine, and shortening and the drops in butter and lard.

Other notable shifts, which were general for households at all income levels within an urbanization category, are the higher consumption of pork by urban and rural nonfarm households and the greater use of commercially canned foods by farm and rural non-farm people.

THE FORMS OF FOOD we use have also changed during the past 50 years. Included are the shift from producing food for our own use in gardens and farmyards to buying more in stores and the shift often described as from fresh to processed.

The extent of the decline in home production is shown by two figures. In the spring of 1942, United States households produced for their own use 18 percent of the food consumed at home. In the spring of 1955, they produced only 8 percent. The proportion for all food (including that eaten away from home) would run a bit lower—perhaps 7 percent.

Data on home production in the early part of this century are so scattered that we cannot measure satisfactorily the full extent of the change over the past 50 years. Very likely at least a third of our food was home produced in the years before the First World War. This decline has increased greatly the demands on our food marketing system and has lightened the work of American housewives.

Now let us consider the shift from fresh to commercially processed foods. It is not easy to define the word "processed," because nearly all foods purchased by consumers have been through some form of processing, such as grading and washing. Although most of us think of fluid whole milk as fresh milk, milk bottlers have pasteurized and bottled most of it.

As a starter, however, we can use as a definition of processing one that excludes fluid whole milk and flour but includes commercially canned, frozen, baked, dried (except beans and peas), cured foods and commercial dairy products (such as butter and ice cream) and fats and oils (such as lard and shortening). By this definition, there was an increase in the proportion of processed food from 33 percent of food used at home in spring 1942 to 39 percent in 1955.

Often we talk about the increase in consumption of convenience or ready-prepared foods. In considering this change, we hit another stumbling block. What is a convenience food? Fluid milk requires no preparation except to pour it in a glass, and we only need to put sliced bread on a plate. Bottling of milk and slicing of bread have been timesaving processes favored by American housewives for a generation.

Probably we intend to refer to newer items among convenience foods, such as cake and cookie mixes, canned and frozen prepared dishes, and canned baby foods. These were minor items or entirely unknown in 1938. Although only 4 or 5 percent of household food expenditures went for these newer items in 1955, collectively they represent a 2-billion-dollar business and have a high growth potential.

The places where we eat also have changed. We ate about 13 percent of our food outside private homes in 1929 and about 17 percent in 1958.

When we eat away from home, we eat in different kinds of places now than we did years ago. Boardinghouses formerly were popular eating establishments and served perhaps as much as one-sixth of the food eaten away from home. In recent years, as incomes have gone up and many more single people have small apartments, fewer persons eat in boardinghouses.

Since the late 1930's, there has been a marked shift in eating away from home toward restaurants, hotels, and lunch counters, which now sell close to three-fourths of the food eaten away from home and handle as much as an eighth of the total United States food supply for civilian consumption.

Two types of large-scale feeding establishments that have become increasingly popular are school lunchrooms and industrial feeding facilities. The share handled by such institutions as hospitals, prisons, and large homes for the aged apparently has remained fairly constant. Some meals are eaten in clubs, fraternities, ships, airplanes, and so on.

These data are largely approximations developed from various sources, but they give a picture of relative significance. But we do not know where particular kinds of foods are eaten away from home, except by casual observation and some studies of limited scope.

We spend much more for food now than we did 50 (or even 30) years ago, because prices are higher, we produce less of our own food in our gardens and farmyards, and we buy foods requiring more farm resources to produce and marketing services to process and distribute.

Our expenditures for food (excluding value of home-produced food) in 1929 averaged 165 dollars per capita, compared with 150 dollars in 1941 and about 390 dollars in 1958. Retail food prices more than doubled between 1941 and 1958.

We learn from special data from household surveys how money for food is allocated among major commodities. Urban households in the United States spent their food money in the spring of 1942 and 1955 in this way:

	1942	1955
	Percent	*Percent*
Meats.....................	22.0	26.3
Dairy products (other than butter)..................	14.8	15.1
Fats and oils.............	7.3	4.1
Poultry and eggs..........	9.6	9.4
Fruits and vegetables.......	23.3	19.9
Sugar and sweets..........	2.8	2.7
Cereals and bakery products.	11.5	10.4
Other (beverages, fish, nuts, etc.)..................	8.7	12.1

WHY THESE CHANGES in food consumption?

The answers lie in two sets of changes—changes in the kinds and amounts of foods available and changes in people's wants and ability to buy food.

Food production has doubled in the past five decades in total. The average per capita has gone up almost a tenth. The yield of crops per harvested acre and livestock production per breeding unit have increased spectacularly. Improvements in seed (such as hybrid corn), fertilizer, and animal husbandry have been remarkable. Seasonal differences in food supplies have been reduced. The location of food production has shifted geographically. A significant change from extensive home production to reliance on commercially produced and marketed supplies has come about primarily because of a drop in the farm population and because fewer nonfarm people raise chickens and gardens.

A greater demand for food marketing services has resulted from this shift to commercially produced supplies, increased specialization of agricultural production in particular areas, and the desires of consumers in all parts of the country for a much wider variety of foods the whole year.

We now have a highly complex and specialized marketing system to meet these increased demands. Technological progress in agricultural marketing has been marked by such developments as the railway refrigerator car, modern motortruck, canning of many more kinds of foods, quick freezing, and the supermarkets.

Consumer demand has changed, too, because of increased purchasing power and shifts in consumers' preferences. Allowing for the rise in prices, we find that income per capita (after income taxes) has gone up 80 percent since the years just before the First World War. Data to measure the market value of food in that period are scanty, but, piecing them together, I have concluded that about a third of income went for food in that period, compared with 27 percent in 1929, 24 percent in 1940, and about 22 percent in 1958.

How INCOME affects food consumption of particular groups of households is revealed by statistics from the 1955

Survey of Household Food Consumption.

Consumption of farm foods per person in households with incomes of 10 thousand dollars or more was half again as high as in those with incomes under 1 thousand dollars in the spring of 1955. The variation in average use of livestock products was somewhat greater between households of high and low income than was the variation in use of foods grown as crops.

An analysis of the effect of income on food consumption over the past 50 years shows that for each 10 percent of increase in income per capita the amount of food consumed per capita goes up about 2 percent. This analysis allowed for the rise in the general price level and used the farm value of food in constant dollars, in order to keep marketing services out of the picture.

Changes in income have had more effect on the consumption of some foods than others. These effects are hard to gage because of concurrent changes in other factors, such as degree of urbanization, the supply situation for individual foods and their alternatives, the age and activity of the population, and the way we live.

But we do know that the consumption of beef, purchased poultry, butter, frozen foods, citrus fruit, salad vegetables, and ice cream tends to rise as incomes rise.

The average consumption of cornmeal and potatoes has fallen as incomes have risen and people have moved from farms.

Variations in income seem to have little effect on how much flour in all forms urban families use per person. The consumption of pork in some parts of the country declines slightly with higher incomes among urban households.

The effect of income on the consumption of such foods as fluid milk and vegetables (other than potatoes, sweetpotatoes, dry beans, and peas) is confused with the effects of other factors, such as the number of children in the family (in the case of milk) and home gardening for vegetables.

These facts are clear, however. Higher incomes have permitted us to consume a greater variety of foods throughout the year, and the availability of purchasing power has prodded the expansion of the United States food marketing system.

The decline in home production of food has been an important factor in changes in food consumption. It has resulted from less opportunity and less desire of American households to produce their own supplies.

Our farm population made up 35 percent of the United States civilian population in 1910, 25 percent in 1929, and 12 percent in 1958. Farm households produced only 41 percent of the food they consumed at home in spring of 1955, compared with 61 percent in spring of 1942. Similar percentages for rural nonfarm households are 8 percent for 1955 and 22 percent for 1942.

CONSUMER PREFERENCES for foods have been altered by changes in the ways we live and eat.

A diversity of factors in addition to income and degree of urbanization have contributed to these changes.

They include: Extent of education of homemakers and their outside employment, variations in the sizes and ages of families, less need for heavy physical labor and for high-energy foods, increasing knowledge of food needs, changes in our ideas of good eating, advertising and promotion of particular foods, and development of new home food-processing and kitchen facilities, such as pressure cookers.

As examples, I review the effects on food consumption of education and employment of homemakers and the use of freezers.

The Institute of Home Economics has tabulated data from the 1955 Survey of Household Food Consumption which show the effect of formal education on food patterns of the urban households at each income level.

The households in which the homemakers had had more formal education used larger amounts per person of dairy products, frozen and canned fruit and vegetables and juices, and less flour and cereal products, potatoes, and dried fruit and vegetables than those with less educated homemakers.

Employed homemakers used more bakery products, meat, poultry, fish, fats, and oils, but about the same amounts of other foods per person.

Freezing facilities have had a great effect on meat consumption of rural households. Farm households with freezing facilities consume substantially more meat per person (with the increase primarily in beef) at each income level than do those not using such facilities. The same relationship holds true for rural nonfarm households with incomes below 4 thousand dollars. Home freezing of meat is much less important for rural nonfarm households with higher incomes and for urban households.

To SUM UP, here are the highlights of how food consumption in the United States has changed and why.

We are eating more food in terms of quantity and quality per capita than our parents and grandparents did 50 years ago. More farm resources are used to produce the additional quantity and improved quality.

Along with more and better food, we are buying more marketing services in the forms of commercial distribution and processing.

These changes in food consumption have resulted from many significant changes in food supply and in consumer demand for food.

On the supply side, our farms have become more and more productive. American food processors and distributors have developed the most extensive and efficient marketing system of the world to supply a great variety of foods the year around to consumers in all parts of the country.

Consumer demand for food has far outrun expectations of even 20 years ago. Although increased purchasing power and urbanization have been the primary causes, a number of other economic and social factors have contributed to changes in the ways we Americans eat.

The process of changes in food consumption has not stopped. It may not even be slowing down.

MARGUERITE C. BURK *in 1945 became head of the Consumption Section in the Agricultural Economics Division of the Agricultural Marketing Service.*

Food Baked at Home

North Central Farm Families,
1948 and 1955

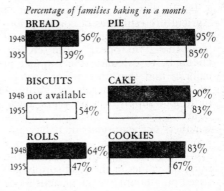

Percentage of families baking in a month

	BREAD	PIE
1948	56%	95%
1955	39%	85%

	BISCUITS	CAKE
1948	not available	90%
1955	54%	83%

	ROLLS	COOKIES
1948	64%	83%
1955	47%	67%

Changes in Sources of Nutrients

BERTA FRIEND AND FAITH CLARK

ONE way to find out whether Americans are changing their eating habits for the better or for the worse is to examine the nutritive value of the assortment of foods that make up our national food supply.

To do that, we use Department of Agriculture estimates of consumption, which are based on the amounts of food that "disappear" into civilian channels, to calculate the number of calories and the amounts of protein, fat, and the key minerals and vitamins in the food supply over the years. These figures give us a basis for judging whether our national diet has improved or worsened.

We need to keep in mind that the nutritive values of the food supply are based on amounts of the various foods estimated to be consumed—that is, "used up" in an economic sense. Because no allowances for loss or waste of food in the home can be made, they are not estimates of nutrients actually ingested. They provide averages per capita or per head in values of food for the country as a whole and are chiefly useful for studying trends.

THE FOOD ENERGY available in the national food supply has had an overall decline since 1909, the first year for which these statistics are available. The increase in the consumption of meat and poultry, eggs, milk, fats, and sugars has not compensated in calories for the decline in the use of grain products and potatoes.

The food energy level in 1909 was almost 3,600 Calories a person a day. In 1956–1958 it stood at 3,200 Calories, a drop of about 10 percent. It remained at a relatively high level of 3,500 Calories through the early 1920's, except for a short decline in the years immediately after the First World War. During the depression in the middle 1930's, it fell to about 3,250 Calories, but it remained constant at 3,400 in 1939–1944. A relatively steady decline since 1945 has brought the food energy of the food supply to 3,200 Calories.

Very likely the chief reasons for the overall decline in calories are shifts in the composition of the population and in people's physical activities, rather than in their interest in weight control.

Our population is now made up of proportionately more older persons and more women than in earlier years.

We have fewer teen-agers in relation to the total population than at any time in our history. These changes have affected the amount of food consumed: Older persons generally eat less food than younger adults, women eat less food than men, and teen-agers eat more food than any other group.

The physical activities of people also have changed. At the beginning of the century many more people lived on farms and engaged in heavy manual labor so that they burned more calories. Our new age has produced many laborsaving devices to lighten farm chores. In fact, the use of laborsaving devices in all areas—factories, farms, and homes—as well as the increasing flow of people to the cities have lessened energy needs. Consequently the amounts of food we eat reflect our smaller need for food.

When we adjust the average number of calories in the food supply to take care of the smaller energy requirements, we see that our calorie supply has changed hardly at all.

THE SOURCES of our calories have changed considerably.

Milk, meat, eggs, and nonstarchy vegetables are providing a larger share of the total number of calories.

The proportion of the total calories provided by grains and potatoes has been steadily declining. At one time they contributed 42 percent of the total calories in the food supply. Now they provide only 24 percent. This often is attributed to the weight-conscious homemaker who does most of the food marketing. If this is true, she is sacrificing these nutritious foods for fats and sugars. Fats and sugars formerly provided a fourth of the total number of calories available for consumption. Now they provide about a third of the total.

CONSUMPTION OF PROTEIN was at a peak level of slightly more than 100 grams a person a day in 1909–1913 and again in 1945. Supplies of protein in 1956–1958 were at a level of slightly less than 100 grams. The lowest amount of protein available for consumption was 88 grams in 1935. People like protein foods, which are relatively expensive items. It is not surprising, therefore, that the increased consumption of meat, poultry, eggs, and milk products reflected the improving economy after the 1930's.

Two-thirds of the total protein supply today comes from animal sources, compared to one-half in earlier years. Meat, poultry, and fish in 1958 provided 35 percent of the protein; in 1909–1913, this group furnished 29 percent of the total. Flour and cereal products provided a fifth of the total protein in the food supply in the late 1950's, compared to more than one-third in the earlier period.

THE MARKET BASKET (per capita quantities) brought into the kitchen now contains larger amounts of food fats and oils than in earlier years.

Dietary fat—that is, fat from the food fats and oils as well as from meat and other foods containing fat—also provides a larger proportion of the total calories.

We averaged about 145 grams of dietary fat a person a day in 1956–1958, compared to 126 grams in 1909–1913. We got 41 percent of our calories from fat in the later years, and 32 percent in the earlier period.

The amount of fat from animal sources declined by about 14 percent from 1909 to 1935, chiefly because of a lower consumption of meat. From the mid-1930's on, the fat content of available food supplies increased because of the increased consumption of meat, poultry, eggs, milk, and many of the fats and oils of vegetable origin. Dietary fat from animal sources was back up to 102 grams in 1956–1958— about the same level it had been in 1909; 91 grams was the level in 1935.

Two big changes occurred within the fats and oils group itself.

Nutrients Available for Consumption per Person per Day—United States Food Supply

Nutrients		1909–13	1915	1920	1925	1930	1935	1940	1945	1950	1955	1956–58
Food energy	calories	3,540	3,480	3,330	3,500	3,500	3,240	3,380	3,340	3,300	3,220	3,200
Protein	grams	102	97	94	95	93	88	93	103	95	96	97
Fat	do	126	127	124	135	136	127	144	140	147	148	146
Carbohydrate	do	501	490	466	483	484	447	437	425	409	386	382
Calcium	do	0.86	0.84	0.89	0.89	0.91	0.92	0.96	1.10	1.02	1.03	1.03
Iron	milligrams	15	15	15	15	14	14	15	19	17	16	17
Vitamin A value	International Units	7,000	7,100	7,500	7,300	7,900	8,300	8,100	9,500	8,000	7,400	7,300
Thiamine	milligrams	1.4	1.3	1.3	1.3	1.3	1.8	1.3	1.8	1.6	1.6	1.5
Riboflavin	do	1.8	1.8	1.8	1.8	1.8	1.8	1.9	2.4	2.2	2.3	2.3
Niacin	do	16	15	15	15	14	14	15	20	18	18	18
Ascorbic acid	do	79	81	81	83	82	90	92	103	85	87	86

One was the decline in the use of butter and the increase in consumption of margarine.

The other was the large increase in the consumption of cooking and salad oils—which in the late 1950's was seven times larger than in 1909–1913 and almost twice as large as in 1935.

Foods high in fat generally are expensive. It has been said that a country's wealth can be measured by its consumption of fat.

We have increased our consumption of fat while lowering our calorie level. The net result is the rather large shift in the proportion of total calories from fat. This shift has been accomplished at the expense of the carbohydrates, which are cheaper sources of food.

CARBOHYDRATES provided only 47 percent of our calories in 1956–1958, against 56 percent in 1909–1913.

The chief sources of carbohydrates are grains and sugars. Americans have been eating less and less grain, but their consumption of sugar has been fairly stable since the early 1930's, except for a few years of relative scarcity during the war.

Grain products and sugars in 1956–1958 contributed about equally to the carbohydrates in the total diet, 37 percent and 34 percent, respectively. Grains provided 55 percent and sugars only 21 percent in 1909–1913.

CALCIUM is the one nutrient that is directly related to the consumption of a specific food. Year by year, the amount of calcium available in the food supply follows closely the supply of fluid milk and the milk products that contain calcium. They provide three-fourths of the calcium in the total food supply.

The trend in the calcium supply was constantly upward until the middle 1940's. The consumption of milk and green and yellow vegetables, which also are sources of calcium, was increasing then.

Grain products, another fair source, have been contributing a smaller and smaller share of calcium to the total

Changes in Sources of Fat in the United States Food Supply

Sources of fat	1909–13	1935	1956–58
	Percent of total	Percent of total	Percent of total
Milk, cream, cheese, ice cream.........	15	16	17
Butter...........	14	14	6
Eggs............	4	4	4
Meat, poultry, fish.	24	19	24
Bacon and salt pork..........	13	9	11
Lard...........	12	10	8
Subtotal....	82	72	70
Margarine.......	1	2	6
Shortening.......	8	12	9
Salad oils and salad dressings..	2	6	9
All other foods....	7	8	6
Subtotal....	18	28	30
Total from all foods...	100	100	100

Changes in Sources of Protein in Our Food Supply

Sources of protein	1909–13	1956–58
	Percent of total	Percent of total
Dairy products, including butter...............	18	26
Eggs..................	5	6
Meat, poultry, fish.......	29	35
Total from animal products........	52	67
Dry beans and peas, nuts.	4	5
Flour and cereal products.	36	20
Other foods............	8	8
Total from nonanimal products........	48	33
Total from all foods.	100	100

food supply. They now contribute only 3 percent of the calcium, compared with 6 percent in earlier years.

The trend in the supply of calcium has been slightly downward since the mid-1940's, but is still well above the level of the 1920's and 1930's.

The indicated increase in calcium in the food supply is more than enough to keep up with any changes in needs due to differences in the makeup of the population, because a small decrease in the ratio of children to adults in the population has meant a slight decline in per capita needs for calcium.

On a straight per capita basis, the calcium content of the diet increased 21 percent from 1910 to 1955. Adjusted for needs of the population, the increase was 27 percent.

RIBOFLAVIN follows much the same trend as the consumption of milk and milk products other than butter. Milk products, the chief source, provide almost 50 percent of the riboflavin in the total food supply.

ENRICHMENT of grain products has been a major reason for the increase in iron, riboflavin, and two other B vitamins, thiamine and niacin. When enrichment began in 1941, small amounts of iron, thiamine, and niacin were added to white bread.

Riboflavin was added later, and the amounts of other nutrients originally added to bread were raised. As a war measure, an order of the War Food Administration in 1943 required that all white bakery bread and rolls be enriched.

White flour for home use began to be enriched on a voluntary basis. Twenty-seven States, Hawaii, and Puerto Rico had made enrichment of white bread and flour mandatory by 1958.

Most, if not all, of the cereal companies enrich their products, and rice, macaroni, and cornmeal are sometimes enriched by the addition of one or more of the nutrients usually added to breads and flour.

Thiamine, niacin, and iron are fur-

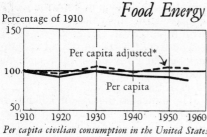

Food Energy

Percentage of 1910

Per capita civilian consumption in the United States
*For actual caloric needs of population

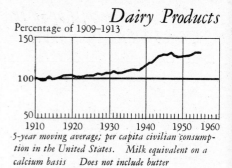

Dairy Products

Percentage of 1909–1913

5-year moving average; per capita civilian consumption in the United States. Milk equivalent on a calcium basis   Does not include butter

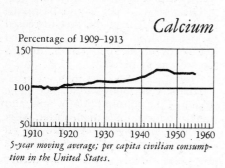

Calcium

Percentage of 1909–1913

5-year moving average; per capita civilian consumption in the United States.

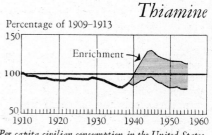

Thiamine

Percentage of 1909–1913

Per capita civilian consumption in the United States. Cooking losses deducted.

Vegetables and Fruit

Per Capita Civilian Consumption in the United States

Percentage of 1909–1913

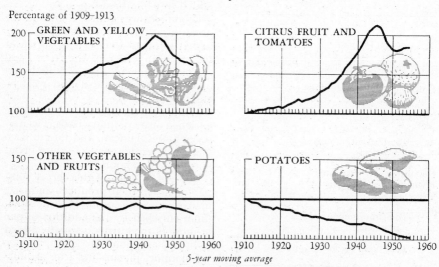

5-year moving average

Ascorbic Acid

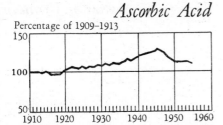

Percentage of 1909–1913

5-year moving average; per capita civilian consumption in the United States. Cooking losses deducted.

nished in large amounts by meat, poultry, fish, and grain products. All of them provided slightly more than 50 percent of the iron and thiamine and about 70 percent of the niacin in the total food supply in 1956–1958.

Until the early 1940's, when enrichment began, iron, thiamine, and niacin were at considerably lower levels than formerly. The lowest level for these nutrients was in 1935. The enrichment program and higher levels of meat consumption meant that the available supplies of these nutrients reached a high point at the end of the war.

Supplies of these nutrients dropped after the Second World War. In the late 1950's, however, they still provided about one-tenth more iron, thiamine, and niacin than in 1909–1913.

The current lower levels for these nutrients are due chiefly to the continued drop in consumption of grain products. A contributing factor in the lower level of thiamine is that beef consumption in 1953 surpassed the use of pork, the richer source of thiamine, for the first time.

Without the enrichment of grain products, supplies of thiamine, iron, and niacin would be no higher than they were in the mid-1930's. Enrichment of grain products in 1956–1958 added the following amounts to the food supply: Thiamine, 30 percent; iron, 14 percent; niacin, 15 percent; and riboflavin, 11 percent.

THE AVAILABILITY of ascorbic acid increased markedly over the years until 1945, mostly because we began to eat more green and yellow vegetables, citrus fruit, and tomatoes. The level of ascorbic acid increased from 79 milligrams a person a day in 1909–1913 to about 100 milligrams in the mid-1940's. The increased consumption of the vegetables and citrus fruits and tomatoes more than offset the lower use of potatoes and sweetpotatoes, which also are good providers of ascorbic acid.

The overall drop in the consumption of the fruit and vegetable groups since the mid-1940's has lowered the ascorbic acid available in the food supply to 86 milligrams. We nevertheless are still somewhat better off than in 1909.

Our sources of ascorbic acid have shifted markedly. Potatoes and sweetpotatoes provided one-third of it in 1909–1913 and only one-sixth in 1956–1958.

The opposite is true of citrus fruit and tomatoes, which furnished two-fifths of the ascorbic acid in 1956–1958 and only one-sixth in the earlier period. Of the 11 major groups of food, citrus fruit and tomatoes now provide the largest proportion of ascorbic acid.

THE VITAMIN A VALUE of the food supply showed some long-term improvement between 1909 and 1945—from about 7 thousand to 9,500 International Units a person a day.

This improvement was due chiefly to the greater use of green and yellow vegetables and, to a lesser extent, the increase in the consumption of dairy products (other than butter) and citrus fruit and tomatoes. The victory gardens in 1943–1946 provided much vitamin A.

A drop in the vitamin A value of the food supply of about 2 thousand International Units between 1945 and 1956–1958 was due chiefly to the decrease in the consumption of fresh carrots, spinach, and sweetpotatoes.

The increases that occurred in the processed forms of these foods were not large enough to compensate for

Changes in Sources of Ascorbic Acid

Sources of ascorbic acid	1909–13 Percent of total	1956–58 Percent of total
Potatoes and sweetpotatoes.	35	17
Citrus fruit and tomatoes..	18	41
Green and yellow vegetables...............	15	15
Other vegetables and fruit.	22	16
Other foods.............	10	11
Total..............	100	100

Changes in Sources of Vitamin A Value

Sources of vitamin A value	1909–13 Percent of total	1956–58 Percent of total
Dairy products, excluding butter................	11	14
Fats and oils, including butter.................	10	10
Potatoes and sweetpotatoes.	27	9
Citrus fruit and tomatoes..	8	10
Green and yellow vegetables................	14	29
Other vegetables and fruit.	11	9
Other foods.............	19	19

the lower consumption of the fresh products.

Some decline in the consumption of milk and cream and of some of the fruits that are fair sources of vitamin A have further contributed to the postwar drop in the amount of vitamin A in our national food supply.

From the period before the First World War to the late 1950's, there have been marked shifts in the sources of vitamin A in the food supply, occasioned chiefly by the decrease in the consumption of sweetpotatoes and the increase in use of green and yellow vegetables. Potatoes and sweetpotatoes furnished less than a tenth of the vitamin A value in the total food supply in 1956–1958 and more than a fourth in 1909–1913. Green and yellow vegetables doubled their proportionate contribution of vitamin A value, contributing about 30 percent in 1956–1958 and about 15 percent in the earlier years.

CHANGES for the better in the nutritive quality of our national per capita food supply have emerged over the years.

Although some persons may question the apparent increasing richness of our diets, as shown by the higher proportion of calories coming from fat,

larger amounts of most of the elements essential to good nutrition are provided than at the beginning of the century.

Some of the improvement has been due to higher levels of consumption of milk, cheese, meat, poultry, eggs, and many of the vitamin-rich fruits and vegetables. Some has come from the program to enrich grain products.

Much of our dietary change took place between the mid-1930's and the early postwar period. Relatively little improvement has occurred since then. In fact, some decline in the availability of several nutrients in the past few years is a challenge to us to produce and eat a selection of foods that would again bring up the national average level of those nutrients—chiefly to eat more vegetables and fruits.

BERTA FRIEND *is a food economist in the Household Economics Research Division, Agricultural Research Service. She has been responsible for the calculations of the nutritive value of the national per capita food supply for the past 10 years.*

FAITH CLARK, *Director of the Household Economics Research Division, has collaborated with Miss Friend for a number of years in studying trends in food consumption and in the nutritive quality of diets. Dr. Clark's graduate work in the University of Chicago was in nutrition and economics.*

Changes in Sources of Iron and Thiamine in the United States

	Iron			Thiamine		
Sources of iron and thiamine	1909–13	1935	1956–58	1909–13	1935	1956–58
	Percent of total	Percent of total	Percent of total	Percent of total	Percent of total	Percent of total
Dairy products..................	3	3	4	12	15	14
Eggs.........................	7	7	8	2	3	3
Meat, poultry, fish, including bacon and salt pork.................	28	24	30	26	22	24
Dry beans and peas, nuts.........	9	13	10	9	11	8
Potatoes and sweetpotatoes.......	9	8	5	12	11	6
Other vegetables and fruit........	13	20	16	11	17	12
Flour and cereal products........	25	19	23	28	21	33
Sugars and sirups..............	6	6	4	0	0	0

Food Used at Home—Households of Two or More Persons

	Amount per person per week		
Foods	Urban	Rural nonfarm	Rural farm
Milk, cream, ice cream, cheese [1]....................qt..	4.3	4.4	5.2
Fresh fluid milk and cream.......................qt..	3.3	3.1	4.3
Processed milk, ice cream, cheese [1]...............qt..	1.0	1.3	.9
Fats, oils.....................................lb..	.8	.9	1.1
Butter.....................................lb..	.2	.2	.3
Margarine..................................lb..	.2	.2	.1
Shortening.................................lb..	.2	.3	.5
Salad dressings.............................lb..	.2	.2	.1
Sugars, sweets................................lb..	1.1	1.3	1.8
Sugar.....................................lb..	.7	.9	1.2
Sirups, molasses, honey.........................lb..	.1	.1	.2
Jellies, jams, preserves........................lb..	.1	.2	.2
Candy....................................lb..	.1	.1	.1
Flour, cereals, baked goods [2].....................lb..	2.6	3.3	3.9
Flour, cereals.............................lb..	1.3	2.1	3.1
Bakery products..............................lb..	2.2	2.0	1.4
Eggs..doz..	.6	.6	.7
Meat, poultry, fish............................lb..	4.4	3.8	3.8
Meats.....................................lb..	3.2	2.8	2.8
Beef.....................................lb..	1.3	1.1	1.2
Pork.....................................lb..	1.1	1.1	1.2
Other....................................lb..	.8	.6	.4
Poultry....................................lb..	.8	.6	.7
Fish, shellfish..............................lb..	.4	.4	.4
Vegetables, fruits, potatoes.....................lb..	10.2	9.6	9.6
Potatoes, sweetpotatoes.......................lb..	1.7	2.1	2.2
Fresh vegetables [3]...........................lb..	2.7	2.4	2.8
Fresh fruit [3].................................lb..	2.9	2.7	2.8
Frozen vegetables and fruit.....................lb..	.2	.1	.1
Canned vegetables and fruit......................lb..	1.3	1.2	.8
Dried vegetables and fruit.......................lb..	.1	.2	.3
Juices, vegetable and fruit.......................lb..	1.2	.8	.6

[1] In terms of fluid whole milk on the basis of calcium content.
[2] In terms of flour and dry cereal content.
[3] Home-canned and home-frozen foods are included.
NOTE: Component items may not add to totals because of rounding.

Percentage of Income Spent for Food, Expense for Purchased Food and Value of Home-Produced Food; Farm Families in Median-Income Group

Family size	Percentage of income spent for food	Expense for food at home and away in a week, per family member	Money value [1] of home-produced food used at home in a week, per family member
2-member families........	29	$6. 92	$3. 86
3-member families........	35	5. 52	3. 02
4-member families........	37	4. 36	2. 78
5-member families........	36	3. 37	2. 76
6-member families........	45	3. 45	2. 80

[1] Foods produced for home use were valued at prices reported by families purchasing similar foods.

Commercially Canned or Frozen Vegetables or Fruits and Juices, City Households of Two or More Persons, by Income

	Percentage of households using at home in a week—		
	Vegetables or fruits		Juices, vegetable or fruit
Income group	Commercially frozen	Commercially canned	
Low income.........................	26	86	55
Median income.....................	43	91	72
High income.......................	55	90	78

Percentage of Income Spent for Food and Money Value of Food; City Families in Median-Income Group

Family size	Percent of income spent for food	Money value of all food eaten at home and away in a week per family member
2-member families.........................	26	$11. 54
3-member families.........................	35	10. 30
4-member families.........................	39	8. 74
5-member families.........................	46	8. 20
6-member families.........................	48	7. 10

What Do We Eat?

JANET MURRAY AND ENNIS BLAKE

WE sometimes get the impression that Americans typically breakfast on a hurried cup of coffee, lunch at a counter, and dine on hotdogs, potato chips, and soft drinks in front of TV sets.

The impression is false.

Most Americans eat a variety of foods in meals served at home. On the average, at least 50 different food items are used at family meals in a week. They include about 10 pounds of vegetables and fruit, 4.5 quarts of milk or corresponding amounts of cheese and ice cream, 4 pounds of meat, 7 eggs, 1 pound of fat, 1.5 pounds of sugar, and 3 pounds of cereal products for each person in the household.

Put another way, the average American eats three or four servings of vegetables and fruit, the equivalent of 2 to 3 cups of milk, an egg, and one or two servings of meat, poultry, or fish each day and bread or other grain products at each meal.

These facts are based on information given to trained interviewers by 6,060 American householders, who comprised a scientifically designed sample of all households in the United States that do enough cooking to be called housekeeping.

They live in all parts of the country and every type of community. They were so selected that average patterns could be obtained, not State by State—that would require a far larger sample—but for each of four regions (the Northeast, North Central, South, and West) and for three types of communities within each region (rural farm, rural nonfarm, and urban) or for any combination of these 12 basic groups. They were interviewed during April, May, and June of 1955.

Each homemaker spent about 2 hours with the interviewer, giving her information on family members and the meals they had at home and away from home, the money spent, the family income, practices with respect to the use of home-produced food, canning and freezing at home, baking, and other details that help to round out the picture of the household and its food.

Information about the size and composition of the household and the family income was needed for more than merely descriptive purposes.

We can classify the households in the sample by these characteristics—by family size, for example, and then get the average food pattern of each of the family groups. Certainly we can

Income and Food Consumption
Per City Family, Spring 1955

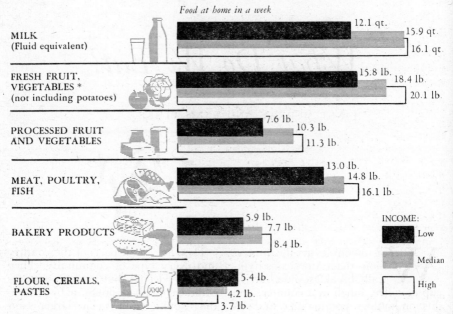

Food at home in a week

	Low	Median	High
MILK (Fluid equivalent)	12.1 qt.	15.9 qt.	16.1 qt.
FRESH FRUIT, VEGETABLES * (not including potatoes)	15.8 lb.	18.4 lb.	20.1 lb.
PROCESSED FRUIT AND VEGETABLES	7.6 lb.	10.3 lb.	11.3 lb.
MEAT, POULTRY, FISH	13.0 lb.	14.8 lb.	16.1 lb.
BAKERY PRODUCTS	5.9 lb.	7.7 lb.	8.4 lb.
FLOUR, CEREALS, PASTES	5.4 lb.	4.2 lb.	3.7 lb.

INCOME:
Low
Median
High

Includes home-canned, home-frozen.

expect the six-person family to spend more for food than the two-person family, although not three times as much.

We may also group families whose incomes are at about the same level and study the differences in use of food and expenditures of families at different positions on the income scale. Again, we will expect the families that earn 10 thousand dollars to spend more for food than those whose income is 2 thousand dollars—but our question will be how much more. Probably not five times as much.

A major purpose of surveys of food consumption, as a matter of fact, is to get the basis for such comparisons. For our overall picture of how much food Americans are getting each year, we can go to statistics of the national food supply. Per capita consumption figures tell us how much food is available for every individual in the country if

it were divided evenly among us all—but it is not divided that way. We need to know not just who is eating more or less, the high- or low-income families, large or small, farm or city, but what are their typical selections of food. Only from household surveys can we get the patterns of eating and the dietary levels of different groups.

Since the mid-1930's, a period of depression, war, recovery, and many developments in processing and marketing foods, the Government has made four nationwide surveys of how and what people eat—in 1935-1936, 1942, 1948 (city families only), and 1955.

More frequent large-scale surveys have been neither feasible nor necessary. Food habits and practices change, but they change slowly. Many people must adopt a new practice or use a new food before much of a dent is made on our averages.

Although, strictly speaking, the data

we present relate to a particular year, 1955, we can accept them as satisfactory representations for a fairly broad span of time.

The survey also relates to one season, spring. We know, of course, that there is seasonal variation in the use of food. People eat more ice cream in summer than in winter, but they also eat more cheese in winter than in summer, and seasonal variation of milk, cream, ice cream, and cheese together is not so great as the individual items that make up the food group.

Moreover, one of the Department's surveys included a study of the way food purchases of urban families varied by season. The study showed that for many foods the purchases in the spring did not differ significantly from the average for the year. Consumption of food in the spring is more like the average for the year than is the consumption in any other season.

For one type of change that occurs over the years—the change in the level of food prices—adjustments can be made readily. For example, the average American family in the spring of 1955 spent 27 dollars for the purchased food used at home or eaten away from home in a week. If the average level of food prices were to increase 15 percent beyond that of the spring of 1955, the family would have to pay about 31 dollars for the same food.

The average money value of the food consumed in a week by an American family in the spring of 1955 amounted to 30 dollars. Nearly one-tenth of this was contributed by the home garden or farm or was received as gift or pay. The money spent for food—27 dollars—took a third of the family income after the deduction of income taxes. Most of this money—22 dollars—was used to purchase the food that came into the kitchen for family meals, snacks, or packed lunches. The rest, nearly 5 dollars, was spent for meals and food away from home.

Eating out, it is sometimes thought, is becoming the usual thing among Americans.

The story is told of the American hostess showing a foreign visitor her kitchen, complete with modern conveniences—rotisserie, electric mixer, garbage disposer, dishwasher, and all—and then saying, "Now we'll go out for dinner."

It is true that Americans now eat out more than formerly. Eighteen percent of food expenditures by housekeeping families went for food away from home in 1955—but only 10 percent in the 1930's.

If we consider all the meals of family members, we find that 9 of 10 of them were eaten at home or at any rate were prepared from the family food supply. About 6 percent of the meals eaten by family members were bought and eaten away from home. Another 3 percent were mostly gift meals. A few were received as payment for services.

Families almost never eat breakfast away from home.

Seventeen percent of the lunches of family members were eaten away from home. Many of these were bought by the men or the children of the family who did not carry their lunches from home to work or school.

If the evening meal was eaten out—and only 7 percent of them were—it was just as apt to be a gift as a purchased meal.

These figures suggest that the story of the American hostess and her foreign visitor is hardly typical.

Expenditures for food brought into the home for household use are of major interest to economists.

The distribution of the food dollar is one way of showing the relative importance of different types of foods. Meat, poultry, fish, or eggs, normally the main dish of our meals, took 35 cents of the food dollar—about 24 cents for beef, pork, veal, and lamb; 5 cents for poultry; 4 cents for eggs; and 2 cents for fish.

Vegetables and fruit, for which 18 cents of the dollar were spent, were next most important as a group. More than half of this was spent for fresh varieties.

Food Consumption: North Central, South

Per City Family, Spring 1955

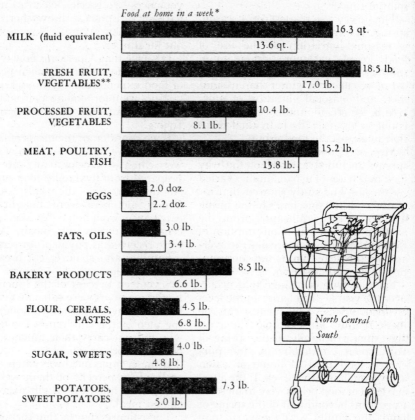

Food at home in a week *

MILK (fluid equivalent)	16.3 qt. / 13.6 qt.
FRESH FRUIT, VEGETABLES **	18.5 lb. / 17.0 lb.
PROCESSED FRUIT, VEGETABLES	10.4 lb. / 8.1 lb.
MEAT, POULTRY, FISH	15.2 lb. / 13.8 lb.
EGGS	2.0 doz. / 2.2 doz.
FATS, OILS	3.0 lb. / 3.4 lb.
BAKERY PRODUCTS	8.5 lb. / 6.6 lb.
FLOUR, CEREALS, PASTES	4.5 lb. / 6.8 lb.
SUGAR, SWEETS	4.0 lb. / 4.8 lb.
POTATOES, SWEET POTATOES	7.3 lb. / 5.0 lb.

North Central
South

*Median income class.   **Includes home-canned, home-frozen.*

Milk and milk products, excluding butter, took 14 cents.

Eleven cents were spent for flour, cereals, bread, and other baked goods.

Beverages took nearly 10 cents—a third of this for alcoholic drinks, which, however, may be underreported by the homemaker.

The remaining 12 cents were divided fairly evenly among fats and oils, sugars and sweets, and a group of such miscellaneous items as soups, nuts, catsup, pickles and olives, fillings, mixtures, and seasonings.

How great is the variation in food practices is illustrated by the fact that although the average money value

of food used at home in a week for all households came to 7.57 dollars a person, in about 7 percent of the households the value of a week's food was less than 4 dollars a person. In an almost equal number of households it came to 14 dollars a person.

Many reasons account for such differences—differences in the family's purchasing power, the size of the household, and the community and section in which it lives.

We may also study the characteristics of the person who takes the major responsibility for planning the meals for the household—usually the homemaker. Her age, employment, and education may have some bearing on what her family eats.

We can detect some systematic variation in food consumption among groups when we classify families by their place of residence, income or size of household, or by certain characteristics of the homemaker.

Even then, however, much variation remains, which probably can be explained only by differences in taste. As R. G. D. Allen and A. L. Bowley say in *Family Expenditure*, "There is no accounting for tastes. Different people have different opinions; some like apples and some like onions."

CITY-FARM DIFFERENCES in the consumption of food are greater than those in most of our comparisons.

Farm families generally have more food (measured in calories), chiefly because their outdoor physical work requires much food energy and because of the food that comes from the farm or home garden. When the home-produced foods are valued at prices the family would normally pay to buy them, they represent about 40 percent of all the food used at home and away by the farm family. That is considerably less than it used to be. The proportion of food produced at home varies among farm families, but nearly every family has some.

Farm families in 1955 ate more food than city families, but its money value was less. The total value of food used by farm families in a week averaged somewhat more than 29 dollars. The urban average was almost 33 dollars.

Having considerably less than city families but somewhat more than the average for those on farms were the rural nonfarm families. These are the families living in communities of fewer than 2,500 persons and outside the fringe areas around cities of at least 50 thousand population but not on farms. Many rural nonfarm families produce some food for themselves, although much less than the average farm family.

Many rural families customarily buy some foods, such as eggs, fruit, and vegetables, from a neighbor or other local outlet. The prices they report are less than the regular retail price usually paid by most city families. For example, the north-central farm families that bought eggs paid only 35 cents a dozen, compared with 41 cents reported by rural nonfarm and 50 cents by city families in the same region.

Food produced by families for their own use was valued at prices paid for similar items purchased by survey families in the same region and type of community. If the food of the farm and other rural families had been valued at prices commonly paid in city markets, the money value of their food undoubtedly would be greater than that of city families.

Farm families paid out only half as much money for food as the urban families. Rural nonfarm families also spent less than urban families. As rural families generally have lower incomes, however, the share of money income going for food—about one-third—was nearly the same for the three groups.

City families ate out much more than rural families did. Some food was purchased and eaten away from home in 10 out of 12 city families, but in only 9 out of 12 rural nonfarm families and 8 out of 12 farm families. Furthermore, the city family that did eat away from home spent nearly one and one-half times as much as the rural nonfarm family and more than twice as much as the farm family.

The most striking differences in the actual consumption of different foods by farm and city families was the relatively greater use of milk, grains, sugars, and fats in the farm family diet and the lesser use of meat.

Farm families had nearly a quart more a person a week of milk and milk products (cream, ice cream, and cheese, as measured in calcium equivalents) than city families. The difference was not only in quantity. The farm families, who as a group home-produced 68 percent of their milk, used a larger proportion in its original form

Food Consumption: North Central, South

Per Farm Family, Spring 1955

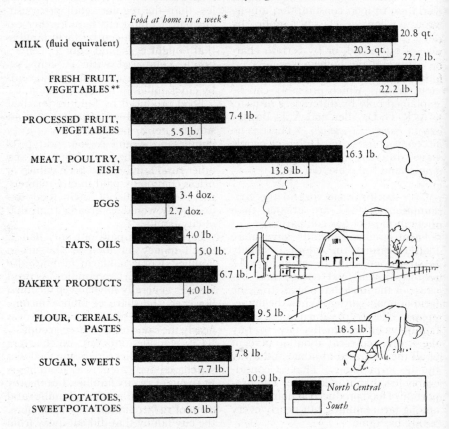

Food at home in a week *

MILK (fluid equivalent)	20.8 qt. / 20.3 qt.
FRESH FRUIT, VEGETABLES **	22.7 lb. / 22.2 lb.
PROCESSED FRUIT, VEGETABLES	7.4 lb. / 5.5 lb.
MEAT, POULTRY, FISH	16.3 lb. / 13.8 lb.
EGGS	3.4 doz. / 2.7 doz.
FATS, OILS	4.0 lb. / 5.0 lb.
BAKERY PRODUCTS	6.7 lb. / 4.0 lb.
FLOUR, CEREALS, PASTES	9.5 lb. / 18.5 lb.
SUGAR, SWEETS	7.8 lb. / 7.7 lb.
POTATOES, SWEETPOTATOES	10.9 lb. / 6.5 lb.

North Central
South

*Median income class.   **Includes home-canned, home-frozen.*

and less as processed milks or cheese than families who generally bought their milk. For example, fluid milk and cream made up 83 percent of the total milk products used by farm families, and processed milks and cheese 12 percent, compared with 76 percent and 18 percent, respectively, for city families.

The rural families not only had considerably more grain products in their diets but they also had a larger proportion as cereal or as flour used in home baking than the city families, who bought more bread and other baked goods. Farm families also used more eggs than city families.

City families, on the other hand, averaged about one-half pound per person of meat, poultry, and fish than farm families. About 90 percent of both city and farm families used pork. More city families than farm families, however, used beef (94 percent, as compared with 79 percent) and poultry (60 percent, as compared with 50 percent).

Nonfarm families used more vegetables, fruit, and potatoes than farm families, but the latter, with their home food production and preservation, had proportionally more of their vegetables fresh or canned or frozen at home and less commercially processed than the nonfarm families.

Even this summary look at their food patterns reveals that farm families are likely to have more food in total pounds than the nonfarm, although the money value is lower, when the food produced for their own use is valued at prices paid by farm families.

REGIONAL VARIATIONS in food patterns are not so great as one might expect in a geographic area as large as the United States.

Differences in the kinds of food produced could account for some differences. Perhaps we might also anticipate some differences lingering on to remind us of the ethnic groups that originally settled the various parts of the country.

Although regional differences were indeed found in the 1955 survey, they were generally slight and often no greater than those among families of different income groups within a region. Of the four broad regions identified in the survey—Northeast, North Central, South, and West—it could be said that the South generally was more different from the other regions than they were from each other.

Food expenditures were lower in the South. The average amounts spent in a week for food at home and away from home by families in the Northeast and the West were 32 dollars; in the North Central, 30 dollars; and in the South, 23 dollars. Relatively less of the southern food dollar went for food away from home. Since the southern families were larger, differences per person were relatively greater.

Because the division of the population between urban and rural is not the same in all parts of the country, many of the seemingly regional differences are actually differences between urban and rural food habits.

Some regional differences remain, to be sure, even when comparisons are made only among urban or among farm groups. They are explained in part by differences in income. Farm families in the South, for example, because their income averaged lower than that of farm families in other regions, had considerably lower expenditures for food. Home-produced food was also a little less in the South, although it made a larger percentage contribution to the food supply than in other regions.

Because family spending is related to the economic level of the community as well as to family income, the clearest picture of regional differences in food patterns may be obtained if we compare families at the same relative levels in their communities. For this purpose we select families at the median-income level.

In the north-central urban community, the median-income group were those families with incomes between 4 thousand and 5 thousand dollars; in the southern urban community, the median-income class was 3 thousand to 4 thousand dollars.

Similarly, the patterns of the farm families in the North Central States and the South may be compared for families at the same relative income level. For the north-central farm families, the median-income class was 3 thousand to 4 thousand dollars; in the South, it was 1 thousand to 2 thousand dollars.

On the basis of both the city and farm comparisons, north-central families used more meat, milk, fruit, vegetables, potatoes, and bakery products than their southern counterparts but less flour and cereals. Greater use of grain products and more home baking traditionally has been a feature of the southern diet. More fats were also used in the South and more sugars, at least in the cities.

FAMILIES TEND TO increase the amount they spend for food as their income increases. The rate is proportionately slower, however, so that the percentage going to food is less for high-income families. Some of this increased spending goes for larger amounts of many foods or more kinds of foods. Much of it is spent for foods that need less preparation by the homemaker and for meals purchased away from home.

The relationship between income and the consumption of food is more direct among urban families than farm families because urban families have less home-produced food.

Even for city families, a study of the food patterns of families classified by net money income does not give so clear an indication of the income-consumption relationship as we might like. The reported income for 1954 of some of the families probably represented their customary level, but for some families it may have been unusually high or unusually low.

Many families do not make adjustments in their spending until some time after their income changes. Illness or other unusual expense may cut into money ordinarily available for food in some families. In other families, such as those of retired persons, savings and other assets may be used to supplement a low income.

With each thousand-dollar increase in income, average expenditures of city families for food increased by about 3 dollars a week. Among families with lower incomes considerably more of a rise in income goes for food. For example, a low-income city family with 1 thousand dollars more to spend would use 28 percent of the extra money for food, but a high-income family that gets 1 thousand dollars more would spend only 5 percent of it on additional food.

For three selected groups of city families—a low-income group (2 thousand to 3 thousand dollars), the median-income group (4 thousand to 5 thousand dollars), and a high one (6 thousand to 8 thousand dollars)—food purchases were 48 percent of income in the low-income group, 37 percent in the median-income group, and only 29 percent in the high-income families.

The average food cost for the week

was 23 dollars for a low-income family 32 dollars for a family in the median group, and 38 dollars for a high-income family. High-income families used nearly one-fourth of their food dollars for meals and other food away from home, and the low-income families only one-eighth.

These are averages—but some families with low incomes spent as much or more money for food as some with high incomes. For example, one in four city families with low incomes served food at home in a week valued at 9 dollars or more a person, while one in four of the high-income families used food valued at less than 7 dollars a person There is a wide range within which a family can plan its food purchases and still not be unusual compared with others in similar circumstances.

Families with higher incomes purchased larger amounts of most foods They used larger amounts of baked goods and smaller amounts of flour and cereals, for example. This illustrates the tendency to shift from services provided by the homemaker to those performed for her as more money becomes available.

Families with high incomes tend to buy more and pay more for food than low-income families. Still, the proportion of the food dollar spent among the major food groups does not change greatly, whatever the income. The high-income family bought more than 4 pounds more of fresh fruit and vegetables than the low-income family, yet in each group 9 cents of the food dollar went for these items.

Likewise, the family with a high income used 3 pounds more meat, poultry, and fish than the low-income family, yet in each case these foods took 33 cents of the food dollar.

In both groups, as well as for the median-income families, the division of the food dollar is not very different from that given earlier for all families.

Families with more money to spend often chose more costly foods within a food group. For example, the low-income families paid 56 cents a pound for meat, while the median- and high-income families paid 62 and 66 cents, respectively.

The low-income families had less beef—and less expensive cuts of beef—than other families. Only 37 percent of the meat of the low-income families was beef, compared with 43 percent for those with median and high incomes. Steak (other than round) appeared on the menu during the week among 24 percent of the low-income families, and 37 and 44 percent, respectively, of the median- and high-income households.

The amount of fats and oils used by households increased relatively little with income, but the average price they paid was higher. For the three groups of city families, the price per pound varied from 34 cents at the low incomes to 37 and 40 cents for the others. This meant, among other things, a drop in the percentage of households using lard from 27 percent at the low income to 10 at the high, and a rise in the percent using salad or cooking oils from 18 to 33 percent. Families with more money to spend were more likely to have butter and less likely to have only margarine.

Frozen fruits and vegetables were used in a week by 55 percent of the high-income families, by 43 percent of the median-income families, and 26 percent of the low-income families.

Most families want variety in meals. Variety is achieved more easily at higher than at lower income levels.

Meat, poultry, fish, eggs, cheese, or dry vegetables, for example, are apt to be used as the main dish in American meals. At the lowest income level, under 1 thousand dollars, 59 percent of urban families used four or more of these six foods in a week. At the top income class, 10 thousand dollars or more, 85 percent used four or more.

Very few families used all six of the following: Coffee, tea, fresh milk, cocoa, soft drinks, and alcoholic beverages. At the lowest income level, 18 percent had four or five kinds; in the top income class, 53 percent used four or five of them. There was a greater tendency to have variety in desserts than in beverages.

Because rural families produce some of their food, the variations in food consumption with income is not quite so marked as among city families, although probably greater than many persons believe. Producing food at home often means using more total food rather than buying less. After a certain point—which differs with family income and with the kinds of food produced—increased home production brings little reduction in food expense.

ALTHOUGH each additional family member adds to the total family budget, expenditures per person in larger families tend to be less.

Comparisons of expenditures of large and small families with about the same income shows differences similar to those observed between low- and high-income families. The food budget takes a larger slice of family funds in the larger families, but dollarwise each member gets less. City families of six members in the median-income class spent an average of nearly half their income for food. Families of two spent only a fourth. Yet the large families had less than two-thirds as much food, dollarwise, for each person. That is, the money value of the food used by each person in the two-member families was 11.54 dollars; in the six-member families, it was 7.10 dollars.

No doubt it is possible to prepare food more economically for a large family than a small one, and there is likely to be less waste. The fact that large families more often include young children means they may need less of some foods per person than small families. The amounts used per person of most foods, particularly those relatively high in price, are considerably less in large households than in small. This would follow from the fact that income per capita is lower in large households.

Dairy Products,* Meat, Grain Products and Vegetables

Urban and Farm Families, Spring 1942 and 1955

Amounts used at home by a person in a week

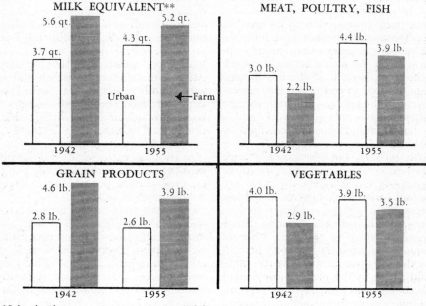

MILK EQUIVALENT**

5.6 qt.   5.2 qt.   4.3 qt.   3.7 qt.

Urban   ←Farm

1942   1955

MEAT, POULTRY, FISH

4.4 lb.   3.9 lb.   3.0 lb.   2.2 lb.

1942   1955

GRAIN PRODUCTS

4.6 lb.   3.9 lb.   2.8 lb.   2.6 lb.

1942   1955

VEGETABLES

4.0 lb.   3.9 lb.   2.9 lb.   3.5 lb.

1942   1955

*Other than butter   **Calcium equivalent*

Another way large households cut costs is by cutting the outlay for food consumed outside the home: Large families eat fewer meals away from home, and a person in a large family who does eat out usually spends less than one in a small family.

The consumption of food by farm families varies with size of family much the same as among city families, with the added factor that food purchases decrease more than home production. In the median-income class, the average person in a family of two spent twice as much for purchased food (in dollar terms) as in a family of six, but only about one-third more food was produced at home.

The value of home-produced food of farm families does not vary in systematic fashion from one income class to another, but it does tend to be larger in larger families. Extending

home production is apparently one way the family with a large number to feed manages to maintain food consumption.

DIFFERENCES IN FOOD patterns as related to the age, education, or employment of the homemaker do not appear so great as one may expect. It is hard, however, to trace their influence on the family food pattern. Each of these characteristics is associated with other factors that affect food practices. Households in which the homemaker is oldest tend to be smaller than others. The households in which the homemaker is college trained or has paid employment tend to have a higher family income than others.

In the North, for example, households at almost every income level in which the homemaker was 30 to 40 years old had a higher money value for food used at home in a week than did households in which the homemaker was younger or older. These households were generally larger than those in which the homemaker was younger or older.

The ages of the other members of the household also make a difference. Many more of the households with homemakers in the 30–49-year group had children under 16 years than did the older groups. The composition of the household associated with the age of the homemaker accounts for the greater importance of milk and milk products in households in which the homemakers were 49 years or younger.

On the other hand, it may be greater flexibility of the younger homemakers that accounts for their greater use of juices and frozen vegetables and fruit. Margarine, too, is used more often by younger homemakers than by older ones.

There is also evidence that college-trained homemakers provided their families with more of these foods—especially frozen vegetables and fruits and juices—than other homemakers. They tended to serve fewer baked goods, flour, cereals, and dried fruit and vegetables.

The money value and quantity of the foods used at home in a week by the households in which the homemaker was employed was consistently less than in households in which the homemaker was not employed, but, again, the size and composition of the family account for much of the difference. Persons in urban households in which the homemaker worked had more meat, poultry, fish, bakery products, fats, and oils than those in which the homemaker was not employed, even at the same income level.

THE OVERALL PICTURE, as we said at the beginning, is a happy one—but averages conceal as well as reveal.

Generous and varied food supplies are available in the market, and American family food patterns are likewise generous and varied. But limited incomes or the lack of knowledge about nutrition lead sometimes to too little of those foods that nutritionists recommend for an adequate and well-balanced diet.

Diets may differ for many reasons, and an understanding of the reasons helps us project the future patterns. The farm population has been declining, for example, and as it does we can predict that unless there are counteracting influences the consumption of milk, grains, and those other foods especially prominent on farms will go down in importance. More of the total food supply would be expected to enter commercial markets as fewer farmers raise less food for home use, unless indeed city families shift into the rural nonfarm group and raise some of the food.

ON THE OTHER HAND, two contrary trends may affect our predictions. Differences in patterns are becoming less important. Regional, urbanization, and income differences are less striking than they used to be. Our population is becoming, as we say, more and more homogeneous. At the same time, as incomes increase and as supplies of many different types of foods become readily available in every section of the country, the scope for individual choice increases. There may then be even greater variation in the food items selected by individual households.

JANET MURRAY *is Chief of the Survey Statistics Staff, Household Economics Research Division, Agricultural Research Service. She has had experience in research on food consumption at the Food Research Institute in Stanford University, the University of Chicago, and for more than 10 years in the Department of Agriculture.*

ENNIS BLAKE *is a food economist with the Household Economics Research Division, Agricultural Research Service. She has assisted in many of the food surveys of the Department and has had a major responsibility in the conduct of the 1955 Household Food Consumption Survey.*

Are We Well Fed?

CORINNE LE BOVIT AND FAITH CLARK

ABOUT one-tenth of the families in the United States have poor diets. What makes them so and what, in terms of nutritive content, enables us to say that most Americans eat very well we discuss in this chapter. An earlier chapter described variations in eating patterns in terms of food consumed.

Average amounts of nutrients in the food available for family use are much more generous than the recommended allowances of the National Academy of Sciences-National Research Council, the yardstick we use in planning diets.

The averages for food energy—calories—are particularly high. Even if we discount by a generous amount for food discarded or wasted in the kitchen and at the table, the calories available would still appear to be more than some people actually need—hence the prevalence of overweight.

Nearly half of the calories are derived from the fat in the food that is brought into the kitchens. Much of it comes from meat, milk, ice cream, cheese, baked goods, and food mixtures—foods not usually thought of as the main sources of fat.

The margin of nutrients in food available to families as compared with the recommended allowances for intakes was greatest for vitamin A. The average family's food supply provided 8,500 International Units a person a day, compared with an allowance of 4,200 units for the average person.

The smallest margin is usually for calcium. A nationwide survey in 195? showed 1.2 grams a person a day in the average food supply, as compared with an allowance of 0.9 gram.

Intakes in moderate excess over the dietary allowances for protein, minerals, and vitamins are not harmful and, indeed, may be desirable.

Furthermore, amounts of all nutrients furnished by the foods in the market basket should also be larger than the recommended allowances, because the allowances represent the quantities for actual ingestion while the market basket includes all discards of edible food in the kitchen or at the table.

We do not know how much is discarded. Some of the fruit may have spoiled. Some of the bread may have dried out and was fed to the birds. Fat may have been trimmed from the meat. John may have spilled a glass of milk. Jean may have left most of her mashed potatoes on her plate.

Surveys of food consumption in

households do not tell us about the food eaten by each individual in a group, but we say, for example, that on the average these households had enough protein for all the people in the group.

What we do not know is whether it was divided within the family according to need. On the other hand, we can be quite certain that if the food supply for a family does not furnish enough key dietary essentials—protein, minerals, and vitamins—to provide the total needed by the family group, the amounts actually eaten by some if not all of the individual members will fall below recommendations. Thus we can make some evaluation of the adequacy of family diets and also compare the adequacy of one group of families with another.

DESPITE THE HIGH average nutritive content of diets in this country, nearly half of the families had food supplies that did not reach recommended amounts in some one or more nutrients. The National Research Council's allowances, however, are designed for use in planning diets that will be adequate for most people. The levels of nutrients so recommended therefore are more than some people actually need and are certainly higher than needed to prevent obvious malnutrition. Because the needs of individuals vary, diets falling below the allowances are not necessarily inadequate nutritionally, and the people consuming them may not be malnourished. They may be faring less well, however, than others whose diets meet the allowances.

Calcium and ascorbic acid (vitamin C) are the nutrients most often in short supply when judged by recommendations of the Council. In the most recent survey in 1955, about 3 households in 10 did not have as much calcium as is recommended. For ascorbic acid, one in four did not meet the allowance. A considerable number of those low in each of these nutrients had diets that were other-wise adequate. Few families had diets that failed to provide at least two-thirds of the recommended allowance in any nutrient.

Nearly two-thirds of the calcium in household food supplies comes from milk, ice cream, and cheese. If a family uses little or none of these products, it is difficult for it to have enough calcium, especially if there are children. The latest survey disclosed that families with less than recommended amounts of calcium averaged less than half as much milk, ice cream, and cheese per person as the group meeting allowances.

People can obtain a considerable amount of calcium from certain grain products. Most baked goods contain milk, and many are made with baking powder or mold inhibitors containing calcium. Self-rising flour, containing calcium salts, is popular for making hot breads in the South. People in this country do not usually eat enough of such bread and baked goods to meet their need for calcium, however.

Of all of the households studied in 1955, only three, representing fewer than 1 percent of the families in the country, had enough calcium without directly using any milk products. These three families each used large amounts of self-rising flour—enough to provide 15 to 20 large biscuits a day for each person.

Nearly all of the ascorbic acid in household food supplies comes from fruit and vegetables—a great deal of it from citrus fruits. Such foods as cabbage or potatoes that are less rich in this vitamin than citrus fruits must be used in larger amounts than when the richer source is used. In the survey, families with recommended amounts of ascorbic acid used more than twice as much fruit and vegetables per person as those whose diets did not meet allowances. Furthermore, a much higher proportion of their fruit consisted of citrus fruits.

From 15 to 20 percent of the families had diets providing less than recommended quantities of vitamin

Need for Improved Diets
Family Diets Not Meeting Allowances of National Research Council

Less than 2/3 NRC   *2/3 NRC but less than 100%*

PROTEIN _____ 1% 🏠🏠 7%

CALCIUM _____ 8% 🏠🏠🏠🏠🏠🏠🏠🏠🏠 21%

VITAMIN A _____ 6% 🏠🏠🏠🏠🏠 10%

THIAMINE _____ 3% 🏠🏠🏠🏠🏠 14%

ASCORBIC ACID _____ 10% 🏠🏠🏠🏠🏠🏠 15%

Each unit represents 5% of the households.

A, thiamine, and riboflavin. Fewer than 10 percent had diets that did not fully meet the allowances in protein, iron, or niacin.

Nearly all that were low in protein were low in at least three other nutrients. This was not unexpected, because the groups of foods that contribute most of the protein—milk, cheese, meat, poultry, fish, and grain products — also supply significant quantities of vitamins and minerals.

Improvement in diets in the United States over the past few decades was greatest for low-income families.

The third of the city families at the low end of the income scale benefited much more from dietary changes between 1936 and 1942 and between 1942 and 1948 than they did later. Although average amounts of nearly all dietary essentials were greater for the third of the families with highest incomes, diets of the third of the families with the lowest incomes showed the greater rate of improvement. The poorer families ate more grain products and thus benefited most from enrichment programs. They also made much greater gains in consumption of meat and citrus fruits.

Much of the dietary improvement of recent decades occurred before 1950, when real income per capita also increased greatly, especially among families ranking lowest in income scale.

Between 1948 and 1955, the rate of increase in nutrient content of the average city diet was smaller than it had been in earlier years. The greatest increases were in protein, thiamine, niacin, and iron. These were related to greater consumption of meat. Some of the increases were canceled by declines in the use of cereals and baked goods, however. Although the amounts of fruit eaten remained the same between 1948 and 1955, the use of vegetables declined. In the later years, furthermore, housewives often selected kinds of fruit and vegetables that were less rich in ascorbic acid. As a result, ascorbic acid values of diets went down about a tenth.

Surveys made in 1936, 1942, and 1948 indicated that diets of low-income families were becoming more like those of the higher income groups. The rate of shift seems to have been arrested between 1948 and 1955, when all of the income groups shared about equally in the changes.

We limit this discussion to city families because only for them have surveys been made that enable us to compare their diets in 1936, 1942, 1948, and 1955. The changes in their diets probably represent the general pattern for the country.

Regional differences in the nutritive quality of family diets arise from many factors—differences in income, the proportion of rural families, and basic food habits.

Southern families used less milk, less meat, and less fruit and vegetables in 1955 than those in the North, and hence their diets were poorer in all nutrients except iron and thiamine. Because they used much more of grain products, much of which was enriched, their diets were as high in iron and thiamine as were diets in the North. Grain products also contributed considerable amounts of protein, calcium, riboflavin, and niacin, but not enough to bring diets in the South up to the levels in the North.

In these days of rapid communication and more even distribution of purchasing power, we are seeing the gradual disappearance of many of the differences we used to associate with particular geographical areas.

When we look at figures on family consumption, however, we find that the South—at least city families in the South—is still different from the North and even more different in 1955 than in 1948. Diets of city families in the South in 1948 averaged only slightly below those in the North in most nutrients and slightly higher in iron and thiamine. Differences were greater by 1955, however.

The average diet of city families in the North between 1948 and 1955 increased 15 percent or more in protein, thiamine, and niacin and about 10 percent in iron. Protein and niacin increased a little less in the South and thiamine and iron much less than in the North. The North had caught up to the South in iron and thiamine and had pushed farther ahead in protein and niacin. Families in both regions

Proportions of Family Diets Not Providing Recommended Amounts of Eight Nutrients

Nutrient	North-east	North-central region	West	South
	Per-cent	Per-cent	Per-cent	Per-cent
Protein.....	7	5	5	12
Calcium....	28	26	26	34
Iron........	12	9	7	10
Vitamin A value.....	12	13	11	26
Thiamine...	22	14	16	15
Riboflavin..	18	16	15	25
Niacin......	7	5	6	10
Ascorbic acid......	17	19	23	37

Source: Household Food Consumption Survey, 1955.

had reduced their use of grains and raised their consumption of meat. Northern families, however, were using slightly more milk in 1955 than in 1948, but southerners were using a little less.

Diets in 1955 in both regions had fallen behind those in 1948 in ascorbic acid, but the South had fallen much farther behind. The total consumption of fruit and vegetables had dropped for both groups, but more in the South—particularly of citrus fruits.

Families in the Northeast, the north-central region, and the West—the three areas that make up what we refer to here as the North—had diets in 1955 that were similar to each other in nutritive quality. The only major difference was in thiamine. The percentage of families in the Northeast with food supplies furnishing less than recommended amounts of thiamine was considerably larger than in any other part of the country. Families in the Northeast used less pork and grain products—both good sources of thiamine if the grain products are whole grain or enriched.

Life on a farm or in the city can also spell differences in nutritive quality of

Diets and Education of Wives

Percentage of Diets Meeting Allowances of National Research Council in All Nutrient

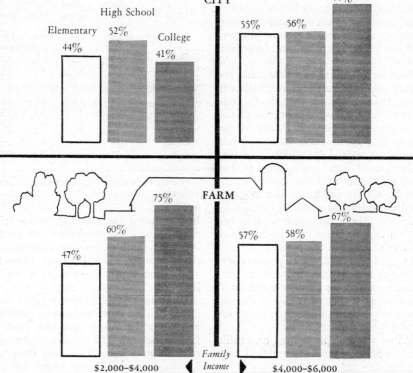

CITY

High School

Elementary   52%

44%   College   55%   56%   70%

                 41%

FARM

                 75%   67%

           60%   57%   58%

47%

$2,000–$4,000   Family Income in a Year ◄ ► $4,000–$6,000

diets. Many of us have a picture of the dining table in the farm home groaning with dishes of meat, vegetables, and milk and pie. We tend to think that farm people are better fed than city people.

Those ideas are not entirely valid today. It is true that farm families eat more food as measured in terms of calories. We found in our survey that a few more farm families than city families in the North had diets that met recommendations in all nutrients. In the South, however, there was no difference in percentage of farm or city families whose diets met allowances in all nutrients.

When diets failed in any nutrient farm families tended to fare the worse Farm diets in both North and South averaged poorer in vitamins A and C

Farm families everywhere used more milk, grain products, fats, and sugars than urban groups. But they used less fruit, particularly citrus fruits, and vegetables, particularly dark-green and deep-yellow vegetables. Most of the large-scale food surveys, however, have been made in the spring when, in some sections, gardens might not yet be producing much and when last year's home-canned food might be all gone. More might have been available another season.

Even though farm housewives bought quite a bit of the food they served to their families, they also made good use of food raised at home.

Nearly half of the calcium and a third of the riboflavin of farm families were supplied by milk from their own cows. The average family without a cow buys some milk, but families who produce their own milk use much more than those who buy all of it.

Fruit and vegetables grown on the farm provided a fifth of the vitamin A and nearly a third of the ascorbic acid. Farm-produced meat animals and poultry provided appreciable amounts of protein, iron, and B vitamins. Despite more purchasing of food by farm families today than formerly, home production still is important in the nutritive quality of their diets.

MANY THINGS besides where families live affect the nutritive quality of their diets. Some of these are the income of the family, how much they actually spend for food, how many people there are to feed, how young and how well educated the homemaker is, and whether or not she has a job.

It is often hard to isolate the effects of one factor from another. For instance, families of older folks tend to be smaller and include fewer children than families of younger folks. Therefore, any difference in family food supplies associated with age of the homemaker is probably also associated with the number and type of persons being fed in the household.

The higher the income that a city family has, the better its diet generally is. Farm families also tend to have better diets when they have more money available. But the nutritive quality of farm diets is also influenced by the amount and kinds of food produced at home for which no direct cash expenditure needs to be made. Besides, the general level of a farm family's income frequently cannot be measured by money taken in during a single year. Less relationship there-fore exists between the quality of diet and income on farms than there is in cities.

High income does not in and of itself insure a good diet, however.

Even in the city group with an annual income of 6 thousand dollars or more, only 63 percent of the families had food supplies that measured up to recommended levels in all nutrients.

For families such as these, good nutrition is clearly an educational problem. They need to be convinced of the importance of choosing a good diet regularly and to be supplied with reliable information to help them.

Not all nutrients are affected to the same extent by income. The nutrient with the closest relationship to income is ascorbic acid. The better off the family, the more likely are diets to meet recommended levels of this vitamin—whether the family lives in the North or South, in city or country. People with more money to spend use more fruits and vegetables that provide nearly all of the ascorbic acid in the diet. In particular, they tend to use a great deal more of citrus fruit, a rich source of this vitamin. Families with incomes over 10 thousand dollars in 1955 used enough citrus fruit to give them a little more than one-half cup of juice a day for each person. Those with incomes under 1 thousand dollars had less than a fourth of that amount.

The nutrient least related to the income level of the family is thiamine. Families with high incomes are just as likely to fall short of the goal of this vitamin as those with low incomes. Some of the best sources of thiamine in the diet are enriched or whole grain flour, cereals, and bread, and lean meat, particularly lean pork. Better-off families tend to use less of both grains and pork, perhaps because of mistaken notions that they are "fattening" or perhaps because they are edged out of the menu by other foods.

HOUSEHOLDS with many mouths to feed tend to have more difficulty in

Nutritive Value of Family Diets in the United States

Nutrient and unit	Average per day from food available for use	Recommended allowances for daily intake
	Per person	Per person
Food energy ....Calories..	3, 200	2, 200
Protein.......................grams..	103	64
Calcium........................do....	1. 2	.9
Iron.......................milligrams..	18	11
Vitamin A value.....International Units..	8, 500	4, 100
Thiamine................milligrams..	1. 6	1. 1
Riboflavin....................do....	2. 3	1. 6
Niacin.........................do....	19	11
Ascorbic acid..................do....	106	68

Source: Household Food Consumption Survey, 1955.

Changes in Nutritive Value of Diets of City Families, Classified by Income

	Percentage of change in nutritive value per person per day					
	1936 to 1942		1942 to 1948		1948 to 1955	
Nutrient	Lowest-income one-third	Highest-income one-third	Lowest-income one-third	Highest-income one-third	Lowest-income one-third	Highest-income one-third
Food energy.............	3	−7	10	4	0	4
Protein..................	15	−1	13	7	9	15
Calcium.................	34	6	19	14	−2	3
Iron.....................	25	−1	22	17	5	9
Vitamin A value..........	41	4	5	6	6	−4
Thiamine................	23	−5	30	17	13	18
Riboflavin...............	37	5	26	18	−1	2
Niacin..................	22	4	29	12	18	20
Ascorbic acid............	78	30	13	−4	−19	−9

getting good diets than do small ones.

Large households use more food and spend more than small households, but the amount that they spend for each person is less. The more people there are to provide for, the more must be spent on nearly all the items a family needs—clothing, housing, medical care, recreation, as well as food. The amount spent on any one portion of the budget therefore may have to be restricted.

For some nutrients, moderate differences in family size have little effect. For instance, about the same proportion of families of two, three, four, or five persons had diets containing enough protein. But more households with six or more persons seemed to find it hard to meet the allowance.

Larger households had the most difficulty providing enough calcium in the diet. Nearly all of the larger households of four or more persons included children, whereas many two- and even three-person families did not.

Income and Food Produced for Home Use

Farm Families, 1941 and 1954

Percentage of families producing in the year

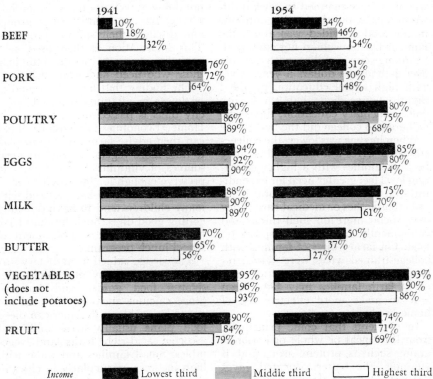

	1941	1954
BEEF	10% / 18% / 32%	34% / 46% / 54%
PORK	76% / 72% / 64%	51% / 50% / 48%
POULTRY	90% / 86% / 89%	80% / 75% / 68%
EGGS	94% / 92% / 90%	85% / 80% / 74%
MILK	88% / 90% / 89%	75% / 70% / 61%
BUTTER	70% / 65% / 56%	50% / 37% / 27%
VEGETABLES (does not include potatoes)	95% / 96% / 93%	93% / 90% / 86%
FRUIT	90% / 84% / 79%	74% / 71% / 69%

Income ■ Lowest third ▨ Middle third ☐ Highest third

Children need more calcium than adults, so that the more children to be fed, the more calcium must be provided. It usually means more milk.

Large households did just about as well as small households in providing recommended amounts of thiamine, because per person they used as much enriched or whole-grain bread, flour, and cereals.

The ability of the homemaker to make wise choices within the limits of the money in her purse determines how well her family is provided with food. Many factors may affect her ability and her interest in making such choices. We have no information on some of these such as her health, her interests, or her training in nutrition.

However, we have studied nutritive quality of diet in relation to the age, employment status, and amount of formal education of homemakers. On the whole, we find few differences.

Homemakers over 60 years of age in the North provided poorer diets for their families than did the younger women, although their households were smaller and fewer had children to feed so that it should have been easier for them to afford good diets.

In the South, the older homemakers tend to provide better diets. One clue to this difference may be that fewer of the elderly northern families lived on farms. They may have had to spend more for other necessities as well as for food.

Whether or not the homemaker had a job that took her away from home made very little difference in the quality of diet she provided. The working wife may have planned somewhat different menus, but the level of nutrients in the food provided was about the same as by the woman not employed.

Among city families with income over 4 thousand dollars a year, wives with high school education provided slightly better diets than those with only elementary education; those who had gone to college did the best.

When income was lower, the college-educated wives did least well. It may be that families with a higher education level feel greater need for expenditures on education and cultural items or better clothes or medical care. They may spend more on such things and consequently have less to spend on food. On farms, diets of families with college-trained wives were better, regardless of income. The better educated farm families may have been able to make more effective use of home production facilities.

In nutrients that come principally from lean meat or whole or enriched grains such as protein, iron, and B vitamins, the better educated wives did not do better than others. However, the food they prepared was higher, for the most part, in calcium and vitamin A and vitamin C supplied principally by milk and fruit and vegetables.

People living alone spent a fifth more on food per person than those in households of two or more. They used a tenth more food per person, measured in terms of calories—more of all groups of foods except milk. Yet their diets were no better. Half of them (the same percentage as for larger households) did not reach recommended amounts in one or more nutrients. Many more than of larger families were low in iron; a few more were low in protein and the B vitamins. Nearly three-fourths of those who lived alone were women. Half were women 55 or more years old.

THE INFORMATION presented here has shown that, on the average, family diets in the United States are good, but that some groups of people are not doing as well as others. From food surveys we can identify these groups and discover their specific problems. This information is then used as a basis for programs designed to help those who need and want help.

The finding that farm diets tend to be lower in vitamins A and C than city diets is passed on to workers in Home Economics Extension. They can then advise farm families to plan to raise more vegetables that are good sources of vitamins A and C and to preserve enough for the whole year.

Families with low incomes and with many children tend to have difficulty getting good diets. Such findings have helped lead to the establishment of school lunch programs.

Knowledge gained from dietary surveys is also used by nutritionists designing food guides and budgets. Since calcium and ascorbic acid are apt to be problems in American diets, food plans usually stress milk and ascorbic acid-rich fruits and vegetables. Small families and those with high incomes, particularly in cities in the Northeast, tend to have less than recommended amounts of thiamine and of iron. Therefore, food recommendations for this group usually stress whole-grain and enriched bread and cereals and lean meat, especially pork.

CORINNE LEBOVIT *is a nutritionist in the Household Economics Research Division of the Agricultural Research Service. She took her graduate training in Cornell University.*

FAITH CLARK *became Director of the Household Economics Research Division in 1957. She received her doctorate from the University of Chicago. Mrs. LeBovit and Dr. Clark have collaborated in several studies of the nutritive quality of family food supplies since 1951, when Mrs. LeBovit rejoined the Division's staff after completing her graduate work.*

Food

LEARNING

Habit—and More

HAZEL K. STIEBELING AND THELMA A. DREIS

PEOPLE at Cornell University wondered why girls living in dormitories disliked some foods, why they were writing home about it, and whether the dislikes meant the girls were being poorly nourished.

In that they were not alone. Many people—parents, teachers, dietitians and others responsible for group feeding, home economists, grocers, sociologists, and anthropologists—would like to know more about why people eat what they do; why they often spurn the good, nutritious things put before them; and why some refuse even to taste new, different, and maybe exciting foods.

Nutritionists at Cornell asked each girl to keep a record for 7 days of the foods she actually ate. They then interviewed each about any influences that might affect what she ate.

They gave each a list of 185 food items on which she was asked to make a check mark in one of several columns with headings such as "Will not eat it because I dislike it or it disagrees with me"; "Will not choose it, but will eat it if it is served"; and "Will eat it frequently."

Finally they determined the extent to which each girl used a number of foods, including milk, eggs, bread, cereals, and potatoes, which were available at mealtime but were served only upon request.

The nutritionists learned that the diets of most of the girls provided less than 70 percent of the recommended allowances for calcium, iron, and thiamine. In general, however, the inadequacy of their diets was not a direct result of distaste for certain foods.

Most of the foods on the "Will not eat" list were seldom served. The list included buttermilk, oysters, turnips, olives, heart, mushrooms, canned figs, pumpkin, cooked celery, soft-boiled and poached eggs, tongue, parsnips, and pimiento. Rejection of these foods, except eggs, would have little effect in the long run on the nutritive content of their diets.

The main reason for the inadequacy was that the students ate too little of some free-choice foods—milk, eggs, bread, cereals, and potatoes. Only a few girls listed them as foods they strongly disliked.

In practically every instance of low intake of calcium and iron, the daily addition of one or two glasses of milk and an egg would have increased the intake to a more satisfactory level.

Use of more bread and cereals would have met their needs for thiamine. More of all of the free-choice foods would have increased the protein and riboflavin in their diets.

Thus, for this group of young people, the failure to get diets as good as those recommended by the National Research Council seemed to result from indifference and misinformation about food values rather than dislikes. The girls apparently did not realize the nutritional importance of milk, eggs, bread, and cereals. Eating more of them would mean more calories, of course; the extra calories would require more physical activity or the reduction in the amounts of some items nutritionally less valuable if the intake and expenditure of energy were to balance.

PREFERENCES among kinds and forms of foods pose problems for military authorities when they come to serve men of varied customs and habits from the same menu and maybe at the same table.

The soldier from Nebraska, for example, may have little interest in hominy, while the man from Georgia likes it. Does the northerner object to hominy itself or to the southern style of cooking?

In a study of feeding problems at Smoky Hill Army Air Field, Salina, Kans., during the Second World War, the food consultants noticed that the plate and kitchen waste of hominy was high for the first shift of a 24-hour period but low for the second shift.

They investigated and discovered that the only difference was in the method of preparation. The cook on the first shift had prepared it southern style. The cook on the second shift, who did not know the way southerners usually prepared hominy, called upon his own ingenuity and had baked it with a cheese sauce in much the same way as he baked macaroni and cheese. His way made hominy seem more familiar to the midwestern men, and they ate it with gusto.

Another investigation made in eight camps by the Office of the Quartermaster General showed that the way fish was prepared had much to do with how well the soldiers ate it. The typical Army cook knew little about cooking fish. His attitude was that fish was unpopular, he had to serve it once a week, the men did not like it, and they were not going to eat it—so why should he take time and trouble of fixing it properly? He simply fried it and dished it out regardless. In camps where the cook added sauces or garnishes, however, the soldiers always ate more fish.

These experiences illustrate that strong dislikes may be a handicap because they make it harder for a person to adjust himself to new situations when he is away from home. They also bring out several aspects of the question, Why do we eat what we do?

Customs, attitudes, and eating habits grow out of cultural, social, and economic backgrounds.

Most people prefer the foods that their family has become used to: The group in which we are born and develop first determines what tastes good to us and what first tends to bring physical and psychological pleasure.

But our behavior as to food also reflects our individual ways of thinking about food, our tastes, and our habits of eating that grow out of our personal experiences. Thus social and individual development go hand in hand. Individual development is produced to a great extent by group interaction.

Choices within major types of foods reflect both our heritage and our response to our environment.

We can cite many examples.

Almost everyone in the United States likes milk and our many kinds of cheese. People in some countries, however, consider fluid milk a food only for young children, but they like cheese, yoghurt, and buttermilk.

Americans consume much meat, poultry, and fish. Beef is preferred; pork is next. Some groups in the world never eat any kind of meat from warm-blooded animals because of religious beliefs. Others refuse pork but accept beef. Still others on fast days or during fasting seasons abstain from any flesh as food.

Take the cereal grain—why do we use wheat or rye or corn or rice or oats for our bread? Agricultural conditions and ease of preparation and preservation at home undoubtedly were among early determining factors.

The continuing relatively high consumption of rice in South Carolina and Louisiana reminds us that rice is of more basic importance in the South than in other parts of the country, where its use is chiefly in desserts. Rice is a staple in tropical and subtropical regions where conditions make it a highly productive food crop.

Mexicans may serve corn—maize—chiefly as tortillas, a kind of unleavened pancake. Corn pone, hoecake, johnnycake, and griddlecakes are inexpensive forms of bread that are widely favored in the United States and once were used in larger quantity than today. There still is preference in some States for white cornmeal for quickbreads or mush, and in others for yellow cornmeal. Hominy, whole or as grits, is popular in the South, but is little known in the North and West. Corn as a food was introduced from America to Africa long ago, but in some countries corn is regarded only as a feed for animals.

Wheat is now our predominant food grain and is used chiefly to make a leavened, ovenbaked bread. White bread once was a rare, prestige food of the rich, but it has become widely used as efficient farm methods of wheat production and factory methods of milling flour and baking bread have lowered the relative cost of bread. Bolted patent flour makes a delicate white product as compared with the heavier, stronger flavored breads made from whole wheat, rye, or maize.

A partial reversal may have begun, however, in ideas as to what is good bread. Some people are acquiring a taste for the more compact, flavorful, nutritious breads—more like those mother used to make from white, whole-wheat, or rye flours. Some of these are similar to the type that some Europeans call "peasantbread."

Custom and habit can become rigid. People sometimes prefer to go hungry rather than to eat unfamiliar food.

Herbert Hoover found that the Belgians after the First World War did not want the rice that was offered for relief of famine. They were used to wheat. The Japanese and Germans after the Second World War did not want corn—most Japanese wanted rice and most Germans wanted wheat or rye. If they are whole grain or enriched, the cereal foods—breads or porridge—are more alike than different in nutritive values, and each is eaten by large groups of the world's population. But even when a food has the approval of large segments of the human race, few of us are adventurous enough to use it as steady diet if it is unfamiliar and far outside the ruts we get into.

WILLINGNESS to accept different foods—to repeat—is affected by many things.

Infancy and childhood are the best times in which to develop a favorable attitude toward variety in food. Children are not highly adventurous about trying new foods, but they are more likely to be willing to adventure with a new food when they feel secure under the influence of father, mother, teacher, or others whom they trust.

The food preferences of parents, especially the father, may limit the variety of food a child will experience at home. In a study in Pennsylvania, it was found that a substantial number of mothers, 89 percent, indicated they served some foods infrequently or left them out altogether from the family's menu in deference to their husbands' food preferences.

Palatability — flavor, appearance, texture, and temperature of food— is important. What we interpret as palatable may depend on the concentration of the flavor. If we eat only a small amount of some food, we may like it because it is very sweet, very spicy, very salty, or very bitter. If we eat much of it, though, we tend to want to have the flavor diluted.

Thus we develop a habit of using mild-flavored potatoes or breads, rice, and other cereal grains as background foods for a meal. We like bread with ham in sandwiches or potatoes with roast beef. People in the Orient like rice with their curries. Young children, more conservative than adults in their judgments of what is palatable, generally prefer foods that are neither very hot nor very cold and that are delicate in seasonings and texture.

Attitudes toward food may result from experiences that have little to do with palatability.

Special food likes may grow out of our associations with food—the foods we had when company came, the foods we had when we ate away from home, or the meals we had on Sundays, birthdays, and holidays.

On the other hand, we may come to dislike foods because of unhappy personal experiences—the green apples and overripe melons that made us sick or mixed dishes made from leftovers that were not properly handled. Nor do we relish food with a color, odor, or texture that we have come to associate with something unpleasant.

Maybe because we have no association with them, we tend also to distrust foods that are unfamiliar or exotic in color, texture, flavor, or origin.

Many people come to like foods that they think will enhance their social position and to avoid foods they fear may lower their status.

Thus children often learn to eat certain foods to win the approval of a teacher. Adults may learn to like the things that their wealthier neighbors eat or things that are scarce or expensive. White bread, white sugar,

white rice once were prestige foods and still are for some groups. Steak, roasts, fried chicken, ice cream, and oranges once were special foods for everyone, and still are for many. Such inexpensive foods as stews, hamburger, and frankfurters often are scorned until people feel secure in their social position. Some first-generation Americans tend to shun delectable mother-country dishes until they are sure that these foods also are accepted by their new associates. Often farm youngsters grow to think of skim milk as fit only for livestock, though it has all the nutritive values of milk except those associated with the fat. And some people do not yet appreciate variety meats, such as liver and heart.

There are still other explanations for accepting or refusing foods. Soft, milky foods unfortunately sometimes are considered suitable only for young children or the ill and therefore not for healthy adults. Some think salads belong to women's parties and rabbits and are not for men. Puddings to be eaten with spoons instead of forks may be considered childish.

Some young people who wish to appear emotionally mature may be influenced to regard food refusals as childish reactions. In spite of earlier dislikes they may accept many foods— for example, strongly flavored vegetables as turnips and cooked cabbage. Even adults to whom the health motive for choosing food wisely is not appealing may want to get a reputation for wide social experience: If a cosmopolitan taste is considered evidence of having dined and traveled with the best, they may eat many unfamiliar foods to achieve or maintain such a reputation. They will then eat what they may once have regarded as exotic—eel, avocado, persimmons, artichokes—besides the everyday foods.

Advertising and other promotion bring familiar and new food products to our attention and influence our choices in countless blunt and subtle ways. There is much in all this to give us thought about human behavior.

WILLINGNESS to accept food does not mean that we have to like every kind of food equally well or that we must be delighted with every vegetable on our plate.

Willingness to eat should mean a promise to ourselves that we will not confine our food selections to favorite foods if doing so leads to an inadequate diet and poor nutrition.

It is not fatal to dislike spinach, for example, if we like and eat some other kinds of leafy greens. But suppose that in addition to refusing the leafy green vegetables because we do not care for them, we also reject nutritionally kindred vegetables for other reasons: Broccoli because it is expensive, carrots because those presently on hand are rather strong flavored or woody, and sweetpotatoes or Hubbard squash because we do not want to take time to fix them. Such a heavy restriction of dark-green and deep-yellow vegetables could leave our diets seriously short in vitamin A value.

Allowing whims, half-remembered childhood experiences, or even downright finickiness to dictate our food selections is risky for good nutrition.

Modifications in diet habits may be necessary for many of us if we are to take full advantage of modern advances of science as they relate to health. By learning to like foods of the kinds and in the amounts that our bodies need, we can achieve the physical and mental vigor that will come with nutritional prosperity.

The Nation's families over the years have improved their food habits. This trend can be speeded up. But such progress calls for application of principles of learning by parents and teachers in the training of children and by all of us who wish to develop better food habits.

By setting goals for ourselves, we can redirect our food ways and modify our food habits for improved nutrition and better living.

HAZEL K. STIEBELING, *Director of the Institute of Home Economics, Agricultural Research Service, has been with the Department of Agriculture since 1930, first as a food economist and since 1942 as the officer responsible for research in human nutrition and other phases of home economics.*

THELMA A. DREIS, *the Institute of Home Economics, joined the Department of Agriculture in 1936. She had been a staff member of the Institute of Human Relations, Yale University and had served with other Government agencies. She received a doctor's degree from American University.*

Food Produced for Home Use

By Farm Families, 1941 and 1954

Percentage of families producing in the year.

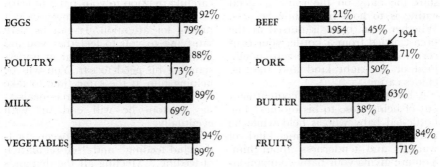

As the Twig Is Bent

WILLA VAUGHN TINSLEY

IT is one thing to know what to eat for good nutrition—that is basic knowledge. It is another type of learning, or wisdom, to know how to influence others, particularly children, to establish the kind of eating practices that will help them all their lives.

Good eating habits begin in infancy, for babies come into the world without established patterns of behavior, and habits formed early develop into lifetime practices.

Start with the child therefore—not with the food.

PROVIDE companionship from the beginning. One of the first ways to start the baby on the route to good eating is to hold him while he eats. Whether your baby is nursed at the breast or fed from a bottle, your concern will be to see that he gets enough food of the right kind and that he enjoys eating.

A breast-fed baby gets contentment out of being close to his mother. The bottle-fed baby who is held while he nurses can feel the same kind of warmth and tenderness about him. You are giving your baby companionship as well as food when you hold him while he eats.

It matters less that you feed your baby by breast or by bottle than that you feel easy and relaxed and confident in your ability to provide for him. The spirit in which you feed your baby counts, as well as the particular kind of milk he gets.

ADAPT THE SCHEDULE to the baby. Babies know when they need to be fed. There is a swing away from beginning with a regulated number of feedings set by the clock.

Letting a baby have a chance to develop a feeding rhythm of his own takes more judgment than feeding him at set intervals. This will require giving careful attention to your baby to learn to judge whether he is hungry or just fussing for attention. It can be very satisfying to you to feel that you are letting the baby guide you in understanding his need to eat. You will be helping him at the same time to take the first step toward the three-meals-a-day custom he will end up with eventually.

There is a difference between "self-demand feeding" and "self-regulation of feeding." Meeting all the demands of a baby does not necessarily prepare him to live happily in a realistic world.

636

Helping him to regulate his meals, to be content with feedings that get farther apart as he advances in age and development because he takes more at each feeding, is teaching him to adapt his eating demands to changing needs. Sooner or later his feedings can become fairly well regulated so family schedules will not be upset, but the move toward regularity should come slowly.

ADD supplementary foods gradually. Regardless of at what age your doctor suggests adding other foods to the initial milk diet, it is essential that the baby enjoy this new experience.

I mentioned the importance of the mother's attitude in influencing the baby's first acceptance of the eating process and his satisfaction in it. Human beings, influenced as we are by emotions, are affected throughout life by attitudes—of ourselves and of others. Emotions apply to eating as well as to other daily habits.

All new experiences in eating are likelier to bring satisfaction if the strange food is introduced slowly, in small amounts, and under pleasant circumstances. Often the mother provides pleasure by holding the baby on her lap and by not becoming disturbed if the experience is not successful from the start.

A wise procedure in introducing a new food is to initiate the baby into some of the sensations of tasting and feeling a new food and then to concentrate on getting the food into him. As taste and touch become less strange, the baby is more apt to swallow the food, which is the second step in accepting a new food.

If you give the baby the new food early in the meal when his hunger is keenest, very likely he will eat it.

Do not crowd him into eating a normal serving of a new food even though he may do so willingly. Follow the new food with a familiar favorite so that the complete process gives the baby a feeling of pleasure with the meal.

CHANGE the form in which food is prepared. Babies can become so accustomed to soft, thin purees that they resist change in the way the food feels to them. Change needs to begin gradually with mashed and chopped foods before the baby gets foods in the coarser forms customarily eaten by the family.

INTRODUCE new methods of eating along with other new eating experiences. Just as it is important to change the flavors and forms of food before habits become so firmly set that change is strongly resisted, it is necessary to change the manner of serving food to babies before these habits also become difficult to change.

Thus a first step in weaning the baby from nursing, whether from the breast or bottle, is to start him gradually taking a few sips from a cup. The object in the beginning is to get him accustomed to the cup. If mothers could accept this as the goal at first instead of feeling frustrated over milk that spills out of the baby's mouth in the first trials, both mother and baby could experience the new practice with more pleasure.

Acquainting the baby with the cup, like all new sensations, should be brief. Then follow it with a familiar and pleasant process, such as nursing.

Even after a baby has learned to drink well from a cup, he may not be ready to take all his milk and other liquids in this way. Nursing has been one of his chief satisfactions since birth. Letting the baby help hold the cup gives him a degree of satisfaction that takes the place of some of the pleasure he had in the sucking process.

A gradual replacement of nursing is likely to be more acceptable than a sudden change. The baby may need a little extra attention during this time to make up to him for the loss of the close companionship he enjoyed while nursing.

DETERMINE amounts of foods on an individual basis. Each baby determines how much food his own body needs. Expecting him to take the same amount at each feeding or to take the amount listed in a chart for his age may cause him to refuse food.

Urging a baby to take the same amounts of food consumed by older brothers or sisters when they were infants may be entirely wrong. Undue urging can destroy appetite. It can also have lasting psychological effects.

A baby by nature grows in a rhythm of getting hungry, demanding food, enjoying food, feeling satisfied after eating—several times a day, day after day.

Such a repetition of satisfactions builds into the child's concept of life feelings of confidence and well-being, and trust in those about him. Any interference in this rhythm tends to disturb the satisfaction that results from completion of the cycle.

If mealtime becomes a struggle between him and his mother, eating becomes a conflict between the baby's drive to satisfy his appetite and his mother's goal, which may differ from the baby's goal. Such conflicts may result in lack of interest in food. Sometimes actual defensiveness and suspicion may develop. Some babies are big eaters. Some have small appetites. Babies, like adults, do not always want the same amounts of food each day or at each meal. Rate of growth is not uniform, even during its period of most rapid progress.

The more disturbed the mother becomes over getting the baby to take food, the more finicky he may become over his eating. Eating is not and cannot be isolated into a mere physical process separated from simultaneous emotional processes.

ENCOURAGE the baby to take a variety of foods. His body's nutritional needs (like ours) are more likely to be met if they are met from many sources instead of a limited number of foods.

Human beings tend to resist change. It usually takes a conscious and concerted effort to convert the baby from satisfaction with a few foods to acceptance and finally enjoyment of a number of different foods.

There are psychological and economical reasons also for teaching the young to eat a variety of foods. As a person widens his living farther and farther away from the home situation to visits away from home, to school, to public eating places, and eventually to his own home, opportunities for food selection expand and vary. Fortunate is the person who can adapt his meal patterns to reasonable circumstances and yet be satisfied and well fed.

Babies and children like best the foods they know best. Give them only a small portion—even as little as a taste—of the unfamiliar food the first time. Introduce it in the same meal with some food the child likes especially. Do not call undue attention to this small amount—maybe only a bite size—and it is more likely to be eaten. Repeat the process in a few days, regardless if the food was eaten or refused the first time it was served.

Watch that your own hunger or liking for a particular food does not cause you to be overly generous or optimistic in the size of the servings.

Purposely serving smaller portions than the child will eat and giving a second small helping if requested mean greater consumption than a larger serving in the beginning. As the child begins to experiment with eating the new food, the amount can be increased gradually to usual family size, and the food can be served as often as it appears in the family menus.

Babies and young children seem to prefer eating all of one food before they start another. They also tend to eat more indiscriminately when they are hungriest—at the beginning of a meal.

The practice of some mothers of mixing a new food with a familiar food may succeed with certain youngsters, but sometimes it may cause a baby to reject not only the new food but the other as well. Alternating bites of less well-liked foods with other foods may be acceptable or even necessary.

If actual unpleasantness occurs at any time during the process of introducing new or unliked foods, it is well to postpone any contact or reference to the food until the baby has had time enough to forget about the previous experience. In reintroducing the rejected food, serve it under circumstances different from the previous time.

EVEN VERY YOUNG children begin copying the eating habits of those near them. A food rejected by one member of the family may also be refused by the baby. Babies at an early age learn to distinguish between sham and reality, particularly in matters as personal and as recurring as eating. Pretending to like a food is not enough. The real attitudes of family members about foods are soon recognized by the baby.

The mother unconsciously may reveal her attitudes toward the flavor, texture, and color of a food as she prepares it with the hungry youngster eagerly watching her. A common method of testing the temperature of strained or pureed vegetables or meat is to taste a small portion from a spoon just before feeding it. So-called baby foods seldom are seasoned to suit adult preferences. Even the look on the mother's face may be enough to condition the child against the food. Misplaced and ill-advised expressions from other family members are to be discouraged.

Fortunate indeed is the child whose parents provide him with the health benefits of highly nutritious liver or greens, even though adults may not care for them. Conscientious and understanding parents often have to learn to eat the variety of foods they want the baby to eat, particularly as the child's age and his drives toward self-assertion increase. This brings us to a consideration of ways to help the child in eating habits as he progresses from dependence upon others in the daily routine—from being fed to feeding himself.

EXPECT FOODS to be handled as the child begins to feed himself and prepare for this by the way you serve his food.

Seek ways of serving suitable foods as "finger" foods during the child's growth period, when coordination of small muscles is too undeveloped to permit the careful handling of spoons, forks, and knives.

A youngster's independence is aided by meats cut into strips before cooking; bacon slices rendered of most of the fat; vegetables, when they are recommended to be served raw, such as carrots and celery, cut into thin sticks; fruit cut into small, convenient-to-eat wedges or chunks; and toast cut into a variety of small shapes. His sense of achievement is stimulated because he can eat foods in these forms without depending upon adult help and without having been fussed at for being so messy with his eating.

The same principle applies to drinking milk and other liquids from a small, flat glass, which perhaps the child may be permitted to refill from a pitcher he can handle.

SELECT suitable equipment to encourage self-feeding. Small, immature hands cannot handle with confidence the same eating equipment used by the older family members. The size and height of his chair, for example, can influence the child's poise in conveying food to the mouth, as can the shape and size of the spoon or the glass.

Such equipment includes thick-bottomed cups and glasses weighted to keep them upright; dishes of unbreakable materials in a variety of colors; bowls having curved inside walls to fit the shape of the spoon as it scrapes around the sides; spoons with the handle attached to the side of the bowl instead of the end (the youngster ladles the food into his mouth); chairs with weight distributed in such a way that they resist toppling over; and blunt tines on short-handled forks.

Whether one purchases furniture and

meal service equipment specially designed for children or improvises it from available home supplies, the result can contribute to greater satisfaction with the eating process for the child as well as for other family members.

ACCEPT growing independence as a stage of normal development and treat it accordingly.

However gradual the growth toward independence may be, with recurring relapses even into adulthood, a time comes when children assume responsibility for feeding themselves. During this process of change, many eating problems occur.

The child has learned by this time that his parents, particularly his mother, are sensitive to matters pertaining to his eating. His own interests in the world about him have expanded to include far more pleasures than those associated with satisfying his hunger for food. His hunger itself has changed as has his rate of physical growth. His memory is getting better. He remembers for a longer time and more vividly. He therefore recalls more readily any unpleasant associations with particular foods: He becomes more choosy as well as less hungry at times.

Try to go along calmly with variable food whims when they occur. The chances are that the child will settle down to normal eating habits more readily if his departures from them are not the focus of attention.

Urging an infant to accept some change in eating practice may bring about some resistance, particularly at first, but pressures on children who are actively asserting their drives toward self-direction may turn temporary rejections into permanent ones. Most foods can be replaced in the diet with others of similar composition to provide the needed nutrients.

Allow the child, if he wishes, to eat a larger amount than usual of one wholesome food at the time he may eat less or none of another.

Remember, however, that a child who for a long time refuses all foods of like composition that supply essential nutrients (citrus fruits, for example, or green vegetables) may develop dietary deficiencies that need medical attention.

The rewards from careful training in sound eating habits from the beginning usually come in periods of child development in which normally there occur problems in eating peculiar to the stage of growth.

On the other hand, a child who has been permitted to follow since birth his inclinations against changes in flavors, forms, and varieties of food and in methods of eating is likely to resist any inroads on his developing drives toward independence. Real nutritional deficiencies can result in the child who limits indefinitely his food intake to a few favorite foods, even though the foods (such as milk) in themselves may be especially nutritious.

RESPECT independence in eating as a desirable trait to be encouraged.

Do not leave to chance, however, the learning of good judgment on the child's part. If we are to permit a child to choose eventually, within reason and to some extent, the foods that will constitute his daily meals, then he needs a knowledge and understanding of the functions of food in life on which to base his choices.

A basic point about the function of food is that food promotes growth. Growth to the young child means, first, body size. He wants to grow big. This is one of his inborn drives and seldom if ever needs motivating.

When a child really learns to the point of being convinced that his food choices affect the way he grows, he has a self-motivated incentive to eat for a conscious purpose. It is through such stages in child learning that his goal in eating and the parents' goal in directing his eating are likely to coincide at last. This is a turning point in parents' responsibility in child feeding.

It deserves understanding and appreciation.

Adults responsible for teaching children to eat sometimes fail to realize that few, if any, concepts are learned by the listening process alone.

The opinions and attitudes children form about the functions of food are no exception.

The words, "Eat this, it will make you grow big," are wasted if the child does not already realize that food can make a difference in the way he grows. He may have tested your promise for growth by having followed your request—only to discover, upon investigating, that he is no larger than he was before he ate the food you said would make him grow. A child often has to see to believe, and even then he may doubt at first. We are not born with knowing what food does for us—but with the hunger that causes us to seek it.

How can we help a child to learn that what he eats makes a difference in the way he grows?

Let him see, with you, how fast some animals, possibly pets, grow when they are fed properly, and you will start the child on the road to understanding. The animals you observe should be of fast-growing species, however, if the young child is to see changes in a relatively short time. Otherwise his interest may lag, doubts creep in, and he may lose trust in those who are trying to convince him.

Children usually find pleasure in watching young animals nurse or eat in whatever ways are natural. Help the child associate eating with growing. This is easier to do when a change in growth is obvious in a few days' time, as with kittens, pups, guinea pigs, pigs, and lambs. Calves and colts and many other larger animals that a child may see in the zoo do not show change in size fast enough to establish the desired association of eating with growing, which the child needs to make in his own mind.

Up to the time the child starts to school, the family is certainly his strongest influence in shaping the direction of all his habits of behavior, including those pertaining to eating.

At school, the child moves into an environment that provides him with two additional influences—his teacher and his age mates or peers.

COORDINATE home and school influences for best results. If your child's eating patterns are satisfactory when he starts to school, these practices need protection and encouragement to continue in a new situation where he may begin eating at least the noon meal regularly away from home.

If you have not achieved all that you wished in helping your youngster to form sound eating habits, the school may provide a turning point in new possibilities. To foster the perpetuation of already established satisfactory patterns or to converge efforts toward major changes in eating practices, the family at home and the teachers at school have much to share in working toward common goals for the well-being of the child.

A child's ever-widening curiosity and interest in the world about him naturally includes interest in finding out more about foods—where foods come from, how they are raised and distributed, their names, what they taste like, what they cost, and what they do for us.

ENCOURAGE the people in your child's school to study food and eating habits.

If the practices of the child measure up well against recommended standards, he will benefit from a feeling of achievement. That in itself can motivate him to continue his good habits.

If his patterns of eating have not developed as far as they need to for his well-being, his finding this out in a class situation as a part of his regular school program can go a long way in impressing him with its importance. Sometimes children pay more attention to "what the teacher says" than to what they hear at home.

A study of food habits—often referred to as a diet survey—can serve for class and home projects over many months. Improved behavior or good habit formation is more likely to occur when there are real problems for pupils to solve within their range of interest.

Most teachers know in general, or can find out, the diet patterns of their children without a diet survey. But because every learner is an individual with different hereditary, home, and social backgrounds and with different purposes or drives, learning takes place more readily when emphasis is placed on the individual. This principle alone would point the necessity for individual pupil food surveys as a sound basis for teaching children to eat wisely.

The teacher knows that many of her children may be eating less than recommended amounts of green and yellow vegetables, citrus fruits, and milk. But her knowledge of this general pattern of the children's dietary shortcomings does not mean that the children (and possibly their parents) have this knowledge. Even if this information is passed on to the children and parents, it still does not reveal the individual child's eating practices, which very likely will be good in some respects and not so good in other ways. Any child (like his parents) is more interested in his own situation than that of the class as a whole.

Studies of the food habits of individual pupils, from the simple, nontechnical types to the more elaborate investigations, are a logical way to determine the needs for emphasizing eating habits. These needs may be a stimulation to both home and school to promote better education in nutrition in the whole community.

Children themselves can understand only the simple studies of food habits. Scientific studies may involve technicians, nurses, physicians, and laboratory analyses and be much more accurate, but they have little value if the child fails to see the relationship between the investigation and his own diet—whether or not he is eating the amounts he needs of a variety of foods.

The very act of learning takes place individually. Since learning can be done only by the individual—it cannot be done for him—every opportunity to relate nutrition education to the individual learner is worth encouraging.

FOLLOW A SIMPLE guide as a basis for food selection.

For convenience in helping the people in our Nation (and in the world) to choose daily meals likely to meet nutritional needs, agencies responsible for promoting nutritional health have grouped together foods making similar nutritional contributions to the body. With the large variety of foods available for human consumption, there is naturally more than one plan for grouping foods of similar composition.

Perhaps the most widely publicized grouping in the past has been the basic seven, which groups foods of similar chemical composition. As a general plan, we are to eat some of the foods from each of the seven groups each day.

A newer and possibly more logical arrangement places foods into four groups. The differences among the groupings are more pronounced than when seven categories are used.

For example, whatever food plan is used as a guide, the amount of milk recommended for daily consumption for elementary school children is 3 to 4 cups. When an individual child's intake falls short of this amount, he can readily see that he needs to include more milk to meet the recommended amounts for children. This fact can also be transmitted to all parents.

USE SIMPLE terms in discussing foods and standards for wise eating, especially with children in the primary grades.

For instance, dark-green and deep-yellow vegetables, of which many children eat less than the recommended amounts, must be identified for the young child by names of individual foods, some of which he can already recognize. The very young child thinks of individual foods, not classifications of foods such as "fruit," "vegetables," and "nuts." We cannot expect a child in primary grades to know subgroups like "citrus" fruits and "green and yellow" vegetables, even though he may begin to be introduced to foods by their classifications.

RESPECT EXISTING meal patterns. Equally important in helping children recognize their individual goals in nutrition is the need for protecting each child from embarrassment over any shortcomings a study of his dietary habits may reveal.

Food practices are personal. As such, they merit respect and confidential treatment.

Eating is an experience around which many cultural forces operate, and some children may feel uneasy and uncomfortable concerning their own eating patterns.

One way of showing respect for existing food habits is to accept the fact that not all families have the same kind of meals. Some families, for instance, prefer cereal foods for the evening meal—others at breakfast; some have meat only for dinner; others have it morning, noon, and evening. The nutritive value of food to the body does not depend on the time of day it is eaten.

Let the child be comfortable in his food pattern. It is important to recognize the good points in each child's food habits. He deserves praise for some practices and should be encouraged to maintain them as a sort of bulwark against the realization that he may have other practices (or, oftener, omissions) that may need changing.

You can do that by checking first to see that recommended foods are included in diets. Bread and cereals are a safe start, because they are likely to measure up well. Thus you have a

point on which the child can be commended. The meat group might come next; it usually measures up well against recommendations, except in extremely poor families.

Replies may be misleading unless children understand which foods are to be included in each group. The teacher therefore must be willing to take the time needed to prepare pupils for their job as recordkeeper. Equally important is the willingness on the parents' part to assist and encourage the child in studying his eating habits.

There is sound argument for a survey of the child's total eating habits as against partial surveys that investigate only their breakfast habits, noon-meal habits, or, worse still, the eating of only one isolated food. Such a practice produces incomplete data, but may develop in the child an unsound concept of good nutrition. He can think, for instance, that quality of eating depends on certain individual foods in large amounts instead of learning that by combination of a well-chosen variety of foods he is more likely to furnish the nutrients his body needs.

If the child is ever to be prepared to choose his foods for good health, he has to know that food aids growth and that different foods do different things for him. Such knowledge can stimulate his interest in trying to eat for specific purposes, which his own individual needs determine.

Experiments in classrooms are more convincing than telling. Directed observation of fast-growing animals and plants can convince a child that food aids growth. Quick-sprouting seeds, such as oats or wheat, can be placed in two glass containers with an inch or so of soil. Water is added in one. The other is left dry. Growth soon starts in the glass that is moist because the moisture permits the seed to utilize available food. Growth will not take place in the dry glass. The sprouted seedlings can be kept from light for a few days, and color changes will soon be evident. The children can be guided to recognize that light, air, and temperature also are factors in growth.

Fast-growing animals such as the albino rat are ideal experimental animals for demonstrating the role of food in growth. Their food habits are more readily comparable to those of human beings than are the nutritive needs of plants. Such experiments are inexpensive.

Schools usually do not conduct feeding experiments with animals commonly used for pets, because some of the animals are deliberately placed on diets that are incomplete in meeting health needs. To treat a pet in this manner would be extremely undesirable.

If your school has not used a rat-feeding experiment in teaching nutrition, perhaps you can be instrumental in encouraging the plan. State departments of health usually can supply information if it is needed in locating suitable experimental animals.

A common practice is to place one weanling rat in a suitable cage. The rat is fed everything that is recommended for boys and girls to eat. This constitutes the "control" experiment. "Some of everything" should be placed in the cage each day in forms the children recognize.

For the very young children, experiments must be extremely simple and in terms they understand. Weighed diets, mixed scientifically to contain all the recommended nutrients, have no place in animal experiments for them. Children need to see milk instead of powdered calcium and carrots or other common deep-yellow vegetables instead of vitamin A concentrate.

Nutritionists know that rats can manufacture ascorbic acid within their bodies, but it seems wise to place foods rich in ascorbic acid (such as oranges, tomatoes, or melons) in the cage along with other foods recommended for children. The concept that one is striving to establish with the child—one should always remember—is that boys and girls need a variety of foods to grow.

The quickest and most convincing experimental comparison with the "good" diet is one that is poor enough to produce some unmistakable signs of poor health in the littermate in another cage. This rat may be given a snack diet, composed largely of carbohydrate foods, such as jelly sandwiches, made of unenriched white bread or crackers (without butter), popcorn, and soft drinks or coffee.

One should be careful in selecting this "poor" diet not to prejudice children against any nutritious food. The teaching of nutrition, to be sound, must always be based on facts.

ACCENT the positive. Let us teach children about the combinations of foods that support good body nourishment and not alienate them by attempting to wean them away from the foods for which they have a natural acceptance—namely sweets.

Negative approaches often accomplish the opposite from desired goals and put barriers between parents and teachers on one side and children on the other. If children can be encouraged to eat what they need, foods they eat that are superfluous to their needs will not loom in importance.

In one Latin American community where children's diets were lacking in milk and green and yellow vegetables, the teacher and the children in one classroom placed one rat on pinto beans (cooked with peppers), meat (occasionally), and tortillas—the typical diet of most of the children. The teacher had commended the children—and the parents—for the food qualities these foods provided, but she insisted that they see if certain additions to family meals could not increase growth in the children.

The other rat was also fed the identical beans, occasionally some meat, and tortillas, but he also was given milk, carrots, fresh greens, and eggs.

The "ratones" proved the point,

although it took about 3 weeks to observe that the more complete diet was having better results than the usual family diet.

Only the imagination of the teacher and perhaps the imagination of the pupils limit the approaches to simple research studies of nutrition.

Dissection of animals, of course, has no place in classroom research used in teaching elementary-age children. No animals should be permitted to die. As soon as all children in the group recognize that the animals on the incomplete diet are developing poorly, the poorly fed animals should be placed on the recommended diet until all children see that the animals' unhealthy signs are lessening.

It is important to demonstrate that a change from poor to more desirable eating habits can result in improvement. Otherwise a child who learns he has been guilty of omitting necessary foods from his diet may feel that he is already doomed to stunted growth—which of course he may be if the omissions have been severe and over too long a period. But the earlier he can be persuaded to begin meeting his body needs for proper nourishment, the more effectively he can offset at least some of the retardation.

The results of one experiment with suitable laboratory animals can influence the eating habits of an entire school and even a whole community, if communication is carefully planned and carried out.

STUDY THE SCHOOL lunch program in your school, and encourage its use in promoting good nutrition of school-age children. The contents of the child's school lunch is no longer determined by his mother in most cases; instead, the noon meal is a matter of concern for the school, the State, and the Nation.

One out of every three children attending American schools ate in an organized school lunchroom in 1959. The number grows as the consolidation of schools continues. The proportion is even higher among children in the lower grades.

As schools consolidate and more and more children are transported between their homes and the schools and as the number of mothers working outside their homes increases, the well-being of more than 10 million children is affected by the school lunch.

The 1946 School Lunch Act designated State educational agencies as responsible for sponsoring school lunch programs in their respective States. They in turn pass on this responsibility to local school officials or school boards. It is possible therefore for parents to help develop and maintain the types of school lunch programs which individual communities decide are best for their situations. Parents have a responsibility in helping local schools to provide suitable and adequate lunch facilities and to cooperate with the school in making the lunch an integral part of the total educational plan of the school and community.

RECOGNIZE the differences in purpose between youth and adults.

When one examines the personal goals of the child, the poor eater may be far more eager for love and attention than he is for good health. A child may or may not desire good health as he perceives it. He may instead seek the attention he gets when he is not well.

As children advance in age (and in independence), perhaps the final realization of parents in guiding them toward sound nutrition is that parents' goals and children's goals may be widely separated or even opposed, particularly when girls are concerned.

Throughout childhood there is little or no difference in the nutritional goals of boys and of girls, but this changes as the life goals of the two sexes begin to diverge. Boys, being usually larger than girls and participating in more active sports, usually have larger appetites. Because they also still want to grow tall and gain in strength, boys eat large amounts of food.

Girls may be as hungry as their brothers, but because they acquire a different goal with respect to body size, they may restrain their hunger, sometimes to the point of actual nutritional deficiency.

BECAUSE adolescence is a period of many changes, some girls, instead of limiting their food intake in their desire to stay thin, seek other avenues of satisfaction. Overeating may be one of them.

Adolescent boys and girls who become overweight are usually self-conscious about it and may experiment with unwise dieting in their efforts to get rid of excess fat.

Parents need to find out why the boy or girl who overeats has to fall back on eating as a way of getting satisfaction. The eating problem, as a rule, will not be solved until the emotional one is faced and solved. Often an understanding family doctor can be more successful than the parents in unearthing subtle emotional anxieties. Obese children are not necessarily happy children.

Parents of adolescents can make special efforts to include in the family meals protein-rich foods such as eggs, meats, fish, cheese, and milk, supplemented with vegetable sources of protein, such as dried peas and beans. These protein-rich foods need to be spread into all three meals, particularly breakfast, which is the meal most likely to be slighted, especially by adolescent girls.

Perhaps the safest insurance against the harm which may come to adolescents who resort to insufficient food intake or overindulgence is for parents to face this problem long before it occurs—during infancy and the preschool years.

SOUND eating practices up to the time of adolescence can go a long way in protecting a girl's health in spite of some irregularities in eating for a time. The girl who has practiced good eating habits for 12 to 15 years is not likely to depart very far from them for any length of time.

Parents and teachers can help the girl to recognize the more subtle influences of food on other forms of growth and development besides body size. She can be helped to understand that gracefulness in movement, pleasing disposition, cheerful outlook on life, clear skin, sound teeth, and good posture characterize the well-nourished person.

Again, however, parents and teachers should realize that the young girl is far more interested in herself at the present time than she is in the fact that at some time in the future she is going to make great demands upon her health in order to assume her adult role as wife and mother.

ALLOW TIME for education in nutrition. Educating the young in good eating habits is a long, slow process.

It consists of guiding the eating practices of an infant, the preschool child, the school-age child, and the adolescent person up to the time that he accepts full responsibility for his own food choices.

This is too big a job for parents alone. We have to look to schools and to other agencies for help in this important responsibility of parenthood. For all who have a part in contributing to the well-being of youth, the rewards are enduring.

WILLA VAUGHN TINSLEY *is Dean of the School of Home Economics of Texas Technological College in Lubbock, Tex. Dr. Tinsley was born in Texas and holds degrees from Texas Woman's University, Colorado State College, and the University of Minnesota. She has taught in high schools and colleges and has written many articles and teaching materials about school lunches, nutrition education, and teacher education. She also has served as consultant in nutrition education for several institutes and commercial food companies. She received a citation in 1957 by the Texas Vocational Association for her outstanding contribution to vocational education.*

Youth Learns About Food

SADYE F. ADELSON, MARGARET ALEXANDER, AND
EVELYN B. SPINDLER

BY the time they are teen-agers, children want more to say about how their home is run. A wise parent is sensitive to their changing needs, interests, and abilities and lets them take part in selecting, preparing, and serving food when they become ready and eager to do so.

Their interests in health and nutrition differ from those of their parents and their younger brothers and sisters. Boys and girls 10 to 12 years old are interested in learning to cook as a new experience and a way to please their parents. Teen-agers are more concerned about preparing special-occasion foods for friends and family and being attractive and strong.

Parents, teachers, and club leaders can use these interests to teach young people about nutrition and the selection and preparation of food.

To what they learn at home children add what they learn in school courses, in science and health clubs, and in such youth organizations as 4-H, Future Homemakers of America (FHA), and Future Farmers of America (FFA).

As a result of their outside activities, young people may want to introduce into home meals and cooking practices some new ideas they got at school, clubs, restaurants, and friends' homes.

Teaching the how and why of food selection has been a growing area in the curriculum of most schools, especially since the start of the school lunch program. Many school kitchens and lunchrooms are now practical laboratories for trying out what is learned about food and nutrition in classes.

The following accounts show the kinds of experiences with food and nutrition that teen-agers may be having in elementary and secondary schools: Learning about nutrition is woven into the total school life in a way that is intended to carry values into home and community life.

A STUDENT menu-planning board of pupils in the 7th to 12th grades contributes to the success of the school lunch program in a school in New York. Having students help with planning the meals they are to eat has proved to be an excellent way to learn community food patterns, find out likes and dislikes, introduce new foods, cut waste, and give students a chance to learn the principles of good nutrition in a practical situation.

647

A boy and a girl from each home-room are elected to a menu-planning board when other class officers are chosen. Their job is to build menus, based on requirements of the type A school lunch pattern, that they, their fellow students, and their teachers will enjoy eating.

One day each month, members of the board meet with the head cook and cafeteria manager to plan menus for the coming month. A representative from each of grades 3 through 6 also brings to the meeting a menu his class has planned. Ideas from all grades are considered. One or two new dishes suggested at the meetings are introduced each month.

The board members act as liaison between the students and the cafeteria as they report to their classmates, both formally and informally.

The homemaking teacher supervises the lunch program and works with students, teachers, and parents on aspects of the nutritional and educational values of school lunches. Classroom teachers contribute to the program by using facts about the school lunch and nutrition and introducing appropriate related activities in their special subjects. By eating with groups of students, teachers get better acquainted with the students and find out about their eating practices.

INDIVIDUAL food problems of some ninth-graders in Virginia were solved in their homemaking class as they studied the kind of breakfast they liked and needed.

Many of the pupils came to school without breakfast, and many who ate breakfast selected a poor one. Many of them said their parents went to work early and left them to prepare breakfast for themselves and younger brothers and sisters. Some girls and boys said they disliked many breakfast foods.

A film, "It's All in Knowing How," was shown. It told the relation of eating well to success in school and in sports and other activities.

The goals the class members set for themselves were: To know dietary needs of the body in terms of customary foods; to understand the contribution breakfast can make to these needs; to learn to prepare quick, nutritious, and delicious breakfasts; and to improve the general ways of eating.

The pupils compared their own menus with a daily food guide. They studied cereals and other breakfast foods to see what nutrients they supply. They planned and prepared simple, nutritious breakfasts.

They shared their knowledge by arranging an assembly program at which a student panel presented their new knowledge. They also planned and arranged exhibits that showed easily prepared, nutritious, and attractive meals.

Every now and then, teacher and students took stock of how near they were to their goals. Planning and giving demonstrations and arranging exhibits provided opportunities for the pupils to determine how well they had grasped an understanding of the problem. They became more discriminating in their choice of foods in the school cafeteria. Parents noted that eating practices at home improved. The boys and girls forgot their earlier excuses and soon began to start the schoolday well fed.

TENTH-GRADE students of home-making in another school in Virginia decided that they needed more information about the wise use of the family's money. The girls chose to study how to buy foods wisely and how to make the dollar go further.

Films were used to introduce material on kinds of stores and services generally available. They visited stores to determine the types of services offered in their community. Sources of information available to the consumer were discussed. Books, magazines, and bulletins were brought to class and studied. Such aids as labels, seals of approval, standardization of products, and the Pure Food, Drug, and Cosmetic Act were investigated.

The girls reported on the amount of money spent by their families for food and the extent to which purchased food supplemented foods from freezer, garden, and home canning.

A girl whose family spent least per person for food reported that there were seven persons and three animals—a dog, a cat, and a cow—to be fed by her family. She gave a report to the class on the money saved in producing their milk, butter, and cottage cheese at home.

Another girl reported on what a planned food supply in the freezer meant to her family.

A third girl reported on the cost of raising garden products at home.

Labels and grades were discussed. Each student collected and classified labels according to standards set up in class. Pupils wrote to firms for information on methods used in labeling products, the meaning of brand names, and the sizes of cans.

The meaning of "bargain" was explored. Demonstrations on cost per unit of purchase and cost per portion of edible food were given.

A final activity included taste-testing of margarine of different prices and a comparison of different grades and brands of canned vegetables and fruit. The brand of margarine that cost the least was voted the most acceptable in flavor by the class.

All the students had home projects. Emphasis was on getting the most from your money. They included comparing prices of foods similar as to use in meals and nutritional content, comparing family food plans at low and liberal cost, and buying groceries for the family for a week.

SEVENTH-GRADERS in a biology class in Arizona conducted a feeding experiment with two sets of white rats. It was designed to show the ill effects of a diet low in milk and low in whole-grain, enriched, or restored bread and cereals and the signs of health in animals properly fed.

The boys and girls planned the diets and kept charts showing the growth of both sets of rats. The whole school became interested in the experiment. The seventh-graders took the rats to other rooms and explained what was happening to their nutritional health. Then the rats on the poorer diet were switched to the more adequate diet, and the students watched their health improve. A better acceptance of milk and other foods served in the school lunch has been noted.

ABOUT 500 thousand homemaking students in junior and senior high schools are members of chapters of the Future Homemakers of America. As the association's name implies, the girls are prepared for their major life work. Activities are directed toward better family living and participation in home, school, and community activities. FHA members are encouraged to share their knowledge with others in the community.

An example: Girls in an Arkansas chapter volunteered to eat in the cafeteria each noon with first- and second-grade children. Each of the members had her own table, and the same seven children ate at her table daily. The member explained new foods or foods prepared different ways to the children, and through daily observation learned individual reactions to foods. The children became proud of their "family" tables, stayed at them longer, and ate more.

SCHOOL PROJECTS also often result from the instruction in nutrition begun in a high school class in homemaking, science, and health.

After studying nutrition in a course in homemaking, for example, 10th-graders in a school in Maine decided to conduct a survey to determine how many students would buy milk to supplement their bag lunches if it were available. As a result, the student council is operating a nonprofit milk sale every noon and more than half of the students who bring their lunches from home buy milk daily.

THE STUDENT BODY of a high school in New Jersey observed nutrition week. The homemaking class previously conducted a survey of the students' eating habits. To the amazement of the students, the girls learned that the boys had better food habits than the girls; fewer boys than girls skipped breakfast; lunch was the most consistently well-selected meal of the day.

The girls planned school lunch menus for the week and served as cafeteria aids.

Concern over the number of students who failed to eat all of the protective foods served in the cafeteria led to a survey of waste, and a poster depicting the waste was displayed.

Classes in mathematics developed statistics for use on charts that pointed up the findings of the survey. Students in the art classes made attractive posters. English classes prepared articles, which were submitted to newspapers during nutrition week. The school paper gave it major attention. The library helped with research and provided space for displays.

Homemaking students wrote and directed a skit about nutrition for an assembly program. They prepared displays of Jewish-American, Armenian, Japanese, Dutch, Scotch, English, and Philippine meals. Language classes added displays of breakfasts typical of Germany, France, and Spain and a poster showing breakfast habits of the early Romans.

Every department in the school participated in some way.

The entire project was evaluated by advanced students of homemaking on the basis of comments made by fellow students during nutrition week.

ONE HIGH SCHOOL girl wrote:

"I am a senior planning to be married shortly after graduation. We have been discussing family finances at school, and I will soon need to put into practice some things I learned. So I started developing a plan for spending the money for foods that will make good, nutritious meals. Encouraged by my teacher and with her help, I roughed out a plan on paper. Then I got my fiance's ideas.

"I used the figures published by the Department of Agriculture in its bulletin, Nutrition . . . Up-To-Date, Up To You, as my guide for determining what foods to buy and how much of each kind. The next step was a cost estimate. I then planned menus for a week, with a daily food guide as reference. I made the market order and went to the store to buy the foods.

"I soon realized that I had gone overboard. I had to rework my plan six times to get the foods down within my budget. Also, I had to do a lot of digging in cookbooks and references on meal planning before I reached my goal. Then my teacher pointed out that locality affected price, and I would have to make a careful study of prices in the community into which I expected to move. As a further aid, I made a list of staple foods that we would need in order to get our housekeeping underway.

"I will have to be a wise shopper and take advantage of every possible food savings that is offered in the stores. Shopping trips made me more conscious of differences in brands, labels, contents, and prices.

"I now have a clearer picture of what I can do with my food money. We will have to be careful and save pennies and nickels, which as they accumulate can be used to stock an emergency shelf for unexpected guests. Preservation of some food at home should also help increase our supplies.

"Mother says that she wishes she had had such an experience before her marriage. She, too, has learned quite a few facts about planning a food budget from my project."

More than a third of the 2 million girls and boys who belong to 4-H Clubs sign up for work in meal planning and preparation and in food preservation. Their projects have such titles as "good food for snacking and packing," "have fun with foods," and "outdoor eats and treats."

As the following accounts show, the skills and knowledge children learn in the projects should have lifetime value. Good nutrition of the boys and girls themselves and other family members are emphasized in the projects, along with basic principles of cooking.

Projects concerned with meal preparation in 4–H Clubs in Virginia have these objectives: To teach young people the importance of good nutrition, develop skills in preparing food and in planning and serving good, attractive meals, make use of home-produced foods, learn how to get the best nutritional return from money spent on food, share responsibility for family meals, and develop good habits.

Nutrition and gardening are combined in 4–H projects in Virginia. Emphasis is on getting the best nutritional return from efforts put into growing and cooking garden produce.

Each boy and girl raises a home garden. Vegetables and fruits that are high in vitamin A and C and that can be raised in home gardens are selected for preparation.

The young people learn the importance of picking their garden produce as close as possible to cooking and serving time and of cooking it quickly in a small amount of water. They also learn and contribute their own ideas on interesting ways of serving fruits and vegetables raw.

Senior 4–H members helped prepare a bulletin, Mix It or Make It, for use of home extension and 4–H groups in New Hampshire.

Under the direction of the nutrition specialist at the first meeting, the group outlined what they would put in their bulletin and selected the recipes they would include. At successive meetings, the girls tested the recipes and judged and scored the results. They showed great interest in the variety of mixes available and how milk puddings and baked goods resulting from them compared in quality and cost with those made from scratch.

It was a challenging experience. It helped the girls make decisions. The scope of their interests, efforts, and participation increased.

Food demonstrations are given by 4–H Club girls in Washington to introduce residents to new ways of using locally raised products and thereby to improve people's diets and increase farmers' sales. To get ready to give these demonstrations, girls have to develop a background of information on food and nutrition. They have also had to become proficient in the preparation of foods and meals and use of professional techniques in demonstrations.

At the State fair, a 15-year-old girl demonstrated how to use cottage cheese in planning the day's menus. She showed the audience how cottage cheese could be used in any course. She made an appetizer, salad, main dish, dessert, and snacks. She talked about the nutritional importance of milk and other dairy products in diets.

She did so well the Dairy Commissioners asked her to repeat her demonstration at their conference in Bellingham. This, in turn, led to an invitation to demonstrate the use of cottage cheese and other dairy products in markets in her county.

Another 15-year-old girl who also was selected to perform before the Dairy Commissioners had chosen beverages for her demonstration. She used charts to compare the nutritional value and cost of a quart of fluid whole milk and a quart of bottled soft drink. She pointed out the superior contribution in calcium, riboflavin, and protein that milk makes.

Community meals are given annually by 18 4–H girls in a county in Washington in which incomes are unstable and health and nutritional levels need to be raised. The meals show what progress the girls have made in learning about foods and nutrition and are a way of extending their knowledge to the community. The girls plan the menus and prepare and serve the meals and clean up afterwards.

Sometimes the meal is a simple supper or tea. One year they served a buffet dinner. It was followed by an evening program, at which the girls were the entertainers. The girls invited the public.

Profits from the small fee they charged were used by them to attend the county's summer camp.

A project in Connecticut revolves about foreign foods and their preparation. It quickens and deepens acquaintance between 4–H Club members and young people of other lands. Connecticut has a number of nationality groups, and the project helps neighbors to understand each other better.

Basic principles of cooking meat, vegetables, and other foods, nutrient values of foods, and food selection are taught as easily in this project as in ones that emphasize American foods and meals. Foreign cookery shows how variety and flavor can be added to everyday meals. A popular series of bulletins, What's Cooking, on how to prepare typical dishes of Finland, Italy, France, Germany, China, and Sweden, has been prepared by extension workers.

Slides and posters of family life, agriculture, and industry, exhibits of native costumes and arts and crafts, talks on customs and traditions, and demonstrations and actual preparation of foods and meals of people in other lands make the project informative and interesting. Returned and visiting International Farm Youth Exchange participants and exchange teachers have contributed to the project.

Outdoor cooking has had long standing on Scout programs for boys and girls. Ingenious leaders have used this enjoyable activity in many ways to help young people appreciate food.

For example, Girl Scouts in Brooklyn tried out a master plan for "fun with food" on a camping trip.

At the first 2-hour session, the girls planned their weekend expedition to stay within their Scout limit of 5 dollars for each girl, including transportation. They discussed which foods to put in their knapsacks, why each food belonged there, and how to prepare the food to get the most nutrition and

enjoyment out of the assortment. As homework, they priced the foods chosen for the expedition.

At a second meeting, the girls talked about the reasons for including each item in the menu. Instead of considering carrots just another ingredient for a stew, the girls learned that carrots are an aid to a better complexion and glossier hair. They also found out that oranges are important for good gums.

Good, wholesome snacks and beverages that the girls could make were the subject of the last session.

This course was sponsored by the Brooklyn Nutrition Committee of the Brooklyn Council for Social Planning in cooperation with the Visiting Nurse Association, Tuberculosis and Health Association, Board of Education, Cumberland Hospital, the Girl Scouts, and Union Gas Co.

YOUTH THUS LEARNS about nutrition as part of homemaking and health education in many junior and senior high schools in the city and in the country. Besides, teachers of physical education, general science, biology, and other courses often weave relevant nutrition facts into their basic subject matter.

If you live in a rural area or in one of several suburban communities your 10- to 21-year-old sons and daughters who agree to learn to do by doing can get a practical education in food and nutrition as members of 4–H clubs.

Many other organizations offer nutrition education programs for youth of high school age. Among them are the Girl Scouts, Boy Scouts, Campfire Girls, and Key Clubs of Kiwanis International.

SADYE F. ADELSON *is a nutrition analyst in the Institute of Home Economics, Agricultural Research Service.*

MARGARET ALEXANDER *is a program specialist, Home Economics Education, Office of Education, Department of Health, Education, and Welfare.*

EVELYN B. SPINDLER *is a nutritionist in the Federal Extension Service.*

Adults Also Learn

SADYE F. ADELSON, MARGARET ALEXANDER, AND
EVELYN B. SPINDLER

ONE way adults can learn more about nutrition is by study in company with others in schools and clubs.

The guidance of a group leader is helpful. Then you have a chance to get acquainted with people who have common interests and problems. Sharing and developing ideas with other learners usually make for a better solution to a problem. There is value in setting a definite time for study.

To keep up with the developing science of nutrition, you have to keep refreshing and adding to your knowledge. New discoveries in laboratories are frequent, and the developments are soon made ready for practical use to help you achieve better diets for yourself and the others in the family.

In the study of elementary nutrition, most instructors start with basic information about the essential nutrients; their contributions to growth and health, how the needs for them differ with a person's sex, age, body size, and physical activity; and the common foods that are sources of the essential nutrients.

Then you probably will go on to learn how to use this knowledge to keep yourself and your family well nourished. Preferences of members of the group often determine what is studied. Among the possibilities are: How to plan the week's food for the family that is right for bodily needs and in line with individual preferences; how to get the best return from food money; how to store and cook food to retain its original nutrient content and to have it look and taste good; how to plan, prepare, and serve meals efficiently; and how to help children develop desirable food habits.

We give some accounts of how adults have learned more about nutrition through activities sponsored by schools, the extension service, and health and community centers.

FEEDING the family was the theme of a series of meetings in the adult homemaking education program in a New York community.

The teacher demonstrated ways to prepare adequate low-cost meals and to use dried milk in making baked goods of high nutritional quality. Films on meat cookery were shown and discussed. Public health workers told about developments in nutrition.

Instructors from a nearby college discussed weight control through diet and increased physical activity. Bulletins were distributed to the homemakers for their further study and as reference materials at home.

At the end of the series, the women planned, prepared, and served four meals to demonstrate what they had learned. Husbands were guests at these meals.

The teacher commented on the interest aroused by these meetings and her pleasure in the homemakers' reports of improved food practices among their family members.

HOME EXTENSION groups in a county in North Carolina were astonished to hear from their home demonstration agent that diets of families in North Carolina were poorer in calcium than those in the country as a whole.

They checked their own food intake during a 24-hour period and found that diets of many of them were low in milk and, therefore, probably in calcium. (American families get nearly two-thirds of their calcium from milk.)

The women decided to learn more about milk and how to get more into the meals they served their families. The county agricultural agent enlisted farmers in a dairy improvement program. Before long, teachers, the public health nurse, 4–H Club leaders, parent-teacher groups, the school lunch administrator, and local newspaper and radio and TV stations added their support.

The effectiveness of the program was shown in greater sales of milk at school, local dairies, and grocery stores. A later recheck of their daily food showed that the women were consuming more milk.

As is usual in extension club projects, volunteer local leaders were in charge. They received special instruction first. At their training sessions, the home demonstration agent presented lectures, materials for home study and reading, filmstrips, movies, and posters on the importance of milk in the

diets of families. For future reference, leaders received teaching guides and additional materials containing facts about milk. Demonstrations were given on basic principles of cooking with milk. The group discussed and exchanged ideas on how to have more milk in diets of family members.

The program for each training meeting was planned carefully in an effort to give the leaders a broad background from which to teach and to make them ready for answering related questions that people might ask. For distribution to her club members, each leader received leaflets containing information on milk.

Besides conducting the meetings of their own extension group, the local leaders shared their knowledge with 4–H Club members, young mothers, and other persons in their community.

FAMILY LIFE education programs, in which many community organizations and agencies work with the schools, often include education in nutrition.

Such a countywide program was organized in Tennessee more than 10 years ago. Persons representing lay and professional groups interested in nutrition formed a steering committee.

Nutrition clinics were conducted in the 10 consolidated schools. A doctor examined each school and preschool child in the presence of one of his parents. The county nurse assisted parents in making arrangements for correcting any physical defect. The mother or father then discussed with the home economics teacher food practices of the child and his family.

As a result, a number of developments have occurred in the county. The schools teach some phase of nutrition in every grade and conduct classes in nutrition for adults. Knowledge of nutrition is spread by club programs and by display of books and bulletins on nutrition in libraries.

Nutrition study groups have been organized in 18 communities. Local leaders were trained by teachers of home economics to hold meetings and give demonstrations on preparing foods that would improve diets. With help from teachers of agriculture, instruction also was given in production and preservation of food at home.

In clinics held recently, the nutritional health of preschool and school children in the community was found to be better than that of children living in it 10 years earlier.

THE USE and value of preservation of food at home was the topic a teacher in Virginia discussed with the men and women in her adult homemaking class on opening night. From long observation she had become convinced that year-round diets of families in the community could be improved through the preservation of more foods in season.

The members of the class decided that emphasis in their course would be on improving the nutritional health of the family through the production and preservation of farm and garden products. They determined which foods and how much of each food to preserve for their families. They planned which varieties were best to plant in their gardens and how much of each kind was needed to provide enough for family meals—fresh in season and preserved out of season.

During the series of lessons, the men and women had demonstrations in which they learned methods of preserving acid and nonacid fruit and vegetables. They made schedules for canning that included dates when each product was expected to be at its best for canning. The teacher helped families with their canning at home. As a result of the project, more products were canned at home. The homemakers felt that their family members were better fed during winter months.

YOUNG WORKING women looking forward to marriage and newlyweds asked the teacher of their homemaking class in Colorado to devote their 3-hour sessions to planning and preparing the family's food.

The women planned a week's menu and market order for a family of four. They considered the needs of family members and nutritional returns from foods in relation to their prices. In groups of four, they prepared and served breakfasts, luncheons, and simple dinners. In getting the meals, the young women made good use of the basic principles of cookery and food selection and the criteria for judging acceptable foods they had learned in their course.

Several of the unmarried women told the teacher that since taking the course they had assumed more responsibility in planning and preparing meals at home.

NUTRITION COURSES in colleges for students majoring in fields other than home economics are becoming increasingly popular.

A course given in a university in Connecticut illustrates what is being offered in many college home economics departments.

Each year about 300 students elect this course, nutrition in health. More men than women take it. The students in the course come from the departments of education, pharmacy, agriculture, physical education, engineering, business administration, and arts and sciences.

Reading, lectures, and discussions cover the foods required for good health and how to select and buy them. Economic as well as physiologic aspects of normal nutrition are included. Chief emphasis is on nutrition of the young adult, but nutrition of the family, of mothers and babies, and of persons requiring special diets is also discussed.

EMPLOYED HOMEMAKERS made up a large part of the membership in several home extension groups in Mississippi, in which all wanted to know how to get good meals on the table quickly and easily.

Planning ahead was stressed as an important element in quick meals.

Homemakers were shown that planning needs to be done at every step from buying and storing the family's food to preparing and serving meals. Demonstrations were given on how to arrange kitchens to save steps in preparing meals and to suit the height and reach of the homemaker. Some shortcuts in food preparation and oven meals that save time, energy, fuel, and money also were demonstrated.

The proof of the value of the project was the many reports from the women that ideas from the demonstrations had become practices in their homes.

INDUSTRIAL WORKERS in a plant in West Virginia were encouraged to try "a better breakfast for a better day" after their poor breakfast habits had come to light in a survey made by the health director and nurse. At the workers' request, nutritionists conducted meetings on the importance of good breakfasts. On a day set aside, in groups of 50 to 100 at a time, men and women in the plant heard from the nutritionists what makes a good meal with which to start the day. They also learned how the right breakfast enhances alertness and well-being throughout the morning and sometimes even into the afternoon.

OLDER PERSONS in New York City attended lecture-demonstrations on how to eat well and feel better. The idea originated in a community day center that serves the social, cultural, recreational, and educational interests of about 600 men and women more than 60 years old.

A study of the diets and nutritional health of some of the men and women at the center revealed a need for improvement. A series of lectures on nutritional requirements of older people and demonstrations of ways to make practical use of the new information seemed a way of meeting the problem.

The series started with a report of the findings of the study. It included the practices of the participants that were good as well as those needing

improvement. Topics at other meetings included: Choose and Use the Right Food; Foods To Keep You Fit and Add Life to Your Years; Tips on How To Buy and Prepare Foods; Shopping and Cooking for Individuals and Couples; and Ideas for Selecting Meals in Restaurants and Cafeterias.

Members were encouraged to send in questions or ask them in class. Refreshments were served at the meetings because of their educational and sociability values.

Pertinent aspects of the series were combined with other center activities, such as postermaking, courses in composition, skits, and field trips.

COUPLES who were 10 percent or more overweight were helped to develop better food habits, lose excessive weight, and maintain normal weight in one Maryland county. The county nurse, who was the leader, worked in consultation with a nutritionist of the State health department.

Each person kept a weight chart of his original weight, desirable weight, and weight at each meeting. The couples learned how to select well-balanced meals, count the calories in foods, and substitute low-calorie for high-calorie foods without sacrificing nutritive value.

Emphasis was put on selecting adequate diets from customary, available foods and on a safe, permanent loss of excessive weight. A basic understanding of nutritional needs and food values was given by the nutritionist and dietitian. The leader often called in a doctor, psychologist, physical education instructor, and other specialists as consultants or speakers.

The participants first consulted a physician, who decided how much and how fast each one could safely lose.

OVERWEIGHT WOMEN in Virginia who joined Take Off Pounds Safely groups soon realized that it was more fun and easier to reduce as a member of a group than alone.

Instead of merely following a reducing diet, they gained a knowledge of their dietary needs and learned how to improve their food habits and how to control their weight. They were helped to face up to the fact that overweight is caused by overeating and that almost everyone who really wants to be the proper weight can achieve that goal.

Carrying on a self-experiment, they saw that a well-balanced diet, fitted to their individual caloric requirements, produced a slow but steady loss of weight on a diet that permitted them to eat what other family members and friends were eating—but less of it.

The Virginia Extension Service developed the program in consultation with the State medical society and State health department.

Workers believe that an important effect of weight control programs is the improvement in the diets of the families of the homemakers who participate.

IF YOU want to study by yourself or cannot attend meetings, you will find that there are many sources of reliable reading material on food and nutrition.

College departments of home economics, State and county extension services, and State, county, and city departments of health and education have pamphlets and can tell you of other sources of good materials.

The Department of Agriculture has many pamphlets that you can get by sending a request (a postal card will do) to the Office of Information, Department of Agriculture, Washington 25, D.C. It is best to make your request as specific as possible.

Among the available publications are: L 424, "Food for Fitness—A Daily Food Guide"; GS 1, "Nutrition—Up-to-Date, Up to You"; G 5, "Food for the Family With Young Children"; G 13, "Food for Families With School Children"; G 17, "Food Guide for Older Folks."

A county nutrition council in Pennsylvania has given several series of educational programs on radio in which physicians, surgeons, psychiatrists, dietitians, nutritionists, and nurses have participated. One was a 13-week series on the nutrition of the child. During another series, authorities discussed problems of overweight, such as how to reduce weight in the midst of a hungry family, choice of restaurant meals by a reducer, and reducing on a budget. A third series was on the later years.

The participants in the three series of broadcasts were experts in nutrition, medicine, and public health, and they gave sound information and advice.

Sometimes, however, the information given over the air and in the press is confusing, contradictory, and even misleading. Consumers often are hard put to be sure what is information and what is misinformation. It is well to check what you hear or read with authorities in your community or State.

You can get some idea about the adequacy of dietary recommendations by asking yourself these questions:

Is this diet limited to a few foods?

Does it stress certain expensive or unusual foods, such as raw sugar, blackstrap molasses, brewer's yeast, or yoghurt?

Does it warn against eating foods rich in protein and those rich in carbohydrates at the same meal or warn against eating any other combination of foods at one time?

Does it omit any food or group of foods of high nutritional value, such as milk and cheese; meat, poultry, fish, eggs, beans, and nuts; vegetables and fruits; bread and other grain products; or fats and oils?

Does it depend on vitamin and mineral concentrates to balance the diet?

If the answer to any of the questions is "yes," it would be wise to check the source and the recommendations. Special diets should not be self-determined; they should be prescribed by a physician or a dietitian for the individual case.

HOME DEMONSTRATION week in each of 5 years in Missouri was devoted to disseminating information statewide about nutrition. The theme was, "Food To Keep Us Strong and Able."

The first year, families were given a wall chart, "A Missouri Plan for Good Eating," a guide in which five groups of food were stressed. Each succeeding year, the emphasis was on a different group. Everyone's need for milk was stressed one year in the slogan, "You never outgrow your need for milk." Other slogans were: "Protein helps us keep fit—meat and eggs have lots of it," and "For health, for pep, for taste appeal, use vitamin C in every meal."

The food of the year was emphasized in demonstrations, recipes in newspapers, milk-bottle collars, leaflets on tables in eating places, grocery store displays, talks at clubs, and pamphlets.

Clubs had displays at local fairs of a great variety of fruit and vegetables. The exhibits were planned early in the spring. Each member grew at least one vegetable that was relatively uncommon in the locality. The value of one club's prizewinning display was summed up by a member who said, "This is a real accomplishment. It has provided our families with a wider variety of fruit and vegetables. Also, it has made us better gardeners."

INDIVIDUAL instruction in nutrition is also a possibility. The schools, the extension service, and health and other community agencies often provide personal consultation and guidance to individuals who have specific nutrition problems.

Extension workers in some States have special programs for working with individual families. For example, a rural family in North Carolina wanted to remodel their home and install some modern conveniences, but they did not have enough money. They learned about the "Raise a Square Meal Around Home" program and the readiness of their county agent to help them with it.

How they accumulated the money and improved their family's general level of living is told by the homemaker:

"This is a family enterprise for the four of us—my mother, my husband, me, and our 3-year-old daughter.

"We now plant a big garden with 22 different kinds of vegetables—some for family use and some for sale. We can and freeze at least 35 quarts of vegetables for each one of us, plus something extra for guests. We work according to a plan. Everything beyond our family needs is sold. We raise strawberries and other small fruits for eating fresh and for jam, jelly, and preserves for freezing.

"We keep 100 laying hens. Some of the culls from our flock are sold, and some are put into our freezing unit for family use. Our hens also provide an average of 46 dozen eggs a week.

"We keep 4 brood sows, from which we average 30 pigs twice a year. Five of them are held for family use.

"Each year we have two milk cows and two beef cows. These give us milk, butter, and beef for sale and our use.

"Our fields produce enough corn for feed and bread. Our flour is also grown right on our farm.

"We have a pond that serves to water our livestock and raise fish. The fish pond adds fun to family life. Sometimes the whole family is out there with rod and reel.

"We have been able to raise our annual net income by about 2 thousand dollars through the guidance of our county agricultural and home demonstration agents, plus our own efforts to raise a square meal around home.

"That extra income has made our dream of a convenient home come true—bathroom, modern range, running water, new refrigerator, and a combination den and dining room on one end of the kitchen. We enjoy more and better food for our family than ever before."

AGENCIES and the programs in practical nutrition they offer in urban and rural places often are different, because ways of living and getting the family's food are different.

A community's program is likely to reflect what its people want, ask to have, and work to get.

In cities and towns you will find that there are adult homemaking programs in schools. In day and night classes, you can get practical instruction in food selection, preparation, and management, separately or as part of other courses in homemaking.

State, county, and city associations of professional societies, such as the American Dietetic Association and the American Home Economics Association, sometimes can supply speakers for clubs and classes.

Your group might invite a nutritionist or dietitian to give a talk or lead a discussion or to attend several meetings to guide you in a study unit on some phase of nutrition.

Community centers, the Young Women's Christian Association, and similar organizations often offer classes in cooking, nutrition, homemaking, and health.

Demonstrations in preparing food and planning meals by home economists who work for gas and electric companies and other commercial firms are sources of information.

In farm areas and villages you will find that the extension workers provide education in food and nutrition through extension groups and through newspapers, radio, and television.

Health departments and other community health agencies provide individual or group instruction in foods and nutrition as part of maternal and child health services and classes for prospective parents or for persons of various ages.

EVERYONE CAN study food and nutrition who wants to do so by knocking on the right door. There are several right doors in a community. They lead to the teacher of homemaking in the school, the nutritionist at the department of public health, the home demonstration agent of the county extension service, and the home economists in utility companies. The agencies are listed in the telephone directory.

If you cannot locate these persons in your community, write for assistance to one of the State agencies that has a nutrition or home economics program. Among these are the departments of home economics in colleges and the extension service at the State college or university and the State departments of education and health, which usually are located in the capital city.

SADYE F. ADELSON *is a nutrition analyst in the Household Economics Research Division of the Agricultural Research Service. Since 1936 she has been making surveys to find out what people eat and how they might improve their food practices.*

MARGARET ALEXANDER *has been program specialist in home economics education, Office of Education, Department of Health, Education, and Welfare since 1949. She assists State supervisors and teachers of home economics in program planning and curriculum development.*

EVELYN B. SPINDLER *has been nutrition specialist in the Federal Extension Service since 1950. She assists the State extension nutritionists in developing, executing, and evaluating their food and nutrition programs to meet the current situation and needs. She was formerly extension nutritionist in New Mexico and instructor in the University of California at Davis.*

Food is eaten for enjoyment, for emotional release, for social prestige, and for attention, adverse or otherwise. Food is refused because of such unconscious emotions as the pleasure of paining others and showing self-assertion. When a person refuses crab, cabbage, or codfish or scorns beans, bananas, or broccoli, he is not showing a connoisseur's discrimination but evidencing an unhappy soul.—JENNIE I. ROWNTREE, Journal of Home Economics, October 1949.

Don't Be Fooled by Fads

HELEN S. MITCHELL

TEN million Americans, who live in a scientific age, waste 500 million dollars a year on quack diets and fake pills and the junk of nonscientific medicine men.

They carry on the myths, magic, superstitions, and taboos that began with the caveman and have persisted because of ignorance, customs, religious beliefs, and the persuasiveness of patent medicine vendors.

Postmaster General Arthur E. Summerfield, in a feature news release from the Post Office Department, commented: "In an era where wonder drugs and great advances in surgery and medicine have produced true medical miracles, it is puzzling that so many people in all walks of life pay big money for the frauds."

The individual food faddist may be sincere in his beliefs, but often he wants fervently to convert his friends to his way of eating. He starts on a by-path of diet because he is worried about health. He fails to get sound advice about proper nutrition. It is easier for him to believe the bizarre and spectacular claims of a quack than the less reassuring but more scientific statement that fails to promise him sure relief from his ills.

660

All degrees of food faddism exist. Enthusiasms for specific foods such as molasses or yoghurt spring up and die young. Every once in a while somebody preaches the miraculous values of oysters or cottage cheese or wheat germ—yet oysters and ice cream have been considered a poisonous combination by another faddist.

The frailty in human nature that the quack and self-styled food expert play upon for personal profit is the psychological need of the chronically ill or the neurasthenic to seek anything that promises relief. They may be ill and insecure and thus find in a nostrum a mental crutch.

The faddist who wants primarily to hand down his ancestors' peculiar notions is relatively harmless but misguided. To tell a child to eat carrots because they will make her hair curl is silly, but carrots are a source of vitamin A, more valuable for eyes than hair. There is no scientific ground for believing that fish are a brain food, but fish are a good source of protein and other nutrients.

I know of no good reason for not eating milk with acid fruits, because the milk will curdle anyway when it reaches the stomach acid, but there is no harm in eating these foods separately if one wants to.

Some people think one must not eat milk and fish, milk and lobster, ice cream and rhubarb, milk and spinach, and buttermilk and cabbage together, but that is nonsense.

Some faddists even tell us to avoid milk entirely because they say that adults do not need milk or that milk is fattening, constipating, or indigestible, or leads to cancer—none of which is true.

A long list of curious fads is given and refuted in "Food Facts Talk Back," a 1957 publication of the American Dietetic Association, 620 North Michigan Avenue, Chicago 11, Ill.

In this chapter, however, we are more concerned with the faddist or quack who spreads his misinformation for personal profit.

THE FOOD QUACK or charlatan is not necessarily a food faddist, but he thrives on those who are.

He may or may not practice the fallacies he preaches, except in public, in order to sell his wares. He may even laugh at his victims while he enjoys his own good meals at home.

Often he is a clever promoter, professing knowledge he does not possess in foods, nutrition, or even medicine— friendly, handsome, poised, and persuasive.

Quacks are sure to be convincing speakers or writers, and their smattering of scientific knowledge gives them a fake plausibility. They mix the true and the false or misleading to fit their whims, to sell their ideas, or to scare people into buying their wares or books.

They accomplish most by personal appearances or books with catchy titles. They also function by way of the mails, radio, television, newspapers, and handbills. They appeal especially to the chronically ill and to retired persons in winter resorts, who have time and inclination to worry about health and hope to recapture their youth.

Smart quacks know all the hidden persuaders. They know also some of the currently fashionable words of science. If they knew more of science they might not be quacks.

THE LAYMAN should be able to spot the earmarks of the self-styled expert.

His advertising and sales approach are direct to the consumer. His products and pamphlets are not distributed through professional channels. He is not eligible to belong to the ethical scientific organizations and he cannot present his theories through the publications of reliable groups, such as the Journal of the American Medical Association and the Journal of Home Economics.

He may offer a money-back guarantee if your diabetes is not cured in 10 days or if you have not lost 5 pounds during the first week of using his reducing nostrum. He may assure you that his elixir will cure whatever ails you, but you will be gullible, indeed, if you believe that diseases such as arthritis, which long has baffled medical scientists, can be cured by a food supplement advertised on the first-come, first-served basis, or by some secret food formula.

The types of food faddism difficult for even the most intelligent layman to recognize are the half-truths and misinterpretations of scientific data that appear in print and are preached from the lecture platform and over the air.

Most of these self-styled authorities distort facts to suit their own ends, much to the embarrassment of the scientists they quote out of context.

It is even possible for them to use a college as a front for their activities so that they may be introduced as authorities, professors of health or nutrition, and founders of such high-sounding but questionable organizations as the "Academy of Applied Nutrition" or the "National Institute of Dietary Foods." They know how to use lingo that sounds like science to promote their own moneymaking projects.

Adelia Beeuwkes, associate professor of public health nutrition in the University of Michigan, wrote in the Journal of the American Dietetic Association in July 1956:

"The pseudo-scientist watches hawk-like for the published reports of the reputable workers. Isolated and sterile fragments of the whole scientific report are torn out and, like a squirrel who runs away to consider the value of the nut he has found, our pseudo-scientist rushes to seclusion with his prize—torn fragments of knowledge. He considers their value to him and sets about weaving a few facts of truth into a garment of many colors—a garment that looks rather impressive at a distance and under dim light. This blend of good and poor threads disintegrates completely before the microscope when a scientist trains his eye on the glass which shows truth and untruth in their proper proportion.

"He snatches bits of information from scientific papers and in the same breath confides to 'his followers' that the field of medicine, nutrition, or other does not accept his theories because the scientists are stubborn and are really not cognizant of the mysteries of life which can be purchased for several dollars. . . . Beware of theories that have not been brought into the daylight of scientific research."

FOOD FADDISM is serious and dangerous for several reasons.

Besides being a waste of money, a fake diet cure may give a person a false sense of security and he may not see a doctor in time to prevent serious trouble. Some diet fads actually are harmful or may lead to malnutrition.

This approach to the treatment of chronic ills, regardless of whether they are of nutritional origin or not, tends to undermine public confidence in scientific nutrition and threatens true progress in the sciences supported by sound agencies.

"Distorting facts into fads is big business today," wrote Dr. Ruth M. Leverton, of the Department of Agriculture, in the Journal of the American Dietetic Association in August 1957.

"Never has so much erroneous information been promoted and accepted by so many people. Never have ignorance and lack of commonsense in matters of food and health held so much danger for the population. The presence of the quackery among us is not new; every age has had its medicine man, alchemist, herb healer, and pseudo-scientist to capitalize on people's ignorance and appeal to their emotions. It does seem that the number of charlatans in our midst today is greater in proportion to the amount of scientific knowledge than ever before."

How can one tell the difference between authenticated facts versus misinformation? In this day of extravagant claims, we are so used to exaggeration that we tend to discount facts as well as fiction.

Mere unvarnished facts about food and nutrition are not considered spectacular enough. We are more apt to hear that a serving of some special cereal and milk is equivalent to a beefsteak, or that one should eat candy for reducing because seven pieces equal only the calorie value of a slice of bread. The wrong implications in these examples are obvious, but there are other fallacies that may really mislead the unwary.

Some persons advocate the theory that the food value of crops grown on depleted soils is poor and that plants are "devitalized" or "demineralized" or otherwise deprived of natural nutrients because they have not been grown according to principles of "organic farming."

This subject has been investigated by the Plant, Soil, and Nutrition Laboratory in Ithaca, N.Y. L. A. Maynard, former director of the laboratory, assured us that no disease or abnormality in man can be traced to a deficiency in the soil except in the case of endemic goiter due to too little iodine. Research at the laboratory gives no evidence that the composition of the crops grown is essentially different as a result of the kind or amount of commercial fertilizer used on the soil. Lack of fertilizer may reduce the yield of a crop but not the amount of nutrients in the food produced.

E. M. Nelson, late Chief of the Division of Nutrition of the Food and Drug Administration, commented on this problem in the Journal of Home Economics for October 1957.

He wrote: "Our tables of food composition would be of little or no value if the composition of a plant were dependent on the composition of the soil on which it was grown. It is the yield per acre that is greatly influenced by the kind and extent of fertilizer used. Composition is controlled by hereditary factors or genes which also control other characteristics of the plant such as size and shape. Thus we find that the seemingly plausible preaching that depleted soils produce foods of poor nutritional quality and that this is the basis for extensive supplementation of minerals and vitamins has no basis in scientific fact."

Nevertheless, a news broadcast introduced a "professor of nutrition" as a guest speaker whose theme was primarily his concern over the poor food value of vegetables grown on depleted soils. He introduced a new twist—that the proteins were of poor quality and the amino acids unstable in foods unless organic fertilizer had been used. It sounded scientific, but no such research finding has been reported in recognized journals.

Faddists are apt to recommend so-called "natural" foods along with raw or unprocessed foods. Many foods, to be sure, we regularly use in their natural state—fruit, nuts, salad greens. But the food faddist has abused the phrase "natural foods" and goes to extremes in condemning such processed items as white flour, milled and enriched cereals, canned products, and pasteurized milk. He would have us use raw sugar in place of refined sugar, sea salt in place of regular table salt,

and lemon juice in place of vinegar. Except for price, there is no objection to these foods, but neither is there anything detrimental about the processed food that is condemned.

Raw—unpasteurized—milk has advocates who believe that milk has lost much of its nutritive value as a result of pasteurization. Almost the only loss of nutrients due to pasteurization is that of ascorbic acid, of which milk has such small and variable amounts that we do not consider it an important source. The nutritive losses are insignificant compared with the protection that pasteurization gives against certain bacteria.

The raw vegetable food fad of a generation ago has given place to a raw vegetable juice fad. "Liquefied vegetables" have no life-giving properties that are not present in the vegetables themselves. Raw vegetables eaten as salad, sticks, curls, or juice all have good value; the juice has no magic just because it is juice. The salesman wants to sell the gadget with which to prepare the juice.

Granted that juice or puree may be the form of vegetable most acceptable to people with inadequate dentures and that juice sometimes is made from vegetable tops not ordinarily eaten. Cooked vegetables retain most of their nutritive value if they are not cooked too long. Some vegetables are more palatable cooked than raw and are more easily digested.

Some vegetables have been credited with more virtues than they actually possess. There is no scientific basis for assertions that celery juice is a cure for indigestion and rheumatism, carrot juice is good for the complexion, parsley juice is a tonic, garlic juice relieves high blood pressure, and white radish and lemon juice are good in the treatment of gallbladder ailments. Many other ridiculous claims are made from time to time.

"MIRACLE" FOOD, food supplements, and food combinations are often credited with therapeutic value far beyond any nutritive factors they contain. It is folly to suppose that blackstrap molasses, wheat germ, and yeast are miracle foods that can in any way correct menopausal difficulties, induce sleep, prevent nervousness, correct baldness, restore original color of hair or skin, aid digestion, or prevent aging—claims typical of the ones made by pseudonutritionists.

One self-styled authority on the "successful treatment of aging" has expounded the ridiculous theory that "the reason why men lose strength and women their beauty was shown to be aging factors in food combinations; while antiaging factors from another group of foods enable a complete mental and physical rebuilding."

Among the Proverbs about life and health, for example, we find, "It is not good to eat much honey," even in a land "flowing with milk and honey."

Royal jelly, the mid-20th-century equivalent of the older "miracles," has been called the miracle food of the queen bee. The promoter would have one believe it can do the impossible—beautify the face or bring back "the joy of life" in a magic capsule. Even though "royal jelly" in face creams was initiated in France and imported to the United States about 1953, no clinical evidence of beneficial effects has been reported. At 140 dollars an ounce, it is truly an extravagant source of certain vitamins of the B complex that are readily available elsewhere.

ARTHRITIS is still one of our most disabling chronic diseases, although doctors have devoted years of research to possible causes and treatment. Yet one writer published the theory that certain oils serve as joint lubricants, but fruit juices consumed at the same meal prevent the oils from functioning in this way. Actually, joints are not lubricated by oils, oils do not circulate in the blood stream to reach the joints in the form in which we consume them, and fruit juices do not change the composition of the oils in our foods. His notion is based on completely erroneous ideas of the chemistry and physiology of the human body, but his jargon appeals to many uncritical readers. The claim that you can eat your way into arthritis and eat your way out again is ridiculous.

According to the Journal of the American Medical Association for January 18, 1958: "There is no diet for the treatment of arthritis . . . . A diet that is liberal in calories and protein and has a high vitamin and mineral content is indicated for the patient who has lost weight and muscle tissue, a situation frequently encountered in rheumatoid arthritis. In patients who are overweight, or obese, caloric limitation is necessary to reduce weight; in some patients with osteoarthritis of weight-bearing joints, such weight reduction is a most important aspect of treatment."

Often food supplements are offered after people have been frightened into believing that their condition is due to a lack of essential nutrients in their regular diet and that the lack can be supplied only by some concoction that is really very expensive but is being made available to them at a special price. You may be sure that the special price is far beyond the value of the ingredients.

TRICK REDUCING DIETS, the mystery foods, and "weight control" pills for losing pounds painlessly are bought and paid for by persons of both sexes and all ages. They fool themselves into thinking that reducing pills and a fad diet may be a substitute that will do what a weak will keeps them from doing—cut down on the calories they ingest.

Some people refuse to believe a hard but simple and established truth: Overweight comes from eating more food than the body requires in terms of energy spent.

Actually, the energy requirement decreases with age, so that the person of the same size and activity needs

21 percent fewer calories at age 65 than he did at 25. Often appetites and eating habits do not adjust to the smaller need, and the extra calories are stored as surplus. We use fewer calories as we get older because we tend to be less active, and expend less energy when we mechanize our homes and transportation. It is easy therefore to eat and drink more calories than the body uses. The surplus calories must be avoided if we do not want to store them as fat.

Somebody has pointed out, for example, that a stenographer who changes from a manual typewriter to an electric typewriter saves enough energy to put on 4 to 6 pounds of weight in a year if she does not use it up in another way or reduce her intake.

Mere futility or actual physical harm or both may be involved in trick devices for reducing. The ultimate futility of a diet of eggs and leafy vegetables or bananas and skim milk is not in the foods as such, but in the lack of variety and poor nutritional balance that are bound to make one give it up in a short time. These and similar combinations of perfectly good but a limited variety of foods are harmless but tiresome. They fail to establish a new pattern of eating, which is the only way to control weight.

Some restricted diets are so poorly balanced that chronic fatigue or actual illness may result. Most people cannot stick to such restricted regimes long enough to suffer permanent damage, however.

The pills and powders advertised for reducing usually are accompanied by instructions to follow a low-calorie diet, which must be followed for the plan to be effective, as guaranteed. The chances are that the diet would be just as effective without the expensive supplement. No food supplement can possibly reduce the caloric value of other foods eaten.

Any type of drugs or pills advertised for weight control should be used only under medical supervision. Not enough is known about the action of the appetite depressants to risk their general use, although some physicians have experimented with them. Yet such drugs are incorporated in some of the reducing pills advertised. An older device, less common today, was the use of cathartic drugs or salts, which tend to dehydrate the body. They cause quick but temporary loss of a few pounds of water—which are soon regained—and may result in irritation of the gastrointestinal tract.

Thyroid extract or drugs that tend to increase metabolism are sometimes prescribed by physicians when diagnosis indicates a need for them. Such endocrine products can be harmful if used indiscriminately. As a protection to the public, thyroid products cannot be sold by ethical druggists without a prescription. Unscrupulous vendors of quack reducing nostrums, however, do not hesitate, regardless of the side effects, to include drugs or endocrine products that may help to accomplish their ends.

Scientific journals and reliable magazines try continually to combat unwarranted enthusiasms for fad diets, whether they are the "Hollywood" or the "holiday" diet or the frivolous or fabulous formulas. But there still are "miracle diets," "revolutionary discoveries," and "reducing formulas" that are worded to appeal to the overweight college professor as well as to the buxom socialite. Advertisements offer tablets that "flush fat right out of your body" or "tranquilize away your reducing problems" or encourage you to "drink your fat away with a reducing cocktail" or "lose ugly fat without dieting or hunger—no calorie counting! no diets! no exercise!" Testimonials such as "I thank you for my new body" or "My husband asked me for a date" play upon emotions rather than appeal to intelligence.

These exaggerated claims and similar ones have aroused concern in Government circles, and a 4-day hearing was held before a subcommittee of the House of Representatives in August of

1957 on false and misleading advertising of weight-reducing preparations. Besides reviewing the misleading statements made about various preparations, several experts testified as to the possible dangers to users of such preparations.

The report of findings can be obtained by writing to the United States Government Printing Office and asking for 33d Report by the Committee on Government Operations, entitled "False and Misleading Advertising (Weight Reducing Remedies), 1958," Union Calendar No. 1071, House Report No. 2553, 85th Congress, 2d Session.

HIGH-POWER ADVERTISING has had a significant effect on the buying and eating habits of Americans despite tradition. Not all advertisers feel a responsibility to consumers to the extent of checking the authenticity and implications of their claims.

Since advertising in mass media is a kind of education for many people, we can attribute some of the present-day interest in foods and special diets to the increasing use of the nutritional claims in advertising.

The pendulum can swing too far, however, when advertisers promote food supplements to such an extent that one is led to believe that a good diet of natural foods cannot be adequate. "High power" vitamin capsules and amino acid supplements should be used only on the advice of a physician, not on the advice of door-to-door salesmen.

It is generally true that reliable companies tend to avoid misleading statements, but an apparently increasing number of unethical promoters indulge in half-truths, exaggerations, "sure-cures," and misinformation to sell their products to gullible consumers.

Many of the supplements widely advertised today are not harmful in themselves. If there exists any pathologic condition, however, the danger lies in the faith that victims may place in the exaggerated and unwarranted claims made for their therapeutic value. The danger is especially great when the concoction is represented as providing adequate treatment for such diseases as cancer, arthritis, diabetes, or pneumonia, which need prompt medical attention. No serious disease or physical disability should be treated by the patient without the advice of a physician.

Several good, reliable books have been published to help people reduce calories sensibly. *Stay Slim for Life*, by Ida Jean Kain and Mildred B. Gibson (published by Doubleday in 1958), offers sound advice and good menus and recipes with which to attain the desired goal.

Diet fads come and go with the changing emphasis—in medicine and nutrition. The pseudoscientist quickly changes his lingo to fit the times. As an example, when this chapter was being written, much emphasis was being given in medical literature to the relationship of fatty acids in foods to the incidence of degenerative heart disease. This relationship is a complex one and is not yet fully understood. Insurance statistics indicate that degenerative heart disease is the foremost cause of death according to their data, and the incidence correlates closely with the degree of overweight.

There is considerable evidence that there is long-range benefit from weight reduction and one way to curtail calories is to reduce the amount of fat in the diet. Eventually science may be able to specify the types of fats which are least harmful, but at the present time no radical changes in dietary habits of people in the normal weight range are recommended. Moreover, any product or dietary regime advertised to be a "sure cure" for atherosclerosis or heart disease should be questioned and inquiry made from reliable medical authority.

We have no censorship to protect us against misleading and incorrect books and articles.

Book reviews in reliable journals,

such as the Journal of the American Medical Association, the Journal of the American Dietetic Association, Journal of the American Public Health Association, American Journal of Nursing, Today's Health, and Science News Letter are likely to be the best guides in the choice of special diet books. Some or all of them can be consulted in most libraries.

The librarian of a public library has to buy books demanded by his patrons, even though he may not recommend them. Moreover, he frequently is not qualified to judge the reliability of theories proposed by authors. Therefore the fact that a book is a bestseller or is on the shelves of a library is not a recommendation of it as a guide to nutrition. Actually, some fad-diet books have enjoyed a popularity far beyond that of most nutrition or diet books by scientific authorities—their only merit being that they are written so people can enjoy them.

MANY reliable agencies and professional authorities are willing to give advice on good sources of information and are able to protect the public against the sales pressure of the quacks. Specific inquiries regarding questioned products or misleading advertising will be answered by the Bureau of Investigation of the American Medical Association, 535 North Dearborn Street, Chicago 10, Ill., or by the better business bureaus or chambers of commerce in your city or vicinity.

The Council of Foods and Nutrition of the American Medical Association also publishes statements and decisions to guide advertisers and include proper use of claims in advertising. Among others, they condemn vague mineral claims, the foods for "building tired blood," trick claims concerning resistance or superresistance of the body, and other superlative claims not supported by facts.

The American Medical Association, in cooperation with the Bureau of Investigation and the National Better Business Bureau, have joined in a program to alert the public to notorious health lecturers, worthless or harmful tonics and food supplements, phony health foods, and related false advertising claims. One project is an exhibit entitled "Nutrition Nonsense and False Claims," which features an actual recording of the pitch made by a door-to-door salesman of food supplements. A film entitled "The Medicine Man," which deals with the health lecturer who promotes his product as a cure-all of diseases, has been shown on television and is available from the American Medical Association for showing to groups.

GENERAL protection against mislabeling of products and fraudulent or misleading claims is provided by the enforcement of the Federal Food, Drug, and Cosmetic Act by the Food and Drug Administration. Examples of the type of legal action which they may take against quack "health lectures" or house-to-house sales based upon false and misleading claims are reviewed by Dr. George P. Larrick, Commissioner of Food and Drugs, in another chapter of this Yearbook.

The Federal Trade Commission and the United States Postal Service can also take legal action against fraudulent use of interstate commerce and of the United States mails, but much harm may be done before legal action can be effective.

In the August 1957 hearings on false and misleading advertising that I referred to, there was considerable discussion of the elapsed time between the receipt of a letter of complaint, the initiations of an investigation, and the issuance of a complaint. Although the average time has been cut down, it is still apt to be nearly a year or more before official action is taken. Much harm can be done in that time.

New fads crop up continually, and quacks use new devices to circumvent the law. The best protection for the consumer should be his own intelligent skepticism about extravagant and mysterious claims and his recourse to reliable agencies for information.

HELEN S. MITCHELL *is Dean of the School of Home Economics, University of Massachusetts. She is the author of a number of articles about nutrition and coauthor of a textbook, "Nutrition in Health and Disease," the 13th edition of which was published by J. B. Lippincott in 1958. She was chief nutritionist in the civilian nutrition program during the Second World War.*

Without a definite program of nutrition education started at the beginning of their school life, children are apt to confine their food choices to favorite foods. Likewise, children cannot project benefits into the future and so have no concern or appreciation for what the future will bring if they fail to eat their vegetables or drink their milk. A willingness to eat and choose the kinds and amounts of food that science has proved we need for good health must be learned. The emphasis and practice must be learned. . . .

Planning of experiences with foods should reflect: the development of children; class teaching of health, social studies, science, or literature; the use of lunch, snack time, parties and other social occasions as practice areas for learnings; the basic food groups; and well-planned lessons with emphasis on very simple directions, sanitation, and safety measures.

Experiences should take into account span of interest, motor control, comprehension, and present need. Children in the primary grades are still very immature and dependent upon adults for their food needs. They are equally dependent upon adults for direction and assistance in developing good eating habits. They can be introduced to food preparation by helping to stir a food mixture, to add ingredients or mold cooking with their hands, to decorate cakes, cookies, salads, or prepare vegetables. The making of a complete recipe would not be in line with their development, but to see and taste many kinds of vegetables and fruits could help establish food choices for growth in knowledge of good eating—as building a vocabulary of words aids growth in reading.—JUSTINE SMEY, in Journal of Home Economics, May 1958.

Reports of current research on the possible relationships of dietary fats, hypercholesteremia, and the incidence of atherosclerosis have aroused more concern on Main Street than any area of nutrition research. Without doubt, further research is necessary to clarify and interpret the influence of dietary factors, specifically fat, on the occurrence of coronary heart disease. Yet questions directed to the nutritionist, the dietitian, the Extension Service specialist, and the home economics instructor about the implication of research findings in terms of daily food patterns should be given careful consideration and answer. Otherwise, the questioner will turn to the food faddist who has the facility for positive, if not validated, statements. . . .

The evidence to date indicates the desirability of teaching moderation in the use of dietary fats, selection of dietary fats from various sources including vegetable oils, and the health hazards of overweight. In essence, these concepts have been a part of nutrition teaching during the past ten years and are in keeping with the principle of a balanced diet selected from a variety of natural foods. Self-chosen diets in which a high proportion of the calories are derived from fat, possibly at the expense of an adequate intake of other nutrients, are not in accord with principles of good nutrition; neither is an incidence of about 30 per cent of our population in the overweight category. Quite possibly further findings in this area of research may justify changes in dietary recommendations. At present, however, the challenge seems to be for more effective nutrition education.—WILMA D. BREWER and LOTTE ARNRICH, in Journal of Home Economics, April 1958.

Food

PROGRAMS

Feeding 6,280 Million

RALPH W. PHILLIPS

SUPPOSE all the people of the world could sit at one table for one meal. How long would that table have to be?

If we allow 2 feet of space for each person and have seats on both sides of the table, we would need 1 foot of table length for each person. For the 2,691 million persons in the world in 1955, the table would have had to be long enough to extend nearly 21 times around the earth at the equator.

But each day we would have to make the table even longer. Because the world's population is expected to increase at the rate of approximately 50 million persons a year during the quarter century from 1950 to 1975, the table would have to be lengthened 9,470 miles a year—about 26 miles every day.

Where would the food for them come from?

To raise the food and the other farm products people need, a little more than 1.25 acres of arable land was available per person for the world as a whole in 1955. In the United States there were about 2.8 acres per person. Besides the arable land, about 2.25 acres were in permanent meadows and pasture for each person in the world and about 3.8 acres for each person in the United States.

It is clear, then, that the United States has relatively more land on which to produce food for its population than has the world as a whole. It is also clear that pressures on the land everywhere will worsen rapidly if populations continue to grow at the present rate.

If, as some experts now predict, the population of the United States increases to approximately 400 million in the year 2000, the amount of arable land will have dropped from 2.8 acres to 1.16 acres per person, or less than the world average in 1955. If we take a much more conservative figure, a population of only 275 million in 2000, the amount of arable land per person will have dropped to about 1.7 acres.

The world population, in the meantime, is expected to rise to approximately 6,280 million persons, so the amount of arable land per person will have been reduced to just over one-half acre at the turn of the century, compared with the 1.25 acres that were available in 1955.

Some new land will, of course, be brought under cultivation, productivity will be increased by using more fertilizer, and so on. Some arable land will be lost by erosion and salting up, however. Buildings and roads will occupy an increasing amount of land. The rate of population increase may slow down before the end of the century.

But it seems certain that advances in medical knowledge and in public health will lengthen the average life-span and tend to offset other factors which slow down the rate of increase. So, even though the effects of these and other factors cannot be estimated very accurately, it is obvious that, as the population increases, the size of the piece of land from which each obtains his food must decrease.

No matter how optimistic is our outlook, the countries of the world have to solve serious problems if their peoples are to get enough food in the future, even though, in some parts, surpluses of a few products create problems of a different type. It is not enough to say that men always have competed among themselves for food and that there never was a time when every man has had enough to eat.

Competition for food or for the land upon which to produce it or for access to the waters from which to procure it has caused many conflicts among men, tribes, countries.

The gigantic task of feeding today's population or the larger population likely in 50 or 100 years is hard indeed to visualize, and we ask ourselves:

How long will it be before a point is reached when increases in food production cannot keep up with increases in population?

How long will it be before limitations on the production of food will force population numbers to become stable?

J. G. Harrar put the dilemma simply and forcefully when he said we must soon decide whether we are prepared to fall behind in each succeeding generation until there is no longer room to move and not enough bread and opportunity for all or whether we will recognize and interpret the laws of Nature in logical fashion and take measures not to violate them at the expense of our descendants.

We can put it another way: Compete (maybe even fight) for food and the places that produce food or cooperate in raising and procuring enough food for everybody.

If countries are to work together on nutritional problems and the related problems of agricultural production and distribution, they need some kind of organizational machinery—boards, committees, organizations, services, or whatever we want to call them—to do so.

The machinery is almost certain to be more cumbersome and to move more slowly than a board or service that deals with a set of problems within a country. Furthermore, international agencies, being the instruments of sovereign member countries, can do no more than the governments of these countries permit them to do. But organization is essential to the conduct of discussions and cooperation.

Some quite effective intergovernmental agencies have been established and now service their member countries, including the United States, to good advantage.

Apart from the intergovernmental agencies, some of which I describe later, many nongovernmental organizations and foundations exist that are interested in better nutrition and ways of improving agricultural production and levels of living.

Not all the activities I describe relate directly to the production, distribution, and utilization of food. Some deal with nonfood products, such as cotton and wool. All have a bearing on improvement of agricultural production, processing, and distribution, however.

Of the international intergovernmental agencies, the Food and Agriculture Organization of the United Nations (FAO) is the primary one having to do with international agricultural activities. The Inter-American Institute of Agricultural Sciences (IAIAS) devotes its efforts to the Western Hemisphere.

Other international agencies work on a regional basis or in some specialized field. The United States maintains active membership in them.

Before I discuss any of the existing agencies, I would like to mention the pioneer, the former International Institute of Agriculture. David Lubin, an American who had seen the misery among farmers in the economic depression of the 1890's, set out to try to help farmers through some international mechanism. After much effort, he persuaded officials in several countries and the King of Italy to accept his ideas. The institution David Lubin had envisaged became a reality in Rome in 1905. It carried out useful work until the Second World War ended its activities.

The Institute assembled and published statistics on world agriculture, convened international meetings in a number of fields, and issued many technical publications.

At the close of the war, countries recognized the need for an organization with broader terms of reference and scope for action. When the Food and Agriculture Organization of the United Nations was established, it absorbed the assets of the Institute, including its excellent library. Now, more than a half century after David Lubin breathed life into the Institute, it no longer exists. It served a useful purpose in its time. In recognition of David Lubin's contribution, an avenue in a beautiful park, the Villa Borghese, in Rome, bears his name. The FAO library is known as the David Lubin Memorial Library.

THE FOOD AND AGRICULTURE Organization was established in October 1945, when representatives of 32 governments signed its constitution at a conference in Quebec.

It had its beginnings in a United Nations Conference on Food and Agriculture conducted in Hot Springs,

Va., in May of 1943, on the initiative of President Franklin D. Roosevelt.

Forty-five countries sent representatives.

Soon thereafter were held the Dumbarton Oaks and San Francisco conferences, which laid the basis for formation of the United Nations.

Thus, among the subjects covered by the various international agencies that have been established since the war, the governments gave first consideration to the basic problems of food and agriculture.

Like each of the agencies in the family of United Nations agencies, FAO is an independent intergovernmental organization. It has its own constitution, its own governing body (the FAO Conference), and its own budget, to which each of its member countries (76 in 1959) contributes.

The preamble of its constitution sets forth as its objective the promotion of the common welfare by furthering separate and collective action by nations for the purposes of raising levels of nutrition and standards of living of the peoples under their respective jurisdictions, securing improvements in the efficiency of the production and distribution of food and agricultural products, bettering the condition of rural populations, and thus contributing toward an expanding world economy.

FAO owns no land on which to produce food—or even the land upon which its headquarters in Rome stands. It has no political control of (or direct contact with) farmers by which to influence the manner in which they use their land. It manufactures no requisites for improving production, such as insecticides and vaccines. FAO maintains no agricultural colleges in which to train leaders. All such activities, which can improve efficiency in producing, processing, and distributing agricultural products, are the responsibility of governmental and private agencies and institutions within the countries.

The task of FAO is rather to assist the governments of its member countries to carry out their functions most effectively in their individual and joint efforts to improve the production, distribution, and use of farm products.

FAO provides forums in which policy-making and technical leaders can exchange information and ideas, arrange coordinated programs or cooperative activities, and agree on procedures for handling the agency's affairs.

Such opportunities are provided in the biennial sessions of the Conference (the governing body of FAO, in which each member country has a seat) and in the Council (a 24-nation body, which meets at intervals between Conference sessions to act on policy questions and to keep under review the state of food and agriculture in the world).

Other meetings are convened to deal with more specialized subjects, including commodity problems, improved ways of gathering statistics, and technical problems of agriculture, fisheries, forestry, and nutrition.

FAO also sends information to its member countries through publications—statistical yearbooks, commodity studies, technical publications, periodicals, monographs, studies of development programs, summaries of meetings and training centers, and reports of missions and the experts who serve in member countries.

The members receive several forms of direct assistance. A survey mission may be sent to study a country's needs and to recommend programs for improvement. Individuals or groups of experts are sent to countries to advise and assist in planning and carrying forward technical and economic projects. Training centers for young workers and development centers for mature officials are held, usually on a regional basis, making use of institutional facilities available in a member country.

Limited amounts of technical supplies, not available in the countries receiving assistance, may be supplied to facilitate the work of experts or the operation of training and development centers. To insure proper followup of service by experts, fellowships may be granted to workers who will return to their countries to carry on work initiated with the advisory assistance of experts.

Member countries are also assisted in their joint efforts to improve agriculture through the establishment of consultative bodies as arms of FAO.

Consultative bodies include the International Rice Commission, the European Commission for the Control of Foot and Mouth Disease, and the European Commission on Agriculture. All are forums for intergovernmental consultation and further the programs sponsored by the governments and by FAO.

FAO sponsored the International Plant Protection Convention (agreement) to facilitate cooperation in the safe exchange of plant breeding materials and preventing the spread of plant pests and diseases from one country to another.

FAO works with other United Nations agencies in carrying out its functions. In the nutritional aspects of its program, there is close cooperation with the World Health Organization (WHO), since WHO is concerned with the medical phases of nutrition.

The United Nations set up as one of its arms the United Nations Children's Fund (formerly the United Nations International Children's Emergency Fund—UNICEF—and still known by these initials). UNICEF is primarily a supply agency, and its facilities are used to support certain long-range activities falling within FAO's sphere. For example, while UNICEF supplies skim milk, thus meeting an immediate need, there remains the problem of how to insure continuing supplies of milk from local sources. FAO gives advice on production and processing problems in many instances like this, and UNICEF supplies essential equipment that is not available locally for use in establishing processing plants.

Another example of such cooperation: UNICEF supplies equipment and materials needed in national programs for training nutrition leaders. FAO provides the professional advisers to give the training.

I could cite many other examples involving the International Labor Organization, the International Bank for Reconstruction and Development, the World Meteorological Organization, the United Nations Education, Scientific and Cultural Organization (UNESCO), and others.

Some examples illustrate the scope of the work of FAO: A team of veterinarians assisted Ethiopia to produce rinderpest vaccine and to organize field teams to vaccinate cattle against this serious plague. Another team assisted in the planning and construction of irrigation works in Iran. A series of farm management training meetings was held to train leaders from the countries of Asia and the Far East. A rice expert brought new methods and new varieties to Egypt (now a part of the United Arab Republic). Experts on small tools and implements assisted Afghanistan, Ethiopia, and other countries to find ways of replacing the sickle with other more modern tools.

Foresters worked with Brazilians to find ways to utilize the vast forested areas of the Amazon Basin.

Fisheries experts assisted Thailand, Ceylon, and other countries to improve fish production from coastal waters, rivers, ricefields, and ponds.

School feeding and other nutrition and home economics projects were started in Burma, Costa Rica, Ecuador, and other countries with FAO assistance.

FAO experts gave India, Libya, and other countries advice on ways to improve the quality of hides by better methods of flaying and curing.

Survey missions visited Greece, Poland, Thailand, Uruguay, Yemen, and other countries to advise on the overall improvement of agriculture and dietary patterns.

The listing of examples could go on and on. These, however, show that much is being done.

THE INTER-AMERICAN Institute of Agricultural Sciences is a specialized agency of the Organization of American States (OAS). OAS is composed of 21 republics in the Western Hemisphere. The Pan American Union in Washington, D.C., is its secretariat.

The Institute has headquarters in Turrialba, Costa Rica. It was recognized formally as a permanent institution in 1944, when the majority of the member nations of OAS had ratified the Convention or the international agreement creating it.

The Institute seeks to encourage and advance the development of agricultural sciences in the American Republics through research, teaching, and extension activities in the theory and practice of agriculture and related arts and sciences.

The work of the Institute is carried out through its departments of plant industry, animal husbandry, and economics and rural life and by its graduate school. It also maintains a Renewable Resources Service and a Communications Service and other means of keeping in touch with agriculturalists in the region it serves. It conducts a technical cooperation program in agriculture for the benefit of its member countries. Special funds are made available to it for the purpose through the Organization of American States.

Research in plants seeks ways to improve production and to protect coffee, cacao, corn, rice, and tropical grasses against pests and diseases. The livestock work is directed primarily toward improving dairy and beef cattle, particularly for tropical conditions. The purpose of the other work is to determine the needs for professional training of extension agents, the usefulness of study circles in community development, key agronomic practices for medium and small farms, and improving the conditions

of rural life. The Renewable Resources
Service conducts research in forestry.

The training of leaders for service
in their own countries is a principal function of the Institute. Eighty
students from 24 countries studied at
Turrialba in 1957; 37 were graduate
students and 43 took special courses
in cacao technology, plant quaran-
tine, animal husbandry, and vocational agriculture.

Members of the technical staff and
the staff of the Communications Service do much to make new information
available to workers throughout the
region. The Institute also publishes a
journal and an information bulletin
and distributes technical information
by other means.

The Institute cooperates with FAO
in certain activities. For example, two
regional meetings dealing with soil
fertility and fertilizers and soil survey
and classification in Latin America
were conducted by FAO and the
Institute in Turrialba in 1957. A
joint meeting on higher agricultural
education in Latin America was held
in Santiago, Chile, in 1958.

OTHER INTERNATIONAL agencies have
various functions.

The Caribbean Commission comprises France, the Netherlands, the
United Kingdom, and the United
States. Established in 1948, it coordinates the efforts of the four governments to improve economic and social
well-being of Caribbean inhabitants.

The South Pacific Commission has
six members—Australia, France, the
Netherlands, New Zealand, the United
Kingdom, and the United States. It
was established in 1948 to further cooperation for the economic and social
development of the 19 dependent ter-
ritories in the South Pacific.

The International Sugar Council
was established by 22 governments in
1937 to administer the International
Sugar Agreement, which is designed
to establish and maintain an orderly
relationship between the supply and
demand for sugar in the world at prices

equitable to producers and consumers.

The International Wheat Council
was established in 1942 by Argentina,
Australia, Canada, the United Kingdom, and the United States. The membership was expanded later. The
Council serves as a forum for discussions and negotiations looking to the
conclusion of wheat agreements aimed
at preventing burdensome surpluses
or critical shortages and to assure supplies to importing countries and markets for exporting countries at fair
prices.

The International Cotton Advisory
Committee provides ways of assembling and analyzing data on world
production of cotton, trade stocks, and
prices and other problems of international scope. It suggests to governments measures that are considered suitable and practicable for the
achievement of international collaboration. It was formed by 10 countries
in 1939.

The International Wool Study Group,
formed in 1946, has representatives of
countries interested in the production,
consumption, or sale of wool. It seeks
to provide continuous, accurate information about the supply and demand
for wool.

The International Seed Testing Association is concerned with the advance of work on seed-testing and the
evaluation of seeds by comparative
tests, the standardization of methods
and terminology, and the development
of standard international certificates
of quality for agricultural seeds in international trade. It began in 1924.

PRIVATELY FINANCED foundations
have made substantial contributions
to the improvement of agriculture and
levels of nutrition in various countries.
Their work has added to our fund of
technical knowledge and has helped
to build international understanding.

Wilmer Shields Rich, of the American Foundations Information Service
in New York City, in her hefty volume,
*American Foundations and Their Fields,
VII,* summarized the purposes and

methods of 4,164 American foundations. She estimated that there are about 7,300 foundations. Relatively few support work in agriculture.

I mention only three to illustrate the types of work they support to improve nutrition and rural living in various parts of the world.

ONE, THE ROCKEFELLER Foundation, among its various fields of interest, gives considerable attention to agriculture. It furnishes grants to other organizations and awards funds for travel and fellowships. It operates some of its own agricultural programs that have to do with the more practical applications of science in improving food production and the training of persons and help to governments in developing programs that can be carried forward on a national scale. The most active programs have been in Mexico and Colombia.

The work in Mexico is aimed at the improvement of corn, sorghums, wheat, rice, beans, soybeans, vegetable crops, potatoes, and forages. Other projects have studied soil fertility and the control of pests in the field and in stored grain.

Varieties of hybrid corn that have yielded 165–200 bushels an acre have been made available for use in the important corn-producing sections of Mexico. Highest yields have been had in the Central Plateau at elevations above 4 thousand feet. At lower elevations, in more tropical climates, yields have been about 100 bushels. The potential is higher, but before higher yields can be obtained in the Tropics, problems of fertilization, drainage, and control of diseases and insects must be solved.

Although hybrids are being promoted, particularly for the irrigated areas, synthetic varieties—varieties resulting from the crossing of two local varieties—have been developed. One of these yields only slightly less than the two hybrids recommended for the Bajío region, but it is still extremely variable in maturity so is not readily acceptable to farmers. The greatest problem of corn improvement continues to be the breeding of hybrids or varieties for the central region, where corn is grown under natural rainfall conditions, the altitude is 4 thousand to 9 thousand feet, and rainfall may be a few inches or 40 inches a year.

Considerable interest has developed in producing sorghums for hog and poultry feed in Mexico. The Foundation has tested standard varieties as well as new Texas hybrids. In the Bajío area, yields from 5 Texas hybrids exceeded by 20 percent the average of 10 standard varieties.

The Foundation has had such a large and diverse program in Mexico that I can give only a few other examples of accomplishments. The national average for wheat production rose from 7.5 bushels an acre in 1948 to 21 in 1957. Lodging has become a limiting factor, and an intensive crossing program with Japanese dwarf varieties has been initiated. A superior, disease-resistant bean, Canocel, has been released for commercial production in the Central Mesa. In an effort to make blight-resistant potato seed available to the small farmers of the high plateau, so they can grow them during the rainy season along with corn and beans without spraying, nearly 10 thousand seedlings from different parts of the world were tested for resistance to late blight at one station during 1956–1957.

Work with forages has progressed rapidly in the Gulf Coast Tropics. A tall, canelike grass (Merkeron) has proved to be outstanding for cutting as green forage; cut 4 times in 7 months at the Cotaxtla tropical station, it produced 42 tons of dry matter per hectare. Eighty-five different legumes, in 20 different genera, some of which appear quite promising, have been studied in the introduction garden.

Thus the Rockefeller Foundation, through an intensive research and development program, in cooperation with the government, has made much new information available to Mexican agriculturists. The results are already evident in increased production of many crops. Young men have been trained to carry on and expand the work. In 1957, 88 young Mexican technicians worked in various phases of the program. Young technicians from other Latin American countries also have received training—26 during 1955–1956.

A similar program was started in Colombia in 1950, also in close cooperation with the Ministry of Agriculture. The research projects involve the development of improved varieties, better methods of soil management, and more economical means of controlling plant diseases and pests. They are intended also to provide training for young Colombian agronomists who will then carry forward the work. An animal husbandry, poultry, and veterinary project has also been initiated.

As an example of practical results, we may take the records of sales of seed during the first 4 years after the seed increase and distribution program was begun. During that period, farmers bought 1,670 tons of corn, 2,050 tons of wheat, and 850 tons of barley seed—enough to plant 100,400 acres in corn, 29,300 acres in wheat, and 17,100 acres in barley. The increased return from these plantings (assuming 30 percent higher yields from the use of improved varieties) was approximately equal to the amount spent by the Ministry of Agriculture on all its agricultural research activities over the 7 years since the joint program with the Foundation was initiated.

Thus, farmers were recognizing the value of improved varieties and were no doubt selling seed from these varieties to their neighbors. At the same time, better soil management and fertilization practices and practical insect and disease control measures were being used by more and more farmers.

THE FORD FOUNDATION has as its gen-eral purpose the advancement of human welfare.

It works toward this objective by making grants to individuals and institutions capable of organizing the search for answers to the problems that confront society. It also awards grants for fellowships, and has set up certain independent, self-governing organizations to undertake programs in special fields. It deals with many subjects.

Much of its resources is expended in the United States, and the work relates only indirectly to the solution of food and agricultural problems. The Foundation, however, supports a number of overseas development projects, which include some agricultural activities.

The work in Pakistan is an example. There, as in other countries, the Foundation operates primarily by giving grants of funds and making available the services of technical advisers to government or private agencies. Pakistan carries the main responsibility for leadership, administration, and financial support.

Under this program, technical institutes have been established in Karachi and Dacca to train technicians and technical supervisors. Home economics colleges have been established at Karachi and Lahore to train professional workers and teachers. Nine institutes have been established to train village workers. Foreign experts have been advisers in the development of effective planning organizations. A modern agricultural college has been designed for construction at Peshawar. Two centers have been planned for East Pakistan and West Pakistan to provide refresher training for primary and secondary teachers, supervisors, and administrators. An international youth exchange was organized whereby Pakistan farm boys visited American farm families while American boys visited Pakistan farm families.

The Ford Foundation has concentrated its support in 13 countries of the Near East, Asia, and the Far East. According to its 1957 annual report, the Foundation was considering extending its program to Africa and Latin America and to the Asian countries where it was not then operating.

THE COUNCIL on Economic and Cultural Affairs began in 1953. It has a small budget and has limited its activities to quite a narrow field. It is an example of a useful type of endeavor, sponsored on a small scale, through private means.

The Council, whose headquarters are in New York, restricts its activities to rural development in Asia. Its program embraces aspects of agricultural economics, community development, rural sociology, and extension education. Activities are aimed at improving the managerial ability of the farmers, gaining a better understanding of the social and cultural factors that must be taken into account in planning and carrying out development programs, and sharpening the educational tools on which the programs depend.

The Council grants fellowships for qualified persons to study abroad, provides visiting professors at key institutions, cooperates in regional training centers, provides books and equipment, and makes special grants for pilot research projects.

One activity, implemented through a grant to FAO, is a study of the farm management aspects of the mechanization of rice culture, an operation that has been carried out mostly with human and animal power. In a machine age, agricultural leaders and farmers themselves naturally look to the machine to bring relief from the drudgery of producing and harvesting a rice crop.

The first problem in many areas is to secure the basic information on farm management practices and labor requirements that is essential to determining where mechanization of any or all of the processes of rice culture may be justified economically. Surveys have been made and international meetings have been held to bring together existing information. Training courses have been conducted, and specialists have visited countries to stimulate interest, train workers to conduct studies, and otherwise try to answer this manysided question.

Other activities sponsored by the Council and aimed at bettering food production and levels of rural living in Asia, include (as examples) grants for a farm management study concerning the application of recommended practices on farms in southern Luzon (the Philippines), a farm management survey in Negros Oriental (also in the Philippines), a sample survey of land and farm records in West Pakistan, assistance in establishing an agricultural economics department at Kasetsart University in Thailand, and support of a farm management research institute at the University of Hokkaido in Japan.

The Council also provides for fellowships for advanced study in the United States, sends visiting professors to selected institutions, and makes grants for books and other educational materials in its specialized field.

HELPING OUR neighbors at home and abroad has become a tradition among Americans—a tradition that is being carried forward abroad by the International Cooperation Administration in the so-called "Point IV" program, by private foundations, through participation by the United States Government in international agencies that carry out programs for the benefit of all their member countries, and other means.

But there are reasons other than good neighborliness for our interest in such activities—reasons that we might group under the phrase "enlightened selfishness."

Bringing plant and animal pests and diseases under control in any country reduces the danger of having them brought to the United States.

As economies of other countries are strengthened, the possibilities of trade are enhanced, including better outlets for our agricultural products.

As the efficiency of production increases, the agricultural products we import should be available at relatively lower prices. The complex problems of supply and demand and the conditions of trade can be resolved only if representatives of the countries concerned sit down together to exchange information and ideas and to find practical solutions.

The United States has profited a great deal from plant exploration and the introduction of new crops and of livestock. We may yet gain much from further activities in this field, however—not only from exploration for yet unused plants but also for improved types of plants and livestock.

For those reasons and others, cooperation among countries will continue to be important to American farmers and to all Americans.

Such activities will almost certainly grow in importance, because developments in rapid communication and transportation will inevitably shrink the world and bring countries into closer relationships and because the relative position of the United States in the world pattern of availability of food may change.

If one projects on a giant graph the figures I cited at the beginning as to the growth of world population and the possession of arable land, he will see the size of the problem of how to feed people.

He will see that the United States will be faced then—in 2000 A.D., say—with quite different problems of production, internal distribution and international trade in agricultural products than we now face.

Population increases will have led to increased pressures on the land. With less land available per person, it will be necessary to intensify the search for more efficient methods of crop and livestock production. Problems of intercountry trade and distribution within countries are almost certain to increase.

Thus it will become more and more important for nations to exchange information, on technical and economic matters, to agree on problems of trade, and to work together in other ways to insure adequate levels of nutrition for their peoples.

The many uncertainties make it impossible to predict population-food relationships in any one country, or in the world as a whole, in some distant year, or even in a not-very-distant year such as 2000, but some trends seem inevitable. Viewed in this light, the activities of international agencies and foundations that are aimed at improving nutrition and levels of living in all countries take on new significance.

RALPH W. PHILLIPS *is Director of International Organization Affairs, Foreign Agricultural Service, the Department of Agriculture. He formerly was Deputy Director, Agriculture Division, Food and Agriculture Organization of the United Nations in Rome. A specialist in animal physiology and genetics, Dr. Phillips first turned his attention to international food problems when he was sent to China and India in 1943–1944 by the Department of State as an adviser on food production problems. He participated in the planning of the FAO program in an advisory capacity during 1944–1946 and late in 1946 joined the FAO staff where for 10 years he took part in many international activities aimed at improving agricultural production, human nutrition, and levels of living.*

There is considerable evidence, both scientific and resulting from practical experience in manufacturing industries, that the health and productivity of workers are greatly dependent upon the foods they eat.—ROBERT S. GOODHART, M.D.

Call it malnutrition, call it undernourishment, call it dietary deficiency or what you will—when men and women and children fail to eat the foods that give them full life and vigor, they are in fact starving.—M. L. WILSON.

Sharing Our Bounty

HOWARD P. DAVIS

THE Department of Agriculture, other Government agencies, the President, Senators, and Congressmen have received thousands of letters asking:

"Why don't you give away your food surpluses to hungry people who need it?"

"Why does the Government continue to hoard huge mounds of stinking butter and all sorts of food until it spoils, while millions of people at home and abroad are going hungry?"

At the same time, there were those who said: "Why are you sending so much of this food overseas? Charity begins at home. Many pensioners, unemployed, and other needy people in this country could use this food."

The questions make the problem seem far simpler than it really is. They do, however, reflect the public's concern over the "farm problem," the enormous cost of storing the commodities, and the moral question of the waste of good food while people who need it cannot buy it.

A PART of the answer is that we have been donating surplus foods to needy people.

In the 5 fiscal years that ended June 30, 1958, the Department of Agriculture donated 9.3 billion pounds of surplus food—at a cost to the Government of 2.1 billion dollars—to an estimated 80 million persons in this country and 87 other countries.

Besides that, the International Cooperation Administration (the Federal agency responsible generally for foreign aid) donated 6.1 billion pounds of surplus food, costing 441 million dollars, to foreign countries in those 5 years to help meet emergency or disaster needs.

Surplus food was donated in fiscal 1958 for use in domestic school lunch programs serving 13.6 million children. In addition, 1.4 million needy persons in institutions and 4.7 million needy persons living in family groups were benefited by Department-donated food. Thus about one out of nine persons in this country were receiving dividends out of our overabundance of food production.

The foods making up these domestic donations included butter, cheese, nonfat dry milk, flour, cornmeal, rice, and beans. The schools—which have first priority on the available supply—also received dried eggs, peanut butter, and canned grapefruit sections.

681

Foreign donations in 1958 went to an estimated 60 million needy persons through the efforts of 20 voluntary agencies in the United States. In accordance with the policy of meeting all domestic requests for surplus food before declaring foods available for donation elsewhere, enough nonfat dry milk, cheese, flour, and cornmeal were available to supply the overseas program for the entire year. Rice was available for overseas distribution during the first half of fiscal 1958.

The total amounts and cost of foods donated in 1958 were: Domestic, 872 million pounds, costing 185 million dollars; foreign, 2 billion pounds, costing 273 million dollars.

Various kinds and amounts of commodities have been available for domestic donation. Besides those that I named, they have included at one time or another beef and beef products, pork and pork products, poultry and poultry products, lard, shortening, oils, fruit, and vegetables. Foreign donations also have included butter and butter oil, cottonseed oil, shortening, and beans.

As to the waste of Government-owned surplus food, the Department's losses through spoilage have been held to the lowest amounts normally experienced under good commercial practice through rotating stocks and periodic inspection.

These food stocks are acquired by the Government under the mandatory price-support and permissive surplus removal programs.

The price-support program is designed to guarantee a reasonable price to the farmer for certain specified commodities. This is done by a number of methods, including loans and purchases, which in turn require the Department actually to take physical possession of large quantities of food from time to time. All such foods must meet high quality standards applied by Federal inspectors. The food is then stored by the Government in more or less unprocessed form until it can be sold back into the market without disrupting it. If these foods cannot be sold or bartered, they are made available for donation in order to prevent waste.

Surplus removal programs for commodities not under price support usually involve the direct purchase by the Department of more perishable, nonstorable foods, to the extent needed to strengthen the farmer's market and in the amounts that can be donated over a relatively short period of time to domestic recipients. The food does not ordinarily go into Federal storage under these programs but is shipped directly to State agencies for distribution.

Foods donated under both types of programs are usually processed, packaged, and delivered in carload lots by the Federal Government to receiving points designated by the recipient agencies.

THE BASIC authorizations for domestic donation are in section 32 of the act of August 25, 1935, as amended (Public Law 320, 74th Cong.), and section 416 of the Agricultural Act of 1949, as amended.

Under section 32 and related legislation, the Department of Agriculture is authorized to donate to schools and for relief purposes food that has been acquired for the purpose of removing market-depressing surpluses. These donations also carry out one of the general purposes of section 32—that is, to increase domestic consumption.

Section 416 provides for the donation of foods acquired by the Department as a result of price-support programs in order to prevent waste. Under this legislation, these foods may be donated to the Bureau of Indian Affairs for needy Indians, to schools for school lunches, and to needy persons residing in institutions or at home.

Foods donated under both these sections are distributed in the same way. The Department donates them, processed and packaged and delivered free of charge, in carload lots to State distributing agencies at receiving points the States designate. Under agreements between the Department and

State agencies, the States assume the responsibility for the proper handling, care, and distribution of the donated foods to eligible schools, institutions, and needy families.

The Department lays down general principles of eligibility in accordance with the laws, but the determination of the eligibility of individual recipient agencies and families is the responsibility of the States, in line with their State and local statutes and welfare standards. Title passes to the States upon receipt of the cars of food, but it is a conditional passage of title, and the Department retains a legal interest in them to see that they are properly cared for and distributed.

An important consideration in the States' distribution is that the foods must not replace normal food expenditures but are in addition to the food the recipients buy. The very purpose of the legislation is to secure additional consumption in a way that will not interfere with normal marketings. This consideration rules out a number of worthwhile, nonprofit organizations (such as university dining halls) or medium-income families and restricts the program to the neediest. If such food donations replaced normal purchases of food, the Department would have to purchase just that much more to remove surpluses and support prices to the farmer.

SECTION 416 also provides for donation of foods held by the Department over and above domestic requests to voluntary American agencies and intergovernmental organizations for distribution to needy persons overseas.

Many United States voluntary agencies, such as CARE, Church World Service, Catholic Relief Services (National Catholic Welfare Council), Joint Jewish Distribution Committee, Lutheran World Relief, American Friends Service Committee, and others have participated over the years in the program. The United Nations Children's Fund (UNICEF) has been the principal intergovernmental agency.

To be eligible for the donations, the programs of the voluntary agencies must be approved by (and the agencies must be registered with) the Advisory Committee on Voluntary Foreign Aid of the International Cooperation Administration. The individual country programs of the agencies are reviewed by the United States overseas missions of International Cooperation Administration. Their recommendations are forwarded to Washington, where they are reviewed by the Interagency Staff Committee on Surplus Disposal before they are approved by the Department of Agriculture.

The foods for approved foreign donations may be processed and packaged by the Department and shipped to appropriate ports of export free of charge to the voluntary agency. Title passes to the agency at the United States port. The United States in many instances pays also for the ocean freight to the foreign port.

The title to the donated foods passes to the voluntary agency at the port of export, but the United States Government retains an interest in the proper distribution of the food to the ultimate recipient. Under agreement with the Department of Agriculture, the voluntary agencies are responsible for the proper distribution in accordance with United States regulations and instructions and are liable for any losses due to negligence. The food must be distributed only to needy people and in a manner that will not interfere with normal trade.

Since one objective of the program is to express the desire of our people to help the needy in other lands, the legislation provides that all packages shall be labeled "Donated by the people of the United States." The agencies are also encouraged to use all possible means of informing the recipients of the origin of the donations.

Agency supervision of the program must be carried out through a United States citizen who is residing in the country during the period the donated food is distributed. Additional assistance and review of operations are provided through representatives of the United States Government in the host country. Actual distribution in the foreign countries is carried out through counterpart voluntary agencies, other indigenous voluntary agencies, and official agencies.

THE UNITED NATIONS Children's Fund (UNICEF) receives donations of nonfat dry milk for its maternal, child health, and other health programs in many countries.

These donations are made under the legislation, regulations, and instructions that govern the donations made to voluntary American agencies. Because of its organizational status with the United Nations, however, UNICEF has not been required to have a United States citizen to supervise distribution in each country. Also, because it operates through foreign governments under arrangements different from those in effect for the voluntary American agencies, UNICEF pays the ocean freight on the donated dry milk. It has never requested any of the other foods available for foreign donations.

SOME FOOD was donated by the Government after the First World War, when war-surplus stocks were liquidated, but large-scale donation of food began when the Federal Government undertook programs to stabilize farm prices during the depressed 1930's. After section 32 was enacted in August 1935, large amounts of surplus foods were acquired by the Federal Government and distributed primarily to needy families.

The program operated through State welfare agencies in that depression period. The agencies had access to ample Works Progress Administration labor to help with distribution. Nearly 13 million needy persons received donated foods in 1939.

The quantities of food available for donation during the Second World War gradually went down, and the participation of needy families dropped to an insignificant number. Some distribution to schools and institutions continued. The availability of some food for the purpose came about largely because the farmers were encouraged by price incentives to produce at the maximum. That and occasional miscalculations in the purchase programs of lend-lease and the Armed Forces meant the Government acquired food from time to time that was in excess of its needs and could not be sold back into the trade without disrupting markets. These foods were then donated to all available outlets. State organizations for the distribution of surplus foods were largely disbanded, and the limited wartime donations were generally distributed through local agencies, which entered into agreements with the Department.

The situation changed quickly after the Second World War. Farmers had been guaranteed prices so they could gear up to maximum production during the war—to buy equipment, use less productive land, apply more fertilizer, and so on. When the abnormal war demand fell off, the Department had to acquire large stocks of some commodities in order to stabilize farm income during the transition from war to peace. Without a cash market for these foods, it was necessary again for the Department to donate them for distribution to eligible domestic outlets.

A new problem arose in this period. Whereas most of the food previously acquired had been nonstorable, perishable goods, the Department began to find itself faced with tremendous inventories of dried eggs, dried milk, and cheese. As a war measure, the Government had encouraged practically a whole new dehydration industry. Many of these plants were closed soon after the war, but the production of dried eggs continued beyond the point of the peacetime demand. As to dried milk, the whole pattern of dairy production was changing, and more and more milk was going into manufactured products.

Before section 416 of the 1949 act was enacted, the Department had had limited authority to dispose of foods except through sales for dollars at prices that would reimburse the agency for their total expenditures for the food sold. Section 416 enabled the Department to donate its food stocks at home and abroad.

The existing stocks of dried eggs had barely been disposed of, however, when the Korean war again reversed the whole situation. The demand for food again reached high levels, and the amounts and kinds of food available for donation dropped. Most of it went to the school lunch programs. High employment meant a reduction in the demand for food assistance for needy families, and, as the stocks of food for donation also decreased, few communities felt it worth while to maintain the necessary machinery for distribution to families.

Following the armistice in Korea, agriculture again had the difficult task of readjusting itself to an uneasy peacetime economy. The Government's inventories of food began to build up to record amounts. Stocks of dairy products, rice, food grains, and cottonseed oil were accumulating at alarming rates by 1954 and 1955. Foreign countries faced serious dollar shortages, and our export prices were high. Our consumption at home was already at relatively high levels. There was little hope of any sizable reduction in the rates of Government acquisitions.

The Agricultural Trade Development and Assistance Act was adopted in 1954 as a way out of this dilemma until a more permanent answer to the "farm problem" could be found.

Title I of the act provided for sales of agricultural commodities for foreign currencies. Title II provided for donations of agricultural commodities to friendly governments or peoples for "famine or other urgent or extraordinary relief."

Section 302 of title III amended section 416. The latter amendment permitted the Department to reprocess, package, and pay inland transportation in the United States on both domestic and foreign donations. This legislation facilitated the domestic donation program. Its major result was to expand greatly the foreign distribution to needy people by voluntary American agencies. (Reimbursement for ocean freight had already been provided for relief shipments to many countries under the Mutual Security Act.)

Distribution overseas jumped from 184 million pounds in fiscal 1954 to 2 billion pounds in 1958. Subsequent amendments, which allowed the Department to process wheat and corn into flour and cornmeal and to provide additional funds for ocean freight, led to continuing expansion of the foreign program.

The expansion of foreign donations has led the voluntary agencies to expand their foreign staffs to insure an effective program and to inform the recipients about the nutritional value and use of the donated foods, some of which are unfamiliar to many peoples.

The expansion also raised some questions about policy: What will be the repercussions when these foods are no longer available? Are large-scale and nationwide programs the proper sphere for voluntary agencies, or should they be carried out on a United States Government-to-foreign government basis? Should these donations be planned on the basis of the most needy countries and as part of our total foreign relations policy?

These considerations have been largely in the hands of the voluntary agencies operating on a people-to-people basis limited only by local conditions, facilities, funds, and available staff. With the expansion of the program, the United States Government has had to concern itself increasingly in the review of the country programs, their operations, and their economic and political effects.

The most far-reaching developments

in our donations since Korea have been abroad. The domestic program also has changed. The major domestic development was the growth in the size and scope of the needy-family program. The first sharp increase came early in 1954 because of unemployment in the coalfields. The drought and subsequent wet weather in the southwestern and southeastern farming regions further increased participation. A recession in early 1958 also caused more needy families to participate. The total number of recipients in needy families increased from 290 thousand in February 1954 to 4.7 million in June 1958.

Only 21 States were distributing surplus foods to needy families in 148 cities and counties in February 1954, but 44 States, the District of Columbia, and Puerto Rico were distributing these foods to needy families in 1,241 cities and counties in June 1958.

IT'S HARD to give food away—and expensive, too. To most people, including those who have written the letters I mentioned in the beginning, nothing could be simpler than giving good, wholesome food away to people who have too little to eat.

Actually, these donation programs require setting up and maintaining domestic and foreign distribution systems that parallel our vast commercial food distribution network in every aspect except advertising and sales— and even in those respects it is necessary to provide for the education of recipients on the value and use of the donated foods.

The physical handling of large quantities of food from original storage points, to processor or packager, to receiving points, to local storage points, to the ultimate recipient without loss or spoilage, is a complicated task.

It is all the more difficult because one has to use noncommercial channels and organizations that have not been set up primarily to handle food. Also, the cost of the distribution falls rather heavily on local agencies. They must provide adequate supervision, the facilities and manpower for handling and distributing the food, and personnel to determine which institutions and families are eligible to receive the food.

Much of the distribution in many instances is carried out through temporary or improvised facilities and with volunteer workers. Since the greatest need for donated food is often in the poorest areas, the lack of adequate funds, facilities, and personnel is apt to limit the use of the program.

A major difficulty in developing and maintaining experienced organizations and facilities is the fluctuation in the volume and kinds of commodities available for donation. That is especially true of domestic donations because under section 32 the need for surplus-removal purchases among the perishable commodities may vary sharply from one crop year to the next.

Many communities have difficulty in maintaining an adequate delivery organization for surplus food when they have no guarantee that enough food will be available to justify the cost of delivery operations. Although the Government has donated food ever since 1933, the program has had to operate under the assumption that the then-current availability of surplus foods was a temporary situation.

The problems have been more acute in foreign lands. To begin with, there are many areas of the world that have never had relief programs for the needy. "Social security" has traditionally been "family security." The concept that any agency outside the family or clan is concerned about the needy as individuals or as a group is difficult for them to grasp. It is particularly difficult for them to believe there is no ulterior motive—no quid pro quo in food donations from the United States.

Many of these countries have always had large groups of the very poor. The better-off people are used to accepting the poor, sick, and starving and regard them as inevitable and hopeless. Even some of the newer, more democratic governments in their awakening social consciousness concentrate on the better-off groups and accept the hopelessness of the large group of very poor.

To a much greater extent than in the United States, food is produced, processed, and consumed on a local basis in many countries. They have no experience in large-scale food distribution. With the possible exception of the larger cities, there are few warehouses, no cold storage, few railroads, and few roads. Our donated foods are often unloaded from a ship into a lighter, held for some time in port storage—which may be in the open or perhaps under just a roof—carried part way to the interior by rail or truck, and then by boat, or cart and, often, on men's backs to the interior.

As I pointed out, even though the United States Government donates the food and pays for processing, packaging, and delivering it to the States or foreign country, the cost to the participating agencies is sizable despite the facilities furnished without charge and volunteer labor.

Aside from assuring that the food is put to the most constructive use possible, the basic consideration in all these donation operations, both at home and abroad, is that they not displace normal markets.

Frequently in places where the domestic need is greatest, the commercial food industry likewise is suffering from the generally low level of economic activity. To the extent that food donations interfered with normal food sales and imports, the program would intensify existing economic problems. Although donations of a specific food may temporarily reduce the normal local sale of that commodity, every effort must be made to maintain the total amount of food purchases of recipient groups. The domestic wholesalers, retailers, and to some extent local processors have been highly critical of the program when the number of recipients or the

quantities of a certain commodity have reached sizable proportions.

The problem of possible disruption of foreign markets has created even more far-reaching effects as the foreign donations have increased. The New York Times on November 5, 1958, in reporting on the annual meeting of the General Agreement on Tariffs and Trade (GATT) in Geneva, Switzerland, said:

"United States farm surplus disposal policies have brought renewed criticism from some agricultural nations of the West. . . .

"These commodities were exported in private sales for local currencies, bartered for strategic materials, included in Mutual Security Act aid, or given to needy persons in the United States and 85 other nations.

"This has prompted agricultural exporters like Canada, Australia, and Denmark to charge unfair competition and disruption of world markets. Their criticism extended to domestic farm policy in the United States which, these nations asserted, has been responsible for the accumulation of large agricultural surpluses. . . .

"United States farm surplus disposals have 'seriously cut into Canada's export markets, particularly for wheat,' said Maurice Schwarzmann, a Canadian representative at the trade talks. . . .

"Three years ago the GATT nations agreed to consultations among themselves to avoid disturbing world markets with farm surplus disposals. 'These consultations have become increasingly effective,' said Godfrey A. Rattigan of Australia, 'but the problem of surplus disposals seems no nearer solution. . . .'

"Australia feared that surplus disposals might become a permanent part of international trade, Mr. Rattigan said. 'A real danger in surplus disposals is that they will lead to a deterioration of the balance-of-payments position of commercial suppliers' and a contraction in the overall level of world trade, he commented. . . .

"Finn Gundelach of Denmark called for broader and more effective consultations.

"He cited 'a very serious experience this year with butter, where marketing of surplus products created complete confusion on the market.' Butter is one of Denmark's major exports. 'Prices dropped to a level only slightly above the level before World War II,' Mr. Gundelach said."

The article concluded: "Several of the GATT nations paid tribute to United States donations of farm products, distributed through voluntary relief agencies and the United Nations Children's Fund. . . ."

Although it must be noted that the major fears and criticisms are directed at the various sales programs and we are complimented on our donation programs, every precaution must be taken to insure that the donated foods are consumed by persons who would not be able to buy them.

During visits to 22 countries in Europe, Asia, and Africa in 1957, I was repeatedly assured by country officials, voluntary agencies, and our own diplomatic posts that there was little or no interference with trade.

Certainly my own observations have confirmed that our donated food was going to very needy people. Considering the unfamiliarity with some of the foods, the destitution of the recipients and the volume of food moved, the "black marketing" was little.

Perhaps the single greatest difficulty in Government food donations is that the foods available for donation are limited by agricultural legislation, funds, and considerations, although the program is regarded as (and is) a "welfare" or "foreign aid" program. The recipients and the public cannot understand why the Government gives them flour, cornmeal, or rice and no meat (or, overseas, no oils).

Worldwide publicity about our large agricultural surpluses has led many people to believe that the Department of Agriculture owns tremendous stocks of all sorts of food. We have had a wide variety of foods for donation over the years, but at any one time the variety is usually rather limited, and at no time do we take most of them into inventory or storage.

Commodities purchased for "surplus removal" under section 32 are limited to the amounts that eligible domestic outlets can accept and consume within a relatively short period. They may be held in storage by the Department of Agriculture for brief periods to facilitate orderly distribution, but no inventories are built up of these commodities as with the mandatory price-support commodities, such as the dairy products and grains.

Because conditions in the farm market determine the kinds and volume of surplus food the Department acquires, the donation program cannot be geared in any important degree to the preferences or nutritional needs of the recipients. Thus the Department may be offering flour to the needy overseas when they would prefer rice and actually, from a nutritional standpoint, need oils and fats. That is not to say, however, that preferences and needs are not taken into consideration in determining which of the available foods, and how much of them, should go to various outlets and areas.

WITH ALL these problems and limitations, why have we continued the donations, and what have been the constructive results?

The most obvious reason for continuing the program has been that the Government has continued to acquire various foods from time to time under farm measures enacted by the Congress. Most of these price-stabilizing measures could not have been carried out without the donation program. The food donations over the years have disposed of the surpluses constructively without seriously disrupting markets at home or abroad.

Aside from the agricultural implications, let us first consider the results in this country.

In the first place, many millions of needy Americans have had more to eat and a better diet than they otherwise would have had. Many of us consider grapefruit, for example, as an important part of our diets, but families who got grapefruit free during the 1930's were entirely unfamiliar with it. They soon learned to eat it and like it.

The introduction of new or unfamiliar foods to many families has been beneficial not only from a nutritional standpoint. It has contributed to the development of new and expanded markets for a more stable and diversified agriculture. This has been especially true with fruit and vegetables and dairy products. Millions of people in low-income groups have learned the value and use of nonfat dry milk. Many of them had never before included much milk in their diets, and all of them were able to obtain much more milk than they would have been able to buy.

Some of the donated foods, such as flour, cornmeal, rice, and beans, have always had high consumption rates in the low-income groups. The preponderance of such foods in the diets of many families—which lack sufficient milk, fruit, vegetables, and animal protein—has concerned nutritionists.

One could argue that donating such foods does not help needy families nutritionally and (because the foods are a large part of their normal food purchases) must disrupt regular markets. That is not true. Low-income families spend a high percentage of their income on food. As they become aware of the importance of good nutrition and the elements of good diets, the donation of these staple foods permits them to use a larger portion of their food money for meats, fruit, and vegetables. Maybe a temporary, local disruption of markets for the donated foods will occur, but the net result will be a greater and better total consumption of food.

Some of us may overlook the significant value of donated foods to many struggling, poorly financed institutions that care for needy people. They have been helped greatly over the years to provide much more adequate meals for their unfortunate ones.

Few people question the contribution of the National School Lunch Program to the nutrition and nutrition education of our schoolchildren—a program that owes its beginning in large part to the early distribution of surplus foods to schools.

Many times over the years surplus foods have been available, through the State and local direct distribution organizations, for relief in times of disaster. Standing procedure has provided for State and local officials to donate stocks of surplus food on hand or to order additional supplies for donation to emergency agencies set up to care for the victims of floods or other natural disasters.

If the commercial channels are destroyed in some major crisis and it is necessary for the Government to supply food to stricken areas, the present system of direct distribution by the Government could be used as the nucleus of an immediate emergency food distribution system. It could be used to get food to mass feeding centers and to families.

From a nutritional standpoint, the foods—particularly the dairy products—have made possible far better diets among foreign recipients. Since most of the donated foods were unfamiliar to many recipients, their most constructive use has depended to a large extent on the ability of the agencies to provide adequate information on the value and use of the foods. Good progress has been made in this direction, especially in clinics, institutions, and schools.

Much remains to be done, however. Although many local nurses, teachers, and volunteers have been instructed and appreciate the nutritional contribution of the food, it is difficult to communicate this to the large numbers of needy who cannot read.

One of the byproducts of the widespread distribution of large quantities of our food abroad should be some development of new markets for these commodities. If the needy themselves may not be able to buy them in the foreseeable future, the groups that are assisting in the distribution—the nurses, teachers, and volunteers—may represent a potential market.

Much has been reported on the results of the UNICEF maternal and child and other health and nutrition programs around the world. Certainly the United States contribution of about 100 million pounds of nonfat dry milk each year for UNICEF programs has been instrumental in the success of many of these programs. And just as certainly, these programs have represented a most constructive use of surplus foods from the United States.

FOOD DONATION to the needy overseas probably has not yet reached its full potential from the standpoint of the most constructive use of the food. Much more has been accomplished than is generally realized, however. Many millions of people have been fed. Some of them otherwise may have starved. Many more would have fallen easier prey to disease, and many who were sick would not have recovered.

Another point that cannot be denied: The food we have shipped abroad has helped greatly in the struggle to maintain world peace. Americans have given proof of their concern for the needy people, the little men, of other countries.

Our other foreign aid and economic development programs have been important and helpful, but often the local villagers have been unable to see and understand the benefits.

But milk, flour, cornmeal—something in his hand to eat—that is something the most remote, the lowliest, the poorest family can understand and appreciate. All the more because the food comes to them not as a result of prolonged diplomatic negotiation, not because of party membership, not because of army service or other obligation, but as a free expression of the American people's concern for the needy throughout the world.

That is enough, but it is not all.

Friendship begets friendship, and charity begets charity. American desires to help and to share have stimulated new concerns and new responsibilities among other peoples to care for their needy.

HOWARD P. DAVIS *has been the Assistant Director and Deputy Director of the Food Distribution Division, Agricultural Marketing Service, since 1950. He joined the Department of Agriculture in 1941 to assist in administering the Food Stamp Plan and later the direct distribution program. As a naval officer during the Second World War, he was stationed in 1945–1946 in Berlin, where he was alternate United States representative on the Four-Power Committee for Feeding Berlin.*

The new science of nutrition does more than show the way to better health and improved physique. It affords a solution to some of our most difficult social and economic problems. If its exponents speak with the authority warranted by the knowledge which they have acquired in recent years and use all their influence to get this knowledge applied, a review on nutrition and human welfare ten years hence may be a record of unprecedented advance in human welfare.— LORD JOHN BOYD-ORR.

School Lunches

MARVIN M. SANDSTROM

SERVING food in schools has become a generally accepted part of the American school system during the present century. To about two-thirds of the children in elementary and secondary schools a lunch service is now available.

Several factors have brought about this happy development.

One is that larger numbers of children cannot go home for lunch—because school districts have been consolidated and schools serve wider areas, mothers may work away from home, and the higher volume of traffic may make it wise to keep children at school at noon.

Secondly, authorities in health and nutrition, educators, social welfare groups, parent-teacher associations, and other community and civic organizations have given eager support to the idea of school lunch as a way to teach the facts of food.

Finally, all State governments have recognized school lunches as an auxiliary service in the public school system, and a number of them provide substantial sums for direct support of the programs.

The Congress has recognized, through the passage of the National School Lunch Act and other legislation, the school lunch program both as a nutrition measure and as an effective means of increasing consumption of agricultural commodities.

The Congress has given substantial support to school lunch programs in the form of appropriations and authorization to the Department of Agriculture for the donation of surplus foods.

Although we can assume that individual, isolated efforts to supply children with a lunch of sorts at school has existed at some time and in some places since the beginning of organized school systems, it is only in the past 100 years or so that we can see the outlines of a conscious attempt to meet at least part of a child's daily food requirements at school.

France was one of the first countries to provide school lunches on a national scale. Some programs were operated as early as 1849. Legislation in 1882 provided for use of local funds to support lunch programs in all schools. In England, Parliament in 1904 authorized local educational authorities to install facilities for preparing and serving food as part of the standard school equipment.

The experience in England and France is typical of the European continent. National legislation in nearly every country has supported lunch service.

The first instance on record of an organized school feeding operation in the United States was that of the Children's Aid Society of New York, which in 1853 opened the first of its vocational schools for the poor and served meals to all who attended.

The Star Center Association of Philadelphia organized municipal school feeding in elementary schools in 1894.

Two books did a great deal to stimulate interest in the movement. Robert Hunter, who wrote *Poverty* in 1904, and John Spargo, who wrote *Underfed School Children, the Problem and the Remedy* in 1906, estimated that several million children were undernourished in the United States, pointed out how Europe had attacked the problem of malnutrition by school feeding, and advocated a similar program for the United States.

School officials also began to recognize that malnutrition affected the ability of the child to learn at school. This recognition gave a quick stimulus for the initiating of a lunch program.

Many cities by 1910 were operating penny-lunch programs in elementary schools, often taking over the task formerly performed by voluntary societies. Small portions of food—a bowl of soup, bread and butter, or cocoa, for example—were sold for 1 to 3 cents during recess. These lunches mostly were self-supporting. They encouraged children to buy nourishing food with their lunch money.

The Department of Agriculture, in Farmers' Bulletin No. 712, in 1916 discussed the importance of an adequate lunch and suggested a number of simple dishes that could be served.

The bulletin stated: "The important elements of a child's diet are milk, supplemented at times by other protein-rich foods but never wholly omitted; bread or cereal food in other forms; butter or other foods containing much fat; vegetables and fruits; and sweets."

The bulletin urged that representative items from each of these food groups should be included in the lunch and stated pretty well the argument in favor of a school lunch program as it was viewed at that time:

"The basket lunch must usually be prepared at a time when the housekeeper is very busy. In places where there are shops near the school, therefore, children are sometimes given pennies with which to buy food at noon. They like this, of course, for it is a pleasure to make their own selections and they are glad to be relieved of carrying baskets.

"If they could choose wisely there would be no objection to this plan and it might even be good training in handling money and keeping accounts.

"In practice, however, it is found that the money is often spent in unclean places and for unwholesome foods; pickles and pies, or, at best, starchy foods and sweets are likely to make up the bill of fare, and in this way, the good effects of careful feeding at home are likely to be overcome.

". . . The meal at school is in some ways a better opportunity for training than those served at home. Unlike the other meals of the child's day, it is eaten during the hours which are set apart for education. The child's mind is, therefore, in a receptive condition, and every precaution which is taken to adapt the lunch to his physical and mental needs is likely to teach a lesson in food and nutrition, silently, to be sure, but effectively."

A survey in 86 cities, made by the Bureau of Municipal Research in 1918, revealed that there was some provision for lunches in high schools in 76 percent of the cities, but that service was maintained in only 25 percent of the elementary schools. The reason for the difference was time and distance— high school students came to school from widely scattered points, while elementary school pupils lived within walking distance of school.

Officials of only five of the high

schools with lunch programs indicated that they had been established to combat malnutrition—to the others, it was simply a convenient accessory to the school system.

Considerable interest was shown in school lunches in rural areas between 1900 and 1920. State and Federal extension workers in home economics cooperated in setting up plans for school lunches. A widely used arrangement was one by which the children contributed food for one hot dish to be prepared by the teacher as a supplement to the cold lunch brought from home. The emphasis was on some simple, inexpensive arrangement that would still meet the essentials of sanitation and nourishment. It called for, and got, a great deal of ingenuity on the part of teachers, parents, and school officials.

Schools soon began to link the school lunch with education in nutrition. The program in New York in 1910 aimed to provide one-fourth of a child's daily nutritional requirements. Publications stressed the importance of teaching children to drink milk. Charts prepared by the Department of Agriculture for schools showed the elements of a balanced, wholesome lunch—the prototype of today's Type A lunch under the National School Lunch Program.

The Director of School Lunch in Philadelphia in 1920 voiced several of the nutritional and educational objectives of today's School Lunch Program:

"The aim of the school lunch is twofold: To meet the food requirements of the child, helping to lay a foundation of physical vigor upon which the structure of mental training can be effectively built; and to serve as an educational factor, instilling wise food habits, offering an opportunity for lessons in courtesy and consideration, and providing a laboratory for the practical demonstration of allied subjects of study such as cooking, hygiene, buying."

The depressed 1930's brought a new stimulus. Many teachers contributed their own money to feed pupils who came hungry to school. Organizations like the American Red Cross and the American Friends Service Committee undertook to feed poor children in some localities. State and local governments passed legislation to encourage lunch programs. Many of them made appropriations for school feeding. Probably the largest of the earlier appropriations was that authorized by the State of New York, which in 1934 appropriated 100 thousand dollars of relief funds for free lunches and milk for poor children.

Fifteen States passed laws by 1937 specifically authorizing school boards to operate lunchrooms. The laws commonly proposed the serving of meals at cost—usually the cost of the food alone—but four States made special provisions for needy children.

The Reconstruction Finance Corporation made loans in 1932 and 1933 to several towns in Missouri to pay people for preparing and serving school lunches. This work was expanded the next 2 years under the Civil Works Administration and the Federal Emergency Relief Administration.

When the Works Progress Administration was created in 1935, school lunch work was assigned to the Division of Professional and Service Projects as a permanent phase of their operation. Funds were provided to employ cooks and servers in schools throughout the United States and in Puerto Rico.

A major incentive to the school lunch program has been the evolution of agricultural policies and legislation whereby surplus agricultural commodities have been available to schools. Surplus foods were distributed on a limited basis for free lunches as early as 1932.

This was expanded following the passage of Public Law 320, 74th Congress, on August 24, 1935. Section 32 of this legislation provided a permanent annual appropriation to the Department of Agriculture for the general purposes of expanding domestic and export markets for agricultural commodities.

Under the legislation, the Department instituted a direct purchase and distribution program to help farmers solve the problem of disposing of commodities that were surplus to the normal commercial market. These surplus foods were distributed to needy people in charitable institutions and family units and to nonprofit school lunch programs.

The Department in 1939 announced a special program to expand school feeding through the use of surplus foods, distributed on the basis of the number of needy children served. This initial relief or emergency aspect of the program gradually shifted to one in which Federal assistance was directed toward the promotion of a broadly based, general program with the dual objective of improving the health of children and encouraging the increased consumption of agricultural commodities.

Distribution of surplus foods was made in 1938 to 9,100 schools, serving about 540 thousand children. This program grew rapidly, reaching 2.5 million children in 1940 and 6.2 million in 1942. In the spring of 1943, when wartime food demands had substantially reduced the volume of surplus foods, the Department of Agriculture inaugurated a cash reimbursement program to pay for a part of the food purchased locally for the lunch program. Participating schools were required to meet certain nutritional standards in the lunches served, provide free meals for children unable to pay, and operate their lunch programs on a nonprofit basis.

The Congress in 1944 for the first time authorized a specific amount of section 32 funds for the operation of the school lunch and penny milk programs and provided that such activities could be carried out without regard to the existence of a surplus.

Then, in 1945, legislation appropriating funds for the Department of Agriculture spelled out for the first time the conditions under which Federal assistance would be provided.

This legislation provided the cornerstone on which was built the National School Lunch Act, enacted in 1946. This is the basic authority for the present National School Lunch Program and provides for assistance to the States in the establishment, maintenance, operation, and expansion of the school lunch program.

The report from the House Committee on Agriculture, which recommended passage of the proposed legislation, said, in part:

"The national school lunch bill provides basic, comprehensive legislation for aid, in general, to the States in the operation of school lunch programs as permanent and integral parts of their school systems, and thus supersedes the prevailing arrangement of a temporary year-to-year program based only upon the authority contained in the annual appropriations therefor for the Department of Agriculture. Such aid, heretofore extended by Congress through the Department of Agriculture, has, for the past 10 years, proven of exceptional benefit to children, schools, and agriculture of the country as a whole, but the necessity for now coordinating the work throughout the Nation, and especially to encourage and increase the financial participation and active control by the several States makes it desirable that permanent enabling legislation take the place of the present temporary legislative structure.

"It appears to this committee that the bill will effectively advance two desirable objectives: the improvement of the health and well-being of the Nation's youth, both immediately and in the period of postwar reconversion, of a substantial market for agricultural production. In this latter objective the committee has in mind not only the maintenance of the present high level of production but the important consideration of a ready and socially desirable means of disposing of irregularly occurring commodity surpluses, a characteristic of agricultural production, which, if left uncontrolled on the market, disrupt the market and seriously injure the ordinary economic processes of pricing and distribution. . . . As to the aspect of children's welfare all surveys point to the need for better nutrition for the Nation's children, and the effective manner in which the school-lunch program meets this need. . . .

"The educational features of a properly chosen diet served at a school should not be underemphasized. Not only is the child taught what a good diet consists of, but his parents and family likewise are indirectly instructed. This also has a direct connection with the second objective of the legislation, for the inculcation of good food habits in the youth of the Nation must soon show up in the Nation's food consumption and the American farmer cannot help but benefit."

UNDER THE National School Lunch Act, basic responsibility for administration is in the hands of State educational agencies. The Secretary of Agriculture is responsible for the establishment of national standards and the maintenance of general supervision. The State educational agency in more than half of the States is not permitted by law to administer the program in private schools; nonprofit private schools in those States enter into agreements with the Department of Agriculture.

The annual appropriation made available under the National School Lunch Act is used for three purposes.

Not less than 75 percent is apportioned to the States under a formula that takes into account the number of school-age children in each State and its per capita income. These funds are used to reimburse participating schools for a part of the cost of local food purchases.

A part of the appropriation is used by the Department of Agriculture to make large-volume purchases of food for distribution to participating schools. These purchases are authorized by section 6 of the act and are designed to provide foods that will help schools meet the lunch standards. Federal administrative expenses are also financed out of the appropriation.

The direct appropriation for the program in the fiscal year 1959 was 110 million dollars. Of this amount, 93.6 million dollars were apportioned to the States, about 1.7 million dollars were budgeted for Federal administrative costs, and approximately 14.7 million dollars were reserved for the direct purchase by the Department of selected foods for distribution to schools participating in the program.

The Congress also provided in the 1959 Appropriation Act for the transfer of 35 million dollars from section 32 for the purchase of commodities in accordance with section 6 of the National School Lunch Act. Foods purchased were those in relatively plentiful supply that would help meet program requirements.

Further assistance is provided to school lunch programs in the form of surplus foods that are acquired by the Department as a result of price support and surplus removal programs. The amount of such foods varies considerably from year to year, depending on market conditions. The value of surplus foods distributed to schools was 132 million dollars in 1957 and about 75 million dollars in 1958.

To participate in the National School Lunch Program, a school must agree to operate its lunch program on a nonprofit basis, serve nutritious lunches that meet the standards established by the Department on the basis of tested nutritional research, and offer the lunch at a reduced price or free to those children determined by local school authorities to be unable to pay the full price of the lunch.

The standards established by the Department of Agriculture are expressed in terms of the broad food groups that make up a well-balanced lunch. The groups are: Protein-rich foods, served in a main dish or in a main dish and one other menu item; two or more vegetables or fruit, or both; whole-grain or enriched bread; butter or fortified margarine; fluid whole milk, served as a beverage.

When the foods from these five categories are used in the amounts specified in the pattern and in combination with other foods needed to prepare certain dishes and to satisfy young appetites, the lunches generally meet one-third of the daily dietary allowances recommended by the National Academy of Sciences-National Research Council for children 10 to 12 years old. Thus, by following these standards, each participating school is able to develop menus that are adapted both to local food preferences and to local food supplies. At the same time nutritional balance is assured.

Major responsibility for program operations rests with State and local governments. State educational agencies undertake a broad and varied program in the supervision of school lunch operations in individual schools. They carry out a planned informational program under which advice and guidance are provided to individual lunch programs on such subjects as planning the menus, purchases of food and equipment, sanitation practices, and management.

Each State agency also carries out a review operation, with visits to schools to offer help in management problems.

The State educational agencies also provide inservice training for local school lunch workers, largely in workshops for groups in cities, districts, and the State.

Assistance of a technical nature also is provided by the Federal Government. Included are aids in menu planning, food buying, standardized quantity recipes, food handling and storage, and equipment requirements for preparing and serving food. Help also is given in the training of lunchroom personnel.

THE NATIONAL SCHOOL LUNCH program was in operation in 1959 in public and private schools in all 50 States, the District of Columbia, Puerto Rico, the Virgin Islands, and Guam.

During the 1957–1958 school year, the peak month of participation was December, when a daily average of 11.5 million children were eating lunches in programs receiving Federal assistance.

Detailed information on pupil participation is available from a study conducted by the Department of Agriculture in March 1957. The study covers operations only in public schools, but it gives us the first comprehensive coverage on a national basis of the various types of operations.

In March 1957, 60,489 public elementary and secondary schools were operating some type of lunch service. This number represented a little more than 57 percent of the 105,966 public schools in the country.

A large proportion of the more than 45 thousand schools without a lunch service were in communities of less than 100 thousand population and were small schools. Many of them, however, did provide children with an opportunity to drink milk at some time during the schoolday.

Seven out of eight (86.8 percent) of the schools with a lunch service were offering complete plate lunches under the National School Lunch Program. Nearly 7 thousand additional schools were offering plate lunches to children outside the National School Lunch Program. The remaining schools (1,169) provided only an a la carte food service.

A substantial majority of the almost 33 million children enrolled in public schools in March 1957 had access to a school lunch service. About 22 million children were enrolled in schools participating in the National School Lunch Program. Student enrollment in schools offering a plate lunch service outside the program totaled 3,109,000. An additional 1 million children were enrolled in schools with only an a la carte food service.

Not all children having access to plate lunches actually participate in the program. In March 1957, a daily average of 45 percent of the enrollment in schools in the National School Lunch Program purchased plate lunches. The daily average of plate lunches served in other schools was equal to 33 percent of the enrollment.

Many factors account for the non-participation. For example, some children live close to school and have their lunches at home. Some bring packed lunches from home. Participation in many schools continues to be restricted by the limited food service facilities available. Moreover, because all children do not regularly participate in the school's lunch program, the percentage of child enrollment that purchases plate lunches one or more times during the month is higher than the daily average indicates.

FOR THE 1957–1958 school year, it was estimated that total expenditures from all sources under the National School Lunch Program amounted to about 800 million dollars. This amount is exclusive of large sums of money expended by localities for the construction of lunchroom facilities.

Although Federal assistance has greatly stimulated the development of the school feeding services, the lunch programs are largely financed by State and local sources. About 78 percent of the expenditures under the national program in 1957–1958 came from sources within the States. Children's payments accounted for 56 percent. About 22 percent of the total cost was represented by Federal contributions in the form of cash grants and food commodities.

WE RECOGNIZE that the school lunch program is limited in its effect on the total food intake and nutrition of children.

Even for students who participate regularly, lunch at school represents only one meal a day, 5 days a week, 9 months of the year. The value of the program to a child's physical development, therefore, must be measured in terms of the nutritive quality of the foods served him when he eats at school and the educational effect of the program on his dietary pattern and food habits away from school now and in the future.

The goal of the school lunch program must be twofold.

First, the lunches offered to children must be nutritionally adequate and designed to develop and encourage the child's liking for a wide variety of the protective foods which frequently are not included in home diets.

Secondly, the school lunch should be closely linked to the school's education program for better health and nutrition.

These objectives have received the fundamental emphasis of the State educational agencies administering the program in the schools. The basic lunch standards established by the Department for the program are stated in the simplest possible terms. They are based on broad food categories that permit a wide range of local accommodation in terms of the items selected for the lunch.

Nevertheless, getting across these relatively simple essentials of a well-balanced school lunch has been a tremendous job. They must get into the hands and the practices of lunchroom managers, cooks, and helpers in thousands of participating schools in every section of the country.

Much progress toward the nutritional goals of the program has been made in the years since the National School Lunch Act was passed.

State agencies have been able to provide increasingly greater technical guidance to individual school lunch programs through employment of additional qualified personnel.

Equally important has been the marked trend toward employment of qualified personnel as school lunch supervisors, working on a county or a city basis and paid from local tax funds.

State educational agencies also have made effective use of workshops as an inservice training device for school lunch workers, and in this effort are receiving increasing cooperation from colleges and universities within the State. The workshops actually cover a tremendous range of subjects involving every phase of school lunch operations, but perhaps their greatest achievement has been that of getting across the nutrition story.

In 24 States and Puerto Rico, workshops held in 1957 were attended by 35,500 persons. Duration of the workshops varied from 1 day to 1 or 2 weeks. Sessions were devoted to cost control, supervisory techniques, menu planning, preparation of food in quantity, food-buying practices, and sanitation.

One or more colleges or universities in 24 States offered courses in management of school lunches. The curriculum for a degree in home economics in a number of States requires some actual job training in the school lunch program. Sometimes students working for graduate degrees base their theses on topics related to school lunch programs—the extent of student participation in lunch programs, the reasons for nonparticipation, evaluation of the workshop technique, and methods of promoting school lunch as part of the education process.

Quite a number of school systems have found that the lunch program is an excellent way to promote better understanding of good nutrition and dietary habits. In these schools, the essential function of the program goes far beyond supplying one well-balanced meal a day. The program becomes one more educational tool to be used intelligently and constructively to educate the student as to the why and how of an adequate diet. School kitchens and dining rooms become laboratories for lessons in nutrition, sanitation, courtesy, and consideration for others.

Some interesting and ingenious ways have been reported by the State agencies for combining education with the lunchroom. Fourth-graders in one school carried out a 2-week nutrition project. The class was divided into committees representing the different food groups in a well-balanced diet. Each committee prepared a report on the contribution that food group made to good health and which individual items were important members of the food group. With this background, the students then planned the menus for the school lunch.

The eighth-grade students in the school undertook a study of plate waste in the lunchroom. Graphs and charts were developed to depict the situation. The students soon expressed concern over the financial loss involved in the waste, and the students began a study of how the entire school lunch program was financed and how much money was available for the lunch program in their school. Graphs and charts were made in the mathematics class to report the results of the study.

Students in another school undertook an analysis of the funds available for school lunch and planned menus based thereon. They learned why steak is not served every day. Other schools take particular pains, before new foods are introduced, to hold advance tasting sessions and to discuss the sources of these new foods before actually serving them as part of the lunch program.

The school lunch program often is the focal point for a communitywide effort to improve dietary levels. Surveys are made of the food intake of children, and the results are published by the local press, highlighting the areas needing nutritional improvement. Specific projects are developed for all grade levels in the school— visits to dairies and supermarkets, use of films about food and good eating habits, posters prepared by the art classes, appropriate tie-in activities with classes in home economics, health, geography, and business. Thus the direct efforts of the school tend to carry over into menu planning in the home.

These examples give only an indication of the infinite possibilities still to be explored in the field of adapting the school lunch program to the role it can play in the curriculum.

SCHOOL FEEDING operations can be a significant factor in helping to bring about a wise and effective use of the Nation's food abundance. The school experience can introduce children to a nutritious, attractive noonday lunch. They can learn to eat and like new foods—or familiar foods in new forms. Children can also learn how to choose well-balanced diets and why good food habits are important.

As school lunch programs make these contributions to the health and general welfare of children, they also work to expand domestic markets for food. The lunch program has been a major factor in the introduction of such new foods as orange juice concentrate, dry milk, and the new-type stabilized dried eggs. It has widened the geographic market for some other foods—such as sweetpotatoes from the Southeast in schools in the Northwest and purple plums from the Northwest for schoolchildren in the South.

In addition, the service of more and better balanced lunches at school means more food purchased in local markets throughout the country.

While the Department of Agriculture regards the school lunch program as its most constructive outlet for surplus foods acquired under various price stabilization programs, most of the food used in school lunch programs is purchased in local markets. In the 1958 fiscal year, schools participating in the National School Lunch Program spent more than 469 million dollars for food with local suppliers. This did not include donated foods valued at 90 million dollars.

Schools represent a sizable market for livestock and poultry products and fruits and vegetables. For example, about 4.5 percent of the fluid milk consumed by the nonfarm population is marketed through schools. To encourage high-level production and consumption of foods of this type—foods that make the greatest contribution to improved diets and health of the Nation—has become a part of public policy in the field of food and agriculture. With the growth and improvement of school feeding services, the lunch program is becoming an increasingly important factor in the implementation of this policy.

WE GET MANY comments from children, educators, and parents about school lunches. I should like to share one or two of them with you.

L. E. Spikes, superintendent of schools in Burlington, N.C., wrote:

"School lunch is a primary factor in our health program—one of the finest tools for our defense program. It assures the children of a balanced, nutritious, healthful meal. A census taken a few years ago showed that over one-half of our students received the best-balanced meal of the day and that over one-third received the only balanced meal in our feeding program.

"School lunch is also an educational program. We feel it must be related to the educational program both in concept and in practice. Educationally, we believe a successful school lunch should have meaning to the pupil, teacher, parent, and community.

"In Burlington, all of our children and teachers eat lunch in the cafeteria. Lunch time is a happy time. Conversation and fellowship abound, within reasonable boundaries of good taste and good manners.

"Burlington has led the State of North Carolina in school attendance for the fifth consecutive year, with over 97 percent attendance. The school lunch program was not, of course, completely responsible; but it was one important factor in maintaining good school attendance."

Robert E. Wilson, superintendent of schools in Mansfield, Ohio, said:

"One of the most satisfying and inspirational sights I have ever experienced is to walk into one of our elementary buildings at noon, a building which is located in a very underprivileged section of the district, to watch a teacher and a sixth-grade pupil sitting at opposite ends of the table acting as hostesses, to watch each child fold his hands and bow his head for a word of prayer, the cleanest hands and faces that the youngsters have probably had all day, learning to use a knife, fork, and spoon as they would not learn any other way, carrying on child talk as they eat slowly a well-balanced diet."

William Henry Shaw, superintendent of education, Muscogee County School District, Columbus, Ga., said:

"Any teacher will tell you that it is impossible to teach a hungry child. Therefore, we must start with the proper feeding of children before we can plan an adequate school program. And so, the school program has taken on one of the responsible functions of the home—that is, feeding each child a hot meal in the middle of the day."

Joyce Juel, a pupil in the Scobey School in Montana, wrote:

"The school lunchroom is always clean and neat. The food is always good. The milk is never sour. Some of the foods I like are potato soup, chili, cabbage salad, scalloped potatoes, baked potatoes and wieners. As for desserts I like cherry pie, chocolate pudding, blueberry muffins, and cookies. The price of a meal is very cheap. My mother and father think that the school lunches are wonderful. I think that the school lunches are truly wonderful."

WITH SCHOOL enrollments increasing and with the school construction program providing more food service facilities, there will be a steady year-to-year increase in the demand for school lunch programs. Advance planning will be necessary if these larger needs are to be met and the quality and effectiveness of the programs are to be further improved.

A major area of planning must involve the sound financing of an expanding program. As in the past, it appears that the major share of school lunch financing must come from State and local sources, with the Federal assistance program supplementing and supporting these efforts. The payments the children make for their lunches have been the most important source of non-Federal financial support for school lunch programs, contributing more than half of the total annual cost of the program. Whether children's payments should continue to finance this large a share of the program's costs is a question that must be faced by those responsible for the future development of the program.

Additional knowledge must be gained of the factors that influence a child's choice of food, for the ultimate purpose of the school lunch experience is to make children want to choose a well-balanced diet.

Supervisory techniques must be improved so that more effective guidance can be given to a larger number of schools. Ways must be found to translate better the results of research into practical working guides for local school lunch workers. Plans must be developed for the greater use of the school lunchroom as a laboratory for learning, supplementing classroom instruction in a wide range of subjects.

A sound school lunch program can help to improve the diets and food habits of children and, thus, eventually lead to better diets and food habits for the population as a whole. As these accomplishments are achieved, farm markets will be further expanded and stabilized.

MARVIN M. SANDSTROM, *Deputy Director of the Food Distribution Division of the Agricultural Marketing Service, has been associated with the Department's marketing and distribution programs for more than 23 years. He has served in an administrative capacity on the distribution programs since the passage of the National School Lunch Act in 1946 and, as Deputy Director, is responsible primarily for the School Lunch and Special Milk Programs.*

The Years Ahead

O. V. WELLS

THE fear of famine hangs over many densely populated, under-developed countries, and many people speculate as to the limits of food production and the possibilities of producing or getting more food.

The question as to whether or how long we can continue to feed a growing population actually has little relevance now.

Consider Japan, a country about the size of Montana. Seven-eighths of Japan is mountainous, and 1 acre in 6 is farmed. It lies within almost the same latitude as the United States. Its area is less than one-twentieth of the area of the United States, not counting Alaska, but its population is 90 million.

We could multiply 90 million by 20 and conclude that the result, 1,800 million, is the population the land in the United States could support if we could make as good use as the Japanese do of each acre and if we would be willing to make some changes in our diet.

Such a calculation, though, is far-fetched.

More to the point—at least now—is to consider three questions:

At what rate is the population of the United States likely to grow?

How well do the American people want to be fed?

What is the probable trend in American farm production?

No fixed answers can be given to any of the questions. Instead, there is a whole family of answers, depending on the assumptions or judgments we start with.

We need to know the assumptions, and we should recognize that we are trying to decide on a rational course of action, rather than trying to forecast what may happen.

Suppose we look at the three questions in some detail.

AGRICULTURE's capacity to produce has been the subject of a series of studies. Each has indicated that agricultural production is likely to outrun or keep pace with population into 1975 or beyond. This means farmers could do over the next 20 years what has been done over the past 20 years. From 1939, the year the Second World War began, to 1957, aggregate farm output increased about 40 percent and the population of the United States increased 30 percent.

A report to the Food and Agriculture Organization of the United Na-

701

tions in 1952 indicated farm output for 1975 could be about 35 percent above the 1947–1949 average.

The report said: "Such an increase would supply the projected domestic and foreign demand for United States farm products. . . . This assumes that economic incentives to farmers to adopt improved production practices will exist. But economic incentive alone will not insure that the needs for food and fiber will be met . . . intensive research and educational efforts will be needed. Special efforts also will need to be devoted to maintenance of soil resources so that higher crop yields can be sustained."

Farm output in the United States has trended upward since colonial days. Over most of this time, however, the increase was chiefly associated with the use of additional acres and additional workers. But significant changes have occurred since the First World War. Total acreage of cropland for the Nation has changed little since the early 1920's. At the same time, numbers of horses and mules fell sharply after 1920 as farmers bought tractors, trucks, and automobiles. Acres formerly used to raise feed for workstock were released for commercial use—a substantial factor in increasing farm output in the interwar years, 1921–1941.

Increasing production continues meanwhile to dominate the American farm picture although the shift to gasoline and motors has about been completed. Average per acre yields and production per livestock unit— milk per cow, eggs per hen, meat per unit of feed—increased by a third from 1935–1939 into 1957, while output per man-hour of farm labor doubled.

It is this increase in agricultural productivity in the past 20 years that is of most interest in analyzing possibilities for years ahead.

Advances in farm technology have been the chief basis for the recent rise in productivity of farm labor, cropland, and animals. This has

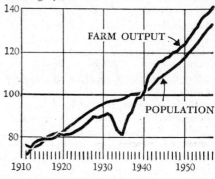

Farm Output and Population
Percentage of 1910–1958

3-year moving averages.

meant an increasing dependence of agriculture on nonfarm goods and services, which has in turn meant increased cash costs.

Mechanization has been an important influence as machines have been substituted for manpower, but farm productivity is also increasingly responsive to chemical and biological developments. Fertilizer and insecticides increase crop yields. Biological research has developed such things as hybrid seed corn and rust-resistant strains of wheat and also has yielded new and more efficient methods for breeding and feeding animals.

New and improved systems of management also contribute to farm productivity. To be most effective, the new chemical, mechanical, and biological practices must be combined into new farming systems—systems that place increasing premiums on management skills. Thus, the substantial increases in farm output are mainly the result of a shift in the resources used (relatively less land, and labor, more machines, seeds, chemicals, and animals) or the way in which they are combined. There have been significant increases in output per unit of total resources used.

Agriculture also continues to transfer substantial resources to other sectors of the economy. In 20 years, for example, the number of farm-workers was reduced by 4 million, or nearly 40 percent; 28 percent of all farm operators worked 100 days or more off their farms in 1954—about twice the proportion for 1939. The size and scale of commercial farms increase, on the one hand; on the other hand, the farm population declines.

Farm population on April 1, 1958, accounted for 12 percent of the total United States population, compared with 24 percent in 1938, and 35 percent in 1910.

This brief review suggests that market needs—rather than production possibilities—will be the major determinant of the level of farm output in the United States over the next 25 to 50 years. That is, how many people will there be to feed and how well will they want to be fed?

How MANY people will there be?
We do not know.

The population experts in the 1920's and 1930's felt fairly confident of their forecasting abilities. They believed—or their calculations assumed—that falling birth rates and increasing urbanization were closely linked, and so they concluded that the United States population would level out sometime in the 1960's or 1970's at somewhere around 155 million to 165 million.

Then came the Second World War and a sharp increase in marriage and birth rates, which has continued during the years that followed. Americans seem to have revised completely their attitude toward children, and the population experts now conclude that marriage and birth rates may vary materially from time to time depending on economic conditions and social attitudes.

So we now have sets or series of projections. Such calculations as to what the future United States population may be assume widely divergent combinations of birth and death rates, with the result that there are wide differences between the minimal and maximal estimates for so close a date as 1975.

Illustrative Population Projections, Continental United States, 1965–2000

[Millions]

Year	Series I	Series II	Series III	Series IV
	Bureau of the Census calculations [1]			
1965......	199.0	195.7	193.6	191.5
1975......	243.9	235.2	225.6	215.8
	Adjusted from Social Security calculations [2]			
2000......	385.6	348.4	334.3	271.8

[1] From the U.S. Department of Commerce, Bureau of the Census, *Statistical Abstract of the United States: 1958*, Washington, D.C., 1958. The Series imply the following assumptions as to fertility: I—fertility averages 10 percent above 1955–1957 level throughout the projection period; II—1955–1957 level continues to 1975–1980; III—1955–1957 level declines to 1949–1951 level by 1965–1970, then remains at that level to 1975–1980; IV—1955–1957 level declines to 1942–1944 level by 1965–1970, then remains at that level to 1975–1980. The Bureau of the Census indicates: "Series I illustrates the size of the future population under very high fertility conditions; it is unlikely that the fertility level implied will persist throughout the projection period."

[2] Adjusted from calculations of the Social Security Administration, Department of Health, Education, and Welfare. Six projections were worked out by the Social Security Administration for the United States and its possessions. The four sets shown exclude the two extremes and were (1) reduced by 4.3 percent to adjust to estimated figures for the continental United States, excluding Alaska, and to eliminate special allowance for underenumeration, and (2) then Series I, II, III, and IV were increased by 6.7, 6.2, 5.1, and 4.3 percent, respectively, to account for differences between Census Bureau projections published in 1955, with which the Social Security projections were relatively consistent, and revised Census Bureau projections published in 1958. From Actuarial Study No. 46, Social Security Administration, May 1957.

Changes in Food Consumption
From 1935–1939 Average Per Capita

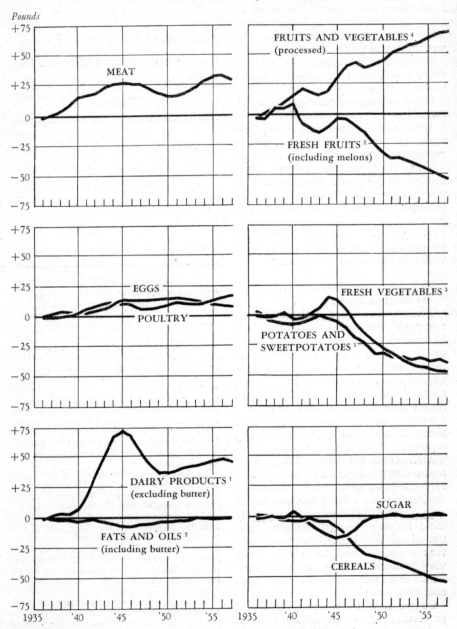

Variations in retail weight. Civilian only. 3-year moving average centered.
  [1] Product weight, except milk and cream content of ice cream.
  [2] Fat content.
  [3] Includes home garden produce.
  [4] Includes frozen concentrated citrus juice on single strength basis.

If we take the population projections which now appear most likely,
assuming that full employment or
something approaching it can be maintained over the intervening years, our
population in 1975 apparently will be
somewhere between 215 million and
235 million (compared with 177 million in mid-1959).

But 1975 is not very far ahead.

What about the year 2000 and later?

Such calculations as can be made
for the year 2000 suggest that our population will not likely be less than 250
million and could equal or actually
exceed 385 million if recent fertility
rates are maintained.

Such analyses and calculations as
these clearly suggest the possibility of
substantial population growth over the
years ahead. At the same time they
emphasize that we cannot now know
within a wide range what actual population may be.

How MUCH and what kind of food
will the American people demand over
the years ahead?

Once again we have a question that
has no fixed answer.

Some marked changes have occurred
in the American diet during the last
two decades—changes that perhaps
will help indicate what may lie ahead.

We may look at these changes in two
ways: In terms of nutritional content
and adequacy and in terms of consumer choices as between particular
foods—choices dictated by consumer
preference and price considerations as
well as nutritional need.

The average per capita disappearance of food measured in terms of calories or food energy shows a small decline, from about 3,300 Calories in
1935-1939 to 3,200 in 1955-1957.
Average per capita supplies of protein
over the same years increased 5 percent, and calcium, 10 percent. Supplies of the vitamins thiamine, riboflavin, and niacin increased 20 to 25
percent. Ascorbic acid and vitamin A,
however, dropped about 10 percent.

Whereas about one-third of the

American families were ill-fed in the
1930's, according to estimated nutrient
requirements at the time, it now appears that only about 10 percent of
American families have diets below
the standards of the 1930's.

Further, poor diets today are due as
much to lack of knowledge about nutrition as to low incomes. Some families in every income level have diets
that could be improved nutritionally.
Also, most families with such diets,
even those at the lower income levels,
could make better choices of food and
so achieve better nourishment at the
same cost.

Protein, mineral, vitamin, carbohydrate, and other nutrient elements
come chiefly from natural foods. Habits and preferences of consumers play
a great part in choosing and eating
them. Costs are also important.

Shifts since the 1930's have meant
not more pounds of food per capita
but, rather, a marked improvement in
the quality of the average American
diet—not only nutritionally but also
in terms of what people prefer to eat.

Many people argue for an increased
"animal agriculture"—an agriculture
that centers increasing attention on
meat, milk, and poultry and cuts down
the acreage devoted to the direct cash
crops that have been in surplus supply.
Farmers have been moving in this
direction.

This shift in agricultural production
is associated also with the main shift in
food-consuming habits. From 1935-
1939 to 1956-1958, as an example,
Americans increased their per capita
consumption of animal foods by almost
100 pounds on a retail-weight basis—
including 22 pounds of beef, 6 pounds
of pork, 5 dozen eggs (the equivalent
of about 9 pounds of eggs), 13 pounds
of chicken, 3 pounds of turkey, and
45 pounds net of fluid milk and other
dairy products (excluding butter).

Over against this, consumption of
other foods, chiefly potatoes and
grain products, has declined by almost 100 pounds (including 15
pounds of cornmeal, 41 pounds of

Factors in Farm Production

Per Unit of Farm Output

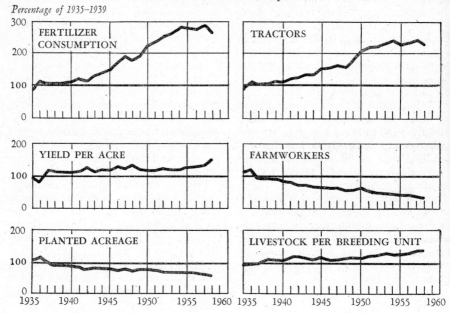

Percentage of 1935–1939

wheat flour, 28 pounds of potatoes, and 12 pounds of sweetpotatoes). Potatoes and grains have given way to livestock products, meat, eggs, and milk.

Some offsetting shifts have occurred in the consumption of fresh versus processed fruits and vegetables; while both the use of sugar and direct consumption of fats and oils (including butter) dipped during the Second World War and then gradually returned to the 1935–1939 level.

Projections of future average per capita food consumption sometimes are made simply by extending current trends.

Such projections generally indicate a further modest improvement in the overall quality of American diets.

Average per capita use of cereals and potatoes may continue to trend slightly down for some years yet.

The consumption of eggs, sugar, and fats may hold about constant.

Dairy products (other than butter),

fruit and vegetables, poultry, and red meat may show some further increase.

Reservations must be made with respect to such projections. Simply drawing trend lines through historical data on the assumption that the trends will continue, food by food or food class by food class, as long as per capita real incomes increase is not enough. We need to know more.

We need to know in what direction greater knowledge of nutrition is likely to influence people. We need to know something about relative costs. We need to know a great deal more than we now do about what influences food preferences.

Earlier chapters indicate we can expect continuing emphasis on the protective foods that are carriers of the scarcer vitamins and minerals and on adequate supplies of protein. Meanwhile, the significance to nutritional health of the nature and amount of various types of fats and carbohydrates in everyday diets is now under intensive study. But nutrition education is not likely to stress any increase in average energy or calorie intake, although this does not mean that the carbohydrates and fats are not excellent, relatively inexpensive, energy-yielding foods.

As for costs, food is now and will apparently continue to be a bargain in the United States, barring great misfortunes, which we shall surely try to avoid. Not only does the average family's food cost fewer hours of wages in the United States than in other countries but the average American family also more nearly gets the particular foods it wants along with a surprising amount of services, or convenience.

Economists generally consider it axiomatic that the percentage of income spent for food declines as income rises. This holds true when we compare the United States with other countries. But over the last 20 years average per capita purchasing power within the United States has risen by two-thirds, while over the same years the percentage of disposable income spent for food has shown little change (averaging about 22 percent). This partly traces to the fact that food processors and handlers are more and more selling not only the basic foods but also increased services. Quality control, packaging, precooking, and free parking space, for example, are all part of this trend. The shift in the quality of the diet is also partly responsible—broilers, eggs, and red meats cost more per pound, for example, than potatoes or flour.

Prices of the same staple foods measured relative to hourly wage rates show a steady decline. Wages for an average hour's factory labor, for example, would buy more bread, or steak, or milk, or butter, or bacon, or eggs, or potatoes, or oranges in 1929 than in 1939 and more in 1958 than in 1939.

It has been suggested, with respect to food preferences, that some useful clues as to possible changes ahead might be provided if we knew how richer families customarily use food, assuming continuing rises in real income per capita. The best available data on this are those from the 1955 food consumption survey of American households.

An analysis has been made of the consumption of certain foods, along with estimated supplies of calories, protein, calcium, and selected vitamins on a per-person basis for the average of all families as well as the average of the 8.6 percent of the families with 1954 money income after income taxes of more than 8 thousand dollars.

The analysis yields some interesting comparisons. Calories per person per day were almost exactly at the same level for the high-income families as for the average of all families.

Consumption of protein, however, was 7 percent greater, because of the more liberal use of the red meats, poultry and eggs, and whole milk and milk products.

Calcium supplies were somewhat better than average for the higher income families, tracing to milk. An increased use of fruit and vegetables also gave increased supplies of vitamin A and C. Thiamine supplies, however, were actually lower, because the high-income families ate less pork per person and less enriched or whole-grain flour.

Improvements in American diets seem probable over the next several years, whatever basis one uses for estimating future trends.

Yet a word of caution is necessary. Should we fail to maintain business and employment, United States diets could be reduced, especially in terms of palatability and the farm resources required to supply food. Surprising changes also sometimes occur in food habits—for example, few people expected butter consumption to be cut in half during and following the war.

We should also remember that the current and prospective high diet levels furnish us a wide margin of food insurance in case of war or drought or,

Weekly Consumption of Selected Foods, per Person, Spring 1955 [1]

Item	Average all United States households	In households with 1954 net income of $8,000 and more	
		Average	As percent of United States average
	Dollars per person		Percent
Average annual money income after income taxes per person..................................	$1,250	$3,225	258
	Pounds per person		
Beef (carcass weight).........................	1.72	2.23	130
Pork (carcass weight).........................	1.49	1.38	93
Chicken (eviscerated weight)..................	.63	.69	110
Eggs [2].......................................	1.04	1.13	109
Fluid milk and cream [3]......................	7.27	8.29	114
Ice cream (milk equivalent)..................	1.15	1.55	135
Butter..	.20	.32	160
Margarine....................................	.20	.17	85
Fruit, fresh equivalent [4]....................	5.09	7.24	142
Vegetables, fresh equivalent [5]...............	5.56	6.56	118
Sugar [2]......................................	1.25	1.25	100
Potatoes, fresh equivalent....................	2.03	1.93	95
Wheat grain [2]...............................	1.66	1.45	87
	Units, per person, per day		
Food energy (calories).......................	3,200	3,245	101
Protein (grams).............................	103	112	109
Calcium (grams).............................	1.15	1.21	105
Thiamine (milligrams).......................	1.56	1.53	98
Vitamin A (International Units)..............	8,540	9,600	112
Vitamin C (milligrams)......................	106	136	128

[1] Derived from Household Food Consumption Survey Report 1955, No. 1, Department of Agriculture, December 1956, covering consumption at home only for 1 week by housekeeping households. About 8.6 percent of households of 2 or more persons had annual money incomes after income taxes of $8,000 or more in 1954.

[2] Includes approximate content in manufactured products as well as shell eggs.

[3] Includes fluid whole milk, half and half, and cream on whole milk equivalent basis.

[4] Farm weight, including melons.

[5] Farm weight, excluding potatoes, sweetpotatoes, dry beans, and peas.

if we take the long view, in case our population should some day press more severely on resources than seems likely during the years immediately ahead.

SOME CONCLUSIONS are now in order.

We have examined the questions that seem relevant in considering our food future. True, we have derived no firm answers. Rather, the effort has been to direct attention to the vari-

ables we face and to the fact that the answers are chiefly matters of conscious choice.

The United States is still a relatively young Nation with a low ratio of population to resources. Further, we have shown ingenuity in discovering or creating new resources as we move through time. The United States can and eventually will support a much larger population than is now the case.

We have good reason to believe that

the trend of farm production and food consumption for quite a few years ahead turns mainly on the questions as to how fast our population increases and as to how well we want to be fed.

We have not discussed exports or our foreign trade in food products. American farms produce 93 or 94 percent of the food consumed in the United States, and we normally export as much or more food commodities than we import even though the commodity mix is different—sugar and coffee, for example, versus soybean oil and wheat.

We have not discussed world food supplies and world population. Our surpluses over domestic needs are useful in supplementing food supplies in many foreign countries.

But the solution to food shortages in most countries lies within themselves; they must eventually rely chiefly upon technical advancement, just as we in the United States must.

Calculations such as those outlined in discussing future population increases do indicate, meanwhile, that we cannot just assume, even in the United States, that there will always be enough food for everybody. Common prudence calls for policies that will maintain and increase our capacity to produce food and such fibers as cotton and wool, recognizing that the decisions as to what and how much are to be produced must be made as we move ahead, year by year.

ON SEVERAL general policies relating to farm production and nutrition there now seems to be general agreement.

We all recognize the need for the conservation of our renewable natural resources—soil, water, and the associated forage and forest cover.

The renewable resources are able to render continuous service if their productive capacities are properly maintained or replaced. There may be argument as to the ways of doing the job, but we seem generally agreed that conservation as a working tool must allow for continuous use of the re-

Money Value of Food
Farm Families

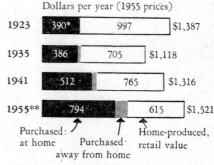

Dollars per year (1955 prices)

1923	390*	997	$1,387
1935	386	705	$1,118
1941	512	765	$1,316
1955**	794	615	$1,521

Purchased: at home / Purchased away from home / Home-produced, retail value

*Includes away from home.
**Survey week, annual rate.

Food Away From Home
Urban and Farm Families

Share of total family food expense in a year

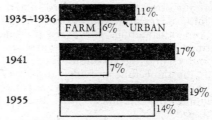

1935–1936	FARM 6% URBAN 11%
1941	17% / 7%
1955	19% / 14%

MEALS AND OTHER FOOD PURCHASED AND EATEN AWAY FROM HOME DURING YEAR.

Canned and Frozen Food
By Farm Families, 1941 and 1954

Amounts preserved per family in the year, processed weight

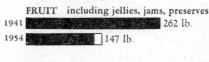

VEGETABLES including pickles, relishes
1941 — 220 lb.
1954 — 184 lb.

FRUIT including jellies, jams, preserves
1941 — 262 lb.
1954 — 147 lb.

MEAT, POULTRY, FISH
1941 — 32 lb.
1954 — 305 lb

█ Home canned   ☐ Home frozen

source in such a way as to assure maintenance and, if possible, gradual improvement. We have a limited land area, which must supply space and also must serve as a primary factor in supplying farm and forestry products for a growing population over the indefinite future.

Continuing emphasis on agricultural research is needed. Most of our recent increases in farm output have come from the use of new technologies, which flow from research, rather than from increase in the total volume of resources used.

We have a new frontier, in terms of individual opportunity and national promise, in the field of new and improved technical development.

More attention is probably paid to research and related educational and developmental activities in the United States today than in any other country at any other time. Our record in agricultural research and extension has been outstanding. If we are to continue using our scarce natural resources into the indefinite future and at the same time provide satisfactory standards of living for a growing population, this emphasis must be continued.

With respect to both conservation and technical advance, however, we must also recognize that the most important single element in American farming is the farmers themselves. Farming today involves sizable capital investments and substantial annual cash expenses.

Conservation of farm resources and the actual use of research findings depend upon technical competence of our farmers, their abilities, and their financial incentives.

Farmers are a part of the American free enterprise system, and it is essential that an economic climate be maintained which allows them to meet their production expenses and maintain their capital, with enough left over for their families to share in the rising American standard of living.

Common prudence also calls for strong continuing emphasis on policies that are designed to improve American nutrition.

Good nutrition is the best guarantee of an able, energetic, long-lived population. That means emphasis on research in and education in nutrition.

Science to be useful must be applied, and nutrition is never an abstract science. Rather, good nutrition comes as each family and each individual knows what is desirable. With such knowledge, most of us can then so arrange our food choices as to meet nutritional needs and also satisfy our own particular food preferences.

O. V. WELLS *is Administrator of the Agricultural Marketing Service. He is one of the representatives of the Department of Agriculture to the National Food and Nutrition Board. He is a member of the Program Committee of the Food and Agriculture Organization of the United Nations. He was Chief of the Bureau of Agricultural Economics in 1946–1953.*

Glossary

ABSORPTION In physiology, absorption pertains to the uptake of nutrients, water, or other substances by stomach or intestinal walls following digestion of food. For example, glucose, a common simple sugar, is absorbed without change, but starches must be broken down into sugars before absorption can take place. In food processing, absorption may also refer to uptake of other substances by foods, such as absorption of fats by foods during cooking in deep fat, or absorption of water by cereals during cooking.

ACETOACETATE A compound formed from condensation of two molecules of acetic acid. Acetic acid is an organic acid commonly formed in the metabolism of sugars and related substances. For example, it is the predominating acid in vinegar where it has been formed by the growth of micro-organisms on sugars, starches, and celluloses.

ADIPOSE Animal fat. Adipose is commonly used in describing the part of the body where fat is stored, which is adipose tissue.

ADOLESCENCE The period of years between the beginning of puberty (when the reproductive organs become functionally active) and maturity.

ADRENAL Near the kidney. The adrenal glands are ductless glands near the upper end of the kidneys. Their secretions are essential for the maintenance of life.

AEROBIC Living or functioning in air or free oxygen.

AFTERBIRTH The placenta and membranes expelled from the womb or uterus after the delivery of a child or a fetus.

AGRICULTURAL RESEARCH CENTER The Agricultural Research Center (ARC) is part of Agricultural Research Service and is located near Beltsville, Md., about 15 miles northeast of Washington, D. C. The center covers about 11 thousand acres and includes 950 buildings of all types equipped to meet specific research needs or to provide office and laboratory space. About 3 thousand experimental farm animals, 10 thousand mature fowls, and 5,500 small laboratory animals are kept at the ARC. There is an apiary for bees. Five acres are under glass in 31 greenhouses. There are experimental pastures, ranges, orchards, gardens, fields for cultivated crops, timber stands, and soil-treatment plots.

AGRICULTURAL RESEARCH SERVICE One of the agencies of the U. S. Department of Agriculture. It has responsibility for conducting farm research, utilization research, and home economics research and for regulating services in animal and plant disease control and eradication and in meat inspection. It also has responsibility for Federal grants to States for agricultural research and for coordinating all the research done within the Department, except research in economics and statistics.

AMINO ACID Organic compounds of carbon, hydrogen, oxygen, and nitrogen. Each amino acid molecule contains one or more amino group ($-NH_2$) and at least one carboxyl group ($-COOH$). In addition, some amino acids (cystine and methionine) contain sulfur. Many amino acids linked together in some definite pattern form a molecule of protein.

ANAEROBIC Living or functioning in the absence of air or free oxygen. The opposite of aerobic.

ANTACID A substance that counteracts or neutralizes acidity.

ANTIBIOTICS Substances that are "against life." They are chemical substances, which are produced by certain living cells, such as bacteria, yeasts, and molds that are antagonistic or damaging to other living cells, such as disease-producing bacteria. Antibiotics may kill living cells or prevent them from growing and multiplying. Penicillin is an example of an antibiotic that damages certain bacteria that cause disease in man.

ANTIBODY One of many specific substances produced in the body to react against disease-producing or other foreign materials in the blood stream. Some antibodies remain in the blood stream for many years and help to give a person immunity to certain diseases.

ANTIOXIDANT A substance capable of chemically protecting other substances against oxidation.

ARACHIDONIC ACID A substance essential to body tissues built by the animal body from the simpler fatty acids that are derived from the food fats.

711

ARTERIOSCLEROSIS A thickening and hardening of the walls of the arteries and capillaries, which lead to loss of their elasticity.

ASCORBIC ACID Another name for vitamin C.

ASEPTIC CANNING A process that involves rapid heating of food to destroy food spoilage organisms, then transferring the cooked food into sterile cans by procedures that prevent the reentry of micro-organisms into the cooked food during the filling and sealing operations.

ATHEROSCLEROSIS A degeneration of blood vessels caused by a deposit of fatty materials along the lining of the wall of the blood vessel. Cholesterol is one of these fatty materials.

AVAILABLE A nutrient is available to the body when it is in the form that can be absorbed from the digestive tract and then used for its intended function in the body.

AVIDIN A protein material that can combine with the B vitamin, biotin, causing the vitamin to be unavailable to the body. Cooking renders avidin inactive.

BACTERIA Very small, one-celled organisms visible only under a microscope and widely distributed in the air, water, soil, and animal and plant tissues. They have some useful functions, such as in decaying of dead matter and in fermentation of fruit or vegetable juices—as in the making of sauerkraut. Many bacteria produce disease or cause harmful spoilage of foods.

BASAL METABOLISM The energy produced by an individual during physical, digestive, and emotional rest, measured directly by the heat evolved and indirectly by the oxygen consumed and carbon dioxide given off.

BATTER A mixture of flour and liquid, usually combined with other ingredients such as sugar, salt, eggs, and baking powder, as for cakes, muffins, waffles, or pancakes. The consistency of a batter is such that it can be stirred with a spoon and is thin enough to pour or drop from a spoon.

BILE A thick green or yellow fluid formed in the liver, collected in the gallbladder, and emptied into the intestinal tract at intervals, particularly during the digestion of fats. It is a complex mixture containing salts of bile acids, which aid in digestion of fats, and cholesterol and other substances from different body sources. It carries cholesterol from the liver into the intestine for excretion or for reuse in digestion as needed.

BIO- (prefix) Living.

BIOCHEMISTRY The chemistry of living things, plant and animal.

BIOLOGICAL Pertaining to the science of life.

BIOLOGICAL CATALYST A substance produced by living organisms that speeds up the rate of a chemical reaction but is not itself used up in the reaction. An enzyme.

BIOLOGICAL FUNCTION The role played or the task performed by a chemical compound or a system of chemical compounds in living organisms.

BIOLOGICAL VALUE The biological value of a food protein is the efficiency with which that protein furnishes the proper proportions and amounts of the amino acids needed, at the time of synthesis of body proteins, by man or animals eating these foods. The more nearly a protein supplies the tissues with the necessary proportions and amounts of these amino acids, the higher is its biological value.

BIOSYNTHESIS The coming together of chemical building units to form new materials in the living plant or animal.

BIOTIN One of the 10 recognized vitamins of the B complex. It is widely distributed in foods. It is needed in the diet of certain laboratory animals, such as the chick, rat, and mouse. A deficiency in man has never been observed under usual conditions.

BLANCH To preheat in boiling water or steam. Blanching is used to inactivate enzymes and shrink food for canning, freezing, and drying. Blanching also is used to aid in removal of skin from nuts, fruit, and some vegetables.

BLAND Mild flavored, not stimulating to the taste; smooth, soft-textured.

BOILING POINT The temperature at which the vapor pressure of a liquid equals the atmospheric pressure. At the boiling point, bubbles of vapor rise continually and break on the surface. The boiling temperature of pure water at sea level (barometer 30 inches) is 212° F. At high altitudes, the boiling point of water is lower because the atmospheric pressure is lower. At 5 thousand feet above sea level, for example, the boiling point of water is 203°; at 10 thousand feet it is 194°.

BRAN The outer coarse coat of grains.

BUFFER A substance that can help a solution resist or counteract changes in free acid or alkali concentration. There are many buffers in the body.

BUTTERFAT The fat in milk; also called milk fat.

CALCIFICATION Process by which organic tissue becomes hardened by a deposit of calcium salts.

CALCIUM A mineral element that is an essential constituent of bone and is essential for blood clotting, muscle tone, and nerve function.

CALORIC Pertaining to heat or energy; used in reference to the caloric value of a food, it means the heat or energy that can be obtained as muscular work and heat when the body uses or metabolizes that food.

CALORIE The unit by which heat is measured. It is defined in terms of the amount of heat required to raise the temperature of a specified amount of water 1 degree centigrade. A small calorie (written with a small c) is the amount of heat required to raise 1 gram of water from $14.5°$ to $15.5°$ C. A large Calorie (capital C) is the amount of heat required to raise 1,000 grams (1 kilogram) of water from $14.5°$ to $15.5°$ C. The large Calorie is used exclusively in expressing the caloric value of foods and the calorie needs of humans and animals. (*Calorie* and *caloric*, as adjectives, usually are not capitalized.)

CALORIMETER An instrument for measuring the heat change and the energy in any system.

CALORIMETRY The science of measuring heat.

CARAMELIZE To heat sugar or foods containing sugar until a brown color and characteristic flavor develop.

CARBOHYDRATE An important group of organic substances that contain carbon, hydrogen, and oxygen. The hydrogen and oxygen are present in the same proportion as in water (H_2O), and there is one molecule of water for every carbon. Starch and sugar are carbohydrates.

CARBON The chemical element present in all substances designated as organic. These include proteins, carbohydrates, and fats. When a compound containing carbon combines with oxygen in the body, energy is liberated and carbon dioxide is formed. Compounds that do not contain carbon are classed as inorganic.

CARBON DIOXIDE A compound that is formed when carbon combines with oxygen. It leaves the body chiefly when air is exhaled from the lung.

CARCASS The part of an animal's body that is used for meat. After an animal is slaughtered and the entrails, head, feet, and lower parts of legs and hide are removed, the carcass remains. It is hung and chilled and later is cut up into steaks, roasts, etc.

CARDIOVASCULAR Pertaining to the heart and blood vessels.

CARIES, DENTAL Tooth decay.

CAROTENE A yellow compound of carbon and hydrogen that occurs in plants and is a form of vitamin A. Alpha, beta, and gamma carotenes may be converted into vitamin A in the body.

CARTILAGE A special form of white connective tissue that is attached to the ends of bones that are either divided into joints or united by joints. It is more flexible but not so strong as bone. Cartilage is the first substance to form in growing bone; then calcium and phosphorus are deposited in the cartilage, thus changing it to bone.

CATABOLISM The breaking down in the body of chemical compounds into simpler ones, usually accompanied by the production of heat.

CATALYST A substance that speeds up the rate of a chemical reaction but is not itself used up in the reaction.

CELL The structural and functional microscopic unit of plant and animal organisms.

CELL-PLATELET A small, colorless, disk-shaped cell in the blood.

CELLULOSE A carbohydrate found in the woody part of plants and trees. It is converted to glucose on hydrolysis. Cellophane and cotton are almost pure cellulose.

CENTIGRADE (C.) A thermometer scale in which water freezes at $0°$ C. and boils at $100°$ C. To change to degrees Fahrenheit, multiply degrees centigrade by nine-fifths and add 32. Also CELSIUS (C.), the preferred form approved by the Ninth General Conference on Weights and Measures in 1948.

CENTRAL NERVOUS SYSTEM The brain and spinal cord.

CHEMICAL ADDITIVES Substances added to foods to improve their flavor, color, texture, or keeping quality.

CHLOROPHYLL The green coloring matter present in growing plants, which under stimulus of light is active in the manufacture of carbohydrates from carbon dioxide and water.

CHOLESTEROL The commonest member of the group of sterols; it is present in many foods and also can be made within the body.

CHROMATOGRAPHY A technique for separating complex mixtures of chemical substances.

CHYLOMICRONS Very small (micro-) globules of fat of varying sizes in transport after digestion and absorption. Chyle is a product of digestion of fats absorbed into the lymphatic circulation and thence into the thoracic duct.

CITROVORUM FACTOR A special substance found in liver. It supports growth and is classified with the B vitamins.

CLINICAL USE A clinic is usually a part of a large hospital. Its physicians diagnose and prescribe for patients who are not hospitalized or are not in need of immediate hospitalization or who can be treated satisfactorily at home. Thus, clinical use means that a treatment or medication is such as can be used for such patients.

COAGULATION The change from a fluid state to a thickened jelly, curd, or clot.

COENZYME A partner needed by some enzymes to accomplish a biochemical change.

COLLAGEN A protein that forms the chief constituent of the connective tissue, cartilage, tendon, bone, and skin. Collagen is changed to gelatin by the action of water and heat.

COLOSTRUM Milk secreted during the first week of lactation.

COMBUSTION The combination of substances with oxygen accompanied by the liberation of energy.

COMPLEX (NOUN) A complicated combination of substances made up of less complicated and interrelated parts.

CONDENSED MILK A liquid or semiliquid food made by evaporating a mixture of sweet milk and refined sugar to such point that the finished sweetened condensed milk contains not less than 28 percent of total milk solids and not less than 8.5 percent of milk fat.

CONDUCTION The transmission of heat or electricity through an object, or from one object to another in direct contact with it, without the motion of the conducting bodies. Conduction is different from convection, which is the transmission of heated particles, and different from radiation, which is the transmission of heated particles effected through the atmosphere.

CONGENITAL A congenital defect is one that exists at birth.

CORONARY In physiology, usually refers to the arteries that supply the heart. For example, coronary thrombosis or coronary occlusion occur in the coronary artery.

CREAM OF TARTAR The common name for potassium acid tartrate, an acid salt that is used in angelcake to stabilize the egg-white foam, to whiten the color, and to increase the tenderness of the cake. It is used also as an acid ingredient in tartrate baking powder.

CREATININE A chemical compound containing nitrogen, carbon, hydrogen, and oxygen, which is present in the urine and results from the metabolism of protein.

CULTURE (i. e., added to milk) Micro-organisms, such as bacteria, molds, and yeasts, which are usually grown under controlled conditions. Specific cultures are used to produce many kinds of cheese and buttermilk and other fermented milks.

CURD The semisolid mass that is formed when milk comes in contact with an acid, such as the acid secretion in the stomach or with an enzyme.

CYSTICERCOSIS Infestation of the body with a form of tapeworm called cysticercus, which is sometimes present in raw beef. Beef should be cooked at least to the rare done stage (140° F.) to avoid danger.

D- (prefix) A chemical prefix that denotes a compound that turns the plane of polarized light to the right.

DECALCIFICATION The withdrawal of calcium from the bones where it has been deposited. It may be caused by an inadequate supply of calcium in the diet so that calcium has to be taken from the bones to help meet the body's needs. It may be caused also by an imbalance in some of the hormone activity in the body.

DEFICIENCY DISEASE A disease resulting from an inadequate dietary intake of something required nutritionally; most commonly refers to diseases resulting from dietary deficiencies of vitamins or trace elements.

DEHYDRATED FOODS Products from which most of the water has been removed in order to improve their stability during storage.

DEHYDRATION The loss of water from the body which is not compensated by drinking water.

DESICCATE To dry.

DIABETES A disorder in metabolism usually accompanied by high water requirements and excretion of large volumes of urine. Sugar diabetes, or diabetes mellitus, the type best known to laymen, is due to low production of insulin, a pancreatic hormone essential for the oxidation of sugar in the tissues. When sugar cannot be burned, the level of sugar in blood and tissues rises and the body demands water for the dilution and elimination of these large quantities by way of the kidney. Eventually inability to utilize sugar gives rise to errors in fat metabolism, including an overproduction of cholesterol.

DIETETICS The application of the science of nutrition to the feeding of individuals and groups of people.

DIGESTION In physiology, the breaking down of foods into simpler components in the alimentary or digestive tract. Foods may be digested by natural body enzymes in the stomach and intestines, or be broken down similarly by the chemist using chemicals and prepared enzymes, heat, or micro-organisms. Proteins are digested to peptides and amino acids, fats to fatty acids and glycerol, carbohydrates to dextrins and sugars. Buttermilk is an example of a food partially digested by natural enzymes and micro-organisms in the milk.

DISPERSE To scatter or distribute over an area or to separate a substance into smaller parts. For example, in making mayonnaise, the oil is separated into small particles by beating and is distributed throughout the egg-acid mixture.

DOUGH A mixture of flour and liquid, usually with other ingredients added. A dough is thick enough to knead or roll, as in making yeast bread and rolls. It is too stiff to stir or pour.

DRY WEIGHT The weight of the residue of a substance that remains after virtually all the moisture has been removed from it. Also called dry matter.

EDEMA Swelling of a part of or the entire body due to the presence of an excess of water. Edema is most noticeable at the end of the day around the ankles, which increase in size. When the condition becomes severe, an impression remains for a few minutes where a finger was pressed against the skin.

EDEMATOUS Refers to the condition of edema, which is the retention of an abnormal amount of fluid in the tissues.

EDIBLE A term applied to food that is fit to eat. It usually refers to food that is suitable for human consumption. The initials E. P. are used to denote the edible portion of a food—for example, a banana without its skin, a pork chop without the bone, a melon without its seeds and rind.

ELASTIN A protein substance that is found in tendons, cartilage, connective tissue, and bone. Elastin is not softened as much as collagen by heat in the presence o water.

ELECTRONIC (OVEN) An electronic oven makes use of microwave energy to heat the food instead of using the ordinary electricity, as in the conventional electric oven. A magnetron tube, or generator, is used as the means of changing electricity into microwaves. The tube gives off energy, which is beamed into the food, where it produces heat.

ELEMENT Any one of the fundamental atoms of which all matter is composed.

EMULSIFICATION A process of breaking up large particles or liquids into smaller ones, which remain suspended in another liquid. Emulsification may be done mechanically, as in the homogenization of ice cream mixtures. It may be hastened by chemicals, as by the use of acid and lecithin (from egg yolk) in emulsification of oil for mayonnaise. It may be accomplished naturally in body processes, as when bile salts emulsify fats during digestion.

EMULSIFY To make into an emulsion. When small drops of one liquid are finely dispersed (distributed) in another liquid, an emulsion is formed. The drops are held in suspension by an emulsifying agent, which surrounds each drop and makes a coating around it.

ENDEMIC An endemic disease is one that occurs in low incidence but more or less constantly in a given population.

ENDOCRINE Secreting internally, or into the blood stream, as endocrine glands, or glands of internal secretion.

ENDOGENOUS Originating within or inside the cells or tissues.

ENDOMETRIUM The mucous membrane that lines the uterus or womb.

ENDOSPERM The starchy portion within the kernel of wheat, corn, or other cereal, from which refined flour is produced after the germ and fibrous outer layers are removed.

ENVIRONMENTAL Pertaining to external influences.

ENERGY Capacity to perform work.

ENZYMATIC Related to that class of complex organic substances called enzymes, such as amylase and pepsin, that accelerate (catalyze) specific chemical reactions in plants and animals, as in digestion of foods.

ENZYME One of a class of substances formed in living cells. It speeds up chemical reactions but does not change during the process.

EPIDEMIC A disease is epidemic when many people in a region are attacked at the same time or when the disease is spreading rapidly.

EPITHELIAL Refers to those cells that form the outer layer of the skin, those that line all the portions of the body that have contact with the external air (such as the eyes, ears, nose, throat, lungs), and those that are specialized for secretion as the liver, kidneys, and urinary and reproductive tract.

ERGOSTEROL A substance belonging to the class of sterols that is found chiefly in plants and animal tissue, yeasts, and molds. It is white and crystalline and similar in appearance to the material that candles are made of. On exposure to ultraviolet light it is converted to vitamin D_2.

ESTROGENS Hormones secreted by the ovaries.

ETIOLOGY Causes of a disease or a disorder.

EVISCERATION Of poultry and fish, refers to removal of the intestinal tract and other organs from the animals.

EXCRETION The products of digestion and metabolism that are discarded from the body—feces from the intestinal tract and urine from the kidneys.

EXOGENOUS Originating from outside the cells or tissues.

EXTRINSIC FACTOR Literally, a constituent from outside; in nutrition something obtained from food, commonly used to refer to vitamin B_{12} in relation to the disease known as pernicious anemia.

FACTOR In nutrition, any chemical substance found in foods. A factor might be a vitamin, a mineral, or any other nutrient or nonnutrient. Usually it has some effect on growth or reproduction of animals. A factor may be "identified" or remain "unidentified." In arithmetic, factor is a value or ratio expressing the relationship between two items, such as liters of oxygen and the equivalent amount of oxygen in grams.

FAHRENHEIT (F.) A thermometer scale that marks the freezing point of water at 32° F. and the boiling point at 212° F.

FAT A glyceryl ester of fatty acids. Fats generally are substances of plant and animal origin. Fat may be in solid form, as butter, margarine, lard, or other shortening, or in liquid form, as the vegetable oils.

FAT-SOLUBLE Refers generally to substances that cannot be dissolved in water but can be in fats and oils, or in fat solvents. The fat-soluble vitamins are vitamins A, D, E, and K.

FATTY ACID Organic compound of carbon, hydrogen, and oxygen, which combines with glycerol to make a fat.

FERMENT To undergo chemical change brought about by the enzymes contained in certain micro-organisms.

FERMENTATION The chemical changes brought about by the activity of enzyme systems of micro-organisms. For example, yeast contains enzymes that produce carbon dioxide and alcohol from sugar. In bread-making, it is this carbon dioxide that causes the dough to rise. The souring of milk is lactic fermentation, some of the milk sugar being converted by the action of lactic acid bacteria into lactic acid. Lactic fermentation also is utilized in making pickles.

FETUS The unborn young or embryo of animals in the later stages of their development before birth. (Adjective: fetal.)

FIBER Meat fibers are the long cells in muscles of the meat. The size and shape of the fibers determine the physical structure and grain of the meat.

FLORA (INTESTINAL) The bacteria and other small organisms that are found in the intestinal contents.

FOLACIN The name officially selected to replace the term folic acid, a vitamin of the B complex.

FOLD In cookery, to combine two mixtures, such as beaten egg white and sugar, gently by cutting down through one side of the mixture with a spatula or other implement, bringing the spatula along the bottom of the mixture, and then folding over before cutting down again. This motion is repeated until blending of the ingredients is achieved. This motion also keeps the air that is already in the mixture (as that in beaten egg whites or whipped cream) and helps to incorporate more air into it.

FOLIC ACID One of the vitamins of the B complex. Its new official name is folacin; it is also known as pteroylglutamic acid. It is a bright-yellow compound needed in very small amounts in the diet of animals and man. A deficiency results in poor growth, anemia, and other blood disorders.

FOLINIC ACID Another name for the citrovorum factor.

FORTIFY To add one or more nutrients to a food so that it contains more of the nutrients than was present originally before processing. Milk often is fortified with vitamin D.

FRACTIONATION A term used by the chemist when he takes natural materials apart in the laboratory by chemical means. He does this for various reasons—usually to isolate or purify some specific compound present in feeds or foods.

FRANK (referring to disease and symptoms) Outright, not just a suggestion.

GALACTOSE A white crystalline sugar obtained from lactose (milk sugar) by hydrolysis.

GAMMA GLOBULIN A protein in the blood that forms antibodies.

GASTRIC Pertaining to the stomach.

GASTROINTESTINAL Refers to the part of the digestive system made up of the stomach and the intestines.

GENE The particle in the cell that carries hereditary characteristics. Genes control the development of the body and its specific functions.

GENETIC Pertaining to heredity.

GENETICALLY Relating to genetics, the science of heredity, variation, sex determination, and related phenomena.

GENITOURINARY Refers to the organs of reproduction and of the excretion of urine.

GERM The part of a cereal seed that grows and produces new plants.

GESTATION Pregnancy.

GIBBERELLINS A group of growth-regulating substances that are produced by certain species of fungi of the genus *Gibberella*.

GINGIVITIS Inflammation of the gums of the jaws.

GLANDULAR Adjective of gland. A gland is an organ that makes and discharges a chemical substance that is used elsewhere in the body or eliminated.

GLUTEN An elastic substance that gives adhesiveness to dough. It is formed when the proteins in flour, especially those in wheat flour, absorb water. Gluten assists in giving shape to the cooked product as it coagulates when heated.

GLYCEROL Same as glycerin. Serves as the backbone radical or framework of the fat molecule, permitting attachment of three fatty acids. Glycerol is an alcohol containing three carbons and three hydroxy (–OH) groups; methyl, or wood, alcohol contains one carbon and one hydroxy group; ethyl, or grain, alcohol contains two carbons and one hydroxy group.

GLYCOLYTIC Pertaining to the chemical breakdown of sugars to lactic acid.

GONADOTROPINS Hormones from embryonic sex glands.

GROWTH-REGULATING SUBSTANCES Chemicals that in extremely small amounts will affect the rate or type of growth of cells, tissues, and organs; sometimes referred to as hormonelike substances.

HARD (WATER) Water containing soluble salts of calcium and magnesium and sometimes iron. Hardness caused by bicarbonate salts of these metals is known as temporary hardness, because boiling expels the carbon dioxide and converts the bicarbonate to the insoluble carbonate, forming incrustation on the walls and bottom of the container. Hardness from chlorides and sulfates of calcium and magnesium is not affected by boiling.

HEAT-LABILE Changeable by heat; unstable to heat.

HEAT-OF-COMBUSTION VALUES The amount of heat produced (usually expressed as calories) when a unit weight of a substance is oxidized.

HEMICELLULOSE A complex carbohydrate that occurs widely in plants as a structural part of their cell walls. It differs chemically from cellulose by being subject to hydrolysis with dilute mineral acids.

HEMOGLOBIN A protein in the blood that contains iron and carries oxygen from the lungs to the tissues.

HEMOLYTIC Refers to the destruction or breakdown of the red blood cells.

HEMORRHAGE Loss of blood.

HERITABLE Capable of being inherited; the tendency of a characteristic to be inherited.

HERMETIC Food containers that do not permit gas or micro-organisms to enter the container or to escape from it. A properly sealed tin can is a hermetic container.

HEXOSE SUGAR A sugar that has six carbon atoms in its chemical structure, as corn sugar.

HOMEOSTATIC Steady biochemical states in the body, maintained by physiological processes.

HOMOGENIZED Broken up into small particles of the same size. Homogenized milk has been treated to break the fat into such small globules that it will not rise to the top as cream.

HORMONE A chemical substance that is produced in an organ called an endocrine gland and is transported by the blood or other body fluids to other cells. A hormone greatly influences the functions of some specific organ and of the body as a whole. Thyroxin is a hormone secreted by the thyroid gland. Insulin is a hormone secreted by the pancreas.

HYDROGEN The chemical element with the smallest atomic weight. Present in proteins, carbohydrates, fats, and water. Hydrogen makes up approximately 10 percent of the human body.

HYDROGENATION The addition of hydrogen to any unsaturated compound. Oils are changed to solid fats by hydrogenation.

HYDROGEN PEROXIDE A chemical substance often used as a bleach to remove color. It is used also in medicine and surgery as an antiseptic agent and as a cleansing agent in mouth washes, tooth pastes and powders. Its antiseptic and cleansing action is due to the fact that it gives off sufficient oxygen to destroy bacteria.

HYDROLYSIS The splitting of a substance into the smaller units of which it is composed by the addition of the elements of water. For example, when starch is heated in water containing a small amount of acid or subjected to the action of digestive enzymes, the simpler sugar glucose is released.

HYPER- A prefix meaning above, beyond, in excess of the normal or average.

HYPERTENSION An abnormally high blood pressure.

HYPERTHYROIDISM Overactivity of the thyroid gland so that it secretes abnormal amounts of the hormone thyroxin.

HYPERTROPHIED Increase in the size of an organ, independent of natural growth.

HYPERVITAMINOSIS The undesirable effects produced by taking an excess of a vitamin concentrate or pure vitamin.

HYPO- A prefix denoting a deficiency or lack or less than the normal or desirable amount.

ICE CRYSTALS When food is exposed to a low enough temperature, the water in food solidifies and forms ice crystals. The formation of large ice crystals in foods such as fruits, vegetables, or meats may rupture the cell walls and affect the appearance and texture of the food. Pure water freezes at 32° F.

IMPERMEABLE Not capable of being penetrated. It is always necessary to name the substance to which a food wrapping material is impermeable. It may be impermeable to water vapor only or to water vapor and to air (or other gases).

INACTIVATE To suspend or terminate certain biological activities, such as by heat, irradiation, or other forms of energy.

INCIDENCE The frequency of occurrence of a situation or of a condition, like a disease.

INEDIBLE A substance that is not fit for food, such as poisonous nuts and plants. Tough skins, seeds, and decayed spots of fruits and vegetables and bones of meat are considered inedible parts because they are not suitable for human consumption.

INERT Relatively inactive.

INERT GAS Does not react with the materials in food. Nitrogen is an inert gas that may be used to replace air (oxygen) in packages of food in order to slow down the deterioration of the food.

INGEST To eat or take in through the mouth.

INORGANIC A large group of chemical compounds that do not contain carbon.

INSEMINATION The planting of seed. The introduction of semen.

INSTITUTE OF HOME ECONOMICS The Institute of Home Economics includes three divisions in the Agricultural Research Service of the U. S. Department of Agriculture—Human Nutrition, Household Economics, and Clothing and Housing. In these fields it undertakes research on problems of national concern.

The Human Nutrition Research Division conducts studies on the nutritive requirements of people, the composition and nutritive value of food to meet these needs, and the physiological availability of nutrients in foods. It develops new and improved methods to prepare, preserve, and care for foods in homes and institutions, to obtain the best nutritive values from food purchases, to prevent deterioration in food quality, to make foods more acceptable in meals, and to make best use of abundant or new foods on the market.

The Household Economics Research Division investigates levels of food consumption and nutritive value and economy of customary diets of various population groups. It conducts research on patterns of rural family expenditures, household production for family use, and economic problems of household management, including the effect of the economic situation on family living. Recommendations are developed for effective and economical use of food and other family resources for higher levels of living. The Division cooperates with other Federal and State agencies in the coordination of nutrition programs.

The Clothing and Housing Research Division is concerned with and evaluates the serviceability of clothing and household textiles in relation to consumer needs, to properties of fabrics, and to the construction, design, care, and reconditioning of garments and home furnishings. It determines the characteristics of housing and household equipment needed to meet family requirements for efficient housekeeping and comfortable living. It develops information basic to wise planning, improved use, and care of clothing, household textiles, the house, its equipment and its facilities.

INSULIN A chemical substance in the group of hormones that is secreted from special cells in the pancreas. It is essential for the normal utilization of sugar by the body. A lack of insulin results in the development of diabetes.

INTAKE Substances or amounts of substances which are taken in by the body— e. g., the intake of food.

INTESTINAL JUICES The digestive juices secreted by the intestinal walls (in contrast to gastric juices secreted by the stomach walls) and pancreatic juices secreted by the pancreas. The intestinal juices contain enzymes, which complete the final stages in digestion of protein, fat, and carbohydrate.

INTESTINAL TRACT The entire intestines, both small and large.

INTRINSIC FACTOR A chemical substance in normal stomach juice. It is necessary for the absorption of vitamin B_{12} from the intestine.

INVOLUTION The change back to a normal condition that certain organs undergo after fulfilling their functional purposes. After pregnancy, the uterus returns to a normal nonpregnant condition.

IRRADIATION To treat with ultraviolet rays from sunlight or an artificial source; to treat with X-rays or other radioactive agent.

IRRITABILITY A term usually applied to nerves. It refers to their ability to respond or react to a stimulus.

I. U. The abbreviation for International Units, the measure of the potency of a vitamin.

KINETIC ENERGY The capacity to do work as a result of motion; for example, the kinetic energy of a waterfall can be used to turn a generator to make electricity.

L- A chemical prefix that denotes a compound that turns the place of polarized light to the left. The opposite of a D-compound.

LABILE Easily destroyed.

LABORATORY ANIMALS Mice, rats, guinea pigs, dogs, and many other small animals that are used in laboratories as the subjects for scientific experiments.

LACTATION The secretion of milk or the period during which milk is formed.

LACTIC ACID A compound formed in the chemical metabolic processes which accompany muscular activity; also a substance formed by the fermentation of lactose, the sugar in milk.

LACTOSE A sugar that occurs in milk. It is a white, crystalline sugar that is less soluble and less sweet than ordinary cane sugar (sucrose).

LINOLEIC ACID One of the digestion products from certain fats, which is essential to body tissues.

LIPIDS A broad term for fats and fatlike substances; characterized by the presence of one or more fatty acids. Lipids include fats, cholesterol, lecithins, phospholipids, and similar substances, which do not mix readily with water.

LOW ACID Meat, poultry, and most of the common vegetables (except tomatoes) contain little of the organic acids and therefore are called low-acid foods. In canning, an acid food, such as tomatoes, can be processed in a boiling water bath because its acid aids in the destruction of certain spoilage organisms and prevents the growth of toxins by other spoilage organisms. To process low-acid foods in a reasonable length of time requires a temperature higher than that of boiling water and requires increased pressure, such as in a pressure cooker.

LYMPH A yellowish liquid that contains corpuscles and is present in the lymphatic vessels or channels of the body.

LYMPHATIC SYSTEM The tissue spaces, all the small and large lymphatic vessels, and the two large ducts or canals in the thorax.

LYSINE One of the amino acids essential to the nutrition of man and animals. It is of special dietary concern because it is one of the amino acids that is present at a relatively low level in some food proteins of plant origin.

MALFORMATION A deformity; an abnormal development or formation of a part of the body.

MAMMARY GLANDS The milk-secreting glands; the breasts.

MATRIX The intercellular framework of a tissue.

MATURATION The process of coming to full development, maturity, or adulthood.

MEAT The flesh of animals used as food. Meat contains proteins, fats, minerals, vitamins, and water. The commonest meats used as food are beef, veal, lamb, and pork. Poultry and fish are sometimes included with the foods classified as meat.

MEMBRANE A thin, soft, pliable layer of animal or vegetable tissue.

MENSTRUATION The monthly discharge peculiar to women. It begins at the age of puberty and continues to menopause.

METABOLIC Refers to metabolism.

METABOLISM The sum of the chemical changes that go on in the body as food is made into body tissues, energy is produced, and body tissue is broken down. There are two parts to body metabolism:
Anabolism is constructive and includes building, maintaining, and repairing tissue;
Catabolism is destructive and includes changing or breaking down tissue or other materials in the body into simple substances for producing energy and for excretion.

MICROBIOLOGICAL Pertaining to micro-organisms—that is, microscopic plants or animals. Refers usually to a method by which certain micro-organisms are used to determine the amounts of a particular nutrient, like a vitamin or an amino acid, in a food. Such assays are possible because these micro-organisms must have these vitamins and amino acids in order to grow. These determinations are called microbiological assays or analyses.

MICRO-ORGANISMS Very small living beings. Bacteria, yeasts, and molds are micro-organisms found in foods.

MICROWAVE A very short electromagnetic wave of high frequency energy produced by the oscillation of an electric charge. Microwave energy is converted into heat when it is absorbed by the food. Microwaves are about 5 inches long—in contrast to radio waves, which average about 0.3 mile in length. A short wave has a greater frequency, or vibrations per second, than a longer wave has. Electronic ovens have a frequency of 2,450 megacycles (million cycles) per second. Ordinary AC electricity, which vibrates 60 times per second, has a frequency of 60 cycles per second.

MISCIBLE Capable of being mixed easily with another substance. For example, sugars are readily miscible in water; fats cannot be mixed with water but are partly miscible in alcohol and are completely miscible in ether.

MOISTURE CONTENT The amount of water in a substance.

MOLECULE A chemical combination of two or more atoms that form a specific substance. For example, the combination of an atom of sodium and an atom of chlorine makes a molecule of sodium chloride, or table salt. This is a comparatively simple molecule. There are also large, complex molecules, such as hemoglobin. Proteins and starches are examples of even larger and very complex molecules containing many atoms.

MORBIDITY Has the same meaning as sickness. The term is used to indicate the extent of illness in a population, as contrasted to mortality or deaths.

MUCOSA The mucous membrane that lines the passages and cavities of the body, as in the gastrointestinal tract.

MUCOUS MEMBRANE A membrane lining the cavities and canals of the body that have contact with the air. It is kept moist by mucus secreted by special cells and glands. The eyes, ears, nose, throat, lungs, digestive tract, genitourinary and reproductive tracts are lined with mucous membrane.

MUCUS (NOUN) A sticky liquid secreted by the mucous glands and mucous membranes.

MUSCULATURE The muscular apparatus of the body or any part of it.

NATIONAL INSTITUTES OF HEALTH The National Institutes of Health are the research arm of the Public Health Service in the Department of Health, Education, and Welfare. There are seven Institutes: Cancer; Heart; Allergy and Infectious Diseases; Arthritis and Metabolic Diseases; Dental Research; Mental Health; and Neurological Diseases and Blindness. Each is engaged in fundamental laboratory and clinical research into the causes, treatment, and prevention of the diseases with which it is concerned.

NEONATAL Newborn.

NEURAL Refers to nerves or nervous tissue.

NEURITIC Refers to nerves. Neuritic pain is pain due to damage to nerves; neuritis is an inflammation of nerves.

NITROGEN A chemical element essential to life. Plants can use nitrogen compounds direct from the soil, and nitrogen-fixing bacteria can use nitrogen directly from the air, but animals must have their nitrogen supplied by protein foods.

NITROGENOUS A substance containing nitrogen is referred to as nitrogenous. Proteins contain nitrogen, as do the chemical components of proteins—amino acids. Protein-decomposition products containing nitrogen are called nitrogenous extractives. They are found in well-ripened meat and contribute to the flavor of meat.

NONFAT SOLIDS The portion of milk remaining after the water and butterfat have been accounted for; nonfat-dried-milk solids.

NRC An abbreviation for National Research Council; usually used when referring to the recommended dietary allowances.

NUTRIENT A chemical compound with specific functions in the nourishment of the body, such as tryptophan, an amino acid; thiamine, a vitamin; or calcium, a mineral. The body depends on food for about 50 different nutrients.

NUTRITIONIST A professionally trained person who applies the science of nutrition and related subjects in research, teaching, or advisory services.

NUTRITURE (OR NUTRITIONAL STATUS) The condition of physical health and well-being of the body as related to the consumption and utilization of food for growth, maintenance, and repair.
Nutriture, or nutritional status, may be appraised by such methods as clinical examinations with special attention to condition of the skin, eyes, mouth, tongue, gums, muscles; determination of overweight or underweight, often by measurement of the thickness of a skin fold; blood pressure and pulse rate; biochemical tests on the blood for various constituents associated with health; and tests of urine samples, with or without the administration of certain nutrients.

OBESE Fat; excessive overweight due to the presence of a surplus of body fat.

477248°—59——47

ORGANIC A large group of chemical compounds that contain carbon.

ORGANIC ACIDS Acids containing only carbon, hydrogen, and oxygen. Among the best known are citric acid (in citrus fruits) and acetic acid (in vinegar).

OSMOSIS The transfer of materials that takes place through a semipermeable membrane that separates two solutions, or between a solvent and a solution, that tends to equalize their concentrations. The walls of living cells are semipermeable membranes, and much of the activity of the cells depends on osmosis.

OSMOTIC PRESSURE The pressure exerted by the movement of a solvent through a semipermeable membrane into a more concentrated solution on the other side of the membrane. This pressure on the walls of the membrane is the driving force that causes diffusion of particles in solution to move from one place to another.

OSSIFICATION The process of forming bone. Cartilage is made into bone by the process of ossification. The minerals, calcium, and phosphorus are deposited in the cartilage, changing it into bone.

OSSIFY To change into bone or bony substance.

OVERWEIGHT An excess of more than 10 percent above the desirable weight.

OVUM A female germ cell.

OXIDATION The removal of electrons, in the most general sense; may also mean the combining with oxygen or the removal of hydrogen.

OXIDATIVE Refers to the processes of oxidation.

OXYGEN One of the most plentiful chemical elements. Oxygen makes up 65 percent of the human body. When other chemical substances combine with oxygen, energy is released.

PALATABILITY The quality characteristics (such as color, flavor, and texture) of a food product that make an impression on the organs of touch, taste, smell, or sight and have significance in determining the acceptability of the food product to the user.

PANCREAS A glandular organ extending across the upper abdomen close to the liver. It secretes into the intestinal tract digestive juices containing enzymes to act upon protein, fat, and carbohydrate. It also secretes directly into the blood the hormone insulin, which is essential for one stage in the oxidation of sugar to carbon dioxide and water. Adjective: Pancreatic.

PANDEMIC A disease that is widespread throughout several countries, regions, or much of the world.

PAPILLAE A small, nipple-shaped elevation. Many such elevations are found on the tongue and give it a velvety appearance.

PARATHYROID Four small glands in the neck situated beside the thyroid gland. They secrete the hormone that affects calcium metabolism.

PARBOILED RICE; CONVERTED RICE Rice that has been especially treated with heat and water before the husks are removed so that the nutrients in the outer layers of the kernel are driven inward to the kernel. This reduces the loss of nutrients when the outer layers are removed in milling.

PART PER MILLION A way of expressing amounts, especially of trace minerals in diets or foods. Examples of how small a part per million is: It is equal to 1 pound in 500 tons, 1 inch in about 16 miles, or 1 cent in 10 thousand dollars.

PATHOLOGY The branch of medicine that deals with the special nature of disease.

PEDIATRICIAN A physician who specializes in the treatment of the diseases of children.

PERCOMORPH Refers to fish of the perch family. Percomorph oil, prepared from the livers of such fish, is a concentrated source of vitamin D.

PERINATAL The interrelated care of both mother and infant during pregnancy, labor, and following delivery.

PERMEABLE Capable of being penetrated.

PEROXIDASE An enzyme that speeds up oxidative changes in certain plant constituents.

PHAGOCYTE A cell that can engulf particles or cells that are foreign or harmful to the body. Phagocytes are present in the blood and lymph and also in the lungs, liver, and spleen.

PHARMACOPOEIA A book that describes drugs and preparations used in medicine. The United States Pharmacopoeia is revised every 10 years after a committee of experts has decided on the necessary changes.

PHOSPHOLIPIDS Fatlike substances containing phosphorus and nitrogen, along with fatty acids and cholesterol. Phospholipids are abundant in brain and nerve tissues, in egg yolk, and in some plant sterols, as in soybean lecithin.

PHOSPHORUS A mineral element necessary for the formation of bone and essential in the blood and soft tissues of the body.

PHOSPHORYLATE A chemical term that applies to the introduction of a phosphorus and oxygen group into a complex chemical compound.

PHYSIOLOGICAL Refers to the science of physiology, which deals with functions of living organisms or their parts.

PIGMENT Any of the coloring materials in the cells and tissues of plants and animals. In fruit and vegetables, the green pigment is chlorophyll; orange to red pigments are carotenoids; red to blue colors are anthocyanins; light-yellow pigments are flavones and flavonols. In meat, the chief pigment producing the pink or red color is myoglobin.

PITUITARY GLAND A gland, in the lower part of the brain, which produces a number of hormones. These hormones regulate the growth of all body tissues and regulate the development and action of other endocrine glands such as the thyroid, pancreas, and adrenal glands.

PLACENTA An organ on the wall of the uterus (womb). The developing young animal is attached to it by means of the umbilical cord. The placenta is the source of nourishment for the young in the uterus.

PLAQUE Tiny patches or unnatural formations on tissues such as on tooth surfaces and on inner arterial walls. The plaques, called atheroma, that are found in walls of arteries contain some lipids, usually cholesterol and oleic acid, and some connective or scar tissue of protein origin. Their formation is related to abnormal fat metabolism. They contribute to stiffening of blood vessel walls, closing of arteries, choking circulation, and ruptured arteries. They may be formed in coronary arteries of people of all ages but appear to be most prevalent in men 45 to 60 years of age engaged in light work or sedentary occupations.

PLASMA The colorless fluid portion of the blood in which the cells are suspended.

POLYPHENOLS An extensive class of organic chemical substances that react readily with oxygen, generally yielding colored substances.

POLYUNSATURATED FATTY ACIDS A class of

fatty acids that have more than one unsaturated linkage in the chain, each lacking two hydrogens. Saturated fatty acids have all the hydrogens the carbon chain can hold. Monounsaturated fatty acids have only one unsaturated linkage. Although there are many kinds of polyunsaturated fatty acids, linoleic appears to be the only one which the body cannot synthesize and so must receive it from food sources.

POTENT Strong, powerful, efficacious.

POTENTIAL ENERGY Energy in chemical form, which may be released either as heat or muscular work when the substance is oxidized.

PRECONCEPTIONAL Before pregnancy.

PRECOOK To heat food before canning, freezing, or drying. Vegetables may be precooked in boiling water, steam, or hot air, as in an oven, and fruits in boiling fruit juice, sirup, water, or steam.

PRECURSOR Forerunner; something that precedes. In biochemistry, a compound that can be used by the body to form another compound.

PREDISPOSE A verb that indicates a special tendency toward a certain disease or other situation.

PREGNANCY The condition of having a developing embryo in the body; the state of being with child.

PREMATURITY Delivery occurring before the expected time.

PRESSURE COOKER An airtight container for the cooking of food at high temperature under steam pressure. It is equipped with a gage for measuring and indicating the pressure on a graduated dial or with some other device. Pressure cookers are used in canning low-acid foods, for cooking less tender cuts of meat and poultry, and for cooking some vegetables.

PROCESSING OF FOODS Subjecting them to various manufacturing procedures to change their characteristics. Processing includes canning, freezing, and dehydrating, so the foods can be stored; it includes changing the form of the food, such as making oil or flour from seeds and making pickles from cucumbers; it includes simply cooking food; for example, baking of bread.

PROGESTERONE A sex hormone secreted by the corpus luteum in the ovary.

PROTEIN One of a group of complex organic compounds that contain nitrogen, carbon, hydrogen, and oxygen and are essential for life and growth. They are formed by various combinations of different amino acids.

PROTOPLASM The essential protein substance of living cells, upon which all the vital functions of nutrition, secretion, growth, and reproduction depend.

PROVITAMIN A Any of a number of substances, called carotenes, that occur in nature and can be converted into vitamin A in the body.

PUBERTY The age at which the reproductive organs become functionally active. It occurs when a person is between 12 and 17 years old and is indicated in the girl by the beginning of menstruation and in the boy by seminal discharge and change of voice.

PUERPERIUM The period in a woman's life between the time her infant is born and the time her uterus returns to its normal size, usually about 6 weeks.

PUREE A smooth, pulpy food product from which the rough fiber has been removed by sieving or other means. Most baby foods are in the pureed form.

PUTREFACTION The decomposition of proteins by micro-organisms under anaerobic conditions, resulting in the production of incompletely oxidized compounds, some of which are foul smelling.

PYRIDOXINE One of the B vitamins, commonly designated as vitamin B_6. Strictly speaking, vitamin B_6 includes a group of three vitamins of nutritional interest—pyridoxine, pyridoxamine, and pyridoxal.

RADICAL In chemistry, a group of elements joined in a set formation, which appears as a unit in a series of compounds or behaves as one piece without decomposition in chemical reactions. Examples are the glycerol radical in fats, the carboxyl group in organic acids, and the phenyl radical (benzene ring) in certain amino acids. The amino acids themselves act as larger radicals in making up proteins.

RADIOACTIVE Giving off atomic energy in the form of radiations, such as in alpha, beta, or gamma rays.

RADIOISOTOPES One of a broad class of elements capable of becoming radioactive and giving off atomic energy, such as is detectable with a Geiger counter. Some radioisotopes occur naturally; others are produced artificially. The word is synonymous with radioactive elements and includes tracer elements.

RANCID Having a disagreeable odor or flavor; usually used to describe foods with a high content of fat when oxidation or hydrolysis of unsaturated fatty acids has occurred. Noun: Rancidity.

RANCIDIFY The process of chemically changing fat or oil with the formation of small amounts of new compounds, which have different characteristics. Rancid fats have typical rank odors and flavors, changed baking properties, and other properties different from those of the original fat.

RECONSTITUTE To restore to the normal state, usually by adding water, such as reconstituting dry milk by adding water to make it fluid milk.

REDUCING (chemical action) The taking up of oxygen from air and from other materials.

REDUCING SUGAR A sugar that can be oxidized readily by chemical means.

REHYDRATION Soaking or cooking or using other procedures to make dehydrated foods take up the water they lost during drying.

RETINA A delicate membrane of the eye connected to the optic nerve (nerve of vision) and necessary for maintenance of sight.

ROLLING BOIL A description of a mixture, usually jelly sirup or candy, when it is boiling rapidly. A full rolling boil cannot be stirred down because bubbles of vapor are continually forming, rising to the top, and breaking on the surface of the mixture.

RUMEN The first stomach of cattle and other animals, such as sheep and goats, which chew a cud. It serves as a storage place for rapidly swallowed food. The food then can be returned to the mouth for more thorough chewing at a later time.

RUMINANT Any of a group of hoofed mammals, including oxen, sheep, goats, antelopes, giraffes, deer, and camels, that have a special stomach compartment, called the rumen, which is designed to aid in the digestion of grasses and other plants that are indigestible to humans.

SALMONELLA A large group of bacteria, some of which are associated with food poisoning. Certain salmonellas are sometimes found in raw and dried eggs and in poultry products. They can be destroyed by sufficient heating.

SALT One of a class of compounds formed when the hydrogen atom of an acid radical is replaced by a metal or metallike radical.

The most common salt is sodium chloride, the sodium salt of hydrochloric acid. Other metal or metallike salts in food may include phosphorus, calcium, potassium, sodium, magnesium, sulfur, manganese, iron, cobalt, zinc, and other metals. They may be present as chlorides, sulfates, phosphates, lactates, citrates, or in combination with proteins, as in calcium caseinate.

SECRETORY The formation of a secretion. Thus, the salivary glands of the mouth secrete saliva and are secretory glands.

SEDENTARY Specifically, the habit of sitting a great part of the time. More generally, it is used to refer to a minimum of physical activity.

SELECTIVE BREEDING (OF PLANTS) The choice of certain varieties or strains of plants as parent stock for breeding purposes in order to develop an offspring that possesses the desired characters present in one or both of the parents.

SERUM The colorless fluid portion of the blood that separates when blood clots.

SOLID A substance that does not perceptibly flow.

SOLUBLE Capable of being dissolved or going into solution.

SOLUTION A uniform liquid mixture containing a solvent and a solute. Salt dissolved in water is a solution—water is the solvent; salt is the solute.

SPECIFIC GRAVITY The relation of the weight of a definite volume of a substance to the weight of an equal volume of water.

SPECIFIC HEAT Heat or thermal capacity of a substance in relation to that of water.

SPOILAGE ORGANISMS Bacteria, yeasts, and molds that cause food to spoil. They live everywhere—in the air, soil, and water and on food, plants, and animals.

SPORE An inactive form of a microorganism that is resistant to destruction and capable of becoming active again.

SQUALENE A chemical compound representing an intermediate step in the formation of cholesterol from acetates. It amounts to the joining of four molecules of acetic acid.

STERILE Free from living micro-organisms. A food container may be made sterile by heating it in a pressure cooker where the temperature will reach 240° F. at 10 pounds pressure or by using dry heat at a high temperature in an oven.

STERILITY (REPRODUCTIVE) As applied to reproduction: Not being able to conceive or produce young.

STERILIZE The process by which micro-organisms, such as bacteria, yeasts, and molds, are killed. In food preparation, this is usually done by the use of high temperatures.

STEROL A complex, fatlike substance that can be dissolved in ether and other fat-solvents. Sterols are found in plant and animal tissues. Cholesterol is a sterol that helps the body to use fat and is used also in the body for making bile salts, hormones, and vitamin D.

STOMACH A saclike organ into which the food passes upon being swallowed. The early stages of digestion, particularly digestion of proteins, occur in the stomach before the partly digested food passes on to the intestines.

STRESS Intense strain. In medicine, any circumstance great enough to disrupt the normal, steady functioning of the body.

SUBCLINICAL DISEASE A disease, usually mild, that has no definite symptoms or signs which can be recognized by the usual visual or clinical means.

SUBSTRATE A substance that is acted upon, as by an enzyme.

SUGAR Usually means cane sugar used as ordinary sugar. May also mean any simple carbohydrate with a sweet taste.

SULFITING The treatment of foods with sulfur dioxide or certain related compounds. The sulfur combines with enzymes in the food and prevents them from causing the quality to deteriorate.

SULFUR DIOXIDE A chemical compound of sulfur and oxygen having antioxidant properties; sometimes used in food technology for control of discoloration.

SYNDROME A medical term meaning a group of symptoms that occur together.

SYNTHESIS A coming together of two or more substances to form a new material.

SYSTEM A functional unit; an arrangement whereby the parts function together toward a common goal, such as the digestive system or the respiratory system.

TERM (AT TERM) The end of the normal period of gestation or pregnancy when birth occurs.

THERAPEUTIC Refers to curing a disease.

THERAPY The medical treatment of disease.

THERMAL Refers to heat.

THYROID The gland in the neck that secretes the hormone thyroxin.

TOXICITY The quality of a substance that makes it poisonous or toxic; sometimes refers to the degree of severity of the poison or the possibility of being poisonous.

TRACER ELEMENT A radioactive element used in biological and other research to trace the fate of a substance or follow stages in a chemical reaction, such as the pathway of metabolism of a nutrient or growth formations in plants or animals. Radioactive elements that have proved useful for tracer work in nutrition research are carbon 14, calcium 45, cobalt 60, strontium 90, and phosphorus 32. Carbon 14 is used widely in studies of fat and sugar metabolism and cholesterol formation.

TRAUMA Physically, wound or injury; psychologically, an emotional shock. Adjective: Traumatic.

TRICHINOSIS Disease caused by trichinae (small worms sometimes present in raw pork or developing from ova in infected pork) embedding themselves in the intestinal tract and muscles. Pork should always be cooked well done (185° F.).

TRIMESTER Three months, or one-third of the nine months of pregnancy. The nine months of pregnancy are divided into the first, second, and third trimester.

TRYPTOPHAN An amino acid that is essential for the nutrition of man and animals. It is frequently present in inadequate amounts in food protein of plant origin; when such foods are the sole diet, tryptophan is often one of the limiting amino acids for the synthesis of animal tissues.

UMBILICAL CORD The connection between the navel of the fetus and the placenta of the uterus.

UNPALATABLE Not pleasing to the senses of taste, smell, sight, or touch.

UNSATURATED FATTY ACID A fatty acid that has a double bond between two carbon atoms at one or more places in the carbon chain. Hydrogen can be added at the site of the double bond. An unsaturated fat is one that contains an unsaturated fatty acid. A saturated fatty acid has no double bonds.

UREA An end product of protein metabolism excreted in the urine.

URIC ACID A chemical compound that contains nitrogen and is present in small amounts in the urine.

URINARY Refers to the urine, which is formed by the kidney and excreted.

UTERUS The organ that holds the offspring before birth; commonly called the womb.

VAPOR PHASE The part of any substance that exists as a gas.

VARIETAL Differences between varieties of the same plant. Groups of plants within the same species may differ in certain characteristics. For example, different varieties of potatoes may contain widely differing levels of ascorbic acid. Such differences between varieties are known as varietal differences.

VASCULAR Full of vessels that contain a fluid. In physiology, the blood and lymph vessels in the body.

VERTEBRATES Animals with backbones or spinal cords (so-called "higher" animals in the animal scale). All mammals, birds, reptiles, and fish are vertebrates.

VISCOSITY A property of fluids that determines whether they flow readily or resist flow. A pure liquid at a given temperature and pressure has a definite viscosity. Viscosity of liquids usually increases with a decrease in temperature. Thus, sugar sirups are thicker when they are cold than when they are heated. Viscosity is important in food preparation. The quality of a baked product, for example, is related to the viscosity of the batter or dough.

VITAL STATISTICS Figures on births, deaths, longevity, disease rates, and other data that indicate the state of health of a population.

VITAMIN One of a group of substances that in relatively small amounts are essential for life and growth.

WATER-EXTRACT Whatever can be removed or dissolved out of a substance with water. A substance like sugar is completely soluble in water, whereas when yeast is shaken up with water only a small portion of it goes into solution. What remains is insoluble and does not pass into the water-extract.

WAXY FLOUR A flour prepared from certain varieties of rice or corn that contain a type of starch that has waxy adhesive qualities. The flour acts as a stabilizer when it is used as an ingredient in sauces or gravies and binds the mixture together, so there is no separation when the mixture is frozen.

WHEAT GERM The heart or kernel of the wheat; the embryo, from which a new plant may develop.

WORK An accomplishment of body activity measurable in work units, such as foot-pounds.

XYLOSE A simple sugar obtained from the woody parts of plants by hydrolysis of the complex carbohydrates they contain.

YEAST One-celled fungi widely distributed in nature. Some convert sugar in fruit juices to alcohol. Some are used to produce carbon dioxide for a leavening agent in breadmaking.

Index

736

PROTEIN

To build and repair all tissues
To help form antibodies to fight
infection
To supply food energy

FAT

To supply a large amount of food ene
in a small amount of food
To supply essential fatty acids

IRON

To combine with protein to make
hemoglobin, the red
substance in the blood that
carries oxygen to the cells

FOOD AN

WHA

FOODS THA

THIAMINE

For normal appetite and digestion
For a healthy nervous system
To help change substances in food
into energy for work and heat

RIBOFLAVIN

To help the cells use oxygen
To help keep vision clear
For smooth skin without scaling
around mouth and nose or cracking
at the corners of the mouth